WIN A FREE CAR CONTEST

1st GRAND PRIZE
WIN A NEW 1984 PONTIAC FIERO SPORTS CAR FROM BUD HASTIN
Drawing November 30th, 1984.

2nd PLACE PRIZE
Win a Weekend in Las Vegas, Dinner with Bud and Vickie Hastin.
Includes Airfare, Hotel, and $100 spending money.
Drawing 4th Week of June 1985.

OFFICIAL ENTRY FORM – Place my Name in Your Free Car Giveaway Contest or Free Weekend in Las Vegas.

Print or type   DATE _____

NAME _____

ADDRESS _____

CITY, STATE _____ ZIP_____

PHONE-AREA CODE _____

NAME OF STORE OR PERSON WHERE 1984 10th EDITION HASTIN'S AVON ENCYCLOPEDIA

PURCHASED _____

CITY-STATE _____

☐ I am an Avon Collector-This is my 1st book on Avon Collecting.

☐ I last purchased Hastin's Avon Book in the year _____.

☐ I am not an Avon Collector-Please enter my entry in your contest. I do not wish to buy an Avon Encyclopedia at this time.

☐ I am an Avon Representative   ☐ Avon Manager.

☐ Send me information on Joining an Avon Collectors Club.

No purchase necessary – Offer void where prohibited by law.
AVON BOTTLE COLLECTING – AMERICA'S #1 FAMILY HOBBY.
CONTEST RULES ON BACK OF ENTRY FORM.
Return Official Entry Form to: Bud Hastin-Fiero Contest
P.O. Box 43690
Las Vegas, NV 89116

Additional Book order blanks and wholesale Prices at end of this book
CUT OUT AND RETURN NOW ——— WIN A NEW PONTIAC FIERO 1984 SPORTS CAR OR TRIP TO LAS VEGAS IN 1985

AVON BOTTLE COLLECTORS
WIN A NEW $12,000.00
1984 PONTIAC FIERO SPORTSCAR FROM BUD HASTIN

CONTEST RULES

BUD HASTIN, PUBLISHER OF THE BUD HASTIN AVON BOTTLE COLLECTORS ENCYCLOPEDIA (ALL NEW 1984-10th EDITION) IS GOING TO GIVE AWAY TO A LUCKY WINNER A BRAND NEW 1984 PONTIAC FIERO SPORTS CAR AS THE 1ST GRAND PRIZE. THE 2ND PLACE PRIZE WILL BE A FREE WEEKEND IN FABULOUS LAS VEGAS. THE WINNER OF THE FIERO WILL BE PICKED IN A RANDOM DRAWING BY THE OWNER OF PAT CLARK PONTIAC IN LAS VEGAS, NEVADA ON NOVEMBER 30th, 1984. WINNER NEED NOT BE PRESENT TO WIN. No purchase necessary. Winner will be notified by telephone on date of drawing or by express mail. In case 1st winner can't be located within 1 week of drawing a second drawing will be held until we have a winner.

The Pontiac Fiero is America's hottest selling sports car and sure to be the envy of all your friends. Your Grand Prize sports car will be bright red, luggage rack on back, white letter tires, fancy wheel rims, air conditioning, AM-FM Stereo radio, 4 speed transmission, 2.5 liter 4 cylinder engine and all standard equipment.

A car you would have to wait months to get at the Pontiac dealer due to backed up demand can now be yours free and under your Christmas tree for 1984.

Each 1984 10th EDITION OF BUD HASTIN'S AVON BOTTLE COLLECTORS ENCYCLOPEDIA has an OFFICIAL ENTRY FORM inside the front cover of each book. All entry forms must be filled out completely and returned to Bud Hastin by 12 Noon November 30th, 1984 to be eligible to win the 1984 Fiero.

For those not wishing to purchase the latest 1984 updated book on Avon Bottle Collecting, you may obtain an OFFICIAL ENTRY FORM by sending a self addressed envelope with a 1st class stamp affixed to Bud Hastin-Fiero Contest P.O. Box 43690 Las Vegas, NV 89116. No Contest Entry Forms will be sent without a SASE.

This offer is void outside the Continental 48 States. All Federal, state and local laws and regulations apply. Void where prohibited by law. Winners will be announced in both the Avon Times magazine, Box 9868, Kansas City, MO 64134 and the NAAC newsletter.

This offer is made by Bud Hastin in the promotion of his latest new 1984 book to further the education of those who collect Avon Cosmetic products. Avon Products, Inc. dates back to the late 1800's when Avon Products was knows as the California Perfume Co. (BUD HASTIN AND HIS AVON BOTTLE COLLECTORS ENCYCLOPEDIA IS NOT AFFILIATED WITH AVON PRODUCTS INC. IN ANY WAY.) The "BUD HASTIN AVON BOTTLE COLLECTORS ENCYCLOPEDIA 1984 10TH EDITION" is available from Bud Hastin, PO Box 43690, Las Vegas, NV 89116 or B-Dalton and Waldron Book Stores throughout the U.S. and any of over 100 active Avon Collectors Clubs in the National Association of Avon Collectors.

Send in the Official Coupon inside the cover before November 30th, 1984 to be eligible to win the sports car and the final drawing coupons must be in before June 15th, 1985 to win the weekend in Las Vegas, Nevada.

2ND PLACE PRIZE-WEEKEND IN LAS VEGAS, DINNER WITH BUD AND VICKIE HASTIN.

All entries not winning the 1984 Fiero Sports Car will have a chance to win 1 round trip Airfare from nearest major airport and Hotel for 3 days-2 nights, $100.00 spending money and dinner on the town with Bud and Vickie Hastin. This 2nd Place Prize will be drawn at a random drawing at the 14th Annual National Association of Avon Collectors Convention to be held in Seattle, Washington the last week of June 1985. Time and date of winners trip for 2nd Place Price to be determined by Bud Hastin and winner. Winner will be notified by telephone the date of drawing or by express mail.

One entry per person only. You must be at least 18 years old to win or of legal age to own an automobile in your home state. Las Vegas Weekend trip winner must be 21 years of age to win. No substitutes will be made. All taxes, freight and registration will be the responsibility of the winners on prizes.

This 1984 Fiero is given by Bud Hastin with consideration by Pat Clark Pontiac, Las Vegas Nevada and Pontiac Motor Division.

This book is updated and the latest information on Avon collecting is released to the public about every 18 months. Send your name and address to Bud Hastin to be first to know when the next book will be released.

Bud Hastin's

Avon Bottle Collectors Encyclopedia™

The Official Guide For

Avon Bottle Collectors

10th Edition

Published, Written, Photographed and Researched by

BUD & VICKIE HASTIN
P. O. Box 43690 – Las Vegas, NV 89116

Bud & Vickie Hastin are in no way responsible for buying, selling or trading Avon bottles at the prices quoted in this guide book. It is published only as a guide and prices vary from state to state as much as 90%. Most prices quoted are top prices in mint condition and it is not uncommon for prices to be quoted differently, usually being lower. Bud Hastin does not solicit Avon bottles to buy or sell. The current values in this book should be used only as a guide. They are not intended to set prices, which vary from one section of the country to another. Auction prices as well as dealer prices vary greatly and are affected by condition as well as demand. Neither the Author nor the Publisher assumes responsibility for any losses that might be incurred as a result of consulting this guide.

The Bud Hastin's Avon Bottle Collectors Encyclopedia™ is recognized by Avon Collectors and Avon Representatives as the official and most complete collector's guide in print.

Acknowledgements & Credits

Bud Hastin personally thanks all the Avon collectors across the nation who have permitted him to photograph their collections to update this book. Much credit goes to all the following people for their assistance and help, be it big or small. For without them there would never have been an Avon Encyclopedia.

Clarine Coggins, CA
Ray & Ralphie Lintz, CA
Evil Hahn, IN
Dortha Bennett, CA
Madeline Seaholm, CA
Dee Schneider, CA
Virginia Wyatt, CA
Lucille Saiia, CA
Diane Truax, CA
George Gaspar, IL
Ray Potter, IL
Rodney Thein, IA
Gene Boyd, CA
Virgil Sinks, IL
Ed Bea, NJ

Ron Federico, CA
Grace Powers, GA
Mary Card, CA
Joan Wesley, PA
Ray Cobb, CA
Joyce Erlichman, PA
Nola Murdock, CA
Maxine Merrick, CA
Mary Foster, CA
Ann Van Sickle, CA
Shirley Fairbanks, MN
Jerry Graham, IA
Ruth Hershberger, Canada
Kate Frisk, Canada
Ogretta Simmons, KS

Phyllis & Clark Popham, Canada
Dorothy Gray, MI
Tony Jotautas, PA
Eola Clark, Canada
Bill Aten, MI
Dick & Beverly Pardini, CA
Lawrence Speegle, TX
Leo Coulter, MI
Adele Norvell, MO
Bud & Roz Hoover, OR
Dwight & Vera Young, MO
O. R. Nicholas, VA
Connie Clark, MO
Vera Shaw, WA
Sara June Lloyd, CA

"Avon Calling" is a
registered trade mark of Avon Products

The phrase "Avon Calling" rings 'round the world' as the signature of a firm devoted to the manufacture and sales of high quality cosmetic and toiletry items for all members of the family.

From its start in 1886, as the California Perfume Company, Avon has grown steadily, expanding its operation throughout the world. Today fourteen manufacturing laboratories and twenty five distribution branches, all using the most modern and efficient equipment and all staffed by well trained and experienced employees, produce a vast variety of ever changing, imaginative products.

The Avon Representative, focal point of the company, employs the oldest method of distribution in the world . . . direct-to-the-home selling. This means she brings the latest news in beauty and grooming, the finest products, and the most personal kind of service directly to her customers in their homes.

Avon's growth from a one room laboratory in downtown New York to the current world wide network of manufacturing laboratories and distribution branches is a success story based on quality . . . quality of product, quality of service, quality of relationships with people.

Avon is the worlds largest manufacturer and distributor of cosmetics, fragrances and costume jewelry. Its products are sold by more than 1,600,000 active Representatives to customers in the home in the United States and other countries. Plus their products are sold in almost every country of the world.

1969

1970

1971

1971

1972

1972

1974

1976 & 1979

1981 & 1982

Bud & Vickie Hastin

Bud Hastin was born April 24, 1939, in Butler, Missouri to Wilbur and Velma Hastin.

He grew up in Butler, where he graduated from Butler High School in 1957. He then spent three years in the United States Air Force. Bud went into the Auto Glass business in 1964 and sold Mobile Auto Glass of Kansas City in 1971 to devote full time to preparing Avon Collector Guides for the collector. Bud met his wife Vickie in 1975 when they immediately became a good working team and have been working together as a team since.

Bud says his father is responsible for getting him interested in the bottle hobby when someone gave him some fancy cut glass bottles and Bud like them so much that he started collecting.

The Avon hobby as a whole, covers a tremendous volume of material. Avon collectables include bottles, tin containers, plastic containers, jars, soaps, samples, candles, jewelry, plates, trays, needlecraft, prizes, catalogs, magazine advertisements, Outlooks, and many more. There is far too much to collect for the average person to work on all categories. **No. 1 Rule in Avon Collecting:** "Set a goal for your hobby and collect only what you want to collect. You rule the hobby, it doesn't rule you. Decide what part of the overall hobby appeals to you, set your goal and work hard toward that goal. Ask yourself some questions. How much room do I have? How much can I spend each month? What do I enjoy the most about Avon Collecting? Base your goal on the answers.

Since 1969 Bud has sold over 605,000 copies of his Avon Collectors book. This book is the 15th book on Avon collecting by Bud Hastin. The first, being sold in 1969, was the Avon Collectors Guide, Vol. I, then followed the 1970 Avon Collectors Guide Vol. II, The Avon Collectors Encyclopedia, the 1971 Avon Collectors Guide for Beginners, the 1972 Avon Collectors Encyclopedia, the 1972 Avon Beginners

Guide, the 1974 Avon Collectors Encyclopedia, and the Avon Collectors Encyclopedia special hardbound edition for collectors. Only 1,000 were printed and each was signed by Bud.

The 1976-77 Avon Collectors Encyclopedia — There were 500 hardbound copies of the 1976 Avon Collectors Encyclopedia. The 1979 Avon Encyclopedia — There were 350 special hardbound collectors editions of 1979 Encyclopedia, 1982-83 Encyclopedia, and 1984 Encyclopedia. Many people are starting to collect the older Avon books published by Bud.

Bud and Vickie travel the world gathering information on Avon collecting. From these travels they have added a Foreign Avon section to this book.

Bud's personal views on Avon collecting are: "I think the Avon collecting hobby is the best hobby around today. It is one of the few hobbies that you will probably never find all of them and that's what collecting is all about, the challenge to find something you don't have. The thrill is finding a high priced Avon bottle in a flea market or garage sale for a low price. You see very few Avon collections the same and this always makes the challenge greater to find the one that your friend has. Avon collecting is one of the biggest hobbies in the U.S. I wonder how many of the old and rare C.P.C. and Avon bottles are lying around in somebodies attics and cellars just waiting to be discovered by some informed collector? Garage sales, rummage sales, etc. are the gold fields and it is almost as big a thrill to find a $100.00 C.P.C. as it was for the treasure hunters of old to find gold. Avon collecting is for all ages, both young and old. It's a hobby for the entire family."

NATIONAL ASSOCIATION OF AVON COLLECTORS

Bud is Chairman of the Board of the National Association of Avon Collectors Clubs, and was the founder of the National Organization in 1971. The N.A.A.C. is not a club, but an organization to help promote Avon collecting in the United States. The N.A.A.C. is run by an elected board of Directors. The N.A.A.C. is ready to help anyone start a new Avon collectors club in your area. For information on starting a new Avon Collectors Club, write to N.A.A.C. in care of Bud Hastin and we will see that all N.A.A.C. material is sent to you. At present there are 140 active Avon Collectors Clubs in the N.A.A.C. A National Convention is held each year along with a National Avon Bottle Show. Each year it is held in a different section of the U.S. The N.A.A.C. is a non-profit organization and financed by the sale of the N.A.A.C. club bottle each year. See the N.A.A.C. section of this book for N.A.A.C. Club Bottles. These club bottles are very limited editions and have skyrocketed in price after they are released. Profits from the sale of the club bottles are used to send a delegate from the member clubs to the National Convention each year.

Helpful Hints & Meaning of Terms In This Book

The 1983 Avon Collectors Encyclopedia has been compiled by Bud and Vickie Hastin. To best understand this book and its contents, please read this before starting through the book.

All items from 1929 to 1984 will give the first year and the last year date that the items were sold by the Avon Company. Dates will read, for instance, 1930-36. This means this item was introduced sometime in 1930 and was discontinued for the last time in 1936. Dates like 1970-71 mean the item sold in both years, but is very possible it sold for less than one year selling time. An item dated for three years like 1958-60 means it sold in all three years, but could have only been on the market for a period of about two years total time. All items dated 1886 to 1928 mean the first and last year sold. All dates from 1929 to 1983 with only one year given, means this item was sold during that one year only and usually for a very short period. These items are usually considered a short-issue and hard to find.

O.S.P. means Original Selling Price. This is the full value price Avon puts on an item. It does not represent a special selling price which is from 20% to 50% off the O.S.P.

S.S.P. means Special Selling Price (reduced in price). The O.S.P. or S.S.P. price may vary as Avon may have put a different special selling price each time it was offered and the O.S.P., may have been changed from the time it was introduced to the time it was taken off the market because of rising cost to make the product. Prices quoted are just to give you an idea of what the item sold for from Avon.

C.M.V. means Current Market Value that most collectors are willing to pay for that particular item. Many items priced in this book are priced both item only and item in box. Items in the original box need not be full. The collectors price is for an empty bottle. If it is current and full, and in the box, then you can expect to pay full retail price or the special selling price that Avon sells this item for. Only after Avon stops selling the item and it has been placed on the annual discontinued list Avon prints each year of items that will not be offered for sale again on its original design, will Avon be considered as a Collectors item and the value could start to increase.

B.O. means bottle only (mint), no box. **M.B.** means mint and boxed in perfect condition.

All Avon tubes priced in this book are for full mint condition tubes. If a tooth paste tube or other type tube has been used then it would not be mint. Tubes and soaps are the only items in this book that have to be full to be mint condition. Most all other items are priced empty unless otherwise stated. In most cases all older items will bring as much empty as they would full.

This book has been compiled from original CPC and Avon Catalogs. Original California Perfume Company catalogs used in the 1984 Avon Collectors Encyclopedia have been copied completely and all items pictured in these original catalogs are pictured in this book. The CPC was used from the years 1896 through 1929. From 1916 to 1929 the CPC sales catalogs were black leather type covers. 1916 to 1923 these books were hard bound. 1924 to 1929 the same size books were soft cover bound. January, 1929, was the introduction of Avon Products with the Avon name first appearing on a number of CPC products.

The CPC sales catalogs 1896 to 1906 were smaller booklet type with soft covers measuring 6 5/8" x 4¾". The 1915 booklet is the last of the small sales catalogs before the large black books in color were issued in 1916. The 1915 book is dated and measures 4" x 7 1/8". 1930 through 1935 the Avon sales catalogs had CPC/Avon Products in them in a 6 3/4" x 10" dark blue soft cover book. 1936 through 1957 the sales catalogs are the same size only with a green cover.

An entire set of Avon sales catalogs from 1930 to 1984 were used to compile the Avon Collectors Encyclopedia. A complete set of Avon Sales Outlook or Avon Calling from 1905 to 1984 were also used. Special Christmas sales catalogs from 1934 to 1984 were also used showing many special sets sold only at Christmas time each year. Some of the CPC and Avon catalogs and Outlooks were borrowed, so we would like to complete our own file of these original books and catalogs. If you have any of the old catalogs both regular or special sales catalog or Outlooks, write to Bud Hastin, P. O. Box 43690, Las Vegas, NV 89116, as I am always trying to buy these books to help keep you the collector, up to date on the true facts about your hobby. I only want catalogs 1947 or older.

Grading Condition of Avons

People have asked me **WHAT A BOTTLE IS WORTH WITHOUT A LABEL.** If it's an old bottle where the label is the main thing that identifies the bottle and it is missing, then it's worth whatever you can get, which is usually not too much. If it is a new figural bottle, then it will usually take a few dollars off the price.

MINT CONDITION means items must be in new condition as originally sold, with all labels bright and correct, and cap and/or stopper. Items need not be full or boxed, but will bring a higher price in most cases if they are in the box. All items in the book are priced empty in mint condition only with right cap and all labels. Bottles with no cap or label are of little or no value. (Examples on the next page.)

GRADING EXAMPLES
A Guide For Selling Or Buying

1969-73 Gold Cadillac . . . Chipped paint, deduct 50% to 90% from CMV

1966-67 Casey's Latern. Chipped paint, broken bail ears, deduct 70% from CMV

1971 French Telephone. . Gold chip on handle, deduct 10 - 40% CMV, label off handle, deduct 40% CMV

1961-63 Cotillion Cologne . Cap turning grey, deduct 25 - 50% CMV, lettering faint

1947-56 Golden Promise Cologne . . . . Letters or printing gone, deduct 20 - 80% CMV. Gold off cap, deduct 40 -70% CMV

1948-50 Quaintance Perfume . . Letters gone on printing, deduct 20 - 80% CMV

1963 Topaze Perfume Oil for Bath . . . . . Letters fading on printing, deduct 50 - 80% CMV

1958 "Old 99" Soap . . . . . Chip on soap, deduct 40% CMV. Box torn, deduct 10 - 50% CMV

1961-62 Avon Slugger . . Crack in handle, deduct 20 - 60% CMV

1896-1908 French Perfume . . . Torn or damaged label, deduct 20 - 70% CMV

Painted Figurals (Gold Cadillac, Casey's Lanterns, French Telephone, Red VW, Silver Warrior, etc.): One or two tiny chips, deduct 10%. Larger flakes that are visible, deduct 50 - 75%. More than ¼ flaked, little or no value.

Other Figurals: Bottom label missing or damaged, deduct 20%. Poor cap, deduct 20%. Both, deduct 50% or more.

Fragrance Line Bottles with Painted Labels (Nearness, Forever Spring, Quaintance, etc.) One or two letters mis-placed or missing, deduct 10%. If more than that, deduct 25 - 90%. Faint writing on gold painted labels, deduct 20 - 80%. Front paper labels (To A Wild Rose, Nearness, Old Cotillion, etc.) if intact but faded, deduct 10 - 30%; if torn or damaged, deduct 30 - 75%.

CPCs (very few are absolutely mint), deduct 10 - 75% for poor caps, damaged labels, scratched bottles, chips, etc.

Soaps: Chips, deduct 20 - 75%. White spots, some are natural, use your judgement. Boxes dirty, stained or torn, deduct 50 - 75%. If used even once, take a bath with it.

Children's Toys . . Paint missing, deduct 25 - 75%. Cracked, holes, .or teeth marks, deduct 50 - 80%. Bottom label missing or damaged, deduct 20%.

IF ANYTHING IS TOO BADLY DAMAGED, DON'T BUY IT OR SELL IT!

CPC bottles may have the same shape but with different labels. Be sure to check labels and boxes to get the right date on your bottles.

All items are dated in this book from actual old Avon catalogs I have in my possession. They did not change the bottles for many years in the early days of CPC. 1896 was the first year a CPC catalog was printed.

TO BUY AND SELL AVONS. Garage sales, flea markets, antique shops, bottle shops are the best places to buy and sell Avon bottles locally. To sell Avons in your own town, place a small ad in your local paper and say Avon bottles for sale with your address or phone number. Have a garage sale and put Avon bottles on your sign. People will come to you. If you have no luck locally, then **Bud Hastin's National Avon Club magazine, The Avon Times is the number one spot in the U.S. to sell those extra Avons.** The National Avon Club is the largest in the world and Avon ads get the best result anywhere. Write Avon Times, P. O. Box 9868, Kansas City, MO 64134, for a sample copy of this club magazine. Send 40c in stamps to cover postage.

IF A SET HAS THE BOTTLE MISSING, look up the individual bottle in this book to determine the price to deduct.

There are several reasons for pricing all items empty. After Shave bottles are known to explode in sun light or heat. Full bottles sitting on glass shelves increase the chance of the shelves breaking. After a few years, the contents become spoiled or unsafe to skin and dangerous in the hands of children. I feel if you buy the item new, use the contents and you will still have the pretty bottles.

Several people ask about **INSURANCE ON BOTTLE COLLECTIONS.** Bottle insurance is available through your home owners policy. Check with your local agent.

EVERY ITEM IN THIS BOOK IS GLASS UNLESS OTHERWISE STATED. Bottles will differ in color shades due to various dates in manufacture. It is difficult to get exactly the same color each time. Unless a bottle comes out in a completely different color, it will be of the same value.

THE SILVER METAL SALT & PEPPER SHAKERS WITH AVON PAT. DATE 1927-28, is not Avon Cosmetic Co. items. **THE AVON NAME WAS NOT USED UNTIL 1929.** The name Avon has been used by several companies and still is. Only the name Avon Products Incorporated is copyrighted.

IF YOU ARE AN AVON SALESLADY, AND WOULD LIKE TO SELL THIS BOOK TO YOUR CUSTOMERS, see volume prices in back of book or write Bud Hastin, P. O. Box 43690, Las Vegas, NV 89116.

I WILL BUY ANY CALIFORNIA PERFUME COMPANY SALES CATALOG, 1929 or older in good condition. I will buy any different complete Avon sales book for 1947 or earlier. Please write to me before you send them.

A HISTORY OF THE
California Perfume Co.
NOW AVON PRODUCTS INCORPORATED

Written by the Founder, D. H. McConnell, Sr., in 1903

To give you a sketch or history of the birth and growth of the *California Perfume Company is, in a measure, like writing an autobiography. Our lives have become so identical and so interwoven that it seem almost impossible to separate us, even in history. I will ask you, therefore, to pardon whatever personal reference I may make of myself in describing to you how the California Perfume Company has become the largest of its kind, not only in the United States, but I believe, in the entire world.

In 1878, when but a mere lad, I left my father's farm located near Oswego City, New York State. Here I spent my boyhood days, and through hard work and proper training developed a good, strong, hardy, rugged constitution. When I started out in the world "to make my fortune", I had this positive advantage over many who were less favored.

My first experience in the business world was as a book agent. I took this up during my school vacation, and developed quite a faculty for talking, which I have since learned is quite essential, and has stood me well in hand many times.

My success in canvassing was such as to invite me into the same field the following year, and after two years hard work in the canvass, I was promoted from local canvasser to that of General Traveling Agent. As General Agent I traveled in nearly every state east of the Rocky Mountains; this gave me a valuable knowledge regarding the country. And my experience, both as canvasser and as General Agent, gave me a good insight into human nature.

It is uninteresting to you to follow me through the different work from Chicago to New York and from New York to Atlanta, Georgia, and back to Chicago, and finally back to New York. During all these years I represented in different ways the same publishing company with which I originally started as a canvasser; canvassing, appointing and drilling agents; starting and drilling General Agents, and corresponding with both after they once entered the field. My work as a canvasser and on the road taught me not to enter right into the everyday work of the canvasser and advise and encourage, so as to obtain the best results. If I learned to be anything, I learned to be practical.

The book business was not congenial to me, although I was, in every sense, successful in it, but there were many things that were not pleasant.

On my return from Chicago, I pruchased the entire business from my employer and managed it myself for sometime. During this time the one thing I learned successfully was how to sell goods to the consumer.

My ambition was to manufacture a line of goods that would be consumed, used up, and to sell it through canvassing agents, direct from the factory to the consumer.

The starting of the perfume business was the result of most careful and thorough investigation, guided by the experience of several years successful operation in the book business. That is, in selling goods direct to the consumer or purchaser. I learned during this time that the proper and most advantageous way of selling goods was to be able to submit the goods themselves to the people. In investigating this matter nearly every line of business was gone over, and it seemed to me, then, as it has since been proved, that the perfume business in its different branches afforded the very best possible opportunity to build up a permanent and well established trade. Having once decided that the perfume business was the business, the question naturally presented itself, "By what name are these perfumes to be known: by what name is this company to be called?" The gentleman who took me from the farm as a boy became in the past years, not only my employer buy my personal friend, and after buying him out he moved to California, and while there wrote me glowing accounts of the country, and to him belongs the idea of the name California, as associated with this business.

I started the perfume business in a space scarcely larger than an ordinary kitchen pantry. At first I manufactured but five odors: Violet, White Rose, Heliotrope, Lily-of-the-Valley, and Hyacinth. I did much experimental work in making these odors, and the selling price to the first batch of perfumes I made did not cover one-half the actual cost of the goods, but experience is a great teacher, and I applied myself to the task of making perfumes with the same vim and energy that I had in selling books and after a short time, I fancied that I could produce as fine an odor as some of the old and tried perfumes. At least my perfumes pleased my customers; they were the natural perfumes of the flower, made in the most natural way and by the process employed by the large French perfumers.

I soon found it necessary to increase the odors, and to add to the line other articles for the toilet. Among those first put out were: Shampoo Cream, Witch Hazel Cream, Almond Cream Balm, Tooth Paste, which afterwards was made in the Tooth Tablet, Toilet Waters, etc.

As the business increased the laboratory must, of necessity grow, so that at the end of two years I was occupying one entire floor in this building for manufacturing purposes alone.

It is perhaps unfair to note the progress of one side of the business without carrying with it the natural development on the other.

My ambition was to manufacture a line of goods superior to any other, to be moneyed value into the goods themselves, and just enough money in the package to make them respectable, and as stated above, take these goods through canvassing agents direct from the laboratory to the consumer.

While in the book business I had in my employ as *General Traveling Agent, a Mrs. P.F.E. Albee, of Winchester, NH. Mrs. Albee was one of

Mrs. P.F.E. Albee
1st CPC—Avon Sales Lady

the most successful General Agents I had in the book work, and it was in her hands I placed the first sample case, or outfit, in the perfume business. Mrs. Albee was the only General Agent employed for the first six months of the business. During that time she secured a number of good workers, some of whom are with us today. It is, therefore, only befitting that we give her the honorary title of Mother of the California Perfume Company. For the system that we now use for distributing our goods is the system that was put in practical operation by Mrs. Albee.

As the business grew, through the work of our agents, we were forced from time to time to increase our laboratory space, and in 1895 we built our own laboratory in Suffern, New York, 32 miles out on the main line of the Erie Railroad. This building has been enlarged and remodeled three different times, until today we have a building 120 feet long, main building 50 feet wide and the wing 30 feet, all three stories and basement giving us four working floors, each floor having 4,800 square feet of floor space, or a total floor capacity of 17,200 feet. This building is equipped with the best possible machinery, the latest devices for bottling goods and so on, until I feel we can truthfully say that there is not a plant of our kind in the country so large and so well fitted for our business, as the laboratory of the California Perfume Company.

As well directed efforts and hard work must eventually win their way to the front, so the manufacturing end of the California Perfume Company grew out of my hands; that is to say, I found that it was almost impossible for me to manufacture, to give the personal attention to both manufacturing and correspondence which the merits of each required. Therefore, in 1896, I secured the services of the best perfumer I could find, a gentleman who had been in the perfume business himself for 25 years and had the reputation in New York and vicinity for making the finest perfumes on the American market. In order to secure his services I was obliged to buy out his business and close up his laboratory, and he now has full charge of the manufacturing of every ounce of goods we put out.

My object in locating the laboratory at Suffern was that as Suffern is my home I can give much more personal attention and supervision to the affairs of the laboratory than if it was located in New York. So that every day in the year, unless when I am out on one of my trips, visiting agents and general agents, I am at the laboratory every morning, and spend an hour with our chemist, going over his work and see that every ounce of goods, every package in every department is made and put up in the best possible shape.

Contrast, if you please, the appearance of our office today with that of when Mrs. Albee first started out with the California Perfume Company's goods. Then, I had one stenographer, and I myself filled the position of correspondent, cashier, bookkeeper, shipping clerk and office boy, and manufacturing chemist. Today we have on our weekly payroll over 125 employees. Mrs. Albee for the first six months was the only general agent on the road. Today we have 48 general agents traveling over this country and selecting and drilling agents for this work. The first six months we had perhaps 100 agents in the field, today we have over 10,000 good, honest, industrious and energetic Depot Managers. All of you have your own customers, so that it is difficult to accurately estimate today the vast number of families that are using our goods. If each of you have 100 customers, or sell goods to only one different family, we are supporting goods to at least one million families in the United States. This will give you an idea of the magnitude of our business. The growth of the California Perfume Company only emphasizes what energy and fair dealing with everyone can accomplish. We propose first to be fair to our customers — your customers — by giving them the very best goods that can be made for the money. We propose to be fair and just, even liberal, with you who form the bone and sinew of our business.

Avon Representatives in the early days of the California Perfume Company were called Agents or Depot Managers.

Gallery Originals by Avon are not considered a collectors item. Only Avon Products are considered collectibles by most Avon Collectors.

David Hall McConnell

Founder

CPC - Avon Products

David Hall McConnell, manufacturer, was born in Oswego, NY, July 18, 1858, son of James and Isabel (Hall) McConnell, who came from Calvin County, Ireland, in 1845 and settled in Oswego, where James McConnell became a farmer and brick manufacturer. Brought up on a farm, David Hall McConnell attended a district school and the Oswego State Normal School and was planning to become a mathematics teacher, but instead entered business life in 1879 as a salesman for a New York book selling agency. In 1880 he joined the Union Publisheing Co. of Chicago and three years later was placed in charge of the southern territory, making his home in Atlanta, GA. He decided that, if books could be sold house-to-house, perfumes could also. Out of this conception grew his California Perfume Co. At first he manufactured his own perfumes at home and went out during the day selling them along with books until the enterprise grew and he had to discontinue his book selling and establish a perfume laboratory in Suffern, NY. Other toiletries and cosmetics were soon added to his line of products which he sold under the name of CPC, standing for California Perfume Co. Later the company also began to manufacture flavoring extracts and other household articles sold under the brand name, Perfection. From the onset McConnell effected distribution of his products through housewives and other women who could devote only a portion of their time to the work. The years brought steadily increasing success and at the time of his death his sales force had grown to over 30,000 agents and the volume of sales was measured in the millions. The California Perfume Co. was incorporated in January 1916, and through subsequent changes in name it became Allied Products, Inc., and later Avon Allied Products, Inc., with the following subsidiaries: Avon Products, Inc, distributors of Avon cosmetics and toiletries, the trade name Avon having been adopted in 1929 because of the similarity of the landscape surrounding the laboratories in Suffern, NY to that of Avon, England; Perfection Household Products; Avon Products of Canada, Ltd., incorporated in 1924, being an outgrowth of the California Perfume Company of Canada, Ltd., which was started in 1906; Hinz Ambrosia, Inc., and Technical Laboratories, Inc. McConnell was president, chairman of the board and principal owner of Avon Allied Products, Inc., and its affiliated companies until his death. He was also treasurer of G.W. Carnrick & Co., manufactureres of pharmaceutical supplies in Newark, NJ, and a director of the Holly Hill Fruit Products, Inc., a large orange grove and canning enterprise of Davenport, FL. He was one of the founders of the Suffern National Bank of which he became vice president in 1901, president in 1922 and chairman of the board in 1927. He was again elected chairman of the board and president in 1933 and continued in one or the other office until his death. For varying periods he was superintendent of schools in Suffern; president of the Suffern Board of Education, and treasurer of the Rockland County Republican committee. During the First World War he was chairman of the Rockland County selective service board. A Presbyterian in religion, he was instrumental in starting and played a major part in building the Suffern Presbyterian Church and for many years was superintendent of its Sunday school. He was a Mason and a member of the Union League Club of New York city, the Ormond Beach Club of Florida, the Arcola, NY Country Club and Houvenkoph Country Club of of Suffern, NY. Fishing, golf and horseback riding were his recreations. He was married in Chicago, March 31, 1885, to Lucy Emma, daughter of Ward Hays of Le Porte, IN, and had three children: Edna Bertha, who married William Van Allen Clark; Doris Hall, who married Edward Hall Faile; and David Hall McConnell, Jr. His death occurred in Suffern, NY, January 20, 1937.

Avon Miscellanea

EARLY DAYS

The company's name suggest a likely California beginning, but it has no such meaning; the manufacturing, shipping, and office work in the beginning was done at 126 Chambers St., New York City. The name followed a suggestion made by a friend of Mr. McConnell's who had just visited California and returned to New York greatly enthused over the gorgeous flowers he had seen there. Since only perfumes were being sold, he suggested that the name of the company be "The California Perfume Company".

A LARGE LINE

By 1915 we had a large line. Our products were well and favorably known among our customers but were not known to the public at large. No advertising was done. The customers told their friends about these splendid products and the CPC Representatives' service. From the beginning all products were sold under the CPC trademark. All were offered to customers by Representatives (our products have never been sold through stores) and, always the products were unconditionally guaranteed. This was most unusual in the early days.

THE PANAMA PACIFIC EXPOSITION

We were invited to exhibit at the Panama Pacific Exposition in San Francisco in 1914 - 1915. This was a World's Fair, and prizes were given for the best articles exhibited in various classifications. Our entire line of perfumes, toilet articles and household products was entered in competition with like products from all over the world, and were awarded the Gold Medal, both for the quality of the products, and the beauty of the packages. This Gold Medal appeared on all packages until it was replaced by the seal that is recognized and followed throughout the world as a consumer's guide to the highest quality of merchandise — The Good Housekeeping Seal of Approval.

NEW NAMES — NEW PACKAGES

Through the years, our chemists were following every avenue of research, improving products wherever possible, and discovering new ones that in every way measured up to the standards of the first one. Manufacturing methods were improved to the point that every product was the sum of perfection as to blending and handling. Then in 1929, the chemist suggested an entirely new line of cosmetics. They had it ready, the managers agreed, and the Avon line was presented to Representatives and customers. The household line was named "Perfection" and given its own trademark.

GOOD HOUSEKEEPING'S SEAL OF APPROVAL

In 1931, the first group of Avon Cosmetics were approved by Good Housekeeping, and from that time on, other groups were sent, tested, approved, and the Seal added to our packages. By 1936, our 50th Anniversary year, Good Housekeeping completed their tests and approved all Avon and Perfection products which came within their scope. All products added since that time bear the Seal of Approval.

A NEW POLICY — NATIONAL ADVERTISING

Steadily increasing business over a period of 50 years without any advertising was a remarkable record, but with the celebration of a Golden Jubilee we changed our policy and began to advertise. All during 1936 and 1937, our advertisements appeared in Good Housekeeping. They are appearing now, telling the public that Avon products are unconditionally guaranteed and that our Representatives give the Avon service. We tell readers how convenient shopping the "Avon Way" is for them.

Avon Products, Inc.

Pictured here are two contrasting buildings that have housed Avon through the years. On the left if the 1900 California Perfume Factory and on the right is the present Avon World Headquarters (50 stories) at 9 West 57th St., New York, NY.

1890'S — TRADEMARKS OF QUALITY —1984

It is interesting to see the changes that have been made over the years in the Avon trademark. As you may know, in the early days your Company was called the California Perfume Company. The founder, Mr. D.H. McConnell, selected this name for his flourishing perfume business because he had heard so many glowing accounts of the great beauty and abundance of flowers in the state of California. This name, however, was changed in the early 1930's to Avon . . . a name that today is known and respected in all parts of the world.

Original Trademark
Circa 1900

CPC Trademark
Early 19 Hundreds

1st Use of Name "Avon" 1936
Ann Hathaway Cottage"

4A Trademark
In Use Today

1930-1936 CPC/Avon Labels Read:
California Perfume Company, New York-Montreal
1937-1947
Avon Products, Inc., Dist., New York-Montreal
1948-1950
Avon Products, Inc., Dist., New York-Padadena
1951-1958
Avon Products, Inc., New York-Pasadena
1959
Avon Products, Inc., N.Y., N.Y. or New York-Pasadena
1960-1967
Avon Products, Inc. New York, N.Y.
1968
Avon Products, Inc. New York, N.Y. 10020
1969-1970
Avon Products, Inc. N.Y., N.Y. 10020
1970 to present
Avon Products, Inc. N.Y., N.Y. 10019

Calendar of Events

Late 1800'S
David McConnell starts the California Perfume Company, at the age of 28, in a room in downtown Manhattan. He and his wife, Lucy, create and manufacture the first products It is sold by the first Representative, Mrs. P. F. E. Albee, who recruits others to sell at the same time.

1894
Mr. McConnell expands to four floors in the Manhattan building.

1896
The first catalog is issued on November 2. Text only (no pictures).

1897
The first laboratory is built, a three story wooden structure in Suffern.

1902
10,000 Representatives are now selling the company's products.

1903
The first branch is opened in Kansas City, Missouri.

1905
The first Outlook is published, with news and selling tips for Representatives.

1906
The first company advertisement appears The product: Roses perfume. The magazine: Good Housekeeping.

1912
Over 5,000,000 products are sold during this year.

1914
A Canadian office is opened in Montreal.

1915
The company wins the Panama-Pacific International Exposition gold medal for quality and packaging.

1920
Sales reach the $1,000,000 mark.

1928
A line of new products, called "Avon" is introduced. It includes a toothbrush, cleaner and talc.

1932
Three week selling campaigns begin in August. Up to this time, Representatives have been asked to send in orders every month. As a result of the change, sales increase by over 70% during America's bleak Depression years. The first Specials also appear with products sold at less than regular prices.

1935
The company sponsors a national radio program, called "Friends", a twice weekly show of music and chatter.

1936
An important step is taken to reach customers in urban and suburban areas. Site of this experiment is the Midwest, where several cities, Kansas City, Wichita and Oklahoma City, are divided into territories. Each Territory is to be covered by a Representative with a manager in charge. Later, after the war, this is to become the universal Avon sales structure.

1937
The home office moves to 30 Rockefeller Plaza in New York City. David McConnell dies at age 79.

1939
On October 6, the California Perfume Company changes its name to Avon Products, Inc.

1942-45
The company joins the war effort, with over 50% of the Suffern plant converted to production for the Armed Forces. Among the items manufactured are insect repellent, pharmaceuticals, paratrooper kits and gas mask canisters.

1949
Avon now has 2,500 employees. 1,175 shareholders, 65,000 Representatives and $25 million in sales. The company has facilities in New York City, Suffern, Kansas City, Middletown, Chicago and Pasadena.

1951
The Atlanta distribution branch opens.

1952
The Newark distribution branch opens.

1954
On TV advertising, the "Ding-Dong, Avon Calling" bell is heard for the first time. Avon goes international with its entry into Puerto Rico and Venezuela.

1955
Sales brochures are introduced to support campaign selling.

1956
The Morton Grove shipping facilities opens.

1959
Monrovia shipping and warehousing facilities open.

1960
The Rye branch opens.

1964
On April 2, the New York Stock Exchange starts trading Avon stock. The "advance call-back" brochure selling plan is adopted, with Representatives leaving mini-brochures at customers homes, then returning for the orders.

1965
The Springdale laboratory distribution facilities open. A new research and development laboratory is completed in Suffern.

1968
Two week selling is introduced in the U.S. The first car decanter appears, launching our most successful decanter series.

1970
The Glenview distribution branch opens.

1971
Jewelry is first introduced in the U.S.

1972 to Present
Avon moves into new world headquarters at 9 West 57th Street in New York City. Sales top the billion dollar mark. Sales continue to climb worldwide. Avon continues to open new operations around the world each year.

1978-79 WINNEBAGO MOTOR HOME
(Top) 5 oz. white painted over clear glass. Stick on trim decals. Holds Wild Country or Deep Woods After Shave, SSP $7 - CMV 9.

1978 STANLEY STEAMER
(Bottom) Silver. 5 oz. silver paint over clear glass. Came in Tai Winds or Deep Woods After Shave. SSP $9 - CMV $10 MB.

MEN'S DECANTERS, CERAMICS, & FIGURINES

SEE 1984 SUPPLEMENT SECTION IN BACK OF BOOK FOR MORE MEN'S DECANTERS

COLLECTORS:
All Containers are Priced Empty

BO means . . . . . . Bottle only (empty)
CMV means Current Market Value(mint)
SSP means . . . . . . Special Selling Price
OSP means . . . . . . Original Selling Price
MB means . . . . Mint and Boxed
See Page 6 for Grading Examples on Mint Condition

1974-75 FERRARI '53
(Left) 2 oz. dark amber glass with plastic closure. Came in Wild Country After Shave or Avon Protein Hair Lotion for Men. OSP $3, CMV $3 BO - $4 MB.

1974-75 THUNDERBIRD '55
(Right) 2 oz. blue glass with blue plastic closure. Came in Wild Country or Deep Woods After Shave. OSP $3, CMV $4 BO, $5 MB.

1978-79 RED SENTINEL "FIRE TRUCK"
4 piece decanter. Engine is 3½ oz. clear glass painted red. Holds Wild Country or Deep Woods After Shave. Plastic hook and ladder center section and 6 oz. rear red plastic section holds talc. Comes with stick on decals, SSP $12 - CMV $13 MB.

1976-77 GREYHOUND BUS '31
5 oz. blue painted over clear glass. Blue plastic front cap. White plastic roof will pop off. Came in Avon Spicy or Everest. SSP $6 - CMV $5 BO, $7 MB.

1975-77 PIERCE ARROW '33
(Left) 5 oz. dark blue sprayed glass with beige plastic cap. Came in Wild Country or Deep Woods After Shave. OSP $6, CMV $5 BO - $6 MB.

1974-75 STOCK CAR RACER
(Right) 5 oz. blue glass with blue plastic cap. Holds Wild Country After Shave or Electric Pre-Shave Lotion. OSP $6, CMV $5 BO - $6 MB.

1973-75 BIG MACK
6 oz. green glass with beige bed. Holds Oland or Windjammer After Shave. SSP $5, CMV $6 MB - $4 BO.

1977-79 EXTRA SPECIAL MALE
(Left) 3 oz. blue glass, dark blue cap and white plastic roof. Separate American eagle and red striped stick on decals. Came in Deep Woods or Everest After Shave. SSP $4.44, CMV $3.50 BO - $5 MB.

1976-78 MUSTANG '64
(Right) 2 oz. size blue glass and blue tail cap. Came in Spicy or Tai Winds. SSP $3 - CMV $3 BO, $4 MB.

1972-74 THE CAMPER
5 oz. green glass truck with After Shave. 4 oz. Talc in beige plastic camper. Came in Deep Woods or Oland. SSP $8 - CMV $9 MB, $7 BO.

GUIDE FOR GRADING SETS

The most important part of a set is the box. It doesn't matter how mint the contents are, if you have a poor box, you have a poor set. Deduct 50% to 75% if the box is soiled, has torn or mended corners, lining stained, or any writing on the outside - especially price marks or dates.

Contents should be bright and clean, but not necessarily full. If they are clear glass, or if you can see through them, they are a little prettier if they are full, but the old ones evaporate even if they are sealed and they must never be filled with another fragrance. Fragrances or colors should match unless they were sold by Avon with mixed fragrances, or colors. For instance, an Unforgettable Rollette does not belong in A Wishing Date Book Set Rouges, lipsticks, and nail polishes should be the same colors when they appear together in a set.

If you pay a high price for a mint condition set, you have a right to expect it to be just that - mint box and mint contents.

1975-76 TRIUMPH TR-3 '56
(Left) 2 oz. blue-green glass with plastic cap. Came with Spicy or Wild Country After Shave. OSP $4, CMV $3 BO - $5 MB.

1976 PORSCHE DECANTER '68
(Right) 2 oz. amber glass with amber plastic cap. Holds Wild Country or Spicy After Shave. OSP $3, CMV $4 BO - $6 MB.

1975-76 STUDEBAKER '51
(Left) 2 oz. blue glass with blue plastic parts. Holds Avon Spicy or Wild Country. OSP $2.50, CMV $2.50 BO - $4 MB.

1975 CORVETTE STINGRAY '65
(Right) 2 oz. green glass with green plastic cap. Holds Wild Country, Deep Woods or Avon Spicy After Shave. OSP $3 - CMV $4 BO, $6 MB.

1978-79 FORD RANGER PICK-UP 1973
5 oz. blue paint over clear glass, blue plastic bed cap. Stick on decals. Came in Wild Country or Deep Woods. SSP $6.99, CMV $5 BO - $8 MB.

1969-73 GOLD CADILLAC
(Left) 6 oz. gold paint over clear glass, gold cap. Came in Excalibur, Leather and Wild Country After Shave. OSP $5 - CMV $7 BO mint, $10 MB.

1970-72 SILVER DUESENBERG
(Right) 6 oz. silver paint over clear glass. Came in Oland & Wild Country After Shave. OSP $6 - CMV $7 BO mint, $10 MB.

1976 CHRYSLER TOWN & COUNTRY '48
4.25 oz. off red painted over clear glass. Beige plastic top. Came in Everest or Wild Country. SSP $5.99, CMV $6 BO, $7 MB.

1972-75 SURE WINNER RACING CAR
(Left) 5.5 oz. blue glass with blue cap. Came in Sure Winner Bracing Lotion and Wild Country. OSP $5, CMV $5 MB - $3 BO.

1973-76 JAGUAR CAR DECANTER
5 oz. jade green glass with green plastic trunk over cap. Holds Deep Woods or Wild Country After Shave. SSP $5 - CMV $6 MB, $4 BO.

1976-77 FORD '36
5 oz. orange paint over clear glass. Plastic stick on hub caps and grill. Came in Tai Winds or Oland. SSP $5.99 - CMV $5 BO, $6 MB.

1972-75 ROLLS ROYCE
6 oz. beige painted glass with dark brown and silver plastic parts. Came in Deep Woods or Tai Winds After Shave. SSP $7 - CMV $7 BO, $9 MB.

1974-75 BUGATTI '27
6.5 oz. black glass with chrome colored plastic trim. Came with Wild Country or Deep Woods Cologne or After Shave. OSP $6, CMV $10 - $12 MB.

1974-76 CORD '37
7 oz. yellow painted with yellow plastic cap and black plastic top. Came in Tai Winds or Wild Country After Shave. SSP $7, CMV $7 MB - $5 BO.

1981-82 JEEP RENEGADE DECANTER
3 oz. black glass, stick on decals. Tan plastic top. Black cap. Sure Winner Bracing Lotion or Trazarra Cologne. SSP $9 - CMV $9 MB, $7 BO.

1980-82 VOLKSWAGON RABBIT DECANTER
3 oz. blue glass and blue plastic cap. Comes with silver stick on windows and hub caps. Choice of Light Musk Cologne or Sure Winner Bracing Lotion. SSP $8 - CMV $6 MB, $5 BO.

1979-80 BUICK SKYLARK '53
(Left) 4 oz. emerald green glass and cap. Stick on decals. Came in Clint or Everest After Shave. SSP $9.99, CMV $10 MB, $8 BO.

1979-80 VANTASTIC DECANTER
(Right) 5 oz. burgundy color glass. Stick on decals. Comes in Wild Country or Everest After Shave. SSP $6.99, CMV, $7 MB, $6 BO.

1973-74 BLUE VOLKSWAGON
(Left) 4 oz. light blue painted with plastic cap. Holds Oland or Windjammer After Shave. SSP $3, CMV $5 BO - $7 BO.

1970-72 BLACK VOLKSWAGON
(Right) 4 oz. black glass with black plastic cap. Holds Wild Country, Spicy or Electric Pre-Shave Lotion. SSP $2 - CMV $4 MB, $3 BO.

1972 RED VOLKSWAGON
(Center) 4 oz. painted red with red plastic cap. Came in Oland or Wild Country After Shave or Sports Rally Bracing Lotion. SSP $3, CMV $5 BO - $7 MB.

1972-73 MINI-BIKE
(Left) 4 oz. light amber glass coated over clear glass with light amber plastic wheel and silver handlebars with yellow grips. Came in Wild Country After Shave, Sure Winner Bracing Lotion, or Protein Hair Lotion for Men. SSP $5, CMV $5 MB - $3 BO.

1973-74 ROAD RUNNER DECANTER
(Right) 5.5 oz. blue glass with blue plastic front wheel, silver handle bars with black grips. Holds Sure Winner Bracing Lotion or Wild Country After Shave. SSP $6, CMV $6 MB - $4 BO.

1971-72 SUPER CYCLE AFTER SHAVE
(Left) 4 oz. gray glass. Came in Wild Country, Island Lime or Sports Rally Bracing Lotion. SSP $5 - CMV $6 MB, $4 BO.

1974-75 SUPER CYCLE II
(Right) Issued in blue glass. Came in Wild Country and Spicy After Shave. SSP $5, CMV $5. BO - $7. MB.

1972-75 AVON OPEN GOLF CART
(Left) 5½" long, green glass bottle with green plastic front end, red plastic golf bags. Holds 5 oz. Wild Country or Windjammer After Shave. Came in light or darker green glass. OSP $6, CMV $5 MB - $4 BO.

1974-75 SNOWMOBILE
(Right) 4 oz. blue glass with yellow plastic front and black runners. Came in Oland or Windjammer After Shave. SSP $6, CMV $4 BO - $6 MB.

PRICING CURRENT MARKET VALUE

Pricing Current Market Value

All pricing in this book for CMV has been set by several qualified Avon bottle dealers and collectors across the United States. The prices reflected are what the item is actually selling for in their respective areas. While many items have increased in value, some have been lowered; only slightly. This in no way reflects a fall out in the market of Avon collecting. It is stronger today than ever and we are trying to reflect the approximate true collector's value; or what a collector will actually pay for the item in Mint condition. All items are priced empty unless otherwise stated. On the pricing of new Avon products dated 1978 to 1983, the CMV is usually the same as the Special Selling Price Avon sold it for, or it is priced a little under the SSP. The future CMV on these products may very well fall somewhat in future issues of this book to reflect the true collector's value. Remember, the price paid to the Avon Representative is not a collector's price, but a new product price. You are paying for the contents. After you use the product, the price usually goes down and it becomes a used item. After you buy the item from Avon it is a used item. It takes some time for the item to become scarce on the collector's market before you see a true collector's price.

WHAT IS CMV?

Current Market Value — Definition: A willing buyer and a willing seller with neither under duress to make the transaction.

What makes an Avon valuable? Shape, color, unusual design, scarcity and how well it will display:

    a.   Too big — takes too much room

    b.   Too small — gets lost in collection

    c.   Odd shapes — doesn't fit shelves, also takes too much room

Condition: Refer to coin collectors. Mint means perfect condition, unused, exceptional and undamaged. Mint means Mint, commands top dollar: (See page 5 for grading examples of Mint items)

a.   Boxes were made to protect the container, keeping it clean and brilliant. Boxes advertise the product and instruct the user. Boxes tell a story. When you say original condition, that was with a box. Boxes (especially men's) were usually thrown away immediately. A good clean, crisp box will help make the item bring a premium.

b.   Grading and condition become even more important for an item with a CMV over $25.00.

c.   Example: 1966-67 Tall Pony Post. The box is probably the hardest to find of the modern figurals. Box should have a premium price.

Sets — The bug-a-boo of Avon grading!! Many sets have a premium value because they display so well. They are packaged in unusual ways and are much harder to find with perfect box and superior contents. I agree with the statement: Poor box - poor set, subtract 50% to 75% of listed value.

A mint box is at least twice as hard to obtain as the mint bottle that came in it. As good as Avon is in packaging - order 10 items of the same thing and only 4 will be truly mint boxes and containers. That is: creased or crushed box, corner of label not securely glued.

1973-75 THE HARVESTER DECANTER

(Left) 5.5 oz. amber glass with amber plastic front. Holds Wild Country After Shave or Protein Hair Lotion for men. OSP $5 - CMV $10 BO, $14 MB.

1975-76 CHEVY '55

(Right) 5 oz. sprayed green glass with white plastic parts. Holds Wild Country or Electric Pre-Shave Lotion. SSP $5 - CMV $6 BO, $8 MB.

1978 TOURING T SILVER

6 oz. silver plated over clear glass. May, 1978 on bottom. Came in Deep Woods or Everest. SSP $8.99, CMV $6 BO, $8 MB.

1978 STERLING SIX SILVER

7 oz. silver plated over clear glass. Came in Tai Winds or Deep Woods After Shave. May 1978 on bottom. SSP $8.99 - CMV $6 BO, $8 MB.

1974-77 STUTZ BEARCAT 1914

(Left) 6 oz. red painted with black plastic seats and cap. Came in Oland or Blend 7 After Shave. SSP $6, CMV $6 MB - $5 BO.

1974-75 MG DECANTER 1936

(Right) 5 oz. red painted with red plastic cap and white plastic top. Came in Avon Blend 7, Tai Winds or Wild Country After Shave. SSP $4, CMV $4 BO - $5 MB.

1970-71 COVERED WAGON

(Left) 6 oz. 4½'' long. Dark amber glass bottom, white painted top and gold cap. Came in Spicy and Wild Country After Shave. OSP $5, CMV $4 MB - $5.

1971-72 SIDE WHEELER

(Right) 5 oz. dark amber glass, black plastic stacks, silver cap, brown label. Came in Wild Country and Spicy After Shave. OSP $6 - CMV $3 BO, $5 MB. Reissued 1976 in Tai Winds, gold cap, white label, same CMV.

1974-75 ARMY JEEP

(Left) 4 oz. olive drab green with plastic closure. Came with Wild Country or Avon Spicy After Shave. OSP $5, CMV $5 BO - $6 MB.

1974-76 GOLDEN ROCKET 0-2-2

(Right) 6 oz. smokey gold over clear glass with gold plastic cap. Came in Tai Winds or Wild Country After Shave. OSP $7, CMV $7 MB - $6 BO. Factory reject from factory is indented sides and gold coated. CMV $20.

1971-72 FIRST VOLUNTEER

6 oz. gold coated over clear glass. Oland or Tai Winds Cologne. OSP $8.50, CMV $8 BO - $10 MB.

1975 FIRE FIGHTER 1910 DECANTER

6 oz. red painted over glass with red plastic back. Came in Wild Country or Tai Winds After Shave. OSP $6, CMV $7 MB, $5 BO.

1973 COUNTRY VENDOR DECANTER

5 oz. brown glass with brown plastic top, has picture of fruits and vegetables on side. Holds Wild Country or Avon Spicy After Shave. SSP $7, CMV $8 MB - $6 BO.

1977-78 CHECKER CAB 1926

5 oz. yellow painted over clear glass. Black plastic trunk cap and top. Stick on decal hub caps, bumper and checker design. Came in Everest or Wild Country. SSP $6.99 - CMV $6 BO, $7 MB.

1968-70 STERLING SIX

7 oz. came in 4 different shades of amber glass, black tire cap, rough top roof. Came in Spicy, Tribute, Leather After Shave. OSP $4 - CMV $5 BO, $7 MB. Smooth top in very light amber glass. Test bottle. CMV $45.

1973-74 STERLING SIX II

7 oz. green glass with white tire cap. Came in Wild Country or Tai Winds After Shave. SSP $4, CMV $5 BO - $7 MB.

1972-74 MAXWELL '23 DECANTER

6 oz. green glass with beige plastic top and trunk over cap. Came in Deep Woods or Tribute Cologne or After Shave. SSP $5-CMV $6, $8 MB

1969-71 STRAIGHT 8

(Left) 5 oz. dark green glass with black trunk cap. No. 8 on hood. Came in Wild Country, Windjammer and Island Lime After Shave. Label says "Avon for Men". OSP $3.50, CMV $6 MB - $4 BO.

1973-75 STRAIGHT 8

(Left) 5 oz. green glass. Came in Wild Country and Island Lime After Shave. Label says Avon - Keep out of reach of children. OSP $3.50, CMV $2 BO - $4 MB.

1971-73 DUNE BUGGY

(Right) 5 oz. blue glass, silver motor cap. Came in Spicy After Shave, Liquid Hair Lotion and Sports Rally Bracing Lotion. OSP $5, CMV $3 MB - $5.

1969-70 TOURING T

(Left) 6½" long, 6 oz. black glass with black plastic top and tire cap. Came in Excalibur or Tribute After Shave. OSP $6, CMV $5 BO - $7 MB.

1972-74 MODEL A

(Right) 4 oz. yellow painted over clear glass, yellow cap. Holds Wild Country or Leather After Shave. SSP $4, CMV $3 BO - $4.50 MB.

1970-72 ELECTRIC CHARGER

(Left) 5 oz. black glass with red trunk cap and red side decals. Came in Spicy, Leather or Wild Country After Shave. OSP $4 - CMV $4 BO, $5 MB.

1970-77 STAGE COACH

(Right) 5 oz. dark amber glass with gold cap. Came in Wild Country, Tai Winds or Oland After Shave. 1977 issue has "R" on bottom for Reissue - hard to find silver cap. CMV $7 for reissue. OSP $5, CMV $3 BO, $5 MB.

1975-76 VOLKSWAGON BUS DECANTER

(Left) 5 oz. red painted glass with silver gray motorcycle plastic closure. Set of 4 "decorate-it-yourself" labels come with each decanter. Came with Tai Winds After Shave or Sure Winner Bracing Lotion. OSP $5, CMV $6 BO, $8 MB.

1974-75 THE THOMAS FLYER 1908

(Right) 6 oz. white painted glass with red and blue plastic parts with white tire cap on back. Came in Wild Country or Oland After Shave. OSP $6, CMV $4 BO - $6 MB.

1971-73 STATION WAGON

6 oz. green glass car with tan plastic top. Came in Wild Country or Tai Winds After Shave. OSP $6 - CMV $6 BO, $8 MB.

1971-72 STANLEY STEAMER

5 oz. blue glass bottle with black plastic seats and tire cap. Came in Wild Country or Windjammer After Shave. OSP $5, CMV $4 BO - $6 MB.

1973-74 HAYNES APPERSON 1902

4.5 oz. green glass with green plastic front over cap. Has silver tiller steering rod. Holds Avon Blend 7 or Tai Winds After Shave. SSP $5, CMV $5 MB - $3 BO.

1972-73 REO DEPOT WAGON
5" long, 5 oz. amber glass with black plastic top and cap. Holds Tai Winds and Oland After Shave Lotion. OSP $6 - CMV $5 MB, $7

1979-80 CEMENT MIXER DECANTER
3 piece bottle. Front section is dark amber glass. Comes in Wild Country or Everest After Shave. Center plastic section connects to 6 oz. pale yellow plastic rear section bottle. Holds talc. Has stick on decals. SSP $12., CMV $11 BO, $13 MB.

1976-77 CANNONBALL EXPRESS 4-6-0
3.25 oz. black glass, black cap. Came in Deep Woods or Wild Country Cologne or After Shave. SSP $6., CMV $4 BO - $6 MB.

1970-72 PACKARD ROADSTER
6 oz. light amber glass and matching plastic rumble seat cap. Came in Oland and Leather Cologne. 6½" long. OSP $6, CMV $4 MB - $6.

1978-79 TRAIN 1876 CENTENNIAL EXPRESS DECANTER
5.5 oz. dark green glass with stick on trim decals. Holds Wild Country or Everest After Shave. SSP $6., CMV $4. BO - $6. MB.

1971-72 GENERAL 4-4-0
5½ oz. dark blue glass and cap. Came in Tai Winds or Wild Country After Shave. OSP $7.50 - CMV $6 MB, $8.

1977-79 HIGHWAY KING
4 oz. green glass bottle with white plastic center connection piece and rear section is 6.5 oz. white plastic talc bottle. Came in Wild Country or Everest. OSP $12.50 - CMV $8 BO, $11 MB.

1974-75 CABLE CAR AFTER SHAVE DECANTER
4 oz. green painted over clear glass has plastic green and white top. Came in Wild Country or Avon Leather. SSP $7, CMV $6 BO - $8 MB.

1973-74 RAINBOW TROUT DECANTER
(Left) Plastic head over cap. Holds Deep Woods or Tai Winds. SSP $5, CMV $5 MB, $4 BO.

1975-76 BIG RIG
3.5 oz. blue glass cab with 6 oz. white & blue plastic trailer. Cab holds After Shave, trailer holds Talc in Wild Country or Deep Woods. OSP $10, CMV $9 BO, $12 MB.

1973-75 ATLANTIC 4-4-2 DECANTER
5 oz. silver over clear glass with silver plastic parts. Holds Deep Woods or Leather After Shave or Cologne. SSP $8, CMV $8 MB - $6 BO.

1972 SEA TROPHY
(Right) 5.5 oz. lt. blue with plastic blue head over cap. Came in Wild Country or Windjammer After Shave. SSP $5, CMV $7 BO, $9 MB.

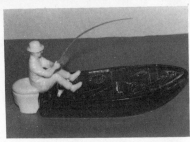

1973-74 GONE FISHING DECANTER

5 oz. lt. blue boat with white plastic man, yellow fishing rod. Came in Tai Winds or Spicy. SSP $6, CMV $7 MB, $5 BO.

1970 CAPTAINS PRIDE

6 oz. bottle with ship decal, tan cap & blue neck label. Sits on black plastic stand. Came in Oland & Windjammer After Shave. OSP $5, CMV $4 BO, $6 MB.

1974-75 AMERICAN EAGLE PIPE

5 oz dark amber glass with gold plastic top & black handle. Holds Wild Country or Tai Winds Cologne. OSP $5, CMV $5 MB, $3 BO.

1974-75 CALABASH PIPE DECANTER

3 oz. yellow gold sprayed glass with yellow gold plastic cap & black plastic stand. Holds Wild Country or Deep Woods After Shave. OPS $8, CMV $9, $7 BO.

1972-73 AMERICAN SCHOONER DECANTER

4.5 oz. blue glass with blue plastic end over cap. Some are blue painted over clear glass. Came in Oland or Spicy After Shave, SSP $5, CMV $5 MB, $4 BO.

1977-79 VIKING DISCOVERER

4 oz. blue green glass & matching plastic cap. Red & white metal sail. Black plastic sail post. Came in Wild Country or Everest. SSP $9.99, CMV $7 BO, $9 MB.

1975-76 UNCLE SAM PIPE

3 oz. white opal glass with blue band & blue plastic stem. Holds Wild Country or Deep Woods After Shave. OSP $5, CMV $5 MB, $4 BO.

1975-76 PONY EXPRESS RIDER PIPE DECANTER

3 oz. white milk glass with black plastic stem. Holds Wild Country or Tai Winds Cologne. OSP $5, CMV $5 MB, $4 BO.

1974-75 CORNCOB PIPE DECANTER

3 oz. amber glass with black plastic stem. Holds Wild Country or Avon Spicy. OSP $3, CMV $3 BO, $4 MB.

1976 BLOOD HOUND PIPE DECANTER

5 oz. lt. tan paint over clear glass, brown & silver cap. Came in Wild Country or Deep Woods After Shave. OSP $7 - CMV $6 MB, $5 BO.

1976 CHIEF PONTIAC CAR ORNAMENT CLASSIC

4 oz. black ribbed glass with silver Indian. Came in Tai Winds or Deep Woods After Shave. OSP $8, CMV $5 BO, $6 MB.

1967 PIPE DREAM

6 oz. dark amber glass, black cap, tan plastic base. Came in Spicy, Tribute & Leather After Shave. OSP $5, CMV $15 BO, $20 MB.

1967 PIPE DREAM CLEAR TEST BOTTLE

6 oz. clear glass factory test bottle. Very Rare. CMV $250.00.

1976-77 WILD MUSTANG PIPE DECANTER

3 oz. white paint over clear glass. Holds Wild Country or Deep Woods cologne. SSP. $5 - CMV $5 MB, $4 BO.

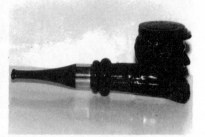

1972-73 BULL DOG PIPE DECANTER
6 oz. cream colored milk glass with black stem. Came in Wild Country or Oland After Shave or Cologne. SSP $4 - CMV $5 BO, $6 MB.

1973-74 DUTCH PIPE
2 oz. white milk glass, blue design, silver handle & cap. Came in Tribute or Tia Winds Cologne. SSP $7, CMV $7 BO, $9 MB.

1973-74 COLLECTOR'S PIPE DECANTER
3 oz brown glass with black stem. Holds Deep Woods or Windjammer After Shave or Cologne. SSP $3, CMV $5 MB, $3 BO.

1968-69 SHORT PONY DECANTER
(Right) 4 oz. green glass, gold cap. Came in Wild Country, Windjammer, Spicy, Leather or Electric Pre-Shave. OSP $3.50 - CMV $3 BO, $4 MB.

SHORT PONY, FOREIGN, DECANTER
Gold cap, greenish amber color. $7 Bright green from Germany MB $15.

1971-72 PIPE FULL DECANTER
2 oz. brown glass with black stem. Holds Spicy, Oland, Tai Winds or Excalibur After Shave. SSP $2, CMV $3 MB, $2 BO.

1972-74 PIPE FULL DECANTER
2 oz. lt green glass with brown plastic stem. Holds Tai Winds or Spicy After Shave. SSP $2, CMV $2 BO, $3 MB.

1973-74 PONY POST MINIATURE
1.5 oz clear glass with gold cap & ring. Holds Oland or Spicy After Shave. OSP $3, CMV $2 BO, $3 MB.

1972-73 PONY POST
5 oz. bronze paint over clear glass with bronze cap & nose ring. Holds Tai Winds or Leather After Shave. OSP $5 - CMV $5 BO, $5 MB.

1966-67 PONY POST "TALL"
8 oz. green glass with gold cap & nose ring. Holds Island Lime, Tribute or Leather After Shave. OSP $4, CMV $13 MB, $6 BO.

1967-69 TWENTY PACES
3 oz. each, 10" long. Gold paint over clear glass, gold cap. Red paper labels on end of barrel. Came in All Purpose Cologne, Wild Country & Leather After Shave. OSP $11.95, CMV brown box lined with red $40, black Lined box $120, blue lined box $160 Very rare gun with raised sight did not break off in glass mold. CMV $100. Raised sight gun only. Regular issue guns $10 each mint.

1980-82 PHILADELPHIA DERRINGER DECANTER
2 oz. dark amber glass with grey stick on parts & gold trim. Came in Light Musk or Brisk Spice After Shave. SSP $10 - CMV $10 MB, $9 BO.

1976-77 PEPPERBOX PISTOL 1850
(top) 3 oz. silver plated over clear glass barrel bottle with gold and brown plastic handle cap. Came in Everest or Tai Winds. SSP $7.77, CMV $8 MB, $6 BO.

1982-83 PEPPER BOX PISTOL
Reissued in gold tone instead of silver came in Clint and Wild Country. SSP $11 - CMV $6.50 MB.

1977 DERRINGER
(bottom) 2 oz. gold plated over amber glass. Came in Deep Woods or Wild Country. SSP $6.66 - CMV $6 BO, $7 MB.

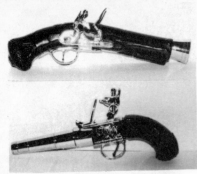

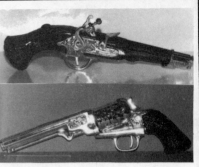

1976 BLUNDERBUSS PISTOL 1780
(top) 12½" long, 5.5 oz. dark amber glass, gold cap & plastic trigger. Came in Everest & Wild Country. OSP $12, CMV $10 MB, $9 BO.

1978-79 THOMAS JEFFERSON HAND GUN DECANTER
(bottom) 10" long, 2.5 oz. dark amber glass with gold & silver plastic cap. Holds Deep Woods or Everest cologne. SSP $9.99 - CMV $10 MB, $8 BO.

1979-80 GAS PUMP - REMEMBER WHEN DECANTER
4 oz. clear glass painted yellow, white top, yellow cap. Came in Light Musk, or cool Sage. SSP $6.99 - CMV $7 MB, $5 BO.

1979-80 VOLCANIC REPEATING PISTOL DECANTER
2 oz. silver coated over clear glass. Silver & pearl plastic handle. Holds Wild Country or Brisk Spice Cologne. SSP $10.99, CMV $9 BO, $11 MB.

1973-74 DUELING PISTOL 1760
(top) 4 oz. brown glass with silver clamp on parts, silver cap. Holds Deep Woods or Tai Winds After Shave. SSP $8 - CMV $8 MB, $6 BO.

1975 DUELING PISTOL II
Same as above but black glass & gold plastic parts. Came in Wild Country or Tai Winds. SSP $8, CMV $8 BO, $9 MB.

1975-76 COLT REVOLVER 1851
(bottom) 3 oz. amber glass with silver plastic barrel. Holds Wild Country or Deep Woods After Shave. OSP $9, CMV $9 MB, $8 BO.

1975-76 LONGHORN STEER
5 oz. dark amber glass with amber plastic head, ivory colored horns. Holds Wild Country or Tai Winds After Shave. OSP $6, CMV $6 BO, $7 MB.

1972-73 OLD FAITHFUL
5 oz. brown glass with brown plastic head & gold keg. Holds Wild Country or Spicy After Shave. SSP $5, CMV $6 BO, $8 MB. Smaller German St. Bernard on right (silver barrel) CMV $12.

HOW TO INVEST
RULES FOR COLLECTING

"The hunger to find a tin toy for $30.00, rather than a good night's sleep drives a painter to wake up at three in the morning in his Brooklyn home. He's rushing to Rennger's flea market in Pennsylvania by the time the rosy fingers of dawn peak over the tents." Does this sound familiar? Of course it does, if you're an Avon collector. How many foolish things have you ever done while seeking that hoped-for bargain or very much sought after item? People are doing this kind of thing in every part of America — and they are doing it for almost anything you could name; be it a tin toy or a campaign button. In today's market, anything is collectible if it has aesthetic vitality, if it's pleasing to the eye and to the senses. However, we are interested in Avon and California Perfume . . . and Avon collecting is now a big collecting field. For the new collectors and to refresh seasoned collectors — we have found collecting, like other investments, has rules to follow for the best results:

● If you don't like an item, don't buy it no matter how much of a bargain it seems to be. The only good investments are those that are enjoyed.

● The old goes up in value, or at least retains its resale value. New items take longer to increase in value and stay around longer. Of course, we all know, there are more collectors today.

● Buy it when you see it. Avons don't stay put . . . some don't have a very long shelf life.

● If you don't know your dealers, be sure you know your Avons. Fakes can be convincing (don't we all know that!).

● It is acceptable to haggle - it cannot hurt to ask if there is a lower price. Often in a booth or flea market there will be a better price available - don't be timid.

● Start small and learn the market. Browse, study the guides and learn all you can before you start buying.

● Measure your space - don't be the collector who buys a lot of items only to bring them home with no place to put them (ha, ha).

● Don't change your item in any way - don't paint it, add lettering, etc. . . . this may destroy the value.

The above rules are good ones to keep in mind — the advice I've found most helpful is to have FUN while collecting . . . whether it be at a flea market, garage sale or convention.

1975-77 NOBLE PRINCE DECANTER

4 oz. brown glass with brown plastic head. Holds Wild Country After Shave or Electric Pre-Shave Lotion. OSP $3.25, CMV $4 MB, $3 BO.

1973-75 CLASSIC LION

8 oz. green glass with green plastic head. Holds Wild Country, Tribute After Shave or Deep Woods Emollient After Shave. OSP $6 - CMV $6 MB, $5 BO.

1973-74 AT POINT DECANTER

5 oz. redish brown glass with redish brown plastic head. Came in Deep Woods or Tribute. SSP $4, CMV $4 MB, $2 BO.

1969-71 SNOOPY SURPRISE

5 oz., 5½" high. White glass with blue or yellow hat & black ears. Came in Wild Country, Excalibur After Shave & Sports Rally Bracing Lotion. OSP $4, CMV $3, $5 MB.

1972-74 PHEASANT DECANTER

5 oz. brown glass with green plastic head. Holds Oland or Leather After Shave. OSP $6, CMV $6 MB, $4 BO.

1973-74 CANADA GOOSE DECANTER

5 oz. brown glass with black plastic head. Holds Deep Woods, Wild Country or Everest After Shave or Cologne. OSP $6, CMV $6 BO, $8 MB. Reissued in 1976 in smaller box in After Shave only. Same CMV.

1977 MAJESTIC ELEPHANT

5.5 oz. gray painted over clear glass. Gray head cap. Came in Wild Country or Deep Woods. SSP $9 - CMV $7 BO, $9 MB.

1977-79 FAITHFUL LADDIE

(Left) 4 oz. light amber glass & amber head cap. Came in Wild Country or Deep Woods. SSP $4.99, CMV $5 MB, $4 BO.

1977 KODIAK BEAR

(Right) 6 oz. dark amber glass & head. Came in Wild Country or Deep Woods. SSP $5, CMV $4 BO, $5 MB.

1971-72 PONY EXPRESS

5 oz. brown glass with copper colored man on cap. Came in Avon Leather or Wild Country After Shave. SSP $4, CMV $6 MB, $4 BO.

1971-72 BUCKING BRONCO

6 oz. dark amber glass horse with bronze plastic cowboy cap. Came in Oland or Excalibur. OSP $6, CMV $6 MB, $4 BO.

1975 SPORT OF KINGS DECANTER

5 oz. amber glass with plastic head. Holds Wild Country, Avon Spicy or Avon Leather After Shave. OSP $5, CMV $5 MB, $4 BO.

1975-76 THE AMERICAN BUFFALO

5 oz. amber glass with amber plastic head & ivory colored horns. Holds Wild Country or Deep Woods After Shave. OSP $6, CMV $6 BO, $7 MB.

1977 PHEASANT DECANTER

Same bottle as 1972-74 issue only came in Deep Woods or Wild Country and box is smaller than early issue. SSP $6 - CMV $7 MB, $6 BO.

1976-77 WILDERNESS CLASSIC

6 oz. silver plated over clear glass. Silver plastic head. Came in Sweet Honesty or Deep Woods. SSP $9, CMV $11 MB, $9 BO.

1974-75 ALASKAN MOOSE
8 oz. amber glass with cream colored plastic antlers. Holds Deep Woods or Wild Country After Shave. OSP $7, CMV $7 BO, $9 MB.

1973-74 TEN-POINT BUCK DECANTER
6 oz. reddish brown glass with reddish brown plastic head & gold antlers. Holds Wild Country or Leather After Shave. OSP $7 - CMV $8 MB, $6 BO.

1967-68 MALLARD DUCK
6 oz. green glass, silver head. Came in Spicy, Tribute, Blue Blazer, Windjammer After Shave. OSP $5, CMV $7 BO, $11 MB.

1974-76 MALLARD-IN-FLIGHT
5 oz. amber glass with green plastic head. Holds Wild Country or Tai Winds Cologne or After Shave. OSP $6, CMV $7 MB, $6 BO.

1974-76 WILD TURKEY
6 oz. amber glass with silver & red plastic head. Holds Wild Country or Deep Woods After Shave. OSP $5, CMV $5 BO, $6 MB.

1973-75 QUAIL DECANTER
5.5 oz. brown glass, gold cap. Came in Avon Blend 7, Deep Woods or Wild Country After Shave. OSP $6, CMV $5 MB, $4 BO.

1971 DUCK AFTER SHAVE
3 oz. glass bottles with gold caps & ducks painted on sides. Came in Collector's Organizer Set only in Tai Winds & Wild Country After Shave. CMV $4 each.

1971-72 AMERICAN EAGLE
6" high, dark amber glass with silver eagle head. Holds 5 oz. Oland or Windjammer After Shave. OSP $5, CMV $4 MB, $5

1973-75 Eagle is black glass with dark gold head. CMV $5 BO, $6 MB.

1964-65 CAPTAIN'S CHOICE
(Right) 8 oz. green glass with green paper label, gold cap. Came in Spicy & Original After Shave Lotion, Electric Pre-Shave Lotion, Spicy After Shower Cologne for men & Vigorate After Shave Lotion. OSP $2.50, CMV $7, $10 in box.

1975-76 REVOLUTIONARY CANNON
2 oz. bronze spray over glass with plastic cap. Holds Avon Spicy or Avon Blend 7 After Shave. OSP $4, CMV $4 MB, $3 BO.

1973-74 HOMESTEAD DECANTER
4 oz. brown glass with gray plastic chimney over cap. Holds Wild Country After Shave or Electric Pre-Shave. OSP $3, CMV $3 MB, $2 BO.

1972-73 BIG GAME RHINO
4 oz. green glass with green plastic head over cap. Came in Spicy or Tai Winds After Shave. SSP $4, CMV $4 BO, $5 MB.

1972-73 BLACKSMITH'S ANVIL DECANTER
4 oz. black glass with silver cap. Came in Deep Woods or Avon Leather After Shave. SSP $4, CMV $4 MB, $3 BO.

1976-77 CAPITOL DECANTER
4.5 oz. white milk glass with white cap & gold tip. Came in Spicy or Wild Country After Shave. OSP $4, CMV $5 MB, $4 BO.

1970-72 CAPITOL DECANTER
5 oz. lt amber glass or clear glass coated amber, gold cap. Came in Leather & Tribute After Shave. OSP $5, CMV $7 MB, $5 BO.

1969-70 WISE CHOICE OWL
4 oz. silver top, lt amber bottom. Came in Excalibur or Leather After Shave. OSP $4, CMV $5 MB $7

1972-73 RADIO
5" high, dark amber glass with gold cap & paper dial on front. Holds 5 oz. liquid Hair Lotion, Wild Country or Spicy After Shave. OSP $4, CMV $4 MB, $5

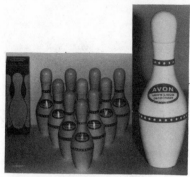

1960-62 BOWLING PIN
4 oz. white plastic trimmed in red. Came in Vigorate, Liquid Deodorant, Hand Guard, Hair Trainer, After Shaving Lotion, After Shower for Men, Liquid Hair Lotion, Shampoo, Cream Hair Lotion & Electric Pre-Shave. OSP $1.19, CMV 10 different. $16 each BO, $20 MB. Vigorate $20 BO, $24 MB.

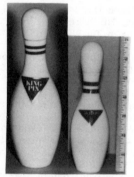

1969-70 KING PIN
(Left) 4 oz. 6½" high. White glass & cap, red label. Came in Wild Country & Bravo After Shave. OSP $3, CMV $4 MB, $3 BO.

1978-79 STRIKE DECANTER
(Right) 4 oz. white milk glass, white cap. Red painted on AMF designs. Came in Sweet Honesty of Wild Country. SSP $3.66, CMV $3 MB, $2 BO.

1973-75 LONG DRIVE DECANTER
4 oz. brown glass with black cap. Holds Deep Woods After Shave or Electric Pre-Shave Lotion. SSP $4, CMV $4 MB, $3 BO.

1973-75 TEE-OFF DECANTER
3 oz. white golf ball on a yellow tee & fits into a green plastic green. Holds Protein Hair Lotion for Men, Avon Spicy After Shave or Electric Pre-Shave Lotion. SSP $3, CMV $4 MB, $3 BO.

1965-66 BOOT "SILVER TOP"
8 oz. amber glass, silver cap with hook on cap. Came in Leather All Purpose Lotion for Men. OSP $5, CMV $7, $10 in box.

1966-71 BOOT "GOLD TOP"
8 oz. amber glass with hook on cap. Came in Leather All purpose Cologne for Men. OSP $5, CMV $3 MB, $4 Gold top boot with no hook on cap is 1971-72 with Leather Cologne. OSP $5 - CMV $3 BO, $4 MB.

1967-70 BOOT SPRAY COLOGNE
3 oz. tan plastic coated with black cap. Came in Leather All Purpose Cologne in early issues. CMV $6 MB, & Leather Cologne Spray in later issues OSP $4 - CMV $4 MB, $5.

1975-76 RAM'S HEAD DECANTER
5 oz. white opal glass on brown plastic base. Holds Wild Country or Avon Blend 7 After Shave. OSP $5, CMV $5 MB, $4 BO.

1975-76 MINUTEMAN DECANTER
4 oz. white opal glass with plastic top. Holds Wild Country or Tai Winds After Shave. OSP $7, CMV $7 BO, $8 MB.

1973-75 WESTERN BOOT
5 oz. dark amber glass bottle, silver cap & clamp on spurs. Came in Wild Country or Leather. SSP $4, CMV $4 MB, $3 BO.

1974-76 SUPER SHOE DECANTER
6 oz. white plastic shoe with blue plastic toe section cap. Holds Sure Winner Liquid Hair Trainer or Sure Winner Bracing Lotion. OSP $3, CMV $3 MB, $2 BO

1974-75 JUST FOR KICKS DECANTER
7 oz. black & white plastic shoe with black plastic cap. Holds Avon Spicy or Avon Sure Winner Bracing Lotion. OSP $4 - CMV $4 MB, $3 BO.

1968-69 OPENING PLAY
6 oz. each, 4" high. Gold caps, white plastic face guards. Came in Sports Rally Bracing Lotion, Spicy & Wild Country After Shave. OSP ea $4, Shiny gold over blue glass was issued one campaign only, on last campaign Open Play was sold. CMV Shiny gold $25. In box $30. Dull gold over blue glass with blue stripe CMV $10, $12 MB. Dull gold over blue glass, no stripe, CMV $14, in box $16.

1973-74 MARINE BINOCULARS DECANTER

Black over clear glass with gold caps. One side holds 4 oz. Tai Winds or Tribute Cologne, other side holds 4 oz. Tai Winds or Tribute After Shave. SSP $8, CMV $8 MB, $6 BO.

1973-74 SURE WINNER BASEBALL DECANTER

White ball with dark blue lettering, dark blue base contains Liquid Hair Trainer. SSP $2, CMV $3.50 MB, $2 BO.

1970 Only FIRST DOWN

5 oz. brown glass, white plastic base. Came in Wild Country or Sports Rally Bracing Lotion. OSP $4, CMV $5 MB, $4 BO.

1973-74 FIRST DOWN — 5 oz. brown glass, white base. Came in Deep Woods & Sure Winner Bracing Lotion. SSP $3, CMV $4 MB, $3 BO.

1975-76 THEODORE ROOSEVELT

(Left) 6 oz. white paint over clear glass. Came in Wild Country or Tai Winds After Shave. OSP $9, CMV $7 BO, $9 MB.

1977-78 THOMAS JEFFERSON

(Right) 5 oz. white paint over clear glass. White head cap. Came in Wild Country or Everest After Shave. SSP $8, CMV $6 BO, $8 MB.

1973-75 PASS PLAY DECANTER

5 oz. blue glass with white soft plastic top over cap. Came in Sure Winner Bracing Lotion or Wild Country After Shave. OSP $5, CMV $7 BO, $8 MB.

1975-76 PERFECT DRIVE DECANTER

4 oz. green glass with white plastic top over cap. Holds Avon Spicy After Shave or Avon Protein Hair/Scalp Conditioner. OSP $6, CMV $7 BO, $8 MB.

1974-76 PRESIDENT WASHINGTON DECANTER

6 oz. white spray over clear glass, white plastic head. Holds Wild Country or Tai Winds After Shave. (1976 came in Deep Woods or Tai Winds After Shave) OSP $6, CMV $6 BO, $7 MB.

1973 PRESIDENT LINCOLN DECANTER

6 oz. white spray over clear glass, white plastic head. Holds Wild Country or Tai Winds After Shave. OSP $5, CMV $9 BO, $12 MB.

1974-76 BENJAMIN FRANKLIN DECANTER

6 oz. white spray over clear glass, white plastic head. Holds Wild Country or Tai Winds After Shave. OSP $6, CMV $6 BO, $7 MB.

CHESS PIECE DECANTER (THE ORIGINAL SET)

3 oz. dark amber glass with silver toned tops.

1971-72 SMART MOVE

Came in Tribute & Oland Cologne. OSP $4, CMV $8.

1973-78 Smart Move came in Wild Country After Shave or Protein Hair/Scalp Conditioner. OSP $4, CMV $4 MB.

1972-73 THE KING

Came in Tai Winds or Oland After Shave. OSP $4, CMV $8 MB.

1973-78 The King came in Wild Country or Oland. OSP $4, CMV $4 MB.

1973-74 THE QUEEN

Came in Tai Winds or Oland After Shave. OSP $4, CMV $7 MB.

1974-78 The Queen came in Wild Country or Deep Woods After Shave. OSP $4, CMV $4 MB.

1973-74 THE ROOK

Came in Oland & Spicy After Shave. OSP $4, CMV $7 MB.

1974-78 The Rook came in Wild Country or Avon Spicy After Shave. OSP $4, CMV $4 MB.

1974-78 THE BISHOP

Came in Wild Country, Avon Blend 7 or Avon Protein Hair Lotion for Men. OSP $4, CMV $4 MB.

1974-78 THE PAWN

Came in Wild Country, Oland, or Electric Pre-Shave Lotion. OSP $4, CMV $6 BO, $8 MB.

(Pieces needed for one side are 2 Smart Moves, 1 King, 1 Queen, 2 Rooks, 2 Bishops, 8 Pawns.) Early issue Chess Pieces do not have name on label.

1979 PRESIDENT LINCOLN BRONZE DECANTER

6 oz. bronze tone over clear glass. Dated 1979 on bottom. Holds Deep Woods or Everest After Shave. SSP $11, CMV $11 MB.

1979 PRESIDENT WASHINGTON BRONZE DECANTER

6 oz. bronze tone over clear glass. Dated 1979 on bottom. Holds Wild Country or Tai Winds After Shave. SSP $11, CMV $11 MB.

CHESS PIECE DECANTER (THE OPPOSING SET) . . . 3 oz. silver over clear or amber glass with amber plastic tips. OSP $3 - CMV $3 BO, $4 MB. Pawns CMV $6 BO, $8 MB. Silver over clear are hard to find.

1975-78 SMART MOVE II
Came in Wild Country After Shave, Avon Protein Hair Lotion or Avon Protein Hair/Scalp Conditioner for Men.

1975-78 THE KING II
Came in Avon Spicy After Shave or Avon Protein Hair Lotion.

1975-78 THE QUEEN II
Came in Avon Spicy After Shave or Avon Protein Hair/Scalp Conditioner.

1975-78 THE ROOK II
Came in Wild Country After Shave or Protein Hair Lotion for Men.

1975-78 THE BISHOP II
Came in Avon Spicy After Shave or Avon Protein Hair Lotion for men. CMV $5 MB, $4 BO.

1975-78 THE PAWN II
Came in Avon Spicy After Shave or Avon Protein Hair/Scalp Conditioner for Men.

(Pieces needed for one side are 2 Smart Moves, 1 King, 1 Queen, 2 Rooks, 2 Bishops, 8 Pawns.)

1973 AVON CALLING 1905 DECANTER
7 oz. brown glass with brown plastic top, has gold bell & black plastic receiver. Holds 7 oz. After Shave and .75 oz. Talc. Came in Wild Country or Avon Spicy. SSP $9, CMV $8 BO - $10 MB.

1969-70 AVON CALLING FOR MEN
8½" high, 6 oz. gold paint over clear glass, gold cap, black mouth piece, black plastic ear piece. Holds 1¼ oz. Talc. Came in Wild Country and Leather Cologne. OSP $8, CMV $10 MB - $12.

1970-72 WASHINGTON BOTTLE
5½" high, 4 oz. bottle with gold eagle cap. Holds Spicy or Tribute After Shave. OSP $3.50, CMV $3 MB - $2 BO.

1971-72 LINCOLN BOTTLE
5½" high, 4 oz. bottle with gold eagle cap. Holds Wild Country or Leather After Shave. OSP $3.50, CMV $3 MB - $2 BO.

1971-72 WESTERN SADDLE
5 oz. brown glass with brown cap, sets on beige fence. Came in Wild Country or Avon Leather After Shave. SSP $6, CMV $5 BO and fence $7 MB.

1977-78 MIXED DOUBLES TENNIS BALL
(Left) 3 oz. light green flock over clear glass. Green cap base. Came in Sweet Honesty Body Splash or Avon Spicy. SSP $3.99, CMV $2 BO - $4 MB.

1977 SURE CATCH
(Right) 1 oz. white milk glass, with red cap, yellow tassel, black eyes. Came in Spicy or Wild Country. SSP $4, CMV $3 BO - $4 MB.

1976-80 GOOD SHOT
(Left) 2 oz. plastic bottle, gold cap. Red bottle in Wild Country or Brisk Spice After Shave and yellow bottle in Deep Woods or Cool Sage After Shave. SSP $2.99, CMV $2 BO - $3 MB. Add $5 for cap on wrong end.

1977-78 WILD WEST "BULLIT"
(Right) 1.5 oz. bronze plated over clear glass. Silver top. Wild Country or Everest. SSP $2.50, CMV $2 BO - $3 MB.

1977-78 FIRM GRIP
(Left) 1.5 oz. silver plated over clear glass. Came in Wild Country or Everest. SSP $3.99, CMV $3 BO - $4 MB.

1977-78 WEATHER VANE
(Right) 4 oz. red painted over clear glass. Silver top with black horse weather vane. Came in Wild Country or Deep Woods. SSP $4.99, CMV $4 MB.

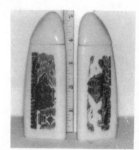

1973 WHALE ORGANIZER BOTTLES
3 oz. ivory milk glass with dark blue design. Holds After Shave & Cologne in Deep Woods or Avon Blend 7. Sold only in Whale Organizer. CMV $5 each.

1978-79 GET THE MESSAGE DECANTER
(Left) 3 oz. black glass base with silver & black plastic top. Came in Clint or Sweet Honesty. SSP $5.99, CMV $4 MB - $3 BO.

1978-80 NO CAUSE FOR ALARM DECANTER
(Right) 4 oz. silver plated over clear glass. Silver plastic top. Came in Deep Woods, or Tai Winds. SSP $7.99, CMV $6.50 MB - $5.50 BO.

1977-80 NBA DECANTER
(Left) Came with your choice of individual NBA team labels. Came in Wild Country or Sure Winner Bracing Lotion. 6 oz. dark amber glass. Silver top. SSP $6.99, CMV $6 MB - $5 BO.

1976-77 NFL DECANTER
(Right) Came with choice of NFL team emblem out of 28 member clubs of the National Football League. Came in Wild Country or Sure Winner Bracing Lotion. 6 oz. black glass with silver top. SSP $5.99, CMV $5 MB - $4 BO.

1976-77 REMEMBER WHEN GAS PUMP
(Left) 4 oz. red painted over clear glass. Red & white plastic cap. Came in Deep Woods or Wild Country. SSP $5.99, CMV $5 BO - $7 MB.

1976 ONE GOOD TURN "SCREWDRIVER"
(Right) 4 oz. clear glass, silver cap. Came in Tai Winds or Avon Spicy. SSP $3.99, CMV $4 MB - $3 BO.

1982-83 EAGLE — PRIDE OF AMERICA
7¾" high porcelain eagle figurine. SSP $29.50, CMV $29.50 MB.

1972-75 INDIAN CHIEFTAIN
(Left) 4 oz. brown glass with gold cap. Came in Avon Spicy After Shave or Avon Protein Hair Lotion for Men. OSP $2.50, CMV $3 MB.

1974-75 INDIAN TEPEE DECANTER
(Right) 4 oz. amber glass with brown plastic cap. Holds Wild Country or Avon Spicy. OSP $3, CMV $3 MB - $2 BO.

1976-77 BIG BOLT
(Left) 2 oz. silver plated over clear glass. Silver cap. Came in Deep Woods or Wild Country. SSP $2.99, CMV $2 MB.

1976-78 DURACELL SUPER CHARGE
(Center) 1½ oz. black glass with bronze & silver cap. Came in Spicy or Everest. SSP $1.99, CMV $1.50 MB.

1977 RIGHT CONNECTION "FUSE"
(Right) 1.5 oz. clear glass, with gold & brown cap. Came in Oland or Wild Country. SSP $2.99, CMV $2 MB.

1976-79 ARCTIC KING
(Left) 5 oz. blue glass bottle, silver bear cap. Came in Everest only. SSP $5.99, CMV $4 MB - $3 BO.

1976-78 BOLD EAGLE
(Right) 3 oz. gold plated over clear glass, gold top. Came in Tai Winds or Wild Country. SSP $7.99, CMV $6 MB - $5 BO.

1976-78 MOTOCROSS HELMET
6 oz. white plastic bottle with stick on decals, blue plastic face guard cap. Came in Wild Country or Avon Protein Hair Lotion for men. SSP $3.99, CMV $3 MB - $2 BO.

1977-78 JUST A TWIST
(Left) 2 oz. silver plated over clear glass. Came in Sweet Honesty or Deep Woods. SSP $3.99, CMV $3 BO - $4 MB.

1977-78 HARD HAT
(Right) 4 oz. yellow paint over clear glass. Yellow plastic base. Came with seven decals. Came in Everest or Deep Woods. SSP $4.99, CMV $4 BO - $5 MB.

1975-76 NO PARKING
(Left) 6 oz. red painted glass with red cap. Came in Wild Country After Shave or Electric Pre-Shave. OSP $4, CMV $3 BO - $4.50 MB.

1975-76 FIRE ALARM BOX
(Right) 4 oz. red painted glass with black cap. Came in Avon Spicy After Shave, Avon Protein Hair Lotion or Electric Pre-Shave. OSP $3, CMV $3 BO - $4.50 MB.

1970-71 FIRST CLASS MALE
(Left) 4½" high, 4 oz. blue glass with red cap. Came in Bravo or Wild Country After Shave or Liquid Hair Lotion. OSP $3, CMV $4 MB - $4.50.

1971-72 FOREIGN FIRST CLASS MALE
(Right) from Canada. Clear glass bottle painted red with red cap. Remove paint & is same as factory test bottle. CMV $7 MB - $8.

1974-75 BARBER POLE
(Left) 3 oz. white milk glass with red & blue paper striped label & white plastic cap. Holds Avon Protein Hair/Scalp Conditioner or Wild Country After Shave. OSP $3, CMV $3 MB - $2 BO.

1976 BARBER SHOP BRUSH
(Right) 1.5 oz. brown glass with black & white plastic brush cap. Came in Tai Winds or Wild Country Cologne. OSP $4, CMV $3 MB - $2 BO.

1974-75 ELECTRIC GUITAR DECANTER
(Left) 6 oz. brown glass with silver plastic handle. Came in Avon Sure Winner Bracing Lotion or Wild Country After Shave. SSP $4, CMV $4 MB - $3 BO.

1975 TOTEM POLE DECANTER
(Right) 6 oz. dark amber glass with plastic cap. Holds Wild Country, Deep Woods or Avon Spicy After Shave. OSP $5, CMV $4 BO - $6 MB.

1971-72 BUFFALO NICKEL
(Left) 5 oz. nickel plated over clear glass with matching cap. Came in Spicy, Wild Country After Shave or Liquid Hair Lotion. SSP $4, CMV $5 MB - $4 BO.

1970-72 INDIAN HEAD PENNY
(Right) 4 oz. 4" high. Bronze paint & cap over clear glass. Came in Bravo, Tribute, Excalibur After Shave. OSP $4, CMV $4 MB - $3 BO.

1970 ANGLER
(Left) 5 oz. 4½" high blue glass with silver reel cap & trim. Came in Windjammer & Wild Country After Shave. OSP $5, CMV $5 MB - $6.50.

1973 EIGHT BALL DECANTER
(Right) 3 oz. black glass with black cap & white 8. Came in Spicy After Shave, Avon Protein Lotion for men or Electric Pre-Shave Lotion. SSP $2, CMV $4 MB - $3 BO.

1970-72 LIBERTY DOLLAR
(Left) 6 oz. silver paint over clear glass, silver cap with eagle. 6" high. Came in Oland and Tribute After Shave. OSP $5, CMV $4 MB - $5. Same bottle only gold, rare, $40 MB.

1971-72 TWENTY DOLLAR GOLD PIECE
(Right) 6 oz. gold paint over clear glass. Gold cap. Came in Windjammer After Shave & Electric Pre-Shave Lotion. OSP $5, CMV $4 BO - $6 MB.

1974-75 AFTER SHAVE ON TAP
(Left) 5 oz. dark amber glass with gold plastic spigot cap. Holds Wild Country or Oland After Shave. OSP $3, CMV $4 MB - $3 BO.

1976 AFTER SHAVE ON TAP
5 oz. amber glass, red spigot cap. Holds Spicy or Wild Country. OSP $4, CMV $4 MB - $3 BO.

1974-76 TRIPLE CROWN DECANTER
(Right) 4 oz. brown glass with red plastic cap. Holds Avon Spicy After Shave or Avon Protein Hair/Scalp Conditioner. OSP $3, CMV $3 MB - $2 BO.

1976-77 CAPTAINS LANTERN 1864 DECANTER
(Left) 7 oz. black glass with black plastic cap & gold ring. Came in Wild Country or Oland After Shave. OSP $5, CMV $5 MB - $4 BO.

1974-75 WHALE OIL LANTERN DECANTER
(Right) 5 oz. green glass with silver toned plastic top & base. Holds Wild Country, Oland or Tai Winds. OSP $4, CMV $4 MB - $3 BO.

1977-78 JUKE BOX
(Left) 4.5 oz. amber glass, silver top. Came in Sweet Honesty or Wild Country. Came with decals. SSP $4.99, CMV $5 MB - $4 BO.

1975-76 AVON ON THE AIR DECANTER
(Right) 3 oz. black glass with silver plastic stand. Holds Wild Country, Deep Woods or Spicy After Shave. OSP $4, CMV $4 MB - $3 BO.

1978 SMOOTH GOING OIL CAN
1.5 oz. silver plated over clear glass. Came in Deep Woods or Everest After Shave. SSP $3.99, CMV $3 MB - $2 BO.

1970-71 IT'S A BLAST
(Left) 5 oz. 8½" high, gold paint over clear glass, black rubber horn on cap. Came in Oland & Windjammer After Shave. OSP $7, CMV $5 BO - $7 MB.

1969-70 MAN'S WORLD
(Right) Brown plastic stand holds 6 oz. globe. Gold paint over clear glass, gold cap. Came in Bravo Windjammer & Tribute After Shave. 4" high. OSP $5, CMV $6 BO - $7 MB.

1977-79 BREAKER 19
(Left) 2 oz. black glass with black & silver plastic cap. Wild Country or Sweet Honesty. SSP $3.99, CMV $2 BO - $4 MB.

1977-79 COLEMAN LANTERN
(Right) 5 oz. green painted over clear glass. Green cap, silver bail handle. Came in Wild Country or Deep Woods. SSP $5.99, CMV $4 BO - $6 MB.

1972 PIANO DECANTER
(Left) 4" high, 4 oz. dark amber glass piano with white music stack cap. Holds Tai Winds or Tribute After Shave Lotion. OSP $4, CMV $4 MB - $5.

1971-72 FIELDER'S CHOICE
(Right) 5 oz. dark amber glass, black cap. Came in Sports Rally Bracing Lotion, Liquid Hair Trainer or Wild Country After Shave. OSP $4, CMV $2.50 MB - $4.

1971-72 LIBERTY BELL
(Left) 5 oz. light amber glass coated over clear glass, brown cap. Came in Tribute or Oland After Shave or Cologne. OSP $5, CMV $5 MB - $4 BO.

1976 LIBERTY BELL
(Right) 5 oz. sprayed bronze with bronze cap. Came in Oland or Deep Woods After Shave. OSP $5, CMV $5 MB - $4 BO.

1973-74 AUTO LANTERN

Shiny gold with amber windows. Left bottle holds 5 oz. Oland or Deep Woods After Shave. Right base holds 1.25 oz. Oland or Deep Woods Talc. SSP $12, CMV $10 BO - $12 MB.

1973 SUPER SHAVER

(Left) 4 oz. blue glass with gray plastic top. Holds Sure Winner Bracing Lotion or Avon Spicy After Shave. SSP $3, CMV $4 MB - $3 BO.

1973 BOTTLED BY AVON

(Right) 5 oz. clear glass with silver lift off cap, holds Oland or Windjammer After Shave. SSP $3, CMV $4 MB - $3 BO.

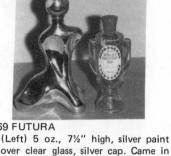

1969 FUTURA

(Left) 5 oz., 7½" high, silver paint over clear glass, silver cap. Came in Excalibur & Wild Country Cologne. OSP $7, CMV $12.50 MB - $10 BO.

1971 WORLD'S GREATEST DAD DECANTER

(Right) 4 oz. clear glass, red cap. Came in Spicy or Tribute After Shave or Electric Pre-Shave Lotion. OSP $3.50, CMV $2 BO - $4 MB.

1975-76 STOP! DECANTER

(Left) 5 oz. red plastic with white plastic base. Holds Wild Country After Shave or Sweet Honesty After Bath Freshener. OSP $3, CMV $3, no box.

1974-75 STOP 'N GO

(Right) 4 oz. green glass with green cap. Holds Wild Country or Avon Spicy After Shave. OSP $4, CMV $5 MB - $3 BO.

1978-79 "HAMMER" ON THE MARK DECANTER

(Left) 8½" long dark amber glass with silver top holds 2.5 oz. of Everest or Wild Country After Shave. SSP $5., CMV $3. BO - $5. MB.

1978-79 ON THE LEVEL DECANTER

(Right) 3 oz. silver coated over clear glass holds Everest or Deep Woods After Shave. SSP $4., CMV $2. BO - $4. MB.

1979-80 ON TAP MUG DECANTER

(Left) 4 oz. clear glass with white plastic top. Holds Wild Country or Deep Woods After Shave. SSP $5.99 CMV $5.99 MB.

1979 PAUL REVERE BELL DECANTER

(Right) 4 oz. clear glass painted gold. Brown and silver handle. 1979 stamped in bottom. Holds Clint After Shave or Sweet Honesty Body Splash. SSP $8., CMV $8. MB.

1975-76 STAR SIGNS DECANTER

(Left) 4 oz. black glass with gold cap. Came in Sweet Honesty Cologne or Wild Country After Shave. Came blank with choice of one of 12 Zodiac signs sticker to apply. OSP $3.50, CMV $3.50 MB each - $2.50 BO.

1975-76 SPARK PLUG DECANTER

(Right) 1.5 oz. white milk glass with gray cap. Holds Wild Country, Tai Winds or Avon Spicy After Shave. OSP $2, CMV $2 MB - $1.50 BO.

1972-73 BIG WHISTLE

4 oz. blue glass with silver cap. Came in Tai Winds or Spicy After Shave or Electric Pre-Shave Lotion. SSP $3.50, CMV $4.50 MB - $3.50 BO.

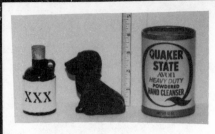

1978-79 LITTLE BROWN JUG DECANTER

(Left) Brown glass, tan plastic cap. Beige painted sides. Holds 2 oz. Deep Woods or Tai Winds After Shave. SSP $3., CMV $3. MB.

1978-79 BABY BASSETT DECANTER

(Center) 1.25 oz. amber glass and matching plastic head. Holds Topaze or Sweet Honesty Cologne. SSP $3., CMV $2. BO - $3.50 MB.

1978-79 QUAKER STATE POWDERED HAND CLEANER

(Right) 12 oz. cardboard sides and gold plastic top and bottom. Holds heavy duty powdered hand cleaner. SSP $3., CMV $3. came without box. box.

FOREIGN DECISIONS

(Left) Smaller than American Decisions. CMV $30 BO - $35 MB.

1965 DECISIONS

(Right) 8 oz. red painted labels, black caps with red centers that say Panic Buttons. Came in Spicy After Shave Lotion. OSP $2.50, CMV $27.50 MB - $20 BO.

1979-80 FARMERS ALMANAC THERMOMETER & SOAPS

Box holds tin top with plastic bottom with 2 bars of Farmers Almanac soap. Comes with copy of Avon 1980 Farmers Almanac. SSP $9., CMV $9. MB complete. CMV Farmers Almanac only $1.

1980 WILSON STEPPING OUT FOOT POWDER

(Left) 5 oz. yellow & red. SSP $2., CMV $1 mint.

1979-80 WILSON CARE DEEPLY LIP BALM

(Right) Yellow & red. 3" high. CMV 50c.

1979-80 LUCKY HORSESHOE SOAP DISH & SOAP

(Left) Brown box holds amber glass horseshoe soapdish & soap. SSP $8., CMV $8. MB.

1979-80 PERPETUAL CALENDAR CONTAINER & SOAP

(Right) Yellow box holds Avon tin can calendar & white bar of soap. bottom of can says Made in England for Avon. SSP $8., CMV $8. MB.

1979-80 SUPER SLEUTH MAGNIFIER

(Left) 10" long. Bottom is dark amber glass and top is real magnifying glass. Came in Wild Country or Everest After Shave. SSP $8., CMV $8. MB.

1979-80 COUNTRY LANTERN

(Center) 4 oz. clear glass painted red. Red wire handle. Holds Wild Country or Deep Woods After Shave. SSP $6., CMV $6. MB.

1979-80 GENTLEMAN'S TALC

(Right) 3.75 oz. green can. Holds Clint, Trazarra or Wild Country Talc. SSP $4., CMV $2. mint, no box.

1979-80 DUTCH BOY HEAVY DUTY POWDER HAND CLEANER

(Left) 12 oz. blue & white paper sides. Yellow plastic top, gray bottom. No box. SSP $4., CMV $3. mint.

1979-80 BATH BREW DECANTER

(Right) 4 oz. dark amber glass, gold cap. Brown box. Holds Wild Country Bubble Bath. SSP $4., CMV $4. MB. MB.

1978-79 WEEKEND DECISION MAKER DECANTER

3 oz. green and white painted over clear glass. Green top. Holds Wild Country or Tai Winds AFter Shave. SSP $6., CMV $6. MB.

1978-79 THERMOS PLAID BRAND DECANTER

3 oz. white milk glass. Red cap and plaid design. Holds Wild Country After Shave or Sweet Honesty Body Splash. SSP $3.66, CMV $3.66 MB.

1978-79 DOMINO DECANTER

1.5 oz. black glass with white spots. Holds Everest or Tai Winds After Shave. SSP $4., CMV $4. MB.

1980 LOVER BOY AFTER SHAVE

3 oz. clear glass. Red letters & cap. Red box, SSP $3.49, CMV $3 MB.

1980 LOVER BOY SCRATCH 'N SNIFF CARDS

Pad of 20 cards for samples. CMV 50c pad.

1968 STEIN - SILVER

(Left) 6 oz. silver paint over clear glass, silver cap. Came in Spicy, Windjammer & Tribute After Shave. OSP $4.50, CMV $6, $8 MB.

1965-66 STEIN - SILVER

(Right) 8 oz. silver paint over clear glass, silver cap. Came in Tribute. OSP $4, Spicy OSP $3.50, Blue Blazer & 4A After Shave OSP $3.75 each. CMV $6 BO, $8 MB.

1981-82 FLYING CLASSIC CERAMIC STEIN

6th in series, 9½" high blue ceramic stein made in Brazil & numbered on the bottom. Sold empty. Metal top. SSP $38, CMV $38 MB.

1980-82 WESTERN ROUND-UP CERAMIC STEIN

(Left) 8¼" high. Made in Brazil & numbered on the bottom. Metal top. Comes with 8 oz. plastic bottle of Wild Country or Trazarra cologne. SSP $38, CMV $38 MB.

1980-82 CASEY AT THE BAT TANKARD

(Right) 6" high beige opaque glass. Comes with a 4 oz. Casey plastic bottle of Wild Country or Weekend After Shave. SSP $16, CMV $16 MB.

1977-79 TALL SHIPS STEIN

Ceramic stein, pewter handle & lid. Came with 8 oz. red plastic bottle of Clint or brown plastic of Wild Country cologne for men. Silver cap. Each stein was hand made in Brazil and numbered on the bottom. OSP $25, CMV $35 MB, $30 stein only.

1978-80 SPORTING STEIN DECANTER

9" tall, ceramic stein marked on bottom "Made in Brazil for Avon Products 1978". Came with choice of 8 oz. Trazarra or Wild Country cologne with gold cap in red plastic bottle. Each stein is numbered on the bottom SSP $27, CMV $35 MB with bottle, $30 stein only.

1972 HUNTER'S STEIN

8 oz. nickle plated over clear glass, has gray & black plastic bottle inside. Holds Deep Woods or Wild Country After Shave. SSP $9, CMV $12 MB, plastic bottle only $2, stein only CMV $8.

1978 TALL SHIPS SHORT STEIN

Smaller stein on right was sold in Trend Setter test area and was later changed to larger regular issue size on left. Both marked Avon on bottom and numbered. CMV $60 small stein.

1976-79 COLLECTORS STEIN
Hand made ceramic blue stein. Made in Brazil and numbered on bottom. Came with 8 oz. plastic bottle of Everest or Wild country. SSP $25, CMV $35 MB, $30 BO stein only.

1979-80 CAR CLASSIC CERAMIC STEIN
9" high ceramic stein made in Brazil & numbered on the bottom. Comes with 8 oz. plastic bottle of Trazarra Cologne. SSP $33, CMV $35 MB, $30 stein only.

1982 PERFECT COMBO MUG & POPCORN
Box holds 12 oz. clear glass mug with geese on side & 10 oz. gold foil wrapped can of popcorn. SSP $10, CMV $10 MB set, mug only $5.

1974-76 IRON HORSE SHAVING MUG
White milk glass mug holds 7 oz. plastic bottle with gold cap. Came in Avon Blend, Deep Woods or Avon Leather After Shave. SSP $6, CMV $6 MB, $2 BO, $3 mug only.

1980-82 HEAVY DUTY DECANTER
10 oz. gray plastic. Holds Care Deeply lotion for problem dry skin. SSP $5, CMV $2 mint no box.

1980-82 HEAVY DUTY HAND CLEANER
Turtle Wax can, 10 oz. green & white. SSP $5, CMV $2 mint, no box.

1980-82 BY THE BARREL DECANTER
8 oz. tan plastic. Holds Wild Country bubble bath or shampoo. SSP $4.50, CMV $2.50 mint no box.

1981-82 CHESAPEAKE COLLECTION GLASSES
(Left) Glass with after shave. 8 oz. drinking glass with 3 ducks on side. Glass does not say Avon. Comes with 7 oz. plastic bottle, green cap. Duck scene on side. Choice of Wild Country & Weekend After Shave. SSP $9, CMV $9 MB.

(Right) Drinking Glasses. Green & brown box holds 2 - 8 oz. drinking glasses with 3 ducks on side. Glasses do not say Avon. SSP $8 set, CMV $8 MB.

1981-82 CHESAPEAKE COLLECTION TRAY
12" green metal tray. Back says "Mallards in Flight" Avon. SSP $7, CMV $7 MB.

1981-82 CHESAPEAKE COLLECTION COASTERS
Set of 4 metal duck coasters with green felt backs. Does not say Avon. SSP $8, CMV $8 MB.

1982-83 WILD MUSTANG AFTER SHAVE SOOTHER
5 oz. black glass. plastic pump dispenser. Choice of Wild Country or Black Suede After Shave Soother. SSP $10, CMV $10 MB.

1982 WILD MUSTANG COMB & BRUSH VALET
Black plastic comb & brush. SSP $10, CMV $5 MB.

1981-82 AVON CLUB COLLECTION
Matching smoke gray glass.

CLUB COLLECTION DECANTER
Wild Country or Weekend after shave or cologne. 4 oz. gold cap. SSP $6 CMV $6 each MB.

CLUB COLLECTION CADDY
4x6 tray. SSP $8, CMV $8 MB.

CLUB COLLECTION HAIR BRUSH
SSP $7, CMV $4 MB.

1980-81 BIRDS OF FLIGHT CERAMIC BOX

Embossed ducks on lid and sides. Bar of duck soap inside. Made in Brazil. SSP $23, CMV $23 MB.

1980-81 ROOKIE COLOGNE FOR BOYS

2.5 oz. clear glass. Red cap & label. SSP $2.80, CMV $2.50 MB.

1980-81 AVON'S FINEST DECANTER

2 oz. dark amber glass. Gold tone cap. Comes in Clint or Trazarra cologne. SSP $5, CMV $5 MB.

1980-81 BOOTS 'N SADDLE DECANTER

7½" high, 7 oz. dark amber glass. Silver label, brown vinyl leather look wrap around bottle. Choice of Wild Country or Weekend After Shave. SSP $10, CMV $10 MB.

1977-78 GIFT COLOGNE FOR MEN

(Left) 2 oz. clear glass bottle, dark blue cap. Came in Wild Country, Deep Woods, Clint or Everest cologne. OSP $3, CMV $1 MB, 50c BO.

1977-78 LOCKER TIME

(Right) 6 oz. green plastic bottle, yellow cap. Came in Sweet Honesty Body Splash or Wild Country. Came with 13 stick on decals. SSP $4, CMV $2 MB, $1 BO.

1982-83 DAD'S PRIDE & JOY PICTURE FRAME

6½" long clear glass. Holds pictures. SSP $8, CMV $8 MB.

1978 GOODYEAR BLIMP DECANTER

2 oz. silver gray paint over clear glass, blue letters. Came in Everest or Wild Country After Shave. SSP $5.99, CMV $5 BO, $7 MB.

1966 VIKING HORN

7 oz. dark amber glass with gold cap & decoration. Came in Spicy, Blue Blazer & original After Shave. OSP $5, CMV $12 BO, $17,50 MB.

1977-80 DESK CADDY

Brown cork holder, silver top made in Spain. Holds 4 oz. clear glass bottle of Clint cologne, red letters, silver cap or Wild Country. SSP $9, CMV $7.50 MB.

1970-72 SPIRIT OF ST. LOUIS

6 oz. silver paint over clear glass. Came in Windjammer & Excalibur After Shave. 7½" long. OSP $8.50, CMV $6, MB $8.50.

1966 DEFENDER CANNON

6 oz. 9½" long, amber glass, brown plastic stand, gold cap & gold center band, small paper label. Came in Leather, Island Lime & Tribute After Shave. OSP. $5, CMV $20 in box, $15 bottle & stand mint.

1967 TRIBUTE SILVER WARRIOR
6" high, 6 oz. silver & blue paint over clear glass, silver cap. Came in Tribute After Shave. OSP $4.50, CMV $12.50 BO, mint, $18 MB. All blue glass $30 mint.

1971-73 TRIBUTE RIBBED WARRIOR
6" high, 6 oz. clear ribbed glass, silver cap. Came in Tribute Cologne. OSP $4, CMV $4, $5 MB.

FOREIGN RIBBED WARRIOR
Same as U.S. except nose & chin is rounded off & U.S. is more pointed. Foreign label on bottom. CMV $14, on foreign, MB $18.

1968-71 TRIBUTE FROSTED WARRIOR
6" high, 6 oz. frosted glass, silver cap. Came in Tribute Cologne. OSP $4, CMV $3 BO, $5 MB.

1969-71 WEATHER-OR-NOT
5 oz. dark amber glass, regular issue on left, gold cap. Came in Leather & Oland, Tribute, Wild Country & Spicy After Shave. OSP $5. There are 5 different Thermometers starting with 20 below, 10 below, 0, 10 above, & 20 above. All same price. CMV $4 BO, $6 MB.

1978 SUPER SHIFT
4 oz. black glass bottle with silver & black shifter cap. Came in Sure Winner Bracing Lotion or Everest Cologne. 7" high. SSP $5.99, CMV $5 MB, $4 BO.

1968-69 SCIMITAR
10" long, 6 oz. gold paint with red windows over clear glass, gold cap. Came in Tribute & Windjammer After Shave Lotion. OSP $6, CMV $18 mint, $24 MB.

1968-70 DAYLIGHT SHAVING TIME
6 oz. gold paint over clear glass. Came in Spicy, Wild Country, Windjammer, Bravo & Leather After Shave. OSP $5, CMV $4 BO, $5 MB.

DAYLIGHT SHAVING TIME Foreign
Gold clock. 150 cc size. CMV $20, MB $25.

1967 WESTERN CHOICE (STEER HORNS)
Brown plastic base with red center, Holds 2 - 3 oz. bottles with silver caps. Came in Wild Country & Leather After Shave. OSP $6, CMV $15 BO, $25 MB.

1967-68 GAVEL
5 oz. dark amber glass with brown plastic handle. 8" long. Came in Island Lime, Original & Spicy. OSP $4, CMV $10 BO, $14 MB.

1970-71 PAID STAMP
5 " high, dark amber glass with black cap & red rubber paid stamp on bottom. Holds 4 oz. of Spicy or Windjammer After Shave. OSP $4, CMV $3 BO, $5 MB.

1969-71 SWINGER GOLF BAG
5 oz. black glass, red & silver clubs. Came in Wild Country & Bravo After Shave. OSP $5, CMV $4 BO, $6 MB.

1970-71 POT BELLY STOVE
5" high, 5 oz. black glass bottle with black cap. Came in Bravo or Excalibur After Shave. OSP $4, CMV $3 BO, $4 MB.

1969-70 INKWELL
(Right) 6 oz. amber with purple tint, black cap with gold or silver pen. Came in Windjammer & Spicy After Shave. OSP $6, CMV $4 BO, $6 MB. (Left) Factory test. No value established.

1969 FOREIGN OLD BARREL
(Left) 6 oz. brown & silver with brown cap. $22 BO, $25 MB.

1965-67 BAY RUM KEG
(Right) 6 oz. brown & silver paint over clear glass bottle. OSP $2.50, CMV $14 BO, $20 MB.

1963 CLOSE HARMONY (BARBER BOTTLE)
8 oz. white glass bottle, gold painted letter & neck band. White cap with tip. Came in Spicy & Original After Shave. OSP $2.25, Vigorate & After Shower Cologne OSP $2.50 CMV, without tip. $7.50, with tip $15 BO $30 MB.

1965-66 ROYAL ORB
8 oz. round bottle, gold cap, red felt around neck. Came in Spicy & Original After Shave. Red letters painted on bottle common issue. OSP $3.50, CMV $16.50 MB, $25. White letter Orb, CMV $75.

1968-69 TOWN PUMP
8" high black glass bottle with gold cap & plastic shoe horn. Holds 6 oz. of Leather, Windjammer, Wild Country. OSP $5, CMV $3 BO, $5 MB.

1966-67 DOLLARS 'N SCENTS
8 oz. white glass bottle with green dollar painted on silver cap. Came in Spicy After Shave. Red rubber band around bottle. OSP $2.50, CMV $28 MB, $16 BO.

1966-67 TOP DOLLAR SOAP ON ROPE
White 1886 dollar soap. OSP $1.75, CMV $40 MB, $27.50 soap only mint.

1966-67 ALPINE FLASK
8 oz. 8¾" high, brown glass, gold cap & neck chain. Came in Spicy, Original, Blue Blazer & Leather After Shave. OSP $4, CMV $60 MB, $45 BO.

1966-67 CASSEY'S LANTERN
10 oz gold paint on clear glass bottle, gold caps. Came in Leather After Shave in red window, Tribute in amber window & Island Lime in green window. OSP ea. $6, CMV amber & green $55 MB. red $45 MB. Bottles only $5 less each mint.

1969 AVON CLASSICS
6 oz. each OSP $3.50. Leather in clear & dark amber glass. Windjammer in blue & clear glass. Wild Country in light & dark amber glass & clear glass. Tribute After Shave in clear glass, light & dark amber glass. All bottle caps & labels must match in color, gold or silver. CMV $5 BO each $8 MB.

1967-68 FIRST EDITION
6 oz. gold cap. Came in Bay Rum, CMV $9 BO, $12 MB. Wild Country & Leather After Shave. OSP $3.50, CMV $5 BO, $8 MB.

SEE 1984 SUPPLEMENT SECTION IN BACK OF BOOK FOR MORE WOMEN'S DECANTERS.

WOMEN'S DECANTERS, CERAMICS, & FIGURINES

BE 1ST TO KNOW
BE INFORMED

If you want to be 1st to know when the next Bud Hastin Avon Collectors Encyclopedia will be for sale in the future, get on Bud's personal mailing list. PLUS you will get a bonus discount on his next book by ordering direct from Bud. Just PRINT your name and address and send it to:

BUD HASTIN
P. O. Box 43690
LAS VEGAS, NV 89116

Just say: "Put me on your next book list."

1975-76 PRECIOUS TURTLE
.66 oz. gold jar with plastic lid. Came in Patchwork, or Roses Roses Cream Sachet. OSP $4, CMV $4 MB, $3 BO.

1971-73 TREASURE TURTLE
1 oz. brown glass turtle with gold head. Holds Field Flowers, Hana Gasa, Bird of Paradise, Elusive, Charisma, Brocade, Unforgettable, Rapture, Occur!, Somewhere, Topaze, Cotillion, Here's My Heart and Persian Wood. OSP $3.50, CMV $4 MB, $3 BO.

1978-80 AUTUMN ASTER DECANTER
(Left) .75 oz. clear glass, gold cap. Holds Topaze or Sun Blossoms cologne. SSP $2, CMV $2 MB.

1978-80 DOGWOOD DEMI DECANTER
(Right) .75 oz. flower shaped bottle, gold flower lid. Came in Apple Blossom or Moonwind, Topaze cologne. SSP $3, CMV $2 MB.

1972-74 COLOGNE ROYAL
1 oz. clear glass, gold cap. Came in Field Flowers, Roses Roses, Bird of Paradise, Sonnet, Charisma, Unforgettable, Somewhere. SSP $1.75, CMV $3 MB, $2 BO.

1973-74 COURTING CARRIAGE
1 oz. clear glass, gold cap. Came in Moonwind, Sonnet, Field Flowers or Flower Talk. SSP $2, CMV $3 MB, $2 BO.

1972-74 PINEAPPLE PETITE COLOGNE
1 oz. clear glass, gold cap. Came in Roses Roses, Charisma, Elusive, Brocade or Regence. SSP $2, CMV $3 MB, $2 BO. Reissued in 1977 in Field Flowers, & Unforgettable.

1970 BOW TIE PERFUME
1/8 oz. clear glass. Shape of bow with gold cap. Came in Pink Slipper Soap in Charisma & Cotillion. CMV $4 mint.

1967 KEY NOTE PERFUME
¼ oz. glass key with gold plastic cap. 4A design on cap. Came in Here's My Heart, To A Wild Rose. OSP $5. Somewhere, Topaze, Cotillion OSP $5.50, Unforgettable, Rapture, Occur. OSP $6.50, CMV $20 in box, $12 key only.

1975-76 LADY BUG PERFUME DECANTER
1/8 oz. frosted glass, gold cap. Came in Sonnet, Moonwind, or Patchwork. OSP $4, CMV $3 BO, $4 MB.

1971-72 SCENT WITH LOVE
¼ oz. frosted glass with gold pen cap, white and gold label around bottle. Came in Field Flowers, Moonwind, Bird of Paradise, Charisma, Elusive, Moonwind. OSP $6, CMV $12.50 $7 BO.

1977 TREASURE TURTLE COLOGNE DECANTER
(Left) 1 oz. clear glass turtle with gold cap. Came in Sweet Honesty or Charisma cologne. Avon on bottom &'R' for reissue on tail. OSP $4.50, CMV $3 MB, $2 BO.

1977-79 EMERALD PRINCE FROG
(Right) 1 oz. green frosted paint over clear glass. Came in Sweet Honesty or Moonwind cologne. OSP $5, CMV $3 MB, $2 BO.

1967-68 ICICLE PERFUME
1 dram, gold cap. Came in Here's My Heart, To A Wild Rose, OSP $2.50, Somewhere, Topaz, Cotillion, OSP $2.75. Unforgettable, Rapture, Occur, OSP $3.25, Regence, OSP $3.75, with gold neck label. CMV $5 in box, $4 bottle only.

1973-74 PRECIOUS SLIPPER
.25 oz. frosted glass bottle with gold cap. Came in Sonnet or Moonwind. OSP, $4, CMV $7 MB, $5 BO.

1969-70 LOVE BIRD PERFUME
¼ oz. frosted bird with silver cap. 2½" long. Came in Charisma, Elusive, Brocade, Regence, Unforgettable, Rapture, Occur!. OSP $6.25, CMV $9 MB, $5 BO.

1972-73 SMALL WONDER PERFUME
1/8 oz. frosted glass with gold cap. Holds Field Flowers, Bird of Paradise, Charisma. OSP $2.50, CMV $7 MB, $5 BO.

1972-73 DREAM GARDEN
½ oz. pink frosted glass with gold cap. Came in Moonwind, Bird of Paradise, Charisma, Elusive or Unforgettable perfume oil. OSP $5, CMV $15 MB, $8 BO.

1973 SNOW MAN PETITE PERFUME
.25 oz. textured glass with pink eyes, mouth & scarf. Gold cap. Came in Cotillion, Bird of Paradise, Field Flowers. OSP $4, CMV $6 BO, $8 MB.

1974-76 PRECIOUS SWAN PERFUME DECANTER
1/8 oz. frosted glass with gold cap. Came in Field Flowers, Bird of Paradise or Charisma. OSP $4, CMV $4 BO, $6 MB.

1975 SEWING NOTIONS
1 oz. pink and white glass with silver cap. Holds Sweet Honesty, To A Wild Rose or Cotillion. OSP $3, CMV $3 MB, $2 BO.

1975 CRYSTALIER COLOGNE DECANTER
2 oz. clear glass. Filled with Field Flower,s Bird of Paradise or Roses Roses Cologne. OSP $4, CMV $4 MB, $3 BO.

1975-77 BABY OWL
1 oz. clear glass, gold cap. Holds Sweet Honesty or Occur! Cologne. OSP $2, CMV $2 BO, $3 MB

1975-76 PERT PENGUIN
1 oz. clear glass, gold cap. Holds Field Flowers or Cotillion Cologne. OSP $2, CMV $2 BO, $3 MB.

1972 PETITE PIGLET
2" long embossed clear glass with gold cap. Holds ¼ oz. perfume in Field Flowers, Bird of Paradise, Elusive & Charisma. OSP $5, CMV $6 BO, $7 MB.

1968-69 SNAIL PERFUME
¼ oz. gold cap, clear glass. Came in Charisma, Brocade, Regence, Unforgettable, Rapture & Occur! OSP $6.25, CMV $13.50 MB, $7 BO.

1970 PERFUME PETITE MOUSE
Forsted glass with gold head and tail, holds ¼ oz. perfume in Elusive, Charisma, Brocade, Regence. OSP $7.50, Unforgettable, Rapture & Occur! OSP $6.25, CMV $17.50 MB, $12 BO.

1974-76 ONE DRAM PERFUME
Clear glass with gold cap. Came in Bird of Paradise, Charisma or Field Flowers, OSP $3.75 Sonnet, Moonwind or Imperial Garden, OSP $4.25, CMV $3.50 MB, $2 BO.

1974-75 STRAWBERRY FAIR PERFUME
1/8 oz. red glass, silver cap. Came in Moonwind Charisma or Sonnet. OSP $4, CMV $4 MB, $3 BO.

NEW Frisky Friends Cologne Decanter

1981 FRISKY FRIENDS DECANTERS
3 different frosted 1 oz. glass cats with blue cap. Honeysuckle, yellow cap has Roses Roses & pink cap has Hawaiian White Ginger. SSP $5, CMV $5 MB each.

1981 HEAVENLY ANGEL DECANTER
(Left) .5 oz blue glass angel, silver cap. Choice of Ariane, Candid, Timeless. Red box dated 1981. SSP $2, CMV $2 MB.

1981 WINGED PRINCESS DECANTER
(Center) .5 oz. swan shaped iridescent glass, gold cap. Choice of Occur! Charisma, Sweet Honesty. Box dated 1981. SSP. $2.25, CMV $2.25 MB.

1981-82 LOVE CHIMES DECANTER
(Right) .5 oz. clear glass bell shape, gold cap. Choice or Roses Roses, Charisma, Moonwind, Sweet Honesty. SSP $1.75, CMV $1.75 MB.

1981 CHRISTMAS CHARMER CANDLESTICK DECANTER

Small white, red & green girl, plastic candle holder. Remove top sleeve to fit small bottle of cologne with red cap. Choice of Zany or Charisma. .33 oz. cologne, red box. SSP $6, CMV $6 set MB.

1982 HUGGABLE HOP-A-LONG DECANTER

1 oz. green glass frog. Plastic hat. Comes with 20 stick on decals. Choice of Sweet Honesty for girls or Light Musk for guys. SSP $5, CMV $5 MB.

1980 COLOGNE GO ROUND DECANTER

.5 oz. clear glass, gold cap. Choice or Roses Roses, Honeysuckle, Hawaiian White Ginger, Field Flowers SSP $1.75, CMV $1.75 MB.

1980-81 SEAHORSE MINIATURE DECANTER

.5 oz. clear glass gold cap. Choice of Sweet Honesty, Charisma, Occur!, or Moonwind. SSP $3, CMV $3 MB.

1980 COLOGNE RONDELLE

5 oz. clear glass, gold cap. Choice of Moonwind, Charisma, Topaze, Occur, Sweet Honesty, Zany, Sprotif or Country Breeze. In special Christmas box. SSP $1.40, CMV $1.50 MB.

1980-81 ROLLIN GREAT ROLLER SKATE DECANTER

2 oz. glass red top. Choice of Zany Cologne or Lover Boy Cologne. SSP $4, CMV $4 MB.

1980 SONG OF CHRISTMAS DECANTER

.75 oz. frosted glass. Red cap. Choice of Moonwind, Sweet Honesty or Bird of Paradise. SSP $2.22, CMV $2.25 MB.

1980 CHRISTMAS SOLDIER DECANTER

.75 oz. clear glass, gold cap. Choice of Sportif, Sweet Honesty, Charisma, or Moonwind. SSP $2, CMV $2 MB.

1980-81 OWL MINIATURE DECANTER

.6 oz. clear glass, gold owl cap. Choice of Tasha, Ariane, Candid or Timeless. SSP $1.95, CMV $1.95 MB.

1979-80 WEDDING FLOWER MAIDEN DECANTER

(Left) 1.75 oz. white painted over clear glass. Holds Unforgettable or Sweet Honesty cologne. SSP $6, CMV $5 BO, $6 MB.

1978-79 GARDEN GIRL DECANTER

4 oz. pink painted over clear glass. Holds Charisma or Sweet Honesty Cologne. SSP $5, CMV $4 BO, $5 MB.

1978-79 ANGEL SONG DECANTER

1 oz. frosted glass base with off white plastic top. Holds Here's My Heart or Charisma cologne. SSP $3, CMV $2 BO, $3 MB.

1978-79 ON THE AVENUE DECANTER

2 oz. blue painted over clear glass. Pink plastic top with lavendar hat. White detachable umbrella. Holds Topaze or Unforgettable cologne. SSP $8, CMV $7 BO, $8 MB.

1978-80 PROUD GROOM DECANTER

2 oz. white painted over clear glass. Holds Sweet Honesty or Unforgettable Cologne. SSP $7, CMV $6 BO, $7 MB.

1979-80 SCENTIMENTAL DOLL ADORABLE ABIGAIL

4.5 oz. clear glass painted beige. Beige plastic top. Comes in Regence or Sweet Honesty cologne. SSP $10 CMV $9 BO, $10 MB.

1979-80 MRS. QUACKLES DECANTER

2 oz. clear glass painted off white. Off white plastic top with white lace and green bonnet. Comes in Delicate Daisies Cologne. SSP $6, CMV $5 BO, $6 MB.

1979-80 SWEET TOOTH TERRIER DECANTER

1 oz. white glass and white plastic top. Comes in Topaze or Cotillion cologne. SSP $4, CMV $3 BO, $4 MB.

1979-80 TUG-A-BRELLA
2.5 oz. clear glass painted yellow, yellow plastic top. Black plastic umbrella on wire. Holds Moonwind or Cotillion Cologne. SSP $10, CMV $9 BO, $10 MB.

1978-80 GOOD FAIRY
3 oz. clear glass painted blue. Blue plastic top. Plastic wand. Blue and pink fabric purse and wings. Holds Delicate Daisies cologne. SSP $6, CMV $5 BO, $6 MB.

1975-77 FLY-A-BALLOON
3 oz. glass sprayed blue with light blue top & red plastic balloon. Holds Moonwind or Bird of Paradise cologne. OSP $7, CMV $7 BO, $8 MB.

1975-77 SKIP-A-ROPE
4 oz. yellow sprayed glass with yellow plastic top and white plastic rope. Holds Sweet Honesty, Bird of Paradise, or Roses Roses cologne. OSP $7, CMV $7 BO, $8 MB.

1975 GARDEN GIRL COLOGNE
4 oz. sprayed frosted glass with yellow plastic top. Holds Sweet Honesty, Somewhere, Cotillion or To A Wild Rose. OSP $3.50, CMV $9 BO, $11 MB.

1973-74 FLOWER MAIDEN COLOGNE DECANTER
4 oz. yellow skirt painted over clear glass with white plastic top. Came in Unforgettable, Somewhere, Topaze, Cotillion. SSP $5, CMV $7 MB, $5 BO.

1974 DEAR FRIENDS COLOGNE DECANTER
4 oz. pink painted with light pink plastic top. Came in Field Flowers, Bird of Paradise or Roses Roses Cologne, SSP $4, CMV $10 BO, $13 MB.

1979-80 ANGEL SONG WITH MANDOLIN DECANTER
(Left) 1 oz. frosted over clear glass. White plastic top. Holds Moonwind or Unforgettable cologne. SSP $3.99, CMV $3.99 MB.

1979-80 SKATER'S WALTZ DECANTER
(Center) 4 oz. blue flock base over clear glass. Light blue plastic top. Holds Charisma or Cotillion cologne. SSP $8, CMV $8 MB.

1979-80 LITTLE JACK HORNER DECANTER
(Right) 1.5 oz. white glass painted white frosted. Came in Topaze or Roses Roses cologne. SSP $6, CMV $6 MB.

1971-72 FASHION FIGURINE
(Left) 4 oz. white plastic top & white painted bottom, over clear glass. 6" high. Came in Field Flowers, Elusive, Bird of Paradise, Brocade. SSP $4, CMV $9 BO, $12 MB.

1973-74 VICTORIAN FASHION FIGURINE
(Center) 4 oz. light green (some call it blue or aqua) painted over clear glass base with green plastic top. Came in Charisma, Field Flowers, Bird of Paradise Cologne. SSP $4, CMV $30 BO, $33 MB.

1972 ELIZABETHAN FASHION FIGURINE
(Right) 4 oz. pink painted glass bottom over clear glass with pink plastic top. 6" high. Came in Moonwind, Charisma, Field Flowers & Bird of Paradise Cologne. SSP $5, CMV $16 BO, $20 MB. Also came pink painted over white milk glass. Remove cap to see difference. CMV $15.

1976 BETSY ROSS DECANTER
4 oz. white painted over clear glass. Came in Sonnet or Topaze Cologne. Sold 2 campaigns only. SSP $7, CMV $6 MB, $5 BO. Also came white painted over white milk glass. Remove cap to see color of bottle. CMV $20 MB. The regular issue Betsy Ross bottle was one of the all time biggest sellers in Avon history.

1976-77 MAGIC PUMPKIN COACH
1 oz. clear glass, gold cap. Comes in Bird of Paradise or Occur! Cologne. OSP $5, CMV $3 BO, $4 MB.

1977 SONG OF SPRING
(Left) 1 oz. frosted glass with frosted plastic bird bath top. Blue plastic bird attachment. Came in Sweet Honesty or Topaze. OSP $6, CMV $4 MB, $3 BO.

1977-78 FELINA FLUFFLES
(Right) 2 oz. blue paint over clear glass, white plastic top, blue ribbon on head. Pink cheeks. Came in Pink & Pretty Cologne. OSP $6, CMV $4 BO, $5 MB.

1974-75 PRETTY GIRL PINK . . . (left)
6 oz. glass sprayed pink base with light pink top. Holds Unforgettable, Topaze, Occur or Somewhere cologne. OSP $4, CMV $7 BO, $9 MB.

1972-73 LITTLE GIRL BLUE
(Center) 3 oz. blue painted glass with blue plastic cap. Came in Brocade, Unforgettable, Somewhere or Cotillion. SSP $4, CMV $7 BO, $9 MB.

1973-74 LITTLE KATE
(Right) 3 oz. pastel orange painted glass with orange plastic hat over cap. Came in Bird of Paradise, Charisma, Unforgettable. SSP $4, CMV $8 BO, $10 MB.

1973 MY PET FIGURINE
(Left) Green & brown, white kitten, ceramic figurine. 1973 embossed in ceramic & printed on box. OSP $10., CMV $35.

1973 JENNIFER FIGURINE
(Right) Pastel turquoise, dress & hat ceramic figurine. 1973 embossed in ceramic & printed on box. Some came with flowers in center of hat & some with flowers on the right side of hat. OSP $10., CMV $45.

Both issued from Springdale, Ohio, branch only.

1976-78 AMERICAN BELLE
(Left) 4 oz. yellow dull paint over clear glass, yellow cap. Came in Cotillion or Sonnet cologne. SSP $5.99, CMV $6 MB, $5 BO.

1976-78 LITTLE BO PEEP DECANTER
(Right) 2 oz. white dull paint over white milk glass base, white plastic top & cane. Came in Sweet Honesty or Unforgettable cologne. SSP $5., CMV $5 MB, $4 BO.

1976-78 CATCH-A-FISH DECANTER
3 oz. dark tan, painted over clear glass, light tan plastic top, yellow hat & brown plastic removable pole. Came in Field Flowers or Sonnet cologne. OSP $9.50, CMV $8 BO, $9 MB.

1977-78 ROLL-A-HOOP DECANTER
3.75 oz. dull pink painted over clear glass base. Light pink plastic top, white plastic hoop. Came in Field Flowers or Cotillion cologne. OSP $10, CMV $8 BO, $9 MB.

1974-75 - 18th CENTURY CLASSIC FIGURINE YOUNG BOY
(Left) 4 oz. white sprayed glass with white plastic head. Choice of Sonnet or Moonwind cologne or foaming bath oil. OSP $5, CMV $7 BO - $9 MB.

1974-75 - 18th CENTURY CLASSIC FIGURINE YOUNG GIRL
(Right) 4 oz. white sprayed glass with white plastic head. Choice of Sonnet or Moonwind cologne or foaming bath oil. OSP $5, CMV $5 BO - $7 MB.

1978-80 LITTLE MISS MUFFET DECANTER
(Left) 2 oz. white painted over milk glass. Came in Sweet Honesty or Topaze. OSP $7, CMV $5 MB, $4 BO.

(Right) 1978-79 CHURCH MOUSE BRIDE DECANTER
Plastic top with separate white veil. Came in Delicate Daisies cologne. Base is white dull paint over milk glass. OSP $6, CMV $5 BO, $6 MB.

1972-73 VICTORIAN LADY
5 oz. white milk glass, white plastic cap. Came in Bird of Paradise, Unforgettable, Occur!, Charisma Foaming Bath Oil. SSP $4, CMV $5 BO, $7 MB.

1975 SCOTTISH LASS

(Left) 4 oz. blue with red, green & blue plaid skirt, blue plastic top. Holds Sweet Honesty, Bird of Paradise, Roses Roses or Cotillion cologne. OSP $5, CMV $6 BO - $8 MB.

1975-76 SPANISH SENORITA

(Center) 4 oz. red base with white designs and pink plastic top. Holds Moonwind, To A Wild Rose or Topaze cologne. OSP $5, CMV $10 BO - $12 MB.

1972-74 ROARING TWENTIES FASHION FIGURINE

(Right) 3 oz. purple painted over clear glass with plastic purple top. Came in Unforgettable, Topaze, Somewhere, Cotillion. SSP $4, CMV $8 BO - $10 MB.

1969-70 CLASSIC DECANTER

(Left) 8 oz. white glass bottle with gold cap. 11" high, filled with Skin-So-Soft bath oil. SSP $5, CMV $7 in box - $5 bottle only.

1971-72 SEA MAIDEN SKIN-SO-SOFT

(Right) 6 oz. gold cap, clear glass, 10" high. SSP $5, CMV $7 MB - $5 BO.

1976-77 LIBRARY LAMP DECANTER

(Left) 4 oz. gold plated base over clear glass, gold cap. Came in Topaze & Charisma cologne. OSP $9, CMV $5 BO - $6 MB.

1976-79 BRIDAL MOMENTS

(Right) 5 oz. white paint over clear glass. White plastic top. Came in Sweet Honesty or Unforgettable cologne. OSP $9, CMV $7 MB - $6 BO.

1973-74 DUTCH GIRL FIGURINE COLOGNE

(Left) 3 oz. blue painted with light blue plastic top. Came in Unforgettable, Topaze or Somewhere. SSP $5, CMV $8 BO - $11 MB.

1974 GAY NINETIES COLOGNE

(Center) 3 oz. orange sprayed bottle with white top and orange hat. Holds Unforgettable, Topaze or Somewhere. OSP $4, CMV $10 BO - $13 MB.

1974 SWEET DREAMS COLOGNE

(Right) 3 oz. sprayed white bottom with blue top. Holds Pink & Pretty or Sweet Honesty cologne. OSP $4, CMV $13 BO - $15 MB.

1982-83 WISHFUL THOUGHTS FIGURINE

5½" high porcelain figurine. Blue & white. SSP $15, CMV $15 MB.

1977-79 DUTCH MAID

(Left) 4 oz. blue painted base over clear glass, flower design & blue plastic top. Came in Sonnet or Moonwind cologne. OSP $7.50, CMV $6 MB - $5 BO.

1977-79 MARY MARY COLOGNE DECANTER

(Center) 2 oz. frosted white over milk glass & white plastic top. Came in Sweet Honesty or Topaze. OSP $7, CMV $5 MB - $4 BO.

1977-78 SKATERS WALTZ - RED

(Right) 4 oz. red flock on clear glass & pink plastic tip. Came in Moonwind or Charisma cologne. OSP $8.50, CMV $6.50 MB.

1982-83 PRECIOUS PRISCILLA DECANTER

(Left) 3 oz. pale pink paint over clear glass. Plastic head top. Holds Sweet Honesty or Moonwind. SSP $10, CMV $10 MB.

1981 AMERICAN HEIRLOOM PORCELAIN HEAD DOLL

(Right) 11" high fabric doll with porcelain head. Blue ribbon around waist. SSP $16.50, CMV $16.50 MB.

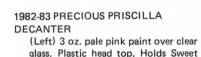

1982-83 PIERROT COLOGNE DECANTER

(Left) 1.75 oz. bottle. Black & white. Choice of Charisma or Occur! SSP $10, CMV $10 MB.

1982-83 PIERRETTE COLOGNE DECANTER

(Right) Same as Pierrot. SSP $10, CMV $10 MB.

1981 BEST FRIENDS PORCELAIN FIGURINE

(Left) 6" high boy figurine. Dated 1981. SSP $19.50, CMV $19.50 MB. 1 made in Taiwan and 1 in Japan.

1981 MOTHER'S LOVE PORCELAIN FIGURINE

(Center) 5½" high girl figurine holding a baby. Bottom tan painted label is dated 1981. Made in Taiwan sticker is tan color. SSP $19.50, CMV $19.50 MB.

1981 MOTHER'S LOVE FIGURINE ADVANCED

(Right) Factory sample. About 75 were given by Avon Products Inc. to Avon collectors at the 10th Annual National Association of Avon Collectors Convention in Long Beach, California. These factory samples do not have Avon label on bottom & is ¼" higher. Made in Taiwan label is green. Rare. Came in plain box. CMV $100 Mint.

1981 MOTHER'S LOVE PORCELAIN FIGURINE TEST PRODUCTS

24 were given to Avon collectors at the 10th Annual National Association of Avon Collectors Convention on the Queen Mary Ship June 1981. It is not in the regular issue box & figurine is not marked on bottom. Came with letter from Avon as very rare. CMV $150 with letter & plain box.

1981-82 FIRST PRAYER DECANTER

(Left) 1.5 oz. light bisque yellow painted bottom over clear glass. Light yellow top. Choice of Charisma, Occur!, Topaze cologne. 4" high. SSP $7, CMV $7 MB.

1981 PRIMA BALLERINA DECANTER

(Center) Pink frosted glass over clear glass, 1 oz. Choice of Zany or Sweet Honesty. Bottle & box label dated 1981. SSP $7, CMV $7 MB.

1981-82 NOSTALGIC GLOW DECANTER

(Right) 1 oz. clear glass lamp bottom, blue plastic shade top. Choice of Moonwind, Wild Jasmine or Topaze. SSP $6, CMV $6 MB.

1982 LOVING TREATS BUTTERMINTS

Flowered tin box filled with buttermint candy. Tin dated 1982. Comes in lavender box. SSP $10, CMV $10 full MB.

1980 FOSTORIA CRYSTAL BUD VASE

(Left) 6" high clear glass. Dated 1980 on bottom. Comes with white scented carnation. SSP $13, CMV $13 MB.

1980 CRYSTAL SNOWFLAKE CHRISTMAS BELL

(Center) 3.75 oz. clear glass. Bottom label dated 1980. Choice of Charisma Topaze, Occur! or Cotillion cologne. SSP $8, CMV $8 MB.

1980-81 MARCHING PROUD DECANTER

(Right) 8½" high, 2 oz. blue base paint over clear glass. White top, red hat, cloth flag. Choice of Sweet Honesty or Topaze cologne. SSP $12, CMV $12 MB.

1980-81 LITTLE DREAM GIRL DECANTER

(Left) 1.25 oz. aqua paint over clear glass. Cream color top. Choice of Sweet Honesty or Occur! cologne. SSP $5, CMV $5 MB.

1980-81 BUNDLE OF FUN DECANTER

(Center) .75 oz. light blue paint over clear glass. Sits on red plastic sled. Choice of Hello Sunshine cologne or Sure Winner Bracing Lotion. SSP $5, CMV $5 MB.

1980-81 FLOWER MOUSE DECANTER

(Right) .75 oz. dull red paint over clear glass and white & yellow mouse cap. Choice of Cotillion or Zany cologne. SSP $4, CMV $4 MB.

1981 HOLIDAY TREATS CANDY CAN
(Left) Green metal can made in England for Avon Christmas 1981. Full of Candy. SSP $9, CMV $9 full MB.

1981 SWEET SCENTIMENTS VALENTINE CANDY
(Right) Metal pink & tan can full of candy. Bottom stamped "Avon Valentine's Day 1981." SSP $8, CMV $8 full MB.

1981 SPRING BOUQUET FRAGRANCED VASE
(Right) 6" glass vase with special plastic coated scented outside. Comes in red, green or amber. SSP $9 each, CMV $9 each MB.

1979-80 CUPID'S MESSAGE SACHET PILLOW & STICKPIN
Red and white box holds 4" red satin heart with white lace trim. Avon on back side of arrow stickpin. Pillow has Timeless Fragrance. SSP $8, CMV $8 MB.

1982-83 SPRING DYNASTY FRAGRANCED VASE
7" high glass vase with fragranced outer coating in blue, pink or green. SSP $11, CMV $11 MB each color.

1981 SHARING THE CHRISTMAS SPIRIT FIGURINE
(Left) First in a series of Christmas figurines from Avon. Dated 1981. 6" high. SSP $45, CMV $45 MB.

1981 NATIVITY HOLY FAMILY FIGURINES SET
Box holds 3 piece white porcelain bisque nativity scene. Each dated 1981. SSP $38.50, CMV $38.50 set MB.

1978-79 DAPPER SNOWMAN
(Left) 1 oz. white milk glass with black painted spots and black hat cap. Holds Moonwind or Sweet Honesty cologne. Brown, blue and red neck scarf. SSP $3, CMV $3 MB.

1978-79 JOLLY SANTA
(Right) 1 oz. clear glass, white painted beard. Red cap. Came in Here's My Heart or Topaze cologne. SSP $1.50, CMV $1.50.

1981 HOLIDAY PLATTER
(Back) 11" clear glass, holly & berry decal. Plate does not say Avon. SSP $15, CMV $15 MB.

1981 HOLIDAY COMPOTE
(Front Left) 4" high clear glass, holly decoration. Avon on bottom. SSP $12, CMV $12 MB.

1981 HOLIDAY CANDLESTICKS
(Front Right) 3" high clear glass, holly decoration. Avon on bottom. SSP $10 set, CMV $10 MB set.

1979 CHRISTMAS TREE HOSTESS SET
9" high ceramic green tree. Comes with Mountain Pine fragrance wax chips and Rag Doll & Teddy Bear ceramic salt & pepper shakers. This was a very short issue at Xmas 1979. SSP $25, CMV $25 MB.

1976-77 HEARTHSIDE CREAM SACHET
(Left) .66 oz. bronze plated over clear glass. Came in Sweet Honesty or Occur! SSP $3.50, CMV $3 MB - $2 BO.

1976-77 GOLDEN ANGEL
(Right) 1 oz. gold plated over clear glass. White angel head cap. Came in Sweet Honesty or Occur! SSP $3, CMV $2 BO - $3 MB.

1968-70 CHRISTMAS TREES
4 oz. bubble bath. Came in red, green, gold & silver painted over clear glass. OSP $2.50, CMV $7 MB - $5 BO Mint.

1974-75 HEAVENLY ANGEL COLOGNE
(Left) 2 oz. clear glass with white top. Holds Occur!, Unforgettable, Somewhere, Here's My Heart, or Sweet Honesty cologne. OSP $4, CMV $4 MB - $3 BO.

1968-69 GOLDEN ANGEL BATH OIL
(Right) 4 oz. gold bottle, gold paper wings. Gold & white cap. OSP $3.50, CMV $7 MB - $4 BO Mint.

1968-69 CHRISTMAS SPARKLERS
4 oz. bubble bath. Came in gold, green, blue & red with gold caps. 2 sides of bottle are indented. OSP $2.50, CMV $7 MB - $5 BO Mint.

1968 CHRISTMAS SPARKLER - PURPLE
4 oz. painted purple over clear glass, gold cap. OSP $2.50, CMV $22.50 Mint. Sold only on West Coast area.

1970-71 CHRISTMAS ORNAMENT BUBBLE BATH
5 oz. Christmas ornament with bubble bath in red, orange or green plastic bottles with silver caps. OSP $2.50, CMV $5 MB - $3 BO.

1974-79 YULE TREE
(Left) 3 oz. green glass with green plastic top and gold star. Came in Sonnet, Moonwind or Field Flowers cologne. OSP $4, CMV $3 BO - $4 MB.

1975 TOUCH OF CHRISTMAS
(Center) 1 oz. green glass with red cap. Holds Unforgettable or Imperial Garden. OSP $2.50, CMV $3 MB - $2 BO. Reissued 1979 in Zany & Here's My Heart. Same CMV.

1975 CRYSTAL TREE COLOGNE DECANTER
(Right) 3 oz. clear glass with gold plastic star cap. Holds Moonwind or Sonnet. OSP $6, CMV $5 BO - $6 MB.

1969-70 CHRISTMAS COLOGNE
3 oz. each. Unforgettable is silver & pink, Occur! is gold & blue, Somewhere is silver & green, Topaze is bronze & yellow. OSP $3.50, CMV Somewhere or Topaze $9 MB, Unforgettable or Occur! $7 MB, $2 less no box.

1979-80 FESTIVE FACETS COLOGNE DECANTER
1 oz. with gold caps. Comes in Charisma "red glass", Sweet Honesty "green glass", and Here's My Heart in "blue glass". SSP $1.50 each, CMV $1.50 MB each.

1978-80 HEAVENLY MUSIC DECANTER
(Left) 1 oz. clear glass, gold cap. Holds Charisma or Topaze cologne. SSP $3, CMV $3 MB.

1978-79 LITTLE BURRO DECANTER
(Center) 1 oz. light gray glass. Straw hat with red flower. Holds Sweet Honesty or Charisma cologne. SSP $3, CMV $3 MB.

1978-80 HONEY BEE DECANTER
(Right) 1.25 oz. amber coated over clear glass. Gold bee on lid. Holds Honeysuckle or Moonwind cologne. SSP $4, CMV $4 MB.

1967 CHRISTMAS ORNAMENTS

Round 4 oz. bubble bath. Came in gold, silver, red, green. Silver caps. OSP $1.75, CMV $9 each MB - $7 each BO Mint.

1979-80 PRETTY PIGLET DECANTER

(Left) .75 oz. clear glass. Holds Roses Roses, pink cap; Honeysuckle, yellow cap; Hawaiian White Ginger, blue-green cap. Fabric flower around neck. SSP $3, CMV $3 MB.

1979-80 MONKEY SHINES DECANTER

(Inside Left) 1 oz. clear glass painted light gray, brown eyes and ears. Red cap and neck strap. Holds Sonnet or Moonwind cologne. SSP $6, CMV $5 BO - $6 MB.

1979-80 BON BON DECANTER

(Inside Right) .75 oz. dark amber glass. Pink and green top came with Sweet Honesty cologne or Cotillion with yellow and green top. SSP $4, CMV $4 MB.

1979-80 GENTLE FOAL DECANTER

(Right) 1.5 oz. dark amber glass and plastic head. Comes in Charisma or Sun Blossoms cologne. SSP $5, CMV $5 MB.

1978-79 KANGAROO TWO

8" red calico stuffed Kangaroo with Avon tag. Green neck ribbon. Came with .75 oz. frosted glass kangaroo bottle with gold head. Holds Topaze or Sweet Honesty cologne. SSP $10, CMV $10 both MB - Bottle only $4 - Stuffed toy - $5.

1979-80 GOLDEN NOTES (CANARY)

(Left) 1.75 oz. clear glass coated light yellow. Yellow head. Came in Charisma or Moonwind cologne. SSP $3, CMV $3 MB.

1979-80 CHURCH MOUSE GROOM

(Center) .75 oz. white glass, white plastic top. Holds Delicate Daisies cologne. SSP $6, CMV $6 MB.

1979-80 FUZZY BUNNY

(Right) 1 oz. clear glass coated with white flock. Pink ears, orange carrot. Holds Sweet Honesty or Honeysuckle cologne. SSP $6, CMV $6 MB.

1978-80 SNIFFY "SKUNK" DECANTER

(Left) 1.25 oz. black glass, white trim. Holds Sweet Honesty or Topaze cologne. SSP $5, CMV $5 MB.

1979-80 "CALCULATOR" IT ALL ADDS UP DECANTER

(Right) 4 oz. black glass. Holds Deep Woods After Shave or Sweet Honesty Body Splash. SSP $6, CMV $6 MB.

1976 FAIRYTALE FROG

(Left) 1 oz. clear glass with gold frog cap. Choice of Sweet Honesty or Sonnet Cologne. OSP $3, CMV $3 MB - $2 BO.

1976-80 LUCKY PENNY LIP GLOSS COMPACT

(Right) 2" diameter copper colored. Contains 2 colors lip gloss. OSP $3, CMV $2 MB, $1 no box. Reissued in 1980 with R on bottom.

1979-80 ROCKING HORSE TREE ORNAMENT DECANTER

.75 oz. clear glass rocker shaped bottle with gold plastic rocking horse top. Bottom of horse says 1979. Holds Sweet Honesty or Moonwind cologne. SSP $5, CMV $5 MB.

1981-82 BEARING GIFTS LIP BALM

Small fuzzy bear, head turns, holds red & green lip balm in red box. SSP $5, CMV $5 MB.

1979-80 MERRY MOUSE DECANTER

(Left) .75 oz. white milk glass bottle & head. Stick on holly leaf. Choice of Zany or Cotillion cologne. SSP $5, CMV $5 MB.

1979-80 PRECIOUS CHICKADEE DECANTER

(Center) 1 oz. white glass. Red & white cap. Came in Here's My Heart or Sun Blossoms cologne. SSP $4, CMV $4 MB.

1979-80 SNUG CUB DECANTER

(Right) 1 oz. milk glass. Green cap. Pink & green paint. Comes in Occur! or Sweet Honesty cologne. SSP $3, CMV $3 MB.

1973-75 LOVE SONG DECANTER
(Left) 6 oz. frosted glass with gold cap. Holds Skin-So-Soft bath oil. OSP $6, CMV $5 MB - $3 BO.

1973-76 BATH TREASURE SNAIL DECANTER
(Right) 6 oz. clear glass with gold head. Holds Skin-So-Soft. OSP $6, CMV $6 MB - $4 BO.

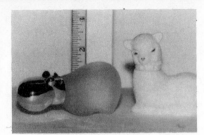

1977-80 BABY HIPPO
(Left) 1 oz. frosted glass with silver head. Came in Sweet Honesty or Topaze cologne. OSP $5, CMV $3 MB - $2 BO.

1977-78 LITTLE LAMB
(Right) .75 oz. white milk glass, white head. Came in Sweet Honesty or Topaze cologne. OSP $5, CMV $3 BO - $4 MB.

1975-76 HIGH-BUTTONED SHOE
(Left) 2 oz. clear glass with gold cap. Holds Occur! or Unforgettable cologne. OSP $3, CMV $3 MB - $2 BO.

1976 GRACEFUL GIRAFFE
(Center) 1.5 oz. clear glass with plastic top. Holds Topaze or To A Wild Rose cologne. OSP $4, CMV $4 MB - $3 BO.

1975-76 ULTRA COLOGNE
(Right) 1 oz. clear glass with gold cap. Holds Timeless or Unspoken. OSP $2.50, CMV $1 MB.

1976-78 TEDDY BEAR COLOGNE DECANTER
(Left) .75 oz. frosted glass, gold cap. Came in Sweet Honesty or Topaze. SSP $3, CMV $2.50 MB - $2 BO.

1976-78 PRECIOUS DOE COLOGNE DECANTER
(Right) ½ oz. frosted glass bottle. Came in Field Flowers or Sweet Honesty. SSP $3, CMV $2.50 MB - $2 BO.

1973-76 ENCHANTED FROG CREAM SACHET
(Left) 1.25 oz. cream colored milk glass with cream colored plastic lid. Came in Sonnet, Moonwind or Occur! OSP $3, CMV $3 MB - $2 BO.

1975-76 HANDY FROG MOISTURIZED HAND LOTION
(Right) 8 oz. white milk glass with red cap. OSP $6, CMV $5 MB - $4 BO.

1975-76 GOOD LUCK ELEPHANT
(Left) 1.5 oz. frosted glass, gold cap. Holds Sonnet, Imperial Garden or Patchwork cologne. OSP $3, CMV $3 MB - $2 BO.

1974-75 SWISS MOUSE
(Right) 3 oz. frosted glass, gold cap. Holds Roses Roses, Field Flowers or Bird of Paradise cologne. OSP $4, CMV $4 MB - $3 BO.

1974-76 PERFUME CONCENTRE
(Left) 1 oz. clear glass with gold cap. Came in Imperial Garden, Moonwind, Sonnet, Charisma or Bird of Paradise. SSP $4, CMV $4 - $2 BO.

1974-75 UNICORN COLOGNE DECANTER
(Right) 2 oz. clear glass with gold cap. Came in Field Flowers, Charisma, Bird of Paradise or Brocade. SSP $4, CMV $4 MB - $3 BO.

1975-76 SNOW BUNNY
(Left) 3 oz. clear glass with gold cap. Holds Moonwind, Charisma, Bird of Paradise or Sweet Honesty cologne. OSP $4, CMV $4 MB - $3 BO.

1974-76 LA BELLE TELEPHONE
(Right) 1 oz. clear glass with gold top. Holds Moonwind, Sonnet or Charisma perfume concentre'. OSP $7, CMV $8 MB - $6 BO.

1980 HUGGABLE HIPPO DECANTER
(Left) 1.75 oz. white glass. Red hat. Holds Zany cologne or Light Musk After Shave. Comes with card of stick on decals. SSP $4, CMV $4 MB.

1980 GREEN-BLUE-BROWN EYED SUSAN COMPACT
(Right) 3 different color centers with yellow flower rim. SSP $5, CMV $2.50 each MB.

1975-76 FLOWER FAIR SSS SKIN SOFTENER

(Left) 5 oz. marbleized glass jar with plastic cap. Holds Skin-So-Soft Skin Softener. SSP $4, CMV $3 MB - $2 BO.

1975-76 FLOWER FAIR COLOGNE

(Right) 3 oz. marbleized glass with plastic top. Holds Roses Roses, Moonwind or Sonnet SSP $4, CMV $4 BO - $5 MB.

1972-73 VICTORIAN MANOR COLOGNE DECANTER

(Left) 5 oz. white painted over clear glass with pink plastic roof. Holds Roses Roses, Bird of Paradise, Unforgettable, Cotillion. SSP $5, CMV $8 MB - $7 BO.

1972-74 HOBNAIL DECANTER FOAMING BATH OIL

(Center) 5 oz. white opal glass. Came in Moonwind, Elusive, Roses Roses, Bath Foam, Lemon Velvet Bath Foam. SSP $6, CMV $6 MB - $4 BO.

1973-74 HOBNAIL BUD VASE

(Right) 4 oz. white milk glass with red & yellow roses. Holds Charisma, Topaze, Roses Roses cologne. SSP $6, CMV $5 MB - $4 BO. Also came 4.75 oz. size.

1971-73 FRAGRANCE HOURS COLOGNE

(Left) 6 oz. ivory glass grandfathers clock, gold cap. Bird of Paradise, Field Flowers, Charisma or Elusive. SSP $5, CMV $5 MB - $4 BO.

1970 EIFFEL TOWER COLOGNE

(Right) 3 oz., 9" high clear glass with gold cap. Came in Occur!, Rapture, Somewhere, Topaze, Cotillion or Unforgettable. SSP $4, CMV $7 MB - $5 BO.

1973-75 VENETIAN PITCHER COLOGNE MIST

(Left) 3 oz. blue plastic coated bottle with silver plastic top. Came in Imperial Garden, Patchwork, Sonnet or Moonwind. SSP $6, CMV $5 MB - $3 BO.

1972-75 COMPOTE COLOGNE DECANTER

(Right) 5 oz. white milk glass bottle, gold cap. Came in Moonwind, Field Flowers, Elusive or Brocade. SSP $5, CMV $4 MB - $3 BO.

1972-74 SWEET SHOPPE PIN CUSHION CREAM SACHET DECANTER

(Left) 1 oz. white milk glass bottom with white plastic back with hot pink pin cushion seat. Came in Sonnet, Moonwind, Field Flowers, Roses Roses, Bird of Paradise or Charisma. SSP $4, CMV $5 MB - $4 BO.

1969-70 FRAGRANCE TOUCH

(Right) 3 oz. white milk glass. Cologne came in Elusive, Charisma, Brocade or Regence. OSP $5, CMV $4 MB - $3 BO.

1974 BUTTERCUP CANDLESTICK COLOGNE

(Left) 6 oz. white milk glass, yellow & white flowers. Holds Moonwind, Sonnet or Imperial Garden cologne. OSP $7. First issue has yellow band around neck. CMV $9 MB. Later issue was plain with no band on neck and yellow or brown decals. CMV $7 MB - $2 less no box.

1974 BUTTERCUP FLOWER HOLDER PERFUMED SKIN SOFTENER

(Center) 5 oz. milk glass with plastic white top. Holds Moonwind, Imperial Garden or Sonnet. OSP $5, CMV $5 MB - $3 BO.

1974 BUTTERCUP SALT SHAKER CREAM SACHET

(Right) 1.5 oz. white milk glass with yellow & white flowers, yellow plastic cap. Came in Moonwind, Sonnet or Imperial Garden. OSP $2.50, CMV $3 MB - $2 BO.

1973-75 COUNTRY KITCHEN DECANTER

6 oz. white milk glass with red plastic head. Holds moisturized hand lotion. SSP $5, CMV $5 MB - $4 BO.

1968-70 BLUE DEMI-CUP BATH OIL
(Left) 3 oz. white glass, blue cap & design, some came with gold top with blue lid. Came in Brocade, Topaze or Unforgettable. OSP $3.50, CMV $7 MB - $5 BO.

1969-70 DEMI-CUP BATH OIL
(Center Two) 3 oz. white milk glass. Charisma has red cap and design. Regence has green cap and design. OSP $3.50, CMV $7 MB - $5 BO.

1969 TO A WILD ROSE DEMI-CUP
(Right) 3 oz. white glass, red rose, pink cap. 6½" high. Contains Foaming Bath Oil. OSP $3.50, CMV $8 MB - $6 BO.

1967 BATH SEASONS
3 oz. foaming bath oil. Each is white glass & top with orange design in Honeysuckle, green in Lily of the Valley. CMV $7 BO - $9 MB each. Lavender in Lilac, yellow in Jasmine. Matching ribbons on each. OSP $2.50 each, CMV $6 BO each - $8 MB.

1972-73 ENCHANTED HOURS
(Left) 5 oz. blue glass bottle with gold cap. Came in Roses Roses, Charisma, Unforgettable or Somewhere cologne. SSP $5, CMV $7 MB - $5 BO.

1973-74 BEAUTIFUL AWAKENING
(Right) 3 oz. gold painted over clear glass front paper clock face, gold cap. Came in Elusive, Roses Roses or Topaze. SSP $5, CMV $4 BO - $6 MB.

1971 DUTCH TREAT DEMI-CUPS
3 oz. white glass filled with Cream Lotion in Honeysuckle, yellow cap; Blue Lotus, blue cap; Hawaiian White Ginger, pink cap. OSP $3.50, CMV $6 - $4 BO. Also each came with white caps.

1972-73 ROYAL COACH
(Left) 5 oz. white milk glass, gold cap. Holds Moonwind, Bird of Paradise, Charisma or Field Flowers foaming bath oil. OSP $5, CMV $5 MB - $4 BO.

1971-73 SITTING PRETTY COLOGNE
(Right) 4 oz. white milk glass with gold cat cap. Came in Topaze, Rapture, Cotillion, Somewhere or Persian Wood. OSP $5, CMV $7 MB - $5 BO.

1963-64 BATH URN (CRUET)
8 oz. white glass top & bottle. Perfume bath oil in Somewhere, Topaze, Cotillion. OSP $3.75 ea. Here's My Heart, Persian Wood, To A Wild Rose, OSP $3.50 ea. CMV $15 in box. $10 bottle with label.

FOREIGN BATH URN
(Right) 180cc size, clear glass. Smaller than American bath urn. CMV $20.

1968-70 SALT SHAKERS
3 oz. pink ribbon, pink flowers. Yellow ribbon & flowers in Hawaiian White Ginger, Honeysuckle & Lilac bath oil. OSP $2.50, CMV $5 MB each - $4 BO.

1971-73 BATH URN
5 oz. white glass & cap with gold top plate. Foaming bath oil in Elusive & Charisma or bath foam in Lemon Velvet & Silk & Honey. 6" high. SSP $4, CMV $3 MB, $2 BO.

1971-74 KOFFEE KLATCH
5 oz. yellow paint over clear glass pot with gold top. Foaming Bath Oil in Field Flowers, Honeysuckle, or Lilac. Also Lemon Velvet Bath Foam. SSP $5, CMV $5 MB, $4 BO.

1975 ORIENTAL EGG — CHINESE PHEASANT
Upside down label mistake made at factory. Upside down bottle only CMV $18

1970-72 LEISURE HOURS

5 oz. white milk glass bottle contains foaming bath oil in 6 fragrances. Gold cap. OSP $4, CMV $4, $5 MB.

1974 LEISURE HOURS MINIATURE

1.5 oz. white milk glass bottle, gold cap. Holds Field Flowers, Bird of Paradise or Charisma cologne. OSP $3, CMV $3, $4 MB.

1974-80 BUTTERFLY FANTASY PORCELAIN TREASURE EGG

5½" long white porcelain multi-colored butterfly decals. Sold empty. 1974 stamped on bottom. Sold 1974-75 then reissued 1978. The 1978 issue has a 1974 ''R'' for reissue on bottom and the big butterfly on top is much lighter than the 1974 issue. OSP $12, CMV $25 MB for 1974 issue. CMV $15 MB for 1974 ''R'' issue. 1979-80 issue has ''R'' 1979 on bottom. CMV $15 MB. Also came with bottom label upside down or backwards. Add $6 CMV.

1971 FRENCH TELEPHONE

6 oz. white milk glass base with gold cap & trim. Holds Foaming Bath Oil, Center of receiver holds ¼ oz. of perfume in frosted glass. Came in Moonwind. OSP $22, Bird of Paradise, Elusive or Charisma OSP $20, CMV $27.50 MB, $20 BO.

1975 ORIENTAL EGG CHINESE PHEASANT

(Left) 1 oz. white opal glass, black plastic base. Came in Imperial Garden, Charisma and Bird of Paradise cologne. OSP $6.50, CMV $10 MB, $8 BO.

1974-75 ORIENTAL EGG PEACH ORCHARD DECANTER

(Right) 1 oz. white opal glass with green marbleized plastic base. Came in Imperial Garden, Sonnet or Moonwind or Patchwork perfume concentre'. SSP $5.99, CMV $7 MB, $6 BO.

1975-76 ORIENTAL EGG DELICATE BLOSSOMS

(Center) 1 oz. light blue opal glass with blue green plastic base. Came in Patchwork, Sonnet, & Charisma cologne. OSP $7.50, CMV $7 MB, $6 BO.

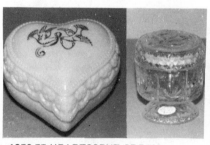

1976-77 HEARTSCENT CREAM SACHET

.66 oz. white glass bottom with white plastic top. Gold dove design. Came in Charisma, Occur! or Roses Roses. OSP $3, CMV $3 MB, $2 BO.

1975-76 FOSTORIA COMPOTE

12 Skin-So-Soft capsules. Clear glass with glass top. OSP $8, MB, $6 BO.

1971-72 VICTORIANA PITCHER & BOWL

6 oz. turquoise glass pitcher with Skin-So-Soft bath oil & turquoise glass bowl with Avon bottom. Some bowls have double Avon stamp on bottom. OSP $7.50, CMV $11 MB, $9 no box, $12 with double stamp on bottom.

1972-73 VICTORIANA PITCHER & BOWL

Same as above only came in Moonwind, Field Flowers Foaming Bath Oil. SSP $7, CMV $8 no box, $11 MB.

1972-74 VICTORIANA POWDER SACHET

1.5 oz. turquoise glass jar & lid. Came in Moonwind, Field Flowers. SSP $5, CMV $6 BO, $8 MB.

1972-73 VICTORIANA DISH & SOAP

Turquoise glass dish with white soap. SSP $4, CMV $8 MB, dish only $3.

1972-76 GRECIAN PITCHER

6½" high, 5 oz. white glass bottle & white stopper holds Skin-So-Soft. SSP $5, CMV $5 MB, $4 BO.

1971-76 CORNUCOPIA SKIN-SO-SOFT

6 oz. white glass, gold cap. 5½" high. SSP $5, CMV $4 MB, $3 BO.

1978 VICTORIANA SOAP DISH

Blue marbleized glass - white soap. May 1978 on bottom. SSP $5.99, CMV $6., $4. no box, $2. dish only.

1978 VICTORIANA PITCHER & BOWL

Blue marbleized glass bowl and 6 oz. pitcher. Holds bubble bath. May 1978 on bottom. SSP $9.99, CMV $8 MB, $6 no box.

1972-75 SECRETAIRE

7" high, pink paint over clear glass, gold cap. Holds 5 oz. of Foaming Bath oil in Moonwind. OSP $7.50, Charisma, Brocade, Lilac & Lemon Velvet, OSP $6, CMV $6 MB, $5 BO.

1972-75 ARMOIRE DECANTER

7" high, 5 oz. white glass bottle with gold cap. Choice of Field Flowers, Bird of Paradise, Elusive or Charisma bath oil. SSP $4, CMV $4 MB, $3 BO. 1975 came in Field Flowers, Charisma & Bird of Paradise only. SSP $4, CMV $4 MB, $3 BO.

1972-76 COUNTRY STORE COFFEE MILL

5 oz. ivory milk glass, white plastic cap & plastic handles on side with gold rim. Came in Sonnet, Moonwind, Bird of Paradise, Charisma cologne. SSP $6, CMV $6 MB, $4 BO. Came in 2 different size boxes.

1972-73 LITTLE DUTCH KETTLE

5 oz. orange painted clear glass with gold cap. Came in Cotillion, Honeysuckle Foaming Bath Oil or Lemon Velvet Bath Foam. SSP $5, CMV $5 MB, $4 BO.

1979-80 SNOW OWL POWDER SACHET II

(Left) 1.25 oz. frosted glass. Holds Moonwind or timeless powder sachet. Blue Rhinestone eyes. Label in black lettering. SSP $7, CMV $7 MB.

1979-80 CUTE COOKIE DECANTER

(Center) 1 oz. dark amber glass. Pink cap & point. Holds Hello Sunshine cologne. SSP $2.75, CMV $2.75 MB.

1979-80 CHARMING CHIPMUNK DECANTER

(Right) 5 oz. clear glass painted frosted peach color. Holds Field Flowers or Sweet Honesty. SSP $4, CMV $4 MB.

1979-80 CHRISTMAS BELLS DECANTER

1 oz. red glass. Silver cap. Holds Topaze or Sweet Honesty cologne. SSP $3, CMV $3 MB.

1979-80 RED CARDINAL DECANTER

2 oz. clear glass painted red. Red cap. Holds Bird of Paradise or Charisma cologne. SSP $5, CMV $5 MB.

1980 PRECIOUS HEARTS DECANTER

(Left) Heart embossed clear glass, 5 oz., gold tone cap. Comes in Here's My Heart, Unforgettable, Moonwind, Topaze or Sweet Honesty. SSP $1.29, CMV $1. MB.

1980 FLUFFY CHICK DECANTER

(Center) 1 oz. clear glass yellow flock coated. Holds Hello Sunshine cologne. SSP $6., CMV $6. MB.

1980 FLUTTERING FANCY DECANTER

(Right) 1 oz. clear glass with pink butterfly on yellow frosted plastic cap. Holds Sweet Honesty or Charisma cologne. SSP $5., CMV $5. MB.

1976-77 LOVABLE SEAL

1 oz. frosted glass, gold cap. Came in Cotillion or Here's My Heart. OSP $4, CMV $3 MB, $2 BO.

1978 LOVE BIRD DECANTER

1½ oz. milk glass bottle with gold cap. Came in Charisma or Moonwind cologne. SSP $4, CMV $3 MB, $2 BO.

1977-79 SILVER SWIRLS SALT SHAKER COLOGNE DECANTER

(Left) 3 oz. silver plated over clear glass. Silver top. Came in Sweet Honesty or Topaze cologne. SSP $4.99 CMV $3 MB, $2 BO.

1977-78 ISLAND PARAKEET COLOGNE DECANTER

(Right) 1.5 oz. blue glass base & blue & yellow plastic top. Approx. 4½" high. Came in Moonwind or Charisma Cologne. OSP $6, CMV $4 MB, $3 BO.

1973-74 REGAL PEACOCK

4 oz. blue glass with gold cap. Came in Patchwork, Sonnet or Moonwind. SSP $6, CMV $9 MB, $7 BO.

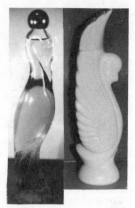

1971-72 FLAMINGO DECANTER
5 oz. clear bird shaped bottle with gold cap. 10" tall. Came in Bird of Paradise, Elusive, Charisma, Brocade, SSP. $4.50 CMV, $5 MB, $4 BO.

1972-76 SWAN LAKE COLOGNE
8" high, 3 oz. white glass bottle with white cap. Came in Bird of Paradise, Charisma & Elusive. OSP $5, Moonwind SSP $5, CMV $4 MB, $3 BO.

THE AVON COLLECTOR

We Avon Collectors are DEFINITELY in a class all by ourselves;
Spending small fortunes on bottles, just to line up neatly on shelves.

Each one collecting in his own special way;
Adding new treasures, one by one, day by day.

Off to a garage sale, a flea market, or still better yet
find the cache of a long time, hoarding type Avon Rep.

Finding a gift set, an old toy, or a mint box of soap;
Keep us ever searching with new rays of hope.

It's that suspense, the anticipation that keeps driving us on;
Many to the point where our savings are about gone.

Some people think we are silly, personally, I find it a thrill;
and I'm gonna keep right on collecting till I go over the hill.

Will my Avons be for sale when from this earth I depart;
My beautiful collection that is so dear to my heart?

You have got to be kidding or just plain out of your tree;
I've already made arrangement to take all of them with me.

I first called on St. Peter, but he said, "I'm so sorry my dear;
We just don't allow worldly possessions up here."

"You might check with Satan, for so I've been told,
He might be willing to accept you into his fold."

I took that advice. I've been granted permission. Isn't that swell;
Can't you just imagine how HEAVENLY HELL'S gonna smell!

By Vera Shaw
Spokane, Washington

1977-79 DR. HOOT DECANTER
(Left) 4 oz. white milk glass owl with blue plastic cap and white gold or green tassel. Came in Sweet Honesty, or Wild Country. OSP $7.50, CMV $5 MB, $4 BO.

1975-76 DR. HOOT DECANTER
4 oz. opal white glass, black cap, gold tassel. Holds Wild Country After Shave or Sweet Honesty Cologne. OSP $5, CMV $5 MB, $4 BO.

1972-74 PRECIOUS OWL CREAM SACHET
(Center) 1½ oz. white bottle with gold eyes. Came in Moonwind, Field Flowers, Charisma, Roses Roses. OSP $3, CMV $3 MB, $2 BO.

1976-77 SNOW OWL DECANTER
(Right) 1.25 oz. frosted glass base and frosted plastic head with blue eyes. Came in Moonwind or Sonnet. Label in blue lettering. SSP $4.99, CMV $5 MB, $4 BO.

1971-72 SONG BIRD COLOGNE
1.5 oz. clear glass with gold base cap. Came in Unforgettable, Topaze, Occur!, Here's My Heart & Cotillion. OSP $3, CMV $5 MB, $4 BO.

1975-76 BIRD OF HAPPINESS COLOGNE
1.5 oz. light blue glass, gold cap. Holds Charisma, Topaze, Occur!, or Unforgettable cologne. OSP $3, CMV $5 MB, $4 BO.

1973-75 CRYSTAL FACETS COLOGNE GELEE
3 oz. clear glass. Choice of Roses Roses, or Field Flowers. OSP $4, CMV $4 MB, $3 BO.

1974-76 OWL FANCY COLOGNE GELEE
4 oz. clear glass. Came in Raining Violets or Roses, Roses. SSP $4, CMV $4 MB, $3 BO.

1976 SILVER DOVE ORNAMENT COLOGNE DECANTER

½ oz. bottle with gold or silver cap. Came in silver metal bird holder marked Christmas '76 on both sides & Avon on inside. Came in Bird of Paradise or Occur! cologne. SSP $4.99, CMV $4 MB, $3 no box.

1975 FLIGHT TO BEAUTY

5 oz. glass jar with white frosted top. Holds Rich Moisture or Vita-Moist Cream or SSS Skin Softener. OSP $5, CMV $4 MB, $3 BO.

1973-75 PARTRIDGE COLOGNE DECANTER

5 oz. white milk glass with white plastic lid. Came in Unforgettable. Topaze, Occur!, Somewhere. OSP $5, CMV $4 MB, $3 BO.

1973-74 SNOW BIRD CREAM SACHET

1.5 oz. white milk glass, white plastic cap. Came in Patchwork, Moonwind, Sonnet Cream Sachet. OSP $2.50, CMV $3 MB, $2 BO.

1974-75 ROBIN RED-BREAST COLOGNE DECANTER

2 oz. red frosted glass with silver plastic top. Holds Charisma, Roses Roses, Bird of Paradise. OSP $4, CMV $4 MB, $3 BO.

1971-72 ROYAL SWAN COLOGNE

1 oz. white glass, gold crown cap. Came in Elusive, Charisma, Bird of Paradise, Topaze, Unforgettable, Cotillion. SSP $3, CMV $5 MB, $3 BO.

1974 ROYAL SWAN COLOGNE

1 oz. blue glass with gold crown cap. Came in Unforgettable, Topaze, Cotillion, Here's My Heart. SSP $2.50, CMV $6 BO, $8 MB.

1978 JOYOUS BELL

Light blue frosted over clear glass. Silver cap. Came in Charisma or Topaze cologne. In blue & white box. SSP $3, CMV $3 MB.

1978-79 SUNNY SHINE UP LIP GLOSS COMPACT

White plastic base with yellow screw on egg lid. SSP $3, CMV $2 MB.

1981-82 MOONLIGHT GLOW ANNUAL BELL

3 oz. glass bell, frosted top. Choice of Moonwind or Topaze. SSP $9, CMV $9 MB.

1975-76 CRYSTALSONG

4 oz. red glass with frosted bow and handle. Holds Timeless or Sonnet. OSP $6, CMV $4 BO, $6 MB.

1974-75 CHRISTMAS BELLS COLOGNE

1 oz. red painted glass with gold cap. Came in Topaze, Occur!, Cotillion, To A Wild Rose, or Sweet Honesty. OSP $2.25, CMV $2 BO, $3 MB.

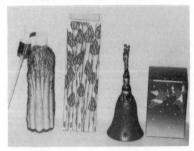

1979-80 GARDEN FRESH HAND LOTION DECANTER

10 oz. clear glass. Yellow & gold pump & cap. Green box. SSP $7, CMV $7 MB.

1979-80 HEAVENLY CHERUB HOSTESS BELL

3.75 oz. clear glass painted frosted tan. Gold plastic handle. 1979 embossed on bottom. Comes in Topaze or Bird of Paradise cologne. SSP $7, CMV $7 MB.

1978 ROSEPOINT BELL DECANTER

(Left) 4 oz. clear glass, clear plastic top. Came in Charisma or Roses Roses Cologne. OSP $8.50, CMV $6 MB, $5 BO.

1976-77 HOSPITALITY BELL COLOGNE DECANTER

(Right) Silver top, 3.75 oz. blue glass bottom. Came in Moonwind or Roses Roses cologne. Avon 1976 stamped in bottom. OSP $8, CMV $6 MB, $5 BO.

1968-69 FRAGRANCE BELL COLOGNE

(Left) 1 oz. gold handle. Bell actually rings. Came in Charisma, Brocade, Regence, Unforgettable, Rapture, Occur!, Somewhere, Topaze, Cotillion, Here's My Heart & To A Wild Rose. OSP $2, CMV $4 MB, $3 BO.

1965-66 FRAGRANCE BELL COLOGNE

(Center) 4 oz. clear glass, plastic handle, neck tag. Came in Rapture, Occur!, OSP $5, Somewhere, Topaze, Cotillion OSP $4, Here's My Heart, To A Wild Rose, Wishing, OSP $3.50, CMV bell with tag, $15, $20 MB.

1973-74 HOBNAIL BELL COLOGNE DECANTER

(Right) 2 oz. white milk glass with gold handle & gold bell underneath. Holds Unforgettable, Topaze, Here's My Heart, To A Wild Rose or Sweet Honesty. SSP $4., CMV $4. MB - $3. BO.

1978-79 ROYAL SIAMESE CAT

Light gray paint over clear glass. 4.5 oz. gray plastic head has blue glass jewel eyes. Came in Cotillion or Moonwind cologne. SSP $7, CMV $7 MB.

1978-79 EMERALD BELL

3.75 oz. light green glass. Gold and green plastic cap. Bottom has "Avon 1978" embossed. Came in Sweet Honesty or Roses Roses cologne. SSP $6, CMV $6 MB.

1974-76 KITTEN'S HIDEAWAY

1 oz. amber basket, white plastic kitten cap. Came in field Flowers, Bird of Paradise or Charisma Cream Sachet. OSP $4, CMV $3 MB, $2 BO.

1975-76 BLUE EYES

1.5 oz. opal glass with blue rhinestone eyes. Available in Topaze, or Sweet Honesty cologne. OSP $4, CMV $5 BO, $6 MB.

1976-77 SITTING PRETTY COLOGNE DECANTER

(Left) 1.5 oz. white milk glass base, white plastic top. Came in Charisma or Topaze. Pink ribbons painted on each corner. OSP $6, CMV $6 MB, $5 BO.

1977-79 ROYAL ELEPHANT

(Right) ½ oz. white milk glass with gold snap on top. Came in Charisma or Topaze. OSP $6, CMV $3 MB, $2 BO.

1979-80 CURIOUS KITTY DECANTER

2.5 oz. clear glass, yellow cat cap. Came in Sweet Honesty or Here's My Heart cologne. SSP $6, CMV $6 MB.

1978-79 PEEK A MOUSE CHRISTMAS STOCKING DECANTER

1.25 oz. green glass with gold mouse cap. Holds Sweet Honesty or Unforgettable cologne. Came with red velvet stocking with gold trim. SSP $5, CMV $5 MB.

1973-74 KITTEN PETITE COLOGNE

1.5 oz. amber glass ball with white plastic cat for cap. Came in Sonnet or Moonwind. SSP $3, CMV $3, $4 MB.

1971 MING CAT COLOGNE

6 oz. white glass & head. blue trim & neck ribbon. Came in Moonwind, Bird of Paradise, Elusive, Charisma. SSP $6, CMV $9 MB.

1972-76 KITTEN LITTLE COLOGNE

3½" high, white glass bottle holds 1½ oz. cologne in Occur!, Topaze, Unforgettable, Somewhere, Cotillion. SSP $2., CMV $3. MB.

1975-76 KITTEN LITTLE COLOGNE DECANTER

1.5 oz. black glass with black head. Holds Sweet Honesty, Bird of Paradise, or Roses Roses. OSP $4, CMV $5 MB, $4 BO.

1975-76 TABATHA COLOGNE SPRAY

3 oz. black glass and plastic. Holds Imperial Garden, Bird of Paradise or Cotillion cologne. OSP $6, CMV $6 MB, $5 BO.

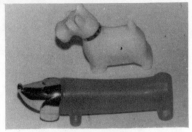

1976-78 PRINCESS OF YORKSHIRE COLOGNE DECANTER

(Left) 1 oz. off white over milk glass. Came in Sweet Honesty or Topaze cologne. SSP $4, CMV $4 MB, $3 BO.

1974-75 ROYAL PEKINESE

(Center) 1.5 oz. white glass & white plastic head. Came in Unforgettable, Somewhere, Topaze. OSP $5, CMV $5 MB, $3 BO.

1977-79 FUZZY BEAR COLOGNE DECANTER

(Right) Tan flock over clear glass base & head. Came in Sweet Honesty or Occur! OSP $6.50, CMV $4.50 MB, $3 BO.

1973-76 QUEEN OF SCOTS

1. oz. white milk glass, white plastic head. Came in Sweet Honesty, Unforgettable, Somewhere, Cotillion, Here's My Heart. SSP $3, CMV $4 MB, $3 BO.

1973-74 DACHSHUND COLOGNE DECANTER

1.5 oz. frosted glass, gold cap. Came in Unforgettable, Somewhere, Topaze, Cotillion. SSP $3, CMV $4 MB, $3 BO.

1973 BON BON COLOGNE

1 oz. black milk glass with black plastic cap. Holds Field Flowers, Bird of Paradise, Roses Roses or Elusive. OSP $2, CMV $6 MB, $4 BO.

1972-73 BON BON COLOGNE

1 oz. white milk glass with white cap. Holds Unforgettable, Topaze, Occur!, Cotillion or Here's My Heart cologne. OSP $2, CMV $4 MB, $3 BO.

1974-79 COUNTRY KITCHEN MOISTURIZED HAND LOTION

10 oz. red glass with plastic top. Holds Moisturized Hand Lotion. OSP $6, CMV $4 MB, $3 BO. Reissued in 1979.

1974-76 LADY SPANIEL

1.5 oz. opal glass with plastic head. Holds Patchwork, Sonnet or Moonwind cologne. OSP $3, CMV $4 MB, $3 BO.

1973-75 FLORAL BUD VASE

5 oz. white milk glass. Holds Roses Roses or Lemon Velvet Bath Foam or Field Flowers or Honeysuckle Foaming Bath Oil. SSP $5, CMV $5 MB, $4 BO.

1973-76 SUZETTE DECANTER

5 oz. cream colored milk glass with cream colored plastic head & a pink-lavender bow around neck. Holds Field Flowers, Bird of Paradise or Cotillion Foaming Bath Oil. SSP $5, CMV $4 MB, $4 BO.

1970-72 SEA HORSE

Clear glass 6 oz. container holds Skin-So-Soft, gold cap. SSP $5, CMV $6 MB, $4 BO.

1973-76 SEA HORSE MINIATURE COLOGNE

1.5 oz. clear glass, gold cap. Came in Unforgettable, Here's My Heart, Cotillion. SSP $3, CMV $4 MB, $3 BO.

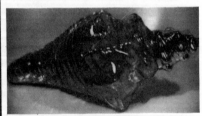

1971-72 SEA TREASURE FOAMING BATH OIL

5 oz. clear glass coated iridescent sea shell shaped bottle, gold cap. Came in Field Flowers, Charisma, Honeysuckle, Lilac. 7" long. SSP $5, CMV $8 MB, $6 BO.

1973-76 SEA SPIRIT FOAMING BATH OIL DECANTER

5 oz. light green glass with green plastic tail over cap. Holds Elusive, Topaze or Cotillion. OSP $5, CMV $5 MB, $4 BO.

1974-75 SONG OF THE SEA EMOLLIENT BATH PEARLS

80 bath pearls, aqua colored glass with plastic head. Holds Moonwind, Sonnet or Imperial Garden. OSP $7, CMV $7 MB, $5 BO.

EUROPEAN DOLPHIN

(Right) Bath oil, 165 cc size, frosted glass, gold tail cap. Foreign Dolphin smaller than U.S. size. CMV $25.

1968-69 DOLPHIN SKIN-SO-SOFT

(Left) 8 oz. frosted glass with gold tail cap. Sold in U.S.A. SSP $4., CMV $6. MB - $3. BO.

DOLPHIN FROM MEXICO

(Center) About same size as American Dolphin, only bottle is clear glass, with gold tail. Aslo came in frosted glass, CMV $20 each.

1972-73 BUTTERFLY COLOGNE

1½ oz. 3½" high, gold cap with 2 prongs. Holds cologne in Occur!, Topaze, Unforgettable, Somewhere & Here's My Heart. SSP $3, CMV $5 MB, $3 BO. Reissued in 1976 in Field Flowers & Sweet Honesty. Same CMV.

1973-74 DOLPHIN MINIATURE

1.5 oz. clear glass, gold tail. Holds Charisma, Bird of Paradise or Field Flowers cologne. OSP $3, CMV $4 MB, $3 BO.

1974-75 PARISIAN GARDEN PERFUME

.33 oz. white milk glass with gold cap. Came in Sonnet, Moonwind, or Charisma perfume. OSP $5, CMV $5 MB, $4 BO.

1974-75 EVENING GLOW PERFUME DECANTER

.33 oz. white milk glass with green flowers, white and gold plastic cap. Came in Moonwind, Sonnet, or Charisma. OSP $6, CMV $6 BO, $7 MB.

1971-74 FRAGRANCE SPLENDOR

4½" high clear glass bottle with gold cap & frosted plastic handle. Holds perfume oil in Bird of Paradise, Elusive, Occur!, Charisma or Unforgettable. OSP $5, CMV $5 MB, $4 BO.

1975-76 MANSION LAMP

6 oz. blue glass with white plastic top. Holds Bird of Paradise or Moonwind cologne. OSP $8, CMV $8 MB, $6 BO.

1975 EMPIRE GREEN BUD VASE

3 oz. green glass with silver base. Holds Moonwind, Sonnet or Imperial Garden cologne. OSP $6, CMV $5 MB, $3 BO.

1975-76 BUTTERFLY GARDEN BUD VASE

6 oz. black glazed glass with gold stopper. Holds Roses, Roses, Bird of Paradise or Topaze cologne. OSP $6, CMV $6 MB, $4 BO.

1972-73 SEAGREEN BUD VASE

5 oz. 9" high green glass bottle holds foaming bath oil in Field Flowers, Honeysuckle or Bird of Paradise. SSP $4, CMV $4 MB, $2 BO.

1972-74 TIFFANY LAMP COLOGNE

5 oz. brown glass base with pink shade, pink and orange flowers, green leaves on lavender background. Came in Sonnet, Moonwind, Field Flowers, Roses Roses. SSP $7, CMV $9 MB, $8 BO. Also came in pink and yellow flowers on shade, also all white flowers. CMV $11 MB.

1973-76 HEARTH LAMP COLOGNE DECANTER

8 oz. black glass with gold handle, has daisies around neck with yellow & white shade. Holds Roses Roses, Bird of Paradise or Elusive. SSP $8, CMV $8 MB, $7 BO.

1973-74 CHIMNEY LAMP COLOGNE MIST DECANTER

2 oz. clear glass bottom with white plastic shade with pink flowers. Holds Patchwork Sonnet or Moonwind. SSP $4, CMV $6 MB, $5 BO.

1976-77 COUNTRY CHARM DECANTER

(Left) 4.8 oz. white milk glass, yellow stove window. Green & white plastic top. Came in Field Flowers, or Sonnet. SSP $7, CMV $7 BO, $8 MB.

1973-74 HURRICANE LAMP COLOGNE DECANTER

(Right) 6 oz. white milk glass bottom with clear glass shade, gold cap. Holds Roses Roses, Field Flowers, Bird of Paradise or Charisma cologne. SSP $8, CMV $11 BO, $9 BO.

1974-76 MING BLUE LAMP

5 oz. blue glass lamp, white plastic shade with gold tip. Holds Charisma, Bird of Paradise or Field Flowers, foaming bath oil. OSP $6, CMV $6 MB, $5 BO.

1975-76 CHARMLIGHT DECANTER

.88 oz. cream sachet in white shade and 2 oz. cologne in pink base. Holds Imperial Garden, Sonnet or Moonwind. OSP $7, CMV $7 MB, $6 BO.

1971-72 PARLOR LAMP

2 sections. Gold cap over 3 oz. cologne top section in light amber iridescent glass. Yellow frosted glass bottom with talc 6½'' high. Holds Bird of Paradise, Elusive, Charisma, Regence or Moonwind. OSP $7, CMV $10 MB, $8 BO.

1970-71 COURTING LAMP COLOGNE

5 oz. blue glass base with white milk glass shade & blue velvet ribbon. Holds Elusive, Brocade, Charisma, Hana Gasa or Regence. OSP $6, CMV $11 MB, $9 BO.

1978-80 FRENCH RIBBON SACHET PILLOWS

Box holds 6 blue satin pillows with blue ribbon. SSP $6, CMV $5 MB.

1979 AVONSHIRE COLLECTION COLOGNE DECANTER

6 oz. clear glass painted blue and white. Holds Charisma or Somewhere cologne. R on bottom for Reissue and dated May, 1979. SSP $9.99, CMV $9.99 MB.

AVONSHIRE BATH OIL DECANTER

6 oz. clear glass painted blue and white. Holds Skin-So-Soft. R on bottom for reissue and dated May, 1979. SSP $10., CMV $10. MB.

AVONSHIRE HOSTESS SOAPS

Blue box holds 3 white bars. SSP $4, CMV $4 MB.

1978-79 COLOGNE RONDELLE

.5 oz. clear glass, gold cap. Came in Sweet Honesty, Charisma, Cotillion, Topaze, Unforgettable, Moonwind, Here's My Heart, Sonnet, Occur!, Bird of Paradise. Came in different color Christmas boxes. SSP 99c, CMV $1 MB.

1978-79 BERMUDA FRESH MOUTHWASH DECANTER

6 oz. purple plastic, green top. SSP $3, CMV $1.50

1978-79 COUNTRY CREAMERY "MILK CAN" DECANTER

10 oz. white painted over clear glass. Holds moisturized hand lotion. SSP $6, CMV $6 MB.

1979-80 FLOWER FANCY DECANTER

1.25 oz. clear glass, gold flower cap. Holds Field Flowers or Roses Roses. SSP $4, CMV $4 MB.

1979-80 SPRING SONG DECANTER

1.5 oz. clear glass. Comes with plastic frosted flower stopper. Came in Lily of The Valley or Sweet Honesty cologne. SSP. $6, CMV $6 MB.

1965-66 SKIN-SO-SOFT DECANTER

10 oz. bottle with gold painted glass stopper. 1st issue came with solid painted gold band around center & later issue not solid band as pictured. OSP $5, CMV solid band $11 MB, $7 BO mint. Not solid band $9 MB, $5 BO Mint.

1966 SKIN-SO-SOFT DECANTER

(Left) 10 oz. bottle with glass & cork stopper. 10'' high. OSP $5, CMV $6 BO, $8 MB.

1967 SKIN-SO-SOFT DECANTER

(Right) 8 oz. bottle with glass & cork stopper. 11'' high. OSP $5, CMV $5 BO, $7 MB.

1964 SKIN-SO-SOFT DECANTER
(Left) 6 oz. gold crown top, came with gold neck tag. OSP $3.50, CMV $12 MB, $7 bottle only with tag, mint.

1962-63 SKIN-SO-SOFT DECANTER
(Right) 5¾ oz. gold neck string with white label, pink & white box. OSP $3.50, CMV $12 MB. Bottle only $7 mint with tag.

1978-79 HUDSON MANOR COLLECTION

1978-79 SALTCELLAR CANDLE & SPOON
Silver plated. Comes with glass lined candle. Bottom says HMC Avon Silver plate on both pieces. Silver and white box. SSP $19, CMV $19 MB.

1978-79 SILVER PLATED DISH AND SATIN SACHET
6" silver plated dish with red satin sachet pillow. Bottom of dish says Avon Silver Plate HMC, Italy. SSP $19, CMV $19 MB.

1978-79 SILVER PLATED HOSTESS BELL
5½" high silver plated bell. Avon silver plate HMC on bottom. SSP $19, CMV $19 MB.

1978-79 SILVER PLATED BUD VASE AND SCENTED ROSE
8" high silver plated bud vase. Came with long stemmed fabric red rose and 2 Roses Roses fragrance pellets. SSP $19, CMV $19 MB.

1979-80 COUNTRY STYLE COFFEE POT
Came in special color of box. 10 oz. clear glass painted red or green, blue or yellow. Holds moisturized hand lotion. Comes with matching hand pump. SSP $8., CMV $8. MB.

1973-75 CREAMERY DECANTER
8 oz. yellow painted over clear glass with brown basket of blue & orange flowers. Holds Roses Roses, Field Flowers, Bird of Paradise, hand & body cream lotion. OSP $5, CMV $5 MB, $4 BO.

1975-76 LIQUID MILK BATH
6 oz frosted glass bottle with gold cap. Holds Imperial Garden, Sonnet or Moonwind. OSP $5, CMV $4 MB, $2 BO.

1973-74 LIP POP COLA'S
.13 oz. plastic tube with plastic top. Came in Cherry (light red case) Cola (brown case) Strawberry (pink case) lip pomade. Strawberry & Cherry also came solid red plastic (rare CMV $7) others OSP $1.50, CMV $2 BO, $4 MB.

1981 OOPS COLOGNE DECANTER
(Left) White glass, brown spots, Ice Cream bottle with tan plastic cone top. 1.5 oz. Sweet Honesty or Country Breeze. SSP $6, CMV $6 MB.

1981-82 BIG SPENDER DECANTER
(Center) 1 oz. green glass, silver cap. Light Musk for men or Sweet Honesty cologne. SSP $4, CMV $4 MB.

1981-82 ULTRA CRYSTAL COLOGNE DECANTER
(Right) Gray box holds 2 oz. clear glass & glass cap. Choice of Tasha, Foxfire, Timeless, Ariane. SSP $10, CMV $10 MB. See Soap Dish section & candle section for other Ultra Crystal Collections.

1979-80 LADY SKATER TALC
3.75 oz. gold top can. Red cap. Choice of Ariane or Sweet Honesty Talc. SSP $4, CMV $3 mint, no box issued.

1979-80 GENTLEMAN SKATER TALC FOR MEN
3.75 oz. gold top can. Blue cap. Choice of Clint or Trazarra Talc. SSP $4, CMV $3 mint. No box issued.

1974-76 ICE CREAM LIP POMADE
.13 oz. white plastic bottom with light pink dark pink or red top for Cherry, Strawberry or Tutti-Frutti flavors. OSP $2, CMV $3 BO, $4 MB.

1974-76 ICE CREAM CONE LIP POMADE
Yellow cone with different color tops for Cherry, Starwberry, Tutti-Frutti, Mint, Chocolate. OSP $2, CMV $3 BO, $4 MB.

1973-74 COLOGNE ELEGANTE ATOMIZER DECANTER

3 oz. clear glass, gold cap with atomizer, also white plastic cap. Holds Imperial Garden, Patchwork, Sonnet or Moonwind. SSP $6, CMV $4 MB, $3 BO.

1974 COURTING ROSE COLOGNE

1.5 oz. red glass rose with gold cap & stem. Came in Moonwind, Sonnet or Imperial Garden. SSP $5, CMV $9 MB. Later issue painted red over clear glass. CMV $5 MB.

1974-76 SWEET TREAT COLOGNE DECANTER

White & brown painted glass with red cap. Came in pink & pretty cologne. SSP $2.50, CMV $2.50

1977 COURTING ROSE

(Right) 1.5 oz. amber coated over clear glass rose bottle with gold top. Came in Roses Roses or Moonwind cologne. SSP $5, CMV $5 MB, $4 BO.

1976 ORANGATAN

6 oz. orange shaped and colored plastic bottle. Holds suntan lotion. OSP $4, CMV $3, no box issued

1969 PYRAMID OF FRAGRANCE

Top is 1/8 oz. perfume, gold cap. Center is 2 oz. cologne. Bottom is 2-3 oz. cream sachet in black glass. 6" high, came in Charisma, Brocade or Regence. OSP $12.50, CMV $12.50, $17.50 MB.

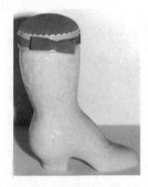

1972-76 FASHION BOOT PIN CUSHION

5½" tall, blue milk glass with lavender bow & velvet cushion that fits over cap. Holds 4 oz. cologne. Roses Roses or Charisma. Regular price $6, Sonnet or Moonwind SSP $6, CMV $6 MB, $4 BO.

1970-71 PICTURE FRAME COLOGNE

4 oz. gold paint on clear glass. Gold cap & gold plastic frame to hold bottle. Came in Elusive, Charisma, Brocade, Regence. SSP $8, CMV $10 mint, $12 MB.

1975-76 MARBLESQUE COLOGNE MIST

3 oz. green plastic coated glass bottle with gold plastic top. Holds Imperial Garden, Sonnet or Moonwind. OSP $7, CMV $6 MB, $5 BO.

1975-76 TOPALENE SPRAY COLOGNE (Non-aerosol)

2.5 oz. glass bottle with tortoise shell colored plastic top and gold band. Holds Moonwind, Patchwork or Roses Roses. OSP $5, CMV $4 MB, $2 BO.

1976-77 CRYSTALPOINT SALT SHAKER

1.5 oz blue glass. Holds Sonnet or Cotillion cologne. OSP $3, CMV $3 MB, $2 BO.

1969 BATH SEASONS

(Left) 3 oz. bath oil. Came in Charisma & Brocade. Black milk glass with silver cap & base. OSP $4.50, CMV $6 MB - $4 BO.

1972-74 EMOLLIENT FRESHENER FOR AFTER BATH

(Center) 6 oz. clear glass with gold cap, holds Sonnet, Charisma, Imperial Garden, or Moonwind pearlescent liquid. SSP $4, CMV $3 MB, $1 BO.

1973-75 AMBER CRUET

(Right) 6 oz. light amber ribbed glass. Holds Field Flowers, Bird of Paradise or Charisma foaming bath oil. SSP $5, CMV $4 MB - $3 BO. 1975 Came only in Field Flowers & Bird of Paradise.

1971-73 ALADDIN'S LAMP
(Left) 7½" long, 6 oz. green glass bottle with gold cap. Holds foaming bath oil in Charisma, Bird of Paradise, Elusive, Occur! or Unforgettable. SSP $7, CMV $7 MB - $5 BO.

1974-76 VENETIAN BLUE EMOLLIENT BATH PEARLS DECANTER
(Right) Frosted turquoise glass with turquoise plastic lid & gold tip. Holds 75 bath pearls. Came in Moonwind, Sonnet or Imperial Garden. SSP $6, CMV $6 MB - $4 BO.

1972-73 ROYAL APPLE COLOGNE
(Left) 3 oz. frosted red glass with gold cap. Came in 4 fragrances. SSP $4, CMV $4 MB, $3 BO.

1973-76 GARNET BUD VASE
(Right) 3 oz. garnet colored translucent glass bottle & stopper. Came in Occur!, Somewhere, Topaze or To A Wild Rose cologne. SSP $5, CMV $4 MB - $3 BO.

1973 GRAPE BUD VASE
(Left) 6 oz. grape frosted glass holds Skin-So-Soft. SSP $5, CMV $5 MB - $3 BO.

1972-74 NILE BLUE BATH URN SKIN-SO-SOFT DECANTER
(Right) 6 oz. deep blue glass with gold trim. SSP $6, CMV $8 MB - $5 BO.

1975 NILE GREEN BATH URN
(Right) Same as above only green glass. CMV $8 MB - $5 BO.

1974-76 DOVECOTE COLOGNE DECANTER
4 oz. clear glass with gold roof & 2 white doves. Holds Field Flowers, Bird of Paradise, Charisma or Roses Roses cologne. SSP $3, CMV $3 MB - $2 BO.

1970 ROYAL VASE DECANTER
(Left) 3 oz. blue cologne bottle in Elusive, Charisma, Brocade or Regence. OSP $5, CMV $5 MB - $3 BO.

1970-71 RUBY BUD VASE COLOGNE
(Right) 3 oz. red box holds ruby glass vase filled with Unforgettable, Rapture, Occur!, Somewhere, Topaze or Cotillion. OSP $5, CMV $5 MB - $3 BO.

1973-74 SAPPHIRE SWIRL
(Left) 5 oz. blue glass with gold cap. Holds Charisma or Bird of Paradise perfumed skin softener. SSP $4, CMV $4 MB - $3 BO.

1972-73 PERIOD PIECE DECANTER
(Right) 5 oz. frosted glass. Came in Moonwind, Bird of Paradise, Charisma or Elusive. SSP $6, CMV $5 MB - $4 BO. 1976 came with Charisma & Bird of Paradise. SSP $6, CMV $5 MB - $4 BO.

1971 LOVELY TOUCH DECANTER
(Left) 12 oz. clear glass, gold cap with dispenser cap. Holds Vita Moist or Rich Moisture body lotion. SSP $4, CMV $4 MB - $3 BO.

1972-73 LOVELY TOUCH DECANTER
(Inside Left) 12 oz. clear glass with dispenser cap. Holds Vita Moist or Rich Moisture body lotion. SSP $4, CMV $4 MB - $3 BO.

1972-76 CLASSIC BEAUTY
(Inside Right) 10 oz. clear glass. Holds Bird of Paradise or Field Flowers hand & body cream. SSP $5, CMV $4 MB - $3 BO.

1973-74 PINEAPPLE DECANTER
(Right) 10 oz. clear glass with green plastic leavs, dispenser top. Holds Moisturized Hand Lotion. SSP $5, CMV $6 MB - $4 BO.

1973-75 BELL JAR COLOGNE DECANTER

(Left) 5 oz. clear glass with bouquet of pink & white flowers. Had gold cap & base with pink ribbon. Holds Field Flowers, Bird of Paradise, Charisma or Brocade cologne. SSP $7, CMV $7 BO - $9 MB. 1976 sold only in Field Flowers, Bird of Paradise & Charisma. Same CMV.

1973-74 CRUET COLOGNE

(Right) 8 oz. clear glass with glass stopper & flat dish. Holds Imperial Garden, Patchwork, Sonnet or Moonwind cologne. SSP $13, CMV $10 BO & dish - $13 MB.

1973-74 APOTHECARY DECANTER

(Left) 8 oz. Spicy After Shave in light brown glass with gold cap.

1973-76 APOTHECARY DECANTER

(Center) 8 oz. Lemon Velvet Moisturized Friction Lotion in light yellow glass with gold cap. Also came in light green or blue green glass.

1973 APOTHECARY DECANTER

(Right) 8 oz. Breath Fresh in dark green with gold cap.
SSP $3 each, CMV $3 MB each - $2 BO each.

1973-74 COUNTRY CHARM BUTTER CHURN DECANTER

(Left) 1.5 oz. clear glass, gold bands & cap. Came in Field Flowers, Elusive, Occur! or Somewhere cologne. SSP $3, CMV $5 MB - $4 BO.

1972-74 GOLDEN THIMBLE

(Right) 2 oz. clear glass with gold cap. Came in Bird of Paradise, Brocade, Charisma or Elusive cologne. SSP $2, CMV $3 MB - $2 BO.

1969-70 PETTI FLEUR COLOGNE

(Left) 1 oz. gold cap. Shaped like flower. Came in Elusive, Brocade, Charisma or Regence. OSP $2.50, CMV $5 MB - $3 BO.

1971 PURSE PETITE COLOGNE

(Right) 1½ oz. embossed bottle with gold trim and cap & chain. Elusive, Charisma, Bird of Paradise, Field Flowers or Hana Gasa. OSP $4, CMV $7 MB - $5 BO.

1974 BAROQUE CREAM SACHET

(Left) 2 oz. white milk glass with gold top & bottom. Came in Imperial Garden, Sonnet or Moonwind. SSP $5, CMV $5 MB - $4 BO.

1973-75 COUNTRY STORE MINERAL SPRING BATH CRYSTALS

(Right) 12 oz. clear glass with gold cap. Holds green Mineral Springs Bath Crystals. SSP $5.50, CMV $4 MB - $2 BO.

1975 COLOGNE CRYSTALIQUE

(Left) 4 oz. clear glass with glass stopper. Holds Moonwind, Sonnet or Imperial Garden. OSP $5, CMV $4 MB - $3 BO.

1974 BREATH FRESH APOTHECARY DECANTER

(Center) 8 oz. clear glass with gold cap. Holds Breath Fresh Mouthwash. SSP $3, CMV $3 MB - $2 BO.

1975 COUNTRY PUMP

(Right) 10 oz. clear glass with plastic top. Holds Rich Moisture or Vita Moist body lotion. OSP $5, CMV $4 MB - $3 BO.

1971-73 KEEPSAKE CREAM SACHET

(Left) 6½" high, gold lid on marbleized glass jar with flower in colors. Came in Moonwind. OSP $5. Bird of Paradise, Field Flowers, Elusive, Charisma. SSP $3, CMV $4 - $5 MB.

1970-73 KEEPSAKE CREAM SACHET

(Right) 5½" high gold metal tree lid on .66 oz. frosted glass jar. Came in Bird of Paradise, Elusive, Charisma, Brocade or Regence. SSP $3.50, CMV $4 - $5 MB.

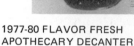

1974-75 DEW KISS DECANTER
(Left) 4 oz. clear glass with pink lid. OSP $3, CMV $3 MB - $1 BO.

1975-76 SEA LEGEND DECANTER
(Right) 6 oz. clear glass with white cap. Holds Moonwind or Sonnet foaming bath oil or Roses Roses creamy bath foam. OSP $5, CMV $5, $3 BO.

1974-75 BY THE JUG BALSAM SHAMPOO
(Left) 10 oz. beige plastic with orange top. Cap is brown, looks like cork. SSP $3, CMV $3.

1974-76 BY THE JUG STRAWBERRY BATH FOAM
(Center) 10 oz. beige plastic with pink top. Brown cap looks like cork. SSP $3, CMV $3. Also came with left handed jug with label reversed. CMV $7.

1974-75 BY THE JUG ASTRINGENT
(Right) 10 oz. beige plastic with blue top. Brown cap looks like cork. SSP $3, CMV $3, no boxes issued.

1977-80 FLAVOR FRESH APOTHECARY DECANTER
6 oz. clear glass bottle & stopper. Holds mouthwash. OSP $4.50, CMV $2.50 MB - $1 BO.

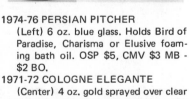

1974-76 PERSIAN PITCHER
(Left) 6 oz. blue glass. Holds Bird of Paradise, Charisma or Elusive foaming bath oil. OSP $5, CMV $3 MB - $2 BO.

1971-72 COLOGNE ELEGANTE
(Center) 4 oz. gold sprayed over clear glass & red rose on gold cap. 12'' high. Came in Bird of Paradise, Hana Gasa, Elusive or Charisma. OSP $8.50. Moonwind. OSP $10, CMV $10 MB - $7 BO.

1971 EMERALD BUD VASE COLOGNE
(Right) 3 oz. green glass & glass top, 9'' high. Came in Topaze, Occur! Unforgettable, Here's My Heart or To A Wild Rose. OSP $5, CMV $3 MB - $2 BO.

1976-78 COUNTRY JUG DECANTER
(Left) 10 oz. gray painted over clear glass. Blue & gray plastic pump. Came with almond scented hand lotion. OSP $8, CMV $5 MB - $4 BO.

1978-79 SEA FANTASY BUD VASE
(Right) 6 oz. bottle. Gold & white fish & seaweed design on both sides. Holds Skin-So-Soft bath oil, bubble bath & Smooth as Silk. SSP $7, CMV $4 MB, $3 BO.

1975-76 COUNTRY STYLE COFFEE POT
(Left) 10 oz. yellow speckled paint over clear glass. Came with yellow & white pump top. Came with moisturized hand lotion. OSP $6, CMV $6 MB - $5 BO.

1977-80 GOLDEN HARVEST
(Right) 10 oz. ear of corn shaped clear & green glass bottle. Gold & plastic pump top. Came with Avon almond scented hand lotion. OSP $8.50, CMV $5 MB - $4 BO.

1975 FOAMING BATH OIL DECANTER
6 oz. clear glass with gold cap. Came in Cotillion, Field Flowers, Bird of Paradise, Charisma, Sonnet, Imperial Garden, Moonwind & Timeless. SSP $2.88. This sold C26 - 1975 only. Very short issue. CMV $8 MB. This is the same bottle as the 1972-74 Emollient Freshener for After Bath. Only label & box is changed.

1975-76 CAMEO DECANTER CREAM SACHET

(Left) .66 oz. painted blue glass with blue & white plastic top. Came in Here's My Heart, Charisma, Topaze or To A Wild Rose. OSP $4, CMV $4 MB - $2 BO.

1975-76 GATHER A GARDEN CREAM SACHET

(Center) .66 painted blue glass jar with floral design on plastic & metal lid. Came in Hawaiian White Ginger, Roses Roses, Lemon Velvet, Lily of the Valley. OSP $4, CMV $4 MB - $2 BO.

1975-76 EMERALDESQUE CREAM SACHET

(Right) 1 oz. green glass with green plastic top. Holds Here's My Heart, Occur! or Sweet Honesty. OSP $3, CMV $3 MB - $1 BO.

1970-72 LOOKING GLASS COLOGNE

6½" high, clear glass mirror. Frame holds 1½ oz. cologne in Bird of Paradise, Elusive, Charisma, Brocade, Regence, Unforgettable, Rapture, Occur!, Somewhere Topaze, Cotillion Here's My Heart, or To A Wild Rose. With gold handle cap. OSP $3.50, CMV $5 BO - $7 MB.

1977-79 TREE MOUSE CREAM SACHET DECANTER

(Left) .66 oz. clear glass & clear plastic top. Gold mouse. Came in Sweet Honesty or Charisma. OSP $6, CMV $4 MB - $3 BO.

1977 SILVER PEAR CREAM SACHET

(Center) .66 oz. silver plated over clear glass. Silver top. Came in Sweet Honesty or Charisma. SSP $4, CMV $3 BO - $4 MB.

1976-78 ENCHANTED APPLE CREAM SACHET DECANTER

(Right) .66 oz. gold plated over clear glass. Gold top. Came in Charisma or Sonnet. OSP $5.50, CMV $4 BO - $5 MB.

1975-76 WINTER GARDEN

(Left) 6 oz. clear glass with gold cap. Holds Here's My Heart, Topaze or Occur! cologne. OSP $5, CMV $4 MB - $3 BO.

1974-75 REGENCY DECANTER

(Right) 6 oz. clear glass filled with Skin-So-Soft bath oil. OSP $5, CMV $4 MB - $3 BO.

1974-76 HONEY BEAR BABY CREAM DECANTER

4 oz. yellow painted glass with blue plastic bear on lid. SSP $4, CMV $4 MB - $3 BO.

1975 GOLDEN FLAMINGO DECANTER

(Left) 6 oz. clear glass with gold flamingo on front. Holds Bird of Paradise, Charisma or Field Flowers foaming bath oil. OSP $6, CMV $3 MB - $2 BO.

1975-76 ATHENA BATH URN

(Right) 6 oz. clear glass. Holds Field Flowers, Bird of Paradise foaming bath oil or Roses Roses cream bath foam. OSP $6, CMV $3 MB - $2 BO.

1975-76 PEAR LUMIERE

(Left) 2 oz. clear glass & plastic with gold leaf. Holds Roses Roses, Charisma or Bird of Paradise cologne. OSP $5, CMV $5 MB - $4 BO.

1975-76 SONG OF LOVE COLOGNE MIST

(Right) 2 oz. clear glass, clear plastic top with white bird. Holds Bird of Paradise, Charisma or Sweet Honesty. OSP $4, CMV $4 MB - $3 BO. 1976 issued with blue base, blue top in Moonwind & Here's My Heart. Same CMV.

1974-76 VICTORIAN SEWING BASKET
(Left) 5 oz. white milk glass basket with lavender plastic, gold cord holds pink flower. Came in Roses Roses, Bird of Paradise or Charisma perfumed Skin-So-Soft. OSP $4, CMV $4 MB - $2 BO.

1975-76 VANITY JAR
(Right) 5 oz. clear glass with silver lid. Choice of Rich Moisture Cream or SSS skin conditioner. OSP $4, CMV $4 MB - $2 BO.

1977-78 FUNBURGER LIP GLOSS
(Left) Came in Frostlight Rose & Frostlight Coral lip gloss. Brown plastic. OSP $4.50, CMV $2.50 - $4.50 MB.

1976 CHRISTMAS SUPRISE DECANTER
(Center) 1 oz. green glass boot. Came in Sweet Honesty, Moonwind, Charisma or Topaze cologne. Red cap or silver cap. SSP 99c, CMV $2 MB - $1 BO.

1977 ORIENTAL PEONY VASE DECANTER
(Right) 1.5 oz. red paint over clear glass with gold design. Came in Sweet Honesty or Moonwind. OSP $6, CMV $4 BO - $6 MB.

1974-75 PETIT POINT PERFUMED SKIN SOFTENER
(Left) 5 oz. translucent purple glass with cloth petit point design on top. Holds Charisma, Bird of Paradise or Field Flowers. OSP $4, CMV $2 MB - $1 BO.

1974-76 PETIT POINT CREAM SACHET
(Center) 1 oz. purple glass with cloth top on lid. Came in Field Flowers, Bird of Paradise or Charisma. OSP $4, CMV $2 MB - $1 BO.

1974-76 PETIT POINT PERFUME
(Right) .25 oz. purple glass jar with cloth top on lid. Holds Field Flowers, Bird of Paradise or Charisma. OSP $6, CMV $4 MB - $3 BO.

1974-76 PETIT POINT LIPSTICK
(Not shown) CMV $2 MB.

1977-78 BATH GARDEN HANGING PLANTER
Light green glass planter, green hanging rope. Came with six 1 oz. packets of mineral spring bath crystals. OSP $12, CMV $9 MB complete - $4 hanging planter only.

1978-79 SCENTIMENTS COLOGNE DECANTER
(Left) 2 oz. clear glass. Came with pink card on front to write your own message. Came in Sweet Honesty or Here's My Heart cologne. SSP $4.99, CMV $4 MB - $2 BO.

1978-79 GOLDEN BAMBOO VASE
(Right) 1 oz. yellow painted over clear glass, black cap, base. Came in Moonwind or Sweet Honesty cologne. SSP $3.99, CMV $3 - $2 BO.

1974-76 CASTLEFORD COLLECTION EMOLLIENT BATH PEARLS
(Left) Holds 60 bath pearls. Clear glass. Came in Imperial Garden, Sonnet or Moonwind. OSP $8, CMV $9 MB - $6 BO.

1975-76 CASTLEFORD COLLECTION COLOGNE GELEE
(Right) 4 oz. glass holds Raining Violets, Roses Roses or Apple Blossoms cologne gelee. OSP $8, CMV $8 MB - $6 BO.

1980 PORCELAIN FLORAL BOUQUET
(Left) 4" high porcelain. Dated 1980 on bottom. SSP $18, CMV $18 MB.

1980-81 ULTRA MIST ATOMIZER DECANTER
(Right) 1.5 oz. clear swirl glass bottle with gold top & atomizer bulb. Choice of Ariane, Timeless, Tasha or Candid. SSP $11, CMV $11 MB.

1982 CRYSTALINE BOWL & FLOWERS
Pink box holds 5" long glass bowl with plastic insert to hold artificial flowers. Comes with fragrance tablet. SSP $18, CMV $18 MB.

1973-74 VICTORIAN WASHSTAND
(Left) 4 oz. buff painted with gray plastic simulated marble top with blue pitcher & bowl for cap. Came in Field Flowers, Bird of Paradise or Charisma Foaming Bath Oil. SSP $5, CMV $6 MB - $5 BO.

1972-74 REMEMBER WHEN SCHOOL DESK DECANTER
(Right) 4 oz. black glass with light brown plastic seat front & deck top, red apple for cap. Came in Rapture, Here's My Heart, Cotillion or Somewhere cologne. SSP $5, CMV $7 MB - $5 BO.

1981-82 NATURE'S BEST WOODEN DISPLAY SPOON HOLDER
(Back) Made of wood, 3½'' by 7''. Does not say Avon. Comes in Avon box. SSP $7, CMV $5 MB.

1981-82 NATURE'S BEST COLLECTOR'S SPOONS
(Front) 4 different stainless spoons with Avon on them. 5'' long in flannel pouch. Porcelain inlaid with fruit - strawberry, orange, plum, raspberry. SSP $10 each, CMV $10 each MB.

1981-82 AMERICAN HEIRLOOM SHIPS DECANTER
(Left) 6 oz. clear glass, glass top. Choice of Wild Country After Shave or Sweet Honesty Body Splash. SSP $9, CMV $9 MB.

1981-82 SOFT SWIRLS BATH DECANTER
(Right) 8 oz. clear glass, frosted cap. Choice of Smooth as Silk bath oil or Skin-So-Soft. SSP $10, CMV $10 MB.

1974-75 TEATIME POWDER SACHET
(Left) 1.25 oz. frosted white with gold cap. Holds Moonwind, Sonnet or Roses Roses. OSP $4, CMV $4 MB - $3 BO.

1975-76 SCENT WITH LOVE
(Right) .66 oz. gold toned glass base with amber plastic top that is a stamp dispenser. Holds Unforgettable, Topaze or Here's My Heart cream sachet. OSP $4, CMV $3 MB - $1 BO.

1980-81 VANITY COLLECTION TRAY
(Bottom) 10'' by 12'' metal tray made in England. SSP $8, CMV $8 MB.

1980-81 VANITY COLLECTION ULTRA COLOGNE DECANTER
(Left) 2 oz. beige painted over clear glass. Choice of Ariane, Candid or Timeless Ultra cologne. SSP $8, CMV $8 MB.

1980-81 VANITY COLLECTION ULTRA SOFT BODY SATIN PUMP
(Inside Left) 10 oz. beige over clear glass. Same choice as cologne. SSP $10, CMV $10 MB.

1980-81 VANITY COLLECTION ULTRA BATH DECANTER
(Inside Right) 6.75 oz. beige plastic bottle. SSP $7, CMV $1 no box.

1980-81 VANITY COLLECTION ULTRA BODY POWDER
(Right) 6 oz. plastic. OSP $10., CMV $10. MB.

1982 HUMPTY DUMPTY BANK
(Left) Box holds ceramic bank made in Korea for Avon. Dated 1982. Sold empty. 5'' high. SSP $12, CMV $12 MB.

1982 BUNNY LUV CERAMIC TRINKET BOX
(Right) Ceramic top & bottom. Rabbit on lid. Sold empty. SSP $15, CMV $15 MB.

1980-81 CRYSTAL CLEAR HOSTESS DECANTER
Clear glass jar & glass lid, Avon stainless spoon. Comes in 5.5 oz. Strawberry Bubble Bath Gelee. SSP $11, CMV $11 MB.

1981 TAPESTRY COLLECTION BELL
(Left) 5'' high white porcelain bell. Dated 1981. Dove on top of bell. SSP $15, CMV $15 MB.

1981 TAPESTRY COLLECTION PICTURE FRAME
(Right) 5'' high white porcelain picture frame. Dated 1981. SSP $13, CMV $13 MB.

1981 AMERICAN HEIRLOOM PORCELAIN BOWL

6" across 4" high, white bowl. "Independence Day 1981" on bottom. Comes with black plastic base stand. SSP $20, CMV $20 MB.

1980-81 BUTTERFLY FANTASY PORCELAIN TREASURE FAN

(Left) Fan shaped porcelain box. Dated 1980 on bottom. SSP $13, CMV $13 MB. Add $5 for backward printed bottom label.

1980 CHRISTMAS REMEMBRANCE CERAMIC WREATH

(Right) White ceramic, gold tassel. Dated 1980. 3" across. SSP $8, CMV $8 MB.

1982 SWEET REMEMBRANCE

(Left) 3¼" porcelain box. Valentines Day 1982 on bottom. "A Token of Love" on inside with a gold foil wrapped chocolate. Short issue. SSP $15, CMV $15 MB.

1981 CHRISTMAS REMEMBRANCE DOVE

(Right) Second in a series of tree ornaments from Avon. White ceramic dove, gold cord. SSP $8, CMV $8 MB.

1979 ANNIVERSARY KEEPSAKE C.P.C. FLACON

.75 oz. clear glass. Silver cap has 1979 on top. Came with Sweet Honesty or Trailing Arbutus cologne. SSP $5, CMV $5 MB.

1979 ANNIVERSARY KEEPSAKE EAU DE TOILETTE

Large 8 oz. clear glass bottle, CPC embossed on back side. Avon 1979 on bottom. Gold cap. Pink and green box. Came in Trailing Arbutus cologne. Pink neck ribbon. SSP $10, CMV $10 MB.

CAPE COD 1876 COLLECTION
(all are ruby red glass)

THIS ITEM IS PICTURED
ON PAGE 71

1979-80 — 1876 HOSTESS BELL
6½" high "Christmas 1979" on bottom. SSP $10, CMV $10 MB. Also came clear glass coated red.

1980 CAPE COD DESSERT PLATES
Box of 2 red glass plates marked Avon. SSP $11, CMV $11 MB.

1975-80 CAPE COD CRUET
5 oz. red glass. Holds Skin-So-Soft. SSP $8, CMV $8 MB.

1975-80 CAPE COD CANDLESTICK COLOGNE
5 oz. red glass. Came in Charisma, Patchwork or Bird of Paradise. SSP $8, CMV $8 MB.

1977-80 CAPE COD WINE GOBLET
Red glass candle. SSP $5, CMV $5. Also issued to Reps with Presidents Celebration 1976 embossed on bottom.

1978-80 DESSERT BOWL & GUEST SOAPS
SSP. $9, CMV $9 MB.

1978-80 SALT SHAKER
May 1978 on bottom SSP $4, CMV $4 MB. Latter issue not dated on bottom. CMV $3 MB.

1976-80 CAPE COD WATER GOBLET
Red glass candle. SSP $9, CMV $10 MB.

1977-80 CAPE COD WINE DECANTER
16 oz. red glass holds bubble bath. SSP $14, CMV $14 MB.

1982-83 CAPE COD DINNER PLATE
Full size ruby red glass dinner plate. SSP $14, CMV $14 MB.

1980-83 CAPE COD SUGAR BOWL
3½" high red glass. Comes with 3 sachet tablets. SSP $10, CMV $10 MB.

1981-84 CAPE COD CREAMER CANDLE
4" high ruby red glass. Holds candle, also came 1983 without candle. SSP $9, CMV $9 MB.

1981-84 CAPE COD DESSERT SERVER
8" long, ruby red plastic handle. Stainless blade made by Regent Sheffield for Avon. SSP $10, CMV $10 MB.

1982-84 1876 CAPE COD PEDESTAL MUGS
Box holds 2 ruby red glass mugs 5" high. SSP $16 set, CMV $16 MB set.

1983-84 1876 CAPE COD COVERED BUTTER DISH
7" long red glass. SSP $15, CMV $15.

1983-84 CAPE COD CANDLE HOLDERS
3¾" wide, 2 in a box, SSP $15, CMV $15 MB.

1975 CALIFORNIA PERFUME CO. ANNIVERSARY KEEPSAKE COLOGNE
(Left) Issued in honor of 89th Anniversary 1.7 oz. bottle, pink ribbon & gold cap. Came in Charisma or Sweet Honesty cologne. Sold in 2 campaigns only. CMV $4, $6 MB. 1st issue Avon Presidents Club Reps received this bottle with 4A design under bottom label. Regular issue had Avon on bottom. CMV for 4A $10 MB. Also came with 4A design & "M" for Managers. Given to Managers only. CMV $15 MB.

1976 CPC ANNIVERSARY KEEP-SAKE COLOGNE
(Right) 1.7 oz. clear glass bottle, gold cap. Bottle is embossed on back side (Avon 90th Anniversary Keepsake). Came in Moonwind or Cotillion cologne. Sold 2 campaigns only. OSP $6, CMV $6 MB, $4 BO.

1977-79 COUNTRY TALC SHAKER
3 oz. gray and blue speckled metal can shaker top. Came in Sweet Honesty or Charisma perfumed talc. SSP $5.50, CMV $4 MB, $3 BO.

1977-78 CALIFORNIA PERFUME CO. ANNIVERSARY KEEPSAKE
3.75 oz. blue can sold to public with Avon 1977 on the bottom. SSP $3, CMV $2.50 MB, $1 BO. Was also given to Avon Reps during 91st Anniversary with "Anniversary Celebration Avon 1977" on the bottom. CMV $4 MB. Came in Roses Roses, or Trailing Arbutus Talc.

1978-79 DINGO BOOT
6 oz. camel tan plastic bottle and cap. Choice of Sweet Honesty Body Splash or Wild Country After Shave. SSP $4.99, CMV $3 MB.

1978-79 VINTAGE YEAR "CHAMPAGNE BOTTLE"
2 oz. green glass, gold cap. 1979 embossed in bottom. Came in Sweet Honesty or Wild Country cologne. Green and gold box. SSP $4.99, CMV $4.99.

1978-79 ANNIVERSARY KEEPSAKE C.P.C.
1.5 oz. clear glass. Old style C.P.C. label and design. Pink neck ribbon. Came in Trailing Arbutus, Sweet Honesty or Somewhere cologne. SSP $5, CMV $5 MB.

DESCRIPTION ON PAGE 70

1981-82 ANNIVERSARY KEEPSAKE DECANTER — Mens

Replica of California Perfume Co. "Early Day Avon". Bay Rum After Shave. 3 oz. clear glass with glass top in plastic cork. SSP $7, CMV $7 MB.

1981-82 ANNIVERSARY KEEPSAKE DECANTER — Women

3 oz. clear glass CPC replica of 1908 design. Holds White Lilac cologne. Dated 1981. SSP $7, CMV $7 MB.

Both came to Avon managers as a Demo empty and marked Not For Sale. CMV $10 ea.

POMANDERS

POMANDERS MUST BE IN THE BOX TO BE MINT

See 1984 Supplement Section in Back of this Book
For More Pomanders

1978-79 PAMPERED PIGLET CERAMIC POMANDER

Avon's 1st ceramic pomander is made in Brazil. White with pink and green flowers. Came in Meadow Morn wax chip refill. Pink box. SSP $8, CMV $8 MB.

1978-80 MEADOW MORN FRAGRANCE WAX CHIPS REFILL

Refill for Pomanders. SSP $1.50, CMV $1.

1981-82 PORCELAIN UNICORN POMANDER

5" long white porcelain. Comes with Garlandia wax chips. SSP $16, CMV $16 MB.

1981-82 BASKETS OF VIOLETS POMANDER

White glass basket with fabric flowers. Comes with Violet fragrance wax chips. SSP $10, CMV $10 MB.

1977-78 FLORENTINE LADY POMANDER

Pink wax, approx. 9½" high. Came in Fragrant Seasons scent. OSP $8, CMV $5 MB.

1972 ORIENTAL FIGURINE POMANDER

10" high. Scented pink wax figurine. OSP $6, CMV $8 MB.

1973 ORIENTAL FIGURINE POMANDER

Same as above except green. SSP $6, CMV $8 MB.

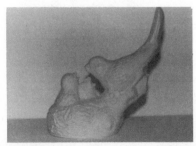

1979-80 TWO TURTLEDOVES POMANDER

Blue box holds white wax doves. SSP $9, CMV $9 MB.

1979-80 UNDER THE MISTLETOE POMANDER

Light blue wax with wire hanging mistletoe. SSP $8, CMV $8 MB.

1979-80 HONEY BEARS POMANDER

Light yellow wax figure. SSP $6.99, CMV $6.99 MB.

1978-79 FRILLY BOOT POMANDER

Pink plastic boot came with wax chip refill. SSP $2.89, CMV $2.50 MB.

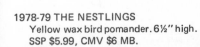

1978-79 THE NESTLINGS

Yellow wax bird pomander. 6½" high. SSP $5.99, CMV $6 MB.

1974-75 DUCK DECOY DECORATIVE POMANDER
Wax statuette (not a bottle) scented with Deep Woods or Wild Country. OSP $6, CMV $7 MB.

1978-79 BOUNTIFUL HARVEST POMANDER
Red spiced apple with tan wax basket. SSP $8, CMV $8 MB.

1978-79 VIENNESE WALTZ POMANDER
6½" high blue wax figurine, bottom label. SSP $7, CMV $7 MB.

1976-77 PARISIAN MODE POMANDER
Pink wax. OSP $7.50, CMV $6 MB.

1977-79 ROYAL PEKINGESE POMANDER
White wax. OSP $7.50, CMV $6 MB.

1975-76 FLORENTINE CHERUB POMANDER
7½" high sculptured wax figurine. OSP $6, CMV $6 MB.

1974-76 DELICATE DOVE POMANDER
4" high light green or olive wax pomander scent Summer Breeze or Sun Forest. OSP $5, CMV $5 MB.

1975 CORAL EMPRESS POMANDER
6½" high coral colored wax figurine. Fragrant Seasons scent. OSP $5, CMV $7 MB.

1974-75 CHRISTMAS CAROLLERS POMANDER
7" high red wax pomander. Bayberry scented. OSP $6, CMV $7 MB.

1974 SIGN OF SPRING POMANDER
6" high yellow fern scented wax. OSP $4, CMV $5 MB.

1975-76 MEADOW BIRD POMANDER
6" high white and blue wax pomander, Fernerie scented. OSP $6, CMV $6 MB.

1982-83 WOODLAND CHARMERS MINI POMANDERS
Wax figures in Racoons, Skunk, or Rabbit & Turtle. SSP $6 each, CMV $6 each MB.

1974-76 PAMPERED PERSIANS DECANTER POMANDER
Wax sculptured cats with Floral Medley fragrance. SSP $5, CMV $5 MB. Yellow cat $7 MB.

1972-73 COCKATOO POMANDER
8½" tall blue scented wax pomander. Came in Floral Medley fragrance. SSP $5, CMV $7 MB.

1982 'LIL CUPID MINI POMANDER
2¼" high white wax angel with red heart. Short issue. SSP $3, CMV $3 MB.

1980-82 SWAN TENDER LOVE POMANDER
6" long white wax. SSP $10, CMV $10 MB.

1980-82 LION PEACEFUL PARTNERS POMANDER
6½" long wax lion and sheep. SSP $11, CMV $11 MB.

1982 GRADUATE POMANDER
Small blue "82" plastic pomander on white cord in yellow box. SSP $4. CMV $4 MB.

1982 AMERICAN TRADITION POMANDER
5x7 plastic wood look frame with green fabric pomander. Does not say Avon. Must be in Avon box. SSP $10, CMV $10 MB.

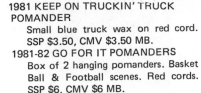

1981 KEEP ON TRUCKIN' TRUCK POMANDER
Small blue truck wax on red cord. SSP $3.50, CMV $3.50 MB.

1981-82 GO FOR IT POMANDERS
Box of 2 hanging pomanders. Basket Ball & Football scenes. Red cords. SSP $6, CMV $6 MB.

1981 HERALDS OF SPRING MINI POMANDERS
Choice of Owl (yellow), Chipmunk (pink) Mouse (blue), chick (white), 3" high each. SSP $5, CMV $5 ea. MB.

1981-82 CUCKOO CLOCK WALL POMANDER
Light brown wax with blue bird. SSP $9, CMV $9 MB.

1981-82 GINGER BREAD JOYS POMANDER
Pink & brown wax with gold hanging cords. Set of 2. SSP $6, CMV $6 set, MB.

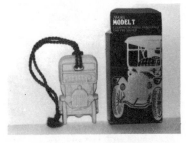

1979 MODEL T CAR FRESHENER
3" high light yellow wax pomander comes in green and yellow box with green hang up rope. SSP $1.99 CMV $1.99 MB.

1979-80 AUTUMN HARVEST POMANDER
10" long, yellow and green wax. Hangs on wall. SSP $8, CMV $6 MB.

1980 FRAGRANT TREE TRIMMING POMANDERS
Set of 3 double sided ornaments 4" high each. Cloth covered, gold hanging cords. SSP $8 set, CMV $8 MB.

1981-82 SURE START CAR KEY POMANDER
Tan wax key. 3" long. SSP $4, CMV $4 MB.

1981-82 VINTAGE MOTOR CAR POMANDER
Green box holds 6" wide antique car hanging pomander. SSP $10, CMV $10 MB.

1981-82 TROPICAL SPLENDOR WINDOW POMANDER
Parrot box holds parrot hanging pomander. Cord not included. SSP $10, CMV $10 MB.

1980-82 FLIRTATION FROG CERAMIC POMANDER
3" high white ceramic frog, yellow and green trim. Made in Brazil. Comes with Fernerie wax chip refill. SSP $10, CMV $10 MB.

1980-82 TRAFFIC STOPPER CAR POMANDER
Small soft green plastic, yellow cord. SSP $3, CMV $3 MB.

1980-82 PINE CONE CLUSTER POMANDER
Small light brown wax with red satin ribbon. SSP $4, CMV $4 MB.

1967-69 LAVENDER POMANDER
Gold tassel on white, pink & gold plastic container. 4" high. Filled with lavender Fragrance tablet. OSP $5, CMV $5 MB.

1970 POTPOURRI POMANDER
Holder is yellow plastic & 4" high in same shape & design as Lavender Pomander. OSP $5, CMV $5 MB.

1980 FRAGRANT FLIGHT POMANDER
Metal frame around soft plastic. Stain glass look. SSP $10, CMV $10 MB.

1980-81 WILD GAME POMANDER
3" long blue plastic, green cord. SSP $4, CMV $2 MB.

1975-77 PARASOL CLOSET POMANDER
Lavender with lavender cord & tassel. Came with Potpourri Fragrance wax chips. OSP $3, CMV $3 MB.

1977-78 SWEET CHERUBS CLOSET POMANDER
Blue & white plastic with blue tassel. Came in Potpourri fragrance wax chips. OSP $5, CMV $3.50 MB.

1979-80 LACY GLOVES CLOSET POMANDER
Lavender box holds Lavender plastic glove. It does not say Avon on it. Comes with packet of Garlandia wax chips. SSP $3, CMV $3 MB.

1979-80 FRESH FLIGHT CLOSET POMANDER
Blue plastic bird holds Potpourri wax chips. Came in colorful box. SSP $4, CMV $2.50 MB.

1975-76 PICTURE HAT CLOSET POMANDER
Yellow & pink plastic hat with yellow cord & tassel. Came in Potpourri fragrance. OSP $4., CMV $3. MB.

1973-74 HEARTSCENT CLOSET POMANDER
Wedgewood blue and white plastic heart with white tassel holds Potpourri scented chips. SSP $3, CMV $3 MB.

1971 POTPOURRI POMANDER REFILL
Orange and white box holds refill in plastic bag. OSP $2.50, CMV $2 MB.

1980 WHISPER OF FLOWERS CLOSET POMANDER
Small hat box type box with green hanging cord & package of Garlandia Fragrance wax chips. SSP $4, CMV $4 MB.

1980 WHISPER OF FLOWERS SACHET PILLOWS
Flowered box holds 5 silk like sachet pillows. SSP $8, CMV $8 MB.

1980-82 CAMEO CLOSET POMANDER
4½" long yellow plastic with white cord. Comes with wax chip Popourri refill. SSP $5, CMV $5 MB.

1980-82 MOON ROCK A BYE BABY POMANDER
5" long yellow wax with blue hanging cord. SSP $7, CMV $7 MB.

1981 CHRISTMAS SURPRISE FRAGRANCE ORNAMENT
(Left) 3x3 inch tree ornament. Teddy Bear on one side & bells on box on the other side. SSP $3, CMV $3 MB.

1981 HIDDEN SCENTS SACHET NUGGETS
(Right) Box holds 3 small tulip shaped see thru fragranced flowers. SSP $5, CMV $2 MB.

1974-75 WISE EYES CLOSET POMANDER
Brown plastic with yellow cord & tassel. Came with Fernerie fragranced wax chips. OSP $4, CMV $4 MB.

CANDLES

SEE 1984 SUPPLEMENT IN BACK OF THIS BOOK FOR MORE CANDLES

1970 DANISH MODERN CANDLE
(Left) Stainless steel candleholder with red candle. OSP $8, CMV $8 with candle, MB.

1973 FLAMING TULIP FRAGRANCE CANDLE
(Right) Red candle in Floral Medley fragrance. Gold holder. OSP $7, CMV $6 CO - $9 MB.

1971 75 FLORAL FRAGRANCE CANDLE
(Left) Metal gold leaf stand & pink or yellow flower candle. OSP $8.50. CMV $6 - $9 MB.

1972-73 WATER LILY FRAGRANCE CANDLE
(Right) Green lily pad base with white plastic petals with yellow center candle. OSP $5, CMV $3 CO - $5 MB.

1979-80 REVOLUTIONARY SOLDIER SMOKERS CANDLE
(left) Clear, or dark amber glass, clear harder to find, 2 different. Red & gold box. SSP $4, CMV $4 MB.

1979-80 FOSTORIA CRYSTAL POOL FLOATING CANDLE
(Right) 6" clear crystal dish, green & white flower candle. SSP $12.99, CMV $12.99.

1974-75 OVALIQUE PERFUME CANDLEHOLDER

(Left) 4" high, clear glass, choice of Sonnet, Moonwind, Patchwork, Roses Roses, Charisma, Bird of Paradise, Bayberry, Frankincense & Myrrh or Wassail. OSP $8, CMV $6 MB.

1975-76 FACETS OF LIGHT FRAGRANCE CANDLETTE

(Center) 4" high, clear glass. Came with Bayberry candle but any refill candlette will fit. OSP $5, CMV $5 MB.

1974-75 GOLDEN PINE CONE FRAGRANCE CANDLETTE

(Right) Gold toned glass. Choice of Bayberry only. OSP $5, CMV $5 MB.

1975-77 WASHINGTON GOBLET FOSTORIA CANDLEHOLDER

(Left) Blue glass by Fostoria. Came with Frankincense & Myrrh or Floral Medley candle. OSP $10, CMV $10 CO - $12 MB.

1976-77 MARTHA WASHINGTON GOBLET

(Right) Blue glass Fostoria candleholder. OSP $12.50, CMV $10 CO - $12 MB.

1966 CANDLESTICK COLOGNE

3 oz. silver coated over clear glass. Silver cap. Came in Occur!, Rapture, Unforgettable. OSP $3.75, CMV $10 mint - $15 MB.

1975-76 COLOGNE & CANDLELIGHT

(Left) 2 oz. clear glass with gold cap and clear plastic collar. Hold Imperial Gardens, Roses Roses or Charisma. OSP $3, CMV $2 BO - $3 MB.

1970-71 CANDLESTICK COLOGNE

(Right) 4 oz. red glass bottle, gold cap. Holds Elusive, Charisma, Brocade, Regence, Bird of Paradise. OSP $6, CMV $5 MB - $3 BO. Also came in smoked red glass. Appears much darker than red glass issue. It looks smokey red. CMV $12 MB.

1972-73 CRYSTAL GLOW PERFUMED CANDLEHOLDER

(Left) Clear glass. Came with Moonwind, Bird of Paradise, Elusive, Charisma, Brocade, Regence, Wassail, Bayberry, Frankincense & Myrrh, Roses Roses. SSP $8, CMV $8 - $11 MB.

1973 FOSTORIA PERFUMED CANDLEHOLDER

(Right) Clear glass. Came with Patchwork, Sonnet, Moonwind, Roses Roses, Charisma, Bird of Paradise, Bayberry, Wassail, Frankincense & Myrrh candles. SSP $6, CMV $6 - $8 MB.

1970-71 CRYSTALLITE COLOGNE CANDLE

(Left) Clear glass bottle with gold cap holds 4 oz. of cologne in Unforgettable, Rapture, Occur!, Somewhere, Topaze & Cotillion. OSP $5.50, CMV $4 MB - $3 BO.

1972-75 CANDLESTICK COLOGNE

(Right) 5 oz. silver painted over clear glass with silver cap. Came in Moonwind, Field Flowers, Bird of Paradise, Roses Roses. SSP $6, CMV $4 MB - $3 BO. 1975 came only in Imperial Garden, Moonwind or Sonnet. CMV $4 MB - $3 BO.

1973-74 REGENCY CANDLESTICK COLOGNE

(Left) 4 oz. clear glass. Came in Bird of Paradise, Charisma, Elusive or Roses Roses. SSP $7, CMV $5 MB, $4 BO.

1976-77 OPALIQUE CANDLESTICK COLOGNE

(Right) 5 oz. swirl glass & cap. Came in Charisma or Sweet Honesty. SSP $8.99, CMV $5 MB, $4 BO.

1975 FOSTORIA CANDLELIGHT BASKET — PERFUMED CANDLEHOLDER

(Left) Clear glass, gold handle. Choice of Sonnet, Moonwind, Patchwork, Charisma, Roses Roses, Bird of Paradise, Wassail, Frankincense & Myrrh or Bayberry candle refill. OSP $9, CMV $9 MB - $6 CO.

1969-70 & 1981 FOSTORIA SALT CELLAR CANDLE

(Right) Clear glass with small silver spoon. OSP $6, CMV $10 in box. $6 candle only, with spoon. Reissued in 1981 with "R" on bottom of foot for Reissue. SSP $10, CMV $7 MB.

1978 HEART & DIAMOND FOSTORIA LOVING CUP PERFUMED CANDLEHOLDER

(Left) Approx. 7" high, clear Fostoria glass. Came with Floral Medley perfumed candle. Embossed with "Avon 1978" on its base. Refillable. OSP $15, CMV $12 MB - glass only $6.

1977-79 MOUNT VERNON SAUCE PITCHER

(Right) Approx. 5½" high. Blue Fostoria glass. Came with Floral Medley perfumed candle. Refillable. Avon on bottom. OSP $15.50, CMV $12 MB - pitcher only $6.

1978-79 HEART & DIAMOND CANDLESTICK

7" high heart embossed Fostoria clear glass candle, Avon 1979 on bottom. Comes with long red candle for one end or turn it over and insert the small glass candleholder on other end. Comes in red box. SSP $13, CMV $13 MB.

1980-82 TULIP CLEARFIRE TRANSPARENT CANDLE

(Left) Clear glass. 4" high. SSP $6.88, CMV $6.88 MB.

1980-82 SPARKLING SWIRL CLEARFIRE CANDLE

(Center) Clear glass 5-1/8" high. SSP $11.99, CMV $11.99 MB.

1980-82 SHERBERT DESSERT CANDLE

(Right) 5" high clear glass. Comes with red, yellow, or pink candle. SSP $8.99, CMV $8.99 MB.

1973-74 HEARTS & FLOWERS FRAGRANCE CANDLE

(Left) White milk glass with red, green & pink design. Came in Floral Medley fragrance. SSP $4, CMV $4 MB - $2 CO.

1972-73 POTPOURRI FRAGRANCE CANDLE

(Right) White milk glass, came with Potpourri candle. SSP $4, CMV $3 CO - $4 MB.

1964-66 WHITE MILK GLASS CANDLE

(Left) OSP $3.50, CMV $6 - $12 MB.

1965-66 AMBER GLASS CANDLE

(Center) Amber paint over clear glass. OSP $4, CMV $17 in box, $12 candle only.

1965-66 RED GLASS CANDLE

(Right) Red paint over clear glass. OSP $4, CMV $11 - $16 in box. Dark red 1968 glass candle, not painted is from Europe. See foreign Avons for picture. CMV $50.

1971-72 FLORAL MEDLEY PERFUMED CANDLES

Box holds yellow & purple frosted glass candleholders. OSP $5.50, CMV $6.50 MB.

1972 TURTLE CANDLE

(Left) White glass turtle candle with green glass shell top. OSP $5, CMV $5 - $7 MB.

1972 MUSHROOM CANDLE

(Right) White glass candle with pink glass mushroom top. OSP $5, CMV $5 - $7 MB.

1974-75 KITCHEN CROCK FRAGRANCE CANDLETTE
(Left) Yellow crock with red, yellow & blue flowers with cork cap. Came in Meadow Morn fragrance. SSP $4, CMV $3 CO - $4 MB.

1969-70 WASSAIL BOWL CANDLE
(Right) Silver paint over red glass with silver spoon. OSP $8, CMV $7 candle only - $10 MB.

1967 FIRST CHRISTMAS CANDLE
(Left) All gold, red inside 1967 had label on bottom and no Avon. OSP $5, CMV $7 CO - $11 MB. 1972 Reissued - Avon on bottom, no label. CMV $8 MB - $5 CO.

FIRST CHRISTMAS CANDLE FOREIGN
(Right) All silver with red inside. CMV $20.

1967 FROSTED GLASS CANDLE
(Left) Gold band around edge, lid makes stand for base. OSP $5, CMV $11 MB - $7 candle only.

1966-67 WHITE & GOLD CANDLE
(Right) White glass top & bottom with gold band. Top makes stand for base. OSP $5, CMV $7 - $11 MB.

1972-73 CHINA TEA POT PERFUMED CANDLE
White china with blue flower design or without decal. Thousands came from factory, not sold by Avon, with or without decals, some had other color decals, some decals were on front, some on back. The factory rejects CMV $9 each. Came from Avon with Roses Roses, Moonwind, Bird of Paradise, Elusive, Charisma, Brocade, Regence, Wassail, Bayberry, Frankincense & Myrrh candles. SSP $10, CMV $12 MB - $8 BO.

1967 REGENCE CANDLE
(Left) Gold paint over clear glass with green paper band. Lid makes base for bottom. OSP $6, CMV $20 in box - $15 candle only mint.

1968-69 REGENCE CANDLE
(Right) Green glass candleholder with gold handle & base. OSP $10, CMV $12 candle only - $17.50 in box.

1970 NESTING DOVE CANDLE
(Left) White base glass & lid with dove on top. OSP $7.50, CMV $6 - $9 in box.

1973 HOBNAIL PATIO CANDLE
(Right) White milk base clear glass top. Came with Sonnet, Moonwind, Roses Roses, Bird of Paradise, Charisma, Wassail, Bayberry and Frankincense & Myrrh candles. SSP $8, CMV $9 MB - $6 CO.

1970's CANDLE PERFUMED REFILLS
Candle refills for the many candleholders Avon has made over the years. Comes in many fragrances. SSP $2.50, CMV $2.50 MB.

1981 CHESAPEAKE COLLECTION JIGGER CANDLE
Amber glass dog head candle. Set dog on head, candle in bottom. SSP $10, CMV $10 MB.

1969-70 CRYSTAL CANDLEIER
(Left) 7'' high, clear glass with blue crystals inside, gold handle on glass lid. OSP $7, CMV $9 in box - $6 candle only.

1969-70 GOLD & WHITE CANDLE
(Right) Painted gold & white over clear glass, lid makes stand for base. OSP $8, CMV $9 in box - $6 candle only.

1968-69 GOLDEN APPLE CANDLE
(Left) Shiny gold over clear glass. OSP $6, CMV $12 mint - $17.50 MB.

1968 SILVER APPLE CANDLE
(Right) Factory test sample same as gold apple only in shiny silver over clear glass. Was not filled. CMV $90 on silver top & bottom. Silver bottom with gold top CMV $55 mint.

1980-81 FLORAL LIGHT CANDLE REFILL
(Left) Comes in lavender, green or yellow. Flower shaped. SSP $4, CMV $4 MB.

1980-81 FLORAL LIGHT FRAGRANCE CANDLE
(Right) Clear glass flower shaped base holds flower shaped refill candle. SSP $7, CMV $7 MB.

1981-82 ULTRA CRYSTAL CANDLE
(Left) 2½" high clear glass. Gray box. SSP $10, CMV $10 MB.

1981-82 ULTRA SHIMMER CANDLE
(Right) 2½" high clear glass octagonal shaped. Gold box. SSP $9, CMV $9 MB.

1982-83 SCENTIMENTS CANDLES
2" high metal can candles, 2 different designs. Lid says "May Love Always Fill Your Heart" or "The Beauty of Friendship is Everlasting." SSP $7 each, CMV $7 MB each.

1978-79 BRIGHT CHIPMUNK CANDLETTE
(Left) Clear glass candleholder. Refillable. SSP $6, CMV $6 MB.

1978-79 FRESH AROMA SMOKERS CANDLE
(Right) Non refillable brown wax like pipe with black plastic and chrome top. Bottom cardboard label. SSP $7, CMV $7 MB.

1981-82 HOT CHOCO-LITE CANDLE
(left) Beige or white color wax cup with brown chocolate smelling candle. SSP $7, CMV $7 MB.

1981-82 PITKIN HAT CANDLE
(Right) Blue swirled glass hat holds candle. Comes in green box. SSP $8, CMV $8 MB.

1981-82 GAMESMAN CANDLE GIFT SET
Green & red box holds small metal green can with candle & set of green playing cards with deer in 2 corners. Made by Arrco Playing Card Co., Chicago. Cards do not say Avon. SSP $10, CMV $10 MB complete set.

1979-80 SHIMMERING PEACOCK CANDLE
(Left) Box holds clear glass peacock. SSP $10, CMV $10 MB.

1979-80 CLEARFIRE TRANSPARENT CANDLETTE REFILL
(Right) Did not come boxed. SSP $3, CMV $3 mint full.

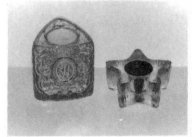

1980-82 PERSONALLY YOURS FRAGRANCE CANDLE
(Left) Clear glass with refillable candle. Comes with sheet of stick on gold letters. SSP $12, CMV $12 MB.

1980-81 STAR BRIGHT FRAGRANCE CANDLE
(Right) Icy clear glass holds refillable candle. SSP $7, CMV $7 MB.

1980-82 SNUG 'N COZY "CAT" FRAGRANCE CANDLE
Clear glass cat candleholder. SSP $10, CMV $10 MB.

1981-82 GLISTENING TREE CLEARFIRE CANDLE
(Left) 4½" high clear ribbed glass tree shaped candle. SSP $10, CMV $10 MB.

1982 LOVE LIGHT CLEARFIRE CANDLE
(Right) Clear ribbed glass heart shape candle. SSP $10, CMV $10 MB.

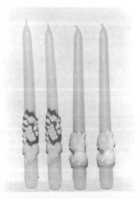

1982 FLOWER FANCY CANDLES
(Left) Same box as Easter Surprise set below only different name. Two 10" green candles with flowers. SSP $8, CMV $8 MB.

1982 EASTER SURPRISE CANDLES
(Right) Green flower box holds two 10" yellow candles with white rabbits. SSP $8, CMV $8 set MB.

1981-82 GEM GLOW CANDLE
(Left) Clear glass multi-faceted. Comes with green, amber or red filled candle. SSP $10, CMV $10 MB.

1981-83 CAPE COD CREAMER CANDLE
(Right) 4" high ruby red glass. Holds candle. Also see Cape Cod Collection. SSP $9, CMV $9 MB. See Cape Cod in Women's Decanters for other Cape Cod candles.

1980 HOLIDAY CANDLE DISH & WREATH
Clear glass candleholder, red candle and holly wreath. SSP $9, CMV $9 MB.

1980 DAPPER SNOWMAN CANDLES
(Pictured) 10" high red candles with snowman on base. Set of 2.

1980 WINTER ROSE CANDLES
(Left in book picture) 10" white candles with roses at base. Set of 2.

1980 CANDY CANE & HOLLY CANDLES
(Center in book picture) 10" high green candles with candy cane at base. Set of 2.
SSP $6 each set, CMV $6 MB each set.

1981 CHRISTMAS CHIMES CANDLES
(Left) Red 10" candles with gold bells. SSP $7 pair in red box, CMV $7 MB.

1981 HOLIDAY HOSTESS CANDLES
(Center) Green & white holly box holds 2 white 10" candles with green & red holly. SSP $7 pair, CMV $7 MB.

1981 MR. & MRS. CHRISTMAS CANDLES
(Right) Red box holds two 10" green candles with Mr. & Mrs. Santa Claus. SSP $7, CMV $7 MB.

1975-76 CATNIP FRAGRANCE CANDLE
(Left) 4" high yellow plastic. Floral Medley fragrance. OSP $3, CMV $4 MB.

1975-76 DYNAMITE FRAGRANCE CANDLETTE
(Right) Red & white. OSP $4, CMV $5 MB.

1978-79 PLUM PUDDING CANDLE
(Left) 4" high brown, green & white candle. Bottom label. SSP $6, CMV $6 MB.

1978-79 WINTER LIGHTS CANDLETTE
(Right) Clear glass square candle-holder. Holds glass candlette. Avon on bottom of both. SSP $8, CMV $8 MB.

1979-81 MRS. SNOWLIGHT CANDLE
(Left) White, red & green wax candle. SSP $7, CMV $7 MB.

1979-80 WINTER WONDERLAND CENTERPIECE CANDLE
(Right) White wax base, green wax trees, red & white wax house. Center holds glass candlette. SSP $15, CMV $15 MB.

1975 ENCHANTED MUSHROOM FRAGRANCE CANDLE
(Left) White wax shell / yellow cover. Meadow Morn fragrance. OSP $4, CMV $4 MB - $3 CO.

1975-76 SLEIGH LIGHT FRAGRANCE CANDLE
(Right) 4" high, red & green. Bayberry scented. OSP $5, CMV $4 MB - $3 CO.

1980 CRYSTALGLOW CLEARFIRE CANDLE
(Left) Clear glass. Avon in bottom under candle. SSP $10, CMV $10 MB.

1980 BUNNY BRIGHT CERAMIC CANDLE
(Right) White ceramic with pink & green trim. 1980 Avon on bottom. SSP $12, CMV $12 MB.

1975-76 BLACK-EYED SUSAN FRAGRANCE CANDLE
(Left) Yellow with brown center. Wild Flowers fragrance. OSP $5, CMV $5 MB - $3 CO.

1974-76 GRAPEFRUIT FRAGRANCE CANDLE
(Right) Yellow with red center. Has grapefruit fragrance. OSP $3, CMV $3 MB - $2 CO.

1981-82 CAROLLING TRIO CANDLES
Comes in separate boxes. Melodic Mouse candle, Howling Hound candle, Crooning Cat candle. SSP $5 each, CMV $5 each MB.

1980-81 HARVEST TIME FRAGRANCE CANDLE
Tan wax candle, 6" high. SSP $10, CMV $10 MB.

1980 GLOW OF CHRISTMAS CANDLE
White wax with red center refillable candle. SSP $10, CMV $10 MB.

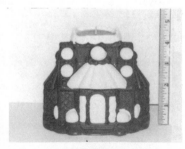

1977-79 GINGERBREAD HOUSE FRAGRANCE CANDLE
Brown & white candle. Came in Frankincense & Myrrh fragrance. OSP $8.50, CMV $6 MB - $3 no box.

1981 MR. SNOWLIGHT CANDLE
5½" high white wax, green trim. SSP $7, CMV $7.

1976-77 TERRA COTTA BIRD CANDLETTE
Reddish brown clay bird candleholder. Avon in bottom. OSP $8, CMV $6 MB - $3 bird only.
Also shown is fragrance candlette refill in Floral Medley. CMV $1.50.

1974-75 LOTUS BLOSSOM PERFUMED CANDLEHOLDER

(Left) Black glass with green & white design. Available with candle fragrance: Bayberry, Frankincense & Myrrh, Wassail, Sonnet, Moonwind, Roses Roses, Bird of Paradise or Charisma. OSP $8, CMV $8 - $12 MB.

1971-72 DYNASTY PERFUMED CANDLE

(Right) 6'' high, white glass jar & lid. OSP $7.50, CMV $7 - $10 MB.

1977-78 DOVE IN FLIGHT CANDLETTE

(Left) Clear glass dove candleholder. Came in Meadow Morn fragrance candlette. Refillable. SSP $6, CMV $5 MB.

1977-79 BUNNY CERAMIC PLANTER CANDLEHOLDER

(Right) 3 different rabbits. One made in Brazil and recessed on bottom; one flat bottom made in U.S. and lighter in weight; 1978 issue same flat bottom only different type letters on bottom. Came with Floral Medley or Roses Roses perfumed candle. SSP $11, CMV $10 MB each - rabbit only $6 each.

1981-82 SUNNY BUNNY CERAMIC CANDLEHOLDER

5½'' high ceramic candleholder. Dated 1981. SSP $15, CMV $15 MB.

1979-80 GARDEN BOUNTY CANDLE

(Left) Beige & pink cart, red candle. SSP $8, CMV $8 MB.

1979-80 COUNTRY SPICE CANDLE

(Center) Light blue green glass jar & lid. Wire bale. Comes with candle inside. SSP $8, CMV $8 MB.

1979-80 FLOWER FROST COLLECTION WATER GOBLET CANDLETTE

(Right) Frosted glass goblet holds glass candle insert. SSP $10, CMV $10 MB.

1979-80 BUNNY CERAMIC PLANTER CANDLE

(Left) Made of ceramic in Brazil for Avon. Green, pink & yellow flowers. Brown eyes, pink inner ears. Comes with Floral Medley or Spiced Garden candle. SSP $15, CMV $12 MB.

1979-80 TENDER BLOSSOM CANDLE

(Right) Light pink wax base with dark pink inner candle. SSP $7, CMV $6 MB.

PERFUME GLACE

SEE 1984 SUPPLEMENT IN BACK OF THIS BOOK FOR MORE PERFUME GLACE

1965-66 PERFUME JEWEL GLACE

Gold & white box contains gold locket. Came as pin or on a chain with solid perfume in Unforgettable, Rapture, Occur!, Somewhere, Topaze, Cotillion, Here's My Heart, To A Wild Rose and Wishing. OSP $5.50, CMV $17 each in box - $12 locket only.

1971-75 MEMORY BOOK PERFUME GLACE

(Left) 1½'' long gold book. Choice of Moonwind, Elusive, Brocade, Regence or Bird of Paradise perfume glace. OSP $7, CMV $9 MB - $6 no box - $5 book only.

1971-72 BABY GRAND PIANO PERFUME GLACE

(Right) 2'' wide gold piano. Came in same fragrances as Memory Book. OSP $10, CMV $14 MB - $8 piano only.

1969-70 RING OF PEARLS GLACE

Perfume glace ring is gold with white pearls. Comes in Charisma, Regence & Brocade. OSP $7.50, CMV $10 MB - $7 ring only.

1966-67 PERFUME GLACE NECKLACE

Silver with black stone & gold with brown stone. Came in Unforgettable, Rapture, Occur! OSP $8.50. Somewhere, Cotillion, Topaze. OSP $8.25. To A Wild Rose, Here's My Heart, Wishing. OSP $8, CMV $17 each MB - $12 locket only.

1968-70 GOLDEN CHARMER LOCKET

(Left) Gold locket holds perfume glace in Somewhere, Topaze, Cotillion, Here's My Heart, To A Wild Rose, Unforgettable, Rapture, Occur!, Brocade & Regence. OSP $9.50, CMV $14 MB - $9 locket only.

1967 PILLBOX PERFUME GLACE

(Top Right) Black & gold with red rose on top. Came in Occur!, Rapture, Unforgettable, Somewhere, Topaze, Cotillion, Here's My Heart & To A Wild Rose. OSP $4.50, CMV $15 MB - pill box only $10 mint.

1969 DAISY PIN PERFUME GLACE

(Bottom Right) White & gold pin. Charisma, Brocade, Regence. OSP $6.50. Rapture, Occur!, Unforgettable. OSP $6. Somewhere, Topaze, Cotillion. OSP $5.75, CMV $6 - $9 MB.

1971-72 MANDOLIN PERFUME GLACE

(Left) 2½" long gold mandolin. Choice of Moonwind, Elusive, Charisma, Brocade, Regence or Bird of Paradise perfume glace. OSP $9., CMV $14 in box - $8 no box, mandolin only.

1971-75 TORTOISE PERFUME GLACE

(Right) 2½" long gold turtle with turquoise back. Came in same fragrances as Mandolin. OSP $9, CMV $10 MB - $6 turtle only.

1966-67 PERFUME GLACE NECKLACE

Special issue gold round box. Came with either silver with black stone or gold necklace with brown stone. CMV $20 MB as shown.

1982 DELICATE HEART PERFUME COMPACT

Pink plastic heart holds solid perfume. Red & white heart decor box. SSP $4, CMV $2 MB.

1970 CAMEO RING & PIN

Both are perfume glace. Comes in Elusive, Charisma, Brocade, Regence & Bird of Paradise. OSP $10 each, CMV $9 each - $15 each MB.

1968-69 OWL PIN PERFUME GLACE

(Left) Gold metal pin with green eyes. Green & gold box. Came in Brocade, Regence. OSP $6.50. Unforgettable, Rapture, Occur! OSP $6. Cotillion, Here's My Heart, To A Wild Rose. OSP $5.75, CMV owl only $7 - $11 MB.

1970-71 FLOWER BASKET PERFUME GLACE

(Right) 1½ x 1¼" gold tone pin. Choice of Bird of Paradise, Elusive, Charisma, Brocade or Regence. OSP $7, CMV $10 MB - $6 pin only.

1978-79 SCENT WITH LOVE "HEART COMPACT"

(Left) Pink box holds red plastic heart compact with Love in gold letters. Holds Sweet Honesty or Here's My Heart solid perfume. SSP $3, CMV $2 MB.

1978-79 GOLDEN TURTLE COMPACT

(Right) .07 oz. gold plastic turtle holds Candid or Sweet Honesty solid perfume. SSP $6, CMV $4 MB.

1969-70 GOLDEN LEAF PIN

Blue box contains gold leaf pin with pearl at stem. Perfume glace comes in Elusive, Charisma, Brocade, Regence. OSP $7. Unforgettable, Rapture, Occur!, Topaze, Somewhere & Cotillion. Same pin also issued without glace. OSP $6.50, CMV $9 MB - $6 pin only.

PLATES

SEE 1984 SUPPLEMENT IN BACK OF THIS BOOK FOR MORE PLATES

1974-75 TENDERNESS PLATE
9¼" Ironstone plate. Blue & white with gold edge. Made in Spain for Avon by Pontesa. The plate sold to public with word "Pontesa" on the back side in blue letters. This was also awarded to Avon Reps. Plate was also sold with no inscription on back. No. 1 (Regular Issue) — all blue lettering on back of plate. No. 2 (Reps Award) — all blue lettering on back of plate, including Pontesa logo. No. 3 (Reps Award) — all blue lettering on back of plate except the Pontesa logo which is red. CMV $20 MB regular issue - $25 Rep plate MB.

1973-77 BETSY ROSS PLATE
White with colored scene, gold trim and lettering. 9" plate. SSP $13, CMV $20 MB.

1974-76 CARDINAL NORTH AMERICAN SONG BIRD PLATE
10" ceramic plate. Green letters on back. SSP $13, CMV $20 MB.

1974-77 FREEDOM PLATE
9" ceramic plate, blue trim with gold edge. Blue printing on back. Made by Wedgewood, England for Avon. SSP $13, CMV $20 MB.

1975-77 GENTLE MOMENTS PLATE
8¾" ceramic plate. Green letters on back. Made by Wedgewood, England. SSP $15, CMV $20 MB.

1978 CHRISTMAS PLATE - 15 YEAR
Same plate as 15 year anniversary plate inscribed on back. We have no info on this or where it came from. Write Bud Hastin if you know what this plate is for. No price established.

1981 MOTHER'S DAY PLATE "CHERISHED MOMENTS"
5" porcelain plate dated 1981, with stand. SSP $10, CMV $10 MB.

1978-79 STRAWBERRY PORCELAIN PLATE & GUEST SOAPS
7½" plate made in Brazil for Avon. Comes with 6 red strawberry soaps. SSP $13, CMV $13 MB - $8 plate only.

1982 MOTHER'S DAY PLATE
5" size plate. Little Things Mean A Lot inscribed on face. Comes in yellow box & plastic plate stand. SSP $10, CMV $10 MB. Same plate given to Presidents Club Reps. Label on back reads "January 1982 Presidents Club Luncheon". CMV $15 MB.

1982-83 CHILDREN'S PERSONAL TOUCH PLATE
7-5/8" ceramic plate. SSP $12, CMV $12 MB.

1973-75 "CHRISTMAS ON THE FARM" 1973 CHRISTMAS PLATE
White with colored scene, turquoise border, gold edge and lettering. 9" plate. SSP $13., CMV $80. MB.

1974-76 PINK ROSES CUP & SAUCER
(Left) White china with pink flowers & green leaves with gold rim. Made by Stoke-on-Trent, England. OSP $10, CMV $12 MB. Also came with double printed letters on bottom. CMV $20 MB.

1974-75 BLUE BLOSSOMS CUP & SAUCER
(Right) White china with blue & pink flowers and 22K gold trim. Made in England. OSP $10, CMV $12 MB.

1973 CHRISTMAS "BETSY ROSS" PLATE
Factory mistake 1973 Christmas plate has inscription on back for Betsy Ross plate. Very rare. CMV $100.

1974-75 COUNTRY CHURCH 1974 CHRISTMAS PLATE
9" ceramic plate. Second in a series of Christmas plates by Avon. Made by Wedgewood, England. Blue writing on back. Blue & white front, gold edge. SSP $13, CMV $35 MB. Rare issue came without Christmas 1974 on front of plate. CMV $75 MB.

1976-80 "SKATERS ON THE POND" 1975 CHRISTMAS PLATE
8¾" ceramic green & white plate. Green letters on the back. Made by Wedgewood, England for Avon. This plate was not sold till 1976 Christmas selling season. SSP $17, CMV $20 MB.

1976-80 "BRINGING HOME THE TREE" 1976 CHRISTMAS PLATE
9" blue ceramic plate, gold edge. Blue printing on back. Made by Wedgewood, England for Avon. SSP $16, CMV $20 MB.

1976 CHRISTMAS PLATE TEST
8¾" test plate. Does not say Avon. Christmas 1976 on front 6 times in gold. Was never sold by Avon. Came from factory. Has blue border. CMV $75.

1980-82 COUNTRY CHRISTMAS PLATE
9" ceramic 1980 Christmas plate. SSP $22, CMV $22 MB.

1977-80 "CAROLLERS IN THE SNOW" 1977 CHRISTMAS PLATE
8¾" ceramic blue & white plate, gold edge. Blue letters on back. Made by Wedgewood, England for Avon. SSP $17, CMV $20 MB.

1978-79 "TRIMMING THE TREE" 1978 CHRISTMAS PLATE
(6th edition) 8-5/8" ceramic plate. Turquoise rim with gold edge trim. Made for Avon by Enoch Wedgewood in England. SSP $20, CMV $20 MB.

1979-80 "DASHING THROUGH THE SNOW" 1979 CHRISTMAS PLATE
8¾" blue & white ceramic plate with gold trim. Christmas 1979 on front. Back of plate says Made for Avon Products by Enoch Wedgewood - in England. SSP $20, CMV $20 MB.

1981-83 "SHARING THE CHRISTMAS SPIRIT" 1981 CHRISTMAS PLATE
9" porcelain plate has 2 kids carrying a Christmas tree. Dated 1981 on back. SSP $21.50, CMV $21.50 MB.

MEN'S AFTER SHAVES & COLOGNES

SEE 1984 SUPPLEMENT IN BACK OF THIS BOOK FOR MORE AFTER SHAVES

1961-63 DELUXE AFTER SHAVE "WOOD TOP"
6 oz. Some have gold letters on bottle, some have gold paper labels. Came in Deluxe Electric Pre-Shave Lotion, Deluxe After Shave Lotion, After Shave Lotion Spicy, Electric Pre-Shave Lotion Spicy. OSP $1.79, CMV each $25 MB - $20 BO mint. 4 different fragrances.

1964-66 4A AFTER SHAVE LOTION SAMPLE
Box holds 10 packet samples. CMV $5 box, mint.

1959-60 AFTER SHOWER FOR MEN
8 oz. gold cap with gold foil on neck & gold neck cord with Stage Coach on bottom. OSP $2.50, CMV with foil top & tag $45 mint - $60 MB.

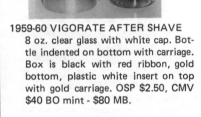

1932-36 AFTER SHAVING LOTION
4 oz. black caps. Two different yellow paper labels. OSP 37c, CMV $40 BO mint each - $50 MB.

1948-49 DEODORANT FOR MEN
(Left) 2 oz. maroon cap & label. OSP 59c, CMV $20.
1948 Only COLOGNE FOR MEN
(Right) 2 oz. size, maroon cap. Came in 1948 Pleasure Case set only. CMV $25.

1959-60 VIGORATE AFTER SHAVE
8 oz. clear glass with white cap. Bottle indented on bottom with carriage. Box is black with red ribbon, gold bottom, plastic white insert on top with gold carriage. OSP $2.50, CMV $40 BO mint - $80 MB.

FOREIGN 4A AFTER SHAVE
(Left) 4 oz. foreign 4A on left with Invigorate. CMV $18 MB - $25.
1964-66 4A AFTER SHAVE
(Right) 6 oz. 4A painted on clear glass, black cap with gold mirror on top. OSP $2, CMV $17 BO - $25 MB.

1936-40 AFTER SHAVING LOTION SAMPLE
(Left) Maroon cap. CPC on back label. CMV $35 mint.
1940-49 AFTER SHAVE LOTION SAMPLE
(Center) ½ oz. maroon cap. CMV $35.
1939 HAIR TONIC SAMPLE
(Right) ¼ oz. maroon cap. CMV $40 - $45 MB.
1940's HAIR LOTION SAMPLE
(Not Pictured) Same as ¼ oz. Hair Tonic. Same CMV.

1946-49 COLOGNE FOR MEN
6 oz. maroon cap. Shield on paper label. OSP $1.50, CMV $75 bottle only. In 2 different maroon boxes, $85.

1965-66 AFTER SHAVE'S MISC.
2 oz. with 4A on black caps. Came in Island Lime, Blue Blazer, Leather, Tribute, Spicy, Bay Rum, Original, 4A After Shaves, Leather All Purpose Cologne & After Shower Cologne. Came in Bureau Organizer, Fragrance Wardrobe & After Shave Selection sets only. CMV each $8 MB - 10 different $5 BO. Add $3 for Blue Blazer.

1969-70 GENTLEMEN'S CHOICE
Red & silver box holds 2 oz. embossed bottles with silver, gold & black caps. Came in Excalibur, Wild Country, Tribute, Leather & Windjammer cologne. OSP $1.75 each - CMV $2 each with black caps - $4 BO - $6 MB.

1975-79 AFTER SHAVE
(Left) 5 oz. clear glass, brown cap. Came in Deep Woods, Everest, Oland, Tai Winds, Wild Country & Clint. Different labels, same bottle. OSP $3, CMV $1.50 each. Issued in 1981-82 in 4 oz. size. Same shape in Wild Country, Weekend, Trazarra & Clint. SSP $4, CMV $1.

1974-75 GIFT COLOGNE FOR MEN
(Center) 2 oz. clear glass with gold cap. Came in Wild Country, Deep Woods, Oland or Tai Winds. OSP $2, CMV 75c.

1975-76 GIFT COLOGNE FOR MEN
(Right) 2 oz. clear glass, gold cap. Choice of Wild Country, Tai Winds, Deep Woods or Oland. OSP $2, CMV $1.

1970 GENTLEMEN'S SELECTION
2 oz. each with gold caps. Came in cologne in Oland, Tribute, Excalibur, Leather, Wild Country & Windjammer. OSP $1.75 each, CMV $2.50 BO - $3.50 MB.

1979-80 COLOGNE ACCENT FOR MEN
(Left) .5 oz. clear glass. Blue cap, blue & silver box. SSP $1.25, CMV $1 MB.

1978-79 GIFT COLOGNE FOR MEN
(Center) 2 oz. clear glass, black cap. Holds Everest, Clint, Wild Country, or Deep Woods cologne. SSP $2, CMV $2 MB.

1978-79 COLOGNE MINIATURE FOR MEN
(Right) 5 oz. clear glass, brown cap. Holds Wild Country, Clint, Everest or Trazarra. SSP $1, CMV $1 MB.

1975-78 ELECTRIC PRE-SHAVE LOTION
(Left) 4 oz. plastic, blue cap. Spicy aroma. OSP $1, CMV 50c.

1976 BRACING LOTION FOR MEN
(Right) 4 oz. plastic with green cap. OSP $1, CMV 50c.

1972 EAGLE ORGANIZER BOTTLE
(Left) 3 oz. clear glass, eagle embossed, gold cap. Came in set only in Deep Woods & Tai Winds. CMV $3 each.

1976 GIFT COLOGNE FOR MEN
(Right) 2 oz. came in Deep Woods, Tai Winds, Wild Country, Everest, or Oland. SSP $2, CMV $1 MB - 50c BO.

1951-52 SERVICE KIT AFTER SHAVE BOTTLE
4 oz. clear plastic with red cap. CMV $12.

1980 GIFT COLOGNE FOR MEN
(Left) .5 oz. black cap, clear glass. Choice of Trazarra, Wild Country, Clint, Weekend, Light Musk, Cool Sage, Brisk Spice or Crisp Lime. SSP $1.50, CMV $1.50 MB.

1977-78 COLOGNE MINIATURE FOR MEN
(Right) 5 oz. smoked glass, black cap. Came in Clint, Everest or Wild Country. SSP 88c, CMV 50c.

1979-82 AFTER SHAVES
(Left) 3 oz. plastic bottle came in different color caps. No box. Came in Cool Sage, Light Musk, Brisk Spice or Crisp Lime. SSP $2, CMV 50c each.

1979-82 COLOGNES FOR MEN
(Right) 3 oz. clear glass bottle. Gold caps. Choice of Brisk Spice, Cool Sage, Light Musk or Crisp Lime. Came in box. SSP $3, CMV $1 each MB.

1970-72 COLOGNE SPRAY FOR MEN
4 oz. silver can with red cap in Leather, brown cap in Wild Country, and tan cap in Oland. This can leaked & most boxes were ruined. OSP $5, CMV $10 each MB - $4 can only.

1981-82 TRAVELER COLOGNES FOR MEN
2 oz. plastic with different color caps. Choice of Wild Country, Weekend or Black Suede in after shave or cologne. SSP $2.99, CMV $1 each MB.

MEN'S ITEMS, MISC.

1948-49 CREAM HAIR LOTION
4 oz. maroon cap. OSP 59c, CMV $20, $25 MB.

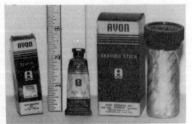

1936-49 STYPTIC CREAM
Maroon & ivory tube. OSP 17c, CMV $8, $15 MB.

1936-49 SHAVING STICK
Avon on maroon base on Soap Stick. Maroon box. OSP 39c, CMV $10 $17 in box.

1936-38 HAIR TONIC EAU DE QUININE
For normal, dry or oily hair. 6 oz. turquoise cap. OSP 78c, CMV $15 Also came in 16 oz. size, $25 BO, $30 MB.

1943-46 TALC FOR MEN
Maroon & ivory colored cardboard. One on left also came with black octagonal cap as shown and also with maroon or black round cap. One on right was smooth top. You punched holes in it. OSP 37c, CMV $35 each mint.

1929 only TALC FOR MEN
(Left) Green can. OSP 25c, CMV $55 mint.

1930-36 TALC FOR MEN
(Right) Greenish yellow, can, black cap. OSP 35c, CMV $45 mint.

1934-36 SHAVING STICK
(Left) Nickel metal container. OSP 36c, CMV $50 MB, $40 mint only.

1929-33 SHAVING STICK
(Right) Green metal can. CPC on lid. OSP 35c, CMV $50 can only mint, $60 MB.

1953-56 SHAVING BOWL
Wood Shaving Bowl, green label. No center handle. OSP $1.25, CMV $30, $40 MB.

1949-53 SHAVING BOWL
Wood Shaving Bowl, green label with red center handle. OSP $1.10, CMV $35, $45 MB.

1949-57 SHAVING STICK
Green & red box holds Shaving Soap Stick with red plastic base. OSP 59c, CMV $12.50 MB, $4 stick only.

1949-57 STYPTIC CREAM
1/3 oz. green tube with red cap. OSP 39c, CMV $10 in box $15.

1938-39 HAIR TONIC
(Left) 6 oz. clear glass, maroon cap and label. OSP 52c, CMV $30 BO mint, $40 MB.

1940-49 HAIR LOTION
(Right) 6 oz. maroon cap & box. OSP 69c, CMV $40 in box. Bottle only $30 mint. Some labels say ''formerly Hair Tonic''.

1965-66 ORIGINAL AFTER SHAVE SPRAY
5½ oz. green can with red cap. OSP $1.50, CMV $6 can only mint, $10 MB.

1949-58 TALC FOR MEN
2 5/8 oz. green can, red cap. OSP 69c, CMV $5, $7 MB. Also came in 2.6 oz. size.

1949-57 CREAM HAIR DRESS
2¼ oz. green tube & box. Came with flat or tall red cap. OSP 49c, CMV $15 MB.

1959-61 STICK DEODORANT FOR MEN
2¾ oz. black & red plastic container. Came with two different caps, 1 flat, 1 indented. OSP $1, CMV $12 ea., $15 MB.

1955-57 KWICK FOAMING SHAVE CREAM
10 oz. green & white can, pointed red cap. OSP 98c, CMV $8, $11 MB.

1957-58 SAME CAN
with flat top, red cap. CMV $8, $11 MB.

1949-59 LATHER & BRUSHLESS SHAVING CREAM
Green tubes, flat red caps, used in 1949-56. Tall red caps used 1957-59. OSP 49c, CMV $10 ea. MB, $8 tube only mint.

1949-58 SHAVING CREAM SAMPLE
¼ oz. green tubes of lather & brushless shaving cream, red caps. CMV $5 each, mint. Also came in ½ oz. size sample tubes. CMV $8 each, mint.

1949-58 COLOGNE FOR MEN
All three sizes have red caps & silver labels, 6 oz. size. 1949-57 OSP $1.50, CMV $15 MB., 4 oz size 1952-57 came in sets only. Also with green label. CMV $9, 2 oz. size 1949-58 OSP 69c, CMV $6.

1953-56 FIRST CLASS MALE
6 oz. cologne for men, box red & white. OSP $1.50, CMV $25 MB as shown.

1949-58 COLOGNE FOR MEN SAMPLE
½ oz. red cap, silver label. CMV $25.
1949-58 AFTER SHAVING LOTION SAMPLE
½ oz. red cap, green label. CMV $5.

1966-68 ORIGINAL SOAP ON A ROPE
White bar with embossed carriage. OSP $1.75, CMV $25 MB, $17.50 soap only mint.
1965-69 ORIGINAL AFTER SHAVE
4 oz. green label, red cap and red & green box. OSP $1.25, CMV $4 BO, $6 MB.

1957 TRIUMPH
Special issue box holds 6 oz. cologne for men. Silver label, red cap. OSP $1.19, CMV $25 MB.

1949-58 DEODORANT FOR MEN SAMPLE
½ oz. bottle with red cap, green label. CMV $25 mint.

1957 KING FOR A DAY
Box holds 4 oz. bottle of Electric Pre-Shave Lotion or choice of cologne for men, or 4 oz. deodorant for men. All had red caps. OSP 89c, CMV $22.50 MB.
1957-58 ELECTRIC PRE-SHAVE LOTION
4 oz. red cap, silver label. OSP 89c, CMV $9, $10 MB.

1952-57 COLOGNE FOR MEN
4 oz. clear glass bottle with red cap. Label is green & red. CMV $9.

1954-57 DEODORANT FOR MEN
4 oz. red cap & green label. Came in sets only. CMV $9 MB, $7 BO.
1949-58 DEODORANT FOR MEN
2 oz. red cap & green label. OSP 63c, CMV $6, $8 MB.

1949-58 AFTER SHAVING LOTION
4 oz. bottle with silver label & red cap. OSP 69c, CMV $6 BO, $9 MB.
1957 AFTER SHAVE 2 OZ.
Silver label. Came in Good Cheer set only. CMV $8.

1957 only ROYAL ORDER
Red & green box holds 6 oz. cologne for men. Silver label. OSP $1.50, CMV $25 MB.

1949-58 HAIR LOTION
4 oz. silver label & red cap. OSP 59c, CMV $7 BO, $12 MB.

1949-58 CREAM HAIR LOTION
4 oz. bottle, silver label, red cap. OSP 59c CMV $7 BO, $12 MB.

1953-54 AFTER SHAVE LOTION
4 oz. silver label, red cap, as above. CMV $15.

1953-54 COLOGNE FOR MEN
4 oz. green label, red cap. Came in Before & After set only. CMV $15.

1958 COLOGNE FOR MEN
2 oz. red cap, black & white label. Came in Happy Hours Set only. CMV $7 BO.

1958-62 DEODORANT FOR MEN
2 oz. red cap. OSP 69c, CMV $8 MB, $6 BO.

1953-54 HAIR LOTION 1 oz.
1 oz. bottle with red cap & green label. CMV $20 BO, $25 MB.

1953-54 CREAM HAIR LOTION 1 oz
1 oz. bottle with red cap, green label. CMV $10 BO, $25 MB in trial size box.

1953-54 LIQUID SHAMPOO
1 oz. bottle with red cap & green label. CMV $22 BO, $27 MB.

1959-62 ELECTRIC PRE-SHAVE LOTION
4 oz. red cap, black & white label. OSP 89c, CMV $12 MB, $8 BO.

1960-62 AFTER SHAVING LOTION PLASTIC
3½ oz. white plastic bottle with red cap. Came in Overnighter Set only. CMV $8. 2 oz. After Shave, red plastic & cap as above came in 1959 Lamplighter Set. CMV $8.

1959-62 SPRAY DEODORANT FOR MEN
2¾ oz. white plastic bottle with red cap. OSP 89c, CMV $6 MB, $4 BO. 1½ oz. size in white plastic, red cap, came only in 1959 Lamplighters Set. CMV $7.

1959-60 AFTER SHOWER FOR MEN
2 oz. black plastic bottle with red cap. OSP $1.25, CMV $8.

1959-60 AFTER SHAVE
2 oz. red plastic bottle & cap. Came in 1959 Lamplighter Set. CMV $8.

1958-62 AFTER SHAVE LOTION SAMPLE
(Left) ½ oz. red cap, black & white label. CMV $8.

1958 AFTER SHAVE LOTION
(Center) 2 oz. red cap. Came in sets only. CMV $6.

1958-62 AFTER SHAVE LOTION
(Right) 4 oz. red cap, black & white label. OSP 89c, CMV $4.

1958-59 COLOGNE FOR MEN
4 oz. black glass, red cap. OSP $1.25, CMV $15 MB, $12 BO.

1959-62 AFTER SHOWER SAMPLE
½ oz. black glass, red cap. CMV $6.

1959-62 AFTER SHOWER FOR MEN
4 oz. black glass, red or gold cap. OSP $1.25, CMV $12.

1960-61 STAGE COACH EMBOSSED BOTTLES
2 oz. size. Red or white caps. Came in First Prize Set only in After Shower for Men. Vigorate, Deodorant for Men, After Shave Lotion, Electric Pre-Shave Lotion, Liquid Hair Lotion. CMV ea $18 MB, $10 BO.

1961 Only - 4 oz. size with white cap came in Spice After Shave Lotion. OSP $1.25, CMV $10 BO, $14 MB.

1960-61 - 8 oz. size with gold metal cap, came in Spice After Shave Lotion. OSP $1.98. After Shave Lotion OSP $1.79, Vigorate $2.50 & After Shower for Men OSP $2.50, CMV ea. $17, with indented gold cap $25 MB.

1960-62 VIGORATE AFTER SHAVE
4 oz. frosted glass bottle, gold or red caps. 2 different painted labels. OSP $1.25, CMV $10, $15 MB.

1962-63 DELUXE STICK DEODORANT NORMAL
2½ oz. brown & gold plastic bottle. OSP $1.35, CMV $8, $10 BO.

1961-62 STICK DEODORANT FOR MEN A SPICY FRAGRANCE
2¾ oz. brown & gold plastic holder. OSP $1.35, CMV $9, $11 MB.

1962-63 DELUXE AFTER SHAVE AFTER SHOWER SPRAY
(Left) 5½ oz. brown can, gold cap. OSP $1.98, CMV $8, $10 MB.

1961 Only - AFTER SHOWER POWDER SPICY
(Center) 4 oz. brown can. OSP $1.35, CMV $12, $14 MB.

1961-62 AFTER SHAVE AFTER SHOWER SPRAY LOTION — A SPICY FRAGRANCE
(Right) 5½ oz. brown can, gold cap. OSP $1.79, CMV $12 mint, $14 MB.

1960-61 AFTER SHAVE FOR DRY & SENSITIVE SKIN
2 oz. white plastic bottle with red cap. OSP 89c, CMV $7 BO, $10 MB. Also came in 2¾ oz.

1960-61 CREAM HAIR LOTION
2 oz. white plastic bottle with red cap. Came in 1st Prize Set only. CMV $7 BO. Also came in 2¾ oz size. $10 MB.

1962-65 CREAM HAIR LOTION
4 oz. white plastic bottle, red cap. OSP 89c, CMV $10 MB, $7 BO.

1962-65 LIQUID HAIR LOTION
4 oz. clear glass bottle, red cap. OSP 89c, CMV $12 MB, $8 BO.

1962-65 HAIR TRAINER
4 oz. white plastic bottle, red cap. OSP 89c, CMV $10 MB, $7 BO.

1962-65 TALC FOR MEN SPICY
3 oz. white can, red cap. OSP 89c, CMV $7. Also came in 3.1 oz. size.

1960-63 ROLL ON DEODORANT FOR MEN
1¾ oz. white plastic with red cap. OSP 89c, CMV $5 MB, $4 BO.

1962-63 DELUXE TALC FOR MEN
4 oz. brown can. OSP $1.35, CMV $8, $10 MB.

1962-63 DELUXE FOAM SHAVE CREAM
6 oz. brown can & cap. Regular or mentholated. OSP $1.35, CMV $8, $10 MB.

1962-65 AFTER SHAVE LOTION SPICY
1962-65 ELECTRIC PRE—SHAVE LOTION SPICY
1962-65 AFTER SHOWER COLOGNE FOR MEN
1962-65 ORIGINAL AFTER SHAVE LOTION
1962-65 VIGORATE AFTER SHAVE LOTION
Each bottle is 4 oz. size with red caps. OSP ea. 89c on Spicy & Electric Pre-Shave and $1 ea. on Vigorate & After Shower cologne. CMV ea $7 BO, $10 MB.

1967-68 BODY POWDER FOR MEN
6 oz. maroon cardboard box. OSP $4, CMV $8 MB, $12.50.

1963-65 VIGORATE AFTER SHAVE' AFTER SHOWER SPRAY
1963-65 ORIGINAL AFTER SHAVE AFTER SHOWER SPRAY SPICY
1963-65 AFTER SHAVE AFTER SHOWER SPRAY SPICY
1963-65 AFTER SHOWER COLOGNE SPRAY
5½ oz. each. White can with red caps. OSP Spicy & Original, $1.50 each, cologne & Vigorate, $1.75 each, CMV $3. each - $5. MB.

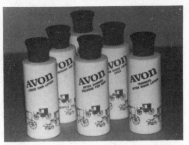

1963-64 MEN'S SQUEEZE BOTTLE
2 oz. white plastic bottles with red caps & letters. Came in Vigorate, Spicy & Original After Shave Lotions, Electric Pre-Shave Lotion, Spicy Liquid Hair Lotion, Hair Trainer, Cream Hair Lotion, After Shower Cologne for Men, Liquid Deodorant for Men, gentle or plain. Came only in 1964 Christmas Trio Set & 1965 Jolly Holly Day Set. CMV $3 each.

1962 AFTER SHOWER COLOGNE SPRAY
5.5 oz. white can & cap. OSP $1.75, CMV $7.
1962-65 FOAM SHAVE CREAM SPICY
6 oz. white can, red cap. Came in regular or mentholated. OSP 89c, CMV $6 MB, $4 BO. Came with tall or flat red caps as shown.

1962-65 STAND UP HAIR STICK
1½ oz. white plastic, red cap. OSP 89c, CMV $4 MB, $3 BO.
1963-66 ROLL ON DEODORANT FOR MEN
1¾ oz. glass bottle, red cap. OSP 89c., CMV $4 MB, $3 BO.
1962-66 SPRAY DEODORANT FOR MEN
2 ¾ oz white plastic bottle, red cap. Came in gentle, normal or plain. OSP 89c, CMV $3 MB, $2 BO.
1962-65 LIQUID DEODORANT FOR MEN - GENTLE OR PLAIN
4 oz. & 2 oz. clear glass bottle, red cap. OSP 79c, CMV 2 oz $6, 4 oz $7.

1962-65 AFTER SHAVE FOR DRY OR SENSITIVE SKIN SPICY 2 oz.
1962-65 LATHER SHAVE CREAM SPICY 4 oz.
All three white tubes with red caps. OSP each 89c, CMV $3, $6 ea. MB.
1962-63 LATHER SHAVE CREAM
4 oz. tube, red cap. OSP 89c, CMV $4 mint, $6 MB.

1966-69 CREAM HAIR LOTION
4 oz. white plastic bottle with red cap and red label. Regular issue OSP 98c. CMV $2. Very short issue sold 1966 only with red cap and red label with black border. CMV $4.

1966-70 LIQUID HAIR LOTION
(Bottles) 4 oz. clear glass bottle with white cap. OSP 98c, CMV $2. 1970-71 bottle is white, red cap, 6 oz. plastic. CMV $1.
1966-71 HAIR DRESS
(Tubes) 4 oz. tube in Cream Clear & Clear for Extra Control. OSP 98c, CMV $2. Also came in 3 oz. tube. CMV $2 each.

1958-62 CREAM HAIR LOTION
4 oz. white plastic bottle, red cap. OSP 89c, CMV $7, $12 MB.
1958-62 HAIR LOTION
4 oz. clear glass, red cap, black & white label. OSP 79c, CMV $14 MB, $10 BO. Glass bottle on right also came in Deer Head box on left.

1959 Only — TALC FOR MEN
(Left) Black & white can, red cap. OSP 69c, CMV $12 MB - $10 can only, mint.
1959-62 AFTER SHOWER POWDER FOR MEN
(Right) 3 oz. black & white can, red cap. OSP 89c, CMV $6 - $7 MB.

1977 TRAVEL-LITE
2 oz. light tan plastic bottle of shampoo, 1.7 oz. spray deodorant, 2 oz. Wild Country after shave. All have brown caps. CMV $1 each.

1970-77 FOAM SHAVE CREAM
11 oz. cans in mentholated (blue cap) and regular (orange cap). OSP $1.79, CMV 50c. With upside down label - CMV $8.

1959-62 BRUSHLESS SHAVING CREAM
(Left) 5 oz. black & white tube, red cap. OSP 79c, CMV $8 MB.

1959-62 LATHER SHAVING CREAM
(Center) 5 oz. black & white tube, red cap. OSP 79c, CMV $8 MB.

1958-62 KWICK FOAMING SHAVE CREAM
(Right) 6 oz. black & white can, red cap. OSP 79c, CMV $8.

1972-76 PROTEIN HAIR CARE FOR MEN
(Left) Blue & white. Shampoo Concentrate. 3 oz. OSP $1.79, CMV 50c.

DANDRUFF SHAMPOO
(Inside Left) 3 oz. OSP $1.79, CMV 50c.

CLEAR HAIR DRESS
(Left Center) 4 oz. OSP $1.79, CMV 50c.

HAIR & SCALP CONDITIONER
(Right Center) 6 oz. OSP $1.79, CMV 50c.

1972-74 HAIR LOTION
(Inside Right) 6 oz. OSP $1.75, CMV 50c.

1974 (late) - 1976 HAIR/SCALP CONDITIONER
(Not Shown) Same as lotion. OSP $2.50, CMV 50c.

1972 Only — HAIR SPRAY
(Left) 7 oz. OSP $1.75, CMV $2.

1973-76 HAIR MANAGING CONTROL
(Not Shown) Same as Hair Spray. OSP $1.75, CMV $1.

1972-76 CREAM HAIR DRESS
(Not Shown) 4 oz. blue tube, white cap. OSP $1.79, CMV 50c.

1966-72 ELECTRIC PRE-SHAVE LOTION
(Left) 4 oz. white cap. OSP $1.50, CMV $1.

1966-70 FOAM SHAVE CREAM
(Right) 6 oz. red & white can in regular; green & white can in mentholated. OSP 98c each, CMV $1 each.

1957-58 HAIR TRAINER
(Left) 6 oz. clear glass bottle with white or blue cap. Came in 1957 Hair Trainer Set. OSP 79c, CMV $20.

1951-52 HAND GUARD & HAIR GUARD
(Right) 2 oz. clear glass with blue cap; hair guard has red cap. Label is red, white & black. Came in Changing of the Guard set only. CMV $20 each.

1954-57 HAND GUARD & HAIR GUARD
(Left & Center) 2 oz. red cap on Hair Guard. 2 oz. green cap on Hand Guard. Both came in Back Field set & Touchdown set. Hair Guard also came in Pigskin Parade set. CMV $18 each.

1955 CREAM HAIR LOTION
(Right) 2 oz. clear glass, red cap. Came in Space Scout set only. Rare. CMV $25.

1957 FOAMY BATH FOR CLEANER HIDES
(Left) 2 oz. red cap, cow hide on label. Came in Trading Post set only. CMV $20.

1957 HAIR TRAINER FOR TRAINING WILD HAIR
(Right) 2 oz. red cap, cow hide on label. Came in Trading Post set only. CMV $20.

1971-74 ANTI-PERSPIRANT DEODORANT FOR MEN
(Left) 4 oz. red, white & black can. OSP $1.50, CMV 25c. With upside down label - CMV $8.

1966-70 LIQUID DEODORANT FOR MEN
(Inside Left) 2 oz. red cap. OSP 79c, CMV $2.

1968-70 STICK DEODORANT FOR MEN
(Inside Right) 2.25 oz. red, white & black plastic. OSP $1.25, CMV $1.

DEODORANT SOAP DRY - FOREIGN
CMV $3.

1975-76 TODAY'S MAN SHAVE CREAM
(Left) 5 oz. white with red & black design, black cap. OSP $2, CMV 50c.

1975-76 TODAY'S MAN HAND CONDITIONER
(Center) 5 oz. white plastic tube with black & red design, black cap. OSP $1.69, CMV 50c.

1975-76 TODAY'S MAN AFTER SHAVE FACE CONDITIONER
(Right) 5 oz. white with red & black, black cap. OSP $2.50, CMV 50c.

1969-72 BATH OIL
(Left) 4 oz. black glass bottle, red cap. OSP $2.50, CMV $2.

1969-72 AFTER SHAVE SOOTHER
(Center) 4 oz. frosted glass bottle with red cap. OSP $2.50, CMV $2.

1969-72 PROTECTIVE HAND CREAM FOR MEN
(Right) 3 oz. black plastic tube with red cap. OSP $1.50, CMV $1.

1958-74 HAIR TRAINER LIQUID
(Left) 4 oz. red plastic bottle, white cap. OSP 89c, CMV $1.

1959-62 ATTENTION CREAM HAIR DRESS
(Center) 4 oz. red & white tube, red cap. OSP 89c, CMV $8 MB - $10.

1958-65 STAND UP HAIR STICK
(Right) Red & white container with white cap. OSP 69c, CMV $3 - $7 MB.

BAY RUM

1968-72 STAY HAIR GROOM FOR MEN
(Left) 7 oz. brown & black can, black cap. OSP $1.50, CMV $1.
1969-73 SKIN CONDITIONER FOR MEN
(Center) 5 oz. black glass, red lid and red & black label. OSP $2.50, CMV $2.50 MB.
1966-68 ALL PURPOSE SKIN CONDITIONER FOR MEN
(Right) 5 oz. black glass, tan lid, gold label. OSP $2.50, CMV $5 MB.

1958-61 HAIR TRAINER BOXES
(Left to Right) 4 oz. red plastic bottle with 1958 box on left, 1962 box center, 1960-61 on right. 1959 box came with basketball player on front of box. CMV add $5 for each box mint - $1 bottle only.

1982-83 TOP CONDITION FACE & BODY SCRUB FOR MEN SOAP
(Left) 5 oz. bar. SSP $2, CMV $1.50 mint.
1982-83 TOP CONDITION AFTER SHAVE MOISTURIZER
(Center) 4 oz. blue plastic bottle. SSP $4.
1982-83 TOP CONDITION HEAVY DUTY HAND CREME FOR MEN
(Right) 3 oz. blue plastic tube. SSP $2, CMV 50c each item.

1958 Only — HAIR GUARD & HAND GUARD
Both 2 oz. bottles with red caps. Came in Avon Guard set only. CMV hand guard $16, hair guard $20.

1980-81 MEN'S TRAVEL CASE
Brown vinyl case with black zipper & trim. Case does not say Avon. Comes in plastic bag marked Avon. Travel case size is 10'' x 4'' x 3''. SSP $6, CMV $6 in Avon bag.

1965-67 AFTER SHOWER FOAM FOR MEN
(Left) 4 oz. silver can, black & red cap. Came in silver box. OSP $2.50, CMV $7 BO - $10 MB.
1965-67 BATH OIL FOR MEN
(Right) 4 oz. silver paint over clear glass, red cap & red Avon plastic tag on gold neck cord. Came in silver box. OSP $2.50, CMV $7 - $10 MB. Foreign Bath Oil same as U.S. only shiny silver & no neck tag - CMV $12.

1936-49 BAY RUM
4 oz. maroon cap. 2 different labels. Both bottles have indented shoulders. Also came in 8 & 16 oz. size. OSP 52c CMV $22. BO, $30. MB. each

1964 BAY RUM GIFT SET
Green box holds 4 oz. Bay Rum after shave with black cap & green 4 oz. paper Bay Rum talc for men. OSP $2.50, CMV $35 MB.

1964-65 BAY RUM SOAP
Green box holds 2 Bay Rum shaped soaps. OSP $1.25, CMV $27.50, MB.

1964-65 BAY RUM AFTER SHAVE
(left) 4 oz. clear glass, black cap. OSP $1.25 - CMV $8.50 bottle only, $12.50 MB.

1962-65 BAY RUM JUG
(center) 8 oz. white painted bottom, green top over clear glass, black cap. Bay Rum after shave. OSP $2.50, CMV $6 BO, $10 MB.

1964-65 BAY RUM TALC
(right) 4 oz. green paper container. OSP $1.25 - CMV $10.

BLACK SUEDE

1980-84 BLACK SUEDE PRODUCTS
Basic Color is tan & black.

1980 Only GIFT SOAP & CASE
Black plastic soap case & soap. SSP $5, CMV $5 MB.

SOAP BAR only
SSP $1.50, CMV $1.50 mint.

AFTER SHAVE & COLOGNE
4 oz. clear glass, black plastic caps. SSP $6 each, CMV $1 each MB.

AFTER SHAVE & COLOGNE SAMPLES
Box of 10 each packets. CMV 25c box of 10.

COLOGNE SPRAY
3 oz. spray can, silver cap. SSP $7, CMV 50c MB.

TALC 3.5 oz. SSP $2, CMV 50c.

SPRAY TALC
4 oz. black cap. SSP $3.50, CMV 50c.

MEN'S GIFT EDITION COLOGNE
.5 oz. clear glass, black cap. SSP $1.25, CMV $1 MB.

AFTER SHAVE SOOTHER
4 oz. clear glass. SSP $5, CMV $1 MB.

TRAVELER COLOGNE OR AFTER SHAVE
2 oz. plastic, black cap. SSP $3, CMV 50c MB each.

ROLL-ON DEODORANT
2 oz. plastic, black cap. CMV 25c.

SOAP ON A ROPE
SSP $3, CMV $3 MB.

BLEND 7

1973-74 BLEND 7 EMOLLIENT AFTER SHAVE
(Left) 5 oz. clear glass with black cap. SSP $4, CMV $3 MB - $1 BO.

1973-76 COLOGNE
(Center) 5 oz. smokey glass with silver cap. SSP $4, CMV $3 MB - $1 BO.

1973-76 SOAP ON A ROPE
(Right) 5 oz. yellow with black cord. SSP $2, CMV $4 MB.

1974-76 BLEND 7 SPRAY TALC
(Left) 7 oz. silver & black can with black cap. SSP $3, CMV $1.

1974-76 BLEND 7 FRAGRANCE SAMPLES
10 foil samples in box. CMV 50c box.

1964-65 BLUE BLAZER 1 SET
Blue & red box holds 6 oz. Blue Blazer after shave lotion & Blue Blazer soap on rope. OSP $3.45, CMV $50 MB.

BLUE BLAZER

1964-68 BLUE BLAZER AFTER SHAVE
(Left) 6 oz. blue glass with red square cap over small red cap. Horses on labels, came in gold or silver & with or without lines across horses. Some labels have 6 oz. at bottom of horse label. OSP $2.50, CMV $22 in box - $20 bottle only.

1964-68 BLUE BLAZER SOAP ON A ROPE
(Right) Blue soap on white rope. OSP $1.75, CMV $22.50 in box - $15 soap only mint.

1966-67 BLUE BLAZER SOAP & SPONGE SET
Red & blue box holds bar of blue soap and red & blue sponge. OSP $2.50, CMV set in box $22.50.

1965 BLUE BLAZER DELUXE SET
Blue & red box holds 6 oz. Blue Blazer after shave, Blue Blazer spray deodorant & silver Blue Blazer emblem tie tac. OSP $5.50, CMV $67.50 MB.

1964-67 BLUE BLAZER SPRAY DEODORANT
2.75 oz. blue plastic bottles, red caps. One bottle has lines on horse design & 1 plain. The plain one is hardest to find. OSP $1.25 each, CMV $8. Different label on right. CMV $7 with 2.75 oz. on front side.

1969 BRAVO AFTER SHAVE
(Left) 4 oz. bottle with black cap, pink label. OSP $2, CMV $4 MB - $2 BO.

1970-72 BRAVO AFTER SHAVE
(Right) 4 oz. black cap, pink label with black border around label. OSP $2, CMV $2 MB - $1 BO.

1964-65 BLUE BLAZER II SET
Blue & red box holds Blue Blazer talc & spray deodorant. OSP $2.50, CMV $25.

1964 BLUE BLAZER TIE TAC
Silver Blue Blazer emblem tie tac. Came in Blue Blazer Deluxe Set only. In blue & red box. CMV $22 in box - $10 pin only.

1970 SANTA'S HELPER
Green box holds 4 oz. Bravo After Shave. Box came with foam stick on decorations. OSP $1.98, CMV $8 MB only.

1964-65 BLUE BLAZER FOAM SHAVE CREAM
(Not Shown) 6 oz. blue can, red cap. OSP $1.25, CMV $10 MB - $7 CO.

1964-65 AFTER SHAVE SPRAY
(Left) Blue 6 oz. can, red cap. OSP $1.95, CMV $10 MB - $7 CO.

1964-65 TALC
(Center) 3½ oz. blue paper box. OSP $1.25, CMV $12 MB - $9 CO.

1964-67 HAIR DRESS
(Right) 4 oz. blue tube, red cap. OSP $1.25, CMV $8 MB - $6 TO.

BRAVO

1969-72 BRAVO AFTER SHAVE TOWELETTES
Pink & black box holds 100 sample packets. CMV $10 MB or 10c per sample.

1969-72 BRAVO AFTER SHAVE SAMPLE
(Left) Box of 10 samples. CMV $1.50 MB.

1969-72 BRAVO TALC
(Right) 3.5 oz. pink & black paper container. OSP $1.25, CMV $1.50.

CLINT

1977-79 CLINT AFTER SHAVE
(Left) 5 oz. glass bottle, brown cap. OSP $5, CMV $1.50.
1977-78 CLINT SHOWER SOAP
(center) Soap on green or white rope. OSP $5, CMV $3.50 MB.
1976-79 CLINT COLOGNE
(Right) 5 oz. bottle with Clint painted on front. OSP $7.50, CMV 75c. Also came in 4 oz. size, same design.

1977 CLINT TRAVEL KIT
(Back) Comes empty, gray, maroon & green bag. OSP $14, CMV $6 MB.
1977-78 CLINT TALC
(Front Left) 3.5 oz. cardboard talc container. OSP $2.50, CMV 50c.
1977-78 CLINT SOAP
(Front Center) 3 oz. soap. OSP $1.25, CMV 75c.
1977 CLINT SPRAY TALC
(Front Right) 7 oz. gray, maroon & green can. OSP $4, CMV $1.50.

1977-78 CLINT GIFT SET
(Left) Gray & green box with outer sleeve. Came with Clint soap on a rope & 5 oz. Clint cologne. OSP $12.50, CMV $10 MB.
1977 CLINT TRAVEL SET
(Right) Cardboard 1.5 oz. talc & 3 oz. Clint in plastic bottle with maroon cap. OSP $3.50, CMV $3.50 MB.

1979-80 CLINT ROLL-ON DEODORANT
(Left) 2 oz. gray & maroon plastic. SSP $1, CMV 25c.
1977-79 CLINT STEIN COLOGNE
(Right) 8 oz. red plastic bottle came in Tall Ships Stein only. CMV $3.

C.J.
SEE 1984 SUPPLEMENT IN BACK OF THIS BOOK

1982-84 CJ AFTER SHAVE
(left) 3 oz. black cap. SSP $6.50, CMV $1 MB.
1982-84 CJ COLOGNE
(center) 3 oz. silver cap. SSP $8.50, CMV $1 MB.
1982-84 TALC FOR MEN
(right) 3.5 oz. SSP $3.50, CMV 50c
1983 CJ INVIGORATING SHAMPOO & BODY CLEANSER
4 oz. gray plastic bottle, black cap. SSP $3 - CMV 25c.
1983 CJ GIFT EDITION COLOGNE
.5 oz. clear glass, gray cap. SSP $2 - CMV $1 MB.

1972-78 DEEP WOODS
(left) light green with brown cap. Looks like a log.
1972-78 COLOGNE
(left) 5 oz. OSP $6.50 - CMV $1.
1973-75 COLOGNE SPRAY
(inside left) 3 oz. OSP $5 - CMV $1.
1973-77 SPRAY TALC
(inside right) 7 oz. OSP $4, CMV 50c. Came in brown or green can. With upside down label - CMV $8.
1973-74 EMOLLIENT AFTER SHAVE
(Right) SSP $5 - CMV $2.

1977-78 DEEP WOODS SOAP BAR
(left) Brown wrapped soap, 3 oz. bar. OSP $1.25 - CMV $1 mint.
1977-78 DEEP WOODS TALC
(right) 3.5 oz. brown and green container, SSP $1.49 - CMV 50c.

DEEP WOODS

1972-79 DEEP WOODS PRODUCTS
1976-79 AFTER SHAVE
(Left) 5 oz. brown cap. OSP $3, CMV $1.50.
1972-75 SHOWER SOAP ON A ROPE
(Center) OSP $2, CMV $6 MB.
1976-79 SHOWER SOAP ON A ROPE
(Right) OSP $3, CMV $3 MB.
1972-79 DEEP WOODS FRAGRANCE SAMPLE
(Back) CMV 25c box.

EVEREST

1975-79 EVEREST SOAP ON A ROPE
(Left) Blue soap, white rope. OSP $3, CMV $3 MB.

1976-78 EVEREST AFTER SHAVE
(Inside Left) 5 oz. glass bottle with bronze cap. OSP $4, CMV 75c.

1975-79 EVEREST COLOGNE
(Inside Right) 5 oz. blue glass, blue cap. OSP $4, CMV $1.50.

1975-77 EVEREST SPRAY TALC
(Right) 7 oz. blue & white with blue lid. OSP $3, CMV $1 mint.

1977-79 EVEREST SOAP BAR
(Left) Blue wrapped 3 oz. bar. SSP $1.25, CMV $1 mint.

1977-79 EVEREST TALC
(Center) 3.5 oz. blue container. OSP $2.50, CMV 50c.

1976-79 EVEREST STEIN COLOGNE
(Right) 8 oz. blue plastic bottle came in 1976 to 1979 Collectors steins. CMV $3.

EXCALIBUR

1969-73 EXCALIBUR COLOGNE FOREIGN & AMERICAN
Smaller foreign Excalibur on left. CMV $12. American on right. 6 oz. gold cap. Bottom of bottle appears to have rocks in glass. OSP $5, CMV $5 MB - $2 BO. American rare issue came with sword pointing to right side low end of rocks. CMV $15 mint.

1969-71 EXCALIBUR SOAP ON A ROPE
(Left) Blue soap on a rope. OSP $2.50, CMV $10 MB.

1970-72 EXCALIBUR SPRAY TALC
(Right) 7 oz. black can & cap. OSP $3, CMV $2.

ISLAND LIME

1966-67 ISLAND LIME AEROSOL DEODORANT
(Left) 4 oz. green & yellow checked can & green cap. OSP $1.50, CMV $3 CO - $5 MB.

1969-73 ISLAND LIME AFTER SHAVE
(Center & Left) 6 oz. green frosted glass & green cap with yellow letters. OSP $4, CMV $1.50. 1973-74 issue has gold cap, green letters. OSP $4, CMV $4 MB - $2 BO.

1974-76 ISLAND LIME SPRAY TALC
(Left) 7 oz. green & yellow with dark green cap. OSP $2, CMV 50c.

1966-69 ISLAND LIME AFTER SHAVE
(Right) First issue 6 oz. dark yellow basket weave. CMV $12 MB - $9 BO. 1967 issue has light yellow weave on clear. CMV $10. 1968 issue has light green weave. CMV $10. All 66 to 68 are clear glass bottles. 1969 issue is green glass bottle & low issue. CMV $20 MB - $14 BO. OSP each $3. All have green & yellow caps. Add $3 each MB. Came with small or large flowers on caps.

1966-68 ISLAND LIME SOAP
Green soap on a rope. OSP $2, CMV $22 MB. Two different weave designs on soap.

LEATHER

1966 LEATHER SOAP
One bar in brown & red box. OSP $1.75, CMV $18 MB.

1966 ALL PURPOSE COLOGNE LEATHER
(Left) 4 oz. black cap, red label. Came in Fox Hunt set only. CMV $10.

1968 AFTER SHAVE LOTION LEATHER
(Right) 3 oz. red cap, clear glass. Came in Boots & Saddle set only. CMV $5.

1966-67 LEATHER AEROSOL DEODORANT
(Left) 4 oz. tan & red can with black cap. OSP $1.50, CMV $5 MB - $3 can only.

1969-72 LEATHER SPRAY TALC
(Right) 7 oz. tan & red can, black cap. OSP $3, CMV $2.

OLAND

1970 OLAND GIFT SET
Brown & silver box holds bar of Oland soap, 3½ oz. Oland talc & 6 oz. Oland cologne. OSP $8, CMV $15.

1970-77 OLAND COLOGNE
(Left) 6 oz. embossed bottle with brown cap. OSP $6.50, CMV $2.

1970-77 OLAND SOAP ON A ROPE
(Center) Tan bar of soap on green rope with plastic "O". OSP $4, CMV $7 MB with plain rope (no "O") - CMV $5 MB.

1970-77 OLAND SPRAY TALC
(Right) 7 oz. brown spray can with brown cap. OSP $3, CMV $2.

1970-72 OLAND SPRAY TALC
(Left) 7 oz. can with O on brown cap. Painted label on can is upside down. Can was filled & sold by Avon by mistake. OSP $3, CMV on upside down label only $15.

1970 OLAND AFTER SHAVE & COLOGNE
(Center & Right) 3½ oz. clear glass with gold cap. Came in Master Organizer only. CMV $5 each.

RUGGER

1981-84 RUGGER PRODUCTS
ALL OVER MOISTURE RUB
(Left) 5 oz. maroon tube.
COLOGNE PLUS
(Inside Left) 4 oz. clear glass, maroon cap.
AFTER SHAVE SOOTHER
(Inside Right) 4 oz. clear glass, maroon cap.
TALC
(Right) 3.5 oz.
GIFT EDITION COLOGNE
(Not Shown) Same shape bottle as 4 oz. cologne only 5 oz. SSP $1.25, CMV $1 MB
ROLL-ON DEODORANT
(Not Shown) 2 oz. plastic
SOAP ON A ROPE
(Not Shown) SSP $4, CMV $4 MB.
CMV 25c each item not marked.
SHAMPOO . . . 5 oz. tube.

SPICY

1967-74 SPICY AFTER SHAVE
4 oz. clear glass, black cap. CMV 50c. 4 oz. amber glass with black cap, OSP $1.50 ea., CMV $2 MB.

1965-66 SPICY SOAP SET
Five brown bars. OSP $2, CMV $22.50 MB.

1965-67 COLOGNE PLUS SPICY
2 oz. gold ribbed cap. OSP $2.50, CMV $20 in box. Bottle only $17.50.
1965-67 AFTER SHAVE LOTION SPICY
4 oz. tan cap. OSP 98c, CMV $7.

1967-75 AFTER SHAVE FOR DRY OR SENSITIVE SKIN - SPICY
2 oz. black, brown & white tube, brown or white cap. OSP 98c. One has all white letters, CMV $1. One has black over print on white letters. Hard to find, CMV $3.

1961 SPICY AFTER SHAVE SAMPLES
Plastic sample tubes of Spicy After Shave Lotion. Full box of 30. Same samples also came in Cream Hair Dress, Rich Moisture Cream & Dew Kiss. CMV 25c each sample or $7 for full box of 30 mint. Comes in 2 different boxes.

1967-74 TALC FOR MEN - SPICY
3½ oz. brown & white container. OSP 98c, CMV $1. Upside down label CMV $8.
1965-67 AFTER SHAVE SPRAY - SPICY
5½ oz. Bamboo style can, gold cap. OSP $1.50, CMV $6.

1965-67 AFTER SHAVE FOR DRY OR SENSITIVE SKIN - SPICY
2 oz. tan & white tube, tan cap. OSP 89c, CMV $4 mint. Upside down label on right is rare. CMV $12 mint.

1961 SPICE AFTER SHAVE LOTION SAMPLES
Small white envelope holds 2 plastic samples. CMV $3.

1965-67 TALC FOR MEN - SPICY
3½ oz. Bamboo style box. OSP 89c, CMV $5 MB - $3 CO.
1965-67 AFTER SHAVE SPRAY - SPICY
5½ oz. Bamboo style can, tan cap. OSP $1.50, CMV $5 MB - $3 CO.

1967-76 OATMEAL SOAP - SPICY
(Left) Large bath size & 3 oz. size in borwn & white wrapper. OSP 60c, CMV $2.
1965-67 OATMEAL SOAP - SPICY
(Right) Brown & white wrapping. OSP 49c, CMV $7.

1966 FORE N AFTER SPICY
Spicy box holds 4 oz. Electric Pre-Shave Lotion Spicy & 4 oz. After Shave Lotion Spicy. White caps on both & wood grained paper label. OSP $1.96, CMV $22 MB.
1966 ELECTRIC PRE-SHAVE & AFTER SHAVE LOTIONS - SPICY
4 oz. white caps & wood grained paper labels. Came in Fore 'N' After Set only. CMV $9 each.

1966 Only - SPICE 'O' LIFE SET
Box holds Spicy Talc for Men & 4 oz. After Shave Lotion. Came out at Fathers Day. OSP $1.96, CMV $22.50 MB.

1965 SPICY THREE
Brown box holds 2 bars of Spicy Oatmeal Soap & Spicy Talc for Men. OSP $1.85, CMV $22.50 MB.

1965 HOLIDAY SPICE
Brown & white box holds Spicy Talc for Men & 4 oz. Spicy After Shave Lotion. OSP $1.85, CMV $22.50 MB.

1965-66 OVERNIGHTER
Brown vinyl zippered bag holds Spicy Talc, 4 oz. Spicy After Shave Lotion & bar of Spicy Oatmeal soap for men. OSP $7.50, CMV $22.50 MB.

1967 TWICE SPICE
Brown striped box holds 4 oz. Spicy After Shave Lotion & Spicy Talc for Men. OSP $2.23, CMV $15 MB.

1965 FIRST EDITION SPICY
Book type box holds 4 oz. Spicy After Shave Lotion & Spicy Talc for Men. OSP $1.69, CMV $22.50 MB.

SPORTS RALLY

1966-68 SPORTS RALLY BRACING LOTION
4 oz. glass bottle with blue cap. OSP $1.50, CMV $10 MB, $6 BO.

1966-68 BRACING TOWELETTE
Blue & white box holds 12 packets. OSP $1.25, CMV $5 MB.

1966-68 SPORTS RALLY SOAP ON A ROPE
4 oz. soap on white rope. OSP $1.50, CMV $12, $17.50 MB.

1966-68 AEROSOL DEODORANT
4 oz. red, white & blue can, white cap. OSP $1.25, CMV $3 MB, $2 BO.

1965 CHRISTMAS WREATH
Gold box holds two 4 oz. bottles of Spicy After Shave Lotion with tan caps. OSP $1.95, CMV $20 MB.

1968 SPICY TREASURES
Brown chest type box holds 4 oz. Spicy After Shave Lotion & 3½ oz. Talc for Men. OSP $2.23, CMV $15 MB.

1966-68 SPORTS RALLY HAIR DRESS
4 oz. red & white tube, red cap. OSP $1, CMV $3, $5 MB.

1966-68 SPORTS RALLY ALL PURPOSE TALC
3½ oz. blue & white cardboard container. OSP $1, CMV $3, $5 MB.

1966-68 SPORTS RALLY CLEAR SKIN SOAP
2 bars with blue band around them. OSP $1, CMV $4 each bar, $10 set.

1966-68 SPORTS RALLY CLEAR SKIN LOTION
4 oz. white plastic bottle, red cap. OSP $1.25, CMV $4 MB, $3 BO.

1966-68 SPORTS RALLY BRACING TOWELETTE
Contains 50 Towellettes in foil packets. CMV $10 MB.

TAI WINDS

TRAZARRA

1978-80 TRAZARRA PRODUCTS
COLOGNE
4 oz. clear glass, gold cap. CMV 50c
AFTER SHAVE
4 oz. clear glass, gold cap. CMV 50c
TALC
3.5 oz. brown cardboard, plastic top & bottom. CMV 50c. With upside down label, CMV $5.

FRAGRANCE SAMPLE INCH
1 inch glass vial in paper holder. CMV 25c.
SOAP ON A ROPE
Tan soap on brown rope. CMV $2 MB.
ROLL ON DEODORANT
2 oz. brown plastic. CMV 50c. Pictured larger than actual size to other products.

1971-79 TAI WINDS COLOGNE
5 oz. green glass, blue-green cap & yellow ribbon. OSP $6.50, CMV 50c.

1971-76 TAI WINDS SPRAY TALC
7 oz. blue-green & yellow can. OSP $4, CMV $1

1971-75 TAI WINDS AFTER SHAVE
5 oz. clear glass, blue-green cap, yellow ribbon. OSP $5, CMV $1.50 MB.

1972-79 TAI WINDS SOAP ON A ROPE
Yellow soap on rope. OSP $4, CMV $5 MB.

1971-72 TAI WINDS GIFT SET
5 oz. green glass bottle with green cap. Yellow bands, 5 oz. embossed soap. SSP $7, CMV $13 MB.

TRIBUTE

1963-68 TRIBUTE AFTER SHAVE SAMPLES
Box holds 30 foil samples. CMV $7 MB

1964-66 TRIBUTE COLOGNE FOR MEN
4 oz. blue & silver top, cap & neck tag. OSP $2.50, CMV with tag $10, $12 MB.

1967-68 TRIBUTE ALL PURPOSE COLOGNE
4 oz. blue & silver top, cap & neck tag. OSP $3, CMV with tag $10, $12 MB. Later issues had no tags. CMV $4 BO, $6 MB.

1963-66 TRIBUTE TALC
4 oz. blue & silver can, blue cap. OSP $1.75, CMV $6 mint.

1963-66 TRIBUTE AFTER SHAVE AFTER SHOWER SPRAY
5½ oz. blue & silver can & cap. OSP $2.50, CMV $6 mint.

1969-72 TRIBUTE SPRAY TALC
7 oz. blue can. OSP $3, CMV $1. Upside down label, rare. CMV $15.

1964-66 TRIBUTE SHAMPOO
Blue & silver tube. OSP $1.75, CMV $8.

1963-66 TRIBUTE ELECTRIC PRE-SHAVE LOTION
4 oz. blue & silver cap. OSP $1.75, CMV $8 MB, $5 BO.

1963-67 TRIBUTE AEROSOL DEODORANT
3 oz. blue & silver can & cap. OSP $1.75, CMV $6 MB, $4 CO. 4 oz. size same can, 1967 only. OSP $1.50, CMV $6 MB, $4 CO.

1963-66 TRIBUTE CREAM HAIR DRESS
4 oz. blue & silver tube & cap. OSP $1.75 - CMV $8 MB.

1963-66 TRIBUTE FOAM SHAVE CREAM
6 oz. blue & silver can & cap. Came in regular & mentholated. OSP $1.75, CMV $6 MB.

1963-64 TRIBUTE GIFT SET NO. 1
Blue & silver box holds Tribute Talc, Foam Shave Cream & After Shave After Shower Spray. OSP $6, CMV $35 MB.

1963-64 TRIBUTE GIFT SET NO. 2
Blue & silver box holds 6 oz. Tribute After Shave Lotion, Talc & Aerosol Deodorant. OSP $6.50, CMV $35 MB.

1966-67 TRIBUTE SOAP
Blue & silver box holds 2 white bars with blue & silver centers. OSP $1.75 - CMV $20 MB.

1963-66 TRIBUTE SOAP
Single bar in blue box. OSP $1.75, CMV $25 MB.

1964-65 TRIBUTE SHAVE SET
Blue box holds 6 oz. After Shave Lotion & can of Foam Shave Cream. OSP $4.25, CMV $35 MB.

1963-68 TRIBUTE AFTER SHAVE LOTION
(Left) 6 oz. silver & blue cap. OSP $2.50, CMV $6 mint.

1968-72 TRIBUTE AFTER SHAVE
(Right) 4 oz. blue label, blue & silver cap. Same bottle also reads After Shave Lotion on label. OSP $2.25 CMV $2.50 mint.

WEEKEND

1979-80 WEEKEND PRODUCTS AFTER SHAVE
4 oz. emerald green glass, wood cap. SSP $4, CMV 50c.

COLOGNE
Same bottle as after shave. SSP $5, CMV 50c

WEEKEND SOAP FOR MEN
Green wrapped bar. SSP $1, CMV 50c.

WEEKEND SAMPLES
Box of 10 green samples. CMV 25c.

WEEKEND GET AWAY BAG
Green nylon bag. Does not say Avon, but does have Weekend tag. SSP $5, CMV $4 mint.

1981-82 WEEKEND AFTER SHAVE SOOTHER
4 oz. clear glass, green cap. SSP $5, CMV $1 MB.

1981-82 WEEKEND TRAVELER COLOGNE OR AFTER SHAVE
2 oz. plastic. SSP $3, CMV 50c MB each.

1979-80 WEEKEND PRODUCTS
Green packaging

SPRAY TALC
CMV 50c

ROLL-ON DEODORANT
CMV 50c

SHOWER SOAP ON A ROPE
Tan soap on green rope. CMV $3 MB.

WILD COUNTRY

1976-80 WILD COUNTRY AFTER SHAVE
5 oz. bottle after shave, brown cap. OSP $5, CMV 50c

1977-79 WILD COUNTRY TALC
3.5 oz. cardboard container. OSP $2.50, CMV 50c

1976 WILD COUNTRY BELT BUCKLE
Sold by family fashions by Avon with purchase of other Wild Country products. OSP $1.99, CMV $3.

1977-80 WILD COUNTRY SOAP
3 oz. soap. OSP $1.25, CMV $1

1981-82 WILD COUNTRY GIFT EDITION COLOGNE'
.5 oz. glass. Same shape as 4 oz. cologne bottle. SSP $1.25, CMV $1 MB.

1981-82 AFTER SHAVE SOOTHER
4 oz. clear glass. SSP $5, CMV $1 MB.

1981-82 WILD COUNTRY TRAVELER COLOGNE OR AFTER SHAVE
2 oz. plastic. SSP $3, CMV 50c ea. MB.

1973-74 WILD COUNTRY HAND CREAM
3 oz. brown & white plastic tube with brown cap. SSP $1.75, CMV $1.75.

1975-77 WILD COUNTRY DEODORANT
4 oz. brown & white, white cap. OSP $1, CMV 75c. With upside down label, $8.

1970 WILD COUNTRY COLOGNE SAMPLES
Box of 10 sample packets. CMV 50c box.

1967-68 WILD COUNTRY BODY POWDER
6 oz. brown & white cardboard box. OSP $4, CMV $8 mint, $12 MB.

1969-70 WILD COUNTRY COLOGNE SPRAY
2½ oz. white coated plastic bottle with silver cap. OSP $4, CMV $4 MB, $2.50 BO.

1978 WILD COUNTRY ROLL ON DEODORANT
2 oz. white & borwn plastic bottle. SSP 99c, CMV 50c.

1978 WILD COUNTRY PENDANT
Silver & ivory bull head. Neck chain for men. Avon on back. SSP $8.99, CMV $4 MB.

1977 WILD COUNTRY TRAVEL SET
Box holds 1.5 oz. talc and 3 oz. after shave in plastic bottle with brown cap. OSP $3.49, CMV $3.50 MB.

1977-78 WILD COUNTRY GIFT SOAP
Metal container holds 5 oz. bar of white Wild Country soap. SSP $2.99, CMV $3 MB. Also came with label printed upside down on bottom of can. CMV $8.

1967-76 WILD COUNTRY SOAP ON A ROPE
Ivory colored bar with bulls head in center. Round. OSP $4, CMV $4, $5 MB.

1970-73 WILD COUNTRY FOAM SHAVE CREAM
11 oz. brown can. OSP $1.75, CMV $1.

1969-77 WILD COUNTRY SPRAY TALC
7 oz. brown can. OSP $4, CMV $2. With special upside down label, CMV $10.

1971-76 WILD COUNTRY AFTER SHAVE
4 oz. silver label & black cap. OSP $4.50, CMV $1.

1971-74-78 WILD COUNTRY TALC
3½ oz. brown shaker top container. OSP $1.50, CMV 50c. Reissued in 1978.

COLOGNE
6 oz. bottle with silver cap & label. OSP $4, CMV $2.50.

1968-80 WILD COUNTRY ALL PURPOSE COLOGNE
6 oz. silver cap & label. OSP $6.50, CMV $1.

1976-78 WILD COUNTRY SOAP ON A ROPE
Not shown, squared side, not round. OSP $4, CMV $4 MB.

WINDJAMMER

1973 CANADIAN WINDJAMMER SOAP ON A ROPE
CMV $12 MB.

1968 WINDJAMMER SPRAY TALC
7 oz. blue can. OSP $2.50, CMV $3. Also came in 4 oz. size. CMV $4.

1969-72 WINDJAMMER RUB DOWN COOLER
10 oz. plastic bottle, blue & gold cap. Lettering gold. Also came with blue lettering. OSP $3, CMV $1, $2.50 MB.

1968-69 WINDJAMMER TOWELETTES
Blue & white box holds 10 packets. CMV $2.50 MB.

MEN'S SETS OF 1930'S

WARNING!! Grading condition is paramount on sets. CMV can vary 50% to 75% on grade. Refer to pages 6 & 16 on Grading Sets.

SEE 1984 SUPPLEMENT IN BACK OF BOOK

1938-39 HEADLINER FOR BOYS
Maroon & gray striped box holds tubes of Hair Dress & Tooth Paste with Tooth Brush. OSP $1.10, CMV $50 MB.

1970-71 WILD COUNTRY SADDLE KIT
Brown & white cowhide kit holds Wild Country 6 oz. cologne, Foam Shave Cream & Spray Talc. OSP $16, CMV $17.50 MB.

1968-69 WINDJAMMER COLOGNE
(Left) 5 oz blue glass bottle & cap with ring. Painted label. OSP $4, CMV $8 MB, $5 BO.

1979-72 WINDJAMMER COLOGNE
(Right) 5 oz. blue glass & cap with blue paper label. OSP $4, CMV $2 BO, $3.50 MB.

1936-37 MEN'S PACKAGE
Maroon box holds can of Talc for Men, 4 oz. After Shave Lotion, turquoise can of Smokers Tooth Powder and tube of Shaving Cream. OSP $1.65, CMV $90 MB.

1936-37 ASSORTMENT FOR MEN
Wood grained paper box holds tube of Shaving Cream and can of Talc for Men with choice of 4 oz. Bay Rum or After Shave Lotion. OSP $1.15, CMV $80 MB.

1938-39 ESQUIRE SET OR COUNTRY CLUB SET
Same set as above and same price, only name changed. CMV $80 each set.

1938-40 MEN'S TRAVEL KIT
Brown leather zipper case holds maroon can of Talc for Men, tube of Shaving Cream, Styptic, and 4 oz. After Shave Lotion. OSP $2.16, CMV $65 MB.

1938-39 SMOKERS TRIO
Green box holds 6 oz. Antiseptic, Tooth Brush and green can of Smokers Tooth Powder. OSP $1.39, CMV $70 MB.

1936-38 MEN'S TRAVEL KIT
Leather case 7¼"x 6½"x 2". Holds 4 oz. After Shave Lotion, Talc for Men, Shaving Cream and tube of Styptic. OSP $2.01, CMV $80 mint.

1938-39 VALET SET
Speckled box holds 4 oz. After Shave, maroon can of Talc for Men, Smokers Tooth Powder & tube of Shaving Cream. OSP $1.65, CMV $100 set mint.

1931-34 ASSORTMENT NO. 7 FOR MEN
Avon box holds can of Talc for Men, 4 oz. bottle of Bay Rum and tube of Bayberry Shaving Cream, 2 yellow Cannon wash cloths and 1 yellow Cannon towel. OSP $2, CMV $110 set mint.

1933-36 MEN'S TRAVEL KIT
Black leather case 7¼"x6½"x2". Holds green tube of Bayberry Shaving Cream, 4 oz. After Shave Lotion, Styptic Pencil and green can of Talc for Men. OSP $1.95, CMV $100 mint.

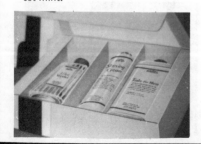

1931-36 ASSORTMENT FOR MEN
Green box holds tube of Shaving Cream and green can Talc for Men with choice of 4 oz. Bay Rum or 2 oz. Lilac Vegetal. OSP $1.20, CMV $110 MB.

1931-35 HAIR TREATMENT SET FOR MEN
6 oz. Liquid Shampoo, 2 oz. Pre-Shampoo, 6 oz. Hair Tonic. All have blue caps. Silver tube Hair Dress. White box. OSP $1.98, CMV $135 MB.

1937-39 BRUSHLESS SHAVING SET
Speckled box holds 4 oz. After Shave Lotion, maroon can of Talc for Men, and tube of Brushless Shaving Cream. OSP $1.10, CMV $75.

1934-35 MEN'S SHAVING SET
Wood grained box holds 4 oz. After Shave Lotion, can of Talc for Men Smokers Tooth Powder and tube of Bayberry Shaving Cream. OSP $1.65, CMV $165 set.

1930-34 SHAVING CABINET
White enamel cabinet with mirror on door. Cabinet is 8" high, 6½" wide and 2 3/8" deep. Label on door reads "Gem Micromatic Shaving Cabinet. Avon Products." OSP $2.50, CMV $90. empty mint.

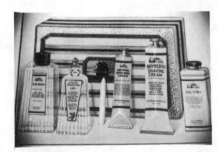

1930-32 HUMIDOR SHAVING SET
Gold & black metal box holds 4 oz. Bay Rum, 2 oz. Lilac Vegetal, Styptic Pencil, tube of Menthol Witch Hazel Cream, Bayberry Shave Cream & green can of Talc for Men. OSP $2.50, CMV $215. MB.

MEN'S SETS OF 1940'S
SEE 1984 SUPPLEMENT IN BACK OF THIS BOOK FOR MORE 1940's SETS.

1946-49 MODERN KNIGHT
Maroon and white box holds 2 oz. Deodorant for Men, can of Talc for Men and 4 oz. After Shaving Lotion. OSP $1.75, CMV $90 MB.

1948 PLEASURE CAST SET
Blue box holds 2 oz. bottles with maroon caps in Deodorant for Men, Cologne for Men and tube of Brushless or Regular Shaving Cream. OSP $1.69, CMV $70 MB.

WARNING!!
Grading condition is paramount on sets.
CMV can vary 50% on grade.
Refer to front of book for grading

1945-46 VALET SET
Maroon and ivory box holds 4 oz. After Shave Lotion, tube of Shaving Cream, Talc for Men and Smokers Tooth Powder. Both came in maroon paper containers with flat top lids and also pouring lids with caps. OSP $1.85, CMV $110 MB.

1940-41 ESQUIRE SET
Maroon box holds 4 oz. bottle of Bay Rum, tube of shaving cream, can of talc for men. OSP $1.15, CMV $80 MB.

1943-46 ARMY & NAVY KIT
Blue and red box holds tube of Brushless Shaving Cream, maroon paper box of Elite Foot Powder and paper carton of Tooth Powder. OSP $1.46, CMV $90 MB.

1940-42 VALET SET
Maroon and white box holds 4 oz. After Shaving Lotion, maroon cans of Talc for Men, Smokers Tooth Powder and tube of Shaving Cream. OSP $1.69, CMV $90 MB.

1946-49 MEN'S TRAVEL KIT
Brown flip open leather case holds can of Talc for Men, 4 oz. After Shaving Lotion, Styptic Cream and choice of tube of Shaving Cream or Brushless Shaving Cream. OSP $4.17, CMV $75 MB.

1941-42 ARMY & NAVY KIT
Blue & red box with Eagle on lid, holds 4 oz. After Shave Lotion, maroon tube of Brushless Shaving Cream and maroon can of Elite Powder. Each in maroon & ivory boxes. OSP $1.35, CMV $85 MB.

1946-49 VALET SET
Maroon box holds maroon can of Smokers Tooth Powder, Talc for Men, 4 oz. After Shaving Lotion and tube of Shaving Cream. OSP $2, CMV $85 MB.

1943-46 COUNTRY CLUB SET
Maroon and white box holds 4 oz. After Shave Lotion, 2 5/8 oz. paper box of Talc for Men and 3 oz. tube of Shaving Cream. Talc came with flat paper top lid or cap lid as shown. OSP $1.15, CMV $80 MB.

1946-49 TRAVELER SET
Maroon & white box holds 4 oz. After Shave Lotion, maroon tubes of Smokers Tooth Paste and Shaving Cream. OSP $1,25, CMV $70 MB.

1941-45 TRAVELER SET
Maroon and ivory box holds 4 oz. After Shaving Lotion, maroon tubes of Smokers Tooth Paste and Shaving Cream. OSP $1, CMV $70 MB.

1943-45 VALET SET
Maroon and ivory box holds 4 oz. After Shaving Lotion, 3 oz. tube in box of Shaving Cream, 2-5/8 oz. paper talc, 3.5 oz. paper side, tin flat top and bottom Smokers Tooth Powder. OSP $1.79, CMV $115 MB.

1943-46 COUNTRY CLUB SET
Maroon and white box holds 4 oz. After Shave Lotion, maroon flat top paper box of Talc for Men and tube of Shaving Cream. OSP $1.15, CMV $80 MB.

1940-42 COUNTRY CLUB SET
Maroon and ivory box holds 4 oz. After Shaving Lotion, maroon can of Talc for Men and tube of Shaving Cream. OSP $1, CMV $80 MB.

1939-41 COUNTRY CLUB SET
Box holds 4 oz. bottle of After Shave, tube of Shaving Cream, can of Talc for Men. OSP $1, CMV $70 MB.

1940-42 COMMODORE SET
Maroon and ivory box holds 4 oz. After Shaving Lotion, maroon can of Talc for Men and 2 white hankerchiefs. OSP $1.35, CMV $75 MB.

1946-49 COUNTRY CLUB
Maroon and white box holds tube of Shaving Cream, 4 oz. After Shaving Lotion and can of Talc for Men. OSP $1.35, CMV $75 MB.

1940-42 BRUSHLESS SHAVE SET
Maroon and ivory box with man fishing, holds 4 oz. After Shave Lotion, maroon can of Talc for Men and tube of Brushless Shave Cream. OSP $1.10, CMV $75 MB.

1943-46 COMMODORE
Maroon and white box holds 4 oz. After Shave Lotion, 2 white hankerchiefs and maroon paper box of Talc for Men. OSP $1.50, CMV $80 MB.

1943-46 BRUSHLESS SHAVE SET
Maroon and white box holds tube of Brushless Shave Cream, 4 oz. After Shave Lotion and maroon paper box of Talc for Men. OSP $1.35, CMV $80 MB.

1946-49 OLYMPIC SET
Maroon and white box holds tube of Shaving Cream, 6 oz. bottle of Hair Lotion and 4 oz. After Shaving Lotion. OSP $1.65, CMV $90 MB.

1946-49 BRUSHLESS SHAVE SET
Maroon and white box holds can of Talc for Men, tube of Brushless Shaving Cream, and 4 oz. After Shaving Lotion. OSP $1.40, CMV $75 MB.

1940-46 OLYMPIC SET
Maroon and ivory box holds 6 oz. bottle of Hair Lotion, tube of Shaving Cream and 4 oz. After Shaving Lotion. OSP $1.29, CMV $95.

MEN'S SETS OF 1950'S

WARNING!! Grading condition is paramount on sets. CMV can vary 50% to 75% on grade. Refer to Page 6 and 16 on Grading Sets.

1949-53 COMMODORE
Stage coach on green flip open box holds 2 oz. cologne & 2 oz. deodorant for men & green tube of brushless or lather shaving cream. OSP $1.90, CMV $50 MB.

1959 GROOMING GUARDS
Black flip open box with red inner box holds can of After Shower Powder for Men, 2 oz. Spray Deodorant for Men in white plastic & tube of Attention Cream Hair Dress & choice of 4 oz. After Shower for Men or After Shaving Lotion. OSP $4.95, CMV $60 MB.

1953-54 PARADE DRESS
Red, white & blue soldier box holds 1 oz. bottle of liquid shampoo, 1 oz. cream or liquid hair lotion & 1 bar of Dr. Zabriskie's Soap. OSP $1.19, CMV $70 MB. Set also came with 2 shampoos & 1 hair lotion with no soap. Same CMV.

1955-56 GOOD MORNING
Red box with geese holds choice of two 4 oz. bottles of cream or liquid hair lotion. OSP $1.18, CMV $26 MB.

1953 SPACE SHIP
Blue box holds plastic spaceship with tubes of chlorophyll toothpaste, creme shampoo & toothbrush. OSP $2.10, CMV $55 MB.

1958 COAT OF ARMS
Red, white, blue & gold box holds 6 oz. Kwick Foaming Shave Cream, 2 oz. Deodorant for Men & 2 oz. After Shave Lotion. OSP $1.98, CMV $37.50 MB.

1952 CHANGING THE GUARD
Red, white & blue guard house box holds 2 oz. hair guard with red cap & 2 oz. hand guard with blue cap. Came with outer box. OSP $1, CMV $65 MB.

1954 SMOOTH SHAVING
Green tubes with red caps had choice of brushless or lather shaving cream. OSP 98c, CMV $25 MB.

1954 BACKFIELD
Red & green box holds 2 oz. bottle of hair guard with red cap, 2 oz. hand guard with green cap, tube of chap check & small brown football soap. OSP $1.95, CMV $60 MB.

1957 ATTENTION
Red & green box holds two 4 oz. bottles in after shave lotion & choice of liquid or cream hair lotion. OSP $1.49, CMV $32.50 MB.

1955 PIGSKIN PARADE
(Left) Red & green box holds tube of creme shampoo, youths toothbrush, chap check, 2 oz. bottle of hair guard & a plastic football. OSP $1.95, CMV $55 MB.

1956-57 TOUCHDOWN
(Right) Green, red & gold box holds 2 oz. bottles of hair guard with red cap, hand guard with green cap & small football soap. OSP $1.29, CMV $55 MB.

1957 HAIR TRAINER & COMB SET
6 oz. bottle, white or blue cap, red & white label. Came in box with comb. OSP 79c - CMV $25 BO, $35 MB.

1957 MAN'S WORLD
Box has choice of 2 cream or liquid hair lotions in 4 oz. size. OSP $1.49, CMV $27.50 MB.

1954-56 PERSONAL NOTE SET
Green & red box holds 4 oz. cologne & deodorant for men with green label & gold ball point pen. OSP $2.95, CMV $50 MB.

1953-54 BEFORE & AFTER
Silver, white & green box opens up to 4 oz. cologne for men & choice of cream or liquid hair lotion. OSP $1.69, CMV $42.50 MB.

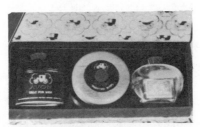

1949-51 PLEASURE SHAVE
Green box holds green can of talc for men, wood shaving bowl & 4 oz. after shave lotion with silver label. OSP $2.35, CMV $65 MB.

1952-54 PLEASURE SHAVE
Green box with red & white barber pole holds 2 tubes of shaving cream in choice of brushless or lather. OSP 98c - CMV $25 MB.

1949-51 DELUXE TRIO
Stage coach on green flip open box with green & red inner box. Holds choice of 4 oz. cream or liquid hair lotion, 2 oz. deodorant for men & 2 oz. cologne for men. OSP $2, CMV $50 MB.

1952 DELUXE TRIO
Same as 1949 set only has green removable lid. OSP $2, CMV $50 MB.

1953-54 QUARTET
Green & red box holds 2 tubes of shave creem brushless or lather, 2 oz. deodorant for men, green label & 4 oz. after shave lotion with silver label. OSP $2.20, CMV $55 MB.

1959 OUT IN FRONT
Box with soldier on horse holds 4 oz. cream or liquid hair lotion & 2¾ oz. spray deodorant for men in white plastic bottles. OSP $1.98, CMV $27.50 MB.

1949-51 COUNTRY CLUB
Green flip open box with red inner box, holds green can of talc for men, 4 oz. after shaving lotion & choice of lather or bruthless shaving cream. OSP $1.85, CMV $47.50 MB.

1952-53 COUNTRY CLUB
Stage coach on green box lid with inner box in red. Holds green talc for men, 4 oz. after shave lotion & tube of brushless or lather shave cream. OSP $1.85, CMV $47.50 MB.

1956 TOP OF THE MORNING
Red, white, green & silver box holds can of Kwick Foaming shave cream & 2 oz. after shave lotion. OSP $1.59, CMV $37.50 MB.

1954-55 COUNTRY CLUB
Red box holds green can of talc for men, 4 oz. after shaving lotion & tube of brushless or lather shaving cream. OSP $1.85, CMV $50 MB. 1956 Country Club Set came in green box with golf ball & red flag on lid & red lined box. Same contents as 1954 set. OSP $2.19, CMV $50 MB.

1954 SPORT WISE
Red, white & green box holds two 4 oz. bottles of after shave lotions. OSP $1.18, CMV $27.50 MB.

1953 ROUGH 'N' READY
White, red & green box holds 4 oz. cream hair lotion, chap check & Dr. Zabriskie's soap. OSP $1.25, CMV $47.50 MB.

1950 YOUNG MAN SET
Red, white & green box holds tubes of cream hair dress & creme shampoo, comb & nail file in brown leather case. OSP $1.50, CMV $55 MB.

1953 KING PIN
Red & green box holds two 4 oz. bottles of after shave lotion wrapped in green King Pin wrappings. OSP $1.18, CMV $40 MB.

1950-51 HI PODNER
White box holds 2 red leatherette cowboy cuffs with tubes of cream hair dress & ammoniated toothpaste or dental cream and toothbrush. OSP $2.39, CMV $60 MB. 1952 Hi Podner set is same except tube of cream hair dress was replaced with green tube of creme shampoo. CMV $60 MB.

1957 GOOD CHEER
Man playing bass fiddle on green & red box. 2 oz. bottles of cologne, deodorant & after shave lotions. All have red caps. OSP $1.98, CMV $40 MB.

1959-60 LAMPLIGHTER
(Left) Lamp post on covered box. 2 oz. bottle of after shave lotion, 1½ oz. white plastic bottle of spray deodorant for men & 2 oz. black plastic bottle of after shower for men. All have red caps. OSP $3, CMV $45 MB.

1958 AVON GUARD
(Right) Red & blue box holds 2 bottles of hair guard & hand guard with red caps, white Avon rocket soap sits on top of bottles. OSP $1.39, CMV $65 MB.

1959 CAPTAIN OF THE GUARD
White tube, red cap of cream hair dress and white plastic bottle, red cap of spray deodorant for men. OSP $1.98, CMV $37.50.

1957 SAILING, SAILING
4 oz. clear glass, red cap, silver label. Choice of any 2 bottles of after shaving lotion, electric pre-shave lotion or deodorant for men. OSP $2.07, CMV $30 MB.

1958 HAPPY HOURS
Coo-coo clock on black & brown box. 2 oz. cologne, deodorant & after shave lotion. All have red caps. OSP $1.98, CMV $40 MB.

1954-55 PENNY ARCADE
Red & white with center foil mirror, holds tubes of cream hair dress, creme shampoo & chlorophyll toothpaste, toothbrush & chap check. OSP $2.25, CMV $60 MB.

1953-54 TWO SUITER SET
Two different olive tan box with airlines painted on sides. Holds choice of two 2 oz. deodorants for men or one 2 oz. deodorant and 4 oz. after shave or 2 oz. deodorant and 2 oz. cologne for men. Sold at Father's Day. OSP $1.26, CMV $50 MB, light color box - $55 MB, dark color box.

1957 REFRESHING HOURS

Red & green hourglass box holds 4 oz. after shaving lotion & 4 oz. deodorant for men. OSP $1.69, CMV $30 MB.

1959 TRIUMPH

Triumph box holds choice of 5 combinations of two 4 oz. after shave lotions or electric pre-shave lotion & after shave lotion or after shave Lotión & after shower powder for men. OSP each set $1.78, CMV each set $30 MB. Electric pre-shave lotion & after shower for men in black glass, or after shower powder for men & after shower for men in black glass. OSP each set $2.14, CMV $30 MB.

1956 FATHER'S DAY SPECIAL SET NO. 1

Box with sail boat holds two 4 oz. bottles of after shave with silver labels. Also came with choice of 4 oz. after shave and green can of talc for men or 4 oz. deodorant & 4 oz. after shave lotion. OSP $1.39, CMV $35 MB.

1958 MODERN DECOY

Blue & brown box with ducks on lid holds silver Paper Mate Capri pen, 4 oz. cream hair lotion & choice of 4 oz. afer shave lotion, cologne, deodorant or electric pre-shave lotion. OSP $4.50, CMV $37.50 MB.

1959-60 CAROLLERS

Xmas box with red & gold base holds red & black stick deodorant for men & black and white can of after shower powder for men & choice of 4 oz. after shower for men in black glass of electric pre-shave lotion or after shave lotion. OSP $3.75, CMV $50 MB.

1958 STAGE COACH

Yellow stage coach box holds 2 oz. bottles of hair trainer & foamy bath. Both have red caps. OSP 98c, CMV $50 MB.

1957 TRADING POST

Red & brown box holds 2 oz. bottle of foamy bath & hair trainer. Both have red caps. OSP 98c, CMV $52.50 MB.

1955 SPACE SCOUT

Blue box holds wall charts of planets, toothbrush, white toothpaste, bottle of hair guard, tube of antiseptic cream & chap check. OSP $2.25, CMV $50 MB.

1955 SATURDAY NIGHT

Plaid box holds 4 oz. deodorant for men, plaid bow tie & choice of 4 oz. cream or liquid hair lotion. OSP $2.69, CMV $45 MB.

1956 VARSITY

Same set as Saturday Night only name changed. OSP $2.19, CMV $45 MB.

1957 MONEY ISN'T EVERYTHING

Red box with money written all over lid, holds 4 oz. cologne for men, 4 oz. after shave lotion & 2 oz. deodorant for men, plus brown leather billfold. OSP $5.95, CMV $55 MB.

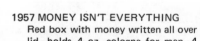

1956 MORE LOVE THAN MONEY
Red, black & gold box holds 4 oz. cologne for men, 4 oz. after shave lotion & 2 oz. deodorant for men. Brown leather wallet with a new 1956 penny in it. OSP $5.95, CMV $47.50 MB.

1955 FLYING HIGH NO. 1 & NO. 2
Red & green box has 4 oz. after shave lotion & 4 oz. deodorant for men. No. 2 box has 4 oz. deodorant for men & green can talc for men. OSP $1.49, CMV $30 each set MB.

1954 PLEASURE CAST NO. 2
(Left) Green & white box holds 4 oz. after shave lotion & green can of talc. OSP $1.25, CMV $32.50 MB.
1954 PLEASURE CAST NO. 1
(Right) Red & white box holds 2 oz. deodorant for men & 4 oz. after shave lotion. OSP $1.25, CMV $32.50 MB.

1955-56 SHAVE BOWL SET
Bronze box holds wood shave bowl & bronze 4 oz. deodorant for men. OSP $2.39, CMV $55 MB.

1955 ROUND THE CORNER
Red & white striped box holds 2 oz. deodorant for men & can of Kwick Foaming shave cream. OSP $1.59, CMV $35 MB.

1956 BEFORE & AFTER
Red & silver box holds 4 oz. electric pre-shave lotion & 4 oz. after shave lotion. OSP $1.59, CMV $27.50 MB.

1954-56 BLACK SHEEP
Red, white, green & black box holds black sheep soap with gold bell on neck & 4 oz. cologne for men & 4 oz. deodorant for men. OSP $2.50, CMV $95 MB.

1957 SEND OFF
Red, white & black box holds two 4 oz. after shave lotions. OSP $1.49, CMV $30 MB.

1957 MERRILY
Red, white & green box holds can of Kwick Foaming shaving cream, 2 oz. deodorant for men & 2 oz. after shave lotion. OSP $1.98, CMV $30 MB.

1955 PLEASURE CAST
Green & white box holds two 4 oz. bottles of after shaving lotion. OSP $1.25, CMV $27.50 MB.

1952-53 U.S. MALE
Green & white mailbox choice of two 4 oz. after shave lotions or 4 oz. after shave lotion & 2 oz. deodorant for men. OSP $1.22, CMV $35 MB.

1957 HOLIDAY HOLLY
Green & white box holds 4 oz. after shave lotion & green can of talc for men. OSP $1.39, CMV $27.50 MB.

1957 NEW DAY
Red top box holds 4 oz. electric pre-shave lotion & 4 oz. after shaving lotion. OSP $1.59, CMV $30 MB.

1951 CLASSIC SET
Green box holds 4 oz. cream hair lotion, tan bar of soap & 2 oz. deodorant. OSP $1.75 set, CMV $55 MB.

1954 CLASSIC SET
Red & white box with horse head on box holds green can of talc for men, 2 oz. deodorant green label, 4 oz. cologne, silver label, all have red caps. Rare. OSP $2.25, CMV $80.

1952-53 AVON CLASSIC
Silver & green box holds 2 oz. deodorant for men, green can talc for men & 4 oz. cologne for men. OSP $2.25, CMV $50 MB.

1957 CUFFLINKS
Black velour covered box holds 2 gold cufflinks and 4 oz. cologne & deodorant for men. OSP $3.50, CMV $47.50 MB.

1956-57 OVERNIGHTER
Brown alligator type bag holds 2 oz. after shaving lotion & 2 oz. deodorant for men, & choice of 4 oz. cream or liquid hair lotion. OSP $2.75, CMV $42.50 MB.

1951 VALET
Green flip open box holds 2 oz. deodorant for men & tube of brushless or lather shaving cream & 4 oz. cream or liquid hair lotion. OSP $2, CMV $45 MB.

1949-50 VALET SET
Green box with choice of green can talc for men or shaving soap & 4 oz. cologne for men. OSP $1.65, CMV $40 MB.

1953 MAN'S SAMPLE CASE
Very rare brown leather case has three partitions inside to hold a Gilette brass razor, ½ oz. green sample tube brushless shaving cream ¾ oz. blue, white & green sample toothpaste tubes, 1 oz. bottle liquid shampoo, green label, 1 oz. bottle cream hair lotion, green label, ½ oz. bottle shaving lotion, green label, ½ oz. bottle deodorant for men, green label, ½ oz. bottle cologne for men. silver label. All bottles have red caps. CMV $125 complete set mint.

1953-54 AVON SERVICE KIT

Green & red box holds tan plastic apron with 4 oz. plastic bottle of after shaving lotion with red cap, tube of brushless shaving cream, shlorophyll toothpaste, Dr. Zabriskie's soap, comb & toothbrush, OSP $3.95, CMV $55 MB.

1958 HAPPY HOURS SUBSTITUTE SET

Outer sleeve marked Happy Hours Sub holds tan vinyl case with 2 oz. cologne, after shave lotion & deodorant. This is a rare set. Factory ran out of regular issue box & used overnighter case for short period. OSP $198, CMV $45 set MB. Must have outer sleeve.

1958 NEAT TRAVELER

Tan soft leather case holds 2 oz. deodorant for men, 4 oz. after shaving lotion choice of Kwick Foaming, lather or brushless shaving cream or electric pre-shave lotion & choice of cream or liquid hair lotion. OSP $8.95, CMV $45 MB.

1951-52 AVON SERVICE KIT

Red & Green box holds canvas apron with 4 oz. plastic bottle of after shaving lotion with red cap, Dr. Zabriskie's soap, tube or brushless shaving cream, toothpaste, toothbrush & comb. OSP $3.90, CMV $55 MB.

1958 OVERNIGHTER

Tan case holds 2 oz. deodorant for men & 2 oz. after shaving lotion & choice of 4 oz. liquid or cream hair lotion. OSP $2.98, CMV $32.50 MB.

1953-55 MEN'S TRAVELING KIT

Choice of brown leatherette or plaid case. Holds 4 oz. after shave lotion, 2 oz. deodorant for men, styptic cream, green can of talc for men and tube of Lather Shaving Cream. OSP $7.50 - CMV $52 MB.

1957 ON THE GO

Brown leatherette bag holds green can of talc for men, 2 oz. deodorant for men, 4 oz. after shave lotion & can of shaving cream in choice of Kwick Foaming lather, brushless or electric pre-shave lotion. OSP $8.95, CMV $45 MB.

1956 THE TRAVELER

Brown leatherette bag holds choice of shaving cream in Kwick, lather or brushless, 4 oz. after shaving lotion, green can talc for men, 2 oz. deodorant for men & styptic cream. OSP $7.95, CMV $50 MB.

1953-56 DELUXE TRIO

Tan leatherette bag holds 2 oz. cologne for men & 2 oz. deodorant for men & choice of 4 oz. cream or liquid hair lotion. Avon on bag. Fold open top, no zipper. OSP $2.25, CMV $45.

MEN'S SETS OF 1960'S

WARNING!! Grading condition is paramount on sets. CMV can vary 50% to 75% on grade. Refer to Page 6 and 16 on Grading Sets.

1965 CHRISTMAS CALL
Red box holds two 4 oz. bottles of Original After Shave Lotion. Red caps. OSP $1.95, CMV $20 MB.

1965 ORIGINAL SET
Horse box holds two 4 oz. bottles of Original after shave with red caps. OSP $1.96, CMV $20 MB.

1960 FIRST PRIZE
Black, gold & red box holds three 2 oz. embossed Stage Coach bottles in choice of after shower for men, 'Vigorate' after shaving lotion, cream hair lotion, deodorant for men, liquid hair lotion, electric pre-shave lotion, after shave for dry or sensitive skin. OSP $2.50, CMV $55 set of 3 MB with outer sleeve.

1966-67 FRAGRANCE CHEST
Brown chest type box holds four 1 oz. bottles with silver caps, of after shave lotion in Tribute, blue glass; Leather in amber glass; Spicy in clear glass; Island Lime in green glass. OSP $4, CMV $40 MB. With outer sleeve $37 as pictured.

1967-68 MEN'S AFTER SHAVE CHOICE
Black box holds 2 oz. after shave lotion in Wild Country with silver cap; Leather with gold cap; & Tribute with blue cap. Late issue set came with all silver or gold caps. OSP $5, CMV $18 MB.

1966-67 BUREAU ORGANIZER
Wood grained plastic tray is 12¼" x 5¼". Came with 2 oz. bottles with black 4A embossed caps in Tribute after shave lotion, Blue Blazer after shave, Spicy after shave & Leather all purpose cologne. OSP $11.95, CMV $50 MB - tray $15.

1965 MEN'S FRAGRANCE WARDROBE
Red box holds three 2 oz. bottles of after shave lotion in choice of Set A: Leather, Blue Blazer, After Shower Cologne; Set B: Leather, Tribute, Spicy; Set C: "4-A", Tribute, Original; or Set D: Spicy, Bay Rum, Original. OSP $3.50 each set, CMV $33 each set boxed with sleeve.

1966 AFTER SHAVE SELECTION
Father's Day box holds three 2 oz. bottles in choice of Leather all purpose lotion for men, Blue Blazer, Island Lime, Tribute, after shave lotion Spicy, Bay Rum, Original & 4A after shave lotions. OSP $2.98, CMV $33 boxed with sleeve.

1968 GENTLEMAN'S COLLECTION
Brown plastic box holds three 2 oz. bottles with gold, silver & bronze caps. Came in Leather, Windjammer & Wild Country cologne. OSP $8, CMV $20 MB.

1966 FOX HUNT
Fox hunt box holds two 4 oz. bottles with black caps in Leather all purpose cologne. OSP $4, CMV $30 MB.

1968 AFTER SHAVE CADDY
6 oz. rectangular bottle with silver cap & top fits in brown plastic box. Came in Leather & Island Lime after shave. OSP $7, CMV $14 MB.

1961 GOLD MEDALLION GIFT SET
Gold box holds three individual men's grooming products in 2 oz. glass or plastic bottles. Glass bottles are: Spicy after shave lotion, Vigorate after shaving lotion, after shaving lotion, after shower lotion, electric pre-shave lotion, liquid hair lotion & deodorant for men. Plastic bottles are: after shave for dry sensitive skin & cream hair lotion. Set of 3 bottles. OSP $2.50, CMV $55 MB with outer sleeve.

1962-63 DELUXE SET FOR MEN
Brown & gold box holds can of deluxe foam shave cream, deluxe after shave, after shower spray & deluxe stick deodorant normal. Box has outer sleeve. OSP $4.98, CMV $45 MB.

1964 CHRISTMAS TRIO FOR MEN
Winter scene box holds three 2 oz. red & white plastic bottles of any three of: Spicy after shave lotion, Original after shave lotion, 'Vigorate' after shave lotion, after shower cologne, Spicy electric pre-shave lotion, liquid deodorant for men, liquid hair lotion, cream hair lotion or hair trainer. OSP $1.98, CMV $22.50 MB.

1969-70 COLOGNE TRILOGY
Brown & gold plastic box holds three 1½ oz. bottles with gold caps & labels in Wild Country, Windjammer & Excalibur cologne. Box is 6'' high. OSP $8, CMV $17.50 MB.

1969 STRUCTURED FOR MEN
Silver box holds black plastic stair step base with 3 oz. bottles of Glass, Wood & Steel cologne. OSP $8.50, CMV $15 in box - bottles & base only $10.

1963 JOLLY HOLLY DAY
Green & white box holds three 2 oz. white plastic bottles with red caps in choice of Vigorate, Spicy & Original after shave lotions, electric pre-shave lotion, liquid or cream hair lotion, hair trainer, after shower cologne for men, & liquid deodorant for men - gentle. OSP $1.98, CMV $22.50 MB.

1965 KING FOR A DAY
Box holds 3 white plastic bottles with red caps in choice of any 3 after shave lotions. Spicy, Original & Vigorate after shave, after shower cologne for men, cream or liquid hair lotion, liquid deodorant for men, electric pre-shave lotion. OSP $1.98, CMV $20 MB.

1967 SMART MOVE

Orange & black box holds three 2 oz. plastic bottles of after shave. Original or Spicy in red, Tribute or Spicy in black. White bottle came in both Original & Spicy. OSP $4, CMV $42.50 MB.

1967 TAG-ALONGS

Box holds 3½ oz. red plastic bottle of after shave lotion Spicy & tan 3 oz. plastic bottle of Squeeze Spray deodorant. Both have black caps. OSP $2.50, CMV $12 MB. Bottles only $3 each.

1961 FOR GENTLEMEN

Black, gold & red box holds 4 oz. plastic cream hair lotion, roll-on deodorant for men, choice of Vigorate or after shower for men in 8 oz. embossed Stage Coach bottle and choice of 6 oz. Kwick foaming shave cream or 4 oz. electric pre-shave lotion. OSP $5.17, CMV $62.50 each set MB, 2 different sets are shown.

1969 THE TRAVELER

Box holds 2 plastic bottles in Bravo or Spicy after shave & spray deodorant. OSP $2.50, CMV $10 MB.

1968 OVERNIGHTER

Black box holds 3 oz. white plastic bottle of Squeeze Spray deodorant & 3½ oz. black plastic bottle of Spicy after shave lotion. OSP $2.50, CMV $10 MB.

1968 BOOTS & SADDLE

Cowhide type box holds 3 oz. bottles of Leather after shave lotion with red cap & Wild Country after shave with black cap. OSP $3., CMV $18. MB.

1963-64 MEN'S TRAVEL KIT

Black leather bag holds can of after shave after shower spray, Spicy, tube of cream hair dress, toothbrush, smokers toothpaste, spray deodorant for men & choice of foam shave cream, Spicy or electric pre-shave lotion. OSP $11.95, CMV $32.50 MB.

1960-61 DASHING SLEIGHS

Black, gold & red box holds 4 oz. plastic bottle of cream hair lotion, can of after shower powder for men, roll-on deodorant for men & choice of Vigorate or after shower for men in 8 oz. embossed stage coach bottle. OSP $5.17, CMV $62.50 MB.

1962 TRAVEL DELUXE SET

Tan plastic bag with front & top zipper. Holds only 2 items, after shave lotion & roll-on deodorant as pictured. Outer sleeve lists only 2 contents. OSP $6.95, CMV $35 MB.

1962-63 UNDER THE MISTLETOE
Green box holds 4 oz. electric pre-shave lotion Spicy & after shave lotion Spicy. Red caps. OSP $1.78, CMV $22.50 MB.

1960-62 OVERNIGHTER
Tan plastic travel case holds after shaving lotion, roll-on deodorant for men & cream hair lotion, cream hair lotion or hair trainer. OSP $1.98, CMV $22.50 MB.

1962-63 GOOD CHEER
Red & gold box holds Spicy talc for men & choice of Spicy or Original after shave lotion. OSP $1.78, CMV $22 MB.

1959-60 TRAVEL DELUXE
Brown soft leather case holds after shave lotion, choice of spray deodorant or roll-on deodorant for men, 4 oz. hair lotion in cream or liquid or Attention & choice of shave cream in Kwick foaming, lather or brushless or electric pre-shave lotion. OSP $9.95, CMV $35 MB.

1962-63 CHRISTMAS CLASSIC
Blue box holds choice of two 4 oz. bottles of 'Vigorate' after shave lotion, after shower cologne for men, original after shave lotion. OSP $1.79, CMV $22.50 MB.

1964 HOLIDAY GREETINGS
Gold box holds 4 oz. bottle of electric pre-shave lotion Spicy & after shave lotion Spicy. OSP $1.78, CMV $22 MB.

1962-63 HOLLY TIME
Red, white & green box holds choice of 2 plastic bottles in cream hair lotion or liquid hair lotion in glass bottle. OSP $1.78, CMV $22.50 MB.

1964 HOLLY STAR
Red, white & green box holds 4 oz. after shave lotion, Spicy & 3 oz. talc for men, Spicy. OSP $1.59, CMV $22 MB.

1966 MEN'S TRAVEL KIT
Brown travel bag holds smoker's toothpaste, clear hair dress, Spicy after shave lotion, Spicy talc for men, aerosol deodorant & choice of electric pre-shave lotion or foam shave cream in regular or mentholated. OSP $12.95, CMV $30 MB.

1964 Only SANTA'S TEAM
Blue box holds 4 oz. each of after shave lotion Spicy & liquid deodorant for men. OSP $1.59, CMV $22 MB.

1962-63 CHRISTMAS DAY
Partridge box holds 4 oz. liquid deodorant for men - gentle & choice of Spicy or Original after shave lotion. OSP $1.78, CMV $22 MB.

1964 CHRISTMAS MORNING
Red & gold box holds two 4 oz. bottles of after shave lotion Spicy. OSP $1.78, CMV $22 MB.

1979 FRAGRANCE GIFT SET FOR MEN
Box holds choice of After Shave in plastic bottles in Cool Sage, Brisk Spice, or Light Musk or the same fragrance in cologne in glass bottles & matching talc. SSP $4, cologne set glass. CMV $4 MB, SSP $3 plastic, CMV $3 MB.

MEN'S SETS OF 1970'S

WARNING!! Grading condition is paramount on sets. CMV can vary 50% to 75% on grade. Refer to Page 6 and 16 on Grading Sets.

1971 Only — COLLECTORS ORGANIZER
Plastic brown duck holds two 3 oz. bottles of Cologne & After Shave. Tai Winds & Wild Country. Painted duck design on bottles & gold caps. 1 yellow bar of duck soap. OSP $25, CMV $27.50 MB.

1973 WHALE ORGANIZER
Brown plastic whale holds 2-3 oz. ivory milk glass bottles and 5 oz. bar of soap. Came in Blend 7 or Deep Woods After Shave and Cologne. SSP $27, CMV $30 MB.

1972 AMERICAN EAGLE BUREAU ORGANIZER
Plastic case, wood carved like finish. Case holds 2 clear glass bottles with embossed eagles & a 5 oz. bar of soap. The bottles hold 3 oz. One has cologne and one after shave. Came in Deep Woods or Tai Winds. SSP $20, CMV $25 MB.

1978 WILD MALLARD
Brown and green ceramic organizer and white Clint Soap On A Roap. Bottom says "Made in Brazil for Avon, May 1978". SSP $20, CMV $16 - $20 MB. Also came no date.

1970 MASTER ORGANIZER
Wood grained plastic flip open box, holds choice of 3½ oz. Cologne or After Shave in Oland with tan bar of soap or Excalibur with blue bar of soap. OSP $25, CMV $32.50 MB.

1974-75 TRAVEL SET FOR MEN
Brown box holds 3 oz. white plastic bottle with white cap. Choice of Deep Woods, Wild Country, Oland or Spicy After Shave and 1.5 oz. brown plastic bottle, white cap of Talc in choice of same fragrances. Short issue OSP $4, CMV $5 MB.

SEE 1984 SUPPLEMENT IN BACK OF THIS BOOK FOR MORE 1980's SETS.

MEN'S SETS OF 1980'S

1981 TRAVELER GIFT SET
Green and red box with deer, holds 1.5 oz. deer decor Talc and 2 oz. plastic After Shave in own box, in choice of Weekend, Wild Country, Black Suede. SSP $5, CMV $5 MB set.

1981 BUCKAROO GIFT SET FOR BOYS
Brown leather look box holds 2 oz. Buckaroo Talc and matching tan 2 oz. plastic bottle of Buckaroo Cologne for Boys. SSP $5, CMV $5 MB set.

1981 NATURALS AFTER SHAVE & SOAP SET
Wood look box holds 3 oz. plastic bottle and bar of soap to match box. Choice of Crisp Lime, Brisk Spice, Light Musk. SSP $4 MB, CMV $4 MB.

1980 MEN'S FRAGRANCE DUO SET
Brown box holds choice of 5 oz. After Shave and 1½ oz. Talc in Wild Country, Trazarra, Weekend or Clint. SSP $6, CMV $6 MB each set.

1980-81 NATURALS AFTER SHAVE SAMPLER SET
Box holds 3 plastic bottles of Brisk Spice, Crisp Lime and Light Musk After Shave. SSP $9, CMV $9 MB.

APPLE BLOSSOM

1974-77 APPLE BLOSSOM AFTER BATH FRESHENER
8 oz. pink plastic, pink cap. OSP $3, CMV 50c

1974-76 APPLE BLOSSOM PERFUMED POWDER MIST
7 oz. white and pink can with pink lid. OSP $3, CMV 50c, with upside down label, CMV $8.

1974-76 APPLE BLOSSOM COLOGNE MIST
2 oz. clear bottle with clear cap has inner pink and white cap. OSP $3, CMV 50c.

1974-76 APPLE BLOSSOM COLOGNE GELLE
3 oz. clear glass pink and white cap. OSP $3, CMV 50c.

1974-78 APPLE BLOSSOM CREAM SACHET
.66 oz. clear glass, pink and white cap. OSP $1.25, CMV 25c.

1974-78 APPLE BLOSSOM PERFUME DEMI STICK
.19 oz. pink and white. OSP $1.25, CMV 25c.

1974-78 APPLE BLOSSOM FRAGRANCE SAMPLES
10 foil packets per box. CMV 25c.

1941-42 APPLE BLOSSOM PERFUME
1/8 oz. gold cap. OSP 75c, CMV in box $45, $27.50 BO. This bottle has two different gold labels and round or flat top caps.

1941-43 APPLE BLOSSOM COLOGNE
6 oz. bubble sided bottle with pink cap. OSP $1, CMV $45 BO, $60 MB.

1941-42 APPLE BLOSSOM TOILET WATER
2 oz. pink, white and blue. OSP $1.04, CMV $30 BO, $40 MB.

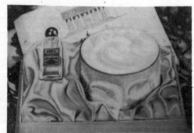

1941-43 APPLE BLOSSOM PERFUME
Box holds 1/8 oz. bottle with gold cap and label. OSP 75c, CMV $27.50 BO mint, $40 MB as shown.

1925 APPLE BLOSSOM COMPLEXION SOAP
Yellow and pink wrapping on 3 bars of soap. OSP 69c, CMV $80 MB.

1946 APPLE BLOSSOM BEAUTY DUST
Special short issue box holds regular issue beauty dust. OSP $1.10, CMV $25 MB as shown.

1941-42 COLONIAL SET
Satin lined box holds Apple Blossom Perfume with gold cap and blue feather box of Face Powder. OSP $1.35, CMV $80 MB. Also came with perfume on right side of box.

1942-43 APPLE BLOSSOM MOTHERS DAY BEAUTY DUST
Special issue blue, pink and white lace design box. Holds feather design Apple Blossom beauty dust. Sold at Mothers Day only in this special box. OSP $1.10, CMV $30 MB as shown.

1941-44 APPLE BLOSSOM BODY POWDER
Blue feather design, flat sifter top container in special issue box as shown. OSP 65c, CMV $25 MB as shown. Can only $22.50 mint.

1941-48 APPLE BLOSSOM BEAUTY DUST
6 oz. size blue and white feather design paper container. OSP $1.10, CMV $18 mint. The Feather Plume outer box shown was issued Christmas 1942 only. Add $7 for this box.

1941-48 APPLE BLOSSOM BEAUTY DUST
6 oz. blue and white paper box. OSP $1.10, CMV $20 MB. $15 for Beauty Dust only mint.

1943-45 APPLE BLOSSOM BEAUTY DUST
Blue and white feather design paper box. OSP $1.10, CMV $35 mint. $40 MB. Outer box pictured in 1943 Christmas issue only. This is rare. CMV $45 MB as shown.

1943 FLOWERTIME SET
Green satin lined box with flower carts on lid. Holds 6 oz. Apple Blossom cologne and Apple Blossom Body Powder. OSP $1.65, CMV $90.

1943-44 PETAL OF BEAUTY
Blue flowered box, pink satin lining, holds 6 oz. Apple Blossom cologne, pink cap and blue feathered Apple Blossom Beauty Dust. OSP $2.20, CMV $100 MB.

1941 BLUE BIRD SET WITH PERFUME
Blue satin lined box holds Apple Blossom Perfume and Apple Blossom Body Powder with blue feather box of Face Powder. OSP $1.65, CMV $90 MB.

1941 BLUE BIRD SET WITH LIPSTICK
Satin lined box holds Apple Blossom, Body Powder, blue feather box of Face Powder and turquoise and gold lipstick. OSP $2.25, CMV $70 MB.

ARIANE

1977-80 ARIANE PRODUCTS SATIN BEAUTY DUST
Red plastic with silver rim. OSP $8.50, CMV $2.

1977-80 PERFUME
.25 oz. glass stopper sealed in plastic. Came in red velvet bag in red box. OSP $15, CMV $10 MB in bag.

1977-80 ULTRA COLOGNE SPRAY
1.8 oz. clear glass bottle, red and silver cap. Red box. First Edition bottle was sold 2 campaigns only. Never pictured in Avon catalog. Regular issue does not say 1st edition. OSP $7.50, CMV 50c regular issue. 1st Edition bottle CMV $5 MB. Rare issue came with 1st Edition marked on backside. CMV not established.

1977-80 ARIANE ULTRA COLOGNE SAMPLE
Small sample packet came 10 to a box for 35c. OSP, CMV 10c each packet. 2 oz. bottle, CMV 50c.

1977 ARIANE "INCH" NECKLACE
Silver container holds small vial of Ariane cologne. 3 different ones, came in red velvet bag, 1 for Avon Reps with black pull cord on bag. CMV $15 in bag. 1 for President's Club members with PC on back of necklace and silver pull cord, CMV $20 in bag. 1 for Managers, sterling silver, back side says "August Conference", has red pull cord, CMV $50 in bag.

1977-80 ARIANE SOLID PERFUME COMPACT
Red and silver box holds red and silver plastic compact. OSP $3.75, CMV 50c.

1977 ARIANE FRAGRANCE SAMPLE
Red and silver packet holds small vial of cologne. Came with introduction sheet. Used by Reps only. Marked "Not for Resale". CMV 50c.

PERFUMED SKIN SOFTENER
5 oz., CMV 50c.

ULTRA SOFT BODY SATIN
6 oz., CMV 50c.

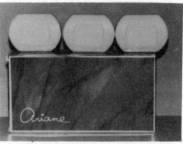

1978 ARIANE PERFUMED SOAPS
Red box holds 3 white soaps. SSP $5, CMV $5 MB.

1977 ARIANE ADDRESS BOOK
Red velvet booklet with note pad and address book. Chrome pen has no markings. Given to team leaders. CMV $6.

1978 ARIANE ULTRA CREME PERFUME
.66 oz. glass jar, silver cap. OSP $4.50, CMV 50c.

1978 ARIANE SATIN PERFUMED TALC
3.5 oz. red and silver container. OSP $3, CMV 50c.

ATTENTION

1942 Only - ATTENTION TOILET WATER
Special issue Christmas box holds 2 oz. Attention Toilet Water with purple cap and label. OSP 25c, CMV $45 MB as shown, $30 BO.

1942 Only — ATTENTION TOILET WATER

(Left) 2 oz. purple cap. OSP 25c, CMV $40 BO, $45 MB.

1943-46 ATTENTION TOILET WATER

(Right) 2 oz. bottle, came with gold ribbed cap or plastic cap. OSP $1.04, CMV $25 BO mint, $35 MB.

1942 ATTENTION SACHET CHRISTMAS BOX

1¼ oz. bottle with turquoise cap sold 1942-48. Regular issue box in Misc. Powder Sachet section. The box pictured here is special issue for Christmas. OSP 25c, CMV $18 MB as shown. $12 BO mint.

1941-43 ATTENTION BODY POWDER

Pink box, flat sifter top on paper container. OSP 65c, CMV $25 MB, can only $20 mint.

1943-47 ATTENTION COLOGNE

6 oz. bubble sided bottle with pink tall or short cap. OSP $1.50, CMV $50 BO, $65 MB.

1942 ATTENTION SACHET

Special 1st issue blue box as shown. 1¼ oz. bottle, turquoise cap. OSP $1.04, CMV $20 MB as shown in this box. See Misc. Powder Sachet section for further details, on regular issue bottles and box.

1943 ATTENTION SACHET 57th ANNIVERSARY BOX

Special issue purple and pink box with flowers. Holds regular issue Attention powder sachet. Sold for 25c, to celebrate Avons 57th Anniversary. CMV $20 as shown, MB.

1943-44, then 46-48 ATTENTION BATH SALTS

Tulip "A" box holds 9 oz. or 8½ oz. glass jar with turquoise lid. OSP 63c, CMV $25 MB, $15 BO mint.

1943-45 PINK RIBBON SET

Blue and pink box holds blue and pink can of Attention Body Powder and paper box of Attention Bath Salts. OSP $1.61, CMV $65 for set in box.

1943-45 ATTENTION BODY POWDER

Blue and pink cardboard container. Came in Pink Ribbon set only. CMV $25.

1943-45 ATTENTION BATH SALTS

9 oz. blue and pink cardboard container. Came in Pink Ribbon set only. CMV $25.

1943-47 ATTENTION BODY POWDER

Blue and white cardboard with feather design. OSP 65c, CMV $25 MB, container only $20 mint.

128

1943-45 FLOWERTIME SET

Box holds 6 oz. Attention cologne and Attention Body Powder. OSP $1.65, 1943 set is green satin lined box with flower carts on lid. CMV $90 MB. 1944 set in plain box with flower design on lid. CMV $90 MB. 1945 set in white box with boy and girl in 1700 style dress under a tree. CMV $90.

1943 Only SCENTIMENTS

2 oz. clear bottle toilet water, gold foil label, white cap or gold cap. White and pink satin sachet pillows. OSP $1.85, CMV $70 MB.

1944 FLOWERTIME SET

Box with flowers on lid holds 6 oz. Attention cologne and Attention body powder. OSP $1.65, CMV $85 MB.

AVON COLOGNE

1941 AVON COLOGNE

6 oz. flat sided bottle. Soon after Avon Cologne was introduced, the name was changed to Orchard Blossoms Cologne. OSP 60c, CMV $50 BO, $65 MB.

1943 AVON COLOGNE' REPRESENTATIVE GIFT

6 oz. clear bottle, maroon and gold label, blue cap. Bottom label reads "This is a gift to our representatives and must not be offered for sale." Came in blue and pink box, pink ribbon on box and bottle. 57th Anniversary Campaign card. CMV bottle only $100 mint, $150 MB as shown.

1945 Only — SCENTIMENTS

Box holds 6 oz. Attention Cologne and 2 satin sachet pillows. OSP $2.50, CMV $90 MB.

AVONSHIRE BLUE

1975-76 AVONSHIRE BLUE BRUSH & COMB

Blue and white plastic. SSP $4, CMV $4 MB.

1975-76 AVONSHIRE BLUE VANITY MIRROR

9½" long blue and white plastic. Avon on handle. SSP $3, CMV $3 MB.

1971-74 AVONSHIRE BLUE
Wedgewood blue and white over clear glass

COLOGNE DECANTER
6 oz. Comes in Field Flowers, Brocade, Elusive, Charisma. SSP $5, CMV $6 MB - $3 BO.

PERFUME CANDLE
Holds Patchwork, Sonnet, Moonwind, Bird of Paradise, Charisma, Wassail, Roses Roses, Bayberry, Frankincense & Myrrh. SSP $8, CMV $8 MB, $6 CO.

BATH OIL DECANTER
6 oz. holds Skin So Soft or Field Flowers, Bird of Paradise. SSP $6, CMV $6 MB, $4 BO.

SOAP
3 bars, 2 oz. blue soap. SSP $2, CMV $6 MB.

1972 AVONSHIRE BLUE SOAP DISH & SOAP
6" long blue dish trimmed in white with white bar of soap. Came with oval soap and round soap. OSP $4.50, CMV $8 oval, $23 round soap MB.

BABY PRODUCTS
SEE 1984 SUPPLEMENT IN BACK OF THIS BOOK
FOR MORE BABY ITEMS

1961-64 BABY CREAM
2 oz. blue and white tube. OSP 89c, CMV $4.

1961-64 BABY SOAP
Blue and white wrapper. OSP 39c, CMV $8.

1959-64 TOT 'N TYKE BABY SHAMPOO
6 oz. white plastic bottle, blue cap. OSP 98c, CMV $6 BO, $7 MB.

1958-64 BABY LOTION
6 oz. white plastic bottle, blue cap. OSP 98c, CMV $5.

1960-64 BABY OIL
6 oz. white plastic bottle, blue cap. OSP 98c, CMV $6.

1955-64 BABY POWDER
9 oz. blue and white can. OSP 79c, CMV $10.

1951-55 BABY TALC
Blue and white box and can. OSP 52c, CMV $18 in box, $13 can only.

1951-55 LANOLIN BABY SOAP
Blue and white box and wrapping, holds 2 bars. OSP 69c, CMV $25 in box.

1951-55 BABY LOTION
4 oz. white plastic bottle, blue cap. OSP $1, CMV $12 in box, bottle only $8.

1954-56 BABY POWDER
2 oz. pink can and cap with paper label around can. Came in Little Lamb set. Rare. CMV $25.

1954-56 BABY POWDER
2 oz. blue, white and pink can, pink cap. Came in Little Lamb set. CMV $20.

1955-60 BABY OIL
8 oz. bottle with indented sides, white cap. OSP 79c, CMV $15.

1955-57 BABY LOTION
8 oz. bottle with indented sides, white cap. OSP 89c, CMV $12.50 BO, $15 MB.

1957-58 BABY & ME SET
Clear glass bottle baby lotion, white cap and Cotillion Toilet Water gold cap, pink paper around neck. Box white, blue and pink. OSP $1.98, CMV $45 MB.

1962-64 SWEETEST ONE BABY SET
Pink and white box holds 1 bar Baby Soap, Baby Powder and Lotion or Oil. Bar of soap came with blue ends, white center and white ends with blue center. OSP $2.07, CMV $40 MB.

1966 TREE TOTS SET
Box holds white plastic hair bursh, 3 oz. plastic tube Non-Tear Gel Shampoo, 3 oz. Baby Soap with Lanolin and 6 oz. Nursery Fresh Room Spray. OSP $3, CMV $20 MB.

1959-64 TOT 'N TYKE BABY SHAMPOO
Special issue box as shown. CMV $12 MB as show.

1968-75 BABY PRODUCTS
1969-74 SHAMPOO
Blue, white and pink, 6 oz. plastic bottle. OSP 98c, CMV $1.
1968-79 NURSERY FRESH ROOM SPRAY
6 oz. blue, white and pink can. OSP $1.50, CMV $1.50. Also came with upside-down label, CMV $8.
1969-72 BABY POWDER
9 oz. blue, white and pink plastic bottle. OSP 98c, CMV $2.
1969-75 BABY CREAM
2 oz. tube, blue, pink and white. OSP 98c, CMV $1.
1969-75 BABY SOAP
3 oz. bar wrapped in blue, pink and white paper. OSP 59c, CMV $2.
1969-75 BABY LOTION
6 oz. blue, white and pink plastic bottle. OSP 98c, CMV $1.

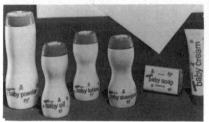

1964-68 BABY SHAMPOO
6 oz. white plastic bottle with blue cap. OSP 98c, CMV $5.
1964-68 BABY LOTION
6 oz. white plastic bottle with blue cap. OSP 98c, CMV $5.
1964-68 BABY CREAM
2 oz. blue and white tube with blue cap. OSP 98c, CMV $3.
1964-68 BABY POWDER
9 oz. white plastic bottle, blue cap. OSP 98c, CMV $5.
1964-66 BABY OIL
6 oz. white plastic bottle with blue cap. OSP 98c, CMV $6.
1964-68 TOT 'N TYKE BABY SOAP
Blue and white wrapper, white cake of baby soap. OSP 39c, CMV $7.

1915 C.P.C. BABY BOOK
CMV $30 mint.

1946-50 LANOLIN BABY SOAP
Pink box holds 2 wrapped bars. OSP 86c - CMV $45 MB, $20 each. bar.

1955-61 BABY SOAP
Blue and white box holds Castile & Lanolin white cake baby soap. OSP 29c, CMV $12 MB. Also came with "Castile with Lanolin" on box and printed on soap horizontally. Same CMV.

1962-64 BABY SOAP
Came in Sweetest One baby set. White ends and blue center line. CMV $8 mint.

BALLAD

1964-68 BABY LOTION SAMPLES
White foil with pink and blue design. Came 10 to a box. CMV $6 box or 50c per sample.

1945 BALLAD AWARD PERFUME
Avon label on bottom, Ballad label across top, glass stopper. CMV $375 mint box.

1939-45 BALLAD PERFUME
3 dram glass stoppered bottle with gold neck cord and gold label at base of bottle. Front of box lays down. OSP $3.50, CMV $130 in box. Bottle only $90. See misc. perfume for 1 dram Ballad Perfume.

1981-82 BABY LOTION REFILL
9.5 oz. plastic, blue cap. SSP $3.50, CMV $1, no box.

1945-53 BALLAD PERFUME
Gold and white box holds 3 dram glass stoppered bottle with gold neck cord and gold label at base of bottle. OSP $3.50, CMV $130 in box. $90 bottle only.

1945 Only — BALLAD PERFUME
3 dram, clear glass with gold neck cord and label, box gray, white and gold. OSP $3.50, CMV $135 in this box. $90 bottle only.

BIRD OF PARADISE

1973-76 BABY BRUSH & COMB SET
Yellow box holds small yellow plastic brush and comb. Avon on both. OSP $3.50, CMV $3.50 MB.

1970-76 BIRD OF PARADISE PERFUME ROLLETTE
1/3 oz. bottle with gold cap, turquoise and green box. OSP $3, CMV $1 MB.
1970-72 BIRD OF PARADISE COLOGNE DECANTER
8" high 5 oz. clear glass with gold head. OSP $6, CMV $4 BO, $6 MB.

1970-71 BIRD OF PARADISE BATH BRUSH & SOAP
Blue box holds blue plastic bath brush and blue soap. OSP $6, CMV $8 MB.

1969-75 BIRD OF PARADISE BATH OIL EMOLLIENT
6 oz. gold cap and neck tag. OSP $7.50, CMV $1.

1969-72 BIRD OF PARADISE 4 OZ. COLOGNE
4 oz. gold cap & neck tag. OSP $5, CMV $2.

1969-74 BIRD OF PARADISE BEAUTY DUST
6 oz. turquoise and gold paper box. OSP $5, CMV $3, $5 MB.

1970-76 BIRD OF PARADISE COLOGNE MIST
3 oz. blue plastic coated bottle with gold cap and neck tag. OSP $7, CMV $1.

1969-75 BIRD OF PARADISE CREAM SACHET
.66 oz. blue glass with gold lid. OSP $3, CMV 50c.

1970-76 BIRD OF PARADISE SOAP
3 oz. bars blue soap in blue & turquoise box. 1st issue no flower on soap. 1972 soap had flower. SSP $3, CMV $4 MB, no flowers $6 MB.

1973-76 BIRD OF PARADISE PERFUMED SKIN SOFTENER
5 oz. blue plastic jar, gold and blue lid. OSP $3, CMV 25c.

1975-75 BIRD OF PARADISE SOAP
3 oz. blue bar with blue wrapper and floral center. OSP $1, CMV $1 mint.

1976-78 BIRD OF PARADISE SOAP
3 oz. blue bar with blue wrapper. OSP $1, CMV $1 mint.

1977-78 BIRD OF PARADISE FOAMING BATH OIL
6 oz. blue plastic bottle and cap. OSP $7.50, CMV 50c.

1976-78 BIRD OF PARADISE CREAM SACHET
.66 oz. clear glass bottom, blue and gold cap. OSP $3, CMV 50c.

1970-72 BIRD OF PARADISE PERFUME GLACE RING
(Left) Gold ring with turquoise top. Perfume glace inside. OSP $10, CMV $7.

1970-72 BIRD OF PARADISE ½ OZ. COLOGNE
(Right) ½ oz. bottle with gold cap. OSP $2, CMV $2 MB.

1971-78 BIRD OF PARADISE PERFUMED TALC
2 different labels. Left and center same labels but top is turquoise on one and dark blue on other. One on right is dark blue label and top. Each is 3½ oz. size. OSP $1.35, CMV 50c. Also came with upside down label, CMV $8.

1971-73 BIRD OF PARADISE PERFUMED SKIN SOFTENER
(Left) 5 oz. blue glass jar with blue & gold lid. OSP $4, CMV $1.

1969-72 BIRD OF PARADISE COLOGNE FLUFF
(Center) 3 oz. blue plastic coated bottle with gold top. Blue & gold neck tag. OSP $5, CMV $2.

1971-77 BIRD OF PARADISE PERFUMED POWDER MIST
(Right) 7 oz. blue and gold can, gold cap. OSP $4, CMV 50c.

1970-78 BIRD OF PARADISE SAMPLES
(Left) Bottle has white cap, blue foil envelopes. CMV 25c each.

1970-78 BIRD OF PARADISE DEMI-STICK
(Inside Left) .19 oz. solid perfume, white cap. OSP $2, CMV 50c.

1971-76 BIRD OF PARADISE EMOLLIENT MIST
(Inside Right) 4 oz. blue & turquoise can with turquoise cap. OSP $4, CMV 50c.

1972-76 BIRD OF PARADISE HAND & BODY LOTION
(Right) 8 oz. & 16 oz. turquoise plastic bottle & cap. OSP $3.50 & $6, CMV 50c each.

1971-72 BIRD OF PARADISE SCENTED HAIR SPRAY
(Left) 7 oz. blue can & lid. OSP $1.50, CMV $3.

1971-74 FOAMING BATH OIL
(Right) 6 oz. blue plastic bottle with gold cap and blue & gold neck tag. OSP $4, CMV $2.

BIRD OF PARADISE ORDER BOOK COVERS

(Left) Canadian. Presidents Club earned for eligibility into Presidents Club. Honor Award earned for sales goal. Each came with pen in matching design. CMV $5 each with pen.

1970 BIRD OF PARADISE ORDER BOOK COVER

Blue & turquoise, awarded for qualifying for Presidents Club, has matching pen. CMV $7.50.

1970 BIRD OF PARADISE SCARF

Awarded for selling cologne mists. Blue and turquoise silk. CMV $10.

1970 BIRD OF PARADISE AVON AWARDS

Gold pin, bracelet and earrings with turquoise stones. CMV pin $12, bracelet and earrings $20 MB.

1970 BIRD OF PARADISE ROBE

Blue terry cloth robe given to Reps for selling 24 Bird of Paradise 3 oz. cologne mists in C-19-1970. Came in S-M-L sizes. Bird of Paradise on pocket. CMV $35.

BLUE LOTUS

BRISTOL BLUE

1975 BRISTOL BLUE COLOGNE

5 oz. translucent blue glass filled with Moonwind, Sonnet or Imperial Garden Cologne. OSP $6, CMV $4 BO, $5 MB.

1975-76 BRISTOL BLUE BATH OIL

5 oz. blue opaline glass decanter with plastic inner bottle that holds Skin So Soft bath oil. OSP $6, CMV $4 BO, $5 MB.

1975-76 BRISTOL BLUE SOAP DISH & SOAP'

Translucent blue opaline glass dish with Moonwind, Sonnet or Imperial Garden soap. OSP $5, CMV $6 MB.

1967-72 BLUE LOTUS AFTER BATH FRESHENER

6 oz. glass bottle with blue cap. OSP $3, CMV $2.

1968-72 BLUE LOTUS CREAM SACHET

.66 oz. blue frosted glass with blue cap. OSP $2.50, CMV $1.

1970-73 BLUE LOTUS FOAMING BATH OIL

6 oz. plastic bottle with blue cap. OSP $3.50, CMV $1.50.

1969-72 BLUE LOTUS CREAM LOTION

5 oz. plastic bottle with blue cap OSP $2, CMV $1.50.

1969-73 BLUE LOTUS DEMI STICK

.19 oz. white plastic with blue and green center. OSP $1, CMV $1.

1967-71 BLUE LOTUS PERFUME SOAP

3 oz. blue, white and purple wrapper. OSP 75c, CMV $2.

1967-71 BLUE LOTUS PERFUMED TALC

3½ oz. cardboard container with plastic shaker top. OSP $1.10, CMV $2.

1967-71 BLUE LOTUS AFTER BATH FRESHENER SAMPLES

Box holds 10 samples. CMV $1.50 per box.

BRIGHT NIGHT

1959-61 BRIGHT NIGHT BEAUTY DUST
White plastic box with gold stars on lid. OSP $2.95, CMV $8 CO, $12 MB.

1954-61 BRIGHT NIGHT COLOGNE
4 oz. gold speckled cap with gold neck cord and white paper label. OSP $2.50, CMV $20 MB, $14 BO mint.

1955-61 BRIGHT NIGHT TOILET WATER
2 oz. gold speckled cap with white paper label on gold neck cord. OSP $2, CMV $20 MB, $14 BO.

1958-61 BRIGHT NIGHT COLOGNE MIST
3 oz. white plastic coated over clear glass. Gold speckled cap, gold neck cord with white paper label. Came with 2 different caps. OSP $2.75, CMV $20 in box. $14 bottle only mint.

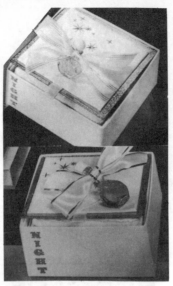

1957-58 BRIGHT NIGHT BEAUTY DUST
(Top) White cardboard box trimmed in gold. Came at Christmas with 5/8 dram Snowflake Perfume bottle with white ribbon and cap. OSP $2.50, CMV $30 MB.

1956 BRIGHT NIGHT BEAUTY DUST
(Bottom) Same as above. Came at Christmas 1956 with long neck perfume bottle with white cap and ribbon. OSP $2.50, CMV $30 MB.

1954-59 BRIGHT NIGHT BEAUTY DUST
Same powder box without perfume. OSP 75c, CMV $18 mint.

1955-61 BRIGHT NIGHT POWDER SACHET
(Left) .9 oz. 1¼, 1½ oz. white glass jar with stars on white lid. Front paper label. OSP $1.50, CMV $8 BO - $12 MB. 1½ oz. rare, CMV $20 MB - $16 BO.

1954-61 BRIGHT NIGHT CREAM SACHET
(Right) White glass jar with stars on white lid. OSP $1.50, CMV $6 MB - $8.

1957 GOLDEN BEAUTY
Gold base box lined with gold acetate with gold plastic lid, holds Bright Night Beauty Dust, 4 oz. cologne, cream sachet and 1 dram perfume. OSP $8.95, CMV $85.

1954-59 BRIGHT NIGHT PERFUME
Gold and white box holds ½ oz. glass stoppered bottle with white label on gold neck cord. OSP $7.50, CMV $120 MB. Bottle only $75 mint. Also came with 1 dram perfume in felt wrapper on top of lid. Add $15 for 1 dram perfume with ribbon around box.

1957 BRIGHT NIGHT GEMS
Gold & white flip open box holds Bright Night 2 oz. toilet water in top & cream sachet in pull-out drawer in bottom. OSP $3.50, CMV $45 mint.

1956 MAGIC HOURS
Gold & white box holds Bright Night 2 oz. toilet water & white cologne stick. OSP $3.50, CMV $45.

1955-56 MELODY
Gold & white box holds Bright Night 1 dram perfume, cream sachet, 4 oz. cologne & beauty dust. OSP $8.75, CMV $85.

1958 GOLDEN GLAMOR
Gold & white box holds Bright Night cologne mist, 1 dram perfume, cream sachet & beauty dust. OSP $8.95, CMV $95 MB.

BROCADE

1968-70 BROCADE COLOGNE SILK
(Left) 3 oz. frosted bottle with gold cap. OSP $4.50, CMV $2 MB - $4.50.

1968-72 BROCADE FOAMING BATH OIL
(Right) 6 oz. plastic bottle with gold cap. OSP $4, CMV $2.

1969-72 BROCADE PERFUMED TALC
(Left) 3½ oz. brown & white cardboard. OSP $1.25, CMV $1.50.

1969-72 SCENTED HAIR SPRAY
(Right) 7 oz. brown & white can. OSP $1.50, CMV $3.

1967-72 BROCADE 4 OZ. COLOGNE
(Left) Frosted ribbed glass with brown & white cap. OSP $6, CMV $2 - MB $3.

1967-72 BROCADE COLOGNE MIST
(Center) 3 oz. ribbed frosted glass with brown & white cap. Some lids have design only & some say Brocade on top. OSP $6, CMV $2 BO - $3 MB.

1967-72 BROCADE COLOGNE MIST REFILL
(Right) 3 oz. brown plastic coated bottle, white cap. OSP $4, CMV $3 BO - $4 MB.

1967-72 BROCADE PERFUME GLACE
Gold case. OSP $5.50, CMV $6 - MB $9.

1967-71 BROCADE BEAUTY DUST
(Left) Brown ribbed plastic, patterned lid. OSP $6, CMV $6 - MB $9.

1971-75 BROCADE BEAUTY DUST
(Right) Pattern printed cardboard, non-refillable. OSP $5, CMV $4 CO - $5 MB. Also came with upside down lettering. CMV $6.

1968-75 BROCADE CREAM SACHET
(Left) .66 oz. brown ribbed glass, designed cap. OSP $3, CMV 50c.

1967-68 BROCADE CREAM SACHET
(Center) .66 oz. brown ribbed glass, label on top. OSP $3, CMV $2 BO - $3 MB.

1968 BROCADE TALC
(Right) 2¾ oz. metal talc, brown, white and gold. Sold only in Perfume Pair set. CMV $2.

1969-72 BROCADE PERFUMED SKIN SOFTENER
(Left) 5 oz. ribbed sides, brown glass, designed top. OSP $4, CMV $2 BO - $3 MB.

1968-69 BROCADE PERFUMED SKIN SOFTENER
(Center) 5 oz. ribbed sides, brown glass, label printed on top. OSP $4, CMV $5 MB - $3 BO.

1968 only BROCADE PERFUMED SKIN SOFTENER
(Right) Manufactured during glass strike, 5 oz. round smooth brown glass, label painted on top. OSP $4, CMV $15 mint.

1969 MANAGER'S BROCADE DEMO KIT
Brocade box holds round Brocade talc & cologne mist. CMV $27.50 MB.

1968 BROCADE SOAP
Brown & white wrapper. Came in Perfume Pair only. CMV $4 mint.

1967 BROCADE DELUXE GIFT SET
Brown & white box with white lining holds Brocade beauty dust, perfume rollette & cream sachet. OSP $12.95, CMV $35 MB.

1967-74 BROCADE PERFUME POWDER MIST
(Left) 7 oz. brown & white painted can with gold cap. OSP $4, CMV 50c.
(Right) 7 oz. brown & white paper label with gold cap. OSP $4, CMV $3. Some came with 7 oz. weight in center label and some at bottom of can in front.

1967-69 BROCADE PERFUME OIL
(Left) ½ oz. frosted brown glass with gold cap. OSP $6, CMV $5 - MB $7.

1970-71 BROCADE ½ OZ. COLOGNE
(Right) Ribbed clear glass with gold cap. OSP $2, CMV $2 MB - $1 BO.

1967-72 BROCADE PERFUME ROLLETTE
(Left) Brown frosted glass, gold cap with 4A design. Ribs horizontal. OSP $3, CMV $3.
(Inside Left) Same as above only no 4A design. OSP $3, CMV $3.
(Inside Right) Brown carnival glass, gold cap. Vertical ribs. OSP $3, CMV $8.
(Right) Brown frosted glass, brown & white paper band on cap. Ribs horizontal. OSP $3, CMV $5.

BUTTONS 'N BOWS

1961-63 BUTTONS 'N BOWS NAIL POLISH
(Left) Pink and white box holds nail polish with white cap. OSP 69c, CMV $8. In box, $6. bottle only.

1961-63 BUTTONS 'N BOWS LIPSTICK
(Right) Pink and white box holds pink and white striped lipstick. OSP 89c, CMV $7. In box, $4. tube only.

1962-63 BUTTONS 'N BOWS CREAM LOTION
(Left) 4 oz. pink plastic bottle with white cap. OSP $1.35, CMV $6 - MB $10.

1962-63 BUTTONS 'N BOWS BUBBLE BATH
(Right) 4 oz. pink plastic, white cap, pink lettering. OSP $1.35, CMV $6 - $10 MB.

BUTTONS 'N BOWS
Cream lotion & bubble bath both came in solid pink plastic & clear frosted plastic bottle. Pink has pink letters. Frosted has white letters.

1961-63 BUTTONS 'N BOWS SOAP
Pink box & soap. OSP $1.35. Some buttons have thread through holes. CMV $25 MB no threads - $27.50 with threads. Two boxes shown. Each box holds 2 bars. Boxes are same.

1960-63 BUTTONS 'N BOWS COLOGNE
(Left) 2 oz. clear glass, white cap, lettering pink, came with pink ribbon bow around neck. OSP $1.35, CMV $12. MB, $9. BO.

1960-63 BUTTONS 'N BOWS COLOGNE MIST
(Center) 2½ oz. pink plastic with white cap. Bottom is 2 shades of pink. OSP $2.25, CMV $9., $12. MB.

1962-63 BUTTONS 'N BOWS ROLL-ON DEODORANT
(Right) 1¾ oz. white and pink painted label on clear glass, pink cap. OSP 89c, CMV $8. BO, $12. MB.

1962-63 PRETTY CHOICE
2 oz. frosted plastic bottle cream lotion, white cap. Cologne, clear glass, white cap, light pink ribbon on neck. Had choice of cream lotion or bubble bath. OSP $2.70, CMV $30 MB.

1960-63 BUTTONS 'N BOWS BEAUTY DUST
(Left) Pink & white cardboard box with clear plastic lid. OSP $2.25, CMV $16.

1960-63 BUTTONS 'N BOWS CREAM SACHET
(Right) Pink glass jar with white & pink lid. OSP $1.35, CMV $9 BO - $12 MB.

1961-62 BUTTON BUTTON
Pink & white box holds Buttons 'N Bows 2 oz. cologne & beauty dust. OSP $3.60, CMV $40 MB.

1961-63 CUTE AS A BUTTON
Pink & white box holds Buttons 'N Bows nail polish with white cap and pink & white lipstick. OSP $1.58, CMV $17 MB.

1949 BUTTONS 'N BOWS SONG SHEET
Green song sheet with words to help sell Quaintance products. 4¼'' wide x 6½'' high. CMV $5.

CAMEO

1969 CAMEO SOAP ON A ROPE
(Top Left) Blue box holds blue soap on white or blue & white rope. OSP $1.75, CMV $7 - $12 MB.

1961-63 CAMEO SACHET
(Top Right) Gold metal base holds pink painted over milk glass jar with white lid with lady's face. Came in Topaze, Cotillion, Somewhere. OSP $3.25. To A Wild Rose OSP $2.75. Persian Wood & Here's My Heart. OSP $3. CMV $7 BO - $11 MB.

1965 CAMEO BROOCH
(Bottom) Gold brooch with pink & white lady's face. Came in Cameo Set only. CMV $15 MB - $9 brooch only.

1973-74 CAMEO SET
Reddish brown plastic with white Cameo beauty dust 6 oz. Came in Sonnet, Moonwind, Hana Gasa, Charisma, Unforgettable, Rapture, Somewhere, Cotillion, Here's My Heart, Topaze, Occur!, To A Wild Rose. SSP $4, CMV $4 brush & comb set. SSP $6, CMV $6 mirror. SSP $4, CMV $4.

1966 CAMEO SOAP
Blue & white box holds 4 white Cameo soaps. OSP $2, CMV $20 MB.

1965 CAMEO SET
White, gold & green box holds Cameo compact, lipstick & Cameo brooch. OSP $6.50, CMV $30.

1965-66 CAMEO LIPSTICK
White lipstick with gold base & lady's face on top. OSP 98c, CMV $2 - $3 MB.

1965-66 CAMEO COMPACT
White plastic with gold edge & pink lady's face on top. OSP $2.50, CMV $6 CO - $8 MB.

CANDID

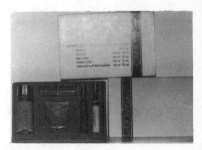

1977-78 CANDID PERFUMED SKIN SOFTENER
(Left) 5 oz. plastic jar. SSP $2.49, CMV 50c.

1977-78 CANDID MAKEUP
(Center) 1.5 oz. glass bottle, gold cap. Came in 3 shades. OSP $3.50, CMV 50c.

1977-78 UNDER MAKEUP MOISTURIZER
(Right) 2 oz. clear glass bottle, gold cap. OSP $3.50, CMV 50c.

1979-80 CANDID SHEER SUNSHINE FACE COLOR
(Left) 1.5 oz. tube, gold cap. SSP $1.50, CMV 25c.

1979-80 CANDID ULTRA CREME PERFUME
(Right) .66 oz. clear glass, gold cap. SSP $1, CMV 25c.

1977 CANDID MAKEUP DEMO KIT
For Reps only. Box lid Candid is in different position than regular set sold. Came with outer sleeve and says (Not for Resale) on back side. Box holds 5 items. Makeup, lip color, eye color, cheek color, mascara with lash builders. CMV $10 MB with outer sleeve only. Sold to public for $10.95. Same CMV.

CANDID PRODUCTS

1976-78 CANDID FRAGRANCE SAMPLE
(Left) Small plastic vial. Came in matchbook-like cover.

1976-78 CANDID COLOR FOR EYES
(Inside Left) .25 oz. CMV 25c.

1977-78 CANDID SOLID PERFUME COMPACT
(Left Center) Plastic container. OSP $3.75, CMV 25c.

1976-78 CANDID COLOR FOR CHEEKS
(Right Center) Plastic .15 oz. OSP $3.50, CMV 25c.

1976-78 CANDID MASCARA
(Inside Right) .25 oz. OSP $3, CMV 25c.

1977-78 CANDID FRESH & FOAMING BODY CLEANSER
(Right) 6 oz. plastic tube. OSP $4.50, CMV 25c.

1977 CANDID SALES LEADER TROPHY
Wood base with brass plaque with bottle of Candid cologne mist glued in base. Given to 1 Rep in each district who sold the most Candid cologne mist on its introduction. CMV $12.50.

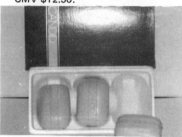

1977-78 CANDID PERFUMED SOAPS
Open end box, 3 cakes each. 3 oz., white bars. OSP $7, CMV $5 MB.

1976 CANDID BAG FOR MANAGERS
Maroon and white canvas bag. Back side says Avon, New York, London, Paris. CMV $10.

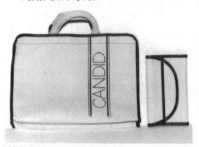

1977 CANDID TOTE BAG
Light colored canvas bag given to Reps for going to C-10 sales meeting. CMV $3. They could also win a Candid matching purse organizer. CMV $3.

1977-78 CANDID PERFUMED TALC
(Left) 3.5 oz. OSP $3, CMV 50c.

1977-78 CANDID ULTRA COLOGNE SPRAY
(Inside Left) 1.8 oz. gold cap. OSP $7.50, CMV 50c.

1977-78 CANDID ULTRA COLOGNE
(Center) 2 oz., gold cap. OSP $6.50, CMV 50c.

1977-78 CANDID ULTRA PURSE COLOGNE
(Inside Right) .5 oz. OSP $3, CMV 50c.

1978 ULTRA PURSE SPRAY COLOGNE
(Right) Refillable .33 fl. oz. SSP $3.95, CMV 50c.

CHARISMA

1969-71 CHARISMA SKIN SOFTENER
(Top) 5 oz. dark red glass jar has red & gold metal caps, or red & silver metal caps. Bottom labels are red with gold lettering. OSP $4, CMV $1 BO - $2 MB.

1972 CHARISMA SKIN SOFTENER
(Top) 5 oz. light red glass, caps are red & gold metal. Paper labels on bottoms are white with red lettering. OSP $4, CMV $2 MB - $1 BO.

1973-78 CHARISMA SKIN SOFTENER
(Not Shown) 5 oz. red plastic with gold & red cap. OSP $5.50, CMV 50c.

1969-72 CHARISMA COLOGNE
(Bottom Left) 4 oz. red glass, some are silver tip (rare) with red plastic cap trimmed in gold. OSP $6, CMV $3.

1968=76 CHARISMA COLOGNE MIST
(Bottom Right) 3 oz. red plastic coated, trimmed in gold. OSP $8, CMV $1.

1968-76 CHARISMA PERFUME ROLLETTE
(Bottom Center) .33 oz. red glass trimmed in gold. OSP $4.50, CMV $1.

1968-76 CHARISMA CREAM SACHET
(Left) .66 oz. red glass jar with red & gold lid. OSP $4.50, CMV 50c.

1969-72 CHARISMA COLOGNE
(Center) ½ oz. red glass, gold cap. OSP $1.75, CMV $2.

1968-76 CHARISMA BEAUTY DUST
(Right) 6 oz. red plastic powder box trimmed in gold. OSP $10, CMV $6 MB - $3 CO.

1970-71 CHARISMA FOAMING BATH OIL
(Left) 6 oz. red plastic bottle with red band on gold cap. Red paper label with gold lettering on bottom. OSP $3.50, CMV $2.

1971-73 CHARISMA FOAMING BATH OIL
(Center) Same as above only cap has no red band. Bottom label is white with red lettering. OSP $4, CMV $2 MB.

1973-74 CHARISMA FOAMING BATH OIL
(Right) Same as above only front lettering says Foaming Bath Oil. Bottom label has number in red. OSP $4, CMV $2 MB.

1970-72 CHARISMA SCENTED HAIR SPRAY
(Left) 7 oz. red can. OSP $1.50, CMV $3.

1970-76 CHARISMA PERFUMED TALC
(Inside Left) 3½ oz. red cardboard. OSP $1.35, CMV 50c.

1971-76 CHARISMA PERFUME POWDER MIST
(Inside Right) 7 oz. red & gold can, gold top, painted label. No longer boxed. OSP $5, CMV $1.

1969-70 CHARISMA PERFUMED POWDER MIST
(Right) 7 oz. red & gold can, gold top, has paper label. Also came boxed. OSP $3.50, CMV $3.

1968-70 CHARISMA TRAY
(Left) Dark red plastic with gold trim. 11" diameter. This one used as introduction. CMV $8 MB.
(Right) Lighter red plastic with gold rim. 10" diameter. OSP $3, CMV $3 - $5 MB.

1968-78 CHARISMA DEMI-STICK
(Front Left) Red & gold with white cap. OSP $2.50, CMV $1.

1968-78 CHARISMA SAMPLES
(Front Center & Left) Clear glass with white cap. CMV 25c. Red foil envelope, 10 in box. CMV 25c.

1968 CHARISMA ORDER BOOK COVER
(Back) Introducing Charisma. Came with red pen. CMV $5 - with pen $6.

1975 CHARISMA SOAP
(Top) 3 pink Charisma soap in special Christmas 1975 design box. OSP $3, CMV $8 MB.

1970-76 CHARISMA SOAP
(Bottom) Red box holds 3 bars. OSP $3.50, CMV $6 MB.

1970-71 CHARISMA COLOGNE SILK
(Left) 3 oz. clear glass, red cap. OSP $4.50, CMV $2 BO - $3 MB.

1969 CHARISMA COLOGNE SILK
(Right) 3 oz. frosted glass, red cap. OSP $4.50, CMV $4 MB - $3 BO.

1968 CHARISMA JEWELRY SET AWARD
Red & gold necklace, bracelet & earrings. Given for meeting or exceeding a prize goal. CMV $37.50 set MB - $12 each MB.

COME SUMMER

COTILLION

All white caps on 1961-74 Cotillion bottles will turn dark gray when exposed to sunlight. The gray or faded caps are not considered to be in mint condition.

1976-78 COME SUMMER PERFUMED TALC
(Left) 3.5 oz. green & white container. OSP $2, CMV 50c.

1976-78 COME SUMMER BUBBLE BATH GELEE
(Center) 4 oz. tube, white flower design and cap. OSP $3.50, CMV 50c.

1977-78 COME SUMMER - A TOUCH OF COLOGNE
(Right) .33 oz. ribbed glass bottle, white cap. OSP $1.75, CMV 50c.

1951-52 COTILLION PERFUME
3 dram glass stoppered swirl glass bottle. White, pink & blue flower design around neck with neck tag. Pink & white box. OSP $3.50, CMV $125 in box - bottle only with tag & flower design $100.

1945-47 COTILLION PERFUME
3 dram glass stopper bottle with gold neck tag. Came in blue, pink & white box as shown. OSP $3, CMV $100 BO mint - $125 MB.

1948-50 COTILLION SWIRL PERFUME
3 dram glass stoppered bottle is swirl glass design, gold neck tag. Purple & white flowered box. OSP $3, CMV $75 mint - $100 MB.

1953-58 COTILLION PERFUME
3 dram bottle with gold cap, pink band around neck with painted label. In pink & white box. OSP $4.50, CMV $100 in box - $65 bottle only. Came with perfume 1 dram smooth glass with gold scroll cap in gold wrapper with pink snap and white & gold ribbon. OSP $6, CMV $12. Complete set CMV $115 with white & gold ribbon.

1975-78 COME SUMMER BODY SPLASH
(Left) 12 oz. white plastic with painted label & white cap. OSP $3, CMV 25c.

1975-78 COME SUMMER PERFUMED POWDER MIST
(Inside Left) 7 oz. green & white with white cap. OSP $3, CMV 50c.

1975-78 COME SUMMER COLOGNE ICE
(Center) 2.25 oz. solid cologne. White & green with white cap. OSP $4, CMV 50c.

1975-76 COLOGNE MIST
(Inside Right) 2 oz. clear glass with green band on bottle & white cap with green band. OSP $3, CMV 50c.

1975-78 COME SUMMER FRAGRANCE SAMPLES
(Right) Box of 10 samples. CMV 50c box.

1935 Only COTILLION PERFUME
¼ oz. gold cap, green & yellow label & box. For 77th birthday of D.H. McConnell. OSP 20c, CMV $80 in box - bottle only $60.

1939 Only COTILLION PERFUME
2 dram, ribbed cap with "A" on cap. Sold for one campaign only for 20c with purchase of other Avons. CMV in box $75 - bottle only $55.

1936 Only COTILLION PERFUME
2 dram, gold ribbed cap. Sold for 20c July 7-27, 1936 only, with purchase of other Avons. In honor of Mr. McConnell's 78th birthday. CMV $80 MB - bottle only $60.

1935 COTILLION TULIP PERFUME CHRISTMAS BOX
Red & green Christmas box holds ¼ oz. glass stoppered perfume with gold label. This bottle sold 1934-39. With this box 1935 Christmas only. OSP $1.04, CMV $90 MB as shown. See Misc. Perfumes for other fragrances in same bottle.

1934 COTILLION PERFUME
¼ oz. metal cap. First Cotillion bottle issued in honor of Mr. McConnell's birthday. OSP 20c, CMV $55 BO - $75 MB.

1937 COTILLION PERFUME
2 dram, gold cap. OSP 20c, CMV in box $70 - bottle only $50.

1938-39 COTILLION TOILET WATER
Flowered box & label. 2 oz. bottle, white plastic cap. Sold for 20c with purchase of other Avons. May 2-22, 1939. CPC on box and back side of label. CMV $52.50 MB - $37.50 BO mint.

1940 Only COTILLION PERFUME
2 dram, ribbed gold cap with "A" on top. Also came plain gold cap. Sold for 20c with purchase of other Avons. CMV in box $75 - bottle only $55.

1946-49 COTILLION TOILET WATER
2 oz. pink, gold or white cap. OSP $1.19, CMV $35 in box - $25 BO mint.

1962 COTILLION BATH OIL
(Left) 6 oz. pink & white plastic bottle. Came in Bath Bouquet set only. CMV $6.
1949-50 COTILLION COLOGNE
(Right) 2 oz. pink cap. OSP $1.25, CMV $22.50 - $25 MB. Toilet water in same design bottle & label. 2 oz. size, pink cap. Same CMV.

1950 COTILLION PERFUME
1/8 oz. pink cap. Very rare. OSP $1, CMV $70 - MB $85.

1951-53 COTILLION CREAM SACHET
(Left) White glass jar with pink & white lid. OSP $1.25, CMV $15.

1950-53 COTILLION TOILET WATER
(Right) 2 oz. pink cap, pink & white label & white box. Box came solid & with open window so label shows through. OSP $1.25, CMV $22 in box - $18 bottle only.

1950-53 COTILLION BEAUTY DUST
Pink & white container. OSP $1.75, CMV $20 mint - $25 MB.

1950-53 COTILLION SOAP
Pink & white box holds pink bars. OSP 69c, CMV $37.50 MB.

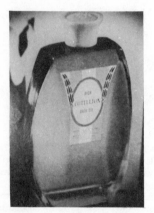

1950-53 COTILLION BATH OIL
6 oz. pink & white label & pink cap. Pink & white box. OSP 95c, CMV $22 in box - $18 bottle only.

1950-53 COTILLION CREAM LOTION
(Left) 6 oz. pink & white label, pink cap and pink & white box. OSP 89c, CMV $22 in box - $18 bottle only.

1950-53 COTILLION COLOGNE
(Right) 4 oz. bottle with pink cap & label. OSP $1.75, CMV $22 in box - $18 bottle only.

1953-61 COTILLION SOAP
Pink & white box holds 3 pink or white bars. OSP 89c. Box came as sleeve top with round edge white soaps. 1953-56 CMV $35 MB. 1956-61 came sleeve top box with 3 flat edge pink soaps. CMV $32.50 MB.

1950-53 COTILLION TALC
(Left) Pink & white can with pink cap. OSP 43c, CMV $12 - MB $15.

1950-53 COTILLION BODY POWDER
(Right) 5 oz. pink & white paper box, sifter on top with metal lid & bottom. OSP 75c, CMV $17 - MB $20.

1947 Only COTILLION TALCUM
(Left) Pink paper box, white shaker top. OSP 39c, CMV $25 - MB $30.

1942-46 COTILLION TALCUM
(Center) 2.75 oz. turquoise & white all paper box. War time. Paper top fits over top of box, shaker top. CMV without top $20 in mint. OSP 39c, CMV $25 mint.

1944-46 COTILLION TALCUM
(Right) Turquoise & white paper box, plastic octagonal cap. OSP 39c, CMV $25 mint.

1961-67 COTILLION SOAP
Gold & white box holds 3 bars with gold centers. OSP $2, CMV $22.50 MB.

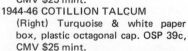

1941 Only COTILLION TALCUM BOX
Blue box with fan. 2.75 oz. can. Sold to Reps for 10c to use as a demonstrator. CMV $30 MB as shown.

1939 Only 53rd ANNIVERSARY COTILLION TALCUM
Special 53rd Anniversary box to first introduce Cotillion talcum. May 23 to June 12, 1939. 2.75 oz. turquoise & white can. This can sold 1939-43 then 1946-50. OSP 37c, CMV can only $10 - in special 53rd box $25.

1946-50 COTILLION COLOGNE
(Left) 6 oz. pink cap. OSP $1.50, CMV $50 BO - $65 MB.

1946-50 COTILLION BODY POWDER
(Center & Right) 4.5 oz. light pink cardboard. Blue metal sifter top. OSP 75c, CMV $15 - MB $20. Came in sets 5 oz. size with pink & white plastic sifter top. Same CMV.

1943 COTILLION TALCUM CHRISTMAS BOX
Pale blue & pink outer box issued only at Christmas 1943 with cardboard large size talc. OSP 98c, CMV $35 MB as shown.

1938-50 COTILLION TALCUM
2.75 oz. turquoise can. Box marked 2¾ oz. size. Can sold 1938-43 then 1946-50. OSP 37c, CMV $10 can only - $15 MB mint.

1940-43 then 1946-50 COTILLION TALCUM
(Left) 14.5 oz. metal can, turquoise & white. OSP $1.05, CMV $20 - add $5 for CPC label.

1943-46 COTILLION TALCUM
(Right) 14.5 oz. paper box used during war. Rare. OSP $1.19, CMV $35.

1962-63 COTILLION BEAUTY DUST
Gold & white paper box with clear plastic lid with 4A design on lid. Came in 1962-63 Fragrance Magic sets only. CMV $17 mint.

1956-61 COTILLION PERFUMED TALC
White can with pink cap & design. Also came just talc. OSP 69c, CMV $8 in box - can only $5.

1940-41 COTILLION TALCUM CHRISTMAS BOX
Special issue blue & white Christmas box holds regular issue metal can of Cotillion talcum in large size. OSP 89c, RARE, CMV $30 MB as shown.

1959-61 COTILLION BEAUTY DUST
Pink plastic bottom, white plastic top with gold center. OSP $2.95, CMV $6 CO - $12 MB.

1953-59 COTILLION BEAUTY DUST
Pink paper sides with pink & white tin top. OSP $1.95, CMV $12 - MB $16.

1939-42 COTILLION FACE POWDER
Gold & turquoise powder box. OSP 78c, CMV $8 - MB $10. Add $3 for CPC label.

1939 COTILLION SACHET SPECIAL ISSUE BOX
Special issue box is blue with lace design. Holds regular issue powder sachet. OSP 20c, CMV $18 MB as shown.

1941 Only COTILLION SACHET BOX
Special issue box to Avon ladies only, for 20c. Holds regular issue Cotillion sachet, 1939-44. CMV $20 MB as shown.

1952 COTILLION SACHET VALENTINE BOX
1¼ oz. pink cap. Came in gold, pink and white Valentine box. Rare in this box. CMV $25 MB as shown.

1946-47 COTILLION SACHET
(Left) 1¼ oz. pink glass & cap with painted label. (Rare) Sold only in Cotillion Garland Set. Same set in 1947 was called Cotillion Duet. CMV $20 - MB $22.

1946-49 COTILLION SACHET
(Center) 1¼ oz. clear glass, pink cap, paper label. OSP $1.15, CMV $16 - MB $18.

1939-44 COTILLION SACHET
(Right) 1¼ oz. turquoise cap, clear glass, paper label. OSP $1.04, CMV $12 BO - $16 MB.

1937-38 COTILLION SACHET
1¼ oz. ribbed glass bottle with turquoise cap. OSP $1.04, CMV $24 MB - $18 BO mint.

1952 COTILLION VALENTINE SACHET
1¼ oz. white cap. OSP 98c, CMV $25 MB. See Misc. Powder Sachet section for box. CMV $18 BO mint.

1961-75 COTILLION CREAM SACHET
(Left) .66 frosted glass with pink & white lid, gold or silver lettering. OSP $2, CMV 25c.

1961-67 COTILLION POWDER SACHET
(Center) 9/10 oz. frosted glass with pink & white cap. OSP $2, CMV $8 MB - $6 BO.

1944-45 COTILLION SACHET
(Right) 1¼ oz. paper box, pink plastic flowers on lid. OSP $1.15, CMV $20 MB - $18 BO mint.

1950-53 COTILLION POWDER SACHET
(Left) 1¼ oz. pink cap and pink & white label. OSP $1.19, CMV $15 - MB $20.

1957-61 COTILLION POWDER SACHET
(Center) 1¼ oz. or .9 oz. pink cap & pink bottom with painted label. Came light or dark pink bottom & also white or pink painted lettering. OSP $1.50, CMV $9 - MB $13.

1953-56 COTILLION POWDER SACHET
(Right) 9/10 oz. or 1¼ oz. clear glass, pink cap & pink painted label. Also white lettering (rare). OSP $1.25, CMV $8 - MB $12. White lettering $18.

1937 COTILLION SACHET
(Left) Red & green box sold Christmas only for 25c, CPC on box & bottle. CMV $25 MB - $18 BO mint.

1937 COTILLION SACHET
(Right) Blue & white box special issue. CMV $25 MB. Bottle only - ribbed glass, turquoise cap, sold 1937-38. OSP $1.04, CMV $18 BO mint.

1957 COTILLION SACHET CHRISTMAS BOX

.9 oz. pink painted glass, pink cap. Bottle sold 1957-61. Pink, green and blue triangle box sold 1957 only. OSP $1.50, CMV $15 MB as shown.

1953-54 COTILLION TALC

4 oz. clear glass bottle with pink cap & pink or white (rare) painted label. 1955 was called Talcum in painted label, pink & white box. OSP $1, CMV $15 each in box - bottle only $10.

1950 Only COTILLION TALC

(Left) 2 oz. white cardboard, pink top & bottom. Came in Always Sweet set only. CMV $15.

1959-61 COTILLION PERFUMED BATH OIL

(Right) 8 oz. pink plastic, pink cap. OSP $2.50, CMV $10.

1957-61 COTILLION POWDER SACHET - NO LABEL

Pink paint over clear glass, pink cap. Rare issue came with no painted label. Plain pink all over. CMV add $5 to price of regular issue.

1954-59 COTILLION BATH OIL

(Left) 4½ oz. pink cap, pink painted label, pink & white box. OSP $1.35, CMV $15 in box - $9 bottle only mint.

1954-61 COTILLION CREAM LOTION

(Right) 4¼ oz. pink cap & pink painted label, pink & white box. OSP 95c, CMV $12 in box - $8 bottle only mint.

1959-61 COTILLION COLOGNE MIST

(Left) 3 oz. pink plastic coated bottle with white cap & paper label. OSP $2.95, CMV $12 BO - $17 MB.

1958-59 COTILLION COLOGNE MIST

(Center) 3 oz. pink plastic coated bottle. OSP $2.50, CMV $16 - $20 MB.

1958 Only COTILLION COLOGNE MIST

(Right) Rare 3 oz. pink plastic bottle. OSP $2.50, CMV $42.50 BO - $52.50 MB.

1953-61 COTILLION TOILET WATER

(Left) 2 oz. gold cap, pink band around neck, pink painted label. OSP $1.50, CMV $15 MB - $10 BO mint. Some have white painted label.

1953-61 COTILLION 4 OZ. COLOGNE

(Right) Gold cap, pink band around neck, pink painted label. OSP $2, CMV $15 MB - $10 BO mint. Some have white painted label.

1956-58 COTILLION TALC

(Left) 3 oz. frosted glass with pink lid & paper label, pink & white box. OSP $1, CMV $14 in box - $9 bottle only mint.

1958-59 BODY POWDER

(Right) 3 oz. frosted glass with pink cap & paper label, pink & white box. OSP $1, CMV $15 in box - $11 bottle only mint.

1953-57 COTILLION CREAM SACHET

(Left) Pink lid, white glass bottom. OSP $1.25, CMV $8 - MB $10.

1957-61 COTILLION CREAM SACHET

Pink lid, pink glass bottom. OSP $1.50, CMV $7 - MB $9.

1957 Only COTILLION COLOGNE
(Left) 3 dram, white cap. Came in Fragrance Rainbow set only. CMV $8 BO - $10 with neck bow.

1961 Only COTILLION COLOGNE
(Right) 2 oz. gold cap, pink band around neck, painted label. OSP $1.50, CMV $20 - $22 MB.

1950-52 THE COTILLION
Pink & white box with green lining holds Cotillion cream lotion & cologne. OSP $2.60, CMV $52.50.

1961-66 COTILLION PERFUMED BATH OIL
(Left) 6 oz. pink plastic bottle, white cap. OSP $2.50, CMV $6.

1966-74 COTILLION FOAMING BATH OIL
(Right) 6 oz. pink plastic bottle, white cap. OSP $2, CMV $2 BO - $3 MB.

1951 COTILLION ENCHANTMENT
Pink, white & green box holds Cotillion toilet water & cream sachet. OSP $2.50, CMV $52.50 MB.

1974-77 COTILLION PERFUME TALC
(Left) 3.5 oz. pink & gold cardboard. OSP $1, CMV $1.

1975-78 COTILLION CREAM SACHET
(Inside Left) .66 oz. clear glass with gold & pink cap. OSP $2, CMV 50c.

1975-78 COTILLION PERFUME DEMI STICK
(Center) .19 oz. white with pink & gold. OSP $1, CMV 50c.

1961-74 COTILLION COLOGNE MIST
(Inside Right & Right) 3 oz. white plastic coated bottle with white cap. OSP $4, CMV $1. Same bottle with yellow plastic coated bottom. CMV $10 MB - $7 BO. 1975-76 issue has white cap, pink top & pink painted label. OSP $5, CMV $1.

1956 Only COTILLION BATH BOUQUET
Pink & white box holds 2 oz. Cotillion cologne, 2 oz. Cotillion bath oil & 1 bar of Cotillion soap. OSP $2.25, CMV $55.

1969-72 COTILLION COLOGNE
(Left) ½ oz. white cap, clear glass. OSP $1.50, CMV $1 BO - $2 MB.

1964-69 COTILLION PERFUMED OIL
(Center) ½ oz. frosted glass with white cap. OSP $4, CMV $5 BO - $7 MB.

1963-64 COTILLION PERFUMED OIL FOR THE BATH
(Right) ½ oz. frosted glass with white cap. OSP $4, CMV $7 BO - $9 MB.

1951-52 JOLLY SURPRISE SET
Pink & white box holds Cotillion powder sachet & 1 dram perfume in pink net lining. OSP $1.99, CMV $42 set.

1960 Only COTILLION COLOGNE
4 oz. clear glass, gold cap, pink paper band around neck with pink painted label. Pink & gold box. OSP $2.50, CMV $22 in this box.

1958 COTILLION BOUQUET

Pink & white box holds Cotillion cologne mist & pink glass cream sachet. OSP $3.95, CMV $65 MB.

1961-70 COTILLION BEAUTY DUST

(Left) White frosted plastic bottom with clear plastic lid. OSP $4, CMV $3 - $5 MB. Some with yellow plastic bottom. CMV $6 - $8 MB.

1961-74 COTILLION PERFUMED TALC

(Center) 2.75 oz. bright pink can with white cap. OSP $1, CMV $1.

1964-73 COTILLION PERFUMED SKIN SOFTENER

(Right) 5 oz. pink glass jar with gold & white lid. Some came with silver lid. OSP $3.50, CMV gold 50c - silver $1. Regular issue came pink painted over clear glass. CMV 50c. Some came pink painted over white milk glass. CMV $5.

1973-75 COTILLION PERFUMED SKIN SOFTENER

(Not Shown) 5 oz. pink plastic with white & gold cap. OSP $3.50, CMV 50c.

1961-71 COTILLION COLOGNE

(Left) 2 oz. frosted glass with white cap. OSP $2, CMV $1 - $2 MB.

1961-63 COTILLION COLOGNE

(Right) 4 oz. frosted glass with white cap. OSP $3, CMV $10 MB - $8 BO.

1961-68 COTILLION CREAM LOTION

(Left) 4 oz. pink plastic, white cap. OSP $1.50, CMV $3.50.

1961-64 COTILLION BODY POWDER

(Right) 4 oz. pink plastic, white cap. OSP $2.25, CMV $6 - MB $8.

1953-55 COTILLION DELUXE SET

Pink & white box flips open in center. Holds Cotillion 1 dram perfume, 4 oz. cologne, powder sachet & talcum. Same set also came with lift off lid. OSP $6, CMV $60 MB.

1953-55 COTILLION DUET

Pink & white flowered box with pink satin lining holds Cotillion 4 oz. cologne & Cotillion talc. OSP $3, CMV $42 MB.

1957 THE COTILLION

Pink & white box holds Cotillion beauty dust, cream sachet with white glass bottom & 4 oz. cologne. OSP $4.95, CMV $45.

1956 COTILLION CAROL

Pink & white box holds Cotillion cream sachet with white glass bottom & Cotillion talc. OSP $2.25, CMV $35.

1966-70 COTILLION SCENTED HAIR SPRAY

(Left) 7 oz. pink can. OSP $1.50, CMV $3.

1966-72 COTILLION PERFUMED POWDER MIST

(Center) 7 oz. (1966-70) pink can has paper label & pink cap & came in white box lined in pink. OSP $3.50, CMV $2.

(Right) 7 oz. (1970-71) pink can, pink cap. Label was painted. Not boxed. OSP $3.50, CMV $1.

1955-56 COTILLION BATH OIL

(Left) 2 oz. clear glass bottle with pink cap, label pink & white. Came in That's For Me set only. CMV $15.

1949 HAND LOTION

(Right) 2 oz. clear glass bottle with pink & blue label, blue cap. Came in Your Charms & Hair-Ribbons set. CMV $15.

1957 COTILLION TREASURES

Gold, white & pink box holds 3 oz. bottles of Cotillion bath oil & cologne with gold caps, 1 pink bar of Cotillion soap. OSP $2.75, CMV $75 MB.

1964-68 COTILLION PERFUME MIST

(Left) 2 dram, pink & white metal with gold band. OSP $3.25, CMV $6 - $7 MB.

1961-63 COTILLION SPRAY PERFUME

(Center) 2 dram, pink & white metal with gold band. OSP $3.50, CMV $10 MB - $8 BO.

1960-61 COTILLION SPRAY PERFUME

(Right) Rose, white & gold box holds rose & gold metal spray container. OSP $2.95, CMV $10 BO - $16 MB.

1954-55 COTILLION GARLAND SET

Pink & white box holds 4½ oz. Cotillion bath oil & cream lotion. OSP $2.15, CMV $37.50 MB.

1956 COTILLION PRINCESS SET

Pink, white & gold box holds Cotillion beauty dust & 4 oz. cologne. OSP $3.95, CMV $40.

1953-56 ENCHANTMENT SET

Pink & white box holds Cotillion powder sachet & 1 dram perfume. OSP $3, CMV $37 MB.

1948 COTILLION TALC

(Left) White, pink & blue paper container came in Hair Ribbon set only. CMV $12.

1951 COTILLION TALC

(Right) 2 oz. blue, white & pink paper container. Came in 1951 Always Sweet set. CMV $12.

1957 Only 1 OZ. COTILLION COLOGNE

(Left) Pink cap. Came in Beautiful Journey set. CMV $15.

1956 Only COTILLION COLOGNE

(Center) 2 oz. white caps. Came in Bath Bouquet only. CMV $20 mint.

1956 Only COTILLION BATH OIL

(Right) 2 oz. white caps. Came in Bath Bouquet only. CMV $20 mint.

1964 COTILLION DUO

White, pink & gold box holds Cotillion powder sachet & 1 dram perfume. OSP $4.50, CMV $22.50 MB.

1963 DEBUTANTE
Pink, white & gold box holds Cotillion cologne mist & beauty dust. Comes in 2 different inner boxes. OSP $8.50, CMV $20 MB.

1947-48 COTILLION DUET
Pink box holds 2 oz. Cotillion toilet water with gold cap & powder sachet. OSP $2.39, CMV $70 MB.

1951 ALWAYS SWEET SET
White, blue & pink box with girls hat on lid, holds straw handbag containing Cotillion talc, 5/8 dram perfume & cream lotion with blue cap. OSP $3, CMV $95 MB.

1948-49 HAIR RIBBONS SET
Pink & white box has bottle of Avon hand lotion, Cotillion talc, 5/8 dram bottle of Cotillion perfume. Also came, this box, with hand lotion & Cotillion talc from 1949 Your Charm set. Set came with or without perfume. OSP $1.59, CMV $65 with perfume - $50 without perfume.

1961-62 SOMEONE LIKE YOU
Pink & white box holds Cotillion 2 oz. cologne & cream sachet. OSP $4. CMV $22.

1950-52 COTILLION BATH ENSEMBLE
Pink & white box holds 2 drawers with Cotillion talc, powder sachet & 2 bars of pink soap in top drawer. Bottom drawer holds Cotillion cream lotion, toiler water, bath oil & 1 dram perfume. OSP $8.25, CMV $175 MB.

1961-62 COTILLION DEBUT
White & gold box holds Cotillion beauty dust, cream sachet & cologne mist, in satin lined flip open compartment. OSP $10, CMV $35.

1949 YOUR CHARMS SET
White, blue & pink box with or without ribbon band around lid came with gold heart & arrow charm on lid. Box contains pink & blue paper box of Cotillion talc, 2 oz. Avon hand lotion, pink & blue label with blue cap, 5/8 dram Cotillion perfume with blue cap. Set came with & without perfume. OSP $1.59, CMV $65 with perfume - $50 without perfume.

1950 COTILLION GARLAND
Pink, white & green box holds Cotillion talc & 2 oz. toilet water. OSP $1.85, CMV $52.50.

1950 ALWAYS SWEET SET
Pink & white box holds straw handbag with green & yellow ribbon & pink flower. Holds bottle of cream lotion with blue cap, Cotillion talc & 5/8 dram Cotillion perfume. OSP $2.39, CMV $95 MB.

1940-41 COTILLION CLASSIC
Satin lined box with people dancing on lid holds 2 oz. Cotillion toilet water & gold box of Cotillion talc. OSP $1.50, CMV $67.50 MB.

1940-43 COTILLION ENCHANTMENT SET
Silk lined gold & green box holds Cotillion powder sachet, 2 oz. toilet water & 1 dram perfume with gold cap. OSP $2.85, CMV $95 MB.

1946 COTILLION GARLAND/ COTILLION DUET
Pink round box holds Cotillion toilet water & pink painted powder sachet. This set was introduced as Cotillion Duet then changed to Cotillion Garland for Christmas 1946. OSP $2.84, CMV $80 MB.

1952 COTILLION FANTASY
Pink & white Cotillion body powder with cream sachet on top under clear plastic lid. OSP $1.95, CMV $40 MB.

1946-47 COTILLION CLASSIC
Pink flowered box holds Cotillion 6 oz. cologne & body powder. OSP $2.48, CMV $95.

1938-39 COTILLION ENCHANTMENT
White box with satin lining holds Cotillion 2 dram glass stoppered perfume, 2 oz. Cotillion toilet water & powder sachet. OSP $2.95, CMV $150 MB.

COUNTRY BREEZE

1980-82 COUNTRY BREEZE PRODUCTS
PERFUMED POWDER MIST
4 oz. can, blue top. SSP $3, CMV 50c.

COLOGNE SPRAY
1 oz. grass embossed bottle, silver & blue cap. SSP $4, CMV $1 MB.
SAMPLES
Box of 10 packets. CMV 25c box.
MINI SPRAY
(Not Shown) SSP $3.50, CMV $1 MB.
COUNTRY BREEZE TOTE
Checkered tote bag given to Reps for selling 10 or more cologne sprays. CMV $2.
DRAWER LINING PAPER & POWDER SACHET
Sachet is 1.25 oz. cardboard sides & box of Country Breeze print lining paper. SSP $6 set, CMV $6 or $3 each.

COUNTRY GARDENS

1971-73 COUNTRY GARDEN FOAMING BATH OIL
4" high, 6 oz. white glass bottle, white cap, green ribbon on neck.

Came in Bird of Paradise, Elusive or Charisma. OSP $5.50, CMV $5 MB - $3 BO.
1971-72 SOAP DISH & SOAP
4" long white soap dish with bar of Country Garden soap. OSP $4.50, CMV $6 MB.
1971-72 BEAUTY DUST
4½" high, 5 oz. white glass jar with white lid & green ribbon. Came in Bird of Paradise, Elusive or Charisma. OSP $6, CMV $6 MB - $4 BO.
1971-73 POWDER SACHET
3" high, 1¼ oz. white glass jar with white lid & green ribbon. Came in Bird of Paradise, Elusive or Charisma. OSP $4.50, CMV $4 MB - $2 BO.

COUNTRY KITCHEN

1980-82 COUNTRY KITCHEN
CERAMIC TRIVET
  (Left) 7½" long, made in Brazil. SSP $10, CMV $10 MB.
MOISTURIZED HAND LOTION
  (Inside Left) 10 oz. glass with pump dispenser. SSP $8. CMV $8 MB.
CERAMIC SALT & PEPPER SHAKERS
  (Center & Inside Right) Made in Brazil. 4" high. SSP $10 set, CMV $10 set MB.
SPICE ROOM SCENT
  (Right) 7 oz. can. SSP 75c, CMV 75c.

1981 COUNTRY KITCHEN MAGNETS & NOTE PADS
  Box holds Country Kitchen design fragranced note pads & packet of sachet. Three small metal magnets. SSP $6, CMV $6 MB.

1940-44 COURTSHIP PERFUME
  Box holds 1/8 oz. bottle, gold cap and label. OSP 75c, CMV $25 mint - $35 MB as shown.

COURTSHIP

1938 Only COURTSHIP PERFUME
  2 dram bottle, gold cap. OSP 20c, CMV $60 MB - $40 BO mint.

1937 Only COURTSHIP PERFUME
  2 dram, gold cap. Sold for 20c with other purchase during Founders Campaign, July 6-26, 1937. CMV $60 MB - $40 BO mint. See Misc. Perfumes & Toilet Water for other Courtship bottles.

CRIMSON CARNATION

CRYSTALIQUE

1946-48 CRIMSON CARNATION
TOILET WATER
  2 oz. gold or plastic caps. OSP $1.19, CMV $40 BO - $55 MB.

1946-47 CRIMSON CARNATION PERFUME
  Blue & white box holds 3 dram bottle with white cap. OSP $3.75, CMV $100 MB - bottle only $60. See misc. perfumes for other Crimson Carnation perfumes.

1972 CRYSTALIQUE BEAUTY DUST
  (Left) Clear crystal plastic powder box & lid with gold base. OSP $8, CMV $5 - $7 MB.
1972 CRYSTALIQUE BEAUTY DUST
  (Right) Clear glass came with choice of powder. Moonwind, Charisma, Regence, Elusive, Rapture, Occur!, Somewhere, Topaze, Cotillion, Unforgettable or Here's My Heart, with matching puffs. SSP $7, CMV $11 - $13 MB.

1966 CRYSTAL BEAUTY DUST
(Left) All glass powder dish. OSP $5, CMV $20 - $22.50 MB.

1966-70 CRYSTAL COLOGNE
(Right) 4 oz., 5½" high glass bottle with matching plastic cap, gold trim. Came in Unforgettable, Rapture, Occur!, Somewhere, Topaze, Cotillion, Here's My Heart or To A Wild Rose. OSP $3.50, CMV $3 BO - $5 MB.

1979-80 CRYSTALIQUE BEAUTY DUST
Clear glass, holds all beauty dust refills. (Sold empty.) OSP $5., CMV $5. MB.

DAISIES WON'T TELL

1957 DAISIES WON'T TELL BEAUTY DUST
(Left) Blue, white & yellow paper powder box with girl on lid. OSP $1.29, CMV $20 - $25 MB.

1959-60 DAISY FLUFF-ON
(Right) Blue paper powder box with Daisy Puff & clear plastic lid. OSP $1.98, CMV $12 - $16 MB.

1956 DAISIES WON'T TELL BEAUTY DUST
Yellow, white & blue paper box. Short issue. OSP $1.29, CMV $20 mint - $25 MB. Also came with blue sided container.

1958 HEARTS 'N DAISIES
(Left) Blue & white box holds 2 oz. Daisies Won't Tell cologne & pink pomade lipstick. OSP $1.59, CMV $22 MB.

1959 LOVE ME - LOVE ME NOT
(Right) Blue, white & green box holds Daisies Won't Tell spray cologne & cream sachet in pink glass. OSP $2.50, CMV $30.

1963-64 DAISIES WON'T TELL CREAM SACHET
(Left) Pink glass jar with white plastic lid. OSP $1.10, CMV in box $11 - jar only $9.

1959-61 DAISIES WON'T TELL CREAM SACHET
(Right) Pink glass jar with floral metal lid. OSP $1.19, CMV $11 - MB $13.

1958 DAISIES WON'T TELL BEAUTY DUST
Blue & white box holds blue & white paper powder box with white daisy on top. OSP $1.49, CMV $23 MB beauty dust only $18 mint.

1959-61 DAISY SHAMPOO
4 oz. white plastic bottle & cap. OSP $1.19, CMV $10 BO - $12 MB.

1956-57 DAISIES WON'T TELL CREAM LOTION
(Left) Yellow & white box holds 2 oz. bottle with rib around center & white flower cap, painted label. OSP 69c, CMV $12 MB, $10 bottle only.

1962-64 DAISIES WON'T TELL HAND CREAM
(Right) Pink tube with white flower cap. In pink & blue box. OSP 59c, CMV $7 in box - $5 tube only.

1956 DAISIES WON'T TELL COLOGNE WITH ATOMIZER
Yellow, white & pink box holds 2 oz. bottle with rib around middle, white & gold spray atomizer. Short issue. OSP $1.25, CMV $15 - MB $20.

1958-62 DAISIES WON'T TELL COLOGNE
(Left) 2 oz. white cap & painted label. OSP $1.19, CMV $7 - $10 MB. Same bottle came in Bubble Bath & Cream Lotion in sets only. Same CMV.

1956-57 DAISIES WON'T TELL BUBBLE BATH
(Center) 4 oz. bottle with rib around center. Painted label, white flower cap. OSP $1.10, CMV $8 - MB $10.

1957-58 DAISIES WON'T TELL COLOGNE
(Right) 2 oz. cologne with rib around center in One I Love set and Daisies Won't Tell set. CMV $12.

1958-61 DAISY DUST
(Left) 2 oz. white plastic bottle & cap. OSP $1.19, CMV $10 BO - $12 MB.

1958-61 DAISY CREAM LOTION
(Center) 4 oz. white plastic bottle & cap. Two different labels. Newer has large letters & painted address at bottom. Older one is smaller letters & embossed address at bottom. OSP $1.19, CMV $10 BO - $12 MB.

1958-61 DAISY BUBBLE BATH
(Right) 4 oz. white plastic bottle & cap. OSP $1.19, CMV $10 BO - $12 MB.

1958-60 DAISIES WON'T TELL SPRAY COLOGNE
(Left) Pink plastic coated bottle with white cap. OSP $1.59, CMV $10 BO - $12 MB.

1957 Only DAISIES WON'T TELL SPRAY COLOGNE
1½ oz. blue plastic coated bottle with white cap & painted label. OSP $1.59, CMV $13 - MB $15.

1962-64 DAISIES WON'T TELL COLOGNE
(Right) 2 oz. glass bottle, white cap & painted label. OSP $1.19, CMV $6 BO - $9 MB.

1962-64 DAISIES WON'T TELL COLOGNE MIST
(Left) 2 oz. white plastic coated bottle with white cap and blue painted label. OSP $2.25, CMV $7. BO, $9. MB.

1962-64 DAISIES WON'T TELL CREAM LOTION
(Right) 4 oz. white plastic bottle and cap. Blue painted label. OSP $1.19, CMV $6. BO, $8. MB.

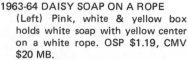

1963-64 DAISY SOAP ON A ROPE
(Left) Pink, white & yellow box holds white soap with yellow center on a white rope. OSP $1.19, CMV $20 MB.

1959-62 DAISY SOAP ON A ROPE
(Right) Blue, white & pink flowered box holds white Daisy soap with yellow center, on a blue rope. OSP $1.19, CMV $20 MB.

1958 FAIRY TOUCH
Blue and white box holds 2 blue & white tubes with yellow caps of Daisies Won't Tell hand cream. OSP 79c, CMV $16. MB.

1960 GAY DAISIES
Blue, white & pink box holds daisy soap on a blue rope & choice of daisy bubble bath, daisy dust, cream lotion or daisy shampoo. OSP $2.35, CMV $35 MB.

1962-64 FIRST RECITAL
Pink & blue fold-over box holds Daisy soap on rope & choice of Daisy cream lotion, bubble bath or Daisy dust. OSP $2.38, CMV $35 MB.

1962-64 DAISIES WON'T TELL BUBBLE BATH
(Top Left) 4 oz. white plastic bottle & cap with blue painted label. OSP $1.19, CMV $6 BO - $8 MB.

1962-64 DAISY DUST
(Bottom Left) 2 oz. white plastic bottle & cap with blue painted label. OSP $1.19, CMV $6 BO - $8 MB.

1958-61 DAISIES WON'T TELL HAND CREAM
(Right) Blue & white box holds blue & white tube with both flat or tall yellow cap. OSP 49c, CMV $6 in box - $4 tube only. 2 oz. Bubble Bath is same type bottle. Came in One I Love set & Daisies Won't Tell set. CMV $8.

1958-59 DAISY POMADE
Blue & white flowered holder holds pink daisy pomade. Also came in lime green color. OSP 59c, CMV $12.50 in holder - $2 pomade only.

1963-64 PICK A DAISY
Pink & blue box holds daisy soap on a rope & Daisies Won't Tell cream sachet. OSP $2.38, CMV $32.50 MB.

1956 WEE TWO
(Left) Blue, white & yellow box has two tubes with yellow caps of Daisies Won't Tell hand cream & cream shampoo. OSP 89c, CMV $18.

1957 DAINTY HANDS
(Right) Pink, white & yellow box holds 2 tubes with pink hearts & yellow caps of Daisies Won't Tell hand cream. OSP 79c, CMV $18 MB.

1957 Only ONE I LOVE
Floral box contains 2 oz. cologne, cream lotion & bubble bath in Daisies Won't Tell. White flower caps with yellow centers. Any sets you find with pink caps are taken off Cotillion bottles and not considered a mint set. OSP $2.49, CMV $50 MB.

1963-64 DAISY CHAIN GIFT SET
Pink & white box holds 2 oz. Daisies Won't Tell cologne & pink tube of daisy hand cream. OSP $1.78, CMV $22 MB.

1958 FIELD OF DAISIES

Blue & white flowered box holds 2 oz. bottles of Daisies Won't Tell cologne, cream lotion with red ribbon & bubble bath. OSP $2.19, CMV $50 MB.

1956 LITTLE CHARMER

Black & white plastic basket with flowers on top holds Daisies Won't Tell 2 oz. cologne, gold pomade & tube of Daisy hand cream. OSP $3.50, CMV $65 MB.

1956 BLOSSOMS

Daisy box holds 2 oz. Daisies Won't Tell cologne with blue ribbon & gold pomade. OSP $1.59, CMV $27.50 MB - gold pomade $5.

1957 DAISY PETALS

Yellow & white box with pink hearts holds 2 oz. Daisies Won't Tell cologne & lime yellow pomade lipstick in corner of box. OSP $1.59, CMV $25 MB.

1959-60 DAISY BOUQUET

Blue & white flowered box holds 4 oz. Daisy cream lotion, Daisy bubble bath & 2 oz. Daisy dust. OSP $3.50, CMV $37.50 MB.

1957 DAISIES WON'T TELL SET

Box holds 2 oz. each in bubble bath, cream lotion & cologne. White & yellow daisy caps. OSP $2.49. Came with outer sleeve. Also came Daisy Talc can in place of cream lotion. CMV $60 MB.

1959 DAISY TREASURES

Pink box with yellow slide open cover with it. Light blue ribbon on daisy flower. Holds 3 bottles of nail polish with white caps & nail file. OSP $2.75, CMV $60 MB.

1961 PRETTY BEGINNER

Blue, white & yellow box holds Daisies Won't Tell 2 oz. cologne & choice of Daisy soap, Daisy dust, cream lotion, shampoo or bubble bath. OSP $2.38, CMV $25 - with soap $35 MB.

1956 DAISIES WON'T TELL SET

Daisy box holds 2 oz. Daisies Won't Tell cologne & bubble bath with center rib on each & can of 3¼ oz. Daisy talc. OSP $2.25, CMV talc can only $20 - $60 MB with outer sleeve.

1956 MISS DAISY SET

Daisy box holds Daisies Won't Tell 2 oz. cologne & beauty dust. Top of bottle sticks through top of box. OSP $2.35, CMV $40.

1957 DAISY BOUQUET
Blue, white & yellow box holds Daisies Won't Tell 2 oz. cologne, beauty dust & lime yellow pomade. OSP $2.95, CMV $45 MB - yellow pomade $5.

1956 PLAYMATE
Daisies carrying case holds Daisies Won't Tell 2 oz. cologne, cream lotion & gold or black pomade with plastic doll with movable arms with satin & net dress. Eyes open & shut, red hair. OSP $3.95 - CMV $90 MB.

1962-64 DAISY POMADE LIPSTICK
Pink box holds pink with gold base lipstick. OSP 59c, CMV $4 MB.

1958 DAISY DARLING
Blue box with daisies & red ribbon holds Daisies Won't Tell spray cologne & beauty dust. OSP $2.98, CMV $42.50 MB.

1957 MY DOLLY
White, yellow & green box holds Daisies Won't Tell 2 oz. cream lotion, cologne, pink or yellow pomade & plastic doll with movable arms, brown hair, blue hat, yellow dress trimmed in pink satin. OSP $3.95 - CMV $90 MB.

1960 FIRST WALTZ
Blue & white Daisies Won't Tell box holds First Waltz nail polish & pink pomade. OSP $1.25, CMV $20 MB.

1960 FIRST WALTZ LIPSTICK
Blue flowered box holds pink lipstick. Came in Daisies Won't Tell. OSP 50c, CMV $6 MB.

1960 DAISY PINK SET
Daisies box holds Daisy pink nail polish, white cap & pink metal pomade in box. OSP $1.25, CMV $20 MB.

1960 DAISY PINK NAIL POLISH
(Left) Blue & white box holds Daisies Won't Tell nail polish, white cap. OSP 69c, CMV $8 MB - $6 BO mint.
1960 FIRST WALTZ NAIL POLISH
(Not Shown) Blue & white box holds Daisies Won't Tell nail polish, white cap. OSP 69c, CMV $8 MB - $6 BO mint.
1960-61 DAISY POMADE LIPSTICK
(Right) Blue & white box holds pink & gold pomade in shades of 1st Waltz or Daisy Pomade. OSP 69c, CMV $6 MB.

DELFT BLUE

1972-74 DELFT BLUE
White milk glass with blue flowers.
SKIN-SO-SOFT SOFTENER
5 oz. SSP $4, CMV $5 BO - $6 MB.
FOAMING BATH OIL
5 oz. holds Patchwork, Moonwind or Sonnet. SSP $6, CMV $7 MB - $6 BO.
PITCHER & BOWL
5 oz. SSP $8, CMV $10 MB - $7 BO & bowl.
SOAP DISH & SKIN-SO-SOFT SOAP
3 oz. SSP $4, CMV $6 MB.

DELICATE DAISIES

1977-78 DELICATE DAISIES COLOGNE
(Left) 2 oz. bottle with white painted daisies on front. White cap. OSP $3.50, CMV $1 MB.

1977-78 DELICATE DAISIES PERFUMED TALC
(Inside Left) 2 oz. blue talc, white plastic top and bottom. OSP $2, CMV 50c. Also came with upside down label. CMV $8.

1977-78 DELICATE DAISIES BRUSH
(Center Left) Blue plastic with Avon on handle. OSP $5.50, CMV $1 MB.

1977-78 DELICATE DAISIES HAND CREAM
(Center Right) 1.5 oz. tube. OSP $2, CMV 25c.

1978 DELICATE DAISIES EARRINGS
(Inside Right) Green and gold flower design, for pierced ears. SSP $4.99, CMV $2.

1978 BUSY BEE BRACELET
(Right) Gold daisy on bracelet. SSP $4.99, CMV $2 MB.

ELEGANTE

1956-59 ELEGANTE PERFUME
Red & silver box holds ½ oz. bottle with silver cap & neck tag with red ribbon. OSP $7.50, CMV $125 in box - $75 bottle only with neck tag & ribbon.

1956-59 ELEGANTE BEAUTY DUST
(Left) Red paper sides with tin top & bottom. Silver letters on lid. OSP $2.25, CMV $15 - MB $20.

1956-59 ELEGANTE COLOGNE
(Inside Left) Red & silver box holds 4 oz. bottle with silver cap & neck tag & red ribbon. OSP $2.50, CMV $40 in box - $20 bottle only with neck tag & ribbon.

1957-59 ELEGANTE TOILET WATER
(Center) Red & silver box holds 2 oz. bottle with silver cap & neck tag & red ribbon. OSP $2, CMV $40 in box - bottle only with tag & ribbon $20.

1957-59 ELEGANTE POWDER SACHET
(Inside Right) 9/10 oz. bottle with silver cap. OSP $1.50, CMV $12 BO - $17 MB.

1956-59 ELEGANTE CREAM SACHET
(Right) .66 oz. jar with silver cap. OSP $1.50, CMV $8 BO - $13 MB.

1957 SPARKLING BURGUNDY
Round neck & silver box with red satin lining. Holds Elegante 4 oz. cologne, cream sachet, 1 dram perfume & beauty dust. OSP $8.95, CMV $115 MB.

1957 SNOW DREAMS SET
White box with red ribbon holds Elegante 2 oz. toilet water, cream sachet & 1 dram perfume in red wrapper. OSP $5.50, CMV $75 MB.

ELUSIVE

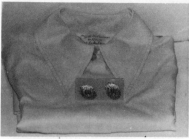

1969-74 ELUSIVE BEAUTY DUST
Pink plastic with gold or silver trim. OSP $6, CMV $3 - $5 MB.

1969-74 ELUSIVE SAMPLES
10 samples to a box. CMV 50c.

1969-75 ELUSIVE ROLLETTE
.33 oz. frosted glass. OSP $3, CMV 75c.

1970-73 ELUSIVE PERFUMED DEMI STICK
Paper center, white cap. OSP $1.75, CMV $1.

1969-75 ELUSIVE ½ OZ. COLOGNE
½ oz. pink frosted glass. OSP $2, CMV $1.

1969-75 ELUSIVE CREAM SACHET
Pink frosted glass. OSP $3, CMV 50c.

1970-72 ELUSIVE PERFUMED SKIN SOFTENER
Pink frosted glass. Lid came with gold or silver trim. OSP $4, CMV $1.

1970-71 ELUSIVE TRAY
Pink plastic, gold trim. OSP $4, CMV $6 MB - $4 tray only.

1970-72 ELUSIVE SCENTED HAIR SPRAY
(Back Left) 7 oz. pink can & cap with gold letters. OSP $1.50, CMV $3.

1971-74 ELUSIVE PERFUMED POWDER MIST
(Back Inside Left) 7 oz. pink painted label. OSP $4, CMV 50c.

1970-71 ELUSIVE PERFUMED POWDER MIST
(Back Center Left) 7 oz. pink paper label. OSP $4, CMV $2.

1971-74 ELUSIVE PERFUMED TALC
(Back Center Right) 3½ oz. pink paper container. OSP $1.35, CMV 50c.

1969-74 ELUSIVE COLOGNE MIST
(Back Inside Right) 3 oz. pink plastic coated bottle. OSP $6, CMV 50c.

1970-72 ELUSIVE FOAMING BATH OIL
(Back Right) 6 oz. pink plastic with pink cap. OSP $3.50, CMV $2.

1970-74 ELUSIVE PERFUMED SOAP
(Front) 3 pink bars in pink box. OSP $3.50, CMV $5 MB.

1969 ELUSIVE BLOUSE & CUFFLINKS
Blouse light lavender silk with label with S.M. Kent signature & Avon. Cufflinks are gold with pink sets. Awarded for selling Elusive cologne mists. CMV $10 blouse - $7.50 cufflinks.

1969 ELUSIVE PINK & GOLD SCARF
Given to Avon sales ladies on first Elusive sales campaign. White box has 4A design & signed by S.M. Kent, designer. CMV $7.50 MB.

1969-74 ELUSIVE COLOGNE MIST
(Left) Pink painted bottle with pink & gold cap. Paint doesn't go to bottom.
(Right) Later issue pink plastic coated bottle, pink & gold cap. OSP $6, CMV painted $1 - plastic coated 50c.

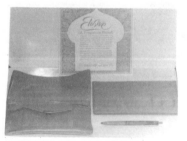

1969 ELUSIVE CLUTCH PURSE
(Left) Pink leather with gold trim. Awarded for selling cologne mists. CMV $10.

1969 ORDER BOOK COVER
(Right) Pink plastic with gold "Avon Honor Award" on cover, came with pink & gold pen. CMV $7.50.

1969 ELUSIVE BALLAD
(Back) Small black record marked Avon in pink sleeve. CMV $6.

EMPRISE

1977 EMPRISE PURSE AWARD
Black satin purse with jewel snap. Has gold carrying chain inside. Purse does not say Avon on it. Given to Reps for top sales of Emprise products. Came in clear plastic bag marked Avon. Designed by S.M. Kent. CMV $11 MB.

1977-80 EMPRISE PERFUME
Box holds ¼ oz. bottle with glass stopper with plastic base seal. OSP $15, CMV $10 BO - $14 MB.

1977 EMPRISE NECKLACE GIFT
Gold double E necklace given to Avon Team Leaders to introduce the new fragrance. T.L. on back side and it came in an Avon box. CMV $10. District Managers also got one marked D.M. on back and in D.M. Avon box. CMV $15 MB. Was also given to Division Managers. CMV $15 MB. Emprise money clip for male Reps. CMV $15 MB.

1977-78 EMPRISE PERFUMED SOAPS
(Left) Open end box holds 3 beige color bars. OSP $7, CMV $5 MB.
1977-78 EMPRISE PERFUMED SKIN SOFTENER
(Center) 5 oz. plastic jar, gold and black cap. OSP $6, CMV 25c.
1977-78 EMPRISE ULTRA CREME PERFUME
(Right) .66 oz. frosted glass jar, gold cap. OSP $4.50, CMV 25c.

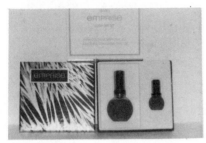

1977-78 EMPRISE ULTRA GIFT SET
Box came with 1.8 oz. Ultra cologne spray and .33 oz. Ultra purse concentre. OSP $11.50, CMV $11.50 MB.

1977-80 EMPRISE FOAMING BATH OIL
(Left) 6 fl. oz. bath oil. OSP $5.50, CMV 50c.
1977 EMPRISE PERFUMED POWDER MIST
(Inside Left) 7 oz. spray can or 4 oz. can. OSP $5, CMV 50c.
1976-80 EMPRISE ULTRA PURSE CONCENTRE
(Center Left) .33 oz. fluid. OSP $5, CMV 50c.
1977-80 EMPRISE PERFUMED TALC
(Center Right) 3.5 oz. OSP $3, CMV 50c.
1976-80 EMPRISE ULTRA COLOGNE SPRAY
(Inside Right) 1.8 oz. non aerosol spray. OSP $7.50, CMV 50c.
1977-80 EMPRISE ULTRA COLOGNE
(Right) 2 oz. OSP $6.50, CMV 50c.

ENGLISH PROVINCIAL

1972-74 ENGLISH PROVINCIAL
White milk glass with blue & pink flowers & aqua blue lid with flowers. Came in Charisma, or Bird of Paradise.

FOAMING BATH OIL
(Left) 8 oz. SSP $5, CMV $5 MB - $3 BO.
COLOGNE
(Inside Left) 5 oz. SSP $5, CMV $5 MB - $3 BO.
POWDER SACHET
(Inside Right) 1.25 oz. SSP $4, CMV $4 MB - $3 BO.
SOAP DISH & SOAP
(Right) 1.25 oz. SSP $4, CMV $4 - $6 MB.

FIELD FLOWERS

1971 FIELD FLOWERS UMBRELLA - AWARD
(Left) 18" spring green nylon umbrella has cream colored floral-relief handle. Given to Reps for making sales goal. CMV $10.
1971 FIELD FLOWERS RAIN CAPE - AWARD
(Center) Given to Pres. Club Reps only for making sales quota. Beige with floral sash. CMV $20.
1971 FIELD FLOWERS TOTE BAG - AWARD
(Right) Cream colored wet looking vinyl tote bag. Field Flowers pattern inside. Given to Reps for achieving sales goal. CMV $12.

1971 FIELD FLOWERS ORDER BOOK COVER & PEN
President's Club. One was given for being eligible for membership. Honor award was earned for sales goal. Cover on left - Canadian President's Club Honor Award. Each came with Avon pen. CMV $5 each with pen.

1970-73 FIELD FLOWERS PERFUMED TALC
(Left) 3½ oz. green paper label. OSP $2, CMV $1. 1973-77 Perfumed Talc had pink label. CMV 50c.

1970-78 FIELD FLOWER DEMI STICK
(Inside Left) Green paper band, white cap. OSP $2, CMV 50c.

1970-77 FIELD FLOWERS FRAGRANCE SAMPLES
(Inside Right) 10 samples in a box. CMV 50c.

1970-78 FIELD FLOWERS COLOGNE SAMPLE
(Right) Clear glass, white cap. CMV 25c.

1971-72 FIELD FLOWERS BATH BRUSH & SOAP
Pink brush approx. 16'' long & 5 oz. flower embossed pink soap. OSP $6, CMV $8 MB.

FIELD FLOWER PRODUCTS
1971-76 COLOGNE MIST
3 oz. green plastic coated over glass, yellow cap. OSP $7, CMV $1.

1971-72 COLOGNE GELEE
3 oz. green ribbed glass & orange cap. OSP $4, CMV $1.50.

1971-73 PERFUMED SKIN SOFTENER
5 oz. green glass, bright or pale blue cap. OSP $4, CMV $1.

1971-75 CREAM SACHET
.66 oz. green ribbed glass with purple cap. OSP $3, CMV 50c.

1971-76 PERFUMED POWDER MIST
7 oz. green, white & pink can. OSP $4.50, CMV 50c. Also came with upside down label. CMV $8.

1971-76 SOAP
Flowered box holds yellow, pink & green flower bars. OSP $5, CMV $6 MB.

1971-72 FOAMING BATH OIL
6 oz. green plastic bottle with pink flowered cap. OSP $4, CMV $1.

1971-72 SCENTED HAIR SPRAY
7 oz. pink & green can with green cap. OSP $1.50, CMV $3.

1971-75 AFTER BATH FRESHENER
Green plastic, blue cap. CMV 50c.

1976 COLOGNE ICE
1 oz. tube. CMV $1.

1976-78 FIELD FLOWERS PERFUMED SOAP
(Front Left) 3 oz. white with flowered band around center. OSP $1, CMV $1.

1972-76 FIELD FLOWERS AFTER BATH FRESHENER
(Back Left) 8 oz. green plastic bottle with aqua cap. OSP $4, CMV 50c.

1974-75 FIELD FLOWERS PERFUMED SOAP
(Front Inside Left) 3 oz. yellow green wrapper with flowers in center. OSP $1, CMV $1.

1974-75 FIELD FLOWERS HAND & BODY LOTION
(Back Right) 8 oz. yellow green plastic with yellow green plastic cap. OSP $2, CMV 50c.

1975-78 FIELD FLOWERS CREAM SACHET
(Front Inside Right) .66 oz. clear glass with gold & green cap. OSP $2, CMV 25c.

1973-76 FIELD FLOWERS PERFUMED SKIN SOFTENER
(Right) 5 oz. yellow green plastic jar, gold lid. OSP $3, CMV 50c.

1980-82 FIELD FLOWERS COLOGNE SPRAY
1.5 oz., yellow cap. SSP $4, CMV 50c.
PERFUMED TALC
3.5 oz. SSP $1.25, CMV 50c.
PERFUMED SOAP
3 oz. bar. SSP $1.25, CMV $1.
COLOGNE
.5 oz. SSP $1.75, CMV 50c.

FLOWER TALK

1972-73 FLOWER TALK
White with orange, blue, yellow, green & purple designs.
PERFUMED TALC
(Left) 3.5 oz. SSP $1, CMV $1.
COLOGNE MIST
(Inside Left) 3 oz. SSP $4, CMV $2 MB - $1 BO.
ROLLETTE
(Center) .33 oz. SSP $1, CMV $1.
DEMI STICK
(Inside Right) .19 oz. SSP $1, CMV 50c.
SAMPLE FLOWER TALK
(Top Right) CMV 25c.
CREAM SACHET
(Bottom Right) .66 oz. SSP $2, CMV $1 BO - $2 MB.

FLOWERTIME

1952 VALENTINE GIFT SACHET
In special red & white gift box. Came in Flowertime, Golden Promise, Quaintance or Cotillion. OSP 98c, CMV $17 MB as shown - $10 BO mint.

1950-53 FLOWERTIME POWDER SACHET
(Left) 1½ oz. with indented pink cap. OSP $1.19, CMV $15 in box - $10 bottle only.
1949-53 FLOWERTIME TALC
(Right) 5 oz. bottle with brass shaker top. OSP 89c, CMV $23 in box - $18 BO mint.

1949 DOUBLY YOURS SET
White & blue swing open box holds 2 oz. bottles of cologne with pink caps in Cotillion & Flowertime. OSP $2.10, CMV $65 MB.

1950-52 FLOWERS IN THE WIND
Blue & silver flip-open box with pink satin lining holds Flowertime cologne talc, powder sachet & 1 dram perfume. OSP $5.50, CMV $95 MB.

FOREVER SPRING

1949-53 FLOWERTIME COLOGNE
(Left) 4 oz. pink cap. OSP $1.75, CMV $20 in box - $16 bottle only. Same bottle came in 2 oz. size in sets only. CMV $20.

1949-53 FLOWERTIME TOILET WATER
(Center) 2 oz. pink cap. OSP $1.25, CMV $23 in box - $18 bottle only.

1949-50 FLOWERTIME POWDER SACHET
(Right) 1¼ oz. bottle has flat or indented pink cap. OSP $1.19, CMV $15 in box - $13 bottle only.

1949 FLOWER CLUSTER
Blue & gold box contains box of face powder, gold lipstick & 1 dram Flowertime perfume. OSP $3, CMV $50 MB.

1949-52 FLOWERTIME SET
Turquoise & gold box with satin lining holds 4 oz. Flowertime cologne & talc. OSP $2.75, CMV $60 MB.

1956-59 FOREVER SPRING PERFUME
Yellow & white box with purple base holds ½ oz. bottle with blue bird on yellow cap & painted label. OSP $5, CMV in box $100 - bottle only with bird $85.

1951-56 FOREVER SPRING PERFUME
Yellow & green box with blue & green ribbon holds 3 dram glass stoppered bottle with blue ribbon on neck & neck tag. OSP $5, CMV $100 in box - $85 bottle only with tag & ribbon.

1951-52 FOREVER SPRING 1 DRAM PERFUME
(Left) 1 dram, ribbed glass, gold cap. Came in green felt folder. OSP $1.75, CMV $17 in sleeve - $12 BO.

1956 FOREVER SPRING POWDER BOX COLOGNE
(Right) 1/16 oz. size bottle came in special beauty dust box set only. Came tied to silk ribbon. CMV $12 BO mint - $15 mint with ribbon.

1951-56 FOREVER SPRING BEAUTY DUST
(Left) Green & white can. OSP $1.75, CMV $20 - $25 MB.

1956-59 FOREVER SPRING BEAUTY DUST
(Right) Yellow & white paper box with tin top & bottom. OSP $1.95, CMV $16 - $20 MB.

1951-56 FOREVER SPRING COLOGNE
(Left) 4 oz. with yellow tulip cap & green painted label. Came in green box. OSP $2.25, CMV $20 in box - $16 mint bottle only.

1953-56 FOREVER SPRING POWDER SACHET
(Right) 1¼ oz. bottle with yellow cap & green painted label. Came in green box. OSP $1.25, CMV $15 in box - $11 bottle only mint.

1951-56 FOREVER SPRING TOILET WATER
2 oz. yellow tulip cap & green painted label. Came in green box. OSP $1.50, CMV $20 in box - $17.50 BO mint.

1956-59 FOREVER SPRING CREAM SACHET
(Left) Yellow glass bottom & cap with flowers on all 3 lids shown. OSP $1.25, CMV $8 - $11 MB.

1956-59 FOREVER SPRING POWDER SACHET
(Center) 9/10 oz. yellow glass & cap. OSP $1.25, CMV $9 - $12 MB.

1956-59 FOREVER SPRING BODY POWDER
(Right) Frosted glass jar with flowered cap, painted label. OSP $1, CMV $12 BO - $17 MB.

1956 SPRING MOOD
Yellow & white box holds Forever Spring body powder & 4 oz. cream lotion in green glass. OSP $1.95, CMV $40 MB.

1956-59 FOREVER SPRING COLOGNE
4 oz. bottle with blue bird on yellow cap, painted label, yellow & white flowered box. OSP $2, CMV in box $20 - bottle only with bird $15.

1956 SPRINGTIME
Yellow & white box holds Forever Spring beauty dust & 4 oz. cologne. OSP $3.95, CMV $50.

1956-59 FOREVER SPRING CREAM LOTION
(Left) 4 oz. clear glass with yellow cap, painted label. No bird on cap. Came in yellow & white box. OSP 95c, CMV in box $14 - bottle only $12 mint.

1956-59 FOREVER SPRING TOILET WATER
(Center) 2 oz. yellow cap with tiny blue bird, painted label. Came in yellow & white flowered box. OSP $1.50, CMV in box $20 - bottle only with bird $15 mint.

1951-56 FOREVER SPRING CREAM SACHET
(Right) Green box holds white glass jar with green lid. OSP $1.25, CMV $12 in box - $9 jar only, mint.

1956 MERRY MERRY SPRING
Yellow, white & blue box holds Forever Spring 2 oz. toilet water and cream sachet. OSP $2.75, CMV $37.50 MB.

1956-59 FOREVER SPRING CREAM LOTION
4 oz. green painted over clear glass bottle with yellow cap. OSP 95c, CMV $18 BO mint - $25 MB.

1957 SPRING GODDESS
Yellow & white box holds Forever Spring beauty dust, cream sachet & 4 oz. cologne. OSP $4.95, CMV $50 MB.

1953 FOREVER SPRING SET
Green & white box with green net lining holds Forever Spring body powder, cream sachet & 1 dram perfume in green felt sleeve. OSP $3.95, CMV $55 MB.

1952 FOREVER SPRING SET
Is same as above only did not have 1 dram perfume. OSP $2.75, CMV $37.50 MB.

1952-53 SPRING MELODY
Forever Spring body powder & cream sachet setting on top under clear plastic lid. OSP $1.95, CMV $35 MB.

1951 FOREVER SPRING REPRESENTATIVE GIFT SET
CMV $80 MB.

1953 SPRING SONG
Blue & green box holds Forever Spring 4 oz. cologne & 1 dram perfume. OSP $3.50, CMV $40 MB.

1956-57 APRIL AIRS
Yellow & white box with blue ribbon top holds Forever Spring body powder & cream sachet. OSP $2.25, CMV $40 MB.

1953 SPRING CREATION
Green box with net lining holds Forever Spring cream sachet & 1 dram perfume. OSP $2.75, CMV $40 MB.

1951-52 SPRING CORSAGE
Green box with clear plastic lid & bouquet of flowers holds Forever Spring 4 oz. cologne & 1 dram perfume. OSP $4.50, CMV $50.

1951-56 FOREVER SPRING BODY POWDER
(Left) Green & white paper container. OSP 95c, CMV $18.

1957-59 FOREVER SPRING PERFUMED TALC
(Right) 2.75 oz. yellow & white can, yellow cap. OSP 69c, CMV $10 - MB $12.

FOXFIRE

1980-83 FOX FIRE FRAGRANCE LINE
Red design color. Ultra Cologne Spray, 1.8 oz. SSP $7, CMV $1.

COLOGNE SAMPLES
Box of 10 packets. CMV 25c.

1980-83 GIFT SOAP & CASE
Red plastic case made in Italy. Bar of soap. SSP $5, CMV $5 MB. Soap only, CMV $1 mint. Case sold in 80-81.

ULTRA COLOGNE
2 oz., gold cap. SSP $6, CMV $1 MB.

LUXURY BATH FOAM
6 oz. plastic. SSP $3.50, CMV 25c.

PERFUME POWDER MIST
4 oz. red spray can. SSP $3, CMV 25c.

ULTRA COLOGNE
.33 oz. ribbed glass. SSP $2, CMV 50c MB.

PERFUMED TALC
3.5 oz. SSP $2, CMV .25.

PERFUMED SKIN SOFTENER
5 oz. red plastic jar. SSP $2, CMV 25c.

FOXFIRE FRAGRANCE FOLIO
C22-80 used by Avon Reps. in envelope. CMV $1.

GARDEN OF LOVE

1948 ONLY — GARDEN OF LOVE SWIRL PERFUME
3 dram glass stoppered bottle is swirl glass design with gold neck tag. Purple and white flowered box. OSP $3, CMV $90 BO mint, $120 MB.

1940-44 GARDEN OF LOVE PERFUME
Orange lid, gold base box holds 3 dram glass stoppered bottle with gold neck tag. OSP $2.50, CMV $100 mint BO, $125 MB.

1946-48 GARDEN OF LOVE POWDER SACHET
(Left) 1¼ oz. turquoise ribbed plastic cap and flowered label. OSP $1.19, CMV $20 in box, $17 bottle only.

1944-45 GARDEN OF LOVE SACHET
(Center) 1¼ oz. pink paper sachet. Came with pink plastic flower on lid. OSP $1.15, CMV $18 mint, $23 MB.

1940-46 GARDEN OF LOVE POWDER SACHET
(Right) 1¼ oz. bottle with black or turquoise metal cap. OSP $1.04, CMV $20, $15 bottle only.

GARDENIA

1940-42 GARDENIA PERFUME
Gold speckled box holds 3/8 oz. bottle with gold octagonal cap. OSP $1.50, CMV $50 BO mint, $80 MB.

1933-36 GARDENIA PERFUME "RIBBED"
½ oz. ribbed glass with black octagonal cap. Came in gold box set. CMV $45 mint.

1933-36 GARDENIA PERFUME "OCTAGONAL"
6 sided bottle and black octagonal cap. Came in Little Folks set and Hankerchief set. CMV $45 mint.

1948-52 GARDENIA PERFUME
3/8 oz. or 3 dram bottle with flowered cap, paper or painted label. Came in satin lined box with clear plastic lid. OSP $2.50 ea - CMV $80 MB, $40 BO mint.

GOLDEN PROMISE

ALL CONTAINERS PRICED EMPTY
See page 6 & 16 for Grading Examples
on Mint Condition

1947—50 GOLDEN PROMISE PERFUME
Gold and white flip open box holds ½ oz. bottle with gold cap and painted label. OSP $3.95, CMV $175 in box. Bottle only $100 mint.

1954-56 GOLDEN PROMISE PERFUME
Gold and white box holds ½ oz. bottle with flat glass stopper and gold & white label. OSP $3.95, CMV $125 in box., $90 bottle only mint.

1947-56 GOLDEN PROMISE BEAUTY DUST
(Left) Standard issue gold and white can. OSP $1.50, CMV $18 CO mint, $22 MB.
1947-51 GOLDEN PROMISE BEAUTY DUST
(Right) Smaller than regular issue. Came in sets only. CMV $20 mint.

1950-54 GOLDEN PROMISE PERFUME
Gold and white box holds 3 dram glass stoppered bottle with gold base label and neck cord. OSP $4, CMV $125 in box, bottle with label and cord $100.

1947 GOLDEN PROMISE BODY POWDER CHRISTMAS DEMO
Regular issue talc in gold box given to Avon ladies in special outer Merry Christmas demo box. OSP $1.50, CMV $30 MB with outer box shown.

1949 ONLY — GOLDEN PROMISE PERFUME
(Left) ¼ oz. glass bottle fits in gold metal case. Came in Golden Duet & Evening Charm Sets. CMV $25.
1953-56 GOLDEN PROMISE CREAM SACHET
(Center) White glass, square base with yellow flowered cap. OSP $1, CMV $9 BO, $13 MB.
1947-56 GOLDEN PROMISE BODY POWDER
(Right) Gold and white shaker top can. OSP $1.50, CMV $16 CO mint, $20 MB.

1952-56 GOLDEN PROMISE POWDER SACHET
(Left) 1¼ oz. yellow plastic cap. OSP $1.25, CMV $12 MB, $9 BO.
1951-52 GOLDEN PROMISE POWDER SACHET
(Center) 1¼ oz. gold cap. OSP $1.25, CMV $12 MB, $9 BO.
1948-50 GOLDEN PROMISE POWDER SACHET
(Right) 1¼ oz. smooth gold cap. OSP $1.19, CMV $12 MB, $9 BO.

1948 GOLDEN PROMISE SACHET
Special gold box, 62nd Anniversary issue. 1¼ oz. ribbed gold plastic cap or threaded brass cap. OSP $1.25, CMV $18.50 MB as shown.

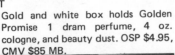

1947-49 GOLDEN PROMISE 3 PIECE SET
Gold and white box holds Golden Promise 1 dram perfume, 4 oz. cologne, and beauty dust. OSP $4.95, CMV $85 MB.

1947-49 GOLDEN PROMISE 2 PIECE SET
Gold and white box holds Golden Promise 4 oz. cologne and body powder. OSP $2.95, CMV $60 MB.

1947-56 GOLDEN PROMISE COLOGNE
4 oz. painted label, gold cap. OSP $2.25, CMV $18, MB $24.

1953-56 GOLDEN PROMISE TOILET WATER
2 oz. gold cap & painted label. OSP $1.50, CMV $20 - MB $24.

1950-51 GOLDEN PROMISE SET
Gold box with clear plastic cover and gold tie down ribbon holds Golden Promise 4 oz. cologne and beauty dust. OSP $3.95, CMV $60 MB.

1952-54 GOLDEN PROMISE DELUXE
Gold box with clear plastic lid and gold satin lining holds Golden Promise 4 oz. cologne, powder sachet, 1 dram perfume and body powder. Gold ribbon around box. OSP $6.25, CMV $100 MB.

1949 GOLDEN DUET
Small gold purse holds Lipstick and gold metal case with ½ dram bottle of Golden Promise perfume inside. OSP $2.50, CMV $35 mint, $40 MB.

1947 GOLDEN PROMISE PERFUME GIFT
Clear bottle, gold cap. Label is gold with red lettering, says "Golden Promise Perfume with Best Wishes of Avon Products Inc., Pasadena, Cal." Came in gold box with same statement. CMV $75 MB, $50 BO.

1953-54 GOLDEN JEWEL
White and gold box with gold jewel on front. Holds Golden Promise 2 oz. Toilet Water and 1 dram Perfume. Toilet Water cap fits through top of box. OSP $2.75, CMV $40 MB.

HANA GASA

1970-71 HANA GASA GIFT NOTES
Yellow with pink flowers, has 15 notes and envelopes. 18 seals. OSP $2, CMV $2.

1970 HANA GASA UMBRELLA
Banboo painted in Hana Gasa colors. Used at sales meetings at introduction of Hana Gasa. Came in Avon box. Very rare. CMV $100 in box.

1970-74 HANA GASA FRAGRANCE SAMPLES
10 in a box. CMV 50c box.

1970-74 HANA GASA COLOGNE SAMPLE
Sample bottle, white cap. CMV 25c.

1970-75 HANA GASA COLOGNE
½ oz. clear glass, yellow cap. OSP $2, CMV $1, $1.50 MB.

1970-74 HANA GASA PERFUME ROLLETTE
Yellow painted glass, yellow cap. OSP $3, CMV $1.

1970-75 HANA GASA CREAM SACHET
.66 oz. yellow painted over milk glass with yellow lid. OSP $3, CMV 50c.

1970-76 HANA GASA BEAUTY DUST
6 oz. yellow plastic. OSP $8.50, CMV $3 CO, $5 MB.

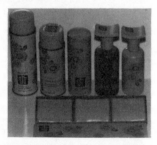

1971 HANA GASA HAIR SPRAY
7 oz. yellow can, OSP $1.50, CMV $3.

1971-74 HANA HASA PERFUME POWDER MIST
7 oz. yellow can. OSP $4, CMV $1.

1971-74 HANA GASA PERFUME TALC
3½ oz. yellow cardboard. OSP $1.35 CMV $1.

1971-77 HANA GASA FOAMING BATH OIL
6 oz. clear plastic bottle, also yellow plastic bottle, yellow cap. OSP $4.50 CMV $1.

1970-76 HANA GASA COLOGNE MIST
3 oz. yellow plastic coated glass, yellow cap. OSP $6, CMV $1.

1971-75 HANA GASA SOAP
3 yellow bars in pink and yellow box. OSP $5, CMV $5 MB.

HAPPY HOURS

1948-49 HAPPY HOURS TALC
2 3/4 oz. metal shaker cap. Sold in sets only. CMV $20 mint.

1948-49 HAPPPY HOURS COLOGNE
1 oz. plastic cap. Came in sets only. CMV $20 mint.

1948-49 HAPPY HOURS PERFUME
3 drams, pink cap. Rare. Came in sets only. CMV $50 mint.

1948-49 HAPPY HOURS SET
Pink and blue box holds Happy Hours Talc, Cologne and Perfume. OSP $2, CMV $115 MB.

1948-49 STAR BOUQUET
Green and pink box holds Happy Hours Talc and Cologne. OSP $1.25, CMV $67.50 MB.

1948-49 MEMENTO
Blue and pink box holds Happy Hours Cologne and Perfume. OSP $1.50, CMV $95 MB.

1970 HANA GASA HAPPI-COAT
Yellow with orange and green flowers. Given when someone a Representative recommended was appointed as a Representative. One size fits all. CMV $10 mint.

1970 HANA GASA JEWELRY
Enameled pin and clip on earrings are deep red and purple. Given when someone a Representative recommended was appointed as a Representative. CMV $15 set.

HAWAIIAN WHITE GINGER

1968 ONLY — HAWAIIAN WHITE GINGER TALC

(Left) 2.75 oz. green and white talc sold in perfume pair only. CMV $2.

1968-73 HAWAIIAN WHITE GINGER TALC

(Center) 3.5 oz. multi-colored cardboard, gold letter label. OSP $2, CMV $1. 1974-77 Talc came with pink letter label. CMV 50c.

1972 HAWAIIAN WHITE GINGER BEAUTY DUST

(Right) Multi-colored cardboard. OSP $3. CMV $4 mint, $5 MB.

1976-78 HAWAIIAN WHITE GINGER COLOGNE SPRAY

1.8 oz. flower embossed bottle, gold cap. OSP $5, CMV 50c.

1976-78 HAWAIIAN WHITE GINGER BODY SPLASH

8 oz. plastic bottle, white cap. OSP $5, CMV 50c.

1972-76 HAWAIIAN WHITE GINGER AFTER BATH FRESHENER

8 oz. white plastic bottle with white cap. OSP $5, CMV 50c.

1971-72 HAWAIIAN WHITE GINGER COLOGNE MIST

2 oz. Light green glass bottle with white cap. OSP $4.25, CMV $1, $2 MB.

1965-67 HAWAIIAN WHITE GINGER AFTER BATH FRESHENER

5 oz. bottle with white painted label and cap. Also came with and without gold 4A design. OSP $2, CMV $6 in box, $5 bottle only.

1967-72 BATH FRESHENER

(Left) 6 oz. glass bottle with white cap. OSP $2.50, CMV $2.

1968-76 HAWAIIAN WHITE GINGER FOAMING BATH OIL

(Center) 8 oz. plastic bottle. OSP $3, CMV 50c.

1969-72 HAWAIIAN WHITE GINGER CREAM LOTION

5 oz. plastic bottle. OSP $2, CMV 75c.

1968-72 HAWAIIAN WHITE GINGER CREAM SACHET

Both .66 oz. green frosted jars and flowered caps. Short jar 1967, same as Lily of the Valley jar. OSP $2., CMV $2. Tall green jar in 1969. CMV $1.

1972-76 HAWAIIAN WHITE GINGER COLOGNE MIST

2 oz. clear glass bottle with clear plastic cap with inner cap of green, red and white. OSP $5, CMV 75c.

1972-74 HAWAIIAN WHITE GINGER ROLLETTE

.33 oz. clear bottle, white cap with colored band. OSP $2.50, CMV 50c.

1970-78 HAWAIIAN WHITE GINGER DEMI STICK

.19 oz. green, red and white, white cap. OSP $1.75, CMV 50c.

1973-78 HAWAIIAN WHITE GINGER CREAM SACHET

.66 oz. glass jar, white, green and red cap. This has 3 different lid labels. Early one - no zip code. .66 oz. Next - zip but no numbers. Doesn't have weight on lid. Later ones have zip and numbers but no weight on lid. OSP $2.50, CMV 50c.

1972-73 FLORAL DUET HAWAIIAN WHITE GINGER

Came with Rollette and bar of soap. OSP $3.25, CMV $5 MB.

1970-78 HAWAIIAN WHITE GINGER SOAP

3 oz. single bar soap (same as shown in set). OSP $1, CMV $1.

1969-75 WHITE GINGER FRAGRANCE KWICKETTES (Not shown) Box holds 14 packets. OSP $1.50, CMV $1 box.

1980-82 HAWAIIAN WHITE GINGER COLOGNE SPRAY

1.5 oz. blue cap. SSP $4, CMV 50c.

PERFUMED TALC

3.5 oz. SSP $1.25, CMV 50c.

PERFUMED SOAP

3 oz. bar. SSP $1.25, CMV $1.

COLOGNE

.5 oz. SSP $1.75, CMV 50c.

HELLO SUNSHINE

1979-80 HELLO SUNSHINE PRODUCTS

LIP BALM
Pink, white and yellow. CMV 50c.

HAND CREAM
White, yellow and pink 1.5 oz. tube. Green cap. CMV 50c.

FUN SHINE NAIL TINT
.5 oz clear glass, pink cap. CMV 75c MB.

COLOGNE
2.5 oz. clear glass, yellow cap. Yellow and pink decal on glass. CMV $1.

1980-83 HELLO SUNSHINE SOLID PERFUME
Yellow plastic jar, white flowered top. SSP $2.50, CMV $1 MB.

BRUSH
White plastic, 6½" long. SSP $4, CMV $2 MB.

1970 ROYAL FOUNTAIN CREME SACHET
Blue base with silver and gold fountain top. Contains Her Prettiness Creme Sachet. OSP $3, CMV $5 MB.

1970-71 HER PRETTINESS TALC
3½ oz. flowered paper box. OSP $1, CMV $2.

HER PRETTINESS

1969-72 HER PRETTINESS ENCHANTED COLOGNE MIST
Brown tree base holds 3 oz. cologne mist in green bubble top and green bird spray button. OSP $5, CMV $6, $7 MB.

1969-72 MAGIC MUSHROOM CREAM SACHET
Green, pink and blue plastic. OSP $3, CMV $4.

1969-72 LADY BUG FRAGRANCE GLACE
Red, black and green plastic bug. OSP $3, CMV $3, $4 MB.

1969-71 LOVE LOCKET FRAGRANCE GLACE
Gold locket and chain, in yellow, gold and pink box. OSP $4.50, CMV $10 MB.

1969-72 SECRET TOWER ROLLETTE
Red cap on bottle. OSP $1.75, CMV $3 MB.

1969-71 PRETTY ME DOLL
5 oz. plastic bottle with gold hair, cap and pink neck ribbon. Holds Powdered Bubble Bath. 6½" high. OSP $6, CMV $8, $6 BO.

1969-72 FLOWER BELLE COLOGNE MIST
Blue top with yellow base has 2 oz. Her Prettiness Cologne Mist. OSP $3.50, CMV $4.

1969-72 BRUSH AND COMB SET
Pink box with yellow comb and brush. OSP $3.50, CMV $5.

1969-72 BUNNY PUFF
3½ oz. white plastic rabbit with pink fluff tail. Holds Her Prettiness Talc. OSP $3.75, CMV $5.

1976 BUNNY FLUFF PUFF
Reissued — Same except holds Pink & Pretty. OSP $4, CMV $4. Also has R on bottom for reissue. 1979 reissue in yellow rabbit. It is shown in childrens toy section.

1969-70 HER PRETTINESS ART REPRODUCTION PRINT
14"x 18" pink, green and white, was free with purchase of any Her Prettiness products. Came in cardboard tube with Her Prettiness sticker and a poem "Her Prettiness Serves Ten in The Garden". CMV $8, three pieces. $4 print alone.

1970-71 HER PRETTINESS LIP KISSES
Lip Pomade, tubes blue and white, pink and white, orange and white in cherry, chocolate, or peppermint. Mirror on back side of cap. OSP $1.95, CMV $2 each, $3 MB.

1969-72 HER PRETTINESS COLOGNE SAMPLE
1/8 oz. clear glass white cap. Painted label. Came in envelope. CMV $1 mint in envelope.

HERE'S MY HEART

1961 HERE'S MY HEART COLOGNE SPECIAL ISSUE
Blue and white box (short issue) holds 4 oz. cologne. OSP $3, CMV $16 MB as shown.

1960-66 HERE'S MY HEART PERFUMED BATH OIL
6 oz. blue plastic, white beaded cap. OSP $2.25, CMV $6 BO, $7 MB.
1966-68 FOAMING BATH OIL
6 oz. blue plastic, white beaded cap. OSP $2.75, CMV $5 BO, $6 MB.

1946-48 HERE'S MY HEART PERFUME
½ oz. glass stoppered bottle with painted label and pink neck ribbons. Bottle is tied to pink satin heart shaped base and box. OSP $7.50, CMV $140 MB. Bottle only with ribbon, $100 mint.

1964-68 HERE'S MY HEART PERFUME OIL
½ oz. painted label and white beaded cap. Came in blue and white box. OSP $3.50, CMV $8 in box. $6 bottle only.
1958-61 HERE'S MY HEART LOTION SACHET
1 oz. blue plastic coated bottle with white beaded cap and painted label. Blue and white box. OSP $2, CMV $8 in box. $5 bottle only.
1961-68 HERE'S MY HEART 2 OZ. COLOGNE
2 oz. white beaded cap and painted label, blue and white box. First introduced in red and white rose box. OSP $1.75, CMV in rose box $8. In blue box $3. Bottle only $2.
1958-76 HERE'S MY HEART COLOGNE MIST
3 oz. blue plastic coated bottle with white beaded cap and painted label. Blue and white box. OSP $7, CMV $1.

1963 HERE'S MY HEART PERFUME OIL FOR THE BATH
½ oz. painted label and white beaded cap. Came in blue and white box. OSP $3.50, CMV $15 MB, bottle only $12.
1970-71 HERE'S MY HEART ½ OZ. COLOGNE
½ oz. painted label, white beaded cap, blue and white box. OSP $1.50, CMV $1 BO - $1.50 MB.

1957-58 HERE'S MY HEART COLOGNE MIST
3 oz. blue plastic coated bottle with indented heart, 2 hearts on gold cap. Also plain lid. OSP $3, CMV $18 BO mint. $23 MB.

1948-49 HERE'S MY HEART PERFUME
½ oz. glass stoppered heart shaped bottle. Painted label, pink satin ribbon and heart shaped box and base. Very rare. OSP $7.50, CMV $125 BO mint, $175 MB.

1959-62 HERE'S MY HEART TOILET WATER
2 oz. painted label and white beaded cap. Came in blue and white box. OSP $2.50, CMV $12 in box, $10 bottle only.

1960-63 HERE'S MY HEART 4 OZ. COLOGNE
4 oz. bottle with white beaded cap and painted label. Came in blue and white box. OSP $3, CMV $12 MB, $10 BO.

1965-66 HERE'S MY HEART PERFUMED SOAP
3 oz. white soap in blue and white wrapper. OSP 39c, CMV $3.

1964-68 HERE'S MY HEART PERFUME MIST
2 dram blue and white metal with gold band. OSP $3, CMV $5, $6 MB.

1970-73 HERE'S MY HEART FRAGRANCE SAMPLE
10 foil samples in a box. CMV 75c box.

1960-66 HERE'S MY HEART POWDER SACHET SAMPLE
CMV $1.

1958-68 HERE'S MY HEART CREAM LOTION
4 oz. bottle with painted label and white beaded cap. OSP $1, CMV $2 BO, $3 MB.

1958-63 HERE'S MY HEART SPRAY PERFUME
Blue, white and gold box holds blue tin container with gold cap with hearts on top. OSP $3.50, CMV $12 in box, $8 container only.

1959 POWDER SACHET CHRISTMAS BOX
Blue box with gold butterflies sold Christmas only 1959 with choice of powder sachet in Here's My Heart, Persian Wood, Nearness, Cotillion (pink painted), Bright Night and To A Wild Rose. OSP $1.50-$1.75, CMV CMV $15 each MB as shown.

1958 LOTION SACHET
½ oz. clear glass fan shaped bottle with blue cap. Came in Here's My Heart and Persian Wood. Came in Wishing set only. CMV $8 ea. MB, $4 BO.

1961-63 HERE'S MY HEART BODY POWDER
4 oz. blue plastic bottle with white beaded cap, painted label. OSP $1.95, CMV $8 MB, $5 BO.

1962-65 HERE'S MY HEART SOAP
Blue and white box holds 2 white heart shaped soaps. OSP $1.29, CMV $24 MB.

1967-68 HERE'S MY HEART PERFUME ROLLETTE
.33 oz. ribbed glass, smooth gold cap. OSP $3, CMV $3.

1963-65 PERFUMED CREAM ROLLETTE
.33 oz. 4A embossed bottle with gold cap. OSP $1.75, CMV $3 mint.

1960-66 HERE'S MY HEART POWDER SACHET
9/10 oz. blue glass, white beaded plastic cap. OSP $2, CMV $8, $10 MB.

1958-60 HERE'S MY HEART POWDER SACHET
Blue and white plastic squeeze bottle with white beaded cap. OSP $1.75, CMV $10 , $12 MB.

1975-78 HERE'S MY HEART DEMI STICK
.19 oz. blue and white, white cap. OSP $1, CMV 25c.

1976-77 HERE'S MY HEART CREAM SACHET
.66 oz. clear glass, gold, blue and white lid. OSP $2, CMV 25c.

1950 HERE'S MY HEART PERFUME SAMPLE
With gold lid. CMV $30.

1957-58 HERE'S MY HEART LOTION SACHET
1 oz. blue plastic coated bottle with hearts on gold cap, painted label. OSP $2, CMV $15, $18 MB.

1960 ROMANTIC MOOD
Blue and white box with blue satin lining with Here's My Heart cologne mist, cream sachet and beauty dust. OSP $8.25, CMV $40 MB.

1958-62 HERE'S MY HEART PERFUMED TALC
2.75 oz. blue and white can, white beaded cap. OSP 79c, CMV $3 CO, $4 MB.

1966-70 HERE'S MY HEART SCENTED HAIR SPRAY
7 oz. blue and white can, 4A on cap. OSP $1.50, CMV $3.

1962-72 HERE'S MY HEART PERFUMED TALC
2.75 oz. blue and white can with white cap. OSP 79c, CMV $1.

1964 HEART FELT SET
Blue and white box holds Here's My Heart 2 oz. cologne and cream sachet. OSP $3.50, CMV $22.50 MB.

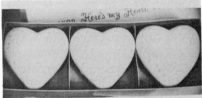

1966-67 HERE'S MY HEART SOAP
Blue and white box holds 3 heart shaped bars. OSP $1.75, CMV $22.50 MB.

1959-64 HERE'S MY HEART SOAP
Blue and white box, holds 2 white heart shaped bars. OSP $1.29, CMV $24 MB.

1958 SWEETHEARTS
Blue and white heart shaped box with white satin lining and white rose on lid. Holds Here's My Heart cologne mist, and plastic powder sachet or lotion sachet. OSP $5, CMV $45 MB.

1964 HEARTS IN BLOOM
Blue and white box holds Here's My Heart cologne mist, cream sachet and cream lotion. OSP $6.50, CMV $37.50 MB.

1961 SENTIMENTAL HEART
Blue box with blue satin lining holds Here's My Heart cologne mist and beauty dust. OSP $6.50, CMV $32.50. MB.

1959-75 HERE'S MY HEART CREAM SACHET
.66 oz. white beaded cap. Came blue painted over clear glass. CMV 50c or blue paint over white milk glass. CMV $3, OSP $3.

1964-73 HERE'S MY HEART PERFUMED SKIN SOFTENER
5 oz. blue painted over milk glass or clear glass jar with gold and white lid. OSP $3, CMV $1.

1958-70 HERE'S MY HEART BEAUTY DUST
White plastic powder box with beaded edge. Some with yellow lid and white handle. CMV $11, OSP $3 white issue. CMV $3 CO, $5 MB.

1959 HEART O'MINE
Blue and white box with blue heart on lid with white rose and blue satin lining. Holds Here's My Heart cologne mist, cream sachet, beauty dust and spray perfume. OSP $11.95, CMV $45 MB.

1961 TWO HEARTS GIFT SET
Blue and white box holds 2 oz. Here's My Heart cologne and cream sachet. OSP $3.50, CMV $25 MB.

1963 NEW REMEMBRANCE
Blue and white box holds Here's My Heart cologne mist and beauty dust. OSP $6.95, CMV $30 MB.

1967-72 HONEYSUCKLE AFTER BATH FRESHENER
8 oz. bottle with orange cap and center band label. OSP $3, CMV $1.

1972-76 HONEYSUCKLE AFTER BATH FRESHENER
8 oz. yellow plastic bottle with yellow cap. OSP $5, CMV 50c.

1967-76 HONEYSUCKLE FOAMING BATH OIL
8 oz. plastic bottle with orange cap. OSP $4.50, CMV $1.

1969-72 HONEYSUCKLE CREAM LOTION
5 oz. yellow plastic bottle. OSP $2, CMV 50c.

1967-77 HONEYSUCKLE PERFUMED TALC
3½ oz. yellow and white paper container. OSP $2, CMV 50c.

1968-69 HONEYSUCKLE SOAP
6 sided box holds 3 yellow bars OSP $3, CMV $9 MB.

1970-74 HONEYSUCKLE PERFUMED DEMI STICK
.19 oz. yellow, green and white. Yellow cap. OSP $1.75, CMV $1.

1971-72 HONEYSUCKLE COLOGNE MIST
2 oz. yellow glass bottle, yellow cap. OSP $4.25, CMV $1.

HONEYSUCKLE CREAM SACHET SAMPLE
Sample in foil. CMV 25c.

1971-73 HONEYSUCKLE KWICKETTES
Box holds 14 Kwickettes. OSP $1.75, CMV $1.

1967-78 HONEYSUCKLE PERFUMED SOAP
3 oz. bar in yellow and orange wrapper. OSP $1.25, CMV $1.25.

1967-75 HONEYSUCKLE CREAM SACHET.
.66 oz. yellow frosted glass with orange lid. OSP $2.50, CMV 50c.

HONEYSUCKLE

1973-77 HONEYSUCKLE CREAM SACHET — (Left to Right)
.66 oz. clear glass jar. Green, orange and white lid. OSP $2.50, CMV 50c.

1975-78 DEMI STICK
.19 oz. yellow, green and white with white cap. OSP $1.75, CMV 50c.

1972-74 HONEYSUCKLE ROLLETTE
.33 oz. clear bottle, white cap with colored band. OSP $2.50, CMV $1.

1972-75 HONEYSUCKLE COLOGNE MIST
2 oz. clear glass bottle with clear plastic cap with inner cap of yellow and green. OSP $5, CMV 75c.

1978 COLOGNE ICE (not shown)
1 oz. size, CMV 50c.

1978 BUBBLE BATH GELEE (not shown)
4 oz. tube, CMV 50c.

1980-82 HONEYSUCKLE COLOGNE SPRAY
1.5 oz. yellow cap. SSP $4, CMV 50c.

PERFUMED TALC
3.5 oz. SSP $1.25, CMV 50c.

PERFUMED SOAP
3 oz. bar. SSP $1.25, CMV $1.

COLOGNE
5 oz. SSP $1.75, CMV 50c.

1972-73 HONEYSUCKLE FLORAL DUET
Box came with Rollette and bar of soap. OSP $3.25, CMV $5 MB.

IMPERIAL GARDEN

1973 IMPERIAL GARDENS AWARDS
Earned for selling certain numbered Cologne Mist for each level.

Level 1 BUD VASE
White china with orange and gold trim. CMV $8 MB.

Level 2 TRAY
White plastic with orange and gold trim. CMV $10, $15 MB.

Level 3 GINGER JAR
White china with orange and gold trim. CMV $25 MB.

Level 4 ROBE
Beige with orangish pink trim and floral sash. CMV $25 MB.

1974-76 IMPERIAL GARDEN PERFUMED SOAP
Three 3 oz. cakes white soap. Came in white and orange box. SSP $6, CMV $7 MB.

1974-77 IMPERIAL GARDEN PERFUMED POWDER MIST
7 oz. orange painted can, white lid. OSP $5, CMV 50c.

1974-76 IMPERIAL GARDEN PERFUMED SKIN SOFTENER
5 oz. orange plastic, white and gold cap. OSP $5.50, CMV 50c.

1973 IMPERIAL GARDEN COASTERS
4 white plastic, orange design. CMV $25 MB set.

1974-76 IMPERIAL GARDEN PERFUME TALC
3.5 oz. white, gold and orange, cardboard. OSP $1, CMV 25c.

1974 ONLY — IMPERIAL GARDEN BEAUTY DUST
6 oz. white plastic with orange and gold. OSP $5, CMV $6, $7 MB.

1974-76 IMPERIAL GARDEN EMOLLIENT MIST
4 oz. white with gold and orange. Has orange cap. OSP $3, CMV 50c.

1973 IMPERIAL GARDEN CERAMIC VASE TEST
Test vase from factory never sold by Avon. Has gold band around top of cap and bottom is glazed over Avon. Blue and green flowers on front different from regular issue. CMV $25.

1973 IMPERIAL GARDEN TEA SET
White Bone China with Imperial Garden design. Given to one Representative in each district when her recommendation name was drawn at the Christmas Party. CMV $175 MB.

1973-75 IMPERIAL GARDEN CERAMIC VASE
Some came with short neck and tall cap and some with long neck and short caps. White with orange flowers and gold stems. 18 oz. ceramic vase. Bath crystals, 7" high. SSP $16, CMV $16 MB.

1973-77 COLOGNE MIST
3 oz. SSP $8, CMV $1.

1973-77 CREAM SACHET
.66 oz. SSP $4.50, CMV 50c.

1973-77 ROLLETTE
.33 oz. SSP $4.50, CMV 25c.

1973-77 SAMPLE BOTTLE COLOGNE
CMV 25c.

1973-77 SAMPLE
CMV 25c box. Box of 10 samples.

1973-77 IMPERIAL GARDEN COLOGNE MIST
3 oz. white with orange flowers and gold stems. 2 different designs as pictured. OSP $8, CMV $1 each.

JARDIN D'AMOUR

See Misc. Perfume & Powder Section for
additional Jardin D'Amour bottles.

**1954 Only JARDIN D'AMOUR
PERFUME SET**
Blue & gold bucket with gold tie
down cord. Holds 1½ oz. bottle with
gold label, clear plastic cap with blue
stone in gold set. Bottom of bucket
holds 1 dram perfume. Came in blue,
white & gold lay down box. OSP
$15, CMV in box complete $200 -
1½ oz. bottle in bucket mint $175 -
1 dram perfume $15 - 1½ oz. bottle
only $100 mint.

**1926-33 JARDIN D'AMOUR
PERFUME**
Orange box with gold base for 1 oz.
glass stoppered bottle. Black label at
neck. OSP $3.50, CMV $100 BO -
$135 MB.

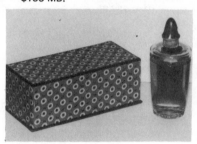

**1929-33 JARDIN D'AMOUR
PERFUME**
2 oz. glass stoppered bottle. Orange
box. Label on top of bottle. OSP
$6.50, CMV $100 BO mint - $135
MB.

1930's JARDIN D'AMOUR PERFUME
1 oz. clear glass bottle with frosted
glass stopper. Silver & blue CPC label.
If you have any information on when
or what this bottle was sold or given
for, please contact Bud Hastin. Very
rare. CMV $150 mint.

1926-30 JARDIN D'AMOUR SACHET
Brass cap, silver & blue label. Rare.
CMV $85 mint.

1932-36 JARDIN D'AMOUR SACHET
1¼ oz. ribbed glass jar, black cap.
OSP $1.04, CMV $25 mint BO - $30
MB.

JASMINE & ROYAL JASMINE

1926-36 JARDIN D'AMOUR TALC
Frosted glass with brass shaker top. Front paper label. OSP $1.04, CMV $60 BO mint - $75 MB.

1926-32 JARDIN D'AMOUR VANITY COMPACT
Silver compact. OSP $2.25, CMV $40 in box - compact only $35 mint.

1934-36 JASMINE SOAP
Beige & gold box holds 3 bars. OSP $1.02, CMV $50 MB.

1939 Only JASMINE SOAP
Gold striped box holds 3 bars. Avon on back of soap. OSP $1.25, CMV $60 MB.

1936-45 JASMINE SOAP
Turquoise & gold box holds 3 embossed bars. OSP $1.02, CMV $47.50 MB.

1966-67 JASMINE GIFT SOAP
Floral box contains 3 yellow Jasmine soaps. OSP $2, CMV $20 MB.

1954-59 ROYAL JASMINE SOAP
Box holds 3 bars, with round or flat edges. Box lid lifts off. OSP $1.69, CMV $25 MB.

1959-66 ROYAL JASMINE SOAP
Same box only lid flips back and not off. The soap has flat edges. CMV $22 MB.

1946-53 JASMINE SOAP
Black flowered box holds 3 bars. OSP $1.25, CMV $40 MB.

1948-49 JASMINE SOAP
Christmas only. Black flowered box holds 3 white bars. OSP $1.28, CMV $40 MB.

1980-82 WILD JASMINE PERFUMED TALC
(Left) 3.5 oz. cardboard, plastic top & bottom. SSP $1.50, CMV 50c mint.

1980-82 WILD•JASMINE PERFUMED SOAP
(Right) SSP $1.25, CMV $1 mint.

1982 WILD JASMINE COLOGNE SPRAY
(Left) 1.5 oz. SSP $4, CMV 50c.

1982 WILD JASMINE PERFUMED TALC
(Center Back) 3.5 oz. SSP $1.25, CMV 50c.

1982 WILD JASMINE PERFUMED SOAP
(Right) 3 oz. bar. SSP $1.25, CMV $1.

1982 WILD JASMINE COLOGNE
(Center Front) .5 oz. SSP $1.75, CMV 50c.

1964-68 JASMIN AFTER BATH FRESHENER
(Left Back) 8 oz. glass bottle with yellow cap & painted label. Yellow flowered box. OSP $2.50, CMV $2 BO - $3 MB.

1966-70 JASMIN FOAMING BATH OIL
(Left Center Back) 8 oz. frosted plastic bottle with yellow cap, green or white painted label, yellow box. OSP $2.50, CMV $1.50.

1964-66 JASMIN PERFUMED BATH OIL
(Not Shown) 8 oz. plastic bottle, green cap. Green or white painted label. OSP $2.50, CMV $2.50.

1964-68 JASMIN PERFUMED TALC
(Right Center Back) 3½ oz. yellow flowered paper container with plastic shaker top. OSP 89c, CMV $2.

1967-72 JASMIN FRAGRANCE KWICKETTES
(Right Back) 14 foil towellettes in box. OSP $1.25, CMV $1 box.

1964-67 JASMIN PERFUMED SOAP
(Front Left) 3 oz. bar in yellow flowered wrapping. OSP 39c, CMV $2.

1967-72 JASMIN CREAM SACHET
(Front Right) .66 oz. yellow frosted glass with gold & white lid. OSP $2.50, CMV 50c.

1957-59 ROYAL JASMINE BATH OIL
Yellow, white & green box holds 8 oz. bottle with yellow cap and flowered label. OSP $1.95, CMV $25 MB - bottle only $20.

1945-52 JASMINE BATH SALTS
9 oz. clear glass with black cap & label. Label came with either a large or small pink flower on front. Came in black box. OSP 75c, CMV $40 in box - $30 bottle only mint.

1936-44 JASMINE BATH SALTS
9 oz. glass jar, turquoise lid. OSP 63c, CMV $20 BO mint - $25 MB.

1946-50 JASMINE POWDER SACHET
(Left) 1¼ oz. bottle with black cap & label. Came in black box. OSP $1.19, CMV $20 in box - $15 bottle only.

1947-50 JASMINE DUSTING POWDER
(Right) 13 oz. black & gold tin can with pink flowers on lid. OSP $1.50, CMV $25 - MB $30.

1946-48 JASMINE TOILET WATER
2 oz. gold cap, also came in black flowered box. Turquoise box shown. OSP $1.19, CMV in box $40 - bottle only $30 mint.

1945 Only FANTASY IN JASMINE
Black box with pink flowers holds Jasmine bath salts & 2 Jasmine soaps. OSP $1.60, CMV $77.50 MB.

1948 FANTASY IN JASMINE
Black box with pink flowers holds 2 bars Jasmine soap & 2 oz. Jasmine toilet water. OSP $2.39, CMV $75 MB.

1954-57 ROYAL JASMINE BATH SALTS
Yellow & white flowered box holds 8 oz. bottle with yellow cap. OSP 89c, CMV $25 MB - $20 BO.

1942-44 FANTASY IN JASMINE SET
Green box holds 2 bars Jasmine soap & 9 oz. Jasmine bath salts with turquoise lid. OSP $1.35, CMV $70 MB.

1956-57 FANTASY IN JASMINE
White box with yellow flowers holds 2 bars Royal Jasmine soap & 2 oz. Royal Jasmine bath oil with white cap & black label. OSP $1.95, CMV $45 MB - 2 oz. bath oil $25 BO.

1940-43 BATH ENSEMBLE
Blue flowered flip open box holds Jasmine bath salts, Jasmine 2 oz. toilet water, 2 bars of Jasmine soap & can of dusting powder. OSP $3.50, CMV $150 MB set.

1940 FANTASY IN JASMINE SET
Blue box with flowers holds 9 oz. Jasmine bath salts & 2 bars soap. OSP $1.35 - CMV $100 MB.

1946-47 FANTASY IN JASMINE
Black box with pink flowers holds 2 bars of Jasmine soap & 9 oz. bottle of Jasmine bath salts. OSP $1.95, CMV $75 MB. Set also came with 2 bottles in boxes of 1¼ oz. Jasmine sachet in place of soaps. CMV with boxed sachets $100 MB.

1954-57 ROYAL JASMINE SET
Yellow & white flowered box holds 8 oz. Royal Jasmine bath salts & bar of Royal Jasmine soap. OSP $1.39, CMV $37.50.

1949 JASMINE POWDER SACHET
(Left) 1½ oz. clear glass bottle, black cap & label. OSP $1.25, CMV $20 - $25 MB.

1949 JASMINE TOILET WATER
2 oz. black cap & label. OSP $1.25, CMV $35 - MB $40.

LAVENDER
SEE 1984 SUPPLEMENT IN BACK OF THIS BOOK FOR MORE POMANDERS

1946-48 LAVENDER SACHET CAKES
(Top) Box holds 2 flower design wrapped cakes of sachet. OSP 79c, CMV $25 MB.

1945-46 LAVENDER SACHETS
(Bottom) Beige box holds 2 foil wrapped cakes of sachet. Plain band. OSP 79c, CMV $25 MB.

1945 LAVENDER SOAP
Pink box holds 3 Lavender embossed bars. OSP 85c, CMV $60 MB.

1944-45 LAVENDER SACHET
Beige box holds 2 lavender wrapped cakes of sachet. One set is wrapped in clear cellophane with a flowered band. The other set is wrapped in lavender flowered paper, no band. OSP 79c set. Some boxes have label printed on box & some boxes plain. CMV $25 MB.

1935 Only LAVENDER SOAP
Box holds 3 lavender bars of soap. OSP 67c, CMV $75 MB.

1946 Only LAVENDER SOAP SET
Box holds 3 lavender bars of soap. OSP 85c, CMV $50 MB.

1935-38 LAVENDER BLOSSOMS
Lavender & pink box holds package of Lavender Blossoms. OSP 50c, CMV $40 MB.

1938-43 LAVENDER TOILET WATER
(Left) 4 oz. lavender cap. OSP 78c, CMV $35 BO - $40 MB. CPC on box, 1938-39 add $5.

1945-46 LAVENDER TOILET WATER
(Right) 4 oz. lavender cap. OSP 89c, CMV $40 BO - $45 MB.

1946-48 LAVENDER TOILET WATER
(Left) 4 oz. pink cap. OSP $1.19, CMV $35 BO - $40 MB.

1934-37 LAVENDER TOILET WATER
(Right) 4 oz. ribbed bottle with blue or gold cap. Lavender label, box shown used 1934-36. OSP 75c - CMV $45 mint BO, $55 MB.

1970-72 LAVENDER & LACE
Lavender & white box holds 1.7 oz. white glass bottle of Lavender cologne with lavender ribbon. A lavender & white lace handkerchief came with it. OSP $4.50, CMV $5 set - bottle only $2 MB.

1934-38 LAVENDER ENSEMBLE
Lavender box holds 4 oz. Lavender toilet water, 2 bars Lavender soap & package of Lavender Blossoms. OSP $1.50, CMV $125 MB set - Lavender Blossoms only $50 MB.

1977-78 LAVENDER BOUQUET SACHET PILLOWS
Pink box holds 6 satin lavender filled sachet pillows. Came with pink ribbon around them. SSP $4.99, CMV $4.

1938-40 LAVENDER ENSEMBLE
Lavender flip open box with cardboard liner holds 4 oz. Lavender toilet water, 2 bars of Lavender soap wrapped in lavender paper & 2 sachet cakes with lavender band around them. OSP $1.50, CMV $80 MB.

1938 Only LAVENDER ENSEMBLE
Lavender flip open box holds 4 oz. Lavender toilet water with same label as 1934 Lavender toilet water, 2 bars of Lavender soap, 2 Lavender sachet cakes. OSP $1.50, CMV $100 MB - bottle only $45.

1940-43 LAVENDER ENSEMBLE
Lavender flowered box with satin lining holds 4 oz. Lavender toilet water, 2 bars Lavender soap & 2 Lavender sachet cakes. OSP $1.75, CMV $90 MB.

1946-48 LAVENDER ENSEMBLE
Blue & pink flowered flip open box holds 4 oz. bottle, pink cap of Lavender toilet water, 2 pink bars of Lavender soap & 2 paper wrapped cakes of sachet. OSP $2.75, CMV $90 MB.

1941 Only LAVENDER ENSEMBLE
Box holds 2 Lavender sachet cakes, bottle of Lavender toilet water & 2 Lavender bars of soap. OSP $1.50, CMV $85 MB set.

1961-68 LAVENDER POWDER SACHET
.9 oz. pink & white label & neck band, glass & plastic stopper. CMV one with 4A design in place of size $4 BO, $7 MB. CMV on 9 oz. $20 MB, $15 BO. Box on right is 1965, box in center is 1961.

LEMON VELVET

1939 LAVENDER SET

Yellow box with lavender, green & pink flowers holds 4 oz. Lavender toilet water, 2 cakes Lavender soap & 2 sachet cakes with plain lavender color paper ribbons. CMV $125 MB.

1973 LEMON VELVET MOISTURIZED FRICTION LOTION
(Left) 8 oz. light yellow glass with gold cap. OSP $4, CMV $2 BO - $3 MB.

1973-75 LEMON VELVET PERFUMED POWDER MIST
(Inside Left) 7 oz. yellow, green & white, green lid. OSP $4, CMV 50c.

1972-76 LEMON VELVET COLOGNE MIST
(Center) 2 oz. clear glass bottle with clear plastic cap with inner cap of yellow & green. OSP $4.25, CMV 75c.

1972-74 LEMON VELVET ROLLETTE
(Inside Right) .33 oz. clear bottle with green & yellow cap. OSP $2.50, CMV 50c.

1973-76 LEMON VELVET PERFUMED SKIN SOFTENER
(Right) 5 oz. yellow plastic jar with gold, yellow & green lid. OSP $2, CMV 50c.

1975-77 LEMON VELVET CREAM SACHET
(Not Shown) .66 oz. white, yellow, green cap. OSP $3, CMV 50c.

1969-77 LEMON VELVET PERFUMED SOAP
Yellow flowered box holds 3 yellow bars. OSP $3, CMV $4.

1969-73 PERFUMED SKIN SOFTENER
5 oz. yellow frosted glass jar with green flowered lid. OSP $3.50, CMV 50c.

1969-76 BATH FOAM
8 oz. yellow plastic bottle with green cap. OSP $3.50, CMV 50c.

1969-76 MOISTURIZED FRICTION LOTION
10 oz. yellow plastic bottle with green cap. First issue green smooth cap, second issue green cap with flower on top. OSP $3, CMV 50c.

1969-74 FRAGRANCE KWICKETTES
Yellow box holds 14 packets. OSP $1.50, CMV $1.50 box.

1969-74 BEAUTY DUST
6 oz. yellow paper box with clear plastic lid. OSP $3.50, CMV $6 - $8 MB.

1971-75 CREAM SACHET
.66 oz. yellow glass & cap. OSP $3, CMV 50c.

1971-75 PERFUMED DEMI STICK
Yellow & green plastic tube with white cap. OSP $1.75, CMV 50c.

1971-72 BATH MIT
Yellow bath mit sponge. OSP $1.50, CMV $1.

1971-74 CLEANSING GEL
6 oz. yellow tube. OSP $3, CMV 50c.

1945-46 LAVENDER ENSEMBLE

Blue, pink & white box with silver bottom holds 4 oz. Lavender toilet water, 2 bars Lavender soap & 2 sachet cakes. OSP $1.95, CMV $90 MB.

1946 LAVENDER ENSEMBLE

Blue, pink & green flowered box with satin lining holds 2 bars of Lavender soap, 4 oz. bottle of Lavender toilet water & 2 flower wrapped cakes of sachet. OSP $2.75, CMV $95 MB.

LILAC

1940 LILAC TOILET WATER
2 oz. gold ribbed cap with "A" on top, gold label. Blue box. Has Avon Products Inc. label. OSP 78c, CMV $35 BO mint - $40 MB. Same bottle sold 1934 to 1939 only bottom of label only says Toilet Water & does not say Avon Products. CPC on backside of label. Same CMV as above.

1966 LILAC SOAP
Lavender box holds 3 piece lavender soap in cellophane wrapper. OSP $2.50, CMV $15 MB.

1968-77 LILAC SOAP
Box holds lavender bars. OSP $5, CMV $5.

1964-68 LILAC AFTER BATH FRESHENER
8 oz. glass bottle with pink cap & pink or white painted label. Pink box. OSP $2.50, CMV $2.

1964-66 LILAC PERFUME BATH OIL
8 oz. frosted plastic bottle with pink cap & painted label, pink box. OSP $2.50, CMV $2.50.

1964-76 LILAC PERFUMED TALC
3½ oz. pink paper container with plastic shaker top. OSP $2, CMV $1.

1971-73 LILAC FRAGRANCE KWICKETTES
Box holds 14 towelettes. OSP $1.75, CMV $1.50 MB.

1970-76 LILAC PERFUMED DEMI STICK
.19 oz. lavender label with white cap & bottom. OSP $1.75, CMV 50c.

1968-70 LILAC PERFUMED DEMI STICK
.19 oz. lavender label & cap & bottom. OSP $1.75, CMV $1.

1964-67 PERFUMED SOAP
1 bar in pink flowered wrapping. OSP 39c, CMV $2.50 mint.

1967-75 LILAC CREAM SACHET
.66 oz. purple frosted glass with gold & white lid. OSP $2.50, CMV 50c.

1975-76 LILAC CREAM SACHET
.66 oz. clear glass, white cap with lilacs on top. OSP $3, CMV 25c.

1966-75 LILAC FOAMING BATH OIL
8 oz. plastic bottle, pink cap. OSP $2.50, CMV 50c.

LILY OF THE VALLEY

1949-52 LILY OF THE VALLEY TOILET WATER
2 oz. white cap. OSP $1.25, CMV $45 MB - $35 bottle only.

1934-40 LILY OF THE VALLEY
2 oz. gold ribbed cap, "A" on top. Gold front label. OSP 78c, CMV $35 BO mint - $40 MB.

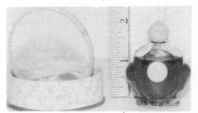

1948-52 LILY OF THE VALLEY PERFUME
3 dram bottle with flower cap. Came in satin lined box with clear plastic lid. OSP $2.50, CMV $80 MB - $40 BO mint.

1946-49 LILY OF THE VALLEY TOILET WATER
Green box holds 2 oz. bottle with gold cap & label. OSP $1.19, CMV $40 MB - $30 BO mint.

1952-54 LILY OF THE VALLEY PERFUME
3 dram, white cap, white satin lined box. OSP $3.75, CMV $85 MB - $40 BO mint. Also came in Gardenia.

1966-68 LILY OF THE VALLEY SOAP
Green box holds 2 green cakes. OSP $2, CMV $18.50 MB.

1974 Only LILY OF THE VALLEY CREAM SACHET
(Left) .66 oz. clear embossed glass with white cap with flowers. First issued with this jar. OSP $1.25, CMV $1 BO - $2 MB.
1975-76 LILY OF THE VALLEY CREAM SACHET
(Center) .66 oz. clear ribbed glass with white cap with flowers. OSP $1.25, CMV $1.
1974-76 LILY OF THE VALLEY PERFUME DEMI STICK
(Right) .19 oz. white with flowers. OSP $1, CMV $1.

1964-68 LILY OF THE VALLEY AFTER BATH FRESHENER
8 oz. glass bottle with green cap, painted label in green or white letters, green box. OSP $2.50, CMV $2 MB - $1 BO.
1964-66 PERFUMED BATH OIL
8 oz. frosted plastic bottle with green cap, painted label in green or white letters, green box. OSP $2.50, CMV $3.
1964-70 PERFUMED TALC
3½ oz. green paper container with plastic shaker top. OSP 89c, CMV $1.50.
1964-67 PERFUMED SOAP
3 oz. bar with green & white flowered wrapping. OSP 39c, CMV $3 mint.

1966-70 LILY OF THE VALLEY FOAMING BATH OIL
(Left) 8 oz. white plastic, green label & cap. OSP $2.50, CMV $2.
1967-75 CREAM SACHET
(Bottom Right) .66 oz. green frosted glass jar with gold & white lid. OSP $2.50, CMV 50c.
1964-68 LILY OF THE VALLEY KWICKETTES
(Top Right) Box of 14 fragrance samples. OSP $1.25, CMV $2 MB.

1979-80 LILY OF THE VALLEY PRODUCTS
COLOGNE ICE STICK
(Left) Yellow & green plastic. SSP $2.49, CMV 50c.
PERFUMED TALC
(Center) 3.5 oz. cardboard sides, plastic top & bottom. SSP $1.29, CMV 25c.
CHATEAU OF FLOWERS BOOK
(Right) Green hardback book on story of Lily of the Valley. Book does not say Avon on it. Must be in Avon box cover as shown. SSP $2, CMV $2 MB.

1979 LILY OF THE VALLEY SCENTED PILLOW
10" x 10" lace green & white scented pillow. SSP $11.99, CMV $8 MB.

SEE 1984 SUPPLEMENT IN BACK OF BOOK FOR MORE PRODUCTS

LITTLE BLOSSOM

1981-82 LITTLE BLOSSOM WHISPER SOFT COLOGNE
1.5 oz. clear glass painted decor. Pink cap. SSP $3.75, CMV $2 MB.
1981-82 LITTLE BLOSSOM CHEEKY ROSE BLUSH
Pink & white plastic jar. SSP $2.25, CMV $1 MB.
1981-82 LITTLE BLOSSOM CHEERFUL LIP TINT
White flowered tube, pink cap. SSP $1.25, CMV $1 mint, no box.
1981-82 LITTLE BLOSSOM SCENTED PICTURE FRAME
Pink plastic frame 4½" x 4½" has scented fabric picture of little blossom. SSP $6, CMV $6 MB.

LUCY HAYS

1936 Only LUCY HAYS PERFUME
2 dram, gold cap. Sold for 20c with other purchase to celebrate Mr. & Mrs. McConnell 51st wedding anniversary. Lucy Hays was Mrs. McConnell's maiden name. Sold March 3 to 23, 1936 only. CMV in box $85 - bottle only $65 mint.

1955-56 LULLABYE SET
Blue & pink box holds baby oil & baby powder. OSP $1.39, CMV $45 MB.

LULLABYE

1946-50 LULLABYE BABY TALC
(Left) 5 oz. pink paper container with pink & white plastic top & bottom. OSP 65c, CMV $35 MB, $30 talc only mint.

1946-50 LULLABYE BABY OIL
(Left Center) 6 oz. clear glass bottle, back side flat. Pink cap & painted label. OSP $1, CMV $50 MB - $40 BO.

1946-50 LULLABYE BABY CREAM
(Right Center) White milk glass jar with pink lid & label. OSP 89c, CMV $30 MB, $25 jar only.

1946-50 LULLABYE BABY SOAP
(Right) Plastic wrapper with pink painted bow & flowers on wrapper. OSP 39c - CMV $25 mint.

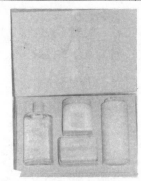

1946-50 LULLABYE BABY SET
Pink box holds Lullabye baby oil, Lullabye baby soap, Lullabye baby cream & Lullabye baby talc. OSP $3.55 - CMV $150 MB.

1951-55 LULLABYE BABY SET
Blue, pink & white box holds baby lotion, baby talc, lanolin baby soap. OSP $2.35, CMV $65 MB.

1964-66 LULLABYE BABY SET
Pink & blue box holds 2 bars baby soap & choice of Tot 'N Tyke baby oil, baby lotion or baby shampoo. OSP $1.96, CMV $27.50 MB.

LUSCIOUS

1950 LUSCIOUS PERFUME AWARD
(Left) Gold & purple box holds 3 dram, ribbed glass stopper. Stopper different from regular issue. Given when Luscious was first issued. CMV $150 in box - $100 bottle only.

1950 LUSCIOUS PERFUME
(Right) 1 dram clear bottle with gold cap & label. Came in brown felt wrapper. OSP $1.75, CMV $12 bottle only - $18 in wrapper.

1950-55 LUSCIOUS PERFUME
(Left) 1 dram, painted label with smooth gold cap. Came in felt wrapper. OSP $1.75, CMV in wrapper $15 - bottle only $10 mint.

1955-56 LUSCIOUS PERFUME
(Right) 1 dram, painted label, embossed gold cap. Came in felt wrapper. OSP $1.75, CMV in wrapper $15 - bottle only $8.

1950 LUSCIOUS PERFUME
3 dram glass stoppered bottle, came with painted label or with gold neck tag label. OSP $2.25, CMV $125 in box - $100 bottle only.

MARIONETTE

1940-44 MARIONETTE PERFUME
(Left) 1 dram bottle, plastic cap. OSP 75c, CMV $25 BO - $30 MB.

1938 MARIONETTE PERFUME
(Right) ¼ oz. size. Gold ribbed cap with "A". CPC on label. Sold in honor of Mr. McConnell's birthday. OSP 20c, CMV $50 MB - $40 BO.

1940-46 MARIONETTE TOILET WATER
2 oz. gold ribbed cap & gold label. Also came with plastic caps. OSP $1.04, CMV $30 BO mint - $35 MB.

1938-46 MARIONETTE SACHET
1¼ oz. with turquoise plain metal cap or ribbed turquoise plastic cap. Shown with regular issue box. OSP $1.04, CMV $20 MB - $15 BO.

1940 Only MARIONETTE SACHET SPECIAL ISSUE BOX
(Left) Short issue blue & pink box holds regular issue marionette powder sachet on left in 1¼ oz. size. Sold for 20c with regular order. CMV $25 MB in this box only.

1938 Only MARIONETTE SACHET
(Right) 1¼ oz. ribbed glass bottle with turquoise plain metal cap or ribbed plastic turquoise cap. OSP $1.04, CMV $25 BO - $28 MB.

1939-40 MARIONETTE TOILET WATER
2 oz. plastic cap, long front label. OSP 20c, CMV $45 in box - $35 bottle only.

1972-73 MINERAL SPRINGS SOAP
(Left) 2 bars in gold & yellow box. OSP $2, CMV $4 MB.

1972-74 MINERAL SPRINGS PERFUMED POWDER MIST
(Inside Left) 7 oz. yellow, gold, brown & beige with beige cap. OSP $2, CMV $1.

1973 BATH MITT
(Inside Right) 9" long sponge with white cord. Sold for use with all bath gelee. OSP $1, CMV $1 mint.

1972-77 MINERAL SPRINGS BATH CRYSTALS
(Right) 12 oz. amber plastic bottle with marbleized cap. OSP $4, CMV 50c.

1972-77 MINERAL SPRINGS BATH CRYSTALS SAMPLE
(Front) Yellow, gold & beige foil packets in box. CMV 50c each box.

MINERAL SPRINGS

MERRIMENT

1955 JOLLY SURPRISE
Pink & blue flip open box holds choice of 4 oz. bottle of Merriment cologne. OSP $1.75. Or bubble bath. OSP $1.50. With pink caps. CMV in box $55 each - bottle only $40 each.

1973-75 MINERAL SPRINGS BATH FOAM
(Left) 8 oz. marbleized plastic bottle with marbleized cap. OSP $3, CMV 50c.

1972-76 MINERAL SPRINGS SPARKLING FRESHENER
(Inside Left) 8 oz. amber plastic bottle with marbleized cap. OSP $3, CMV 50c.

1972-74 MINERAL SPRINGS CLEANSING GEL
(Inside Right) 6 oz. amber plastic tube with marbleized lid. OSP $2, CMV 75c.

1972-74 MINERAL SPRINGS MOISTURIZING BODY RUB
(Right) 8 oz. amber bottle with marbleized cap. OSP $3, CMV 75c.

1976-78 MINERAL SPRINGS BATH CRYSTALS
12 oz. green container. OSP $6, CMV 50c.

MISS LOLLYPOP

1967-69 MISS LOLLYPOP COLOGNE BOOT
2 oz. glass boot with gold cap & red tassel. Red & white box. OSP $2, CMV $8 MB - bottle only with tassel $5.

1967-70 MISS LOLLYPOP CREAM SACHET
(Left) .66 oz. dark or light yellow glass jar with white kitten on red, white & pink cap. Kittens eyes are blue or black, head also turns on some. OSP $2, CMV $5 MB, $4 BO. Also came with white base. CMV $7 MB - $6 BO.

1967-70 MISS LOLLYPOP COLOGNE MIST
(Right) 3 oz. pink plastic coated bottom with red band, white hat with red & yellow ribbon. OSP $3, CMV $6 MB - $5 BO.

1968 MISS LOLLYPOP HAND CREAM
(Left) 2 oz. white plastic tube, white boots & purse, yellow cap. OSP 75c, CMV $3.

1968 MISS LOLLYPOP HAND CREAM
(Right) 2 oz. white plastic tube, black boots & purse, yellow cap. OSP 75c, CMV $3.

1967-68 MISS LOLLYPOP POWDERETTE
(Left) 3½ oz. container of perfumed talc, red plume on top is long handled puff. OSP $2.50, CMV $10 MB.

1969 PRETTY TOUCH
Yellow, pink, green & orange plastic light switch plate. OSP 29c with purchase of Miss Lollypop items. Hard to find. Sold only 1 campaign. CMV $9 MB.

1968-70 MISS LOLLYPOP POWDER MITT
(Left) Yellow, orange & white plastic mitt filled with powder. Pink & white box. OSP $2.50, CMV $5 MB.

1967-70 MISS LOLLYPOP SOAP & SPONGE
(Right) Pink soap & 9'' long sponge. Pink & white box. OSP $2.50, CMV $12 MB.

1967 MISS LOLLYPOP LIP POP
(Left) 1st issue pink & white dots, mirror top with face on back. OSP $1.50, CMV $4 MB - $8 lip pop.

1968 MISS LOLLYPOP LIP POP
(Right) Same box came with 2 pink & white dot lip pops, no mirror top. OSP $1.75, CMV $5 MB.

1968-70 MISS LOLLYPOP ICE CREAM PUFF
(Left) 3½ oz. yellow plastic bottom with pink fluff. Holds talc. OSP $3, CMV $4 BO - $6 MB.

1968-70 MISS LOLLYPOP DOUBLE DIP BUBBLE BATH
(Right) 5 oz. orange & white plastic bottle, red cap. OSP $2, CMV $4 BO - $5 MB.

1967-69 MISS LOLLYPOP LIP POPS
(3 on Left) Girls face on handle. Pink lemonade, cherry, raspberry, peppermint & cola. OSP $1.75 each, CMV $3 - $4 MB.

1968-69 MISS LOLLYPOP ROLLETTE
(Center) Pink, yellow & white cap. 1/3 oz. size. OSP $1.50, CMV $3 MB - $2 BO.

1968-70 MISS LOLLYPOP PERFUMED TALC
(Right) 3½ oz. paper container with plastic shaker top. OSP $1, CMV $5 MB - $4 CO.

1968 PRETTY ME
Box with white plastic tray holds Miss Lollypop perfume rollette & lip pop in choice of peppermint, pink lemonade, cherry, raspberry or cola. OSP $3.25, CMV $12 MB.

MOONWIND

1971 MOONWIND TRAY
(Top Left) Blue glass tray trimmed in silver emblem of Diana in center. Given for selling 10 Moonwind cologne mist during C18-19. CMV $22 - MB $25.

1971 MOONWIND JEWELRY BOX
(Bottom Left) Blue & silver. Emblem of Diana on top in silver. Given for selling 20 Moonwind cologne mist in C18-19. CMV $25 - $30 MB.

1971 MOONWIND ROBE
(Right) Blue, zipper front with silvery trim. Zipper pull is emblem of Diana. Given to President's Club representatives for selling 35 Moonwind Cologne mists. CMV $30 - MB $35.

1972-73 MOONWIND PIN/SCARF HOLDER
Silver with blue enamel & blue set. SSP $6, CMV $6 MB.

1975-78 MOONWIND PERFUMED SOAP
3 cakes blue soap. Blue & silver lid slides over gold box. OSP $4, CMV $4 MB.

1971-80 MOONWIND FRAGRANCE
All are blue trimmed in silver.
1971-75 COLOGNE MIST
(No. 1) 3 oz. blue with silver painted top. OSP $7.50, CMV $1.

1975-80 COLOGNE MIST
(No. 2) Blue with flat top, 2.7 oz. size. OSP $8, CMV 50c.

1971-76 PERFUME ROLLETTE
(No. 3) 1/3 oz. OSP $4.50, CMV 50c.

1971-76 BEAUTY DUST
(No. 4) 6 oz. OSP $10, CMV $3 - $6 MB.

1972-77 PERFUMED POWDER MIST
(No. 5) 7 oz. silver or blue caps. OSP $5, CMV 50c. Some with upside down painted label. CMV $8.

1972-73 PERFUMED SKIN SOFTENER
(No. 6) 5 oz. blue glass. OSP $5, CMV 50c.

1971-75 CREAM SACHET
(No. 7) .66 oz. OSP $4, CMV 50c.

1972-73 PERFUMED SOAPS
(No. 8) 3 bars, blue, in blue box. OSP $6, CMV $7 MB.

1972 FOAMING BATH OIL
(Not Shown) 6 oz. OSP $5, CMV $1.50.

1976-78 CREAM SACHET
(Not Shown) Blue with silver cap. OSP $4.50, CMV 25c.

1973-78 MOONWIND PERFUMED TALC
(Left) 3.5 oz. blue cardboard trimmed in silver. OSP $2.50, CMV 25c.

1972-73 MOONWIND BATH PEARLS
(Left Center) Blue plastic jar with silver trim. Contained 75 capsules of emollient oil. OSP $5, CMV $3 - $5 MB.

1971-78 MOONWIND FRAGRANCE SAMPLES
(Right Center) 10 foil samples in box. CMV 25c.

1971-78 MOONWIND COLOGNE SAMPLES
(Right) Clear glass bottle with white cap. CMV 25c.

1975-76 MOONWIND EMOLLIENT MIST
(Left) 4 oz. blue & silver, blue cap. OSP $3, CMV 50c.

1973-78 MOONWIND PERFUMED SKINSOFTENER
(Inside Left) 5 oz. blue plastic jar with blue & silver lid. Came with 2 different lids, one has silver edge and one is blue edges. OSP $3, CMV 25c.

1974 MOONWIND DEMI STICK
(Left Center) .19 oz. white with blue & silver. OSP $1, CMV 25c.

1975-78 MOONWIND POWDER SACHET
(Right Center) 1.25 oz. blue & silver, cardboard. OSP $2, CMV 25c.

1976-78 MOONWIND PERFUMED SOAP
(Inside Right) 3 oz. blue bar with blue & silver wrapper. OSP $1, CMV $1.

1974-75 MOONWIND PERFUMED SOAP
(Right) 3 oz. blue bar with blue wrapper & multi-colored center. OSP $1, CMV $1.50.

1973 MOONWIND COLOGNE & BATH OIL
4 oz. clear glass bottles, gold caps. Came in Treasure Chest set only. CMV $3.

1971 MOONWIND ORDER BOOK COVERS
Dark blue with silver trim. President's Club cover earned for entry into President's Club. Honor Award earned for sales goal. Each came with pen. CMV $4 Honor cover with pen - $6 President's cover with pen.

NEARNESS

1956-58 NEARNESS BODY POWDER
(Left) Frosted glass bottle with blue cap & label. Blue & gold box. OSP $1., CMV $16. MB - bottle only $12.

1957-61 NEARNESS PERFUMED TALC
(Center) Blue can & cap. OSP 69c, CMV $10 in box - can only $7.

1956-61 NEARNESS POWDER SACHET
(Right) 1¼ oz. blue glass bottle with blue cap & label. OSP $1.50, CMV $12 in box, $8 bottle only. Also came .9 oz. size. Same CMV.

1957-59 NEARNESS COLOGNE MIST
(Left) 3 oz. blue plastic coated bottle with blue cap, blue & gold box. OSP $2.75, CMV $27.50 MB - $22.50 BO mint.

1959-61 NEARNESS COLOGNE MIST
(Right) 3 oz. blue plastic coated bottle with pearl on pearl colored cap. Cap will turn gray in sunlight & not considered mint. Blue & gold box. OSP $2.95, CMV $20 BO mint - $25 MB.

1959-61 NEARNESS BEAUTY DUST
Plastic pearl color lid with lavender rim & turquoise bottom. General issue. OSP $2.95, CMV $15 MB - $10 container only. Rare issue came all lavender matching rim & bottom. CMV $18 MB - $13 CO.

1956 Only NEARNESS SEA SHELL NECKLACE
Gold finished pendant with pearl on fine chain. Came only in Always Near set. CMV $25.

1956-61 NEARNESS TOILET WATER
(Left) 2 oz. bottle with blue cap & see through label on back side. Came in blue & gold box. OSP $2, CMV $20 in box - $15 bottle only.

1955-61 NEARNESS COLOGNE
(Right) 4 oz. bottle with blue cap & see through label on back side. Came in blue & gold box. OSP $2.50, CMV $20 in box - $15 bottle only.

1957 Only NEARNESS COLOGNE
(Left & Center) ½ oz. clear glass. Sold in Gems & Crystals set only. Came with 2 different caps. Available in 4 fragrances. CMV $12.50.

1955-61 NEARNESS CREAM SACHET
(Right) Blue glass bottom, blue metal cap. OSP $1.50, CMV $8 BO - $10 MB.

1955-59 NEARNESS 1 DRAM PERFUME
(Left) 1 dram, clear smooth glass, gold scroll cap. Came in blue felt wrapper. OSP $2.25, CMV $8 BO - $15 in wrapper.

1956-57 TWO PEARLS SET
(Right) Blue & gold box with 2 pearls on lid holds Nearness body powder & cream sachet. OSP $2.50, CMV $40 MB.

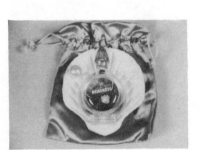

1955-59 NEARNESS PERFUME
Blue satin draw bag holds clam shell with pearl & ½ oz. bottle with blue cap & see through label on back side. OSP $7.50, CMV in bag $100 - bottle only $75.

1956-59 NEARNESS BEAUTY DUST
Blue cardboard container with tin bottom. OSP $2.25, CMV $20 MB - $15 container only, mint. CMV $22 for special 1956 Christmas issue box as shown, MB.

1957 Only NEARNESS CHARM
Blue box holds Nearness toilet water & can of talc. OSP $2.50, CMV $40 MB.

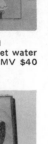

1958 SEA MIST SET
Blue & gold box with net lining holds Nearness cologne mist & cream sachet. OSP $3.95, CMV $60 MB.

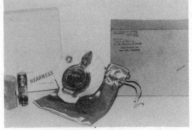

1956 NEARNESS GIFT PERFUME COMBO SET
½ oz. Nearness perfume on the clam shell in blue satin bag. Came with 1 dram Nearness perfume in blue felt wrapper in white box & outer sleeve. OSP $7.95, CMV $130 MB.

1956 ALWAYS NEAR SET
Blue sea shell box with pink satin lining holds Nearness 2 oz. toilet water, 1 dram perfume & gold sea shell necklace with pearl. OSP $5.95, CMV $75 MB.

1957 CIRCLE OF PEARLS
Blue plastic box with blue plastic cover holds Nearness 2 oz. toilet water, cream sachet & pearl necklace. OSP $5.95, CMV $65 MB.

OCCUR!

1964-68 OCCUR! CREAM LOTION
(Left) 4 oz. gold cap & painted label. Came in black & gold box. OSP $1.75, CMV $4 MB - $2 BO.

1970-71 OCCUR! ½ OZ. COLOGNE
(Center Left) ½ oz. size with gold cap & painted letters. Came in black & gold box. OSP $1.50, CMV $1 BO - $2 MB.

1964-69 OCCUR! PERFUME OIL
(Center Right) ½ oz. gold cap & painted label. Came in black & gold box. OSP $5, CMV $6 MB - $4 BO.

1964-71 OCCUR! 2 OZ. COLOGNE
(Right) 2 oz. bottle with gold cap & painted label. Came in black & gold box. OSP $2.50, CMV $1 BO - $2 MB.

1964-74 OCCUR! PERFUMED TALC
(Left) 2.75 oz. black can & cap, gold painted label. OSP $1, CMV 50c.

1966-74 OCCUR! FOAMING BATH OIL
(Center) 6 oz. black plastic bottle with gold cap & painted label. Came in black & gold box. OSP $3.50, CMV $3 MB - $2 BO.

1963-76 OCCUR! COLOGNE MIST
(Right) 3 oz. black plastic coated bottle with gold cap & painted label. Came in black & gold box. Older issue was gold bottom under plastic coating. CMV $3. Came with & without 3 oz. on front of bottle. CMV $2. OSP $7, CMV $11.

1971-75 OCCUR! BEAUTY DUST
(Left) 6 oz. black cardboard, non-refillable. OSP $8.50, CMV $3 - $4 MB.

1963-70 OCCUR! BEAUTY DUST
(Center Back) Black plastic box with gold handle on black lid. OSP $5, CMV $3 - $5 MB.

1964-72 OCCUR! PERFUMED SKIN SOFTENER
(Right) 5 oz. black painted over white milk glass or clear glass jar with black & gold lid. OSP $1.75, CMV $1. Also came white milk glass painted black or solid black glass. CMV $7 each.

1965-68 OCCUR! PERFUMED SOAP
(Center Front) Black wrapped soap. OSP 49c, CMV $2.

1964-65 OCCUR! PERFUMED BATH OIL
6 oz. black plastic bottle with gold cap & painted label. Black & gold box. OSP $2.75, CMV $5 BO - $6 MB.

1963-67 OCCUR! POWDER SACHET
(Left) 9/10 oz. black glass & cap, painted label. OSP $2.50, CMV $9 MB - $7 BO.
1963-75 OCCUR! CREAM SACHET
(Center) .66 oz. black glass & cap. 2 caps: 1 says Occur!, 1 says Occur! Cream Sachet. OSP $3, CMV 50c.
1976-78 OCCUR! CREAM SACHET
(Right) .66 oz. clear glass with black & gold lid. OSP $3, CMV 25c.

1963 OCCUR! PERFUME OIL FOR THE BATH
(Left) Black & gold box holds ½ oz. bottle with gold cap & painted label. OSP $5, CMV $12 in box - $8 BO.
1963-66 OCCUR! COLOGNE MIST
(Center & Left) 2 oz. frosted glass with black cap & gold painted label. Came in black & gold box. OSP $3, CMV $4 BO - $6 MB. Also came with 4A embossed bottle with black neck label & gold plastic cap. OSP $2.50, CMV $5 MB - $3 BO.

1965-67 OCCUR! SOAP
Black & gold box holds 3 yellow bars. OSP $2.25, CMV $17 MB.

1966-70 OCCUR! SCENTED HAIR SPRAY
(Left) 7 oz. black can with black cap. OSP $1.50, CMV $3.
1965-69 PERFUME ROLLETTE
(Center Left) .33 oz. gray ribbed carnival glass, gold cap. OSP $2.50, CMV $6 BO - $7 MB.
1963-65 PERFUMED CREAM ROLLETTE
(Center Right) .33 oz. 4A embossed bottle with gold cap. OSP $2.50, CMV $2 - MB $3.
1963-68 OCCUR! PERFUME MIST
(Right) Gold box holds 2 dram black & gold metal case with white cap. OSP $3.75, CMV $6 MB - $5 BO.
OCCUR! PRODUCTS NOT SHOWN
1970's PERFUMED TALC
3.5 oz.
FOAMING BATH OIL
6 oz. plastic.
PERFUMED SKIN SOFTENER
5 oz. plastic jar.
COLOGNE SPRAY
2.7 oz. glass.
CMV 50c each.

1964-65 OCCUR! FRAGRANCE FORTUNE SET
Black & gold box holds Occur! 2 oz. cologne & ½ oz. perfume oil. Both have gold caps. OSP $6.95, CMV $30 MB.

1963-64 OCCUR! SOPHISTICATE SET
3 oz. Occur! cologne mist, perfume cream rollette & beauty dust. Black & gold box. OSP $12.95, CMV $35 MB.

1964 OCCUR! ELEGENCE SET
Black & gold box holds Occur! 4 oz. cream lotion, perfumed talc & 2 oz. cologne. OSP $5.75, CMV $35 MB.

1965 OCCUR! DELUXE SET
Black & gold box holds Occur! beauty dust, perfumed skin softener & cologne mist. OSP $13.95, CMV $35.

ODYSSEY

1981-83 ODYSSEY PRODUCTS
Blue & lavender colors.
PERFUMED POWDER MIST
4 oz. spray can.
SOAP
1 bar.
ULTRA COLOGNE SPRAY
1.8 oz. frosted glass, silver cap.
LUXURY BATH FOAM
6 oz. blue plastic bottle.
SAMPLE VIAL ON CARD
CMV 25c.
CMV soap $1 - all other products 25c each.

ORCHARD BLOSSOMS

1941-45 ORCHARD BLOSSOMS COLOGNE
(Left) 6 oz. bubble sided bottle, short front label has tree with flowers on it. OSP $1.50 pink cap. CMV $50 BO - $60 MB.

1945-46 ORCHARD BLOSSOMS COLOGNE
(Right) Same as above with long blue & white front label, pink cap. OSP $1.50, CMV $65 MB - $55 BO.

1945-46 PETAL OF BEAUTY
Blue & white box holds 6 oz. Orchard Blossoms cologne and blue & white box beauty dust. OSP $2.20, CMV $100 MB.

1043-44 PETAL OF BEAUTY
Blue box with pink satin lining holds 6 oz. Orchard Blossoms cologne & blue feather design beauty dust or Apple Blossom beauty dust. OSP $2.20, CMV $100 MB.

PATCHWORK

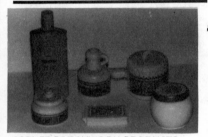

1973-77 PATCHWORK PRODUCTS
1973-74 HAND & BODY LOTION
8 oz. SSP $2, CMV 50c.
1973-75 FOAMING BATH OIL
6 oz. SSP $3, CMV $1.
1973-74 PERFUME CANDLE
SSP $6, CMV $6.
1973-76 COLOGNE GELEE
3 oz. SSP $4, CMV $1.
1973-74 EYESHADOW
SSP $4, CMV $1.
1973-76 SAMPLES
In foil pouch. CMV 25c box.
1973-76 PATCHWORK CREAM SACHET
5 oz. white plastic jar with red, yellow & orange lid. OSP $3, CMV 50c.
1973-76 PERFUMED SKIN SOFTENER
5 oz. plastic jar. OSP $4.50, CMV 25c.

1973-76 PATCHWORK PRODUCTS
White with orange, red & green designs.
1973-76 SOAP
3 cakes, yellow, orange & green. SSP $5, CMV $6 MB.
1973-76 COLOGNE MIST
3 oz. SSP $4, CMV $1.
1973-76 PERFUME POWDER MIST
7 oz. SSP $2, CMV 50c.
1973-76 PERFUME ROLLETTE
.33 oz. SSP $3, CMV 50c.
1973-77 CREAM SACHET
.66 oz. SSP $3, CMV 50c.
1973-76 COLOGNE SAMPLE BOTTLE
CMV 25c.

1972 PATCHWORK REFRIGERATOR AWARDS
Level 1. Earned by selling cologne mists. White plastic with orange, green, red & yellow patchwork decals. CMV $10 set - $12 MB.

1972 PATCHWORK COOKER AWARD
Patchwork design. Level 4. Earned for selling cologne mists. CMV $30 - MB $35.

1972 PATCHWORK CANNISTER AWARD
Level 3. Earned for selling cologne mists. White glass 3 piece cannister set with Patchwork decals. CMV $25 set MB.

1973 PATCHWORK BINGO CARD
9½" paper bingo card used by Reps at meetings. CMV $2.

1972 PATCHWORK COOKIE JAR AWARD
Level 2. Earned for selling cologne mists. White glass with orange, green, red & yellow. CMV $12 - MB $15.

PATTERNS

1969 PATTERNS
1969-70 TRAY
10" black plastic tray with gold edge when held to light shows purple, red, gray (these are transparent). There is an opaque black one - rare. CMV red, gray & purple $4 MB - $2 TO. Re-issued in 1975. Black (no light comes through) $7.50.
1969-70 POWDER SHADOW COMPACT
Black & white plastic. OSP $5, CMV $2 - $3 MB.
1969-70 LIPSTICK
Black & white metal tube. OSP $1.50, CMV $1.
1969-74 CREAM SACHET
.66 oz. black & white glass jar, plastic lid. OSP $3, CMV 50c.
1969-72 COLOGNE MIST
3 oz. black & white spray can & cap. OSP $6, CMV $1.
1969-74 PERFUME ROLLETTE
.33 oz. black & white bottle & cap. OSP $3, CMV $1.50.
1969-70 PATTERNS PERFUME GLACE RING
Black, white & red box holds gold ring with black set. OSP $6, CMV in box $6 - ring only $3.

PENNSYLVANIA DUTCH

1973-76 PENNSYLVANIA DUTCH DECANTERS
Yellow painted over clear glass with orange fruit and yellow caps. All items CMV $4 BO - $6 MB.

1973-76 HAND & BODY LOTION
10 oz. came in Patchwork or Sonnet only. SSP $5.
1973-74 COLOGNE DECANTER
(Salt or pepper shaker) Holds Moonwind, Patchwork or Sonnet. 4 oz. SSP $5.
1973-76 FOAMING BATH OIL
6 oz. SSP $5.
1973-75 POWDER SACHET SHAKER
1.25 oz. SSP $5.
1973-76 PERFUMED SKIN SOFTENER
5 oz. OSP $5.

PERSIAN WOOD

1959-64 PERSIAN WOOD MIST
(Left) 3 oz. red plastic coated glass, gold crown cap. Came in red & gold box. OSP $3, CMV $6 in box - $5 bottle only.
1964-76 PERSIAN WOOD COLOGNE MIST
(Center) 3 oz. red plastic coated glass, gold crown cap. Came in red & gold box. OSP $7, CMV $1 - $2 MB.
1963 PERSIAN WOOD PERFUME OIL FOR THE BATH
(Right) ½ oz. bottle with gold cap, painted label. Came in red & gold box. OSP $3.50, CMV $12 bottle only - $15 in box.

1959-61 PERSIAN WOOD TOILET WATER
(Left) 2 oz. gold cap, painted label. Came in red & gold box. OSP $2.50, CMV $10 MB - $8 BO.
1957-59 PERSIAN WOOD MIST
(Center) 3 oz. red plastic coated glass, smooth gold cap. Came in red & gold box. OSP $3, CMV $10 BO - $12 MB.
1956-59 PERSIAN WOOD MIST
(Right) 3 oz. red plastic coated glass, raised gold cap with 4A on top. Came in red & gold box. OSP $3, CMV $10 BO - $12 MB.

1964-66 PERSIAN WOOD PERFUME OIL
(Left) Red & gold box holds ½ oz. bottle, white lettering & gold cap. OSP $3.50, CMV $10 in box - $8 BO.
1961-66 PERSIAN WOOD COLOGNE
(Center) 2 oz. clear glass, gold lettering, gold cap. In red & gold box. OSP $1.75, CMV $6 in box - $4 BO.
1960-63 PERSIAN WOOD COLOGNE
(Right) Red & gold box holds 4 oz. bottle with gold lettering & gold cap. OSP $2.75, CMV $10 in box - $8 bottle only.

1957-66 PERSIAN WOOD POWDER SACHET
(Left) 1¼ oz. red plastic squeeze bottle, gold cap, red & gold box. OSP $2, CMV $10 MB - $8 bottle only.
1957-61 PERSIAN WOOD LOTION SACHET
(Right) Red plastic coated, gold cap. Came in red & gold box. OSP $2, CMV $10 MB - $7 bottle only.

195

1961-66 PERSIAN WOOD CREAM LOTION
(Left) 4 oz. clear glass, gold lettering, gold cap. Came in red & gold box. OSP $1.25, CMV $5 MB - $3 BO.

1960-66 PERSIAN WOOD PERFUMED BATH OIL
(Center) 6 oz. red plastic bottle with gold cap. Came in red & gold box. OSP $2.25, CMV $8 MB - $6 BO.

1961-63 PERSIAN WOOD BODY POWDER
(Right) 4 oz. red plastic bottle with gold cap, in red & gold box. OSP $1.95, CMV $12 in box - $8 bottle only.

1958-62 PERSIAN WOOD PERFUMED TALC
(Right) Red & gold box holds red can with brass cap & trim. OSP 79c, CMV $5 MB - $3 can only, mint.

1962-68 PERSIAN WOOD PERFUMED TALC
(Left) Same as above only with a white or red plastic cap. OSP 79c, CMV $3 MB - $2 can only.

1957-60 PERSIAN WOOD BEAUTY DUST
(Left) Red glass bottom with red & gold tin lid. Lid also came in cardboard just like tin lid shown. Same CMV. OSP $3, CMV $10 mint - $15 MB.

1960-66 PERSIAN WOOD BEAUTY DUST
(Right) White plastic with red design around gold handle. OSP $3.25, CMV $8 mint - $12 MB.

1959-76 PERSIAN WOOD CREAM SACHET
(Left to Right) .66 oz. red bottom with smooth gold lid. CMV $10 BO - $12 MB. Gold embossed cap with curved sides. CMV $4 BO - $5 MB. Same cap with straight sides. CMV 50c. Came red paint over clear or milk glass.

1962-63 PERSIAN WOOD COLOGNE
(Left) 2½ oz. clear glass, gold cap. Red label on front of flat sided bottle. Came in Refreshing Hours set only. CMV $10.

1975-76 PERSIAN WOOD CREAM SACHET
(Right) .66 oz. clear glass, red & gold cap. OSP $1.50, CMV 50c.

1960's PERSIAN WOOD BEAUTY DUST REFILL
Box holds plain paper refill pack with red powder puff. OSP $2.98, CMV $6 MB.

1963-67 PERSIAN WOOD PERFUME MIST
(Left) 2 drams, red base, white cap, in gold box. OSP $3.25, CMV $6 - $7 MB.

1957-63 PERSIAN WOOD SPRAY PERFUME
(Right) 2 dram, red metal with gold cap, red & gold box. OSP $3.50, CMV $10 in box - $8 container only.

1960-64 PERSIAN WOOD PERFUMED SKIN SOFTENER
(Left & Center) 5 oz. off-white glass bottom with straight sides. Red & gold cap with either curved or straight sides. OSP $3, CMV $5 MB - $3.50 BO.

1964-66 PERSIAN WOOD PERFUMED SKIN SOFTENER
(Right) 5 oz. white glass, round bottom, red & gold cap. OSP $3, CMV $3 BO - $4 MB.

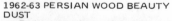

1962-63 PERSIAN WOOD BEAUTY DUST
Red paper sides with gold writing around sides & clear plastic top. Came in Fragrance Magic sets only. CMV $16 mint.

1960-62 PERSIAN WOOD 4 OZ. COLOGNE
Red & gold flip open box holds 4 oz. Persian Wood cologne. OSP $3, CMV $20 MB.

1963-64 PERSIAN INTRIGUE
Red & gold box holds Persian Wood mist, cream lotion & perfumed cream rollette. OSP $6.50, CMV $32.50.

1961-62 PERSIAN MAGIC
Red & gold box holds Persian Wood 2 oz. cologne & cream sachet. OSP $3.50, CMV $22 MB.

1959-60 PERSIAN TREASURE
Fancy gold box with white satin lining holds Persian Wood mist, 2 oz. toilet water, perfume spray & cream sachet. OSP $10.75, CMV $60 MB.

1961-62 PERSIAN LEGEND
Red & gold box with red satin lining holds Persian Wood mist & beauty dust. OSP $6.50, CMV $40 MB.

1964 PERSIAN MOOD
Red & gold box with white lining holds Persian Wood cream sachet & 1 dram perfume. OSP $4, CMV $22 MB.

1957-58 PERSIAN FANCY
Red & gold box with red lining holds Persian Wood mist & lotion sachet or powder sachet. OSP $5, CMV $40 MB.

PINE & ROYAL PINE

1954-57 ROYAL PINE BATH SALTS
8 oz. clear glass with green lid. Green & brown label. OSP 75c, CMV $20 - $25 MB.

1957-59 ROYAL PINE BATH OIL
8 oz. bottle with green cap & pine cones on label in yellow, white & green box. OSP $1.95, CMV $25 in box - $22 bottle only.

1953 PINE BATH SALTS
8 oz. clear glass jar, green lids, painted pine branch. Came 2 different ways. Both came in 1953 Royal Pine set only. CMV $30 each mint.

1944-45 PINE BATH OIL
(Left) 6 oz. flat sided bottle with green cap & brown label. OSP $1, CMV $25 - $30 MB.

1955-57 ROYAL PINE BATH OIL
(Center) 6 oz. flat sided bottle, green cap. OSP $1.25, CMV $25 BO - $30 MB.

1955-56 PINE BATH OIL
(Right) 2 oz., pink cap. Pink & white curtain label. Came in "That's for Me Set" only. CMV $15.

1963-68 ROYAL PINE BATH OIL
8 oz. green plastic bottle & cap. OSP $2, CMV $6 MB - $4 BO. See Misc. Bottle section under Misc. Bath Oils for different labels.

1942-51 PINE BATH OIL
6 oz. flat sided bottle with turquoise cap. OSP 95c, CMV $22 - MB $28.

1940-59 PINE SOAP
(Top) Green box with pine cone on lid holds 3 green round bars of Pine soap. OSP 69c, CMV $30 MB.

1959-65 ROYAL PINE SOAP
(Bottom) Same design box & same design on soap, only edge of soap is flat instead of round. OSP $1.25, CMV $25 MB.

1959 PINE SOAP
Plain green box with gold printing on lid. 3 green flat edge bars. CMV $30 MB.

1954-57 ROYAL PINE SET
Pine covered box holds 8 oz. jar with green lid of Royal Pine bath salts & green bar of Pine soap. OSP $1.39, CMV $35 set - bottle only $20.

1940 Only PINE SOAP
Special box holds 3 green bars of Pine soap. OSP 69c, CMV $45 MB.

1955-57 PINE BATH OIL
4 oz. bottle with green cap. Came in Pinehurst Set only. CMV $30.

1953 ROYAL PINE SET
Pine box holds 1 bar of Pine soap & 8 oz. jar with green lid & pine cone & branch painted on bottle. OSP $1.25, CMV $45.

1940 PINE SOAP SUBSTITUTE
3 green bars of pine soap came in brown and green box that was the Royal Pine set box. A letter from Avon stating the regular soap boxes were not available & Royal Pine set box was substituted. Rare, with letter. OSP ?, CMV $45 MB with letter as shown.

1940-42 BREATH OF PINE
Green & white box holds 2 green bars of Pine soap & 9 oz. bottle of Pine bath salts. OSP $1.25, CMV $55 MB.

1943 ROYAL PINE SET
Beige box with pine cones & crest on lid, holds 6 oz. Royal Pine bath oil with brown label & 2 bars Pine soap. Came in 2 different size boxes as shown. OSP $1.60, CMV $60 MB each set.

1941-42 TOWERING PINE
Pine cones on lid of box, holds Apple Blossoms body powder, green bar of Pine bath soap & 6 oz. bottle of Pine bath oil with tulip A on label. OSP $1.65, CMV $65 MB.

1955-57 PINEHURST
Pine box holds 2 green bars of Pine soap & 4 oz. bottle of Pine bath oil with green cap. OSP $1.75, CMV $52.50 MB.

PRETTY PEACH

1940 Only BREATH OF PINE
Box holds 9 oz. bottle of Pine bath salts & 2 green bars of Pine soap. OSP $1.25, CMV $60 MB.

1964-67 PRETTY PEACH "SODA" COLOGNE MIST
2 oz. pink plastic coated bottle with pink top with white flowers & blue straws. Came in 2 different silver stands. OSP $2.50, CMV $8 each - $12 MB.

1964-67 PRETTY PEACH CREAM LOTION & BUBBLE BATH
4 oz. pink plastic bottle with peach on cap, painted label, pink box. OSP $1.35, CMV cream lotion $8 - MB $10. CMV bubble bath $6 - MB $8.

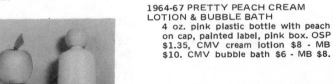

FOREIGN PRETTY PEACH EAU DE COLOGNE
(Left) Peach cap & painted label. CMV $10.
FOREIGN PRETTY PEACH HAND CREAM
CMV $6.

1940-43 ROYAL PINE
Pine cones on lid of box, holds 2 green bars of Pine soap & 6 oz. bottle of Pine bath oil with brown label. OSP $1.35, CMV $55 MB.

1964-67 PRETTY PEACH CREAM SACHET
(Left) Yellow glass jar with peaches on lid. OSP $1., CMV $7. MB, $5. jar only.

1964-67 PEACH POMADE
(Right) Foam peach with green leaf holds pomade lipstick. OSP $1, CMV $16 - MB $18.

1964-67 PRETTY PEACH COLOGNE
2 oz. bottle with peach cap with green leaf & painted label. Pink box. OSP $1.50, CMV $7. MB, $4. bottle only.

1964-65 PRETTY PEACH SOAP ON A ROPE
(Left) 5 oz. peach shaped soap on white rope. OSP $1.35, CMV $17 MB - $11 soap only.

1964-67 PRETTY PEACH PERFUMED TALC
(Center) 2½ oz. pink & white paper container. OSP 79c, CMV $6 - MB $8.

1964-67 PRETTY PEACH BEAUTY DUST
(Right) Pink & white cardboard box. OSP $2.50, CMV $10 - MB $14.

1964-66 PRETTY PEACH SOAP
Pink box holds 2 peach halves & brown seed center soap. OSP $1.50, CMV $24 MB - $15 soap only, mint.

1965 PRETTY PEACH NECKLACE
(Left) Small peach on gold chain. Came in Peach Delight Set only. CMV $20 - $25 on card.

1964-67 PRETTY PEACH SACHET SAMPLES
(Right) Box holds 10 peach shaped samples of cream sachet packets. CMV $2.50 box of 10.

1965-66 PRETTY PEACH TALC PUFF
Pink box holds pink & white puff filled with powder. OSP $1.50, CMV $6 MB - puff only $2 mint.

1965 PEACH DELIGHT
Box holds Pretty Peach necklace, beauty dust & cologne. OSP $5.95, CMV $55 MB set.

1965 PEACH SMOOTH
Peach box holds 2 tubes of Pretty Peach hand cream. OSP $1.35, CMV $12 MB, $4 tube only mint.

1964-65 JUST PEACHY
Pink & white box holds Peach soap on a rope & Peach pomade. OSP $2.35, CMV $42.50 MB.

1964 PEACH SURPRISE SET
Pink & white box holds Pretty Peach 2 oz. cologne with choice of 4 oz. bubble bath or cream lotion. OSP $2.85, CMV $20 MB.

1966-67 PEACHY KLEEN SET
Pink box holds pink & white sponge & soap. OSP $2.25, CMV in box $12 - soap & sponge only $8.

1965-66 PRETTY PEACH PRINCESS
Box holds Pretty Peach talc & cream sachet. OSP $2.25, CMV $20 MB.

QUAINTANCE

1964-65 MISS AVON SET
Blue & black plastic case holds Pretty Peach cologne, bubble bath, perfumed talc & 10 Lip Dew samples in a bag. Also talc samples. OSP $7.50, CMV $50 set in blue case - $55 set MB.

1950 QUAINTANCE PERFUME
White box with white lace trim holds 3 dram perfume with plain red cap & green leaf. OSP $4, CMV $125 in box.

1948-56 QUAINTANCE BODY POWDER
(Left) 5 oz. red & white paper box, shaker top. OSP 75c, CMV $16 in box - $12 container only.
1948-50 QUAINTANCE PERFUME
(Right) 1 dram size with red rose cap, painted label in large or small lettering. Blue & white box. OSP $1.50 - CMV $80 in box, $70 bottle only.

PRIVATE WORLD

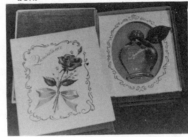

1949-56 QUAINTANCE DIARY PERFUME
3 dram glass bottle, painted label, rose flowered cap & green leaf. Box green felt. Diary has white cover with red rose & turquoise design. OSP $4, CMV $150 in box.

1948 Only 62nd ANNIVERSARY QUAINTANCE COLOGNE
1st issued in white lace design box. 4 oz. size. Given to Reps for selling 62 Avon items on 62nd anniversary celebration. CMV $65 MB.

1982-83 PRIVATE WORLD PRODUCTS
FRAGRANCED LINGERIE WASH
8 oz. green plastic bottle. CMV 25c.
FRAGRANCED LINGERIE WASH SAMPLES
Box of 10 packets. CMV 25c.
POWDER SACHET
1.5 oz. green cardboard. CMV 50c.
SOFT SACHET
2 green fabric pillows with green satin ribbon. SSP $8, CMV $4 MB.
BUTTERFLY FRAGRANCES
Box of 2 green Butterfly pomanders on pink cards. SSP $6, CMV $4 MB.
PRIVATE WORLD PICTURE FRAME
6" x 7¼" fabric frame. SSP $9, CMV $7 MB.
PRIVATE WORLD BOOK MARK
CMV 50c each.

1949 QUAINTANCE DIARY PERFUME AWARD
Given to Representatives in 63rd anniversary compaign for selling 63 pieces of Avon. Green felt cover trimmed in gold, holds 3 dram bottle with rose flowered cap & painted label, green leaf around neck. Not shown in picture. Must have leaf to be mint. 63rd anniversary inscribed inside cover. CMV $100 MB.

1949-56 QUAINTANCE BATH OIL
(Left) 4 oz. clear glass, white painted label. Rose on cap. OSP $1.25, CMV $20 in box - bottle only $16 mint.
1949-56 QUAINTANCE CREAM LOTION
(Right) 4 oz. clear glass, white painted label. Rose cap. OSP 89c, CMV $14 in box - $12 bottle only mint.

1948-56 QUAINTANCE POWDER SACHET
9 oz. clear glass, white cap & painted label. Cap same as Bright Night without stars, but came this way. Very rare. CMV $15. BO, $20. MB.

1948-56 QUAINTANCE COLOGNE
(Left) 4 oz. clear glass, green painted label, ribbed corners, rose cap with green leaf. OSP $1.75, CMV $15 in box, bottle only $13.

1948-50 QUAINTANCE 2 OZ. COLOGNE
(Center) 2 oz. bottle with rose cap, painted label & ribbed corners. Came in Quaintance Set & Quaintance Bow Knot Set only. CMV $20.

1953-56 QUAINTANCE TOILET WATER
(Right) 2 oz. clear glass, green painted label, ribbed corners, rose cap with green leaf. OSP $1.25, CMV $20 in box - $15 bottle only.

1948-56 QUAINTANCE POWDER SACHET
(Left) 9/10 oz. or 1¼ oz. clear glass with red cap, painted label. OSP $1.19, CMV $11 in box - $10 jar only.

1948 Only QUAINTANCE POWDER SACHET
(Right) 9/10 oz. clear glass with red cap & larger painted label. OSP $1.19, CMV $20 MB - $16 BO. Also came in 1¼ oz. size with large size label. CMV $20 MB - $16 BO.

1955-56 QUAINTANCE SOAP
3 blue bars with embossed bows. OSP $1.59, CMV $40 MB.

1955 BATH BOUQUET
White & blue box with red rose on lid holds 2 oz. bottles of Quaintance cream lotion & cologne with blue caps. Blue bar of Quaintance soap. OSP $1.95, CMV $52 MB.

1955-56 QUAINTANCE COLOGNE
(Left) 2 oz. bottle with blue cap, came in Daintiness Set and Bath Bouquet Set. CMV $15. Quaintance cream lotion in same sets. CMV $12.

1953-56 QUAINTANCE CREAM SACHET
(Right) White square glass jar with red rose on white cap. OSP $1.25, CMV $12 in box - $10 jar only.

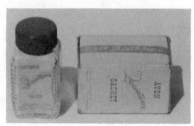

1949 QUAINTANCE SACHET 63RD BIRTHDAY BOX
Regular issue powder sachet came in special issue Avon's 63rd Birthday box. CMV $15 MB as shown.

1952 QUAINTANCE SACHET VALENTINE BOX
Short issue box at Valentine time. Holds regular issue powder sachet. OSP $1.19, CMV in this box $19 mint.

1948-57 QUAINTANCE BEAUTY DUST
Red rose on tin lid, white paper sides & tin bottom, white box. OSP $1.50, CMV $18 in box - $12 beauty dust only mint.

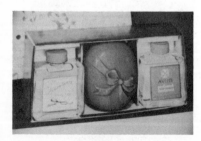

1955 DAINTINESS SET
White box with pink & blue ribbons holds 2 oz. bottles of perfumed deodorant & Quaintance cologne with blue caps & blue bar of Quaintance soap. OSP $1.95, CMV $52 MB.

1955-56 QUAINTANCE BATH OIL
2 oz. pink cap, pink & white label. Came in That's For Me set only. CMV $15 mint.

1956 DAINTINESS SET
White box with pink & blue ribbon holds 2 oz. bottles of Quaintance cream lotion & cologne with blue caps & blue bar of Quaintance soap. OSP $1.95, CMV $55 MB.

1954-56 ROSE GAY SET
Blue & white box holds Quaintance 4 oz. cream lotion & body powder. OSP $1.95, CMV $55 MB.

1952-53 MISS QUAINTANCE SET
Blue & white octagonal box holds Quaintance body powder & 4 oz. cream lotion. OSP $1.95, CMV $50 MB.

1948 QUAINTANCE SET
Blue & white box contains 2 oz. Quaintance cologne & powder sachet. Both have red caps. OSP $2.35, CMV $55 MB.

1948 GAY BONNET SET
White hat shaped box with black ribbon & red rose around hat lid contains gold lipstick & 1 dram bottle of Quaintance perfume with rose cap. OSP $2.35, CMV $125 MB.

1952-53 QUAINTANCE HARMONY
Box with blue ribbon on clear plastic lid holds 4 oz. Quaintance cream lotion & cologne. OSP $2.75, CMV $45 set MB - 4 oz. cologne with rose cap $20.

1950 QUAINTANCE BOW KNOT
Box holds Quaintance 2 oz. cologne & powder sachet. OSP $2.25, CMV $50.

1954-55 QUAINTANCE HARMONY
Blue & white flip open box holds Quaintance cologne & cream lotion. OSP $2.15, CMV $55 MB.

1950-51 QUAINTANCE ROSE GAY SET
Blue & white box with red rose holds Quaintance body powder & 4 oz. cream lotion. OSP $1.85, CMV $50 MB.

1950-51 QUAINTANCE HARMONY
White box with blue ribbon over clear plastic lid holds Quaintance 4 oz. cologne & body powder. OSP $2.95, CMV $50 MB.

QUEEN'S GOLD

1954-55 LEISURE HOURS SET
Blue & yellow fold up box holds 4 oz. Quaintance bath oil & cream lotion. OSP $2.75, CMV $55.

1949 BEAUTY MUFF SET
(Left) Red, white & blue box with blue ribbon on lid contains white lambswool muff with 1 dram Quaintance perfume with rose cap & gold lipstick. OSP $2.35, CMV $135 MB.

1950 BEAUTY MUFF SET
(Right) Same set & box only came with 1 dram gold scroll top perfume. CMV $65 MB.

1975 "WE WANT TO PAMPER YOU" SAMPLE
Sent to all President's Club members campaign 3, 1975, introducing new fragrance Queen's Gold. Clear glass bottle with white cap. White envelope with yellow printing. CMV $2.

1975-76 QUEEN'S GOLD FRAGRANCE SAMPLES
(Left) 10 foil packets in box. CMV 25c box.

1975-76 QUEEN'S GOLD FOAMING BATH OIL
(Inside Left) 10 oz. yellow plastic bottle with gold cap. OSP $5, CMV 50c.

1975-76 QUEEN'S GOLD COLOGNE MIST
(Left Center) 3 oz. yellow plastic coated bottle, gold cap. OSP $5, CMV 50c.

1975-76 QUEEN'S GOLD CREAM SACHET
(Right Center) .66 oz. clear glass with gold & yellow cap. OSP $3, CMV 25c.

1974-76 QUEEN'S GOLD DEMI STICK
(Inside Right) .19 oz. white with brown, pink & blue. OSP $1, CMV 25c.

1974-75 QUEEN'S GOLD PERFUME POWDER MIST
(Right) 7 oz. gold, brown, pink & blue. OSP $2, CMV 50c.

RAINING VIOLETS

1974-76 RAINING VIOLETS COLOGNE MIST
(Left) 2 oz. clear plastic with clear plastic lid with purple & blue inner cap. OSP $5, CMV 50c.

1974-76 RAINING VIOLETS MOISTURIZING BATH OIL
(Left Center) 6 oz. white plastic, pink cap. OSP $2, CMV 50c.

1974-76 RAINING VIOLETS PERFUME DEMI STICK
(Right Center) .19 oz. white with violets. OSP $1, CMV 50c.

1974-76 RAINING VIOLETS CREAM SACHET
(Right) .66 oz. clear glass with metal lid with violets. OSP $3, CMV 50c.

1973-75 RAINING VIOLETS
White with violet & lavender caps.
CLEANSING GEL
(Left) 6 oz. SSP $2, CMV 50c.
MOISTURIZED FRICTION LOTION
(Left Center) 10 oz. SSP $3, CMV 50c.
EMOLLIENT MIST
(Right Center) 4 oz. SSP $2, CMV 50c.
PERFUMED POWDER MIST
(Right) 7 oz. SSP $2, CMV 50c.
COLOGNE GELEE
(Front) 3 oz. SSP $3, CMV $1.

RAPTURE

1966 Only RAPTURE COLOGNE MIST
2 oz. medium blue glass, gold trim. OSP $3.

1966 Only RAPTURE COLOGNE MIST
2 oz. dark blue glass. OSP $3.

1965-66 RAPTURE COLOGNE MIST
2 oz. light blue glass, no gold trim. OSP $3.

1965-66 RAPTURE COLOGNE MIST
2 oz. very light, appears almost frosted glass.
CMV each $4 BO - $5 MB.

1966-72 RAPTURE FOAMING BATH OIL
(Left) 6 oz. blue plastic bottle & cap. OSP $2.75, CMV $2.

1965-66 RAPTURE PERFUMED BATH OIL
(Center) 6 oz. blue plastic bottle & cap. OSP $2.75, CMV $3 BO - $4.50 MB.

1965-68 RAPTURE CREAM LOTION
(Right) 4 oz. blue plastic bottle & cap. OSP $1.75, CMV $2 BO - $3 MB.

1964-66 RAPTURE POWDER SACHET
(Left) 9/10 oz. blue frosted glass with blue lid with 2 white doves. OSP $2.50, CMV $6 in box - $4 BO.

1964-75 RAPTURE CREAM SACHET
(Right) .66 oz. dark purple glass jar with 2 white doves on purple plastic lid. OSP $3, CMV 50c.

1964-69 RAPTURE PERFUME OIL
(Top Left) ½ oz. green glass & cap. OSP $5, CMV $4 - $6 MB.

1964-71 RAPTURE COLOGNE
(Top Center) 2 oz. blue glass & cap. OSP $2.50, CMV $1 BO - $2 MB.

1964-74 RAPTURE COLOGNE MIST
(Top Right & Bottom Two) 3 oz. turquoise plastic coated cap, all have gold letters. OSP $5, CMV $1 BO - $1.50 MB. Pictured above with regular issue box on right & special issue 1970 box on left. Add $1 for 1970 box.

1966-70 RAPTURE SCENTED HAIR SPRAY
(Left) 7 oz. blue can. OSP $1.50, CMV $3.

1965-72 RAPTURE PERFUMED TALC
(Left Center) 2.75 oz. blue can. OSP $1, CMV $1.
(Right Center) Foreign Rapture perfume talc is 2.75 oz. blue can, but shorter than U.S. can. CMV $2.

1971-74 RAPTURE BEAUTY DUST
(Right) 6 oz. blue & gold cardboard. OSP $4.50, CMV $3 CO - $5 MB.

1964-73 RAPTURE PERFUMED SKIN SOFTENER
(Left) 5 oz. with blue & gold lid. Came blue painted over clear glass. CMV $1. Also came blue painted over white milk glass. CMV $3, OSP $3.50.

1964-70 RAPTURE BEAUTY DUST
(Right) Light blue plastic, white doves on lid. OSP $5, CMV $3 CO - $5 MB.

1964-65 RAPTURE RHAPSODY TRAY
Rapture powder sachet, 1 dram perfume & 2 oz. cologne sit on blue velvet, trimmed in gold. Rapture mirror in center with 2 doves on mirror. OSP $10.95, CMV $30 tray, set mint - $40 set MB.

1964-68 RAPTURE PERFUME MIST
(Left) 2 dram, dark turquoise & white metal with gold band. OSP $3.25, CMV $5 - MB $6.

1966-67 RAPTURE PERFUMED SOAP
(Inside Left) 3 oz. soap in turquoise wrapper. OSP 49c, CMV $4.

1964 RAPTURE PERFUMED SKIN SOFTENER SAMPLE
(Center) Turquoise foil packet holds skin softener. CMV $2.50 box of 10.

1964 RAPTURE COLOGNE SAMPLE
(Inside Right) 10 foil samples per box. CMV $1.50 box.

1964 RAPTURE POWDER SACHET SAMPLE
(Right) Paper folder with sample inside. CMV $1 each.

1965-68 RAPTURE SOAP
Blue box holds 3 blue bars with 2 doves embossed. OSP $2, CMV $17.50 MB.

1969-72 RAPTURE ½ OZ. COLOGNE
(Left) ½ oz. green cap. OSP $1.50, CMV $1 BO - $2 MB.

1964-65 RAPTURE PERFUMED CREAM ROLLETTE
(Left Center) Gold cap, embossed 4A design on 1/3 oz. bottle. OSP $2.50, CMV $3.

1965-69 RAPTURE PERFUMED ROLLETTE
(Right Center) 1/3 oz. blue ribbed glass, gold cap. OSP $2.50, CMV $6 - MB $7.

1964 RAPTURE PIN
(Right) Silver gray in color. CMV $15 pin only - $20 on Avon card pictured.

1965 RAPTURE DELUXE
Turquoise box contains beauty dust, perfumed skin softener & cologne mist in Rapture. OSP $13.95, CMV $32.50.

1965 RAPTURE AWARD BOWL
Fostoria glass bowl with Rapture doves etched in bottom. Given to each Representative in the winning district during the 79th Anniversary campaign. CMV $35 - MB $40.

1965 RAPTURE BLOUSE AWARD
Cotton blouse with 2 doves on upper left side of shirt. Came in blue and white. Won by Avon Reps. Modeled by Sally Omann. Avon neck label made by Lady Manhatten. Won by selling 50 Rapture and/or Occur! products. CMV $20.

REGENCE

1966-69 REGENCE PERFUME
1 oz. frosted glass bottle & stopper, trimmed in gold, green & white box. Gold neck tag. OSP $30, CMV $27.50 BO - $40 MB.

1966-69 REGENCE PERFUME
½ oz. frosted glass with gold plastic cap. Bottle trimmed in gold, green & white box. Gold neck tag. OSP $15, CMV $20 BO - $30 MB.

1966 REGENCE HAND MIRROR
(Left) Green & gold metal 4½" long. Came in Regence gift set. CMV $10 in box - $7 mirror only.
1967-71 REGENCE FRAGRANCE SAMPLE
(Right) Foil packet. CMV $1 box of 10.

1970-71 REGENCE ½ OZ. COLOGNE
(Left) ½ oz. clear glass bottle with gold cap. OSP $1.75, CMV $2 MB - $1 BO.
1968-69 REGENCE PERFUME OIL
(Inside Left) ½ oz. gold cap. Came with either clear bottom label or gold neck tag label. OSP $6, CMV $4 BO - $6 MB.
1967-69 REGENCE COLOGNE
(Center) 2 oz. gold cap. OSP $3, CMV $2 MB - $1 BO.
1968-70 REGENCE COLOGNE SILK
(Inside Right) 3 oz. gold cap, frosted glass bottle. OSP $4.50, CMV $2, MB - $1 BO.
1968-70 REGENCE SKIN-SO-SOFT
(Right) 6 oz. gold cap. OSP $5., CMV $2. MB, $1. BO.

1969-71 REGENCE 4 OZ. COLOGNE
(Left) 4 oz. gold cap. OSP $6, CMV $2.
1969-72 REGENCE FOAMING BATH OIL
(Center) 6 oz. light green plastic bottle with gold cap. OSP $4, CMV $1 BO - $2 MB.
1966-71 COLOGNE MIST REFILL
(Right) 3 oz. green plastic coated. OSP $4, CMV $3 BO - $4 MB.

1968 REGENCE CREAM SACHET
.66 oz. clear glass painted green. Green & gold tone cap & base. Sides are smooth, no design. CMV $4 BO - $6 MB.

1966-71 REGENCE COLOGNE MIST
(Left) 3 oz. green & gold plastic. Base is gold on older ones and green on newer ones. OSP $6, CMV gold base $3, green base $2 MB - $1 BO.
1968-71 HAIR SPRAY
(Center) 7 oz. green & gold with green cap. OSP $1.50, CMV $3.
1966-73 REGENCE BEAUTY DUST
(Right) Green & gold plastic bottom, clear plastic lid with gold crown. OSP $6. Paper side older - CMV $8 MB. Plastic side newer - CMV $5 MB. $2 less each for no box.

1967-68 REGENCE PERFUME ROLLETTE
(Left) .33 oz. ribbed glass, smooth gold cap. OSP $3, CMV $2 MB - $1.50 BO.
1969-73 REGENCE PERFUME ROLLETTE
(Center) .33 oz. ribbed glass & green cap. OSP $3, CMV $1 BO - $1.50 MB.
1967-70 REGENCE PERFUMED GLACE
(Right) Green & gold box holds green & gold glace compact. OSP $5.50, CMV $8 in box - $5 compact only.

1966-67 REGENCE CREAM SACHET
(Left) Green painted glass with green paper band. Green & gold cap, gold base. OSP $3, CMV $2 - $3 MB.
1968-75 REGENCE CREAM SACHET
(Right) Solid green glass, green plastic cap. OSP $3, CMV 50c. Both also came green painted over clear or milk glass. Same CMV.

1968-72 REGENCE TALC
(Left) 3½ oz. green paper box. OSP $1.25, CMV $1.
1967-72 REGENCE PERFUMED POWDER MIST
(Right) 7 oz. green can with gold cap, painted label. OSP $4, CMV $1 - with paper label $3.

1968-71 REGENCE PERFUME SKIN SOFTENER
(Left) 5 oz. green ribbed glass, small silver edged cap. Gold center & multi-color cap. OSP $4, CMV $2.
1971-74 REGENCE PERFUMED SKIN SOFTENER
(Center) 5 oz. green ribbed glass, large silver edged, gold center & multi-color green cap. OSP $4, CMV $1.
1967-68 REGENCE PERFUMED SKIN SOFTENER
(Right) 5 oz. green ribbed glass, small silver edge cap with with gold center & plain green cap. OSP $4, CMV $3 - $4 MB.

1966 REGENCE EARRINGS
(Top) Gold with turquoise settings. Customer service award campaign 14-18, 1966. Has green velvet box. CMV $60 in box.
1966 REGENCE NECKLACE
(Bottom) Crown performance award. Gold with turquoise setting & gold crown set in center, can also be worn as a pin. Has green velvet box. CMV $50 in box.

1966 REGENCE GIFT SET
Green box holds cream sachet, cologne mist, green & gold hand mirror. OSP $12.50, CMV $37.50.

ROSE GERANIUM

1957-58 ROSE GERANIUM BATH OIL
8 oz. bottle with red cap. OSP $1.95, CMV $20 MB, $15 BO.

1942 Only — ROSE GERANIUM LIQUID SOAP FRAGRANCE
(Left) 6 oz. flat sided bottle came in Rainbow Wings and Bath Bouquet Set only. CMV $45 MB.
1943-48 ROSE GERANIUM BATH OIL
(Right) 6 oz. flat sided bottle, pink cap. OSP 95c, CMV $25 BO, $35 MB.

1943-50 ROSE GERANIUM BATH OIL
6 oz. flat sided bottle has Tulip A label, pink cap. OSP 95c, CMV $25 BO, $30 MB.

FOREIGN ROSE GERANIUM CREAM SACHET
Frosted rose colored glass, gold cap. CMV $2.

1966-67 ROSE GERANIUM SOAP
Flowered box holds 4 flower shaped soaps. OSP $2.25, CMV $18 MB.

1964-68 ROSE GERANIUM AFTER BATH FRESHENER
8 oz. glass bottle with rose colored cap, red flowered box. OSP $2.50, CMV $4 BO, $5 MB.

1964-67 PERFUMED BATH OIL
8 oz. frosted plastic bottle with rose colored cap. Red flowered box. OSP $2.50, CMV $3 MB, $2 BO.

1964-66 PERFUMED TALC
3½ oz. rose covered paper container with plastic shaker top. OSP 89c CMV $4 MB, $3 CO. Also came with upside down label. CMV $8.

1964-66 PERFUMED SOAP
3 oz. bar with rose design wrapping. OSP 39c, CMV $4.

ROSES ROSES

1972-73 GLOW OF ROSES PERFUMED CANDLE
4½" high, pink frosted glass. SSP $6, CMV $5 BO, $6 MB.

1972-73 SCENT OF ROSES DECANTER
6 oz. red glass jar with gold lid, filled with Cologne Gelee. SSP $5, CMV $3.

1972-73 DEW OF ROSES PERFUMED SKIN SOFTENER
5 oz. frosted pink glass jar with gold lid. SSP $2. CMV $2.

1972-76 SCENT OF ROSES COLOGNE GELEE
3 oz. clear or tinted glass jar, gold lid. SSP $2 - CMV 75c.

1974-77 ROSES PERFUME TALC
3.5 oz. pink and gray cardboard. OSP $1, CMV 25c.

1976-78 TOUCH OF ROSES SOAP
3 oz. pink soap, pink and gray wrapper. OSP $1, CMV $1.

1974-75 ROSES ROSES SOAP
3 oz. pink soap, pink wrapper with floral band. OSP $1, CMV $1.50.

1973-76 ROSES ROSES PERFUMED SKIN SOFTENER
5 oz. pink plastic with pink and gold metal lid. OSP $3, CMV 25c.

1975-78 SACHET OF ROSES CREAM SACHET
.33 oz. clear glass with pink metal lid. OSP $3, CMV 25c.

1972-77 MIST OF ROSES COLOGNE MIST
3 oz. pink plastic coated bottle, gold cap. OSP $7, CMV $1.

1972-76 FOAM OF ROSES CREAMY BATH FOAM
5 oz. pink plastic bottle with gold cap. OSP $5, CMV 50c.

1972-77 TOUCH OF ROSES PERFUMED SOAP
Pink box holds 3 pink flowered soaps. OSP $5, CMV $5 MB.

1972-75 ROSES CREAM SACHET
.66 oz. pink glass jar with pink rose on gold lid. Also came in clear glass. OSP $3, CMV 50c.

1980-82 ROSES ROSES COLOGNE SPRAY
1.5 oz. pink cap. SSP $4, CMV 50c
PERFUMED TALC
3.5 oz. SSP $1.25, CMV 50c
PERFUMED SOAP
3 oz. bar. SSP $1.27, CMV $1.
COLOGNE
.5 oz. SSP $1.75, CMV 50c.

1976 ROSES ROSES PERFUMED SOAP BAR
3 oz. bar wrapped in red paper. Short issue. OSP $1.25, CMV $2.

1977-78 ROSES ROSES COLOGNE SPRAY
1.8 oz. flower embossed bottle, gold cap. OSP $5, CMV 50c.

1972 ROSES ROSES ORDER BOOK AND PEN
Redesigned size is larger than older Order Books, pink with darker pink rose and green leaves. Given to all President Club members. CMV $5 mint.

1972-75 ROSES ROSES FRAGRANCE KWICKETTS
14 per box, pink foil packets. OSP $1, CMV 50c.

1972-77 ROSES ROSES AFTER BATH FRESHENER
8 oz. pink plastic bottle, pink cap. OSP $5, CMV 50c.

1972-78 ROSES ROSES FRAGRANCE SAMPLES
10 samples per box, CMV 25c box.

1972-78 ROSES, ROSES COLOGNE SAMPLE
Clear glass with white lid. CMV 25c.

1973-77 ROSES ROSES HAND & BODY LOTION
8 or 16 oz. pink plastic bottle with pink lid. OSP $3.50 for 8 oz., $6 for 16 oz., CMV 50c each.

1972-76 ROSES ROSES PERFUME POWDER MIST
7 oz. pink and gray can, pink lid. OSP $4.50, CMV 50c.

1973-77 ROSES ROSES BATH GELEE
4 oz. clear plastic tube with pink cap. OSP $3.50, CMV 25c.

1978 COLOGNE ICE
1 oz. CMV 50c.

SEA GARDEN

1972 ROSES ROSES HOT PLATE
6" square, white Corning Ware with pink and green rose. Given for selling Mist of Roses Cologne. CMV $12 MB.

1972 ROSES ROSES GOBLET
Gold trimmed goblet with bouquet of pink artificial roses. Came with card of congratulations. Given for selling Mist of Roses Cologne. CMV $18 MB.

1972 ROSES ROSES CLOCK
3" clock by Hamilton, 4 small roses on front. Given for selling Mist of Roses Cologne. CMV $15 MB.

1972 ROSES ROSES GOWN
Pink floor length gown with sash. Given for selling Mist of Roses Cologne. CMV $20 mint. $25 MB.

1970-73 SEA GARDEN PERFUMED BATH SOAP
6 oz. blue bar with blue box. OSP $2, CMV $4 MB.

1970-73 SEA GARDEN EMOLLIENT MIST
4 oz. dark or light blue spray can with green cap. OSP $3, CMV $1 each color.

1970-74 SEA GARDEN PERFUMED POWDER MIST
7 oz. blue can with green lid. OSP $3.75, CMV 50c.

1970-75 SEA GARDEN EMOLLIENT BATH FOAM
5 oz. green and white frosted bottle with green cap. OSP $5, CMV 75c.

1970-71 SILK & HONEY MILK BATH
6 oz. gold plastic milk can bottle with flowers around neck. OSP $5, CMV $4.

SILK & HONEY

1975-76 SILK & HONEY BUBBLE BATH GELEE
4 oz. plastic tube. OSP $3.50, CMV 25c.

1973-74 SILK & HONEY BATH GELEE
4 oz. clear plastic tube with yellow cap. OSP $2, CMV 50c.

1970-76 SILK & HONEY PERFUME SOAP
3 oz. gold and yellow wrapper. OSP $1.25, CMV $1.25.

1969 SILK & HONEY BANK
Yellow plastic Beehive Bank. CMV $25.

1970-71 SILK & HONEY PERFUME POWDER MIST
7 oz. yellow and gold paper label, yellow cap. OSP $3.75, CMV $2. 7 oz. yellow and gold painted can, yellow cap. "Shake vigorously before use" on front of can, newer issue. OSP $3.75, CMV $1.

1969-74 SILK & HONEY BATH FOAM
6 oz. gold plastic bottle and cap. OSP $3, CMV 50c.

1969-74 CREAMY LOTION
6 oz. gold plastic bottle and cap. OSP $2.50, CMV 50c.

1969-74 CREAMY MASQUE
3 oz. gold ribbed plastic jar and cap. OSP $2.50, CMV 50c.

1969-71 SOFTALC
3 oz. gold plastic bottle and cap. OSP $1.50, CMV $1.50.

1970-76 PERFUMED POWDER MIST
7 oz. gold and yellow can. OSP $4.50. CMV 50c.

1969-70 BATH GELEE
4½ oz. gold frosted glass jar with gold beehive lid and gold spoon. OSP $6, CMV $7 MB, $5 BO with spoon.

SMALL WORLD

1970-73 SMALL WORLD PRODUCTS
(Back row left ro right)
1970-72 COLOGNE (SPLASHU)
2 oz., 4½" high. OSP $3.50, CMV $6.
1970-71 BUBBLE BATH (BUBBLY-O-BATH)
5" high, 5 oz. green plastic bottle.
OSP $3.50, CMV $8, $10 MB.
1971-73 PERFUMED TALC
3½ oz. blue paper container. OSP
$1.25, CMV $4.
(Front row left to right)
1970-73 LOVE CAKES SOAP
3 pink heart shaped bars in blue box.
OSP $2, CMV $9 MB.
1971-72 ROLLETTE
3" high, .33 oz. Indian design. OSP
$1.75, CMV $3.
1970-73 DEMI STICK
3" high with pink cap. OSP $1.50,
CMV $2.
1970-71 PIN PAL PERFUME GLACE
Black hair, white and red body.
OSP $2.50, CMV $5, $7 MB.
1970-71 NON-TEAR SHAMPOO (POOLU)
5½" high, red bottle, black hair.
OSP $3.50, CMV $6.
1970-71 COLOGNE MIST (HEIDI)
3 oz. 5" high, purple bottle, yellow
hair. OSP $5, CMV $6.
(Add $2 each item MB)

1970-73 SMALL WORLD PRODUCTS
(Back row left to right)
1971-72 CREAM LOTION (WENDY)
5 oz., 5" high cowgirl plastic bottle.
OSP $5, CMV $6, $8 MB.
1971-72 BUBBLE BATH (BRITISH MISS)
4½" high, 3 oz. pink plastic bottle.
OSP $5, CMV $6, $8 MB.
1971-72 COLOGNE MIST (GIGI)
5" high, 5 oz. blue plastic coated
bottle with white collar and blue &
red hat. OSP $3.50, CMV $6, $8 MB.
1971-72 NON-TEAR SHAMPOO (SENORITA)
5" high, 5 oz. orange plastic bottle
with pink flower in hair on cap. OSP
$3.50, CMV $10 BO, $12 MB.
(Front row left to right)
1971-72 CREAM SACHET
.66 oz. white jar with pink and white
lid. OSP $2.50, CMV $3 MB, $2 BO.
1970-73 LIPKINS
3" high with pink, yellow and orange
caps in Dutch Chocolate, Tropical
Fruit or French Mint. OSP $1.75,
CMV $3 each MB, $2 BO.
1970-73 LOVE DOVE CREAM SACHET
White jar and dove lid. OSP $3,
CMV $4, $5 MB.

1974 SMALL WORLD COLOGNE SAMPLE — Canada
1/8 oz. clear glass, white cap. Used
by Avon Reps. as sample in Canada.
CMV $3.

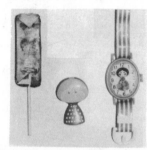

1970 SMALL WORLD SUCKER
Sent to representatives at introduction of Small World. Red and yellow
wrapper says "Avon Watch for the
Small World". CMV $25 mint.
1971-72 SMALL WORLD PERFUME GLACE
Blue and white polka-dots. OSP
$2.50, CMV $5, $6 MB.
1971 SMALL WORLD GLACE WATCH
Orange with striped band. OSP $3,
CMV $6, $8 MB.

SOMEWHERE

ALL CONTAINERS PRICED EMPTY
See front of book for Grading Examples
on Mint Condition

1961-63 SOMEWHERE PERFUME
1 oz. pink jewel cap, jewels in glass
around bottom of bottle. Has 4
butterflies on lid. OSP $20, CMV
$80 in box. $50 BO mint.

1964-66 SOMEWHERE PERFUMED SKIN SOFTENER
5 oz. pink glass jar with pink and
gold lid. OSP $3.25, CMV $6.
1965 SOMEWHERE PERFUMED SOAP
3 oz. pink soap with pink and white
wrapper. OSP 39c, CMV $4 mint.

1963 SOMEWHERE PERFUMED OIL FOR THE BATH
½ oz. clear glass, white lettering, pink
cap. OSP $4, CMV $7 BO, $10 MB.
1964-66 SOMEWHERE PERFUMED OIL
½ oz. clear glass, white lettering, pink
cap. OSP $4, CMV $5 BO, $7 MB.

1962-66 SOMEWHERE BATH OIL
6 oz. pink plastic bottle and cap. OSP $2.50, CMV $4 BO, $6 MB.

1961-66 SOMEWHERE COLOGNE MIST
3 oz. pink plastic coated glass, pink jeweled lid. OSP $4, CMV $3 BO, $5 MB.

1967-70 SOMEWHERE BEAUTY DUST
White plastic with green around bottom. Gold handle. OSP $4, CMV $10 MB, $6 CO.

1968 PERFUME TALC
3½ oz. green cardboard with gold trim. Came with Fluff Puff set. CMV $2.

1962-66 SOMEWHERE POWDER SACHET
1¼ oz. pink glass bottom, pink jeweled lid. OSP $2, CMV $6 MB, $4 BO.

1962-66 SOMEWHERE CREAM SACHET
Pink glass and pink jeweled lid. OSP $2, CMV $1, $3 MB. Some came pink paint on milk glass. Same CMV.

1963-66 SOMEWHERE CREAM LOTION
4 oz. pink lid without jewels. OSP $1.50, CMV $3, $5 MB.

1961-66 SOMEWHERE COLOGNE
2 oz. pink jeweled lid. OSP $2, CMV $3, $5 MB.

1961-66 SOMEWHERE DUSTING POWDER
Pink plastic bottom, clear plastic top with pink jeweled crown. OSP $4, CMV $10 MB, $6.

1967 Only - SOMEWHERE POWDER SACHET
(Left) 9/10 oz. white glass bottom, white and gold cap with green ribbon. Issued during bottle strike in 1967. Bottom is same as Wishing Powder Sachet. OSP $2, CMV $23, $25 MB.

1966-68 SOMEWHERE POWDER SACHET
9/10 oz. white glass, green label, white lid with gold band. Hard to find. OSP $2, CMV $18 MB, $15 BO.

1961 PERFUME MIST AWARD
Given to each representative sending in an order during the 75th Anniversary Campaign. This was also the introduction to a new fragrance - Somewhere. CMV $15 MB.

1962-66 SOMEWHERE TALC
2¾ oz. pink can and lid. OSP 89c, CMV $3, $5 MB.

1964-66 SOMEWHERE 2 DRAM PERFUME MIST
White lid, pink bottom, gold band. OSP $3.25, CMV $9 in box, $7 Mist only.

1962-63 UNFORGETTABLE SET
Pink, yellow and blue box holds Somewhere Cologne Mist, Cream Sachet and Beauty Dust. OSP $10.95, CMV $45 MB.

1966-76 SOMEWHERE PRODUCTS
(Left to Right)

1966-75 CREAM SACHET
White glass trimmed in green and gold. .66 oz. OSP $3, CMV 50c.

1966-72 SKIN SOFTENER
Green and gold lid, 5 oz. glass jar. Came in green paint over clear glass. CMV $1, or green paint over white milk glass, CMV $3. OSP $3.50.

1966-69 PERFUME OIL
½ oz. green label, gold cap. OSP $4, CMV $4, $6 MB.

1966-71 COLOGNE
2 oz. gold cap. OSP $2.50, CMV $1.50.

1966-76 COLOGNE MIST
3 oz. green plastic coated, gold cap, green label. OSP $7, CMV $1.

SOMEWHERE
(Green and white design)

1976 CREAM SACHET
Gold and green lid. OSP $1, CMV 50c.

1975-76 DEMI STICK
OSP $1, CMV 50c.

1970-71 COLOGNE
½ oz. gold cap. OSP $1, CMV $2 MB, $1 BO.

1967-68 CREAM LOTION
4 oz. gold cap. OSP $1.50, CMV $3 BO, $4 MB.

1973-76 SOMEWHERE TALC
3.5 oz. green cardboard, round container. OSP $2, CMV $1.

1966-68 SOMEWHERE SOAP
Green and white box holds 3 bars. OSP $2, CMV $17.50 MB.

1962-66 SOMEWHERE SOAP
Pink box holds 3 bars with embossed name. OSP $1.75, CMV $22 MB.

1968-69 SOMEWHERE SOAP
3 white bars in green box. OSP $3, CMV $13 MB.

1966-72 SOMEWHERE FOAMING BATH OIL
6 oz. green plastic bottle with gold cap. OSP $3.50, CMV $2 BO, $3 MB.

1966-68 SOMEWHERE PERFUME MIST
2 dram, white cap, green bottom. OSP $3.25, CMV $6 MB, $5 BO.

1964 DREAMS OF SOMEWHERE
Box holds 2 dram bottle of Somewhere Perfume Mist, 6 oz. Beauty Dust and 4 oz. bottle of Cream Lotion. OSP $9.25, CMV $40 MB.

1966-71 SOMEWHERE SCENTED HAIR SPRAY
7 oz. green can. OSP $1.50, CMV $3.

1966-67 SOMEWHERE SOAP
Single bar in green wrapper. OSP 49c, CMV $4.

1966-72 SOMEWHERE TALC
2¾ oz. green and white can, green cap. OSP $1, CMV $1.

1964 DREAM CASTLE
Pink and green box holds 2 oz. bottle of Somewhere Cologne and Cream Sachet. OSP $4, CMV $30 MB.

SONNET

1973-78 SONNET PRODUCTS
(White and gold design)

1973-77 PERFUMED POWDER MIST
7 oz. metal can, white cap. SSP $2, CMV 50c.

1973-77 PERFUMED POWDER MIST
(Double stamped label)
Can came out of factory with a double stamped label all over can. Rare. CMV $8.

1973-78 PERFUMED TALC
3.5 oz. cardboard with plastic top and bottom. OSP $2.50, CMV 25c.
Rare upside down label, CMV $5.

1973-76 CREAM SACHET
.66 oz. jar. OSP $4.50, CMV 50c.

1973-76 BEAUTY DUST
6 oz. plastic, pink puff. OSP $10, CMV $2, $5 MB.

1973-78 PERFUMED SKIN SOFTENER
5 oz. plastic jar. OSP $5.50, CMV 50c.

1973-75 PERFUMED ROLLETTE
.33 oz. bottle. SSP $2, CMV 25c.

1973-78 COLOGNE MIST
3 oz. spray bottle. OSP $8. 1st issue 1973. Issued with no gold ring around neck. CMV $2. 1973-78 issued with gold ring around neck. CMV 50c.

1973-74 FOAMING BATH OIL
6 oz. white plastic bottle, gold cap. SSP $2, CMV $1 BO, $2 MB.

1973-74 SONNET HAND & BODY LOTION
8 oz. white plastic. OSP $2, CMV 75c.
1975-76 SONNET EMOLLIENT MIST
4 oz. white and gold with white cap. OSP $3, CMV 50c.
1975-78 SONNET POWDER SACHET
1.25 oz. white and gold cardboard. OSP $2, CMV 50c.
1976-78 SONNET PERFUMED SOAP
3 oz. white bar with gold and white wrapper. OSP $1, CMV $1.
1974-75 SONNET PERFUMED SOAP
3 oz. white with multi-colored center. OSP $1, CMV $1.
1974-78 SONNET PERFUMED DEMI STICK
.19 oz. white and gold. OSP $1, CMV 25c.
1975 FOAMING BATH OIL
6 oz. plastic. CMV 50c.

1972 SONNET AWARDS
(All earned for selling Cologne Mist)
VANITY TRAY
10" white plastic, gold trim. CMV $10.
VANITY BOX
White plastic, gold trim. CMV $18 MB.
THREE PANEL MIRROR
White and gold. CMV $24 MB.
HOSTESS ROBE
White satin, gold trim. (won by Presidents Club members only) CMV $30 MB.

1941-46 SONNET TOILET WATER
2 oz. gold ribbed cap and gold front label. OSP $1.04, CMV $30 BO mint, $35 MB.
1941-43 SONNET BODY POWDER
Special issue box, angel on box, blue and white paper container with plastic shaker top. OSP 65c, CMV $25 MB as shown, $18 CO.

1940-42 FRAGRANCE MIST SONNET
Blue and gold box holds 2 oz. Sonnet Toilet Water, gold cap and label and Spray atomizer. Also came in other fragrances. See Fragrance Mist Sets of 1940's. OSP $1.35, CMV $50 MB, $35 BO mint.

1973 SONNET COLOGNE & SONNET SKIN SO SOFT BATH OIL
4 oz. clear glass bottles, cap is gold. Came in Treasure Chest set only. CMV $3 each.

1941-43 SONNET BODY POWDER
Flat sifter top, scroll box. CMV $22 MB, can only $18 mint.
1973-77 SONNET PERFUME POWDER MIST (double stamped label)
Regular issue can came out with double stamp label on entire can. Rare. CMV $8.

1941-42 SONNET SET
Satin lined lavender box holds 2 oz. Sonnet Toilet Water with gold top atomizer & Sonnet Body Powder. OSP $2, CMV $70 MB.

1974-77 SONNET PERFUMED SOAP
3 oz., three pink oblong shaped bar soap, in gold and white box. OSP $4, CMV $4 MB.
1972-74 SONNET PERFUMED SOAP
3 oz., three pink round shaped bars of soap, in gold and white box. OSP $3, CMV $6 MB.

1943-44 BLUE BIRD SET
Blue and white box, blue satin lining holds feather design face powder, cardboard or plastic lipstick and Sonnet or Apple Blossom Body Powder. OSP $2.25, CMV $75.

1941 Only - SONNET TOILET WATER
2 oz. purple cap and label. 2 different labels. One has yellow dress on box and label and the other has green dress on box and label. OSP 20c, CMV $30 BO, $40 MB each.

SPORTIF

STRAWBERRY

1980 SPORTIF PRODUCTS
(Green in color)
COLOGNE SPRAY
1.8 oz. CMV 50c.
COLOGNE SAMPLES
Box of 10, CMV 25c
COLOGNE INCH SAMPLE
Small glass vial in folder. CMV 25c.
PERFUMED TALC
CMV 25c.

1971-72 STRAWBERRY BATH GELEE
4 oz. red strawberry base and gold cap and spoon. OSP $7, CMV $4, $6 MB.
1971-72 STRAWBERRY GUEST SOAP
Red box holds 3 strawberry soaps. OSP $3, CMV $7 MB.
1971-72 STRAWBERRY BATH FOAM
4 oz. red glass and top. 6" high. OSP $4, CMV $4, $5 MB.

1978-79 STRAWBERRY PORCELAIN NAPKIN RINGS & SOAP SET
Box holds 2 porcelain napkin rings and 1 red strawberry shaped soap. Porcelain made in Brazil. SSP $9.99, CMV $9.99 MB set.

1975-78 STRAWBERRY BUBBLE BATH GELEE
4 oz. plastic tube. OSP $3.50, CMV 25c.
1973-74 STRAWBERRY BATH GELEE
4 oz. clear tube, red cap. SSP $2, CMV 50c.
1973-74 BIG BERRY
10 oz. red plastic with green cap top. Holds Bath Foam. SSP $4, CMV $2, $3 MB.

(Left to right)
1979-80 STRAWBERRY BODY LOTION
6 oz. white plastic. SSP $2.99, CMV 25c.
1979-80 STRAWBERRY FAIR BUBBLE BATH
8 oz. white plastic. SSP $2.99, CMV 25c.
1979-80 STRAWBERRY FAIR PERFUMED TALC
3.5 oz. white, green and red paper sides, plastic top and bottom. SSP $1.49, CMV 25c.
1979-80 BERRY NICE STRAWBERRY COMPACT
Small red and green plastic holds lip gloss. SSP $3.49, CMV $2.50 MB.
1979-80 STRAWBERRY FAIR SHOWER SOAP
Red strawberry soap on a green roap. SSP $3.49, CMV $3.49 MB.
1979-80 SUNNY MORN STRAWBERRY SHAMPOO
8 oz. pink plastic. SSP $1.69, CMV 25c.

1970 STRAWBERRIES & CREAM BATH FOAM
4 oz. white milk glass, red cap and design, or orange cap and design. OSP $3.50, CMV for red cap $6, orange cap $4.
1969-70 STRAWBERRY FAIR SOAP
Red soap in yellow plastic basket with green grass, wrapped in celophane and bow. OSP $3, CMV $7 $10 MB.

1979-80 STRAWBERRY PORCELAIN DEMI CUP CANDLETTE
Box holds 4" saucer and 2¼" high cup. Starwberry design. Made in Brazil for Avon 1978 on bottom of each. SSP $7, CMV $7.99 MB.

1979 STRAWBERRY PORCELAIN SUGAR SHAKER & TALC
Box holds white porcelain shaker and 3.5 oz. box of strawberry perfumed talc. Made in Brazil. Avon 1978 on bottom of shaker. SSP $11.99, CMV $12 MB set. Early orders and demos had 1978 on bottom of sugar shaker and regular issue had only "Avon" and no date on bottom. Talc only CMV $2, shaker only CMV $8 no date, CMV $12 1978 date. Talc also came with upside down label from factory by mistake. CMV $8 upside down label on talc.

SUN BLOSSOM

1978 BURST OF SPRING SCARF
Yellow, green and white acetate scarf designed by S.M. Kent. 28" square. OSP $2.50, CMV $2.50.

1978 SUN BLOSSOMS PERFUMED TALC
Yellow flower design. 3.5 oz. container. SSP $1, CMV 25c.

1978 BURST OF SPRING BEAUTY DUST CONTAINER
Yellow, pink and green metal can to put beauty dust in. Sold empty. SSP. $4.99, CMV $4 MB.

1978 SUN BLOSSOM COLOGNE SPRAY
1.8 oz. flower embossed bottle, gold cap. SSP $2.50, CMV 25c.

1978 SUN BLOSSOM COLOGNE
½ oz bottle, yellow cap. SSP $1, CMV 50c.

1978 COLOGNE ICE
1 oz. CMV 50c.

1947-49 SWAN LAKE 2 PIECE SET
Blue and white box holds 6 oz. Swan Lake Bath Oil and 9 oz. blue box of Swan Lake Body Powder. OSP $2, CMV $100 MB.

SWAN LAKE

1947-49 SWAN LAKE BATH OIL
6 oz. flat sided bottle, pink cap, painted label. OSP $1.25, CMV $55, $65 MB.

1947-50 SWAN LAKE COLOGNE
4 oz. pink cap, painted label. OSP $1.35, CMV $45 BO mint, $55 MB.

1947-50 SWAN LAKE 3 PIECE SET
Blue and white box holds 9 oz. blue boxes of Swan Lake Bath Salts, Body Powder and 4 oz. cologne with white cap. OSP $3, CMV $120 MB.

1947-49 SWAN LAKE BODY POWDER
9 oz. blue, pink and white paper box. Came with swan or ballerina on side. OSP 85c, CMV $30, $35 MB. Also came 4½ oz. size in sets. CMV $30 mint.

1947-49 SWAN LAKE BATH SALTS
9 oz. blue, pink and white paper box. OSP 85c, CMV $30, $35 MB.

SWEET HONESTY

1973-76
SWEET HONESTY PRODUCTS
COLOGNE MIST
2 oz. SSP $3, CMV $1.
GENTLE MOISTURE GEL
1.8 oz. SSP $1, CMV 25c.
JUST ENOUGH COLOR LIQUID FOUNDATION
1.5 oz. SSP $1, CMV 25c.
CREAM SACHET
.66 oz. SSP $1.50, CMV 25c.
LIP GLOSS POT
.12 oz. SSP $1, CMV 25c.
VERY REAL BLUSH
.25 oz. SSP $1, CMV 25c.
COMPACT
5 oz. SSP $2.50, CMV $1.

SWEET HONESTY PRODUCTS
1973-76 AFTER BATH FRESHENER
10 oz. OSP $3, CMV 50c.
1973-77 PERFUMED POWDER MIST
7 oz. OSP $2, CMV 50c.
1973-78 PERFUMED TALC
3.5 oz. OSP $1, CMV 25c.

1973-77 COLOGNE GELEE
1.5 oz. OSP $1, CMV 25c.
FACE BEAMER
1.5 oz. OSP $1, CMV 25c.
BRIGHT & SHINING SHADOW
.25 oz. OSP $1, CMV 25c.
LIP COLOR AND/OR SUNNY LIP GLEAMER
.13 oz. OSP $1, CMV 25c.
WIDE EYES MASCARA
.15 oz. OSP $1, CMV 25c.
1973-78 DEMI STICK
.19 oz. OSP $1, CMV 25c.
1973-77 ROLLETTE
.33 oz. OSP $2, CMV 25c.
1973-78 FRAGRANCE SAMPLES
10 foil samples per box. CMV 25c.

1981-83
SWEET HONESTY PRODUCTS
COLOGNE SPRAY
1.8 oz. SSP $5
FRESH & FOAMING BODY
CLEANSER
6 oz. tube. SSP $3.50
BODY SPLASH
10 oz. plastic bottle. SSP $3.50
PERFUMED POWDER MIST
4 oz. spray can. SSP $2.50
PERFUMED TALC
3.5 oz. SSP $2.50
STROKE OF SWEET HONESTY
SOLID COLOGNE
Pencil form. Pink and gold. SSP $3.
1982-83 SWEET HONESTY SOAP
Single Bar. CMV 75c.
FLUTED PETITE COLOGNE
.5 oz. gold cap.
(CMV all products 25c)

1976-78 SWEET HONESTY BUBBLE BATH
10 oz. plastic bottle, pink cap. OSP $4.50, CMV 50c.
1977-78 SWEET HONESTY COLOGNE
2 oz. bottle, gold and pink cap. OSP $5, CMV 50c.
1977 SWEET HONESTY RECORD
Small 33 1/3 size cut out plastic record in green folder. Sent to Avon managers on introduction of Sweet Honesty. CMV $4 mint.

1977-78 SWEET HONESTY GIFT SET
Came with 2 oz. cologne and 2 perfumed soaps. OSP $9, CMV $7 MB.

1978 SWEET HONESTY PERFUMED SOAPS
Boxed 3 cakes, 3 oz. each. OSP $6.50, CMV $5.50 MB.
1976-77 SWEET HONESTY BY THE JUG BUBBLE BATH
10 oz. plastic jug. OSP $5, CMV $1.50

1977 SWEET HONESTY SCARF
Red, white, blue and green scarf sold for $1 with order of Sweet Honesty products. CMV $3 in Avon plastic bag.

TASHA

1979-80 TASHA PRODUCTS
DREAM DIARY
Given to Reps. CMV $1.
ULTRA COLOGNE SPRAY
1.8 oz. CMV 50c
ULTRA COLOGNE
.33 oz. gold cap. CMV 50c.
LIGHT PERFUME
.5 oz. gold cap. CMV 50c.
PERFUMED SOAP
Single bar. CMV 75c.
PERFUMED POWDER MIST
4 oz. can. CMV 50c.
LUZURY BATH FOAM
6 oz. plastic. CMV 50c.
ULTRA COLOGNE
2 oz. glass, gold cap. CMV 50c.
TASHA ULTRA COLOGNE
2 oz. not shown. CMV 50c.
1979-80 SSP $4.50, 50c.

1980 TASHA ULTRA CREME PERFUME
.66 oz. clear glass, gold tone lid. CMV 50c.
1980 TASHA PERFUMED TALC
3.5 oz. purple color. SSP $1.75, CMV 50c.

1980-83 TASHA PRODUCTS
Burgandy color
SOAP   SSP $1, CMV $1 mint.
PERFUMED SKIN SOFTENER
5 oz. plastic jar. CMV 25c.
PERFUMED POWDER MIST
4 oz. spray can. CMV 25c
BEAUTY DUST REFILL
Box holds white plastic dish powder refill with burgandy puff. SSP $3.50, CMV $3.50 full MB.

TEMPO

1979-80 TEMPO PRODUCTS
(Colors are beige, silver and red)
ULTRA SOFT BODY SATIN
6 oz. plastic.
PERFUMED TALC
3.5 oz. paper, plastic top and bottom.
PERFUMED SKIN SOFTENER
5 oz. plastic.
ULTRA CREAM PERFUME
.66 oz. glass.
(CMV 25c each on all products)

TENDER BLOSSOMS

1977-79 TENDER BLOSSOMS
FRAGRANCE CANDLE
Came in Floral Medley fragrance.
OSP $6.50, CMV $5, $6.50 MB.
1977 TENDER BLOSSOMS BEAUTY
DUST CONTAINER
Flower shaped metal container with
Tender Blossoms design. OSP $6.50,
CMV $4.50 MB.
1977-79 COLOGNE
½ oz. bottle. Came in Field Flowers,
Honeysuckle, Raining Violets, Roses
Roses, Hawaiian White Ginger, Apple
Blossom. Each cologne had different
colored caps. Box shown in Tender
Blossoms design issued Christmas
1977 only. OSP $2, CMV $1.50
MB as shown.
1978 TENDER BLOSSOMS TALC
3½ oz. Came in Field Flowers, Roses
Roses, Hawaiian White Ginger and
Honeysuckle. OSP $2, CMV 50c.

TIMELESS

TIMELESS PRODUCTS
Yellow & light amber.
1975-77 PERFUMED POWDER MIST
4 or 7 oz. OSP $3 - CMV 50c.
1975-78 PERFUMED TALC
3.5 oz. cardboard. OSP $1.50, CMV
25c. Also came with upside down
label. CMV $6.
1975-78 POWDER SACHET
1.25 oz. cardboard. OSP $3.50, CMV
75c.
1975-77 ULTRA PERFUME
ROLLETTE
.33 oz. gold cap. OSP $3, CMV 50c.
1975-78 ULTRA CREAM SACHET
.66 oz. gold cap. OSP $3, CMV 25c.
1975-78 ULTRA COLOGNE SAMPLE
10 foil packets per box. CMV 25c.
1978-80 ULTRA PERFUME
CONCENTRE
.33 oz. gold cap. CMV 25c.

1974 TIMELESS ULTRA COLOGNE
MIST FOR PRESIDENT'S CLUB ONLY
(Right) 2 oz. size, gold cap. 1st issue
to Avon President's Club members
only, had 4A design on bottom under
label. Regular issue had Avon on bottom. Box also came with special card
saying it was collectors edition, fall
1974. CMV $6 MB as shown.
1974-78
(Left) Regular issue 1.8 oz. size, gold
cap. Avon on bottom. OSP $7.50,
CMV 50c.

1977-78 TIMELESS BEAUTY DUST
CONTAINER
(Left) Amber plastic base and lid.
OSP $9.50, CMV $4 MB.
1976-78 TIMELESS PERFUMED SOAP
(Center) 3 oz. bar. OSP $1.25, CMV
75c.
1976-78 TIMELESS ULTRA COLOGNE
(Right) 2 oz. amber glass bottle, gold
cap. OSP $7.50, CMV 50c.

1975-78 TIMELESS SOAP
(Left) 3 cakes amber soap in amber,
gold & yellow box. OSP $4, CMV $4
MB.
1975-78 TIMELESS PERFUMED SKIN
SOFTENER
(Right) 5 oz. light amber plastic jar
with gold lid. OSP $2, CMV 50c.

1975 TIMELESS MANAGERS GIFT
SET
Gold box holds perfume rollette,
cologne mist & creme perfume. Given
to Avon Managers only at introduction of Timeless. CMV $35 MB.

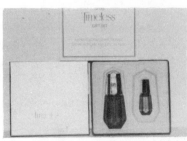

1977-78 TIMELESS ULTRA GIFT SET
Box came with 1.8 oz. Ultra cologne
spray and .33 oz. Ultra perfume
rollette. OSP $11.50, CMV $9 MB.

TO A WILD ROSE

1976 TIMELESS GIFT SET
Amber bottles with gold caps. Box yellow & gold. Contains Ultra cream sachet & cologne mist. OSP $10, CMV $10 MB.

1950-56 TO A WILD ROSE PERFUME
(Left) Pink flowers on pink & blue box. 3 dram bottle with blue cap & flower around neck. OSP $4.50, CMV in box $110 - bottle only with tag $75.

1960-63 TO A WILD ROSE SPRAY PERFUME
(Right) Red, white & gold box holds pink & white metal spray perfume with pink flowers. OSP $2.95, CMV in box $11 - spray only $7.

1955-59 TO A WILD ROSE PERFUME
Pink & white box holds ½ oz. white glass bottle with pink cap & painted label. OSP $5, CMV $100 in box - bottle only $70.

1957 TO A WILD ROSE COLOGNE
(Left) 2 oz. white glass with paper label, pink cap. Came in Trilogy Set only. CMV $16 mint.

1957 TO A WILD ROSE LOTION
(Right) 2 oz. white glass with paper label & pink cap. Came in Trilogy Set only. CMV $16 mint.

1961-68 TO A WILD ROSE 2 OZ. COLOGNE
(Left & Center) 2 oz. white glass, pink letters & cap. Came with & without painted flowers around base. OSP $1.50, CMV $3.

1960-63 TO A WILD ROSE SPRAY PERFUME REFILL
(Right) Box holds small metal refill. CMV $4 MB - $2 refill only.

1956-62 TO A WILD ROSE TOILET WATER
(Left) 2 oz. white glass, pink cap, has paper flower band around base. OSP $1.50, CMV $10 BO - $12 MB.

1963 TO A WILD ROSE PERFUME OIL FOR THE BATH
(Right) ½ oz. white glass, pink cap, pink & white box. OSP $1.50, CMV $10 MB - $8 BO.

1956 TO A WILD ROSE TOILET WATER
(Not Shown) ½ oz. size. Same size & design as perfumed oil shown above. White glass with pink cap & lettering. Came in Special Date Set, rare. CMV $27 mint.

1965-68 TO A WILD ROSE CREAM LOTION
(Left) 4 oz. painted label, white glass, pink cap. OSP $1.25, CMV $4 BO - $5 MB.

1956-65 TO A WILD ROSE CREAM LOTION
(Right) 4 oz. white glass, pink cap, paper label. OSP $1.25, CMV $5 BO - $7 MB.

1970-71 TO A WILD ROSE COLOGNE
(Left) ½ oz. white glass with pink cap & letters. OSP $1.75, CMV $2 MB - $1 BO.

1962-72 TO A WILD ROSE PERFUMED TALC
(Center) 2¾ oz. white & pink can with pink cap. OSP $1, CMV $1.

1954-55 TO A WILD ROSE TALC
(Right) Blue can & cap with pink flowers. OSP 49c, CMV $8 CO - $10 MB.

1955-59 TO A WILD ROSE BODY POWDER
(Left) 4 oz. white glass & cap with rose on lid, paper label around bottom, pink letters. OSP $1, CMV $10 BO - $13 MB.

1961-63 TO A WILD ROSE BODY POWDER
(Center) 4 oz. white hard plastic bottle, white lid with roses. OSP $1.79. Also came 3 oz. size & with short issue pink cap. CMV $12 pink cap. CMV $8 BO - $10 MB.

1955-59 TO A WILD ROSE BODY POWDER
(Right) 4 oz. white glass & cap with rose on lid. paper label. OSP $1, CMV $10 BO - $13 MB.

1955-63 TO A WILD ROSE COLOGNE
(Left) 4 oz. white glass bottle, pink cap, has flowered paper border around base. OSP $2.50, CMV $15 - $17 MB.

1950-55 TO A WILD ROSE BODY POWDER
(Right) 5 oz. blue paper container, 2 different bottoms. One is refillable from the bottom. OSP 85c, CMV $15 - $20 MB. Some issued as shown with To A Wild Rose Body Powder on side & some only say Avon Body Powder.

1956-59 TO A WILD ROSE BATH OIL
4 oz. white glass bottle with pink cap. OSP $1.35, CMV $12 in box - $10 bottle only. 2 oz. white glass bottle with pink cap, same label came in Trilogy Set only. CMV $15.

1960-61 TO A WILD ROSE 4 OZ. COLOGNE
Pink, green & white Christmas box holds 4 oz. white glass bottle with pink cap & neck ribbon. No flower band around base, but also came with a paper flower band around base as shown. OSP $2.50, CMV $25 in box pictured.

1950-55 TO A WILD ROSE CREAM SACHET
(Left) Blue cap with pink flowers, white glass, 3 cornered shape. OSP $1.25, CMV $10 MB - $8 BO.

TO A WILD ROSE CREAM SACHET
(Center) Same shaped jar as one on right only has blue lid as on the left jar. Lid will not interchange with jar on right. Also came with white lid, label on bottom with no zip code, is older. Rare. CMV $9 BO - $11 MB.

1955-72 TO A WILD ROSE CREAM SACHET
(Right) White glass, white lid with painted rose. OSP $1.25, CMV 50c - $1 MB.

1959-61 TO A WILD ROSE PERFUMED BATH OIL
8 oz. white plastic bottle with pink cap. OSP $2.25, CMV $5 BO - $7 MB.

1961-66 TO A WILD ROSE PERFUMED BATH OIL
(Not Shown) Same only 6 oz. size. CMV $6 MB - $4 BO.

1960-61 TO A WILD ROSE 4 OZ. COLOGNE
Pink & white box holds 4 oz. white glass bottle, pink cap, painted label, pink silk ribbon on neck. OSP $2.50 CMV $15 BO with ribbon mint - $17 MB. Came with and without painted flowers around base.

1958-59 TO A WILD ROSE COLOGNE MIST
(Left) 3 oz. white plastic coated over clear glass, pink cap. Came with or without embossed rose on lid. OSP $2.50, CMV $17 BO - $22 MB.

1966-67 TO A WILD ROSE SOAP
(Right) 3 oz. white embossed soap in pink & green wrapper. OSP 49c, CMV $3.

1956-62 TO A WILD ROSE TALC
(Left) White can with pink flowers & cap. OSP 69c, CMV $5 - $7 MB. Add $4 for 1959 Christmas box shown.

1966-68 TO A WILD ROSE FOAMING BATH OIL
(Right) 6 oz. white plastic bottle with pink cap. OSP $2.50, CMV $3.50 - $5 MB.

1959-75 TO A WILD ROSE COLOGNE MIST
(Left) 3 oz. white plastic coated with pink flower on cap. OSP $5, CMV $1 - $2 MB.

1976 TO A WILD ROSE COLOGNE MIST
(Not Shown) 3 oz. white bottle, pink letters, pink cap, no flower. OSP $7, CMV 50c.

1964-68 TO A WILD ROSE PERFUMED MIST
(Right) 2 dram, pink & white, gold band. OSP $3, CMV $7 in box - $6 mist only.

1969 TO A WILD ROSE TALC
(Left) 2.75 oz. pink & white can, pink cap. Came in 1969 Perfumed Pair set only. CMV $2.

1955-56 TO A WILD ROSE BATH OIL
(Right) 2 oz. pink cap & label. Came in "That's Me Set" only. CMV $15 mint.

1966-69 TO A WILD ROSE SCENTED HAIR SPRAY
(Left) 7 oz. pink & white can, pink cap. OSP $1.50, CMV $3.

1968-73 TO A WILD ROSE PERFUMED POWDER MIST
(Center & Right) 7 oz. pink & white can, 2 different labels. CMV paper label $4 - painted label $2. OSP $3.50 each.

1955-67 TO A WILD ROSE POWDER SACHET
(Left) White glass, white lid with painted rose. Paper band around bottom with roses. Came in 9 oz. & 1.25 oz. OSP $1.25, CMV $7 in box - $6 bottle only.

1964-68 TO A WILD ROSE PERFUME OIL
(Right) ½ oz. white glass, pink letters & cap. OSP $3.50, CMV $6 BO - $8 MB.

1964-70 TO A WILD ROSE BEAUTY DUST
(Left) White plastic trimmed in pink. OSP $3.25, CMV $4 - $6 MB.

1959-70 TO A WILD ROSE PERFUMED SKIN SOFTENER
(Right) 5 oz. white glass, pink & white lid. OSP $3.50, CMV $2.

1950-55 TO A WILD ROSE TOILET WATER
(Left) 2 oz. blue cap, with or without embossed roses. Three cornered bottle. OSP $1.50, CMV $20 MB - $17 BO.

1953-55 TO A WILD ROSE CREAM LOTION
(Right) 4 oz. blue cap & label, with or without embossed roses. OSP 89c, CMV $15 bottle only - $17 in box.

1950-55 TO A WILD ROSE BEAUTY DUST
Blue can with flowers on lid. OSP $1.75, CMV $15 CO - $20 MB.

1953-55 TO A WILD ROSE SACHET
1¼ oz. blue cap with embossed flower on top. Blue box. CMV $15 MB - $12 BO mint.

1953-55 TO A WILD ROSE BATH OIL
4 oz. bottle with blue cap, with or without embossed roses. Blue label. OSP $1.25, CMV $20 in box - bottle only $17.

1962-63 TO A WILD ROSE BEAUTY DUST
(Left) Pink & green flowers, clear plastic top, cardboard. Came in Fragrance Magic Sets only. CMV $16 mint.

1955-59 TO A WILD ROSE BEAUTY DUST
(Right) Pink ball on top, trimmed in pink, tin lid & bottom. Sides cardboard. OSP $1.75, CMV $12 - $16 MB.

1954 TO A WILD ROSE COLOGNE OR CREAM LOTION
2 oz. clear glass with blue caps. Came in Bath Bouquet Set. CMV $17.50 each mint.

1950-55 TO A WILD ROSE COLOGNE
(Left) 4 oz. clear glass, blue cap, blue label. OSP $2, CMV $20 MB - $16 BO.

1953-55 TO A WILD ROSE POWDER SACHET
(Center) 1¼ oz. blue smooth top cap, blue label, clear glass. OSP $1.25, CMV $12 - $15 MB.

1975-76 TO A WILD ROSE CREAM SACHET
(Right) .66 oz. clear glass jar, red & gold lid. OSP $3, CMV 25c.

1969-73 TO A WILD ROSE SOAP
Floral box holds 3 white bars. OSP $3, CMV $7 MB.

1955 BATH BOUQUET SET
White & pink box holds To A Wild Rose 2 oz. cologne & cream lotion with white caps & 1 bar of soap. OSP $1.95, CMV $52 MB.

1954 TO A WILD ROSE COLOGNE BATH OIL, COLOGNE, CREAM LOTION
2 oz. clear glass with white cap, blue label. Came in Miss Coed Set only. CMV $17.50 each.

1952-56 TO A WILD ROSE SOAP
White box holds 3 white bars. OSP $1.50, CMV $26.50.

1954 TO A WILD ROSE SOAP
Blue box of 3 bars. CMV $30 MB.

1954 MISS COED
Blue box holds three 2 oz. bottles of To A Wild Rose cologne, cream lotion & bath oil. All have white caps. OSP $2.35, CMV $75 set - $17.50 each bottle.

1955 TO A WILD ROSE COLOGNE OR CREAM LOTION
2 oz. clear glass with white caps. Came in Bath Bouquet Set. CMV $15 each mint.

1957-68 TO A WILD ROSE SOAP
Pink & white box holds 3 bars in 2 different size boxes. OSP $1.59, CMV large box $25 MB - small box $17.50 MB.

1954 BATH BOUQUET SET
Pink & blue box. To A Wild Rose 2 oz. cologne & cream lotion with blue caps & white soap. OSP $1.95, CMV $52 MB. One box has sleeve top and one with a lift off lid. Came with and without flowers on bottom of box.

1956 TO A WILD ROSE BATH OIL & COLOGNE
Both 2 oz. bottles with white caps. Came in 1956 Bath Bouquet Set only. CMV $15 each mint.

1956 BATH BOUQUET SET
White & pink box holds To A Wild Rose cologne & bath oil with white caps & 1 bar of soap. OSP $2.25, CMV $52 MB. Also came with 2 bath oils as substitutes.

1956 SWEETHEART SET
White & pink box holds To A Wild Rose beauty dust & 4 oz. cologne. OSP $3.95, CMV $45 MB.

1956 TO A WILD ROSE SPECIAL DATE SET
Pink & gold box holds black lipstick, powder pak & ½ oz. of To A Wild Rose Toilet Water. OSP $2.50, CMV $45 MB.

1957 TRILOGY SET
Box holds 3 To A Wild Rose 2 oz. bottles of bath oil, cream lotion & cologne. OSP $2.95, CMV $57.50 MB.

1961 LOVELY AS A ROSE
Pink & white box holds 2 oz. To A Wild Rose cologne & cream sachet. OSP $3.50, CMV $20 MB.

1963-64 HOLIDAY ROSES
Box holds To A Wild Rose beauty dust, splash cologne, cream lotion, with paper label. Same set in 1964 with painted label. OSP $6.50, CMV $37 each set MB.

1956 ADORABLE SET
Pink & white box with pink ribbon on lid holds To A Wild Rose body powder & cream sachet. OSP $2.25, CMV $32.50 MB.

1958 A SPRAY OF ROSES
Pink & white box holds To A Wild Rose cologne mist & cream sachet. OSP $3.95, CMV $37 MB.

1955-56 ADORABLE SET
Pink & white box with pink flowers on top holds To A Wild Rose body powder & cream sachet. OSP $2.25, CMV $32.50 MB.

1957 ROSES ADRIFT
Pink & white box holds To A Wild Rose beauty dust, cream sachet & cologne. OSP $4.95, CMV $50 MB.

1964 WILD ROSES
Multi-pink flowered box holds 2 oz. bottle of To A Wild Rose cologne & cream sachet. OSP $3.50, CMV $25 MB.

1955 SWEETHEARTS
Pink & white box holds To A Wild Rose beauty dust with pink ribbon & 4 oz. cologne. OSP $3.95, CMV $50 MB.

1961 SPRAY OF ROSES
White & pink box with pink satin lining holds To A Wild Rose beauty dust & cologne mist. OSP $5.90, CMV $30 MB.

1953 WILD ROSES
To A Wild Rose body powder with cream sachet on top. Pink ribbon around set. OSP $1.95, CMV $35 MB.

1950-52 TO A WILD ROSE SET
Blue & pink box holds To A Wild Rose body powder & 4 oz. cologne. OSP $2.85, CMV $57.50 MB.

1955 PINK BELLS
Pink box holds 2 blue cans of To A Wild Rose talc. OSP $1, CMV $22.50 MB.

1954-55 PETAL OF BEAUTY
Blue & pink box with blue ribbon around outside holds 4 oz. cologne & beauty dust. OSP $3.75, CMV $60 MB.

1953-54 ROSE PETALS
Two clear glass bottles, blue caps, holds bath oil & cream lotion. OSP $2.15, CMV $55 MB.

1953 PETAL OF BEAUTY SET
Pink box holds blue & pink satin bag, all blue bag, or all pink bag with To A Wild Rose 4 oz. cologne & beauty dust. with 5/8 dram perfume, "Small Square Bottle" with ribbon tied around it. Inside beauty dust. OSP $5.25, CMV in box $75. Bag & contents only $55. 1950-52 set sold without 5/8 dram perfume. CMV $60 MB, $40 no box, in bag.

1956 ANNIVERSARY SPECIAL
Pink & white box holds 2 cans of To A Wild Rose talc. OSP $1.10, CMV $20 MB.

TOCCARA

1981 TOCCARA SWEATER AWARD
(Bottom) Navy blue sweater made by Lady Botany only for Avon. Given to Reps for selling 12 bottles of Toccara cologne spray. CMV $15.
1982 TOCCARA CAFTAN AWARD
(Top) Blue, lavender & silver caftan given to Reps for selling 20 bottles of Toccara cologne spray. CMV $25.

1982 TOCCARA DELUX GIFT SET
Blue box holds white bar of soap & jar of renewable creme cologne. Short issue. SSP $9, CMV $9 MB.

1981-84 TOCCARA PRODUCTS
Basic color is blue & silver.
LUXURY BATH FOAM
6 oz. plastic.
SOAP
Single bar.
RENEWABLE COLOGNE SPRAY
1.25 oz. blue paint over clear glass.
Frosted cap.
RENEWABLE CREME COLOGNE
1 oz. jar, blue paint over clear glass.
SOLID COLOGNE PENCIL
FRAGRANCE PENCIL SHARPENER
RENEWABLE PERFUME LUSTRE
.5 oz.
PERFUMED TALC
3.5 oz.
DUSTING POWDER
3 oz.
PURSE SPRAY - SPECIAL EDITION
CMV soap & dusting powder $1 -
all other products 25c each.
CMV soap & dusting powder $1 - all
other products 25c each.

TOPAZE

See Stockholders Gift section for 1960
Topaze Treasure Set.

1959-63 TOPAZE PERFUME
1 oz. amber glass & amber jeweled
glass stopper. Bottle cut like a gem.
In yellow & white box. OSP $20,
CMV in box $135 - bottle only $100.

**1959-61 TOPAZE 4 OZ. GIFT
COLOGNE**
Gold cap, clear glass in yellow & gold
satin lined box. OSP $3.75, CMV $8
BO - $17 MB.

1935 Only TOPAZE PERFUME
¼ oz. gold cap, gold & white label &
box. Introducing Topaze for the 50th
wedding anniversary of Mr. & Mrs.
D.H. McConnell. OSP 20c, CMV
bottle only $50 - $70 MB.

1959-63 TOPAZE 4 OZ. COLOGNE
(Left) Gold cap. OSP $3, CMV $8
in plain yellow box $14.
1960-71 TOPAZE 2 OZ. COLOGNE
(Right) Gold cap, painted label. OSP
$2, CMV $1 - MB $2.

1960-70 TOPAZE BEAUTY DUST
(Left) Yellow plastic bottom. white
lid with yellow jewel. OSP $4, CMV
$3 - $5 MB.
**1964-72 TOPAZE PERFUMED SKIN
SOFTENER**
(Right) 5 oz. yellow painted over
white milk glass or clear glass, gold &
white lid. OSP $3.50, CMV $2 MB -
$1 BO.

1964-69 TOPAZE PERFUME OIL
(Left) ½ oz. gold cap & painted label.
OSP $4, CMV $4 - MB $6.
**1963 TOPAZE PERFUME OIL FOR
THE BATH**
(Center) ½ oz., gold cap, painted
label. OSP $4, CMV $40 BO - $45
MB.
1970-71 TOPAZE ½ OZ. COLOGNE
(Right) Gold cap & painted label.
OSP $1.50, CMV $2 MB - $1.50 BO.

1964-68 TOPAZE PERFUME MIST
(Left) 2 dram yellow bottle, white
top with gold band, box gold. OSP
$3.25, CMV $5 - $6 MB.
1959-63 TOPAZE SPRAY PERFUME
(Right) Yellow box holds 2 dram
metal spray perfume, gold top &
yellow bottom. OSP $3.75, CMV $7 -
$12 MB.

1974-76 TOPAZE PERFUMED TALC
(Left) 3.5 oz. yellow with gold, cardboard. OSP $1, CMV 50c.
**1975-78 TOPAZE PERFUMED DEMI
STICK**
(Center) .19 oz. white with yellow &
gold. OSP $1, CMV 50c.
1975-76 TOPAZE CREAM SACHET
(Right) .66 oz. clear glass, gold &
yellow cap. OSP $2, CMV 50c.

1965-69 TOPAZE PERFUME ROLLETTE
(Left) .33 oz. ribbed carnival glass, gold cap. OSP $2, CMV $6 BO - $7 MB.

1966-70 TOPAZE SCENTED HAIR SPRAY
(Right) 7 oz. yellow can. OSP $1.50, CMV $3.

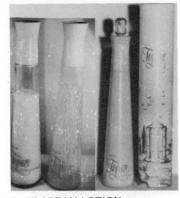

1959-67 CREAM LOTION
(Left) 4 oz. clear glass, yellow cap. OSP $1.50, CMV $2. Also came with yellow cap with jewel, rare. CMV $8.

TOPAZE BODY LOTION - FOREIGN
(Center) CMV $6.

1959-68 TOPAZE COLOGNE MIST
(Right) 3 oz. yellow plastic coated, yellow jewel on lid, in round yellow box. OSP $7, CMV $3 in round box. 1969-76 issue came in square box. Same bottle. CMV $1.

1977-78 TOPAZE PERFUME SKIN SOFTENER
5 oz. plastic jar, yellow and gold lid. OSP $6, CMV 50c.

1976-78 TOPAZE CREAM SACHET
.66 gem like cut glass base. Gold and brown cap. SSP $1.50, CMV 50c.

1970's TOPAZE FRAGRANCE SAMPLE
Yellow packet came 10 to a box. CMV 50c box of 10.

1965-66 TOPAZE SOAP COLUMN
Holds 3 yellow bars. OSP $1.75, CMV $22, $26 MB.

1961-66 TOPAZE BATH OIL
(Left) 6 oz. yellow plastic bottle & cap. OSP $2.50, CMV $4.

1966-73 TOPAZE FOAMING BATH OIL
(Center) 6 oz. yellow plastic bottle & cap. OSP $2.75, CMV $1.50.

1961-63 TOPAZE BODY POWDER
(Right) 4 oz. yellow plastic bottle & cap. OSP $2.25, CMV $7 - $9 MB.

1961-62 TOPAZE PERFUMED TALC
(left) 2¼ or 2¾ oz. yellow round can & cap. OSP $1 - CMV $5, $7 MB.

1962-74 TOPAZE PERFUMED TALC
(Right) 2¾ oz. yellow & white can, yellow cap. OSP $1, CMV $1.

1961-64 TOPAZE SOAP
Yellow box holds 2 bars of Topaze soap. OSP $1.50, CMV $22 MB.

1959-67 TOPAZE POWDER SACHET
Both 9/10 oz. yellow glass, yellow caps. OSP $2 common issue with large cap. CMV $6 MB - $5 BO. CMV small cap $6 BO - $7 MB.

1976-78 TOPAZE COLOGNE SPRAY
2 oz. clear glass gold cap. SSP $3.99 CMV 50c.

1977 TOPAZE PERFUMED POWDER MIST
7 oz. yellow and brown can, plastic cap. OSP $5, CMV 50c.

1976-78 TOPAZE FOAMING BATH OIL
6 oz. yellow plastic bottle and cap. SSP $5.55, CMV 50c.

1960-61 GOLDEN TOPAZE
Gold box with plastic cover holds Topaze Cream Sachet, Cologne Mist and Beauty Dust. OSP $9.95, CMV $40 MB.

1964 TOPAZE SETTING
Yellow box holds 2 oz. bottle of Topaze Cologne and Powder Sachet. OSP $4, CMV $25 MB.

1961 GOLDEN GEM
Gold box holds 2 oz. Topaze Cologne and Cream Sachet in .75 oz. size. OSP $4, CMV $25 MB.

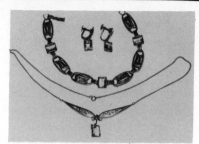

1960 TOPAZE JEWELRY AWARDS
Awarded for sales of Topaze products. 12 carat gold filled with imported Topaze stones. CMV necklace-$40-$50 MB, bracelet - $60-$70 MB, earrings $30-$40 MB.

1960-61 TOPAZE TEMPLE OF LOVE
Yellow and gold. Holds yellow and white plastic holder. Came with .75 oz. Topaze Cream Sachet. OSP 75c, CMV in box $20, $10 holder only, $6 for .75 oz. Cream Sachet only.
1960-75 TOPAZE CREAM SACHET
.66 oz. yellow paint on clear or milk glass, yellow cap. OSP $3, CMV 25c.

1964 TOPAZE PRINCESS
Gold box holds Topaze 3 oz. Cologne Mist and 4 oz. Cream Lotion. OSP $5.95, CMV $25 MB.

TRACY

1981-83 TRACY PRODUCTS
All are pink & white plastic.
TWICE A DAY SKIN LOTION
6 oz. bottle, pink cap.
DEEP CLEAN CREAM
4 oz. tube, white cap.
NATURAL GLOW MOISTURIZER
3 oz. tube, pink cap.
SSP $3 each, CMV 25c each, no boxes.

1961 TOPAZE JEWEL
Gold box holds Topaze Cologne Mist and Cream Lotion. OSP $4.95, CMV $30 MB.

1963 TOPAZE ELEGANCE
Gold and white box holds Topaze Beauty Dust, 4 oz. Creme Lotion, and 2 oz. Cologne. OSP $7.95, CMV $35 MB.

UNFORGETTABLE

1965-69 UNFORGETTABLE PERFUME OIL
(Left) Clear glass, gold cap, no neck trim. OSP $5, CMV $7 MB - $6 BO.
(Center Left) Clear glass, gold cap, cut out gold neck trim. OSP $5, CMV $7 MB - $6 BO.
(Center Right) Clear glass, gold cap, solid gold neck trim, scalloped edge. OSP $5, CMV $7 MB - $6 BO.
(Right) Solid gold neck trim with smooth edge. CMV $7 MB - $6 BO.

1965-70 UNFORGETTABLE BEAUTY DUST
(Left) Pink plastic trimmed in gold. OSP $5, CMV $3 - $6 MB.
1965-73 UNFORGETTABLE SKIN SOFTENER
(Right) 5 oz. pink painted over clear or milk glass, pink & gold lid. OSP $3.50, CMV $1.

1966-68 UNFORGETTABLE POWDER SACHET
(Left) 9 oz. pink glass, gold pattern printing & gold cap. No neck trim. OSP $2.50, CMV $6 - MB $8.

1965 Only UNFORGETTABLE POWDER SACHET
(Center Left) 9 oz. pink glass, gold lettering, cap & trim. Neck trim has cut out pattern. OSP $2.50, CMV $8 MB - $6 BO.

UNFORGETTABLE POWDER SACHET
(Center Right) 9 oz. pink glass, no trim. OSP $2.50, CMV $6 - $8 MB.

1965 Only UNFORGETTABLE POWDER SACHET
(Right) 9 oz. pink glass, gold letter-ing, cap & trim. No holes in trim. OSP $2.50, CMV $6 - MB $8.

1966-71 UNFORGETTABLE SCENTED HAIR SPRAY
(Left) 7 oz. orange & gold can. OSP $1.50, CMV $3.

1971-73 UNFORGETTABLE BEAUTY DUST
(Center Left) Orange & gold 6 oz. cardboard box. OSP $4.50, CMV $3 mint - $5 MB.

1968-72 UNFORGETTABLE PERFUMED POWDER MIST
(Center Right & Right) 7 oz. orange & gold can, 2 different labels painted on paper. OSP $3.75, CMV $1 - $3 paper.

1970-71 UNFORGETTABLE COLOGNE
(Left) ½ oz. with gold cap. OSP $1.75, CMV $2 MB - $1.50 BO.

1966-74 UNFORGETTABLE PERFUMED TALC
(Right) 2¾ oz. pink can & cap. OSP $1, CMV $1.

1965-76 UNFORGETTABLE COLOGNE MIST
(Left & Center) 3 oz., pink plastic coated, gold cap. Two different gold trims around neck. OSP $5, CMV 50c with holes in gold trim - $4 on solid gold neck trim.

1965-75 UNFORGETTABLE CREAM SACHET
(Right) Pink painted over clear or milk glass bottom with gold plastic cap & gold trim. OSP $2.50, CMV 50c.

1965 UNFORGETTABLE PERFUMED SOAP
(Left) 3 oz., pink & gold wrapper. OSP 49c, CMV $4.

1965-74 UNFORGETTABLE CREAM SACHET SAMPLE
(Center Left) Pink, gold plastic. CMV box of 10 - $1.50.

1965-76 UNFORGETTABLE FRAGRANCE SAMPLE
(Center Right) Box holds 10 samples in pink foil. CMV 50c box.

1966-68 UNFORGETTABLE POWDER SACHET SAMPLE

1965-68 UNFORGETTABLE SOAP
Orange box holds 3 orange soaps with gold centers. OSP $2.25, CMV $20 MB.

1965 UNFORGETTABLE DELUXE
Gold & white box holds beauty dust, cream sachet & cologne mist. OSP $12.95, CMV $32.50 MB.

1966-68 UNFORGETTABLE CREAM LOTION
(Left) 4 oz. orange plastic bottle with gold cap. OSP $1.75, CMV $2 - $3 MB.

1966-72 UNFORGETTABLE FOAMING BATH OIL
(Right) 6 oz. orange plastic bottle with gold cap. OSP $3, CMV $2 BO - $3 MB.

1966-71 UNFORGETTABLE COLOGNE
(Left) 2 oz. gold cap, painted label. OSP $2.50, CMV $2.

1964-68 UNFORGETTABLE PERFUME MIST
(Right) 2 dram, rose colored bottom, white cap, gold trim, all metal. OSP $3.25, CMV $5 - $6 MB.

1965 UNFORGETTABLE INTRODUCTION BROCHURE
Gold cover has red & gold 3D glasses inside cover and 8 pages of intro-ducing new Unforgettable products for Reps only. CMV $30.

UNSPOKEN

1965-66 UNFORGETTABLE HEIRLOOM
Gold & white tray holds 1½ oz. pink & gold cardboard perfumed talc. CMV $15. 9/10 oz. powder sachet, gold cap & ½ oz. perfume oil with gold cap. OSP $10.95, for set CMV $30 - $40 MB.

1976-78 UNSPOKEN FOAMING BATH OIL
(Left) 6 oz. bath oil, also came in 12 oz. size. OSP $5.50, CMV 25c. 12 oz. size: OSP $8.50, CMV 25c.

1977 UNSPOKEN PERFUMED POWDER MIST
(Inside Left) 7 oz. size. OSP $5, CMV 50c.

1976-78 ULTRA COLOGNE SPRAY
(Center) 1.8 oz. size. OSP $7.50, CMV 25c.

1977-78 ULTRA COLOGNE
(Inside Right) 2 oz. size. OSP $6.50, CMV 25c.

1977-78 ULTRA PURSE SPRAY COLOGNE
(Right) Refillable .33 fl. oz. SSP $3.95, CMV 50c.

1975-78 UNSPOKEN PRODUCTS
1975-78 FOAMING BATH OIL
6 oz. light blue & dark blue. OSP $4, CMV 24c. Also came in 12 oz. size. CMV 25c.

1975-77 ULTRA CREAM PERFUME
Clear glass with silver lid. OSP $3, CMV 25c.

1975-77 ULTRA PERFUME ROLLETTE
.33 oz. clear glass, silver cap. OSP $3, CMV 25c.

1975-78 UNSPOKEN FRAGRANCE SAMPLE
10 foil packets to box. CMV 25c.

1975-78 ULTRA COLOGNE SPRAY
(Non-aerosol) 1.8 oz. clear glass with silver cap. OSP $5, CMV 25c.

1975-78 PERFUME SOAPS
3 oz. light blue soap in two-toned blue box. OSP $4, CMV $4 MB.

1976-77 UNSPOKEN ULTRA GIFT SET
Box came with 1.8 oz. Ultra cologne spray and .33 oz. Ultra perfume rollette. OSP $10.50, CMV $10.50 MB.

1976-78 UNSPOKEN PERFUMED TALC
(Left) 3.5 oz. blue paper carton. OSP $2.50, CMV 25c.

1976-78 UNSPOKEN PERFUMED SKIN SOFTENER
(Right) 5 oz. blue plastic jar, silver & blue lid. OSP $5.50, CMV 25c.

1975 UNSPOKEN PRESIDENT'S CLUB VELVET BAG
Blue velvet bag with President's Club tag. Came in plastic bag. CMV $10 bag.

1975 UNSPOKEN PERFUME VIAL
Blue box holds small 1-5/8" vial Unspoken perfume. Given to Managers only. Outside sleeve on box. CMV $10 box.

VIOLET BOUQUET

1946-49 VIOLET BOUQUET COLOGNE
6 oz. bottle. Came in different color caps. OSP $1, CMV $80 MB - $70 BO.

**1945 VIOLET BOUQUET
REPRESENTATIVE GIFT**
   Avon's 59th Anniversary gift to each
representative. Violet colored net
ribbon around white cap. 16 oz.
crackle glass bottle. CMV $150 mint -
$175 MB.

WHITE MOIRE

1946 WHITE MOIRE SACHET
   White cap & small plain paper label.
CMV $30 BO - $35 MB.

1946-49 WHITE MOIRE SOAP
   Blue & white box, white bow tie
soap. OSP $1.22, CMV $47.50 MB.

**1946 WHITE MOIRE SACHET
60th ANNIVERSARY BOX**
   1¼ oz. regular issue bottle, white cap.
Came in special issue blue & white
box with white ribbon and blue &
silver tag saying "Avon Diamond
Anniversary 60th Year". OSP $1.15,
CMV $30 MB as shown.

**1948-49 WHITE MOIRE POWDER
SACHET**
   (Left) 1¼ oz. clear glass, blue and
white label, blue cap. OSP $1.15,
CMV $20 - $25 MB.
**1946-47 WHITE MOIRE POWDER
SACHET**
   (Right) 1¼ oz. clear glass, white or
blue plastic cap. OSP $1.15, CMV
$18 - $23 MB.
Both bottles pictured have same label.

**1945-49 WHITE MOIRE BODY
POWDER**
   (Left) 5 oz. or 4½ oz. size, blue &
white paper container with plastic
sifter top, came in blue & white box.
OSP 65c, CMV $30 MB - $25 container only, mint.
1945-49 WHITE MOIRE COLOGNE
   (Right) 6 oz. white or blue cap. Blue
& white label. OSP $1.75, CMV $65
BO - $75 MB.

1945-49 WHITE MOIRE SET
   Blue & white box with white silk
bow on lid contains 6 oz. White
Moire cologne with white cap. Blue
& white label. Also 5 oz. White Moire
body powder, blue & white cardboard. OSP $2.50, CMV $110 MB.

229

WISHING

1947 WISHING COLOGNE
4 oz. bottle with gold cap, painted label. Same bottle as Golden Promise cologne. Came in fancy open front & top box. Given to Avon Representatives for calling on 61 customers during 61st Anniversary Campaign in campaign 9 - 1947. CMV $85 bottle only - $110 MB.

1964-67 WISHING PERFUME OIL
(Left) ½ oz. clear glass, white cap, gold lettering with small gold wishbone on gold string. White box. OSP $3.50, CMV $8 BO - $10 MB.

1963-67 WISHING COLOGNE
(Right) 2 oz. clear glass, white cap, gold lettering with gold wishbone on neck, white box. OSP $1.75, CMV $7 MB - $4 BO.

1963-67 WISHING BEAUTY DUST
(Left) 4 oz. white plastic trimmed in gold. OSP $2.95, CMV $8 - $10 MB.

1964-69 WISHING PERFUMED SKIN SOFTENER
(Right) 5 oz. white glass jar with gold & white lid. OSP $3, CMV $4 in box - $2.50 jar only.

1952 WISHING TOILET WATER
(Left) 2 oz. white cap. Same as Flowertime bottle. OSP $1.25, CMV $25 BO - $30 MB.

1947-49 WISHING TOILET WATER
(Right) 2 oz. white cap. OSP $1.25, CMV $35 MB - $30 BO. Also came in gold 61st Anniversary box. CMV $40 MB.

1964-68 WISHING POWDER SACHET
(Back Two) 9/10 oz. white glass bottom. Bottle on right has white plastic cap, bottle on left has yellow plastic cap, not faded. Both have wishbone in center of cap. White box. OSP $1.75, CMV yellow cap $10 - white cap $6 - add $2 MB each.

1963-70 WISHING CREAM SACHET
(Front Two) White glass bottom with white plastic cap, gold wishbone in center of cap. Also came with Wishing written on lid. CMV $2 with wishbone - $25 with Wishing lettering, OSP $1.75.

1966-67 WISHING SCENTED HAIR SPRAY
(Left) 7 oz. white can with gold lettering, white cap. OSP $1.50, CMV $10.

1965-66 WISHING PERFUMED SOAP
(Right) 3 oz. white soap with white & gold wrapper. OSP 39c, CMV $4 mint.

1963-70 WISHING COLOGNE MIST
(Left) 2½ oz. white plastic coated, gold trim. Gold wishbone on neck, white box. OSP $2.95, CMV $3 BO - $5 MB.

1963-66 WISHING BUBBLE BATH
(Center) 4 oz. white plastic bottle & cap, white box. OSP $1.35, CMV $7 in box - $5 bottle only.

1963-67 WISHING CREAM LOTION
(Right) 4 oz. white plastic bottle & cap. White box. OSP $1.35, CMV $6 in box - $5 bottle only.

1964-66 WISHING BATH OIL
6 oz. white plastic bottle, gold lettering, white box. OSP $2.25, CMV $12 in box - $10 bottle only.

1965-67 WISHING PERFUME MIST
(Left) 2 dram, white metal, gold trim, white box. OSP $3, CMV $6.

1963-66 WISHING PERFUMED TALC
(Right) 2.75 oz. white can, gold lettering. OSP 79c, CMV $4.

1963-65 SECRET WISH SET
White box holds Wishing perfumed talc & 4 oz. cream lotion. OSP $2.10, CMV $20 MB.

1964-65 CHARM OF WISHING
Gold & white box holds Wishing beauty dust, cologne mist & 22K gold plated Wishbone necklace on 9" chain. OSP $8.50, CMV $62.50 MB.

1964 WISHING PERFUMED PAIR
White box holds Wishing perfumed talc & bar of soap in white wrapper. OSP $3.50, CMV $19 MB.

1964-65 WISHING NECKLACE
22K gold wishbone necklace came in Charm of Wishing set only. CMV $25 in small pink & white box - $17 necklace only.

1963-64 WISH COME TRUE SET
White & gold box holds Wishing bubble bath & 2 oz. cologne with wishbone on neck. OSP $3.10, CMV $26 MB.

YOUNG HEARTS

1952-53 YOUNG HEARTS TALC
1 2/3 oz. cardboard talc. Came in sets only. CMV $20.
1952-54 YOUNG HEARTS COLOGNE
2 oz. cologne with pink cap and painted label. OSP $1.25, CMV $30 BO mint.
1952-54 YOUNG HEARTS BUBBLE BATH
2 oz. pink cap and painted label. OSP $1.25, CMV $30 BO mint.

1964-65 WISHING DUETTE
White, gold & pink box holds Wishing cream rollette & cream sachet. OSP $3.50, CMV $19 MB.

1965 WISHING DATE SET
White & gold box holds Wishing perfume skin softener, perfume rollette & white vinyl covered Wishing date book. OSP $6, CMV $32.50 MB.

1952-54 YOUNG HEARTS
1 dram perfume, pink cap and painted label. Came in sets only. CMV $60. ½ oz. Toilet Water with pink cap and painted label. Came in sets only. CMV $30. 1 oz. Cologne with pink cap. Came in sets only. CMV $30.

1963 Only WISHING SET
White & gold box holds Wishing 2 oz. cologne & cream sachet. OSP $3.10, CMV $25 MB.

1963-66 WISHING SOAP
White box holds 3 white wishbone embossed soaps. OSP $1.35, CMV $25 MB.

1954-55 KIDDIE COLOGNE
2 oz. bottle of Young Hearts Cologne has pink cap with white foam dog head on cap, in yellow, white and blue box. OSP $1.25, CMV $50 MB, $25 BO. Add $15 for foam head on bottle only mint.

1954-55 YOUNG HEARTS BUBBLE BATH
White foam dog head on pink cap, in yellow, white and blue box. OSP $1.10, CMV $25 BO. Add $15 for foam head on bottle only mint. $50 MB.

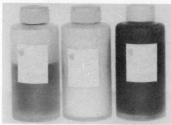

1945-46 FOR YOUNG HEARTS SET BOTTLES
Each are 2 oz. frosted glass with pink caps. In Cotillion Toilet Water, Cream Lotion, and Bubble Bath. CMV $22.50 each.

1954 YOUNG HEARTS CREAM LOTION
Bottle has pink cap, in pink and white heart shaped box. OSP 50c, CMV $25 in box, $20 bottle only.

1952-54 YOUNG HEARTS KIDDIE BUBBLE BATH
2 oz. bottle with pink cap and white foam cat head on cap. Blue and white box, painted label. OSP $1.10, CMV $50 in box with foam head. $30 bottle only. Add $10 for foam head.

1952-53 YOUNG HEARTS KIDDIE COLOGNE
2 oz. bottle with white foam cat head over pink cap, painted label. Blue and white box. OSP $1.25, CMV $50 in box with cat head. $30 bottle only. Add $10 for foam head.

1952-53 YOUNG HEARTS CREAM LOTION
2 oz. pink cap. Came in set only. CMV $20 mint.

1952-53 YOUNG HEARTS POLISH REMOVER
2 oz. pink cap. Came in 'N Everything Nice set only. CMV $20 mint.

1954-55 YOUNG HEARTS TALC
Pink and white metal can.
COLOGNE
Pink cap.
BUBBLE BATH
Pink cap. All 3 came in sets only. CMV $25 each, mint.

1945-46 YOUNG HEARTS SACHET
One pink lace net with pink ribbons on each end. Came in For Young Hearts set only. CMV $25 MB.

1945-46 YOUNG HEARTS SACHET
Box holds two pink lace net sachets with pink ribbons on each end and flower in the middle. Refills for the Young Hearts Set. CMV $40 MB.

1954-55 YOUNG HEARTS BEAUTY DUST
Blue, white and yellow paper box. OSP $1.19, CMV $20, $25 MB.

1954-55 RAIN DROPS SET
Red umbrella hand bag holds Young Hearts Cologne, Pomade and Cream Lotion. OSP $3.25, CMV $90 set MB.

1954-55 HONEY BUN SET
Young Hearts Cologne and gold Lipstick in white, blue and yellow box. OSP $1.19, CMV $45 MB.

1952 RAIN DROPS
Red umbrella bag holds 1 oz. Young Hearts Cologne, Perfume and Cream Lotion. All have pink caps. OSP $2.95, CMV $125 MB.

1953 YOUNG HEARTS SET
Blue and white box holds Young Hearts Cologne, Bubble Bath and Talc. OSP $1.75, CMV $95 MB.

1954 HONEY BUN SET
Blue white and yellow box holds Young Hearts Toilet Water, and gold Pomade Lipstick. OSP $1.19, CMV $50 MB.

1953 RAIN DROPS
Red umbrella hand bag holds Young Hearts Cologne, Pomade and Cream Lotion. Pink caps. OSP $2.95, CMV $90 set MB.

1945-46 FOR YOUNG HEARTS SET
Pink box holds three 2 oz. frosted glass bottles of Cotillion Toilet Water, Cream Lotion and Bubble Bath. All have pink caps. Pink net sachet in top of box. OSP $3.75, CMV $110 set MB, or $22.50 each bottle. $20 for net sachet.

1954-55 MISS FLUFFY PUFF SET
Young Hearts Beauty Dust and Cologne in blue and pink. Pink cap in pink and white box. OSP $2.35, CMV $60 MB.

1953 HONEY BUN SET
Blue and pink round box holds 2½ oz. Young Hearts Toilet Water with pink cap and gold Pomade Lipstick. OSP $1.19, CMV $50 MB.

1952 HONEY BUN SET
Pink and white 8 sided box holds Young Hearts Toilet Water and gold Pomade Lipstick. OSP $1.19, CMV $50 MB.

1954-55 NEAT & SWEET SET
Young Hearts Cologne and Cream Lotion with pink heart shaped soap. Pink caps in yellow, white and blue box. 1955 set came with green and gold spray atomizer. OSP $2.50, CMV $75 MB. Add $10 for atomizer set.

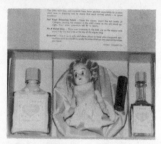

1954-55 LITTLE DOLL SET
Plastic doll with blond hair. Blue dress is a zipper handbag containing Young Hearts Cream Lotion, Cologne and Gold Pomade. OSP $2.95, CMV $115 set MB.

1952 YOUNG HEARTS SET
Blue, white and pink box holds Young Hearts Cologne, Talc and Bubble Bath. OSP $1.50, CMV $85 MB.

1954-55 YOUNG HEARTS SET
Cologne, Talc, and Bubble Bath with pink caps and pink hearts on label, in pink and white box. OSP $1.95, CMV $85 MB.

1953 'N EVERYTHING NICE
Box holds Young Hearts Cream Lotion, Polish Remover with pink caps and Nail Polish, white cap, Emery Board and Orange Stick. OSP $1.65 - CMV $60 MB. Top lid different from back of lid.

1952 'N EVERYTHING NICE
Box holds Young Hearts Cream Lotion, pink cap. Polish Remover, pink cap. Nail Polish, white cap, Emery Board and Orange Stick. OSP $1.50, CMV $60 MB.

ZANY

1979-80 ZANY PRODUCTS BUBBLE BATH
10 oz. pink plastic jug. Pink cap. SSP $4.99, CMV 50c.
SHAMPOO
10 oz. orange plastic jug. Pink cap. SSP $4.99, CMV 50c. Neither came in box.

1979-80 ZANY PRODUCTS
The colors are orange and pink
ZANY BUBBLE BATH
10 oz. plastic. SSP $3.49, CMV 25c.
BODY SPLASH
Not shown. 10 oz. plastic. SSP $3.49, CMV 25c.
PURSE CONCENTRE
.33 oz. glass. SSP $1.99, CMV 50c.
PERFUMED TALC
3.5 oz. paper and plastic. SSP $1.25, CMV 25c.
COLOGNE SPRAY
1.8 oz. glass. SSP $3.99, CMV 25c.
COLOGNE ICE
1 oz. plastic. SSP $2.75, CMV 25c.
CREME PERFUME
.66 oz. glass. SSP $1.99, CMV 25c.
ZANY INCH
Small demo vial of Zany on demo card used by Reps. CMV 25c.

1979 ZANY RADIO
Orange and pink Zany bottle shaped AM radio made in Hong Kong for Avon Products. Given to Avon customers in a drawing. Came in pink bag and certificate. CMV $25 MB, $20 mint in bag complete, radio only $15.

1979 ZANY BAG AWARD
Given to Reps for ordering 10 Zany products. Orange canvas bag. CMV $4 mint.

WOMEN'S SETS OF 1930'S

1935 BATH ENSEMBLE
Box contains Jasmine Bath Salts, 2 bars Jasmine Bath Soap, Avon Dusting Powder in silver can and bottle of Trailing Arbutus Toilet Water. OSP $3.50, CMV $175 MB.

1933 CHRISTMAS PERFUME SET
Small blue box with winter snow scene holds 4 octagonal shaped perfumes with black caps. Came in choice of perfumes. OSP 90c, CMV $200. Very Rare!

1938-40 WINGS TO BEAUTY
Hinged lid box holds 4 oz. bottle of Lotus Cream and choice of Ariel or Cotillion Face Powder and choice of astringent or skin freshener. OSP $1.60, CMV $65 MB.

1936-39 BATH ENSEMBLE
Plaid box holds 9 oz. Jasmine Bath Salts, 2 oz. Trailing Arbutus Toilet Water, 2 bars of Jasmine Soap and can of Beauty Dust. OSP $3.50, CMV $145 MB.

1931-32 ASSORTMENT SET FOR WOMEN
Contains 2 bars Verna Fleur Toilet soap, blue and silver can Avon Dusting Powder, bottle of Verna Fleur Bath Salts, 1 bath towel and 2 wash cloths. All in orange and blue box. OSP $3.50, CMV $150 MB.

1939 COLONIAL SET
Blue and gold box holds 2 dram Gardenia Perfume and Face Powder in choice of Ariel or Cotillion. OSP $1.30, CMV $65 MB.

1934 CHRISTMAS SET NO. 49
Red and green holly design box holds 2 white and green linen hand towels. 4 oz. bottle of Vanilla Tonka and Vanilla Extract in box with tube of Mending Cement in box. Rare set. Comes with outer sleeve with Set No. 49 on sleeve. OSP $1.29, CMV $100 MB with sleeve.

1931-35 HAIR TREATMENT SET FOR WOMEN
Contains Liquid Shampoo, Pre-Shampoo Oil, Wave Set and Hair Tonic. All have blue plastic caps, blue and white box. OSP $2, CMV $170 MB.

1937 LYRIC SET
White and gold box holds Trailing Arbutus Toilet Water, turquoise and white can, Daphne Talcum, turquoise and white can, turquoise cap, white jar, turquoise lid cold cream. OSP $1.65, CMV $75 MB.

1937 HARMONY SET
Blue and white box contains Lily of the Valley Toilet Water, gold cap and label. White milk glass jar with turquoise cap of Rose Cold Cream and turquoise and white tube Hand Cream. OSP $1.80, CMV $75 MB.

1932-33 VANITY SET
Gray velvet lined blue box contains blue and gold double Compact and Lipstick. OSP $2.50 - CMV $70 MB.

1931-32 VANITY BOOK
Silver and blue box contains blue and silver Compact and Lipstick. OSP $1.82 - CMV $75 MB.

1938-41 CHARMER SET
Satin lined box contains lipstick, mascara and rouge. All green and gold. OSP $2.15, CMV $60 MB.

1933 VANITY BOOK
Silver and blue box contains blue and silver double compact and lipstick. OSP $1.75 - CMV $75 MB.

1939 MAYFAIR SET
Blue lid box holds 2 dram glass stoppered bottle of Bolero Perfume, box of Face Powder and turquoise double Compact. OSP $3.57, CMV $110 MB.

1936-37 VANITY BOOK
Satin lined box holds green and gold Compact and Lipstick. OSP $2.27, CMV $47.50 MB.
1938-40 SPORT WISE
Same set as 1936-37. Vanity Book only name changed. OSP $2.27, CMV $47.50 MB.

1934-35 VANITY BOOK
Blue and silver box holds blue and silver compact and lipstick. OSP $2.27 - CMV $70 MB.

1937-38 PERFUME HANDKERCHIEF SET
Two 1/8 oz. bottles of Gardenia and Cotillion Perfume on four colored handkerchiefs. OSP $1, CMV $70 MB.

1933-36 PERFUME HANDKERCHIEF SET
Two small bottles of Ariel and 391 perfume or Bolero, with black caps, 4 handkerchiefs under green and red flower cutout. OSP $1, CMV $85 MB.

1939 Only HANDKERCHIEF SET
Gardenia and Cotillion Perfumes with 4 handkerchiefs. OSP $1, CMV $75 MB.

1936 Only — HANDKERCHIEF SET
Avon box holds 2 perfume bottles of Bolero and Ariel. OSP $1, CMV $90 MB.

1939-42 FAIR LADY
Green, yellow and white flowered box with gold base holds 4 perfumes in Narcissus, Gardenia, Cotillion, Trailing Arbutus, or Sweet Pea. Each came in different colored caps. OSP 94c, CMV $100 MB.

1936-37 POWDER COMPACT SET
Box holds box of face powder and green and gold compact. OSP $2.50, CMV $45 MB.

1938 ARISTOCRAT SET
Same set as Powder Compact Set only name changed in 1938. OSP $2.50, CMV $45 MB.

1936 TRIO GIFT SET
Box holds 2 oz. Trailing Arbutus toilet water with tulip label and gold ribbed cap. Silver can of Daphne Talcum and ribbed glass. Ariel powder sachet. OSP $1.29, CMV $110 MB.

1931-33 ATOMIZER SET NO. 6
Blue and silver box contains red 1 oz. glass bottle with silver atomizer with Ariel or Vernafleur perfume, in 1 oz. bottle with cork stopper. Set comes in 2 different boxes. OSP $2.86, CMV $160 MB.

1937-39 BATH DUET
Box holds turquoise and white can of Daphne Talc with choice of bath salts in Jasmine, Pine, Ariel or Verna Fleur. OSP $1, CMV $55 MB.

1934-35 TRIO SET
Red and blue box contains Trailing Arbutus Toilet Water, Daphne Talcum and Ariel Sachet. OSP $1.60, CMV $115 MB.

1934-35 THREESOME SET
Silver and blue box contains compact, face powder and 2 dram bottle of Bolero Perfume. OSP $3.57, CMV $110 MB.

1938-39 BEAUTY KIT FOR FINGERS
Green box holds bar of Lemonal soap, turquoise tube of hand cream, bottle of polish remover and cream or nail polish. OSP $1.35, CMV $65 MB. Same set also came in gold design box as substitute.

1935 GIFT SET "A"
Satin lined box contains face powder in Ariel or Vernafleur and 2 dram bottle of Gardenia perfume with gold ribbed cap. OSP $1.30, CMV $80 MB.

1936-37 THREESOME SET
Box has green and gold compact, box of face powder and glass stoppered 3 dram of Bolero Perfume. OSP $3.57, CMV $115 MB.

1939 SPECTATOR
Turquoise and white box holds 2 dram bottle with gold cap of Trailing Arbutus Perfume, lipstick and rouge compact. OSP $1.56, CMV $80.

1936-37 GIFT SET "A"
Box has box of face powder, 3 dram size of Ariel, Vernafleur or Gardenia perfume with gold caps. OSP $1.30, CMV $70 MB.

1936-37 GIFT SET "B"
Green and silver box holds green and gold lipstick and rouge with 3 dram Trailing Arbutus perfume with gold cap. OSP $1.56, CMV $90 MB.

1935 GIFT SET "B"
Box contains blue and silver lipstick and rouge compact and 2 dram bottle of Trailing Arbutus perfume. OSP $1.56 - CMV $95 MB.

1935 GIFT SET "D"
Blue and yellow box contains choice of Ariel or Vernafleur face powder in silver and blue box and 2 dram Ariel perfume with gold cap and Ariel sachet with silver label. OSP $2.34, CMV $105 MB.

1936 GIFT SET "D"
Blue and yellow box contains Ariel or Vernafleur face powder in green and gold and 2 dram Ariel perfume with gold cap and Ariel powder sachet with black cap. OSP $2.34, CMV $90 MB.

1936-37 GIFT SET "F"
Box holds green and gold compact, lipstick and box of face powder in Ariel or Vernafleur. OSP $3.05, CMV $60 MB.

1938 MASTERCRAFT SET
Same set as Gift Set "F" only name changed in 1938. OSP $3.05, CMV $60 MB.

1935 GIFT SET "F"
Red and gold box contains blue compact, face powder in Ariel or Verna Fleur and lipstick. OSP $2.80, CMV $85 MB.

1936-37 GIFT SET "K"
Blue and gold box has green and gold lipstick and compact and 2 dram perfume with gold cap. OSP $2.79, CMV $90 MB.

1938 Empress set
Same set as Gift Set "K" only name is changed. CMV $90 MB.

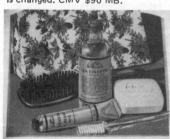

1934 GIFT SET NO. 19
Red and green box contains Deluxe Hair Brush, toothpaste, 1 bar of Savona soap, bottle of antiseptic and tube of Dental Cream No. 2. OSP $1.85, CMV $110 MB.

1935 GIFT SET "K"
Box contains blue compact, 2 dram perfume in Gardenia and blue and silver lipstick. OSP $2.54, CMV $115 MB.

1936-37 GIFT SET "W"
Satin lined box holds two ribbed bottles of nail polish and polish remover, green and gold lipstick and rouge. OSP $1.67, CMV $80 MB.

1935 GIFT SET "W"
Box contains nail polish, lipstick, rouge compact and polish remover. OSP $1.67 - CMV $105 MB.

1936-37 GIFT SET NO. 21
Striped box holds turquoise and white box face powder, turquoise and white cake rouge, turquoise and gold lipstick. OSP $1.56, CMV $60 MB.

1933-35 GIFT SET NO. 21
Contains box of face powder and table rouge. Silver and blue. Blue lipstick in green, white and red box. OSP $1.56, CMV $55 MB.

1934 GIFT SET NO. 24
Holly decorated box contained box of face powder, rouge and jar of vanishing cream. OSP $1.56, CMV $85 MB.

1934 GIFT SET NO. 36
Red and green box contains bottle of Rosewater Glycerine, Lily of the Valley Toilet Water, can of Daphne Talcum and Vernafleur Bath Salts. OSP $1.95, CMV $175 MB.

WOMEN'S SETS OF 1940'S

WARNING!!
Grading condition is paramount on sets.
CMV can vary 50%-75% on grade.
Refer to page 6-16 on Grading.

1944-45 LITTLE JEWELS SET
Pink box holds 3 paper powder sachets in 1¼ oz. Cotillion, Attention Garden of Love. OSP $3.25, CMV $62.50 MB, mint.

1943-44 RAINBOW WINGS SET
Box holds 6 oz. bottles of Cream Lotion and Rose Geranium Bath Oil with pink caps. Both bottles are flat on one side. Butterflies on box. OSP $2, CMV $60 MB.

1942 MINUET SET
Box with music notes on lid, satin lined holds lipstick, powder compact, rouge, and face powder. All are blue and white feather design. OSP $2.95, CMV $70 MB.

1947 BEAUTY BASKET
Straw basket with pink ribbon holds two 6 oz. bottles of Avon Cream Lotion and Rose Gardenia Bath Oil. Both bottles are flat on the back side and have pink caps. OSP $2, CMV $65 basket mint with bottles. $90 mint in box.

1945-46 RAINBOW WINGS SET
Pink box holds two 6 oz. flat sided bottles of Cream Lotion and Rose Geranium Bath Oil. Pink net ribbon on top of box. OSP $2, CMV $75 MB with net.

1943-44 MINUET SET
Pin and blue box with yellow satin lining holds blue plastic rouge compact, cardboard feather design lipstick, Cotillion perfume with gold cap and neck tag, and blue satin sachet pillowette. OSP $3.95, CMV $105 MB.

1940 SPECTATOR SET
Box contains green and gold rouge, 1 dram Garden of Love perfume, gold cap, green and gold lipstick. OSP $1.56, CMV $65 MB.

1946 DOUBLE DARE SET
Red and gold box holds bottle of Double Dare nail polish and gold Bamboo lipstick. OSP $1.25, CMV $50 MB.

1949-50 COLOR MAGIC THREE PIECE SET
Multi-colored box holds gold lipstick, gold rouge and ½ oz. nail polish with green cap. OSP $2.19, CMV $47.50 MB.

1946 Only — LEADING LADY
Red, blue and gold box holds Bamboo lipstick and nail polish. OSP $1, CMV $45 MB.

1946-47 COLOR CLUSTER SET
Red and gold box holds gold Bamboo lipstick and rouge with ½ oz. nail polish with black cap. OSP $2.15, CMV $50 MB.

1940-43 MR. & MRS. SET
Blue & pink box contains smokers tooth-powder, after shaving lotion for men, Cotillion toilet water & Cotillion talcum for women. OSP $2.50, CMV $130 MB.

1948 COLOR CLUSTER
Red and gold box contains gold lipstick, gold rouge and ½ oz. nail polish with green cap. OSP $2, CMV $45 MB.

1948 BEAUTY MARK
Red and gold box contains gold lipstick and ½ oz. nail polish with green cap. OSP $1.35, CMV $40 MB.

1943-44 BATH BOUQUET
Blue box holds 6 oz. of Rose Geranium bath oil & Apple Blossom beauty dust. OSP $2.35, CMV $75 MB.

1940 MAYFAIR SET
Blue box contains 1 dram perfume with gold cap. Green & gold compacts & box of face powder in Ariel or Cotillion. OSP $3.35, CMV $75 MB.

1949-50 COLOR MAGIC TWO PIECE SET
Multi-colored box contains gold lipstick and ½ oz. nail polish with green cap. OSP $1.35, CMV $40 MB.

1940-43 BATH DUET
Blue, pink & white box holds can of Daphne or Cotillion talc & choice of Jasmine, Pine, Ariel or Vernafleur bath salts. OSP $1, CMV $60 MB.

1940-41 MILADY SET
Satin lined box contains two small bottles of perfume in Gardenia, Cotillion, Apple Blossom or Ballad & white lace edged hankey. OSP $2.25 - CMV $85 MB.

1943 COLONIAL DAYS SET
6 oz. clear glass bottle, pink cap cream lotion & cardboard body powder, shaker cap. OSP $1.60, CMV $65 MB.

1940 COLONIAL SET
Blue box holds 1 dram Garden of Love perfume, gold cap & label & box of face powder. OSP $1.25, CMV $55 MB.

1940-41 COLONIAL SET
Feather face powder & Garden of Love perfume in blue box. OSP $1.25, CMV $55 MB.

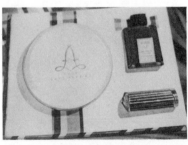

1947-49 THAT'S FOR ME SET
Multi-colored box contains choice of cream cake or cake makeup, gold lipstick & ½ oz. nail polish. OSP $2, CMV $37 MB.

1941 TANDEM SET
(Left) Box holds gold bamboo compact & turquoise & gold lipstick. OSP $1.75, CMV $47 MB.
1942 TANDEM SET
(Right) Same set only with matching bamboo lipstick. CMV $47 MB.

1944 Only PEEK-A-BOO
Blue, white & pink box with yellow satin lining holds cardboard compact covered with pink satin & white net. Cake rouge in blue plastic compact & cardboard feather design lipstick. OSP $2.50, CMV $55 MB.

1941-42 RECEPTION SET
Satin lined box holds gold compact, blue box of face powder & 1/8 oz. perfume. OSP $2.75, CMV $70 MB.

1940 ORCHID SET
Red & white box, green & gold lipstick & rouge. Cream polish with green cap. OSP $1.50, CMV $50.

1941-42 ELYSIAN SET
Satin lined box contains lipstick, rouge & 1 dram perfume with gold cap. OSP $1.75, CMV $80 MB.

1945-47 FAIR LADY SET
Blue & white box holds 4 small bottles with colored caps of perfume in Cotillion, Lily of the Valley, Gardenia, Garden of Love, Trailing Arbutus & Sweet Pea. OSP $1.50, CMV $90 MB. Also came with all blue caps.

1950 FRAGRANT MIST
Turquoise & gold box holds 2 oz. toilet water with green & gold atomizer in the choice of Flowertime, Cotillion, Lily of the Valley & Wishing. OSP $2.35, CMV $50 MB.

1940-42 MERRIMENT SET
Rouge, lipstick & eyebrow pencil. All green & gold. OSP $1.50, CMV $45 MB.

1943 PEEK-A-BOO SET
Pink & blue box with yellow satin lining holds blue & white feather design cardboard compact, cardboard lipstick & rouge. OSP $2.50, CMV $65 MB.

1947-54 PERFUMED DEODORANT SET
Turquoise box holds two 2 oz. bottles of perfumed deodorant. OSP 98c, CMV set $15 MB.

1940-42 HANDKERCHIEF SET
Box holds white, pink, blue & yellow handkerchiefs, 1/8 oz. Cotillion perfume with red cap, Gardenia perfume with blue cap. OSP $1, CMV $57.50 MB.

1941 WINGS TO BEAUTY SET
Red designed box contains choice of two 2 oz. skin conditioner, astringent, finishing lotion or Lotus cream, and box of face powder. OSP $1, CMV $55 MB.

1948-49 FAIR LADY SET
Pink & blue box contains four 1/8 oz. perfumes in Lily of the Valley, Garden of Love, Quaintance, Gardenia & Cotillion. All have blue caps. OSP $1.50, CMV $100 MB.

1940-42 FRAGRANT MIST
Blue & gold box holds 2 oz. toilet water with gold or plastic cap & label and spray atomizer. Came in Cotillion, Marionette, Sonnet, Jasmine or Apple Blossom. OSP $1.35, CMV $50 MB.

BE 1ST TO KNOW
BE INFORMED

If you want to be 1st to know when the next Bud Hastin Avon Collectors Encyclopedia will be for sale in the future, get on Bud's personal mailing list. PLUS you will get a bonus discount on his next book by ordering direct from Bud. Just PRINT your name and address and send it to:

BUD HASTIN
P. O. Box 43690
Las Vegas, NV 89116

Just say: "Put me on your next book list."

WOMEN'S SETS OF 1950'S

WARNING!! Grading condition is
paramount on sets.
CMV can vary 50% to 70% on grade.
Refer to Page 6 and 16 on Grading

1954-55 LADY BELLE
White bell shaped box trimmed in blue & gold has two 1 dram perfumes. Ribbed glass with gold cap. Choice of Cotillion, To A Wild Rose, Golden Promise, Quaintance, Bright Night or Forever Spring. OSP $3, CMV $80 MB.

1955 TWO LOVES
Red, white, blue & gold Christmas tree ornament box holds 2 gold fashion lipsticks. OSP $1.10, CMV $33 MB.

1957 TWO LOVES
Red Christmas tree hang on box came with black fashion lipstick & liquid rouge. OSP $1.10, CMV $33 MB.

1955 JEWELED LIPSTICK
(Left) Blue & gold box with gold lipstick with pearl & rhinestones on top. OSP $1.75, CMV $20 MB.

1955 CHARMER SET
(Right) White, gold & red brocade case holds jeweled lipstick & 1 dram perfume. OSP $3, CMV $25 mint.

1959 TOPS STYLE BEAUTY
(Left) Red & white box holds lipstick & 1 dram Top Style perfume. OSP $2.95, CMV $22.50 MB.

1956 TWO LOVES SET
(Right) Box holds 2 black lipsticks. OSP $1.40, CMV $33 MB.

1950-51 AVONETTE
Blue & white brocade bag holds 1 dram perfume & deluxe gold lipstick. OSP $2.65, CMV $22 - $25 MB.

1954 CONCERTINA
Two gold fashion lipsticks in red, white & green box. OSP $1.10, CMV $35 MB.

1959 - 2 LIPS SET
Two white enamel lipsticks, white box with pink & gold design. OSP $1.69, CMV $14 MB.

1958 FASHION FIRSTS
White & gold box holds 2 light tan fashion lipsticks. OSP $1.69, CMV $15 MB.

1953-54 AVONETTE
Black case holds 1 dram perfume &
gold deluxe lipstick. OSP $2.50,
CMV $22 - $25 MB.

1952-53 HOUSE OF CHARM
With windows open. You find four
1/8 oz. or 5/8 dram bottles of per-
fume¾ Lily of the Valley, Cotillion,
Golden Promise or Quaintance. In
pink box, all blue caps. OSP $1.95,
CMV $100 MB.

1957 BEAUTY PAIR
White, blue & yellow box with 2
black & pink fashion lipsticks. OSP
$1.49, CMV $27 MB.

1953 HOLIDAY FASHION
White box holds 2 gold fashion lipsticks in green holly leaves. OSP
$1.10, CMV $25 MB.

HOUSE OF CHARM PERFUMES
Shown only to identify size & labels.
Left square bottle is 1954 set only.
Center bottle has same label as short
one on left issued in 1953-54. Right
one issued 1952-53 sets only.

1954-56 LITTLE LAMBS SET
Box holds 2 lamb soaps and can of
baby powder. Two different boxes.
One has 2 lambs & the other has 2
lambs holding an umbrella. OSP
$1.30, CMV $70 each set MB.

1954 HOUSE OF CHARM
Pink box holds four 5/8 dram bottles
of perfume with turquoise caps or
white caps. Choice of To A Wild
Rose, Cotillion, Golden Promise or
Quaintance. OSP $1.95, CMV $110
MB.

1955-56 THAT'S FOR ME
Pink box holds four 2 oz. bottles
with pink caps of bath oil. Quaintance, To A Wild Rose, Cotillion &
Pine. OSP $2.50, CMV $85 MB.

1952 TIME FOR BEAUTY
Blue, white & pink box with pink
ribbon holds gold lipstick & nail
polish. OSP $1.65, CMV $30 MB.

1957 GEMS IN CRYSTAL
½ oz. bottles of Nearness, Bright
Night, Cotillion & To A Wild Rose.
Pointed plastic caps. OSP $2.95.
CMV with flat top caps (left) $65 -
with pointed caps (right) $75 MB.

1953 PRECIOUS PEAR
Gold bell box holds 1 dram perfumes in Golden Promise, Quaintance, Cotillion, To A Wild Rose & Forever Spring. OSP $2.75, CMV $75 MB.

1954 FRAGRANCE RAINBOW
Flowers on top of box. Choice of Cotillion, To A Wild Rose, Forever Sping, Quaintance. Cologne in ½ oz. bottles, white caps & painted labels. OSP $2.50, CMV $65 MB.

1956 Only FRAGRANCE RAINBOW SET
Box holds four 3 dram bottles with white painted caps. Came in To A Wild Rose, Nearness, Bright Night, Cotillion, Quaintance & Forever Spring. OSP $2.75, CMV $75 MB.

1953 FRAGRANCE TIE INS
White box with bows holds four ½ oz. bottles with white caps. Came in Cotillion, Forever Spring, Quaintance & To A Wild Rose cologne. OSP $2.50, CMV $65 MB.

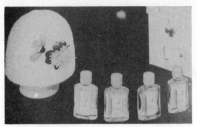

1951 SWEET AS HONEY "BEEHIVE"
Foam beehive holds four 5/8 dram bottles of perfume in Cotillion, Quaintance, Golden Promise, Luscious, Forever Spring & To A Wild Rose. All have different colored caps. OSP $2.50, CMV in box $115. Beehive and bottles only $90 mint.

1950 AVON BLOSSOMS SET
Four 1/8 oz. or 5/8 dram perfume bottles set in white foam with wire fence behind it. Flowers around bottles. Plastic cap. Quaintance, Cotillion, Luscious and Golden Promise. OSP $2, CMV $85 set only, $100 MB.

1956 CREAM SACHET PETITES
Gold box holds 4 plastic cream sachets in blue boxes. Came in Cotillion, Bright Night, Nearness and To A Wild Rose. OSP $3.25, CMV $55 set. $10 each jar in box.

1955 CUPID'S BOW
White and pink box holds four ½ oz. bottles of cologne with white caps. Bright Night, To A Wild Rose, Quaintance and Cotillion. OSP $2.50, CMV $60 MB.

1957 OVER THE RAINBOW SET
Blue box holds 4 cream sachet jars in Cotillion, To A Wild Rose, Bright Night and Nearness. Jars are white glass with green, and yellow, and have two pink lids. OSP $3.25, CMV $50 set MB, $55 MB with outer box as shown, $8 each jar.

1950 Only — JOLLY SURPRISE
Pink, white and green Santa box holds 2 oz. cream lotion, nail polish and 1 dram perfume in ribbed glass. OSP $1.95, CMV $55 MB.

1955 SHOWERS OF STARS
Silver box with fluff on top holds cream sachet and body powder in choice of Golden Promise, Quaintance, and Forever Spring. OSP $2.10, CMV $40 MB.

1958 WISHING COIN TRIO
Blue and gold box. Holds choice of cream sachet, lotion sachet and ½ oz. cologne in To A Wild Rose, Cotillion, Nearness, Forever Spring, Bright Night, Elegante, Here's My Heart and Persian Wood fragrances. Blue caps on all three. OSP $2.50, CMV $40 MB.

1956 SINGING BELLS
White bell box holds 2 cans of talc in Cotillion or To A Wild Rose. OSP $1.10, CMV $20 MB.

1955 SPECIAL DATE SET
Blue and white box holds gold lipstick, 2 different powder paks and ½ oz. Cotillion Toilet water. OSP $1.95 - CMV $37 MB.

1957 MODERN MOOD
Pink and gold box holds 2 cans of talc in choice of Cotillion or To A Wild Rose. Same box in blue and gold holds 2 cans of talc in choice of Nearness or Forever Spring. OSP $1.29, CMV $22.50 each set MB.

1954 SILVER WINGS SET
Box holds cream sachet and body powder in choice of To A Wild Rose, Quaintance, Golden Promise or Forever Spring. OSP $2.10, CMV $40 each set MB.

1953-55 CHRISTMAS ANGELS SET
Blue and white box holds gold lipstick and cream sachet in To A Wild Rose, Quaintance, Cotillion, Forever Spring and Golden Promise. To A Wild Rose pictured sold 1955 only and 1953-54 came with older 3 corner white jar with blue cap. Both are same CMV. OSP $2, CMV $27.50.

1957 TRI COLOR SET
Blue and white box holds Nearness or choice of cream sachet, gold satin sheen lipstick and white leather purse trimmed in gold. OSP $7.75, CMV $45 MB.

1955 BATH DELIGHTS
Box holds bottle of Avon Bubble Bath and choice of body powder in Golden Promise, Quaintance or Forever Spring. OSP $2.10, CMV $50 MB.

1952-53 SUNNY HOURS
White umbrella holds 1 dram perfume and deluxe gold lipstick. OSP $2.50, CMV in box $50. Umbrella and contents only $30.

1958 CLASSIC STYLE
Black and gold box holds Top Style lipstick and gold Top Style compact. OSP $5, CMV $20 MB.

1957 AVON JEWELS SET
Box contains liquid rouge, nail and longlife gold lipstick. OSP $2.50, CMV $25 MB.

1958 MAKEUP MATES
Green box holds lipstick and face powder. OSP $1.98, CMV $17.50 MB.

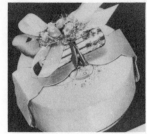

1954-55 COLOR CORSAGE
Turquoise box of face powder with gold lipstick on top. OSP $1.90, CMV $25 MB.

1950-51 LADY FAIR
Red, white and silver box holds gold Deluxe Lipstick and bottle of nail polish. OSP $1.65, CMV $30 MB.

1958 TOUCH OF PARIS
Box holds white lipstick and compact. OSP $2.10, CMV $16 MB.

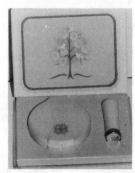

1959 PEARL FAVORITES
Blue, green and white box holds white compact and white enamel lipstick. OSP $2.19, CMV $17.50 MB.

1955-56 TOP STYLE SET
Box holds gold lipstick, ½ oz. nail polish and liquid rouge. OSP $1.95, CMV $22 MB.

1954-55 GADABOUTS
Gold and white box holds turquoise and white compact and gold lipstick. OSP $2.10, CMV $18 MB.

1955-56 BEAUTY BOUND
Turquoise and white plastic compact, jeweled lipstick. Box pink and turquoise. OSP $2.75, CMV $18.50 MB.

1954 BEAUTY PAIR
Red and gold box holds gold Deluxe Lipstick and nail polish. OSP $1.50, CMV $25 MB.

1952-53 GADABOUTS
Gold and white box holds compact and cologne stick. Both are turquoise in color. OSP $2.25, CMV $25 MB.

1950-51 ADORABLE SET
White box holds blue satin with white lace pillow with powder pak and lipstick inside. OSP $2.95, CMV $35 MB.

1950 ADORABLE
Foam holder has powder pak and gold lipstick. Trimmed in blue feathers and pink ribbon and flowers. Came in green box. OSP $2, CMV $35 mint as shown, $40 MB.

1951-52 FRAGRANCE MIST
Turquoise box with pink and gold inside holds 2 oz. toilet water and 1 dram perfume in choice of Cotillion, Flowertime and Lily of the Valley. OSP $2.35, CMV $50 MB.

1957 BEAUTIFUL JOURNEY SET
Pink zippered bag holds 1 oz. bottles of Cotillion cologne, Deep Clean Cleansing Cream, Deodorant, Hand Lotion, Skin Freshener and ½ oz. jar of Rich Moisture Cream with peach colored cap. $10 each bottle, $15 Cotillion cologne, $7 Rich Moisture Cream. OSP $5.95, CMV set $70 MB.

1958 SAFE JOURNEY
Gold and white zippered travel kit holds 6 plastic containers of Perfumed Talc, Hand Lotion, Lotion Sachet, Cleansing Cream, Rich Moisture Cream and Deodorant. OSP $6.95, CMV $35 mint.

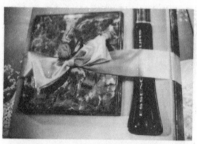

1958 DRAMATIC MOMENTS SET
Essence de Fleurs Cologne Mist and paper box of powder in blue box. Came in To A Wild Rose, Cotillion, Forever Spring. OSP $5 Nearness, Elegante and Bright Night. OSP $5.25, CMV $40 MB.

1958 BEAUTIFUL YOU
Pink and white box with ladies face holds 3½ oz. Rich Moisture Cream, 2 oz. of Skin Freshener and Rich Moisture Suds or Deep Clean. OSP $3.50, CMV $22.50 MB.

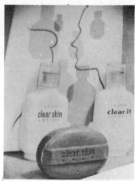

1956 FOR YOUR BEAUTY SET
Blue and gold box holds Cleansing Cream in plastic bottle, 2 oz. bottle of Skin Freshener and Rich Moisture Cream in jar. OSP $2.95, CMV $22 MB.

1959 CLEAR-IT-SKIN CARE KIT
White box holds shampoo and lotion in white plastic bottles and bar of Clear Skin soap. OSP $2.50, CMV $20 MB.

1956 DOUBLY YOURS SET
Blue and gold box holds two bottles of hand lotion. OSP $1.29, CMV $18 MB.

1954 HAND BEAUTY SET
Red box holds two bottles of hand lotion. OSP $1.10, CMV $18 MB.

1955 HAND BEAUTY SET
Pink box holds two 4 oz. bottles of hand lotion with turquoise caps. OSP $1.18, CMV $18 MB.

1955 FOAM 'N SPRAY SET
Green box holds can of Avon Hair Spray and 6 oz. bottle of Cream Lotion Shampoo. OSP $2.19, CMV $20 MB.

1950-54 HIGH FASHION SET
Black case with white satin lining holds 1 dram perfume, gold lipstick, gold compact and gold rouge compact. OSP $10, CMV $45 MB.

1954-55 FOR YOUR LOVELINESS
Green and silver box holds 3½ oz. jar of Moisture Cream and choice of 4 oz. bottle of Hand Lotion or Skin Freshener. OSP $2.75, CMV $18 MB.

1957 BOUQUET OF FRESHNESS
Pink and lavender box holds two 2 oz. bottles of Perfumed Deodorant. OSP $1.38, CMV $12 MB.

1955-56 HAPPY TRAVELER SET
Black bag with pink and blue stripes holds Cleansing Cream, Skin Freshener, Rich Moisture Cream, Hand Cream, Flowing Cream Deodorant, 1 empty plastic jar, packette of tissues. OSP $5.95, CMV $35 MB.

1951 SPECIAL SET
Blue and pink Christmas box holds 2 bottles of hand lotion. OSP $1, CMV $30 MB.

1956 Only — SHOWER OF FRESHNESS SET
Turquoise and white box holds 2 bottles of Perfumed Deodorant. OSP $1.38, CMV $12 MB.

1954 HAPPY TRAVELER SET
Black and white bag holds Perfumed Deodorant, Hand Cream, Rich Moisture Cream, Skin Freshener, Cleansing Cream and a plastic jar. OSP $5.95, CMV $35 MB.

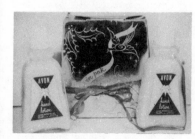

1952-53 TWIN PAK
Silver box holds 2 bottles of hand lotion. White caps, red ribbon on box. OSP $1.10, CMV $30 MB.

1954-55 FASHION JEWELS SET
Black velvet case holds 1 dram perfume, jeweled lipstick and gold compact. OSP $10.50, CMV $40 MB.

1955 HAPPY TRAVELER SET
Black zipper bag with pink and blue stripes. Came with pack of Kleenex tissues, 2 turquoise and white plastic jars, tube of hand cream and cleansing cream and rare 2 oz. bottle of skin freshener with turquoise cap. OSP $5.95, CMV $35 mint, $40 MB.

1955-57 SPECIAL NAIL CARE SET
Red and white box contained Silvery Base and Top Coat. OSP $1.10, CMV $10 MB.

1951 HOME PERMANENT REFILL KIT
Kit contains 4 oz. permanent wave lotion. CMV $25. Neutralizer, end tissues. OSP $1, CMV $45 MB set.

1953 HAPPY VACATION
Plastic bag and tie string says Avon Happy Vacation. Bag holds Cotillion Talc, tooth paste, cream deodorant, and tube of Ammoniated Tooth Paste. OSP $1.39, CMV $50 mint in bag.

1957 A THING OF BEAUTY
White, pink and black box holds 6 oz. Avon Cleansing Cream, 2 oz. Skin Freshener and 3½ oz. Rich Moisture Cream. OSP $3.50, CMV $22.50 MB.

1954 CAMPING KIT
Navy blue cotton twill draw string bag. Came with 2 oz. Sun Lotion, Chap Check, Antiseptic Cream and choice of either Creme Shampoo or Cream Hair Dress. OSP $1.95, value complete set $50 MB.

1951 HAPPY VACATION SPECIAL GIFT BAG
Folder has plastic bag and Avon tie tag to hold cream deodorant, tooth paste, tooth brush and Cotillion Talcum, all boxed. CMV $7 as pictured.

WOMEN'S SETS OF 1960'S

WARNING!! Grading condition is paramount on sets.
CMV can vary 50% to 75% on grade.
Refer to Page 6 and 16 on Grading.

1968 FRAGRANCE FLING TRIO
½ oz. cologne, gold cap. Set of 3. Came in Charisma, Brocade, Regence, Occur!, Unforgettable, Rapture, Somewhere, Topaze, Cotillion, Here's My Heart, Wishing, To A Wild Rose, Persian Wood. OSP $4, CMV $12 MB.

1964 FRAGRANCE GOLD SET
Box holds 3 heart shaped ½ oz. colognes in Occur!, Somewhere, Wishing, Topaze, Cotillion, Here's My Heart, Persian Wood, To A Wild Rose. OSP $3.50, CMV $22 MB.

1965 FRAGRANCE ORNAMENTS
Three bottles 5/8 dram perfume oil. Same as the Bullet bottle. White paper trimmed in gold. Gold & white box. Set A: Wishing Somewhere, Occur!; Set B: Rapture, Topaze, To A Wild Rose; Set C: Unforgettable, Here's My Heart & Cotillion. OSP $4.50, CMV $40 MB.

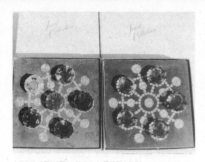

1964 JEWEL COLLECTION
(Left) With 6 gem shaped bottles of perfume oil & gold caps. Blue & gold box. Somewhere, Topaze, Cotillion, Persian Wood, Here's My Heart & To A Wild Rose. OSP $5.95, CMV $50 MB.

1964 JEWEL COLLECTION - CANADA
(Right) Box is same as American set only center bottle hole is not punched out. Came in Somewhere, Topaze, Cotillion, Here's My Heart, To A Wild Rose in perfume oils, 5/8 dram each. Very rare set. OSP $6.95, CMV $225 MB.

1966-67 RENAISSANCE TRIO
Box holds 3 boxes with ½ oz. colognes in Unforgettable, Rapture, Occur!, Somewhere, Topaze, Cotillion, Here's My Heart, To A Wild Rose & Wishing. OSP $3.50, CMV $17.50 MB.

1965 STAR ATTRACTIONS
Box contains ½ oz. cologne & metal lipstick in Rapture, Occur!, Somewhere, Topaze, Cotillion, Here's My Heart, Persian Wood, To A Wild Rose & Wishing. OSP $2.50, CMV $20 MB.

1966 PERFUME OIL PETITES (PIN CUSHION)
Gold box with red velvet pin cushion top & inner box holds three 5/8 dram heart shaped bottles with gold caps & labels. Came in choice of Set A: Wishing, Somewhere, Occur!; Set B: Rapture, Topaze, To A Wild Rose; Set C: Here's My Heart, Unforgettable, Cotillion. OSP $4.50, CMV $45 MB.

1965 FRAGRANCE GOLD DUET
Two heart shaped ½ oz. colognes in gold & white box. Came in Rapture, Occur!, Cotillion, Somewhere, Topaze, Here's My Heart, Persian Wood, To A Wild Rose, Wishing & Unforgettable. OSP $2.50, CMV $17.50 MB.

1967-68 GIFT MAGIC
3½ oz. clear glass rocker bottle with gold label & lid. Box red & purple with gold & white sleeve. Came in choice of Brocade, Regence, Unforgettable, Rapture, Occur!, Somewhere Topaze, Cotillion, Here's My Heart, To A Wild Rose, Wishing & Persian Wood cologne. OSP $2.98, CMV $15 MB.

1960 GIFT MAGIC SET
Flat rocker bottles in same set that sold in 1967-68 with round cap rocker bottles. OSP $2.49, CMV $20 MB.

1966 FRAGRANCE VANITY TRAY
Three hearts on tray. ½ oz. cologne. Heart shaped bottles on 1966 glass tray with Avon insignia on tray. OSP tray $1.25, CMV $3 tray - MB $4. Colognes OSP $3.75, CMV $2 each bottle - $4 MB. CMV set $18 MB.

1965 FRAGRANCE FAVORITES
Box holds 3 heart shaped ½ oz. colognes in Unforgettable, Rapture, Occur!, Cotillion, Somewhere, Topaze, Here's My Heart, Persian Wood, To A Wild Rose, Wishing. OSP $3.50, CMV $22 MB.

1968 GOLDEN HEIRLOOM CHEST
6" long gold metal, glass lid. red velvet in bottom of chest. Avon on bottom. Came in perfume rollette in Brocade or Regence & deluxe refillable gold lipstick. Came in pink box. OSP $15, CMV complete set in box $35 - chest only $25.

1965-66 GOLDEN VANITY
Gold metal stand with removable mirror in center. Came with perfume rollette & gold refillable lipstick. OSP $10, CMV complete set $30 MB, stand with mirror only $15.

1964-65 VANITY SHOWCASE
Silver & gold plastic holder. Avon on bottom. Came with 1 dram ribbed perfume & deluxe silver lipstick with 4A on top. OSP $5, CMV complete set $20 in box - holder only $9.

1967 MANICURE TRAY
Dark brown plastic tray with 4A design. Came with tubes of Nail Beauty & Cuticle Remover, ½ oz. bottle of Double Coat & Nail Enamel with white caps & box of 10 Enamel Remover Pads, 1 orange stick & emery board. OSP $5, CMV complete set $16 MB - tray only $5. Also came in amber color tray. CMV $10 tray.

1962-64 MANICURE TRAY
Clear plastic, Avon on bottom, 4A design. Came with 3 oz. bottle of Oily Polish Remover, ½ oz. bottle of Nail Polish & Base Coat or Double Coat & 2 tubes of Cuticle Remover & Nail Beauty. OSP $3.98, CMV complete set $20 - tray only $7.

1966-67 COLOGNE GEMS
Gold & white box contains two 1 oz. Gem Colognes, clear glass with plastic caps. Came in Unforgettable, Rapture, Occur!, Somewhere, Topaze, Cotillion, Here's My Heart, To A Wild Rose. OSP $3.50, CMV $12 MB.

1968 VANITY TRAY
Brown plastic tray. Came with brown plastic fashion lipstick shown on right & perfume rollette in choice of Unforgettable, Rapture, Occur!, Somewhere, Topaze, Cotillion, Here's My Heart or To A Wild Rose. OSP $6, CMV complete set $11 in box - tray only $6 MB.

1965 PERFUMED PILLOWETTES
Box contains two sachet pillows & gold top powder sachet in Occur!, Rapture. OSP $3.75. Lavender, Somewhere, Cotillion, Topaze. OSP $3.25. Here's My Heart, To A Wild Rose & Wishing. OSP $3, CMV $20 MB.

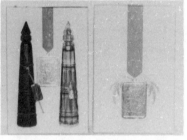

1965 JUST TWO
3 oz. each, Tribute after shave, black glass; clear Rapture cologne with gold tags. OSP $5.50, CMV $70 MB - bottles only with tags (black) $25, (clear) $20.

1968 SPLASH & SPRAY SET
Purse size cologne spray & 2½ oz. splash cologne bottle with refill funnel. Both trimmed in gold. Gold box. Came in Brocade & Regence. OSP $7. Unforgettable, Somewhere & Topaze. OSP $6.50, CMV $20 MB.

1959-60 PARIS MOOD
Gift set came with spray essence, beauty dust & cream sachet in Persian Wood, Here's My Heart, Cotillion, To A Wild Rose, Bright Night & Nearness fragrances. OSP $7.95, CMV $47 MB. See stockholders gifts for additional information.

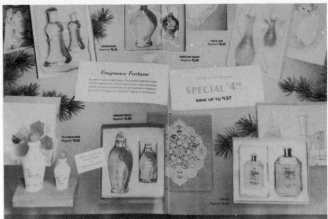

1964 FRAGRANCE FORTUNE
Matching boxes hold 2 oz. cologne & ½ oz. perfume oil in Somewhere, Here's My Heart, Cotillion, To A Wild Rose, Persian Wood & Topaze. OSP each $4.98, CMV $27.50 MB.

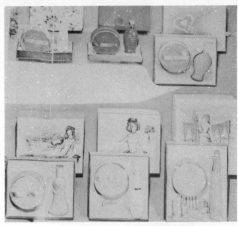

1962-63 FRAGRANCE MAGIC
Matching boxes holds cologne mist & beauty dust with clear plastic top. Came in To A Wild Rose, Persian Wood, Here's My Heart, Somewhere, Cotillion & Topaze. OSP $6 to $8, CMV $35 MB each.

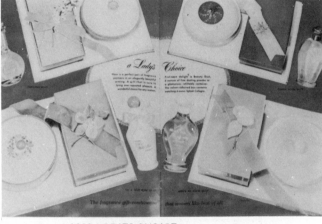

1960 LADIES CHOICE
Matching boxes hold 4 oz. cologne & beauty dust in Cotillion, Persian Wood, To A Wild Rose, Here's My Heart. OSP $5.45 to $6.25, CMV $40 each set MB.

1960-61 MODERN SIMPLICITY
Lavender blue & white box contains soap, 4 oz. bath oil, 3 oz. beauty dust in choice of Cotillion, To A Wild Rose & Here's My Heart. OSP $3.98, CMV $45 MB.

1959-60 TWO LOVES SETS
Matching boxes hold cologne mist & cream sachet in To A Wild Rose, Here's My Heart. CMV $20 each. Nearness CMV $38. Cotillion CMV $23. 1959 only for Persian Wood CMV $27. Bright Night CMV $30. OSP $4.25 to $4.75.

1965 FLOWER FANTASY
Floral box holds cream sachet & perfume rollette in Here's My Heart, To A Wild Rose, Wishing, Somewhere, Cotillion, Topaze & Occur! OSP $5, CMV $15 each - MB $18 with carnival glass rollette.

1963-64 FLOWER FANTASY
Cream sachet & cream rollette in Here's My Heart, Persian Wood, To A Wild Rose, Cotillion, Somewhere, Topaze, Occur! OSP $5, CMV $17 MB.

1969 SCENTIMENTS
Box holds ½ oz. clear glass jar with gold cap with cream sachet in Unforgettable, Rapture, Occur!, Somewhere, Topaze or Cotillion with 4A embossed soap. OSP $3.50, CMV $10 MB. Each fragrance came with different color soap.

1969 TWO LOVES
Red & gold box with red felt inside holds perfume rollette & cream sachet in Charisma, Brocade or Regence. OSP $6, CMV $12 MB. Brocade is gray inside box.

1968-69 SCENTIMENTS
Gold, white & silver box holds cream sachet & perfumed rollette in Brocade, Regence, Unforgettable, Rapture, Occur!, Somewhere, Topaze or Cotillion. OSP $4, CMV $12 MB.

1. Elusive

2. Bird of Paradise

3. Charisma

1970 TWO LOVES
Cream sachet & perfume rollette in Elusive in pink & gold box, Bird of Paradise in turquoise & gold box and Charisma in red & gold box with white, gold or red liner. OSP $6 each, CMV $12 each MB.

1967 TWO LOVES
Gold & green box has cream sachet & perfume rollette in Unforgettable, Rapture, Occur!, Somewhere, Topaze, Cotillion, Here's My Heart & To A Wild Rose. OSP $5, CMV $13 MB.

1967 MERRY LIPTINTS
Red flocked sleeve holds 2 white & gold Encore lipsticks with boxes to match sleeve but not flocked. OSP $1.99, CMV $9 MB.

1960 GOLDEN RINGS SET
Red & gold box holds 2 pink & white lipsticks. OSP $1.79, CMV $15 MB.

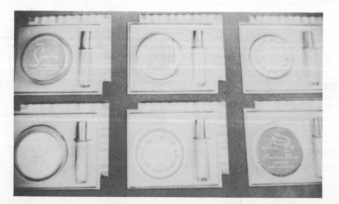

1963-64 BEAUTY SCENTS
Box holds 5 oz. perfumed skin softener & matching perfume creme rollette in Somewhere, Topaze, Cotillion, To A Wild Rose, Here's My Heart & Persian Wood. OSP $5.25, CMV $16 MB. 1965 Beauty Scents issued same box but with perfume rollette and dropped Persian Wood and added Rapture and Occur! OSP $5.25, CMV $15 each - MB $17 with carnival glass rollette.

1963 FASHION STAR
Blue, pink & white box holds two Fashion lipsticks. OSP $1.69, CMV $13 MB.

1963 COLOR NOTE
Gold & white box holds bottle of nail polish & pink Fashion lipstick. OSP $1.67, CMV $14 MB.

1966 CANDY CANE TWINS
Candy cane box holds 2 Cameo lipsticks. OSP $1.96, CMV $20 MB.

1962 COLOR TRICK
Blue & gold foil box has 2 black Fashion lipstick tubes, gold bottom. OSP $1.96, CMV $15 MB.

1963-64 TOUCH-UP TWINS
Mult-colored box holds lipstick & perfume cream rollette in Here's My Heart, Persian Wood, To A Wild Rose. OSP $3.10 each. Somewhere, Topaze, Cotillion. OSP $3.35. Occur! OSP $3.85, CMV $17 MB.

1965 FASHION TWINS
Multi-colored box holds 2 Cameo lipsticks. OSP $1.95, CMV $15 MB.

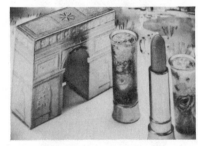

1964 GOLDEN ARCH
Gold arch box holds 2 floral Fashion lipsticks. OSP $1.96, CMV $17.50 MB.

1965 Only TOUCH-UP TWINS
Angel box holds deluxe lipstick & perfume rollette in Here's My Heart, Wishing, To A Wild Rose. OSP $2.70. Somewhere, Topaze, Cotillion. OSP $2.95. Rapture, Occur! OSP $3.45, CMV $12 MB. Add $2 for carnival glass rollette.

1962 CLEVER MATCH SET
Pink & red box holds black lipstick & nail polish with white cap. 1961 set same only has white plastic lipstick with pink flowered top. OSP $1.83, CMV $15 MB.

1967 MERRY FINGERTIPS
Pink velvet box holds 2 bottles of nail polish. OSP $1.70, CMV $12 MB.

1964 PAIR TREE
Gold, white & blue holds nail polish & floral Fashion lipstick. OSP $1.83, CMV $15 MB.

1966 SLEIGH MATES
Red and gold box holds Fashion Cameo lipstick & bottle of nail enamel. OSP $1.83, CMV $20 MB.

1962-63 HAWAIIAN DELIGHTS
Box holds 4 bottles of nail polish. White caps. OSP $2.98, CMV $20 MB.

1963 BATH BOUQUET
8 oz. plastic bottle of bath oil & soap in Royal Jasmine, Royal Pine, Rose Geranium. OSP $2.39, CMV $14 each MB.

1965 BATH BOUQUET
Green box contains 1½ oz. green cardboard talc, 2 oz. bath oil & ½ oz. cologne in Here's My Heart, To A Wild Rose, Wishing. OSP $4. Somewhere, Topaze, Cotillion. OSP $4.25. Rapture & Occur! OSP $4.50, CMV $35 MB.

1964 COLOR GARDEN
Red & white floral box holds 4 nail polish bottles with white caps. Came with pearl or cream polish only. OSP $2.76, CMV $20 MB.

1962-63 REFRESHING HOURS
Red & white box holds 2¾ oz. can of perfumed talc & 2½ oz. bottle of cologne in Somewhere, Topaze, Cotillion, Here's My Heart, Persian Wood & To A Wild Rose. OSP $2.50, CMV $25 each set.

1960 PARTY FUN
Blue & gold box holds gold lipstick & 1 dram perfume in Topaze, Here's My Heart, Persian Wood, Cotillion, To A Wild Rose, Bright Night, Nearness. OSP $3.50, CMV $22 MB.

1962-63 BATH CLASSIC
1½ oz. with gold design, gold cap in gold box with large red powder puff. Box has clear plastic top. Cologne came in Somewhere, Cotillion, Topaze. OSP $5. Here's My Heart, Persian Wood. OSP $4.75. To A Wild Rose. OSP $4.50, CMV $35 MB.

1960 CLASSIC HARMONY
Red, pink & gold box holds Top Style lipstick, compact & perfume. Came in choice of shades & fragrances. OSP $6.95, CMV $25 MB.

1964 BATH BOUQUET
Pink box holds white plastic 6 oz. bottle of perfumed bath oil & perfumed soap in Topaze, Somewhere, To A Wild Rose, Persian Wood, Here's My Heart & Cotillion fragrances. OSP $2.89, CMV $14 each MB.

1962 FASHION TWIN SET
Blue & white silk cosmetic case holds gold & black compact & lipstick. OSP $3.29, CMV $15 - $18 MB.

1963 BATH BOUQUET
Gift box holds 8 oz. plastic bottle of bath oil & soap in Lily of the Valley, Lilac. OSP $2.39, CMV $14 each MB.

1965-66 MANICURE TRAY
White plastic tray & tissue holder. Came with pink box of Kleenex Tissue with 4A design on box. 8½ x 6 x 3 inches. OSP $5, CMV tray only $5 - MB $7. Avon Kleenex box mint $7. Complete set MB $14.

1965 BATH SPARKLERS
Silver box holds 3 colored tubes of bubble bath powder in Lilac, Jasmine & Lily of the Valley. OSP $2.50, CMV $25 MB.

1962 BATH BOUQUET
White & gold box holds 6 oz. pink & white plastic bottle of bath oil & wrapped soap in Somewhere, Cotillion, Here's My Heart, Topaze, Persian Wood, Royal Jasmine, Rose Geranium, Royal Pine, Floral & To A Wild Rose. OSP $2.79, CMV $17 MB.

1966 FRAGRANCE DUETTE
Blue & gold box holds 2 oz. splash on cologne & perfumed rollette in Occur!, Rapture & Unforgettable. OSP $5, CMV $15 MB.

1962-63 FRAGRANCE GEMS
Box holds creme sachet & cream lotion in Topaze, Cotillion, Somewhere, Persian Wood, Here's My Heart & To A Wild Rose. OSP $2.75, CMV $16 MB.

1960 BEGUILING SET
Multi-colored box holds spray essence & cream sachet in Bright Night, Nearness, To A Wild Rose, Cotillion. OSP $4.50. Here's My Heart & Persian Wood. OSP $5, CMV $25 MB.

1967-68 KEEPSAKES
Gold, floral & white box holds 3 oz. cologne mist, perfume rollette in Occur!, Rapture & Unforgettable. OSP $8.50, CMV $14 MB.

1966 FRAGRANCE CHIMES
Red & gold box holds perfumed talc & cream sachet in Rapture, Occur!, Unforgettable, Somewhere, Topaze, Cotillion, Here's My Heart & To A Wild Rose & Wishing. OSP $2.89, CMV $12 MB.

1964 DECORATION GIFT SET
Purple, gold & white box holds cream sachet & spray essence in Here's My Heart, Persian Wood, To A Wild Rose, Somewhere, Cotillion & Topaze. OSP $5.50, CMV $20 MB.

1967 FLORAL MEDLEY
Floral box contains perfumed talc & cream sachet in Honeysuckle. OSP $3.48. Jasmine, Lily of the Valley, Lilac. OSP $2.89, CMV $13 each set MB.

1965 DOUBLE PAK SET
Box in green, pink & red foil design. Came with choice of 2 tubes of moisturized hand cream or Avon hand cream or silicone glove or bottle of hand lotion as shown. OSP $1.29, CMV $10 MB.

1967 FLUFF PUFF SET
Issued during bottle strike. Green box holds 2 boxes 3.5 oz. of powder. White plastic bottle, gold base & pink puff. Does not say Avon. Came in Unforgettable, To A Wild Rose, Cotillion, Regence. OSP $5.50, CMV $18 MB. Regence came in dark pink & light pink & green. Green is rare. CMV green only $25 MB.

1963-64 FLORAL ENCHANTMENT
Floral box holds cologne mist & cream sachet in Occuri, Persian Wood, Here's My Heart, To A Wild Rose, Topaze, Somewhere & Cotillion. Came with 2 different bottles. CMV $17 MB.

1965 FLORAL TALC TRIO
Floral box holds three 3½ oz. talcs in Lily of the Valley, Lilac & Jasmine. OSP $2.65, CMV $12.50 MB.

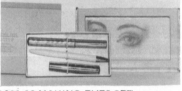

1961-62 MAKING EYES SET
Blue & green box with checkerboard top holds Eye Shadow Stick, Curl 'N' Color & Eyebrow Pencil. Box came with outside sleeve. OSP $3.95, CMV $25 MB.

1967 FLUFF PUFF
Floral box contains one puff & beauty dust. White plastic. Comes in Unforgettable, To A Wild Rose, Cotillion & Regence. OSP $5.50, CMV $12 MB. Also came in white puff in Regence. CMV $20.

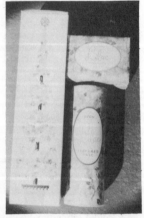

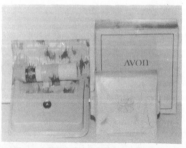

1964 FLOWER BATH SET
Talc & 2 bars of soap in choice of Lily of the Valley, Lilac, Jasmine & Rose Geranium. OSP $1.67, CMV $13 MB.

1965 PRETTY NOTIONS
Pink vinyl case contains pink compact & Cameo lipstick. OSP $4.50, CMV $10 set only - $12 MB.

1967-70 ROLL-A-FLUFF
Fluff holds 3½ oz. beauty dust. Red puff is Charisma. Green puff is Regence. White puff is Brocade. Gold top & handle. OSP $13.50, CMV $15 MB.

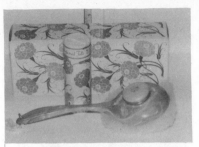

1968 FLUFF PUFFS
3½ oz. talc & matching puff comes in Somewhere with green puff, Honeysuckle with yellow puff, Here's My Heart with blue puff & To A Wild Rose with pink puff. OSP $6, CMV $10 MB.

1969 FLUFF PUFF
Cardboard talc, blue & gold design on white, puff white with marbleized handle, white knob with 4A. Came 3 different colors: Rapture, turquoise; Occur!, yellow; & Unforgettable, coral. OSP $4.99, CMV $10 MB.

1965-66 WOMEN'S TRAVEL KIT
Yellow floral "hat box" contains cream deodorant, Skin-So-Soft, hand cream, white Velex Cleansing cream, Hormone cream, Rich Moisture, Vita Moist & Cream Supreme. OSP $12.95, CMV complete set $30 MB - hat box only $12.

1963-64 WOMAN'S TRAVEL KIT
White floral bag holds moisturized hand cream, perfumed talc, 4 oz. Skin-So-Soft, 2 oz. perfumed deodorant & choice of night cream. OSP $11.95, CMV $25 MB.

1959-60 ON THE WING SET
Blue plastic bag holds choice of perfumed talc in Here's My Heart, Persian Wood, To A Wild Rose, Nearness, Cotillion & Floral. Skin freshener, deep clean & 2 oz. plastic bottle of choice of 1½ oz. jar of Vita Moist or Rich Moisture cream. OSP $6.25, CMV $30 MB.

1962 TOTE ALONG SET
Tapestry bag holds 4 oz. cologne & cream lotion, cream sachet, 3 cakes of wrapped soap in Somewhere, Topaze, Cotillion, Here's My Heart, Persian Wood & To A Wild Rose. OSP $12.95, CMV $32 MB.

WOMEN'S SETS OF 1970'S

WARNING!! Grading condition is paramount on sets.
CMV can vary 50% to 75% on grade.
Refer to Page 6 and 16 on Grading.

1973 TREASURE CHEST SET
White plastic chest with deep purple velour inside & on top. Bottles are clear glass with white on front & gold rose & gold cap. One bottles holds 4 oz. Skin-So-Soft, other holds 4 oz. cologne in Moonwind or Sonnet. Soap 5 oz. in Moonwind (blue) or Sonnet (pink). SSP $20, CMV $27.50 MB.

1970 ULTRA FLUFF SET
Box holds 3½ oz. beauty dust, 1/8 oz. perfume, Lamb's Wool Puff & white pedestal dish in Brocade, Charisma & Regence. OSP $10, CMV $12 MB.

1972-73 PAST & PRESENT BRUSH & COMB SET
Antique ivory colored, nylon bristled plastic brush & comb. SSP $4, CMV $6 MB.

1972-75 FRAGRANCE FANCY
Pink, blue & white. Has .33 oz. roll-ette & 1.5 oz. perfumed talc. Choice of Unforgettable, Somewhere, Cotillion, Occur!, Topaze, Here's My Heart or Rapture. OSP $3, CMV $4 MB.

1971-73 PRECIOUS PAIR
Multi-colored box holds matching 1½ oz. perfumed talc & ½ oz. cologne in Occur!, Rapture, Unforgettable, Somewhere, Topaze & Cotillion. OSP $4, CMV $5 MB.

1973-75 FRAGRANCE TREASURES
.66 oz. clear glass cream sachet with pink & gold lid. Pink & gold soap wrapper & box. Choice of Sonnet, Charisma or Moonwind. OSP $3, CMV $4 MB.

1978-79 FRAGRANT NOTIONS
Floral design box with gold & blue felt inner box holds .33 oz. bottle, gold cap & porcelain thimble with Avon stamped in bottom. Box came with outside sleeve. Choice of Ariane or Timeless cologne. SSP $6.99, CMV $6.99 MB.

1969-72 LIGHTS & SHADOWS COLOGNE
(Left) Lights is clear glass & gold cap. Shadows is smoked glass & cap. 2 oz. each. OSP $4, CMV $6 MB.
1969 LIGHTS & SHADOWS SAMPLES
(Right) Each sample has both fragrances. Box of 10 sample packets (box on top). CMV 50c each.

1973 MINUETTE DUET
5 oz. cologne in clear bottle with gold cap. 1.5 oz. talc in paper cylinder with Christmas scene. Came in set of Unforgettable, To A Wild Rose, Occur!, Somewhere, Topaze or Cotillion. SSP $3, CMV $5 MB.

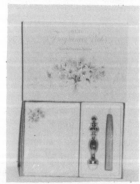

1977-78 FRAGRANCE NOTES
Fragranced writing paper & sealing wax. Came with 18 notes scented with Earth Flowers fragrance, sealing wax stick, and goldtone seal. OSP $9, CMV $7 MB.

1977-78 FLUFF PUFF SET
Perfumed talc dispenser. Pink plastic holder approx. 11½" long. Came with 2 oz. cardboard talc in Roses Roses or Sonnet. SSP $5.99, CMV $4.50 MB.

1971 SOPHISTICURL
A salon permanent wave used only in Avon Beauty Salons. Box holds 4 oz. bottle of waving lotions and 3.75 oz. white tube of neutralizer. CMV $10 set MB.

1971-74 HAIR PERFECT SET
Blue & white box holds 2 oz. brown glass bottle of Color Perfect & 2 oz. white plastic bottle of cream developer. OSP $2.50, CMV $4 MB.

1971 ORIGINAL BODY SALON PERMANENT WAVE
Pink box holds 4 oz. bottle of neutralizer and waving lotion. Used only in Avon Beauty Salons. Not sold. CMV $11 MB.

1969 HAIR COLOR SET
2 oz. brown glass bottle of hair color & 2 oz. white plastic bottle of cream developer in blue box. Short issue. OSP $2.50, CMV $16 MB.

1971 BUILT-IN BODY SALON PERMANENT WAVE
White box holds 4 oz. bottle of waving lotion & 4 oz. bottle of neutralizer. Used only in Avon Beauty Salons and not sold. CMV $12 MB.

1971 CURL SUPREME SALON PERMANENT WAVE
Purple box holds 3.75 oz. white tube of neutralizer & 4 oz. bottle of waving lotion. Used only in Avon Beauty Salons. No sold. CMV $12 MB.

SEE 1984 SUPPLEMENT IN BACK OF BOOK FOR MORE SETS OF 1980'S.

WOMEN'S SETS OF 1980'S

WARNING!! Grading condition is paramount on sets.
CMV can vary 50% to 75% on grade.
Refer to Page 6 and 16 on Grading.

1982 FLORAL ACCENT GIFT SET
Box holds 1 oz. cologne & matching trim handkerchief. Choice of Wild Jasmine & Honeysuckle in yellow trim; Hawaiian White Ginger or Field Flowers in green trim; Roses Roses or Sweet Honesty in pink trim. SSP $6, CMV $6 MB each set.

1982 ENVIRA SKIN CARE KIT
Handle carton holds .5 oz. tube of conditioning cleansing cream, .5 oz. plastic bottles of clarifying toner & protective moisturizing lotion. Short issue. SSP $2, CMV $2 mint set.

1981 HOLIDAY GIFT SOAP SET
Red & green handle box holds 3 bars soap in gold wrappers. Choice of mix & match in Tasha, Foxfire, Odyssey, Candid, Timeless, Unspoken, Ariane or Emprise. SSP $5 set, CMV $5 MB set.

1981 HOLIDAY GIFT SET ULTRA
Red & green carry box holds gold 1.5 oz. talc & 1 oz. Ultra cologne spray in gold box. Choice of Timeless, Candid, Ariane, Tempo or Tasha. SSP $8, CMV $8 MB.

1981 HOLIDAY TAPESTRY GIFT SET
Red & green handle carry box holds green & red tapestry design 1.5 oz. talc & 1.8 oz. cologne spray in choice of Occur!, Topaze, Moonwind, Charisma, Sweet Honesty or Zany. Colognes come in own box. SSP $8, CMV $8 MB set.

1980-82 SILKEN SCENTS SCARF & COLOGNE
25 x 25 inch scarf & 1.75 oz. swirled glass cologne in Candid or Timeless. SSP $13 set, CMV $13 set MB.

1980 COLORCREME & ULTRA WEAR GIFT SET
Blue & red box holds blue & silver Colorcreme moisture lipstick & Ultra Wear nail enamel. Each item in own box inside set box. SSP $4, CMV $4 MB.

AVON FACIAL SETS

WARNING!! Grading condition is paramount on sets. CMV can vary 50% to 75% on grade. Refer to Page 6 and 16 on Grading.

1938-40 FACIAL SET
Green box holds 4 oz. bottles of astringent & Lotus cream, jars of tissue cream & cleansing cream and box of face powder in Ariel or Cotillion. OSP $1.89, CMV $65 MB.

1933-36 FACIAL SET
Silver & blue box contains 2 oz. jar of cleansing cream & 1 oz. jar of tissue cream, 1 bottle of astringent, silver box of Ariel face powder, package of tissues. OSP $1.68, CMV $110 MB.

1941-48 FACIAL SET
Green box contains jar of cleansing cream, foundation cream, night cream with green lids. Skin freshener, 2 oz. green cap & box of face powder, blue & white feather design, 2 packs of Avon facial tissues. Jars had green or white metal lids. OSP $1.89, CMV $50 MB. Add $10 set for white lids.

1949-54 FACIAL SET FOR DRY SKIN
Green box contains Fluffy cleansing cream, skin freshener, special dry skin cream & lipstick.
SAME SET FOR OILY SKIN
Contained liquifying cleansing cream, astringent, night cream & lipstick. OSP $3.39 each set, CMV $50 MB each set.

1936-37 FACIAL SET
Turquoise flip up box holds Ariel face powder, 2 oz. jar cleansing cream, tissue cream & 2 oz. bottle of astringent. All products are marked CPC. Also came with packet of tissues. OSP $1.60, CMV $50 MB.

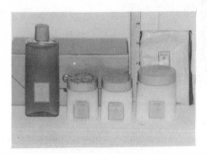

1937-38 FACIAL SET
Green box contains choice of 2 oz. bottle of skin freshener or astringent, green caps, 2 oz. jar of cleansing cream, 1 oz. jar of tissue cream and Ariel of Vernafleur face powder. OSP $1.68, CMV $65 MB.

GOLD BOX SETS

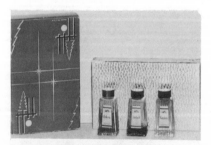

1932 GOLD BOX SET
Metal gold with black strips. Can holds 3½ oz. ribbed glass bottles of 391, Ariel and Vernafleur perfume. All have black octagonal caps. This is the same metal can as the 1925-30 manicure set. OSP $1.40, CMV $140.

1933-36 GOLD BOX SET
Gold box contained three ½ oz. bottles of Vernafleur, Ariel, 391, Bolero or Gardenia. Black caps. OSP $1.46, CMV $125 MB.

1937-38 GOLD BOX SET
Gold box holds three 1/8 oz. bottles of Cotillion, Narcissus & Gardenia perfumes. OSP $1.25, CMV $80 MB.

1939-40 GOLD BOX
Gold open front box holds 3 bottles of perfume in Gardenia, Cotillion, Narcissus or Trailing Arbutus. White plastic caps on all. OSP $1.25, CMV $90 MB.

1944 GOLD BOX
Ribbons & flower design box holds three 1/8 oz. perfumes in Trailing Arbutus, Cotillion & Gardenia. OSP $1.50, CMV $90 MB.

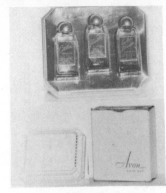

1949 GOLD BOX SET
Turquoise plastic bottom with gold insert, clear plastic lid contains three 1 dram bottles of Cotillion, Flowertime & Golden Promise perfumes. All have gold caps & labels. OSP $2.25, CMV $80 MB.

1941-44 GOLD BOX SET
Pink & gold box contains 1/8 oz. perfumes in Gardenia, Cotillion & Trailing Arbutus. White caps, pink & gold box. OSP $1.35, CMV $85 MB.

MAKEUP ENSEMBLE SETS

1939-40 MAKE-UP ENSEMBLE
Box holds can of face powder in choice of Cotillion, Ariel or Vernafleur, and table rouge in green & gold boxes. Lipstick in green & gold. OSP $1.40, CMV $40 MB.

1943-44 MAKE-UP ENSEMBLE
Blue & pink box holds feathered box of face powder, rouge & plastic or cardboard lipstick. OSP $1.75, CMV $40 MB.

1945-46 GOLD BOX
Pink & white box holds three 1/8 oz. bottles in Crimson Carnation, Gardenia & Cotillion perfume. OSP $1.50, CMV $80 MB.

1941-42 MAKE-UP ENSEMBLE
Box contains face powder, rouge in feather design, turquoise & gold lipstick. OSP $1.52, CMV $40 MB.

1947-48 GOLD BOX SET
Three 1/8 oz. perfume bottles, gold caps, pink labels. Ballad, Garden of Love, Cotillion. OSP $2.50, CMV $80 MB.

1945 MAKE-UP ENSEMBLE
Lipstick designed box holds feather design face powder, lipstick & rouge. Also came with metal bamboo lipstick. OSP $1.75, CMV $37 MB.

1946 Only MAKE-UP ENSEMBLE
Pink & blue feather design box holds gold bamboo lipstick, rouge & box of face powder. OSP $2.25, CMV $40 MB.

1947 Only MAKE-UP ENSEMBLE
White, pink box with Eiffel Tower on box holds pink & blue feather design powder with bamboo lipstick & rouge. OSP $2.35, CMV $40 MB.

1948 MAKE-UP ENSEMBLE
Same except lipstick gold with swirl design around bottom. OSP $2.35, CMV $40 MB.

1952-53 MAKE-UP ENSEMBLE
Turquoise & gold box holds gold compact, lipstick & face powder or powder pak. OSP $2.75, CMV $30 MB.

1949-51 MAKE-UP ENSEMBLE
Blue, pink & white box contains face powder, gold lipstick & rouge. Eiffel Tower on box. OSP $2.35, CMV $30 MB.

MANICURE SETS

WARNING!! Grading condition is paramount on sets.
CMV can vary 50% to 75% on grade.
Refer to Page 6 and 16 on Grading.

1930 MANICURE SET NO. 1
Silver box holds 2 small bottles of nail polish & polish remover. Black caps. Booklet "What Story Do Your Hands Tell?" came with set. OSP 52c, CMV $60 MB.

1937 MANICURE SET NO. 2
Turquoise & white lid, gold inside box holds cans of nail white & nail cream, bottles of polish remover, cuticle softener & nail polish, orange stick, nail file, 3 cotton rolls in glass tube & booklet "What Story Do Your Hands Tell?" OSP $1.67, CMV $80 MB.

1936-37 MANICURE SET NO. 1
Green & white box has bottles of nail polish & polish remover with 2 rolls of cotton & booklet "What Story Do Your Hands Tell?" OSP 52c, CMV $45 MB.

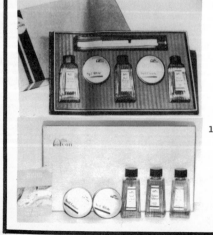

1931-36 MANICURE SET NO. 2
Silver box holds 3 small ribbed glass bottles of polish remover, nail polish, cuticle softener. All have black caps. Two small silver cans of nail white & nail cream, 1 fingernail file & booklet "What Story Do Your Hands Tell?" OSP $1.67, CMV $110 MB. Same set also came with no stripe on box as shown & 2 different linings inside box as shown.

1938-39 MANICURE SET NO. 2
Brown case holds orange stick, nail file, can of nail white, nail cream, bottles of cuticle softener, cream polish & polish remover. OSP $1.89, CMV $55 MB.

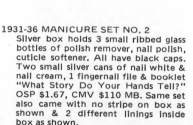

1938-49 MANICURE SET NO. 1
Turquoise box holds ½ oz. nail polish and cream polish, 2 cotton rolls and booklet "What Story Do Your Hands Tell?" CPC on box, 2 different boxes. Some say Manicure Set No. 1 at top of box and some at bottom of box. Add $5 for CPC box. OSP 52c, CMV $30 MB.

1940 MANICURE SET NO. 2
Brown case holds fingernail file, orange stick, white Avon nail white pencil, ½ oz. bottles of clear or cream nail polish, polish remover, cuticle softener & cuticle oil. Turquoise or black caps. OSP $2.25, CMV $55 MB.

1941-43 MANICURE SET DELUXE
Same set as above only name changed. OSP $2.25, CMV $55 MB.

1945-50 NAIL POLISH TWOSOME
Turquoise box holds ½ oz. bottles of cream polish & cuticle softener and small 30 page booklet. OSP 85c, CMV $30 MB.

1938-49 TWOSOME SET
Turquoise & white box holds ½ oz. of nail polish & ½ oz. of cuticle softener, 2 cotton rolls & booklet "What Story Do Your Hands Tell?" CPC on box in 1938-39. Add $5 for CPC box. OSP 52c, CMV $30.

1942-43 THREESOME SET
Pink & white box has 3 small bottles with turquoise caps of cream polish, nail polish base & oily polish remover. Comes with story booklet on hands. OSP 85c, CMV $40 MB.

1948-49 AVON THREESOME SET
Red, white & green tray with green box holds three ½ oz. bottles with white caps for oily polish remover, Cling Tite & nail polish. OSP $1.19, CMV $28 MB.

1938-49 NAIL POLISH THREESOME
Turquoise & white box holds ½ oz. double coat, ½ oz. nail polish, ½ oz. oily polish remover, 2 rolls cotton & booklet. OSP 85c, CMV $42.50.

1950-52 AVON THREESOME SET
Red & white box holds 3 nail polish bottles with white caps. OSP $1.29, CMV $28 MB.

1941-44 ROYAL WINDSOR SET
Blue box holds choice ½ oz. nail polish base & ½ oz. cream polish or ½ oz. top coat. OSP 52c, CMV $17 MB as shown.

1944-49 MANICURE SET DELUXE
Black & red bag holds 5 bottles of nail polish, top coat, nail polish base, cuticle softener, oily polish remover. All have black or turquoise caps. White nail white pencil, orange stick & 2 nail files. OSP $3, CMV $45 MB.

1949 MANICURE SET DELUXE
Same black & red bag only holds 4 bottles with turquoise caps in Cling Tite nail polish, nail polish remover & cuticle softener. OSP $2.50, CMV $40 MB.

1950-51 DELUXE MANICURE SET
Black & red box holds three ½ oz. bottles nail polish, ½ oz. bottle of clear nail polish, ½ oz. bottle cuticle softener, 1 orange stick, 1 white nail white pencil & booklet. OSP $2.75, CMV $25 MB.

1950-52 DELUXE MANICURE SET
Black & red box holds bottles of cuticle softener, nail polish, oily polish remover & Cling Tite. OSP $2.50, CMV $25 MB.

1956-57 POLKA DOT SET
Red & white plastic case holds ½ oz. bottles of nail polish, top coat & 2 oz. oily polish remover. OSP $1.69, CMV $18 MB.

1959 MANICURE DELUXE SET
Box holds cuticle softener, silvery base, oily polish remover, top coat & cream polish. OSP $3.95, CMV $20 MB.

1953-54 MANICURE SET DELUXE
Gray case holds ½ oz. bottles of cuticle softener, nail polish, double coat, 2 oz. oily polish remover, white caps on all. OSP $2.65, CMV $22 MB.

1956-57 MANICURE SET DELUXE
Pink plastic container holds ½ oz. bottles of polish remover, cuticle softener, silvery base, top coat & polish. All have white caps. OSP $3.25, CMV $25 MB.

1960-61 MANICURE PETITE SET
Black vinyl case holds top coat, oily polish remover & cream or pearl nail polish. White caps. OSP $2.98, CMV $12 MB.

1955 DELUXE MANICURE SET
White plastic with gold dots, red lining holds oily nail polish remover, cuticle softener, Silvery Base, choice of nail enamel, all white caps & emery board. OSP $2.95, CMV $25 MB.

1957 COLOR CHANGE SET
Pink, turquoise & gold design on white plastic case, holds 2 oz. bottle, white cap, oily nail polish remover & top coat & nail polish. OSP $1.95, CMV $18 MB.

1960-61 DELUXE MANICURE SET
Black vinyl case holds silvery base, oily polish remover, cuticle softener, top coat & cream nail polish. All have white caps, OSP $4.98, CMV $17.50 MB.

1955 LITTLE FAVORITE SET
Plastic turquoise case holds bottles of nail polish, oily polish remover & cuticle softener, all have white caps. OSP $1.50, CMV $18 MB.

1958 COLOR BAR SET
White plastic tray holds 4 bottles of nail polish or silvery base coat, top coat, & cuticle softener. Mix or match. OSP $3, CMV $15 complete - $18 MB.

1966 MANICURE KIT
Gold & white plastic case holds 1 bottle of nail enamel, long last base coat, enamel set, cuticle remover cream, nail beauty, 10 enamel remover pads, emery board & orange stick. OSP $8.50, CMV $15 complete set MB.

PERFUME PAIR SETS

1968-69 MANICURE BEAUTI-KIT
Black & white vinyl case holds ½ oz. bottles of nail enamels, 1 oz. plastic tube cuticle conditioner, 1 oz. plastic tube cuticle remover, 10 enamel remover pads, ½ oz. bottle of enamel set, long-last top coat & emery boards. Red plastic tray. OSP $12, CMV $12 MB.

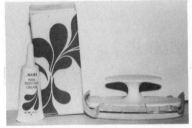

1974 NAIL BUFFER SET
Box holds .25 oz. tube of nail buffing cream & nail buffer. OSP $3, CMV $1.50 MB.

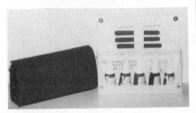

1979-80 NAIL CARE KIT
(Left) Blue plastic kit holds 5 bottles of Avon nail care products. 3 emery boards & wood cuticle stick. SSP $6.50, CMV $5 MB.
1978-79 NAIL CARE KIT
(Right) Same as above only beige color alligator grain case. CMV $5 MB.

1979-80 NAIL CARE KIT
Blue plastic kit holds 5 bottles of nail care products & 3 emery boards & 1 cuticle stick. SSP $6.99, CMV $5 MB complete.

1963 PERFUMED PAIR
Gold & white box with perfumed talc & bar of soap in To A Wild Rose, Here's My Heart, Persian Wood, Topaze, Somewhere & Cotillion. OSP $1.18, CMV $14 MB each set.

1962 PERFUMED PAIR
Box holds 2¾ oz. can of perfumed talc & perfumed soap in Somewhere, Topaze, Cotillion, Persian Wood, Here's My Heart & To A Wild Rose. OSP $1.18, CMV $15 MB.

1966 PERFUMED PAIR
Brown, gold & white box holds 2¾ oz. perfumed talc & wrapped soap in Unforgettable, Rapture, Occur!, Cotillion, Somewhere, Topaze, Here's My Heart, To A Wild Rose & Wishing. OSP $1.39, CMV $11 MB.

1964 PERFUMED PAIR
Box holds perfumed talc & soap in Here's My Heart, Persian Wood, To A Wild Rose. OSP $1.18. Somewhere, Topaze, Cotillion. OSP $1.28, CMV $14 MB.

1967 PERFUMED PAIR
Box contains perfumed talc and matching soap. Comes in Unforgettable, Here's My Heart, To A Wild Rose, Somewhere, Topaze, Cotillion, Rapture & Occur! OSP $1.49, CMV $10 MB.

1953 EVENING CHARM SET
Choice of black velvet bag or brocade bag. Came with 1 dram embossed top perfume, gold deluxe compact & gold jeweled lipstick. OSP $10.95, CMV $30 MB.

1968 PERFUMED PAIR
Box holds 2¾ oz. can of talc and matching soap in Brocade, Regence, Unforgettable, Hawaiian White Ginger, Honeysuckle & To A Wild Rose. OSP $1.79, CMV $8 MB.

1969 PERFUMED PAIR
Box holds perfumed talc & bar of soap in Charisma, Brocade, Blue Lotus, White Ginger, Honeysuckle & To A Wild Rose. OSP $2, CMV $7 MB.

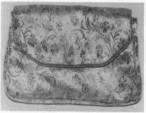

1951 EVENING CHARM SET
Brocade hand bag, or black satin bag with gold trim. Came with same contents as 1953 Evening Charm Set listed. OSP $10.95, CMV purse only $6 - complete set MB $30.

1970 PERFUMED PAIR
Each box contains perfumed talc & matching soap in Hawaiian White Ginger, Honeysuckle, Elusive, Blue Lotus, Bird of Paradise & Charisma. OSP $2.25, CMV $6 MB.

1974-75 PERFUMED PAIR
1.5 oz. perfumed talc & .5 oz. cologne. Choice of Roses Roses, Unforgettable, Cotillion, Sonnet or Moonwind. Came in 2 different boxes. OSP $3, CMV $5 MB.

PURSE SETS — WOMEN

1953 EVENING CHARM PURSE
Avon box holds black velvet purse. Avon on tag inside. CMV $15 MB - purse only $6.

1949 EVENING CHARM SET
Black purse holds gold compact, lipstick & 1 dram bottle in gold metal case with Golden Promise perfume. Also came with beige purse. OSP $10, CMV $40 MB.

1952 EVENING CHARM SET
Gold purse holds 1 dram perfume, lipstick & gold deluxe compact. OSP $10.95, CMV $35 MB.

1954 EVENING CHARM SET
Choice of black velvet or white brocade purse with 1 dram perfume, gold deluxe compact & gold jeweled lipstick. Both have zipper tops. OSP $12.50, CMV $30 MB.

1955 DRESS UP SET
Black & gold purse with gold satin lining holds 1 dram perfume, jeweled lipstick & deluxe gold compact. OSP $10.95, CMV $32.50 MB.

1955 EVENING CHARM SET
Gold brocade purse. Has Avon tag inside. Also came in matching black satin bag. Holds 2 dram embossed top perfume, gold deluxe compact, and gold jeweled lipstick. OSP $12.50, CMV $30 MB.

1955-56 DRESS UP SET
Black & gold reversible purse holds 1 dram perfume, gold compact & gold jeweled lipstick. OSP $10.95, CMV $30 complete MB.

1956 AROUND TOWN SET
Black leather bag holds gold lipstick, powder compact, 1 dram perfume & cologne stick. OSP $12.50, CMV $35 MB.

1956 LADY FAIR SET
Gold box holds 1 dram perfume, gold lipstick & red leather billfold. OSP $5.95, CMV $35 MB.

1957 IN STYLE SET
Black satin purse holds Persian Wood spray perfume, white compact, gold lipstick & black coin purse. OSP $12.95, CMV $32 MB.

1957 MAKE-UP TUCK IN SET
Black striped purse contains pink powder-pak, liquid rouge & lipstick. OSP $3.50, CMV $25 MB.

1959 PAK-PURSE SET
White leather purse holds lipstick, 1 dram perfume & compact. OSP $8.95, CMV $20 MB.

1960 HIGH STYLE SET
Blue satin lined bag holds gold deluxe compact & lipstick. OSP $5.95, CMV $18 MB.

1958 ON THE AVENUE SET
Black purse holds Top Style lipstick & Top Style compact with Here's My Heart or Persian Wood spray perfume. OSP $12.95, CMV $30 MB.

1960 GOING STEADY SET
Gray bag holds white compact & lipstick. Purse does not say Avon on it. OSP $3.50, CMV $15 MB.

1961 MODERN MOOD SET
Gold & white sequin bag holds deluxe lipstick & compact. OSP $6.50, CMV $20 MB.

1962 DELUXE TWIN SET
Blue clutch bag holds deluxe compact & lipstick. OSP $7.50, CMV $17.50 MB.

1964 PURSE COMPANIONS SET
Brocade beige purse with pockets to hold floral fashion lipstick & cameo compact. OSP $6.50, CMV $17 MB. Same set in 1965 only with cameo lipstick. OSP $6.50, CMV $15 MB.

1965 Only EVENING LIGHTS PURSE SET
White box with gold purse came with deluxe compact, lipstick & perfume rollette. OSP $14.95, CMV $20 MB.

1963 MODERN MOOD SET
Gold & white or pink & gold purse holds deluxe compact & lipstick. On left: OSP $7 - CMV $17.50 MB. Or pearl pink compact & floral fashion lipstick (on right). OSP $4.75 - CMV $15 MB.

1964 BEAUTY BOUND SET
Black leather handbag holds deluxe compact & lipstick & choice of creme rollette. OSP $14.95, CMV $30 MB.
1965 BEAUTY BOUND SET
Same set as 1964 only with perfume rollette instead of creme rollette. OSP $14.95, CMV $30 MB.

1978-79 POLISHED GOLD EVENING BAG
Gold plastic purse. Does not say Avon on it. Comes in white Avon box. SSP $6.50, CMV $8 MB.

SOAPS CPC

All Soaps Must Be Mint For CMV.

1905 JAPAN TOILET SOAP
Box of 3 cakes. OSP 25c - CMV $110 MB.

1905 ALMOND MEAL TOILET SOAP
Box of 3 cakes. OSP 25c, CMV $100 MB.

1925 ALMOND BOUQUET TOILET SOAP
Yellow, green & pink wrapping around 3 bars of soap. Soap is embossed. OSP 30c - CMV $85 MB.

1896 SAVONA BOUQUET SOAP
Maroon colored box & wrapping. Two bars. OSP 50c, CMV $100 MB.

1915 PEROXIDE TOILET SOAP
Box of 3 cakes. OSP 50c - CMV $90 MB.

1936-43 SAVONA BOUQUET TOILET SOAP
Turquoise & white box holds 6 square bars. OSP 72c. 1936-39 has CPC label on soap & box. CMV $75 MB. 1940-43 Avon label only on soap and box. CMV $65 MB.

1936 SAVONA BOUQUET SOAP SAMPLES
(Left) CMV $15 each.
1929 SAVONA BOUQUET TOILET SOAP SAMPLES
(Right) CMV $15 each.

1932-36 SAVONA BOUQUET TOILET SOAP
Box of 6 bars. OSP 50c - CMV $70 MB.

1906 ALMOND, BUTTERMILK & CUCUMBER SOAP
Yellow, pink & green box & wrapping holds 3 bars soap. OSP 40c. CMV $100 MB.

1923-25 CASTILE IMPORTED SOAP
Box holds 2 silver wrapped bars. OSP 60c, CMV $45 MB. Same box also came with 1 large bar. OSP 33c, CMV $60 MB.

1936-38 VEGETABLE OIL SOAP
Three light orange colored bars wrapped in turquoise & white paper & box. OSP 46c, CMV $45 MB.

1931-36 VEGETABLE OIL SOAP
Box of 3 bars. OSP 45c, CMV $50 MB.

1908 CPC IMPORTED CASTILE SOAP
5 oz. cake. First came out about 1893. OSP 25c - CMV $60 MB.

1931-36 CASTILE IMPORTED SOAP
Box holds 2 silver wrapped bars. OSP 60c, CMV $45 MB.

1925 CASTILE SOAP
One bar of soap. OSP 33c - CMV $50 MB.

1915 A.B.C. SOAP
Six bars in yellow box with pink flowers on box. OSP 40c - CMV $100 MB.

1936-43 CASTILE SOAP
Two white bars wrapped in silver paper & turquoise box. OSP 62c. CMV $45 MB.

1911 STARCH DRESSING SAMPLE
1" size box holds 3 samples. CMV $60 MB.

DR. ZABRISKIE'S SOAP

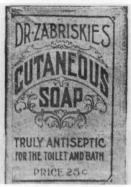

1925 EASY CLEANER
Box of two ½ lb. cakes. OSP 33c - CMV $75 MB.

1925 NAPTHA LAUNDRY CRYSTALS
Two different box labels. One box has blue letters & 1 box has green letters. Thirteen white crystals in box, with instruction sheet. OSP 33c, CMV $45 MB.

1925 STARCH DRESSING
25 tablets in box. Each tablet is marked CPC & has instruction sheet in box. OSP 33c - CMV $45 MB.

1911 STARCH DRESSING DIRECTION SHEET
Came in box of Starch Dressing. Printed on both sides. CMV $5 mint.

1911 CPC STARCH DRESSING
(Right) Paper box holds 25 blue tablets. OSP 25c - CMV $50 MB.

1915 CPC NAPTHA LAUNDRY CRYSTALS
(Left) White tablets, paper box. OSP 25c - CMV $50 MB.

1895 Dr. ZABRISKIES CUTANEOUS SOAP
One bar in box. OSP 25c, CMV $70 MB.

1915 DR. ZABRISKIES SOAP
Brown or green bar embossed, came in blue box. OSP 25c - CMV $60 MB.

1920 DR. ZABRISKIES CUTANEOUS SOAP
Green cake & box. OSP 24c, CMV $50 MB.

1931-33 DR. ZABRISKIES CUTANEOUS SOAP
(Right) Gray box holds 1 bar. OSP 31c, CMV $30 MB.

1933-36 DR. ZABRISKIES SOAP
Gray box holds 1 bar. CPC & Avon on box & soap. Two different labels on boxes. OSP 33c, CMV $30 MB.

1936-56 DR. ZABRISKIES CUTANEOUS SOAP
Green bar in turquoise box. OSP 33c, CMV $22.50 MB. Add $5 for CPC label on box.

1940-47 DR. ZABRISKIES CUTANEOUS SOAP
3 oz. green bar and box with Ichthynat. OSP 33c, CMV $22.50 MB.

1956-62 DR. ZABRISKIES SOAP
Turquoise box holds 1 green bar. OSP 43c, CMV $20 MB.

SEE 1984 SUPPLEMENT IN BACK OF BOOK FOR MORE MEN'S SOAP.

MEN'S SOAP

1908 CPC SHAVING SOAP
White bar embossed. Came in yellow box. OSP 20c, CMV $60 MB.

1930-36 SHAVING SOAP
White bar. OSP 25c, CMV $30 MB.
1930 STYPTIC PENCIL
OSP 10c, CMV $5 MB.

1936-49 SHAVING SOAP
Two bars in maroon box, white soap. OSP 31c, CMV $42.50 MB.

1963-64 MOST VALUABLE SOAP SET
Yellow box holds 3 yellow bars. OSP $1.35, CMV $25 MB.

1949-57 SHAVING SOAP
Two bars in green & red box. OSP 59c, CMV $32.50 MB.

1960-62 CARRIAGE SHOWER SOAP
Red, white & black box contains 6 oz. cake embossed Stage Coach soap on red or white rope. OSP $1.35, CMV $30.

1961-63 OATMEAL SOAP
Two brown bars, 2 different boxes. "A spicy fragrance." OSP $1.35, CMV $25. MB, deluxe box $30. MB.

1963-64 OATMEAL SOAP FOR MEN SPICY
Embossed stage coach on brown bar of soap. OSP 39c, CMV $10 in wrapping.

1966-67 LONESOME PINE SOAP
Green & gold box holds woodgrained soap cut in half. OSP $2, CMV $20 MB.

1966-67 BATH SOAP FOR MEN
Two white soaps with red buttons, silver & white box. OSP $2.50, CMV $22.50 MB.

1972-73 SHAMPOO SHOWER SOAP FOR MEN
5 oz. bar on red & black rope. Also came with white rope. Red & black box. OSP $2.50, CMV $7 MB.

1975 MODEL 'A' 1928 SOAP SET
Two 3 oz. white bars of soap with dark & light blue wrapper & box. OSP $3, CMV $4 MB.

1975 GOLF BALL SOAPS
Three white soaps in yellow & green box. Spicy scented. OSP $2, CMV $4 MB.

1978-79 BUFFALO NICKEL 1913 SOAP DISH & SOAP
5" nickel plated Buffalo Nickel metal soap dish & light gray or off white color soap. SSP $8, CMV $8 MB.

1978-79 BARBER SHOP DUET MUSTACHE COMB & SOAP SET
Box holds white bar man's face soap & small brown plastic mustache comb. SSP $3.99, CMV $3.99 MB set.

1977-84 ON DUTY 24 SOAP
Deodorant soap. OSP 3 for 99c, CMV 50c each. 3 different labels.

1978-79 ROYAL HEARTS SOAPS
(Left) King & queen box holds 2 white bars with king & queen of hearts soaps. SSP $4.99, CMV $4.49 MB.

1978-79 SUITABLY GIFTED SOAP
(Right) Blue box holds blue bar that is shaped like a shirt and tie. SSP $4.99, CMV $4.49 MB.

WOMEN'S SOAP
ALL SOAPS MUST BE MINT FOR CMV
SEE 1984 SUPPLEMENT IN BACK OF THIS BOOK FOR MORE WOMENS SOAP

1921-33 LEMONOL SOAP
Box of 12 cakes. OSP $1.50, CMV $100 MB.

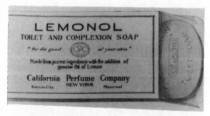

1923-31 LEMONOL TOILET SOAP
Box of 3 bars. OSP 45c - CMV $80 MB.

1936-41 LEMONOL TOILET SOAP
Three yellow bars in turquoise and white box and wrapping. OSP 51c, CMV $40 MB. Box of 12 bars OSP $1.79, CMV $60 MB. Add $3 per bar for CPC label mint.

1958-66 LEMONOL SOAP
Yellow and green lemon box holds 3 yellow bars with flat edges. Box comes lift off, (older) and flip up as shown. OSP $1.19, CMV $22.50 MB.

1931-36 LEMONOL TOILET SOAP
Yellow soap wrapped in blue and silver paper. Came in box of 3. OSP 50c, CMV $45 MB. Box of 12 bars $1.75, CMV $65 MB.

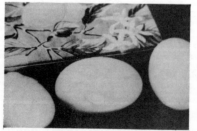

1941-58 LEMONOL SOAP
Yellow and green lemon box holds 3 yellow bars with round edges and flat on bottom. OSP $1, CMV $30 MB.

1966-67 LEMONOL SOAP
Blue and yellow box holds six 2½" yellow bars. OSP $2.25, CMV $22.50 MB.

1945-55 FACIAL SOAP
Box holds 2 bars. OSP 89c, CMV $25 MB.

1955-61 FACIAL SOAP
Turquoise box holds 2 bars. OSP 89c, CMV $20 MB.

1959-61 HOSTESS BOUQUET SOAP
Pink and yellow box holds 4 bars. OSP $1.39, CMV $22 MB.

1962-64 GIFT BOWS SOAP
Box holds 6 bow tie soaps. OSP $2.25, CMV $23 MB.

1963 SOAP TREASURE
Gold and white box holds 5 bars of perfumed soap in choice of Lilac, Lily of the Valley, Floral, Lemonol, Cotillion, Here's My Heart, Rose Geranium, To A Wild Rose, Royal Jasmine, Persian Wood, Somewhere, Royal Pine and Topaze set. Came with 2 different kinds of soap as shown. OSP $1.95, CMV $25 MB each set.

1964-65 HOSTESS SOAP SAMPLER
Floral box holds 12 cakes of soap. OSP $2.50, CMV $22.50 MB.

1965-66 LADY SLIPPERS SOAP
4 shoe soaps in box. OSP $2.25, CMV $23 MB.

1968 WHIPPED CREAM SOAP
Green, blue, pink and yellow soap. OSP $3, CMV $10 MB.

1967 BAY BERRY SOAP
Blue and gold box holds 3 wrapped bars in plastic holder. OSP $3, CMV $22 MB. Soap only $4 each.

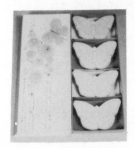

1966-67 BUTTERFLY SOAP
4 bars in box. OSP $2, CMV $22.50 MB.

1966-67 CHERUB SOAP SET
Blue box holds 2 pink angel soaps. OSP $2, CMV $22.50 MB.

1968-70 PARTRIDGE & PEAR SOAPS
Two green pears and white partridge. OSP $3, CMV $9 MB.

1969 FRUIT BOUQUET SOAP
Orange, lavender, and green soap. OSP $3, CMV $9 MB.

1969 DECORATOR SOAPS
Pink box holds 3 egg shaped soaps in green, pink and blue. OSP $3, CMV $10 MB.

1970-73 PINE CONE GIFT SOAPS
Box contains blue, yellow and green pine scented soaps. OSP $3, CMV $9 MB.

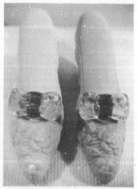

1970-71 SLIPPER SOAP & PERFUME
1/8 oz. bow tie perfume sits in light pink slipper soap in Cotillion, and dark pink soap in Charisma. OSP $5 each, CMV $9 MB. $6 soap and perfume only mint.

1970-73 SPRING TULIPS SOAP
Blue and pink box holds 6 green, white and pink soaps. OSP $3.50, CMV $9 MB.

1971-72 GRADE AVON HOSTESS SOAPS
Plastic carton holds 2 blue and 2 pink egg shaped soaps. OSP $4.50, CMV $8 MB.

1972-73 CUP CAKE SOAP
Green, pink and orange soap, 2 oz. each. SSP $2.50, CMV $7 MB.

1972-75 HIDDEN TREASURE SOAP
Two 3 oz. turquoise soaps with pearl colored and shaped 1/8 oz. bottle of perfume. Came in Bird of Paradise only. SSP $5, CMV $8 MB.

1972-73 LACERY HOSTESS BATH SOAP
Cream colored with foil center design. Box gold and pink. SSP $3, CMV $6 MB.

1972-73 HOSTESS BOUQUET GUEST SOAP
3 pink bars shaped like flower bouquet tied with green ribbon. Came in pink and blue bouquet box. OSP $3.50, CMV $7 MB.

1972-75 FRAGRANCE & FRILLS SOAP
4 lavender soaps in lavender plastic box. In center a 1/8 oz. bottle of Dazzling perfume in Field Flowers or Bird of Paradise. SSP $6, CMV $9 MB.

1973 MELON BALL GUEST SOAP
1 oz. honey-dew and cantaloupe colored balls inside cantaloupe shaped plastic container. SSP $4, CMV $6.50 MB.

1973 SOAP SAVERS
9 oz. total of 6 green soaps in spearmint fragrance. SSP $3, CMV $7 MB.

1975-76 PETIT FOURS GUEST SOAPS
Eight 1 oz. soaps, 3 pink hearts, 2 yellow squares, 3 rounds. OSP $4, CMV $5.50 MB.

1975 BAYBERRY WREATHS GIFT SOAPS
3 Bayberry scented soaps in Christmas box. OSP $3, CMV $5 MB.

1976 LITTLE CHOIR BOYS HOSTESS SOAPS
Box holds 3 pink soaps. Came in light or dark pink. SSP $2.88, CMV $4.

1973 SOAP FOR ALL SEASONS
1.5 oz. each, 4 soaps, yellow, green, blue and orange. SSP $3, CMV $7 MB.

1976 TIDINGS OF LOVE SOAPS
3 pink soaps in pink and white box. OSP $3, CMV $5.50 MB.

1974-75 PARTRIDGE 'N PEAR HOSTESS SOAP
3 yellow soaps in festive Christmas box. OSP $3, CMV $6 MB.

1974-75 RECIPE TREASURES
5 orange scented soaps in yellow and orange decorative metal file box. OSP $5, CMV $6 MB.

1974-75 COUNTRY KITCHEN SOAP DISH & SOAP
Red plastic scooped dish contains 5 green apple fragranced soaps. OSP $6, CMV $7 MB.

1975-76 ANGEL LACE SOAPS
3 blue soaps in blue and white box. OSP $3, CMV $5 MB.

1975 TOUCH OF LOVE SOAPS
3 white soaps in lavender box. Spring lavender fragrance. OSP $4, CMV $5 MB.

1974-76 GOLDEN BEAUTIES HOSTESS SOAP
2 oz. each, 3 cakes yellow soap. SSP $2, CMV $4.50 MB.

1976-1876 WINTERSCAPES HOSTESS SOAPS
Two Currier & Ives scenes soaps. Came in Special Occasion fragrance. OSP $5.50, CMV $6 MB.

1975-76 PICK-A-BERRY STRAWBERRY SOAPS & CONTAINER
4½" high red plastic with 6 strawberry scented soaps. OSP $6, CMV $7 MB.

1977 MERRY ELFKINS GUEST SOAPS
Box holds 3 green soaps. OSP $5.50, CMV $6 MB.

1976-77 BOUQUET OF PANSIES SOAP
Blue box holds 2 flower decorated special occasion white soaps. OSP $5.50, CMV $6.50 MB.

1977-78 TENDER BLOSSOMS GUEST TOWELS & SOAPS
Came with 12 paper hand towels and 3 special occasion fragranced soaps. OSP $6.50, CMV $7 MB.

1977-78 WINTER FROLICS HOSTESS SOAPS
Came with 2 Festive Fragrance scented soaps with long lasting decals. 3 oz. each. OSP $5.50, CMV $6 MB.

1977-78 SUMMER BUTTERFLIES HOSTESS SOAPS
Two scented soaps with long lasting decals. 3 oz. each. OSP $5.50, CMV $6 MB.

1978 ANGEL FISH HOSTESS SOAPS
Box holds 3 blue fish soaps. SSP $3.66, CMV $4 MB.

1978-79 TREASURE BASKET GUEST SOAPS
Silver basket holds 2 yellow and 2 pink tulip soaps. SSP $9, CMV $9 MB.

1978-80 BLUE TRANQUILITY REFRESHING SOAP
5 oz. blue embossed bar on white rope. Blue box. SSP $3, CMV $3 MB.
1978-80 BLUE TRANQUILITY RELAXING BUBBLE BATH
8 oz. blue plastic bottle. Came without a box. SSP $3, CMV 25c.

1978-80 COUNTRY GARDEN SOAPS
Box holds 2 Avon bar flower soaps with 2 different flower decals. SSP $4, CMV $4 MB.
1978-79 CHRISTMAS CAROLLERS SOAPS
Box holds 2 turquoise color carollers soaps. SSP $3, CMV $3.50 MB.

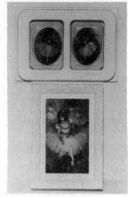

1978-80 BALLET PICTURE SOAPS
White plastic box and lid holds 2 blue picture decal bars of soap. SSP $6.99, CMV $6.99 MB.

1978 A TOKEN OF LOVE HOSTESS SOAPS
All three pieces are special occasion fragranced soaps. Light pink outside, dark pink inside soap. OSP $6, CMV $6 MB.

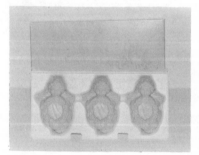

1980-81 LITTLE ANGELS HOSTESS SOAPS
Blue box holds 3 blue angel soaps. SSP $4, CMV $4 MB.

1981 TAPESTRY HOSTESS SOAPS
Box holds 2 decorator bars. SSP $4, CMV $4 MB.

1980-81 BUBBLY BEAR SOAP-IN-SOAP
Blue box holds small ribbon box of blue soap with small white bear soap inside. SSP $6, CMV $6 MB.
1980-81 CALIFORNIA PERFUME CO. 1980 ANNIVERSARY SOAPS
1980 CPC box holds two Violet bars. SSP $4, CMV $4 MB.

1960-63 CLEAR SKIN SOAP
Brown bar in gray and white box. OSP 49c - CMV $4.
1964-69 CLEAR SKIN SOAP
Brown bar in gray and white wrapper. OSP 59c - CMV $3.

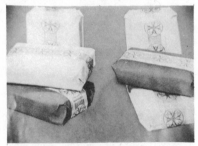

1961-64 PERFUMED SOAPS & PERFUMED DEODORANT SOAPS
1 bar each in Lemonol, Persian Wood, Somewhere, Facial, Floral, Royal Pink, Royal Jasmine, Here's My Heart, Cotillion, To A Wild Rose, Topaze, and Rose Geranium. OSP 39c, CMV $4 each mint.

1978-83 FEELIN' FRESH SOAP
Regular issue bar on left, CMV 50c. Introductory trial size bar on right, short issue. CMV $2.

1963-67 PERFUMED DEODORANT SOAP
OSP 39c - CMV $4 mint.

1966-70 COMPLEXION BAR
4 oz. bar. OSP $1.25 - CMV $4 MB.

1971-73 SCENTED SOAPS
3 oz. bars in matching soap and wrapping. Mint, Pine Tar, Almond, Camomile, Papaya, Avacado. OSP 75c - CMV $4 MB.

1977 PERFUMED SOAP HOLIDAY WRAPPING
Came in Charisma and Touch of Roses in red poinsetta wrap. Sonnet and Field Flowers in green, and Moonwind and Bird of Paradise in blue. SSP $1.25, CMV $1.50 each.

1979-80 PERFUMED SOAP CHRISTMAS WRAP
Single fragrance bar in red, Tempo or Ariane, bronze, Candid, blue, Emprise or Unspoken. SSP 99c, CMV $1 mint.

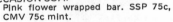

1981-83 CREAM SOAPS
1 pink and white wrapped bar. SSP 50c, CMV 50c.
1981 HEARTS & LACE SPECIAL OCCASION SOAP
Pink flower wrapped bar. SSP 75c, CMV 75c mint.

1982-83 FRESH AS NATURE SOAP
3 different bars in Aloe Vera, Wheat Germ and Glycerine, Witch Hazel and Lyme. SSP $2, CMV $1.50 each MB.

SOAP DISHES & SOAP

SEE PAGE 6 & 16 FOR GRADING
EXAMPLES ON MINT CONDITION

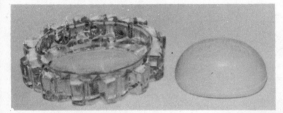

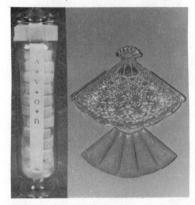

1981-82 ULTRA CRYSTAL SOAP DISH & SOAP
5" long clear glass soap dish and bar of cream color soap. SSP $10, CMV $10 MB.

1979-80 MOUNT VERNON PLATE & SOAPS
9" long blue glass plate. Has Mount Vernon, George and Martha Washington on front. Came with 2 white George and Martha bars of soap. SSP $11, CMV $11 MB.

1965-66 AVON SOAP JAR
Pink ribbon on clear glass jar and lid. Came with 12 cakes of soap. OSP $4.50, CMV $20 in box, jar only with ribbon and no soap $6. Jar and soap with ribbons mint $16.

1975-76 HOSTESS FANCY SOAP DISH & SOAP
8" wide clear glass with 5 pink soaps. OSP $6, CMV $7 MB.

1973-75 SITTIN' KITTENS SOAP DISH AND SOAPS
White milk glass dish with 3 kitten soaps in gold colored, yellow and orange. SSP $4, CMV $7.50 MB.

1979-80 FLOWER FROST COLLECTION CRESCENT PLATE & GUEST SOAPS
Frosted glass soap dish holds 3 yellow flower soap bars. SSP $13, CMV $12 MB.

1970-71 DOLPHIN SOAP DISH AND HOSTESS SOAPS
Silver and aqua plastic soap dish holds 4 blue soaps. OSP $8, CMV $11 MB.

1979-80 FLOWER FROST SHERBERT GLASS AND SOAPS
Frosted glass holds 6 yellow Avon balls of soap. SSP $10, CMV $9 MB.

1978-80 BIRD IN HAND SOAP DISH AND SOAPS
5½" long white glass hand soap dish with 3 small blue bird soaps. SSP $6, CMV $5 MB.

1979-80 BUTTERFLY FANTASY DISHES & SOAPS
Two 4" porcelain with butterfly design. 1 pink butterfly soap. SSP $10, CMV $10 MB.

1975-76 BICENTENNIAL PLATE & SOAP
Clear glass plate with blue soaps embossed with the face of George & Martha Washington on each. Some have Avon on bottom and some don't. OSP $7, CMV $8 MB.

1975-76 WINGS OF BEAUTY SOAP DISH & SOAP
White milk glass dish with 2 pink soaps. OSP $5, CMV $7 MB.

1974-76 NUTTY SOAP DISH & SOAPS
Plastic dish with 2 peanut scented soaps. OSP $4, CMV $6 MB.

1971-73 DECORATOR SOAP DISH & SOAPS

7" long frosted glass dish on gold stand. Came with 2 pink soaps. OSP $7, CMV $8 MB.

1972-73 GIFT OF THE SEA SOAP DISH & SOAPS

Iridescent white glass dish looks like a shell. 6 cakes, 1 oz. each, pink soap. 2 each of 3 different shells. SSP $5, CMV $8 MB.

1973-75 LOVE NEST SOAP DISH & SOAPS

White dish with green plastic lining, holds 2 aqua and 1 blue bird soap. OSP $4, CMV $6 MB.

1974-76 BEAUTY BUDS SOAP DISH & SOAP

6" long white milk glass with 4 yellow soaps. OSP $5, CMV $6 MB.

1975-76 HOSTESS BLOSSOMS FLOWER ARRANGER SOAP DISH & SOAP

4½" high white milk glass, plastic top and light green soap. OSP $6, CMV $6 MB.

1973-74 BUTTER DISH & HOSTESS SOAPS

Clear glass with 2 yellow 3 oz. butter pats. SSP $7, CMV $12 MB.

1976-78 NATURE BOUNTIFUL CERAMIC PLATE & SOAPS

Wedgewood ceramic plate made in England, edged in 22K gold. Two soaps decorated with pears decals, Avon stamped on plate. OSP $25, CMV $16 MB. Plate only $7.

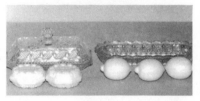

1975-76 CRYSTALUCENT COVERED BUTTER DISH & SOAP

7" long clear glass with 2 yellow soaps. OSP $10, CMV $12 MB.

1975-76 SUNNY LEMON SOAP DISH & SOAP

8½" long clear glass with 3 lemon scented yellow soaps. OSP $4, CMV $7 MB.

1974 LOVEBIRDS SOAP DISH & SOAPS

White milk glass dish with two 4 oz. pink soaps. SSP $6, CMV $8 MB.

1971-73 OWL SOAP DISH

5½" long white glass soap dish with 2 owl eyes in bottom of dish. Holds 2 yellow bars of owl soap. OSP $4.50, CMV $8 MB.

1972-74 FLOWER BASKET SOAP DISH & SOAPS

Clear glass dish with gold handle Came with 5 cakes of soap (2 yellow, 3 pink) 1 oz. each. Hostess Fragrance. SSP $5, CMV $8 MB. Also came with double stamp on bottom, add $4.

1973 NESTING HEN SOAP DISH & SOAP

White milk glass hen with beige painted nest. Holds 4 yellow egg soap, 2 oz. each. SSP $7, CMV $10 MB.

1969-70 TOUCH OF BEAUTY

White milk glass hands holds 4 small bars of pink soap. OSP $5, CMV $9 MB.

1970 HEAVENLY SOAP SET

White glass dish and 2 pink soaps. OSP $5, CMV $10 MB.

SOAPS WITH SPONGES
SEE 1984 SUPPLEMENT IN BACK OF BOOK FOR MORE SOAPS & SPONGES

1977-79 COUNTRY PEACHES SOAP JAR & SOAPS
Replica of a 19th century mason jar. Holds 6 yellow peach seed soaps. Blue glass jar with wire bail. Avon on Bottom. OSP $8.50, CMV $7 MB. Jar only $3.

1977 FOSTORIA EGG SOAP DISH & SOAP
Blue soap came in Spring Lilacs fragrance. Egg dish about 4½" long clear glass. Avon on bottom. OSP $15, CMV $10 MB. Egg dish only $5. 1st issue had "Mothers Day 1977" on bottom. CMV $12 MB.

1978 LOVE NEST SOAPS
Light green glass dish holds 3 yellow bird soaps in Special Occasion fragrance. SSP $5, CMV $5 MB.

1977 "HEART AND DIAMOND" SOAP DISH & SOAP
Fostoria clear glass soap dish. Came with red heart shaped Special Occasion fragranced soap. Avon on dish. OSP $9, CMV $8 MB.

1969-71 CHARLIE BROWN BATH MITT & SOAP
Red and white sponge with white bar of Snoopy embossed soap. OSP $3 - CMV $7 MB.

1965-66 BATH FLOWERS SOAP & SPONGE
Pink and white floral box contains 1 bar To A Wild Rose soap, pink, green and white sponge. OSP $2.50, CMV $12 MB.

1966-67 SPONGAROO SOAP & SPONGE
Brown kangaroo sponge is 15"x 5 3/4". White kangaroo soap. OSP $2.25, CMV $12 MB, soap only $7 mint.

1965-66 MINNIE THE MOO SOAP & SPONGE
White foam cow with yellow ears and black eyes. Soap is in green wrapper. OSP $1.75, CMV $6 soap and sponge only mint. $11 MB.

1969-70 POLLY PARROT PUPPET SPONGE & SOAP
Green and orange sponge with bar of soap. OSP $3 - CMV $9 MB. Soap and sponge only $4.

1968-69 CLARENCE THE SEA SERPENT
Orange and yellow sponge with bar of serpent soap in blue and yellow wrapper. OSP $2.25 - CMV $9 MB.

1966 LITTLE PRO SOAP
White baseball soap and brown sponge. OSP $2.25 - CMV $12 MB, $8 soap and sponge only.

1969 MONKEY SHINES
Brown and pink sponge and bar of soap. OSP $3, CMV $7 MB. Soap and sponge only $4.

1972 LITTLE LEAGUER SOAP AND SPONGE
Tan sponge mitt and white baseball soap. Sponge is different from Little Pro soap and sponge in 1966. CMV $10 MB, $6 soap and sponge only mint.

1967-68 NEST EGG SOAP & SPONGE
Box holds yellow nest sponge and pink soap. OSP $2.25, CMV $12 MB.

1979-80 BATH BLOSSOM SPONGE AND SOAP
(Left) Box holds yellow, green and blue sponge and yellow soap. SSP $6, CMV $6 MB.
1979-80 SWEET PICKLES WORRIED WALRUS SOAP AND SPONGE
(Center) Purple, green and brown sponge. Comes with wrapped bar of Sweet Pickles childrens bath soap. SSP $5, CMV $5 MB.
1979-80 FEARLESS FISH SPONGE AND SOAP
(Right) Green fish sponge and Sweet Pickles wrapped soap with fish on a scooter. SSP $4, CMV $4 MB.

1970-71 HUBIE THE HIPPO SOAP & SPONGE
Turquoise and red sponge with Hippo wrapped soap. OSP $4, CMV $8 MB.

1969 BATH BLOSSOMS
Pink and yellow sponge with pink soap. OSP $3.50, CMV $8 MB. $4 soap and sponge only.

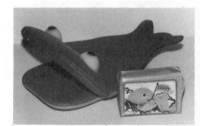

1973-74 SOAPY THE WHALE BATH MITT AND SOAP
8½" long blue and red sponge mitt with blue soap. SSP $3, CMV $5 MB.

1974 GOOD HABIT RABBIT BATH MITT & SOAP
White and pink foam mitt with yellow carrot soap. SSP $2.50, CMV $5 MB.

1977-80 PINK PANTHER SPONGE MITT AND SOAP
Pink mitt, yellow eyes. Blue green and pink wrapped soap. OSP $6, CMV $4.50 MB.

1978-79 YAKETY-YAK TAXI SOAP AND SPONGE
Box holds yellow taxi sponge and bar of wrapped Sweet Pickles soap. SSP $4, CMV $4 MB.

1973 CEDRIC SEA SERPENT SPONGE AND SOAP
(Left) 9½" long, green and pink sponge, white soap. OSP $2.50, CMV $6 MB.
1974-75 CEDRIC SEA SERPENT SPONGE AND SOAP
(Right) 9½" long, purple and pink sponge. OSP $3, CMV $5 MB.

1980 SPIDERMAN SPONGE & SOAP
Blue and red sponge. Red wrapped soap. SSP $4, CMV $4 MB.

1980-81 OSCAR OCTOPUS & SOAP
Yellow and orange with blue and green trim sponge. Green, red and purple rings, 1 bar of Oscar Octopus soap. SSP $6, CMV $6 MB.

CHILDREN'S SOAPS

SEE 1984 SUPPLEMENT IN BACK OF THIS BOOK FOR MORE SOAPS

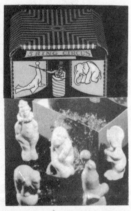

1958 FORWARD PASS
7½ oz. brown football soap on a white rope on side of soap. OSP $1., CMV $40 MB.

1939-41 CIRCUS SOAP SET
5 ring circus on box holds 5 figural soaps. This set is Avon's first figurals. Soaps are clown, elephant, monkey, seal & horse. OSP $1.19, CMV $300 MB. Very rare.

1959 POOL PADDLERS SOAP
Pond display box holds green frog, yellow fish & blue turtle soap. OSP $1.39 - CMV $40 MB.

1957-58 CIRCUS WAGON SOAP SET
Pink, yellow, black & white circus wagon box contains 1 blue elephant, 1 pink monkey, 1 yellow lion soaps. OSP $1.25, CMV $65. MB.

1958 "OLD 99" SOAP
Yellow train engine soap. OSP 69c, CMV $50 MB.

1957 FIRE ENGINE SOAP
Red box contains red fire truck soap. OSP 59c - CMV $50 MB.

1953-54 BO PEEP SOAP
Blue & green box holds 3 white sheep soaps. OSP $1 - CMV $65 MB.

1956 BEST FRIEND SOAP
Blue & white box holds blue dog soap. OSP 59c - CMV $50 MB.

1960 FRILLY DUCK SOAP
Box contains yellow & blue soap 5¾ oz. OSP 89c, CMV $20. MB.

1955 AWAY IN THE MANGER SOAP SET
Box holds 4 bars of pink, blue, white & yellow soap. 2 different scenes as shown. Remove panel on bottom picture to show inner panel as shown on top picture. OSP $1.49 - CMV $75 each set, MB.

1960-61 AVONLITE SOAP ON A ROPE
Green bowling ball shaped soap in green box. Brochure says "Bowl 'em Over", soap says "Avon Lite". OSP $1.19, CMV $35. MB - soap only $20. mint.

1955 KIDDIE KENNEL SOAP
Blue & yellow box holds blue, yellow & pink dog soaps. OSP $1.49, CMV $110 MB.

1956 SANTA'S HELPER SOAP
(Left) Box holds 3 green, yellow & red Santa & 2 helpers soaps. OSP $1.19 - CMV $100 MB.
1955 SANTA'S HELPER SOAP
(Right) Box holds green, red & yellow soap. Red Santa soap much larger than 1956 set. OSP $1.49, CMV $100 MB.

1956-57 CASEY JONES JR.
Red, white & blue box holds red engine soap, yellow passenger car & red caboose. OSP $1.19, CMV $55. MB.

1961-62 LI'L FOLKS TIME SOAP ON A ROPE
Red box holds yellow clock soap on a rope. OSP $1.19 - CMV $30 MB.

1954 THREE LITTLE BEARS SOAP SET
3 brown bear soaps. OSP $1.19, CMV $75 MB.

1959 HIGH SCORE
Green net box holds brown basketball soap on a rope. OSP $1.19, CMV $15 soap only mint - $30 MB.

1961-62 A HIT! SOAP ON A ROPE
Box holds white baseball soap on a rope. OSP $1.19, CMV $25. MB.

285

1962-63 SHERIFF'S BADGE SOAP
Box holds yellow soap on a rope with embossed sheriff's badge. OSP $1.19, CMV $30 MB.

1966-67 LITTLE SHAVER SOAP
(Left) Yellow shaver soap on a rope. OSP $1.35 - CMV $25 MB.
1958 TEXAS SHERIFF SOAP
(Right) Box holds 2 blue pistol soaps & silver sheriff's badge. Box comes with band around outside of box as shown at top. OSP $1.19, CMV $55. MB.

1964-65 PACKY THE ELEPHANT SOAP
Green box holds pink elephant with white hat. OSP 98c - CMV $30 MB.

1965 HANSEL & GRETEL SOAP
Blue & pink soap in box. OSP $1.35, CMV $25. MB.

1962-64 "WATCH THE BIRDIE" SOAP
White molded camera soap on a rope. OSP $1.19 - CMV $30 MB.

1963-64 LIFE PRESERVER SOAP
White life preserver soap on a rope. OSP $1.19, CMV $25. MB.

1962-63 LIL TOM TURTLE SOAP
Box holds green turtle soap with white hat. OSP 98c - CMV $25 MB.

1966 SPEEDY THE SNAIL
Green snail soap on a rope. OSP $1.35, CMV $20.

1966-67 GOLDILOCKS SOAP
5 oz. yellow soap. OSP $1., CMV $12. MB.

1965 GINGERBREAD SOAP TWINS
Pink, white & brown box holds 2 blue plastic gingerbread cookie cutters with 2 yellow bars of gingerbread soap. OSP $1.50, CMV $25.

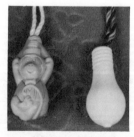

1965 MR. MONKEY SOAP ON A ROPE
(Left) Brown monkey soap. OSP $1.35, CMV $16. MB.
1967 LIGHT BULB SOAP ON A ROPE
(Right) Yellow soap on black, orange & yellow rope. OSP $1.50, CMV $15. MB.

1966 SUNNY THE SUNFISH SOAP
Yellow fish soap on a rope. OSP $1.19, CMV $17. MB.

1966-67 YO YO SOAP SET
Pink & red wood Yo Yo & pink soap. OSP $1.50, CMV $20. MB - Yo Yo only $6.

1969 TUB RACERS SOAP
Green box holds red, yellow & green racer soap. OSP $1.75, CMV $8. MB.

1964-66 SEA BISCUIT - THE SEA HORSE SOAP ON A ROPE
Box holds green soap on a rope. Sea Horse. OSP $1.25, CMV $18.50 MB.

1967 BUNNY'S DREAM SOAP ON A ROPE
Box holds orange carrot soap on a green rope. OSP $1.25, CMV $15 MB.

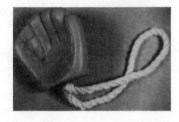

1969-72 MIGHTY MIT SOAP ON A ROPE
Brown soap. OSP $2., CMV $8. MB.

1968 EASTER QUACKER SOAP ON A ROPE
Yellow soap. OSP $1.35, CMV $11. MB.

1969-70 YANKEE DOODLE SHOWER SOAP
White drum shaped soap on a rope. OSP $2., CMV $9. MB.

1966-67 CHICK-A-DEE SOAP
Yellow soap on a rope. OSP $1.35, CMV $15 MB.

1968-69 RUFF, TUFF & MUFF SOAP SET
Blue, pink & yellow dog soaps. OSP $1.25, CMV $7. MB.

1969-70 MODELING SOAP
Pink 6 oz. soap in blue & pink box. OSP $2., CMV $7. MB.

288

1969-70 MITTENS KITTENS SOAP
Pink, green & yellow soap. Blue box. OSP $2 - CMV $10 MB.

1974-75 TUBBY TIGERS SOAP SET
3 orange soaps in orange & green box. OSP $2., CMV $4. MB.

1971 SCRUB TUG SOAP
(Left) 4" long plastic boat scrub brush holds 2 oz. yellow boat soap. OSP $2.50, CMV brush & soap $5. MB - brush only $1.

1973-75-79 PIG IN A TUB SOAP
(Right) 3" long yellow scrub brush holds 2 oz. pink pig soap. SSP $2.20, CMV $4. MB. Reissued 1979.

1977-79 M.C.P. SOAP
(Left) Tan color Male Chauvinist Pig soap. Came in Deep Woods scent. OSP $5., CMV $5. MB.

1977-79 BUTTON BUTTON GUEST SOAPS
(Right) Cardboard spool container holds 5 blue button shaped soaps. OSP $6., CMV $6. MB.

1974-75 FOOTBALL HELMET SOAP ON A ROPE
(Left) Yellow soap, white cord. OSP $2., CMV $4. MB.

1974-75 WILBUR THE WHALE SOAP ON A ROPE
(Right) 5 oz. blue soap with white rope. SSP $2., CMV $5. MB.

1973-74 SNOOPY'S PAL SOAP DISH & SOAPS
4½" diameter red plastic dish says "Snoopy" on front with yellow bird. Comes with two 2 oz. white bone shaped soaps. SSP $3., CMV $6. MB.

1970-71 FIRST DOWN SOAP
Box holds brown 5 oz. football soap on a rope. This soap is different from older one. Rope is on end of football. OSP $1.50 - CMV $10 MB.

1972-73 PERCY PELICAN SOAP ON A ROPE
(Left) 5 oz. yellow soap on white rope. SSP $1.50, CMV $5. MB.

1973-74 PETUNIA PIGLET SOAP ON A ROPE
(Right) 5 oz. pink soap on white rope. SSP $2., CMV $5. MB.

1973-75 HOOTY & TOOTY TUGBOAT SOAPS
2 oz. yellow & orange tugboat shaped soaps. SSP $2., CMV $4. MB.

1971 TWEETSTERS SOAPS
Yellow box holds 3 pink bird soaps. OSP $2., CMV $7. MB.

1970 PEEP A BOO SOAP ON A ROPE
(Left) Yellow chick soap on pink or white rope. OSP $1.35, CMV $8. MB.

1970 EASTER BONNET SOAP ON A ROPE
(Right) Yellow soap. OSP $1.35, CMV $8. MB.

289

1973-75 SURE WINNER SOAPS
(Left) 3 snowmobile soaps in blue, red & yellow. SSP $2., CMV $4. MB.

1972-73 SURE WINNER SHOWER SOAP
White with blue cord. SSP $2., CMV $6. MB.

1978-79 FURRY, PURRY, & SCURRY SOAPS
Red box with white dots holds 3 kitten shaped soaps in yellow, blue & green. SSP $3., CMV $3. MB.

1970-72 TREE TOTS SOAP
Red & green box holds 3 squirrel soaps. OSP $1.75, CMV $6. MB.

1972 BLUE MOO SOAP ON A ROPE
(Left) 5 oz. blue cow soap on a rope. OSP $1.75, CMV $5. MB.

1971-72 HONEY LAMB SOAP ON A ROPE
(Center) 5" high yellow soap on blue rope. OSP $1.19, CMV $5. MB.

1971-72 AL E. GATOR SOAP ON A ROPE
5" high green soap on white rope. OSP $2., CMV $5. MB.

1978-80 TUBBO THE HIPPO SOAP DISH & SOAP
(Left) Blue box holds light green plastic hippo soap dish & 3 oz. pink embossed wrapped bar of hippo soap. SSP $5., CMV $5. MB - soap dish only $1. - soap only wrapped $1.50.

1978-79 ALKA SELTZER SOAPS
Blue, white & red box holds 2 white embossed bars. SSP $4., CMV $4. MB.

1971 ARISTOCAT KITTENS SOAP
Box holds white, brown & blue kitten soaps. OSP $2., CMV $6.50 MB.

1974 HOOPER THE HOUND SOAP HOLDER & SOAP
White & black plastic head with pink, green & yellow hoops. Has yellow soap. SSP $4., CMV $5. MB.

1978-79 SAFE COMBINATION BANK & SOAPS
Black & gold tin bank comes with 2 yellow bars of soap embossed "Avon, 99.9 mint". Bottom of bank says "Made in England, exclusively for Avon". SSP $8., CMV $8. MB.

1970-72 TUB RACERS
Three speed boat soaps in red, blue & yellow. OSP $2., CMV $6. MB.

1972-73 HYDROJET SCRUB BRUSH & SOAP
Red plastic jet with yellow soap. SSP $2., CMV $4.50 MB.

1970-72 PEANUTS GANG SOAP
Red Lucy, yellow Charlie, white Snoopy soaps. OSP $2., CMV $7.50 MB.

1973-74 HAPPY HIPPOS NAIL BRUSH & SOAP
3" long pink nail brush with yellow soap. SSP $2., CMV $5. MB.

CHILDREN'S TOYS
All items are priced mint condition
See front of book for grading examples
SEE 1984 SUPPLEMENT IN BACK OF BOOK FOR
MORE TOYS

1980-81 SCRIBBLE DEE DOO PENCIL SOAPS
(Top) 3 pencil shaped yellow soaps. SSP $4.50, CMV $4.50 MB.

1980-81 ORCHARD FRESH GUEST SOAPS
(Bottom) Choice of orange, lemon or peach shaped soaps. 6 bars in each box. SSP $5., CMV $5. each kind.

1975 GOOD HABIT RABBIT SCRUB BRUSH & SOAP
(Left) Pink plastic with white bristles. OSP $2.50, CMV $3.50 MB.

1974-75 GAYLORD GATOR SCRUB BRUSH & SOAP
(Right) Green plastic with white bristles. OSP $2.50, CMV $3.50 MB.

1975-76 GRIDIRON SCRUB BRUSH & SOAP
Brown plastic with yellow soap. OSP $4., CMV $4. MB.

1974-75 SNOOPY'S SKI TEAM
7 oz. white plastic bottle, red skis, yellow "Woodstock". Holds bubble bath. OSP $5, CMV $5 MB.

1975-78 WOODSTOCK BRUSH & COMB
Yellow plastic brush, green comb. OSP $4, CMV $1 BO, $2 MB.

1969-72 SNOOPY MUG
5 oz. white glass, 5 inches high. Came 2 ways, red or blue top. Blue top is more rare. Also came with tall decal or round decal. OSP $3.50, CMV $7 red to MB, $9 blue top MB, $2 less no box.

1973-74 SNOOPY COME HOME SOAP DISH AND SOAP
6" long, brown raft with white sail, has 3 oz. brown soap. SSP $3, CMV $5 MB.

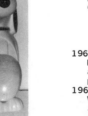

1968-72 CHARLIE BROWN
4 oz. red, white and black plastic bottle of Non Tear Shampoo. OSP $2.50, CMV $5 MB, $3 BO.

1970-72 LUCY
4 oz. red, white and black plastic bottle holds bubble bath. OSP $2.50, CMV $5 MB, $3 BO.

1966-67 PERRY THE PENGUIN
Black and white penguin soap dish and white plastic soap dish. OSP $6, penguin $4, vest soap $5, set $12 MB.

1968-76 SNOOPY SOAP DISH
White bar of Avon soap sets in black and white plastic soap dish. OSP $6., CMV $6 MB, Snoopy only $1.

1971-72 THREE MICE SOAPS
Box holds green, white & pink mice soaps. OSP $2., CMV $6. MB.

1969-72 SNOOPY & DOG HOUSE
8 oz. white plastic dog and red plastic 3" high dog house, holds Non Tear Shampoo. OSP $3, CMV $3, $5 MB.

1968-74 LINUS
Red, white and green plastic 4 oz. tube of Gel Bubble Bath with red, white and black plastic Linus, plastic holder. OSP $3.50, CMV $4 MB. $2 Linus & tube only.

1973-74 BO BO THE ELEPHANT
6 oz. pink plastic with squeeze head. Filled with baby shampoo. SSP $3, CMV $2 BO, $4 MB.

1973 SNOOPY'S SNOW FLYER
10 oz. red, white and black. Holds bubble bath. SSP $4, CMV $4 MB, $2 BO.

1971-72 SNOOPY'S BUBBLE TUB
5" long, 12 oz. blue and white plastic tub. bottle holds bubble bath. OSP $4, CMV $2 BO, $4 MB.

1971-72 PEANUTS PALS SHAMPOO
6 oz. plastic, white, red and black bottle with yellow cap. 6" high. OSP $3.50, CMV $4 MB, $2 BO.

1971-75 SNOOPY COMB & BRUSH SET
5½" long black and white brush and white comb. OSP $3.50, CMV $3.50 MB.

1972 CHARLIE BROWN COMB & BRUSH
4½" long, red, black and white with white comb. SSP $3, CMV $4 MB.

1973-74 GRID KID BRUSH & COMB
4½" long, red, black and white with white comb. SSP $3, CMV $3 MB.

1968 LITTLE RED RIDING HOOD
4 oz. yellow plastic bottle, red cap. Holds bubble bath. OSP $1.50, CMV $2 BO, $6 with glasses MB.

1968 WOLF
4 oz. yellow and blue plastic bottle, green cap, holds Non Tear Shampoo OSP $1.50, CMV $2 BO, $6 MB with white fang teeth.

1969-70 LUCY MUG
5 oz. white glass, yellow top and label. White cap, Non Tear Shampoo. OSP $3.50, CMV $8.

1969-70 CHARLIE BROWN MUG
5 oz. white glass, blue top and label. White cap, bubble bath. OSP $3.50, CMV $8.

1969 SNOOPY THE FLYING ACE
4 oz. 6" high white plastic with blue hat, yellow glasses, holds bubble bath. OSP $3, CMV $2, $5 MB.

1969-73 JUMPIN' JIMMINY
8 oz. 6" high, green, red and yellow pull toy with yellow cap. Holds bubble bath. OSP $3.50, CMV $3.50 MB, $2 BO.

1962-63 SIX SHOOTER
6 oz. gray plastic and white gun with No Tears Shampoo. OSP $1.98, CMV $18 BO mint, $24 MB.

1960-61 CLEAN AS A WHISTLE
8 oz. red & white plastic bottle, real whistle cap. Came in bubble bath. OSP $1.79, CMV $15. MB - $10. BO.

1965-66 MR. MANY MOODS
6 oz. white plastic bottle with blue and yellow hat, red nose and mouth, black eyes. Holds shampoo. OSP $1.98, CMV $8, $10 MB.

1968 MR. PRESTO CHANGO
6 oz. yellow plastic bottle with red hat, black eyes and pink lips. Holds No Tear Shampoo. OSP $2.25, CMV $5, $6 MB.

1964-65 BUBBLE BUNNY
Pink and white rabbit puppet with 6 oz. tube of bubble bath gel. OSP $1.98, CMV $5 puppet only, $11 MB.

1965 BUGLE
6 oz. blue plastic bugle with yellow cap. Holds Tot 'N Tyke Shampoo. OSP $1.79, CMV $10 BO, $15 MB.

1965 FIFE
6 oz. yellow plastic bottle with red cap. Came in hand lotion or hair trainer. OSP $1.49, CMV $10 BO, $15 MB.

1966-67 THREE BEARS
4¾" high each. 3 oz. each. White plastic bottles with blue caps. OSP $1.25 each. Papa Bear holds baby oil, CMV $10 BO, $14 MB. Mama Bear holds baby lotion, Baby Bear holds shampoo. CMV $8 BO, $12 MB each.

1967 GOOD HABIT RABBIT
3 oz, 4½" high. White plastic rabbit, green hat and orange carrot. Came in Tot 'N Tyke Shampoo. OSP $1.50, CMV $8, $11 MB.

1967-68 THREE LITTLE PIGS
3 oz. each, 4½" high. Blue pigs, yellow hat holds bubble bath, yellow pig, green hat holds baby shampoo, and pink pig with pink hat holds baby lotion. OSP $1.35, CMV $5 each, $8 MB.

1960-62 A WINNER
4 oz. maroon plastic boxing gloves with white caps. Tied together with white plastic cord. Hand Guard and Hair Guard. OSP $1.98, CMV $20 MB, $7 each bottle.

1967-68 LITTLE CHAMP
½ oz. each with white caps. Blue boxing glove holds Non Tear Shampoo, yellow glove holds Hair Trainer. OSP $2.50, CMV $17 set in box. Each glove $5.

1965-66 CUCKOO CLOCK
10 oz. red, white and blue plastic clock holds bubble bath. OSP $2.50, CMV $8, $9 MB.

1969-70 WRIST WASH BUBBLE BATH
2 oz. orange plastic clock with blue cap. OSP $3, CMV $6 MB, $3 BO.

1970-72 RING 'EM UP CLEAN
8 oz. orange plastic bottle with red or white cap holds Non Tear Shampoo. OSP $2.50, CMV $2.50, $4 MB.

1965 SAFE SAM
8 oz. red and black plastic safe holds bubble bath. OSP $1.98, CMV $8, $11 MB.

1966-67 WHISTLE TOTS
6¾" high, 4 oz. white plastic bottle with whistle cap. Red cap fireman holds Tot 'N Tyke Shampoo. Blue cap policeman holds Hair Trainer and green clown holds bubble bath. OSP $1.50 each, CMV $7 BO mint, $10 MB.

1966-67 SCHOOL DAYS
8 oz. red and white plastic ruler holds Non Tear Shampoo. Yellow cap. OSP $1.98, CMV $7, $10 MB.

1968-69 MILK BATH
6 oz. pink plastic milk can holds powdered bubble bath. OSP $4, CMV $2 BO, $3 MB.

1967 MR. LION
4 oz. white plastic bottle with red bubble pipe over white cap. Holds bubble bath. OSP $1.50, CMV $6 BO, $8 MB.

1967 TIN MAN
4 oz. white plastic bottle with blue bubble pipe over white cap. Holds Non Tear Shampoo. OSP $1.50, CMV $6 BO, $8 MB.

1967 STRAW MAN
4 oz. white plastic bottle with yellow bubble pipe over white cap. Holds hand lotion. OSP $1.50, CMV $6 BO, $8 MB.

1966-67 GLOBE BANK
10 oz. blue plastic globe holds bubble bath. Black base. Bank has 5 different colored sets of stick on countries. North America came in orange, blue, tan, pink or yellow. OSP $2.50, CMV $16 MB, $10 BO.

1970 MAD HATTER
6 oz. bronze plastic with pink hat and clock. Came in bubble bath. OSP $3, CMV $3 BO, $5 MB.

1970-72 CONCERTINA
8 oz. blue and yellow plastic squeeze bottle. Holds bubble bath. Musical cap with pink strap. OSP $2.50, CMV $6 MB, $4 BO.

1962-65 CONCERTINA
8 oz. red and yellow plastic squeeze bottle with musical cap. Holds bubble bath. OSP $1.98, CMV $12, $15 MB.

1969 BIRD HOUSE
7" high orange plastic bottom with tan roof. Holds 8 oz. of Powdered Bubble Bath. OSP $3.75, CMV $5 BO, $7 MB.

1968-69 SPACE ACE
4 oz. silver and yellow plastic rocket holds liquid hair trainer. OSP $1.50, CMV $3, $5 MB.

1970 BO BO THE ELEPHANT
5 oz. light or dark pink plastic bottle of Non Tear Shampoo. OSP $2.50, CMV $3 BO, $5 MB.

1972-73 RED STREAK BOAT
5 oz. red plastic boat, white cap. Holds bubble bath. OSP $2, CMV $5 MB, $3 BO.

1966-67 SPINNING TOP
4 oz. red and white top holds bubble bath, yellow top spinner. OSP $1.75, CMV $10 MB, $6 BO.

1961-62 LAND HO
(Left) 8 oz. blue & white plastic telescope holds Hair Trainer. OSP $1.49, CMV $17. MB - $12. BO mint.

1961-62 NAUGHTY-LESS
(Right) 8 oz. red & white submarine with white & blue cap. Holds bubble bath. OSP $1.79, CMV $15. BO mint - $20. MB.

1961-62 AVONVILLE SLUGGER
6 oz. tan plastic bat holds shampoo. OSP $1.49, CMV $12 BO, $17 MB.

1973 SURE WINNER SLUGGER DECANTER
6 oz. yellow plastic bat. Holds Sure Winner Bracing Lotion or Liquid Hair Trainer or Avon Spicy After Shave. SSP $2, CMV $3 mint, no box issued.

1966-67 LITTLE MISSY ROLLING PIN
12" long, 8 oz. pink plastic center with orange ends. Holds Non Tear Shampoo. OSP $2.25, CMV $9. BO mint - $13. MB.

1963-64 FIRST MATE SHAMPOO
8 oz. blue and white plastic sailor with white hat. OSP $1.98, CMV $15 in box, $11 BO.

1963-64 CAPTAIN'S BUBBLE BATH
8 oz. white, yellow and black plastic bottle with blue hat. OSP $1.98, CMV $15 MB, $11 BO.

1967-68 BIRD FEEDER
11" high, black and white plastic center with red base and yellow top. Holds 7½ oz. powdered bubble bath. OSP $3.50, CMV $7 bottle only, $9 MB.

1965 Only — TOPSY TURVEY CLOWN
10 oz. red, white and yellow plastic clown. Blue hat, black feet. Holds bubble bath. OSP $2.50, CMV $16 MB, $12 BO mint.

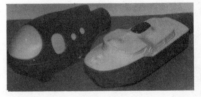

1964-65 AQUA CAR
(Left) 8 oz. red & white plastic bottle of bubble bath. OSP $1.98, CMV $10. - $15. MB.

1970-71 S.S. SUDS
(Right) 8 oz. blue & white plastic boat holds No Tear Shampoo. OSP $3., CMV $4. - $6. MB.

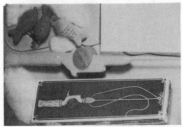

1968-69 ONE TWO LACE MY SHOE
8 oz. bubble bath. Pink plastic shoe with orange tie on and yellow cap. Green or yellow roof. OSP $2.98, CMV $5 BO, $8 MB.

1968-69 TIC TOC TURTLE
8 oz., 5½" high. Green turtle, yellow clock face with pink hands. Bubble bath. OSP $2.50, CMV $5 BO, $8 MB.

1967-68 SANTA'S HELPER
Red and white sponge with 6 oz. tube of Gel Bubble Bath. OSP $2.50, CMV $8 MB.

1968-69 TUB CATCH
2 ft. long yellow rod & reel holds 6 oz. of bubble bath. Pink, green & blue plastic fish. OSP $3.50, CMV $9. MB.

1967-68 SMILEY THE WHALE
(Left) 9" blue plastic whale holds 9 oz. bubble bath. OSP $1.98, CMV $5. BO - $8. MB.

1959-62 WHITEY THE WHALE
(Right) 8 oz. white plastic whale holds bubble bath. OSP $1.79, CMV $15. MB - $10 BO.

1961-64 LIL FOLKS TIME
(Left) 8 oz. yellow & white plastic clock with yellow cap & red time hands, holds bubble bath. OSP $1.79, CMV $10. MB - $6. BO.

1967-69 TIC TOC TIGER
(Right) 8 oz. orange & white plastic clock with yellow cap & hands, holds bubble bath. OSP $1.75, CMV $4. BO - $6. MB.

1969-70 CHIEF SCRUBBEM
(Left) 4 oz. red & yellow plastic Indian holds liquid soap. OSP $2.50, CMV $4. MB - $3. BO.

1968-69 SCRUB MUG
(Right) 6 oz. blue plastic mug with blue brush lid. Holds liquid soap. OSP $2.50, CMV $5. MB - $3. BO.

1964-65 SANTA'S CHIMNEY
Red & white box holds 5 oz. of powdered bubble bath. Top of box makes a puzzle game. OSP $1.98, CMV $20. MB.

1968-69 MARY NON TEAR SHAMPOO
(Left) 3 oz. pink plastic bottle. OSP $1.35, CMV $5. BO - $7. MB.

1968-69 LITTLE LAMB BABY LOTION
(Center) 3 oz. white plastic lamb with blue cap. OSP $1.35, CMV $5. BO - $7. MB.

1968-69 LITTLE RED SCHOOLHOUSE
(Right) 3 oz. red plastic school with yellow cap. Contains bubble bath. OSP $1.35, CMV $5. BO - $7. MB.

1967-68 TOOFIE TOOTHPASTE
3½ oz. white tube with racoon & pink cap & toothbrush, pink & white box. OSP $1.25, CMV $6. MB - $2. tube only.

1968-69 EASTER DEC A DOO
(Left) 8 oz. pink & yellow plastic egg holds bubble bath. Came with stick on decorations. OSP $2.50, CMV $5. MB - $3. BO.

1963-65 HUMPTY DUMPTY
(Right) 8 oz. plastic bottle of bubble bath. Blue bottom, white top, black belt. OSP $1.98, CMV $8. MB - $5. BO.

1963-64 TOOFIE TWOSOME
This is the 1st issue of the Toofie series. 3½ oz. green & blue tube & green cap. Choice of red, yellow, blue or green toothbrush. OSP $1.25, CMV $8. MB - tube only $3.

1964-65 PACKY THE ELEPHANT
3 oz. each. OSP $1.10 each. Each has white hat. Blue holds baby oil, yellow holds baby shampoo, baby lotion in red. CMV red & blue $10. BO each - $15. MB; yellow $15. BO - $20. MB.

1962-64 LITTLE HELPER IRON
(Left) 8 oz. blue plastic iron with white handle. Holds bubble bath. OSP $2., CMV $13. mint - $17. MB.

1962-64 WATERING CAN
(Right) 8 oz. yellow plastic bottle holds bubble bath. Blue cap. OSP $2., CMV $13. mint - $17. MB.

1961-63 LIL TOM TURTLES
3 oz. plastic turtles. OSP $1.10 each. Each has white hat. Yellow holds baby shampoo, blue has baby oil & baby lotion in red. CMV $10. each - $15. MB.

1966-67 PADDLE 'N' BALL SET
6 oz. tan plastic paddle with red cap. Holds shampoo. Rubber ball hooked to paddle. 8" long by 4½" wide. OSP $1.75, CMV $12. - $15. MB.

1969-70 TOOFIE TOOTHPASTE
3½ oz. blue & green tube with pink cap & toothbrush in blue & green box. OSP $1.35, CMV $5. MB - $2. tube only.

1965 Only JET PLANE
3 oz. red, white & blue plastic tube with white plastic wings came in gel bubble bath, children's gel shampoo or Hair Trainer. OSP $1.50, CMV $10. mint - $15. MB.

1969 TUB TALK TELEPHONE
(Blue) 6 oz. blue plastic telephone with yellow cap & holder. Holds No Tear Shampoo. OSP $2.25, CMV $5. - $7. MB.

1964-65 VERY OWN TELEPHONE
(Red) 6 oz. red plastic telephone & base. Holds Baby Shampoo. OSP $1.98, CMV $9. BO - $13. MB.

1967-68 TUB TALK TELEPHONE
(Yellow) 6 oz. yellow telephone with red cap & holder. Holds Tot 'N' Tyke shampoo. OSP $1.75, CMV $7. BO - $10. MB.

1960-62 FRILLY DUCK
(Left) 3 oz. yellow plastic duck with blue cap. Came in baby oil, baby lotion & Tot 'N' Tyke shampoo. OSP 98¢, CMV $9. - $13. MB.

1960-62 PIG IN A POKE
(Right) 8 oz. pink plastic pig holds bubble bath. Came in pink bag. OSP $1.79, CMV $9. BO - $14. BO with bag - $18. MB.

1969-71 MICKEY MOUSE
(Left) 4½ oz. red pants, black & white plastic Mickey with yellow feet. Holds bubble bath. OSP $3.50, CMV $4. BO. - $6. MB.

1970-71 PLUTO
(Right) 4 oz. yellow & black plastic dog with red collar. Holds Non Tear shampoo. OSP $3.50, CMV $4. BO - $6. MB.

1964 TOY SOLDIERS
4 oz. each. Red, white & blue plastic bottles, black caps. Came in Hair Trainer, shampoo, hand lotion, bubble bath. OSP $1.25 each, CMV $10. each BO - $12. MB.

1970-72 TOPSY TURVEY
(Left) 4 oz. green plastic bottle with white cap holds bubble bath. OSP $2., CMV $3. MB - $1. BO.

1972-73 BALL & CUP
(Right) 4 oz. blue bottom with green cup & ball. Holds shampoo. OSP $2., CMV $4. MB - $2. BO.

297

1973 BARNEY BEAVER TOOTHBRUSHES & HOLDER
(Left) 4" high, brown plastic with white & blue. Has pink & blue toothbrushes. Comes with a sticker to put on wall. SSP $2.50, CMV $4. MB.

1973 'I LOVE TOOFIE' TOOTHBRUSHES & HOLDER
(Right) 5" high, white & pink, holds red & blue toothbrushes. Comes with sticker to put on wall. SSP $2., CMV $4. MB.

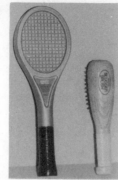

1975-76 TENNIS ANYONE?
(Left) 5 oz. gray & black plastic. Holds Sweet Honesty after bath freshener or Avon Spicy after shave. OSP $3., CMV $2.50.

1974-75 SLUGGER BRUSH
(Right) 7" long brown & black plastic. OSP $3.50, CMV $2.

1978-79 ON THE RUN "JOGGING SHOE"
(Left) 6 oz. blue plastic with white stripes. Holds Wild Country after shave or Sweet Honesty body splash. SSP $4., CMV $3. MB.

1978-79 CONAIR "HAIR DRYER"
(Right) 6 oz. off-white plastic. Blue letters and cap. Holds Naturally Gentle shampoo. SSP $5., CMV $3.50 MB.

1973-74 BABY SHOE PIN CUSHION
(Left) 7 oz. white plastic with pink pin cushion & blue bow. Filled with baby lotion. SSP $4., CMV $4. BO - $5. MB.

1973-76 SUNNY BUNNY BABY POMANDER
(Center) Wax figurine with nursery fresh fragrance. SSP $5., CMV $5. BO - $6. MB.

1973-74 SAFETY PIN DECANTER
(Right) 8 oz. yellow plastic filled with baby lotion. SSP $3., CMV $3. BO - $4. MB.

1979 TOOTHBRUSH DUO (CHILDREN'S)
(Left) Red & pink box holds 1 red & 1 white toothbrush for kids. SSP 89c, CMV 50c MB.

1979 PINK PANTHER TOOTHBRUSH HOLDER
(Right) Pink plastic holder. Yellow & red toothbrushes. Blue & pink box. SSP $5., CMV $3. MB.

1978-79 ACCUSING ALLIGATOR
(Left) 6 oz. green, yellow & tan plastic. Holds bubble bath. SSP $5., CMV $3.50 MB.

1978-79 SUPERMAN BUBBLE BATH
(Right) 8 oz. blue, red & gray plastic. Holds bubble bath. Box came with 2 red and yellow plastic cut out capes. SSP $6., CMV $4. MB.

1979-80 BUNNY FLUFFPUFF
(Left) 3.5 oz. yellow plastic with yellow fluff tail & pink eyes & ears. Holds children's talc. SSP $6., CMV $3.50 MB.

1979-80 RED STREAK CAR
(Right) 7 oz. red plastic with blue & silver stick on decals. Holds bubble bath for children. SSP $4., CMV $2. MB.

1966-67 TOOFIE THE TIGER
(Left) 3½ oz. green & orange tube, green cap, toothbrush. OSP $1.35, CMV $6. MB - $3. tube only mint.

1968-69 TOOFIE ON GUARD
(Right) 3½ oz. red, white & blue tube, blue cap. Avon toothbrush. OSP $1.25, CMV tube only $2. mint - $5. MB.

1978-79 BATMOBILE
(Left) 6 oz. blue & silver plastic with stick on decals. Came in bubble bath for children. SSP $5., CMV $3. MB.

1978-79 LIP POP POMADE "PEPSI"
(Right) Dark amber plastic. Gray cap. Looks like Pepsi Cola bottle. SSP $3., CMV $2. MB.

1978-79 SWEET PICKLES FUN BOOK & RECORD
Book & record issued by Avon Products. Came in an envelope. There are 4 different ones. SSP $2., CMV $3. complete mint.

1979-80 SPACE PATROLLER DECANTER
(Left) 8 oz. gray plastic, black cap & stick on decals. SSP $5., CMV $3.

1979-80 SPIDERMAN TOOTHBRUSH & HOLDER
(Right) Red & blue plastic. Yellow & green Avon toothbrushes. SSP $5., CMV $2.50 MB.

1976-77 SPOTTY TO THE RESCUE TOOTHBRUSH HOLDER
Red, white & black plastic toothbrush holder holds 2 Avon toothbrushes. SSP $2.49, CMV $2. MB.

1974-75 GRID KID LIQUID HAIR TRAINER
(Left) 8 oz. red, black & white plastic. OSP $2., CMV $1. BO - $2. MB.

1975-76 ARCH E. BEAR BRUSH & COMB
(Right) Red, white & blue brush with white comb. OSP $3., CMV $1. - $2. MB.

1975-76 HOT DOG! BRUSH & COMB
(Left) Yellow & red plastic comb. OSP $3., CMV $1. - $2. MB.

1974-76 SUNANA BRONZE GLORY TANNING LOTION
(Right) 6 oz. yellow plastic banana. OSP $2.75, CMV $2. BO, no box issued.

1978-79 HANG TEN SKATEBOARD DECANTER
(Left) 5.5 oz. yellow plastic with top stick on decal. Holds bubble bath for children. SSP $5., CMV $2.50 MB.

1978-79 - 14 KARROT TAN DECANTER
(Center) 4 oz. orange plastic with green leaf top. Holds Bronze Glory tanning lotion. SSP $5., CMV $2.50 BO, no box issued.

1978-79 HEAVY HITTER DECANTER
(Right) 4 oz. dark blue plastic. White letters. Holds non tear shampoo. SSP $5., CMV $2.50 MB.

1974-76 JACKKNIFE COMB & BRUSH
(Left) Blue & silver plastic comb. Cub Scout gold label on top. OSP $5., CMV $3. MB.

1977-78 ICE CREAM COMB
(Center) Orange plastic comb with pink & brown ice cream & red cherry on top. OSP $3., CMV $2. MB.

1977 REGGIE RACCOON HAIRBRUSH & COMB
(Right) 6¼" long. Brown, white, pink & black brush & white comb. SSP $4., CMV $2. MB.

1977-78 WALLY WALRUS TOOTHBRUSH HOLDER & TOOTHBRUSH
Adhesive back holder sticks to wall. Came with 2 child sized Avon toothbrushes in red & white. Plastic holder is blue & red with white hat & trim. SSP $2., CMV $2. MB.

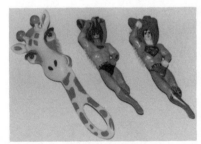

1977-79 GIRAFFABATH BATH BRUSH
(Left) Orange & beige plastic. Blue eyes. OSP $6., CMV $3.50 MB.

1977-78 BATMAN STYLING BRUSH
(Center) Blue, grey & black plastic brush. OSP $6., CMV $4. MB.

1977 SUPERMAN STYLING BRUSH
(Right) Red & blue plastic brush. OSP $6., CMV $4 MB.

1974-75 TED E. BEAR TOOTHBRUSH HOLDER
Box holds tan, pink & white plastic holder & pink & white Avon toothbrushes. OSP $2.75, CMV $3. MB.

1971-73 TOOFIE TOOTHPASTE
(Left) 3½ oz. yellow & orange tube & box. OSP 89c, CMV $1. - $2. MB.

1973-74 TOOFIE TOOTHBRUSH DUO
(Right) Pak of 2, green worm & yellow bird. SSP $2., CMV $2. MB.

1979-80 MOST VALUABLE GORILLA
(Left) 4 oz. orange & blue plastic stick on front & back decals in any letter. Holds bubble bath for children. SSP $6., CMV $3.50 MB.

1979-80 WILLIE WEATHERMAN
(Center) 6 oz. tan plastic, pink cap. Blue umbrella changes color with the weather. Holds Non Tear shampoo. SSP $5., CMV $3. MB.

1980 IMP THE CHIMP BATH BRUSH
(Right) Brown plastic, yellow, black & pink trim. 10" long. SSP $7., CMV $4. MB.

1975 SCRUBBO THE ELEPHANT BATH BRUSH
White plastic, pink ears & cheeks. SSP $2.99, CMV $2. MB. 1976 issue was all pink plastic. Each is 8" long. SSP $2.99, CMV $2. MB.

1979-80 ELLA ELEPHANT SCENTED STUFFED ANIMAL
Pink box holds pink scented elephant with turqoise ears & pink ribbon. Has Avon tag. Made in Taiwan. SSP $8., CMV $6. MB.

1975-76 BRONTOSAURUS BUBBLE BATH
(Left) 10 oz. blue gray plastic. OSP $3.50, CMV $2. BO - $3. MB.

1974-76 LOVABLE LEO
(Right) 10 oz. yellow plastic, pink cap. Children's shampoo. OSP $3., CMV $2. BO - $3. MB.

1976-79 SCHOOL DAYS RULER COMB
Box holds yellow plastic 6" ruler comb. OSP $3., CMV $2. MB.

1978-79 LOVING LION DECANTER
(Left) 8 oz. plastic purple, yellow, pink & orange. Holds Non Tear shampoo. SSP $5., CMV $3.50 MB.

1978-79 THREE RING CIRCUS CHILDREN'S TALC
(Center) 5 oz., 2 sections of center turn around. SSP $2.49, CMV $2. MB.

1978-79 OCTOPUS TOOTHBRUSH HOLDER
(Right) Purple & orange plastic toothbrush holder. Comes with orange & white Avon toothbrushes. SSP $4., CMV $2.50 MB.

1975-76 PRECIOUS LAMB BABY LOTION
6 oz. white plastic lamb with blue bow. Holds baby lotion. SSP $3., CMV $3. MB.

1978 TOOFIE THE CLOWN
Orange, yellow & white plastic toothbrush holder. Blue & pink toothbrushes. SSP $3., CMV $2. MB.

1976 TOOFIE TIGER TOOTHBRUSHES & HOLDER
(Left) Yellow, black, white & pink. Has 1 pink & 1 white toothbrush. OSP $2.50, CMV $2. MB.

1971-73 TOOFIE TOOTHBRUSH DUO
(Center) One yellow giraffe, 1 pink rabbit brush. OSP $1., CMV $2. MB.

1975-76 TORTOISE 'N' HARE TOOTHBRUSH DUO
(Right) Green tortoise & yellow hare. OSP $1.80, CMV $1. MB.

1974-75 SURE WINNER CATCHER'S MITT
(Left) 6 oz. brown plastic with brown cap. Holds Avon liquid hair trainer. OSP $2., CMV $2.

1975-76 WINKIE BLINK CLOCK BUBBLE BATH
(Right) 8 oz. yellow with blue clock hands & blue cap. OSP $4., CMV $2. BO - $3.50 MB.

1977-79 KISS 'N' MAKEUP LIP GLOSS COMPACT
(Top) Came with Frostlight Peach & Frostlight Pink lip gloss. Red plastic container. OSP $4., CMV $1.

1972 LOVE LOCKET GLACE
(Bottom) CMV $6. MB - $4. CO.

1972-74 TURN A WORD BUBBLE BATH
8 oz. pink plastic bottle with white cap & green lettered sides. OSP $3.50, CMV $2.

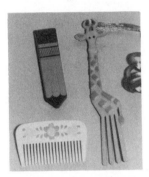

1973-75 SCHOOL DAYS BARRETTE
(Top Left) Brown & yellow pencil barrette. SSP $1.50, CMV $1.50 MB.

1973 COMB BARRETTE
(Bottom Left) 2" long, white plastic with red, pink & green design. SSP $1.50, CMV $2. MB.

1973 JENNY GIRAFFE
(Right) Yellow & brown with coral cord. SSP $1.50, CMV $2.50 MB.

1976 JACK IN A BOX GLACE
(Left) White plastic with pink & green trim. SSP $2., CMV $3.50 MB.

1977 CHICK A PEEK GLACE
(Right) Yellow plastic back & chick with purple plastic egg. SSP $2., CMV $3.50 MB.

1974-75 TOOFIE TRAIN
Red plastic train, yellow plastic cup. Red & blue toofie toothbrushes & yellow with red cap Toofie toothpaste. OSP $5., CMV $5. - $7. MB.

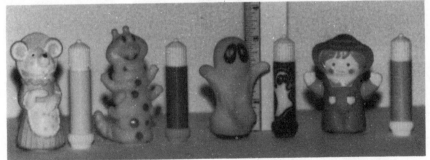

1977-78 MILLICENT MOUSE DEMI STICK
(Left) Came with Pink & Pretty fragrance demi stick. Colors are pink & white. OSP $3.75, CMV $3.50 MB.

1977-79 GLOW WORM
(Inside Left) Came with Care Deeply lip balm. White rubber top with purple spots. Demi stick is blue & green. OSP $3.50, CMV $3.50 MB.

1977-78 GILROY THE GHOST
(Inside Right) Came with Care Deeply lip balm. White & black rubber top with black, green & white demi stick. OSP $3.50, CMV $3.50 MB.

1977-78 HUCK L. BERRY
(Right) Came with Care Deeply lip balm. Blue, yellow & white rubber top with yellow & white demi stick. OSP $3.75, CMV $3.50 MB.

1974-75 RAPID RABBIT PIN PAL
(Left) White plastic with pink & green. Feet swing. Filled with perfumed glace. SSP $2., CMV $2. - $3. MB.

1974 MYRTLE TURTLE PIN PAL
(Right) Green plastic with pink & green. Filled with perfumed glace. SSP $2., CMV $2. - $3. MB.

CHILDREN'S FUN JEWELRY

1973 LUV-A-DUCKY
(Top Left) Yellow & orange. SSP $2., CMV $3.50 - $5. MB.

1973 PANDY BEAR PIN
(Bottom Left) Black & white. SSP $1.50, CMV $3.50 - $5. MB.

1973 FLY-A-KITE
(Center) Red, white & blue. SSP $2., CMV $3.50 - $5. MB.

1973-74 FUZZY BUG
(Top Right) Blue with green fur. SSP $2., CMV $3.50 - $5. MB.

1973 PERKEY PARROT
(Bottom Right) Red & green. SSP $1.50, CMV $3.50 - $5. MB.

1971 LOONEY LATHER BUBBLE BATH
(Left) 6 oz. spray can, pink cap. OSP $2., CMV $4.

1971 LOONEY LATHER SHAMPOO
(Right) 6 oz. size, green cap. OSP $2., CMV $4.

1973-75 ROTO-BOAT FLOATING SOAP DISH & SOAP
9" long blue & white boat with red rudder holds 3 oz. blue soap. SSP $3., CMV $4. Reissued with "R" on bottom.

1975-76 BOBBIN' ROBIN PIN
(Top Left) White cage, red bird (bird movable). OSP $2., CMV $3. MB.

1974-75 MINUTE MOUSE PIN
(Bottom Left) White with blue clock, orange hands & numbers. OSP $2., CMV $3. MB.

1975-76 PEDAL PUSHER PIN
(Top Center) Blue elephant with green jacket & pink bike. OSP $1.89, CMV $3. MB.

1974-76 LICKETY STICK MOUSE PIN
(Bottom Center) White plastic with green hat & pink striped stick. OSP $2., CMV $3. MB.

1975-76 MAGIC RABBIT PIN
(Top Right) White & pink rabbit with grey hat. OSP $2., CMV $3. MB.

1976-78 COTTON TAIL GLACE
(Bottom Right) Yellow & pink with white tail. OSP $2., CMV $3. MB.

1973-74 BUMBLEY BEE PINS
Yellow with black stripes. One with big stripes & 1 with narrow stripes. OSP $2., CMV $4. - $6 MB.

1975-76 GREAT CATCH, CHARLIE BROWN, SOAP HOLDER & SOAP
(Left) Red, white, black & brown plastic. OSP $4., CMV $5. MB.

1974-75 QUACK & DOODLE FLOATING SOAPDISH & SOAP
(Right) Yellow rubber with yellow soap. OSP $3.50, CMV $4. MB.

1966-67 RING AROUND ROSIE
Pink rubber elephant sticks on wall with blue bar of Avon soap. OSP $2.25, CMV $15. MB - soap only $6. - elephant only $4.

1970-72 CLEAN SHOT
Orange net holds orange basketball sponge & 1 bar of clean shot soap. OSP $4.50, CMV $6. MB set.

CHILDREN'S PERFUME GLACE PIN PALS
Add $1. each MB.

1973-74 FUNNY BUNNY
(Top Left) Pink & white. SSP $2., CMV $4.

1973 CALICO CAT
(Top Center) Red with white dots. Also came red & no dots. SSP $2., CMV $4.

1974-75 CALICO CAT
(Repeat Top Center) Blue with white dots. Also came blue with no dots on bottom half. OSP $2., CMV $3. each.

1972 BLOUSE MOUSE
(Top Right) Green & pink. Also came green with white trim. SSP $2., CMV $4.

1974 BLUE MOO
(Middle Left) Blue & pink. SSP $2., CMV $3.

1972-75 SNIFFY PIN PAL
(Middle Center) Black, pink & white. SSP $2., CMV $3.

1973 ELPHIE THE ELEPHANT
(Middle Right) Yellow & pink. SSP $2., CMV $4.

1973 GINGERBREAD PIN PAL
(Bottom Center) Brown & pink. Also came brown & white. SSP $2., CMV $5. pink - $6. white.

1975 PUPPY LOVE PIN PAL GLACE
(Top Left) Beige dog with black ears & pink pillow. OSP $2., CMV $4. MB.

1974-75 WEE WILLY WINTER PIN PAL GLACE
(Top Center) White snowman with pink hat, scarf & mittens. OSP $1.88, CMV $4. MB.

1974-75 SUNNY FRESH ORANGE GLACE NECKLACE
(Top Right) Orange & yellow with green cord. OSP $3., CMV $4. MB.

1975-76 PETER PATCHES PIN PAL GLACE
(Bottom Left) Yellow with red & blue trim. OSP $2., CMV $4. MB.

1975 CHICKEN LITTLE PIN PAL GLACE
(Bottom Inside Left) Yellow chicken with pink flower & green leaf. OSP $2.49, CMV $4.

1974-75 WILLIE THE WORM PIN PAL GLACE
(Bottom Inside Right) Red apple, green worm. OSP $2., CMV $4. MB.

1975-77 ROCK-A-ROO PIN PAL GLACE
(Bottom Right) Pink with dark pink rocking pouch. OSP $2., CMV $3. MB.

1973 REGGIE RACOON HAIR BRUSH AND COMB
6½" long, tan and black with tan comb. SSP $3., CMV $4. MB.

1966-67 WASH AWEIGH SOAP & DISH
Green plastic boat dish & yellow anchor soap on a rope. OSP $1.98, CMV boat $6. - anchor soap $9. - set $18. MB.

1973-74 CLANCY THE CLOWN SOAP HOLDER & SOAP
Orange, pink and white clown holds green and white, pink and orange 3 oz. soap. SSP $3.50, CMV $5. MB.

1969-70 FREDDIE THE FROG
(Left) Green rubber frog soap dish & green vest soap. Pink lips & pink band around hat. OSP $1.75, CMV frog only $2. - with soap $6. MB.

1965-66 FREDDIE THE FROG
(Right) Green rubber frog with yellow hat & eyes, pink lips, green soap. OSP $3., CMV frog only $5 - with soap $10. MB.

1970-71 REGINALD G. RACOON III
Black, brown and white rubber soap dish and 3 oz. pink vest soap. OSP $3.50, CMV racoon only $2., $6. set MB.

1972-74 RANDY PANDY SOAP DISH
Black, white & pink rubber soap dish & 3 oz. white soap. OSP $3.50, CMV panda only $2. - set $6. MB.

1967-69 GAYLORD GATER
10" long green and yellow rubber soap dish with yellow soap. OSP $2.25, CMV gater only $2., $6., set MB.

1973-74-79 TOPSY TURTLE FLOATING SOAP DISH & SOAP
7" long green rubber soap dish with 3 oz. green soap. SSP $2, CMV $3. MB. Reissued 1979. Some came light green body and dark green head. Also came matching body and head.

1971-72 BARNEY BEAVER SOAP DISH & SOAP
10½" long, brown soap dish and brown vest soap. OSP $3.50, CMV $5. MB. Beaver only $2.

1965-67 FIRST DOWN
Large box holds real junior size football & 6 oz. brown football soap on a rope. Rope comes out side of soap. OSP $3.95 Avon soap & ball, CMV soap $9. MB - ball $15. - set in box $27.50 MB.

1975-76 PADDLEWOG FROG FLOATING SOAP DISH & SOAP
Green plastic with pink propeller and yellow soap. OSP $4., CMV $3. MB.

1973-74 SOAP BOAT, FLOATING SOAP DISH AND SOAP
7½" long blue and red boat with white sail and white soap. SSP $2., CMV $5. MB.

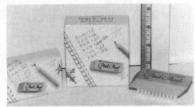

1977-78 PINK PEARL SCRUB AWAY NAIL BRUSH AND SOAP
3 oz. soap, pink brush shaped like pink pearl eraser. OSP $4., CMV $4. MB.

1972-73 SPOOL-A-DOO ROLLETTE
.33 oz. Rollette with red cap. Came with yellow plastic spool, eight yards of pink yarn and blue and pink plastic needles. SSP $2., CMV $4. MB.

1971-72 MR. ROBOTTLE
8" high plastic bottle with blue body and red legs and arms. Silver and yellow cap. Holds bubble bath. Came with white plastic wrench to put together. OSP $3.50, CMV $3.50 BO, $5. MB.

1970 FREDDY THE FROG MUG
5 oz. white glass with red or orange top and white cap. Holds bubble bath. OSP $3.50, CMV $5., $7. MB.

1970-72 GAYLORD GATOR MUG
5 oz. white glass mug with yellow top and white cap. Holds Non Tear Shampoo. OSP $3.50, CMV $5., $7. MB.

1970-71 SPLASH DOWN BUBBLE BATH
8 oz. white plastic bottle with red cap and yellow base ring. Came with 3 plastic toss rings. OSP $4., CMV $2. BO, $4. MB.

1977-78 TERRIBLE TUBBLES FLOATING SOAP DISH AND SOAP
(Left) Blue plastic dish with 3 oz. soap. SSP $4., CMV $4. MB.

1976-77 RANDY PANDY SOAP DISH AND SOAP
(Right) Black, light blue and red rubber soap dish and 3 oz. blue and white soap. SSP $4., CMV (Panda only) $1. Set $4. MB.

1971-72 HICKORY DICKORY CLOCK
5½" high, 8 oz. yellow plastic cheese clock with orange face and pink hands, purple mouse cap. Contains Non Tear Shampoo. OSP $4.50, CMV $5. MB, $3. BO.

1971-72 KANGA WINKS
7" high yellow and orange plastic bottle with pink hat, holds 8 oz. of bubble bath. Box also holds black and white plastic target and package of 16 plastic chips for tiddlywinks. OSP $4., CMV $4. complete set, $1. Kangaroo only, $6. set MB.

1970-72 MOON FLIGHT GAME
4 oz. white Space Capsule holds Non Tear Shampoo. Comes with black game sheet. OSP $4., CMV $4. MB, $1.50 BO.

1971-72 CHOO-CHOO TRAIN
Soap coach is 4" long plastic soap dish with yellow bar of soap. OSP $1.50, CMV $4. MB, with soap. $1. soap coach only. Caboose is pink plastic bottle, 3" long with Non Tear Shampoo, OSP $2., CMV $4. MB. Puffer Chugger is 4" long green plastic bottle with yellow cap and nose. Holds bubble bath. OSP $2., CMV $4. MB.

1975-76 ROCKABYE PONY DECANTER
6 oz. yellow plastic, holds Clearly Gentle Baby Lotion. OSP $4., CMV $2. BO, $3. MB.

1975-76 JACK-IN-THE-BOX
4 oz. yellow and pink plastic, holds baby cream. OSP $4., CMV $2. BO, $3. MB.

1978 EASTER DEC-A-DOO FOR CHILDREN
(Left) 8 oz. plastic yellow base, pink top. Came with stick on decals. This is different from 68-69 issue. Old one does not say for children on label. Holds bubble bath. SSP $3.99, CMV $3. MB, $2. BO.

1978-82 DUSTER D. DUCKLING FLUFF PUFF
3.5 oz. yellow plastic and fluff top. Holds Delicate Daisies or Sweet Pickles perfumed talc. SSP $4.44 CMV $3 MB, $2 BO.

1976-78 TYRANNOSAURUS REX
4 oz. green plastic bottle, green rubber head. Holds bubble bath for children. SSP $3., CMV $2. BO, $3. MB.

1978-79 TUB SUB
6 oz. yellow plastic, 10" long. Holds bubble bath for children. SSP $4., CMV $2. BO, $3. MB.

1971-72 POP A DUCK
6 oz. blue plastic bottle holds bubble bath. 3 plastic ducks and ball. OSP $3.50, CMV $5. complete set MB.

1971-72 MAZE GAME
6 oz. green plastic bottle, white cap. Holds Non Tear Shampoo. OSP $2.50, CMV $5. MB, $3. BO.

1971-72 HUGGY BEAR
8 oz. brown plastic bottle with lace-up vest, holds bubble bath. OSP $3.50, CMV $5. MB, $3. BO.

1973 LITTLE WIGGLEY GAME & BUBBLE BATH
8 oz. green with pink legs, red and yellow hoops. Holds bubble bath. SSP $3.50, CMV $3.50 MB.

1978 POP-A-DUCK GAME
6 oz. blue plastic with red orange cap. Came with 3 green balls. Pink, orange and yellow ducks and red orange ball holder. Bottle holds bubble bath for children. SSP $4., CMV $4. MB.

1972-75 LOOP-A-MOOSE GAME AND SOAP
7" high brown plastic moose, yellow antlers. Has green, pink and yellow rings to toss. Comes with 3 oz. yellow soap. SSP $3., CMV $3. - $4. MB.

1970-72 SCHROEDER
6 oz. red, white, black and yellow plastic bottle holds bubble bath, in piano shaped box. OSP $3.50, CMV $3., $7. MB in piano box.

1970-72 LINUS
4 oz. red, white and black plastic bottle holds Non Tear Shampoo. OSP $3., CMV $5. MB, $2. BO.

1974-75 CURLEY CATERPILLAR COMB
6" long green and pink plastic. OSP $1.50, CMV $1.50 MB.

1975-76 SHAGGY DOG COMB
5" long white plastic. OSP $1.25, CMV $1.50 MB.

1974 AL E. GATOR COMB & BRUSH
5" long green plastic with green comb. OSP $3., CMV $3. MB.

1971-72 ARISTOCAT
4 oz. gray cat with pink collar holds Non Tear Shampoo. OSP $3., CMV $4. BO, $5. MB.

1971 CLUCK A DOO
8 oz. yellow bottle, pink hat. Came with stick on decals. Holds bubble bath. OSP $3., CMV $5. MB, $3. BO.

1975-77 SUNBONNET SUE DEMI STICK
.19 oz. red and white plastic. Pink & Pretty fragrance. OSP $2.50, CMV $3. MB, $2. BO.

1974-75 NUTSHELL COLOR MAGIC LIPSTICK
Peanut shaped case came in Pink Sorcery (blue lipstick) or Peach Sorcery (green lipstick). OSP $2., CMV $3. MB, $2. BO.

1975-76 SCHOOL DAYS PENCIL LIP POMADE
.13 oz. red, white and yellow plastic. Choice of strawberry, cherry or tutti-frutti. OSP $2.50, CMV $3. MB, $2. BO.

1975-76 SWEET LIPS LIP GLOSS COOKIE
Brown plastic with 2 shades of lip gloss. OSP $3,., CMV $3. MB, $2. BO.

1978-79 BED OF NAILS COMB
5½" comb, tan, white and red. SSP $2.49, CMV $2. MB.

1978-79 WONDER WOMAN MIRROR
7½" long plastic mirror. SSP $6., CMV $4. MB.

1978-79 SWEET PICKLES ZANY ZEBRA HAIR BRUSH
White, black, pink and green plastic. SSP $5., CMV $2.50 MB.

1978-79 TASTI MINT LIP GLOSS COMPACT
Green and silver plastic. SSP $3., CMV $2. MB.

1979-80 COMBSICLE
Popsicle box holds brown and beige Avon comb. SSP $2., CMV $1. MB.

1979-80 CHOCOLATE CHIPLICK COMPACT
Tan and brown plastic, holds lip gloss. SSP $3.50, CMV $2. MB.

1979-80 POWER DRILL
5 oz. yellow plastic with silver plastic drill cap. Holds Wild Country or Electric Pre Shave. SSP $6., CMV $4. MB.

1980-81 TUGGABLE TEDDY TOOTHBRUSH HOLDER
Tan and blue plastic. Pink and green Avon toothbrushes. Orange ring on gold cord. SSP $5., CMV $5. MB.

1980-81 SMILEY SNAIL TOOTHBRUSH HOLDER
Yellow and green plastic. Orange and blue Avon toothbrushes. SSP $6., CMV $6. MB.

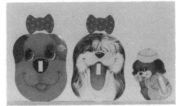

1982 PLAYFUL PUPS LIGHT SWITCH COVER
"(Left & center) 3½"x 4½" plastic dog light switch covers. Both came with blue and yellow dot stick-on fragrance bows. Golden pup, and white and gray pup. SSP $4.50, CMV $4.50 each MB.

1982 PLAY PUPS WALL HOOK
(Right) Plastic wall hook, Avon on back. SSP $3., CMV $3. MB.

1981-82 CLEAN-' EM-UP-PUMP
8 oz. yellow plastic with white and yellow pump dispenser. Comes with card of stick on decals. Come in Liquid Cleanser. SSP $5., CMV $5. MB.

1981-82 TED E. BEAR BABY LOTION DISPENSER
10 oz. plastic in choice of pink or blue bear. Comes with matching pump dispenser. SSP $7., CMV $7. MB.

1981 SPONGIE THE CLOWN
6 oz. plastic bottle with green cap and comes with orange sponge for top. SSP $5., CMV $3. MB.

1980-81 AUTOGRAPH HOUND STUFFED ANIMAL & DIPLOMA LIP BALM
8½" high tan cotton. Blue plastic cap. White tassel, red stainribbon on neck. Comes with Care Deeply lip balm Diploma. SSP $10., CMV $10. MB.

1976-78 CUSTOM CAR
7 oz. blue plastic bottle with red tire cap. Filled with bubble bath for children. OSP $5., CMV $2. BO, $3.50 MB.

1977-78 TRICERATOPS
8½ oz. green plastic bottle. Came with bubble bath for children. OSP $5.50, CMV $2. BO, $3. MB.

1981 AVON IN SPACE
(Left) Liquid Cleanser, blue and white, 1 oz. tube.
(Center) Non Tear Shampoo - Blue 1 oz. plastic robot bottle, gold cap.
(Right) Lip Balm - Blue and green., No boxes. SSP $1. each, CMV $1. each.

1980-81 I.M. CLEAN II
Blue plastic robot with pump dispenser. Comes with card of stick-on decals. Holds 8 oz. of Liquid Cleanser. SSP $7., CMV $7. MB.

1980-81 TUB TUG
5 oz. plastic. Comes in yellow and green cap with Non Tear Shampoo, red and lavender cap with bubble bath, and blue and red cap with Liquid Cleanser. SSP $3. each, CMV $3. each. No boxes.

1981-82 GOOD HABIT RABBIT BRUSH AND COMB
Yellow rabbit brush and comb. SSP $5., CMV $3. MB.

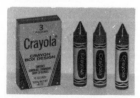

1980-81 CRAYOLA LIP GLOSS SET
Crayola box holds 3 plastic crayon shaped Avon lip gloss in chocolate, grape and strawberry. SSP $5., CMV $5. MB.

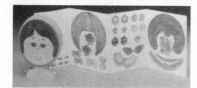

1982 MARIA MAKEOVER BATH DECANTER
6 oz. plastic face bottle and sheet of stick-on decals. Choice of Non Tear Shampoo or childrens Liquid Cleanser. SSP $5., CMV $3.50 MB.

1981-82 SNEAKIN' 'ROUND POMANDER
White plastic tennis shoe with white cord and blue stick-on decals. Comes with Country Morning wax chips. SSP $6., CMV $6. MB.

1981 CHICK POMANDER
White egg shaped wax pomander. 3" high. SSP $5., CMV $5. MB.

1980-81 NESTLE CRUNCH LIP GLOSS COMPACT
2¾" long white, blue and red plastic. SSP $3., CMV $3. MB.

1980-81 REFLECTOR PROTECTOR LIP GLOSS COMPACT
Grey with red reflector top. SSP $5., CMV $5. MB.

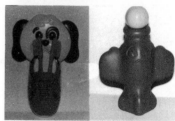

1981-82 PLAY PUPS TOOTHBRUSH HOLDER
Blue and orange shoe, brown ears, holds green and pink Avon toothbrushes. Dated 1981 on back. SSP $6., CMV $6. MB.

1982 CLEAN FLIGHT DECANTER
6 oz. plastic sea plane shaped. Choice of Non Tear Shampoo in yellow plastic with blue cap or Liquid Cleanser in orange with yellow cap. SSP $3., CMV $3. No box issued.

MISC. — AVONS, BOTTLES, ETC.

ALL CONTAINERS PRICED EMPTY
See pages 6 and 16 for Grading Examples on Mint Condition

SEE 1984 SUPPLEMENT IN BACK OF BOOK FOR MORE MISC. BOTTLES

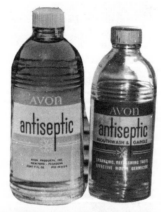

1955-59 ANTISEPTIC MOUTHWASH
(Left) 7 oz. white cap. Label says antiseptic only. OSP 59c, CMV $7. BO, $10. MB.

1959-68 ANTISEPTIC MOUTHWASH
(Right) 7 oz. white cap. OSP 59c. CMV $6. MB, $5. BO.

1940-50 ANTISEPTIC
6 oz. clear glass bottle with turquoise cap. Early issue had metal cap. Also came in 12 oz. size. OSP 62c, OSP 36c, CMV 6 oz. size, $12. BO, OSP MB., 12 oz. size, $16. BO, $20. MB. Add $5. for CPC label.

1936-41 LIQUID POWDER RACHEL OR PEACH
4 oz. green cap, clear glass. OSP $1.04, CMV $20. MB, $15. BO. Add $5. for CPC label on box.

1936-54 ASTRINGENT
2 oz. and 4 oz. size with turquoise caps. OSP 78c, CMV in box $15. Bottle only $12.50 each mint. Add $5. for CPC label.

1931-36 HAIR TONIC EAU DE QUININE FOR OILY HAIR
1 pint size. Silver metal cap. (For dry hair, same price and date). OSP $1.75, CMV $45. MB, $40. BO.

1931-36 HAIR TONIC EAU DE QUININE
6 oz. ribbed glass bottle with dark blue cap with silver and blue label. Came in Tonic for Dry Hair and for Oily Hair. OSP 90c, CMV $40. in box, $35. bottle only.

1930 LOTUS CREAM
4 oz. ribbed glass. OSP 75c. Rare with flowered label. CMV $50. BO, $60. MB.

1930-36 LIQUID POWDER
4 oz. ribbed glass bottle with dark blue cap, silver and blue label. OSP $1., CMV $40. in box, $35. bottle only.

1946 Only ANTISEPTIC
6 oz. round bottle, black cap. Rare. OSP 39c, CMV $45. MB, $40. BO.

1932-36 ANTISEPTIC
(Left) Metal cap, green label. 6 oz. size. OSP 36c, CMV $35. MB, $30. BO. Also came in 12 oz. size with same label. OSP 62c, CMV $40. in box, $35. bottle only.

1936-40 ANTISEPTIC
(Right) 6 oz. metal cap. Turquoise box and label. OSP 36c, CMV $35. MB, $30. mint BO.

1930-36 ASTRINGENT
Came in 2 and 4 oz. size as pictured on right for size comparison. Both are ribbed glass bottles with dark blue caps and silver and blue labels. OSP 75c for 4 oz. 40c, for 2 oz., CMV $40. MB, $35. BO. Mint each size.

1951-55 COCOANUT OIL SHAMPOO
6 oz. bottle with turquoise cap and label. OSP 59c, CMV $17. MB, $12. BO.

1936-38 PRE-SHAMPOO OIL
2 oz. bottle with turquoise cap and label. OSP 52c, CMV $22. MB, $18. BO. Add $5. for CPC label on bottle in box.

1954-58 SKIN FRESHENER
2 oz. bottle with turquoise cap and label. Came in Beautiful You Set, A Thing of Beauty Set, For Your Beauty Set and Happy Traveler Set with white cap. CMV $3.

1951-55 COCOANUT OIL SHAMPOO
1 pint bottle with black pouring, or flat black cap. OSP $1.19, CMV $22.50, BO. $27.50 MB.

1956-57 LIQUID COCOANUT OIL SHAMPOO
1 pint with green label and double pouring cap. OSP $1.59, CMV $18. BO, $22. MB.

1954-65 SKIN FRESHENER
4 oz. bottle with green cap and label. OSP 89c, CMV $1. each. 1965 bottle has For Dry Skin and For Normal Skin added to label. CMV $2. BO, $3. MB.

1954-65 ASTRINGENT
4 oz. bottle with green cap & label. OSP 89c, CMV $3. MB, $2. BO.

1965 ASTRINGENT FRESHENER FOR OILY SKIN
Same 4 oz. bottle as 1954-65 Astringent only name is changed. OSP $1.25, CMV $3. BO, $4. MB.

1931-36 BRILLIANTINE
2 oz. ribbed glass bottle with dark blue cap and silver and blue label. OSP 52c, CMV $45. in box, $40. bottle only.

1930-36 SKIN FRESHENER
2 or 4 oz. ribbed glass, blue or black cap. OSP 75c, 2 oz. size came in sets only. CMV $40. BO, $45. MB each.

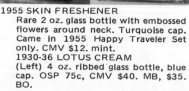

1936-44 LOTUS CREAM
4 oz. clear glass, green cap. OSP 52c, CMV $17. MB, $12. BO. Add $5. for CPC label on bottle in box. Came with 2 different labels and 2 different boxes.

1955 SKIN FRESHENER
Rare 2 oz. glass bottle with embossed flowers around neck. Turquoise cap. Came in 1955 Happy Traveler Set only. CMV $12. mint.

1930-36 LOTUS CREAM
(Left) 4 oz. ribbed glass bottle, blue cap. OSP 75c, CMV $40. MB, $35. BO.

1953-55 CREME HAIR RINSE
6 oz. clear glass bottle with green cap and label. OSP 89c, CMV $10. in box, $6. BO.

1954-56 CREME LOTION SHAMPOO
6 oz. bottle with turquoise cap, painted label. 1956 label has 4A design. OSP $1., CMV $9 MB, $5. BO.

1937-50 LIQUID SHAMPOO
6 oz. turquoise cap. Indented top of bottle. OSP 59c, CMV $20. MB, $15. BO. Add $5. for CPC label on bottle in box.

1943-45 LIQUID SHAMPOO
6 oz. round shoulder bottle, black cap. This bottle is rare with round shoulders. OSP 59c, CMV $30. mint, $35. MB.

1956 Only - CREME LOTION SHAMPOO
6 oz. clear glass, green cap. OSP $1., CMV $9. MB, $5. BO mint.

1956-57 LIQUID COCOANUT OIL SHAMPOO
6 oz. clear bottle with green cap, painted label. OSP 79c, CMV $9. MB, $5. BO.

1956 CREME HAIR RINSE
6 oz. bottle with white cap and painted label with 4A design. OSP 89c, CMV $9. MB, $5. BO.

1946-49 SOAPLESS SHAMPOO
6 oz. turquoise cap. OSP 59c, CMV $20. BO, $25. MB. Also came in 16 oz. round size with same label. 1946-49. OSP $1.19, CMV $20. BO - $25. MB.

1931-36 PRE-SHAMPOO OIL
2 oz. ribbed glass bottle with dark blue cap, silver and blue label. OSP 52c, CMV $40. in box, $35. bottle only.

1936-54 SKIN FRESHENER (Left to right)
2 and 4 oz. size bottles. Both 4 oz. bottles in center have 2 different labels. Turquoise caps. OSP 78c, CMV in box $15. Bottle only $12.50 each. Add $5. for CPC label on bottle or box.

1936-54 BRILLIANTINE
2 oz. green cap and label, 3 different labels. OSP 59c, CMV $20. MB, $15. BO. Add $5. for CPC label.

1950-51 FOUNDATION LOTION
2 oz. bottle with turquoise cap. OSP
59c, Formerly called Finishing
Lotion. CMV $20. MB, $15. BO.

1943-49 LEG MAKE-UP
4 oz. clear glass with black cap, or
turquoise cap on left. 2 different
bottles as shown. OSP 69c, CMV
$20. MB, $15. BO each.

1930-36 LIQUID SHAMPOO
(Left) 1 pint size, metal cap. OSP
$1.02, CMV $35. BO, $40. MB.

1931-36 LIQUID SHAMPOO
(Right) 6 oz. ribbed glass bottle with
dark blue cap and silver and blue
label. OSP 75c, CMV $40. in box,
$35. bottle only.

1926 ROSE WATER, GLYCERINE & BENZOIN
(Left) 4 oz. ribbed bottle with cork
stopper, front and neck label. OSP
50c, CMV $60. mint, $75. MB. See
CPC bottles for different label.

1930-36 ROSE WATER, GLYCERINE & BENZOIN
(Right) 4 oz. ribbed glass bottle, blue
cap. OSP 75c, CMV $40. BO, $45.
MB. Regular issue box in center. Add
$5. for 1935 special issue Christmas
box shown on right.

1936-44 ROSE WATER, GLYCERINE & BENZOIN
4 oz. bottle with turquoise cap.
OSP 52c, CMV $17. MB, $12. BO.
Add $5. for CPC label on bottle in
box.

1937-50 LIQUID SHAMPOO
1 pint size with raised pouring or flat
cap. OSP $1.19, CMV $20. BO, $25.
MB. 1937-39 has CPC label. $30.

1938-50 FINISHING LOTION
2 oz clear glass bottle with turquoise cap. OSP 52c, CMV in box $17., bottle only $12.50. Add $5. for CPC label on bottle in box.

1936-44 WAVE SET
4 oz. bottle with turquoise cap and label. OSP 52c, CMV $20. MB, $15. BO. Add $5. for CPC label on bottle in box.

1931-36 DEODORANT
2 oz. ribbed glass bottle with silver label and dark blue cap. OSP 50c, CMV in box $40., bottle only $35.

1936-48 WITCH HAZEL
4 oz. green cap and label. Also came with black cap. OSP 37c, CMV $15. BO, $20. MB. Add $5. for CPC label on bottle in box. (Also came in 8 and 16 oz. size).

1970 Only - ULTRA DRY ANTI PERSPIRANT (Left to Right)
7 oz. orange and yellow can. OSP $1.89, CMV $2.
1971-76 ULTRA DRY ANTI PERSPIRANT
7 oz. orange and yellow can. OSP $1.89, CMV 25c. Upside down label CMV $8.
1970 Only - AEROSOL DEODORANT
7 oz. blue and white can. OSP $1.75, CMV $2.
1971-76 AEROSOL DEODORANT
7 oz. blue and white can. OSP $1.75, CMV 25c.

1971 Only - HABIT ANTI PERSPIRANT DEODORANT
1.25 oz. size. Pink and white plastic bottle. OSP $1.25, CMV $1.50.
1972-75 HABIT ANTI PERSPIRANT DEODORANT
1.5 oz. pink and white bottle. OSP $1.50, CMV 25c.
1971-76 ROLL-ON ANTI PERSPIRANT DEODORANT
2 oz. clear glass with white and pink label. Pink cap. OSP 98c, CMV 25c. Also came in plastic bottle.
1960-70 HABIT CREAM DEODORANT
1¼ oz. turquoise plastic container and cap. OSP $1.25, CMV $1. mint. Also came for normal skin.

1930-36 WITCH HAZEL
4 oz. ribbed glass bottle with dark blue plastic cap, green label. OSP 50c, CMV $45. in box, $40. bottle only. Also came in 8 and 16 oz. size.

1930-36 WAVE SET
4 oz. ribbed glass bottle with dark blue cap. and silver and blue label. OSP 52c, CMV $40. in box - $35. bottle only.

1965-68 STICK DEODORANT (Left to Right)
2.75 oz. white plastic with aqua cap. OSP $1, CMV $1.50.

1968-70 SQUEEZE SPRAY DEODORANT
3 oz. white, blue and green plastic with blue cap. OSP 98c, CMV $1.50.

1968-69 ROLL-ON DEODORANT
1¼ or 1¾ oz. clear glass with painted blue, white and green label with blue cap. OSP 98c - CMV $1.50.

1965-66 TOUCH ON DEODORANT
1.75 oz. clear glass, painted label, white and aqua with aqua cap. OSP $1, CMV $2.

1965 BATH OILS - MISC.
Came in Bath Bouquet Set only. 2 oz., gold cap and label. Came in Rapture, Occur!, Somewhere, Topaze, Cotillion, Here's My Heart, To A Wild Rose and Wishing. CMV $9. each.

1967-72 PERFUMED DEODORANT
4 oz. size. Turquoise cap and label. OSP $1.25, CMV $1.50 BO, $2.50 MB.

1973-77 DRY 'N DELICATE DEODORANT
4 oz. pink and white can with pink cap. OSP $1, CMV 25c.

1976 ULTRA DRY DEODORANT
7 oz. blue, white and gold with white cap for powder. Same design only red white and gold with white cap for scented. OSP $1.98, CMV 50c.

1968-76 AEROSOL PERFUMED DEODORANT
4 oz. white, gold and aqua can with aqua cap. OSP $1, CMV 25c.

1936-48 DEODORANT
(Left) 2 oz. turquoise cap and label. OSP 52c, CMV $20. in box, $14. bottle only. Add $5. for CPC label on bottle in box. 1946-48 came with black applicator with sponge end. CMV $25. MB, $20. BO.

1944-45 LIQUID DEODORANT
(Right) 2 oz. turquoise cap with applicator. OSP 59c, CMV $20. BO, $25. MB.

1961-62 STICK DEODORANT
1¾ oz. white cap, green glass jar with painted label. OSP 89c, CMV $5., $7 MB.

1956-61 STICK DEODORANT
Green cap and label on clear glass jar, 2 different caps. Older has 4A design on top and newer on has "New" spelled on lid. OSP 79c, CMV $6., $7. MB each.

1955-59 FLOWING CREAM DEODORANT
2 oz. turquoise plastic bottle with white cap. OSP 79c, CMV $2. BO, $4. MB.

1958-60 FLOW-ON DEODORANT
2 oz. white plastic bottle. OSP 89c, CMV $2. BO, $3. MB.

1966-70 TOUCH ON DEODORANT
1¾ oz. white cap, clear glass, white design and green and white label. OSP $1.25, CMV $1.

1960-66 FLOW ON DEODORANT
1¾ oz. green cap and painted label, green and white label on clear glass. OSP 89c, CMV $3.

1966-67 ROLL ON DEODORANT
1¾ oz. green cap and green and white 4A design and label on clear glass. OSP 89c, CMV $2.

1960-66 CREAM DEODORANT
1.75 oz. white tube with aqua cap. Also sold with word "Normal" on tube. OSP 79c, CMV $1.

1970 Only - HABIT DEODORANT
1.25 oz. aqua with white cap. OSP $1, CMV $1.50.

1966-67 SPRAY DEODORANT
3 oz. turquoise plastic bottle with white cap. OSP 98c, CMV $2.

1954-72 PERFUMED DEODORANT
(Left) 2 oz. turquoise cap and label with 4A design. OSP 79c, CMV 50c.

1942-54 PERFUMED DEODORANT
(Right) 2 oz. green cap, old Avon label. OSP 59c, CMV $9. MB - $6. BO.

1936-37 NAIL POLISH
Clear glass with turquoise cap. CPC label. OSP 37c, CMV $15. BO - $20. MB.

1946-47 DOUBLE DARE NAIL POLISH
½ oz. black cap, red paper label. OSP 43c, CMV $8. BO, $10. MB.

1936-39 CUTICLE SOFTENER
½ oz. bottle with turquoise cap. CPC on label. CMV $15. BO, $20. MB.
1955-62 OILY POLISH REMOVER
2 oz. white cap and label. OSP 49c, CMV $4.

1936-39 POLISH REMOVER
½ oz. bottle, turquoise cap. CPC on label. OSP 31c, CMV $15. BO, $20. MB.

1931-36 NAIL POLISH
Ribbed glass bottle with black octaginal cap. Gray and blue box. OSP 50c, CMV $30. MB.
1931-36 POLISH REMOVER
1931-36 CUTICLE SOFTENER
Both ½ oz. ribbed glass, black 8 sided caps. Silver labels. OSP 50c, CMV $25. each BO, $30. MB.

1936-40 POLISH REMOVER
Has Good Housekeeping seal on turquoise and gold label. Black cap. OSP 50c, CMV $15. BO, $20. MB.

1946-50 OILY POLISH REMOVER
2 oz. bottle with turquoise cap. OSP 43, CMV $15 MB, $10. BO.
1950-53 OILY POLISH REMOVER
2 oz. white cap. OSP 49c, CMV $6. BO, $10. MB.

1950-54 NAIL POLISH
½ oz. bottle with white cap and gold line through label. Came in nail polish, cuticle softener, cling-tite, oily polish remover, clear nail polish and double coat. OSP 39c to 49c, CMV $3. on nail polish bottle - $3.50 on all others.

1954-58 NAIL POLISH
With 4A design on label, came in long last nail polish, cuticle softener, silvery base, top coat, oily polish remover. OSP 39c to 59c, CMV $2. for nail polish bottles and $3. for all others.

1938-50 NAIL POLISH
½ oz. and ¼ oz. bottle came in polish remover, cream polish, cuticle softener, cuticle oil, oily polish remover, nail polish base and top coat. 1946-50 same bottles and labels with black caps. Also came in double coat, nail polish and cling tite. OSP 29c, to 43c, CMV in box $7., bottle only $6. Nail polish bottles only $5.

315

1978-79 PEARL NAIL ENAMEL
.5 oz. white cap, gray and white box.
SSP 99c, CMV 25c MB.
1978-79 COLORWORKS SAMPLES
LASTING COLOR EYE SHADOW
Box of 10 samples
SUPERSHINE LIP GLOSS
Box of 10 samples. CMV 50c each
box.

1967 FLOWER PRINT NAIL ENAMEL
½ oz. bottle, white cap. Flower on
label and box. OSP $1.25, CMV $2.
MB.

1966 ICED CREAM NAIL ENAMEL
½ oz. nail enamel in tangerine, toffee,
rasberry, blueberry, pistachio, whipped cream and sugar frost. White caps.
OSP $1.25, each, CMV $4. MB, $1.
BO.

1965-66 ENAMEL REMOVER PADS
Red and white box holds 10 samples.
CMV $2. MB.
1969 NAIL ENAMEL
½ oz. white tall cap. CMV $1.50 MB.

1979-80 CRYSTAL LIGHTS
NAIL ENAMEL
CMV 50c. MB.
CREAMY POWDER EYE SHADOW
CMV 50c. MB.
LIP STICK
CMV 50c MB.

1970's MISCELLANEOUS NAIL ENAMELS
CMV 50c each.

1970's SKYLIGHTERS NAIL ENAMEL
(Left) .5 oz. white cap. In New York
City designed box. CMV $2. MB.
1970 STROKE OF BRILLIANTS NAIL POLISH
(Center) .5 oz. white cap. CMV $2.
MB.
1971 SHINE DOWN STICK
(Right) .6 oz. brown and gold plastic
tube. CMV $1. MB.

1945 TOILET WATER, CREAM LOTION & BUBBLE BATH
All are 2 oz. size, frosted glass and
pink caps. Came in 1945 Young
Hearts Set. CMV $20. each. Toilet
Water is in Cotillion fragrance.

1967 FIRE WORKS NAIL POLISH
½ oz. each, with white caps. Came in
blue, orange, violet, green, pink and
base coat. OSP $1.25, CMV $3. ea.
BO, $4. MB.

1962-68 OILY ENAMEL REMOVER
(Left) 3 oz. white cap. OSP 75c,
CMV $2.
1968-77 OILY ENAMEL REMOVER
(Center) 3 oz. bottle with white lid.
OSP 90c, CMV 25c.
1970-74 CUTICLE SOAK
3 oz. plastic bottle with white cap.
OSP $1., CMV 25c.

1951 CREAM LOTION
2 oz. bottle with blue cap. Came in 1951 Always Sweet Set. CMV $18.

1950-51 CREAM LOTION
2 oz. clear glass with turquoise cap, label has red, yellow and blue streamers. Came in 1951 Always Sweet Set and 1950 Jolly Surprise. CMV $12.

1965-67 BUBBLE BATH
8 oz. white plastic bottle and white cap. OSP $1.98, CMV $1.

1972-84 BUBBLE BATH
16 oz. pink plastic bottle with white cap. OSP $4., CMV 25c.

1973-84 BUBBLE BATH
8 oz. pink plastic bottle with white cap. OSP $2 - CMV 25c. 1982-84 Same bubble bath bottle in 24 oz. size. CMV 25c. 1984 issued in green plastic bottle, 16 oz. CMV 25c.

1975-76 BUBBLE BLOSSOM BUBBLE BATH DECANTER
14 oz. pink or white plastic bottle with white cap. OSP $5 - CMV $1.

1944-48 BUBBLE BATH
Blue and white box with pink ribbon holds 8 oz. bottle with blue cap and label. OSP $2.25, CMV $45. MB, $35. BO mint.

1958 LOTION SACHET
Came in Safe Journey only. White plastic with turquoise cap. CMV $5. mint.

1974-78 ONE STEP CREME HAIR RINSE
8 and 16 oz. white plastic with white cap. OSP $2. and $3., CMV 50c each.

1942-49 CREAM LOTION
6 oz. pink cap, back side of bottle is flat. Flowered box shown sold in 1942 only. OSP 79c, CMV $30. MB, $25. BO.

1948-51 BUBBLE BATH
4 oz. bottle with blue cap. Round blue and pink box with top of bottle sticking through lid. OSP $1.29, CMV $25. In box. Bottle only $15.

1951-58 BUBBLE BATH
Same bottle as above in a square box of same design. OSP $1.29, CMV $20. In box. Bottle only $15.

1942-43 CREAM LOTION BOX
Box shown sold 1942-43 only. 6 oz. flat sided bottle with pink cap sold 1942-49. OSP 49c, as pictured. CMV $30. MB as shown. $25. BO mint.

1944-45 LIQUID TWIN-TONE
2 oz. bottles. OSP 89c, CMV $15. BO, $20. MB.

1957-65 HAIR COSMETIC
3 oz. pink plastic with white cap. OSP $1., CMV $2. mint.

1957-61 MOISTURIZED HORMONE LOTION
6 oz. green plastic bottle with 4A embossed turquoise cap. OSP $2., CMV $2.

1957-60 RICH MOISTURE SUDS
6 oz. turquoise plastic bottle, white cap. OSP $1.50, CMV $3. MB, $2. BO.

1962 WASH OFF FACIAL CLEANSER
6 oz. pink plastic bottle, pink cap. 1963 came out for dry or oily skin. OSP $1.25, CMV $3. MB, $2. BO.

1958-65 MOISTURE BATH
6 oz. white plastic bottle, turquoise cap. OSP $1.25, CMV $3. MB, $2. BO.

1954-58 FASHION FILM
(Left) 1 oz. white cap. OSP 95c, CMV $4. BO.

1951-54 FASHION FILM
(Center) 1 oz. white cap. OSP 75c, CMV $5. BO.

1958-61 FASHION FILM
(Right) 1 oz. pink cap. OSP $1.10, CMV $4. BO. Add $1. each for each box.

1959-63 BATH OILS - MISC.
Royal Pine Bath Oil, green plastic. Rose Geranium, pink; Floral, lavender; and Jasmine, yellow. All are 8 oz. plastic bottles with matching caps. OSP $2., CMV $3. each.

1959-63 BUBBLE BATH
8 oz. pink plastic bottle and cap. OSP $1.69, CMV $2.

1957-59 CLEAR SKIN LOTION
6 oz. bottle with white cap. OSP $1., CMV $5. MB, $4. BO.

1963-69 CLEAR SKIN LOTION
3 oz. white plastic bottle with red cap. OSP 59c, CMV $1.

1959-63 CLEAR SKIN LOTION
3 oz. white plastic with clear plastic lid with red on inside white cap. OSP 79c, CMV $2.50.

1970-73 CLEAR SKIN BLOTTING CREAM
.65 oz. white tube with blue cap. OSP $1.50, CMV 25c.

1959-65 INSECT REPELLENT
2 oz. bottle with red and white caps. OSP 59c, CMV $5. MB, $3. BO.

1957 BEAUTIFUL JOURNEY BOTTLES
1 oz. clear glass bottles came in Beautiful Journey Set only. Pink caps. Came in hand lotion, skin freshener, deep clean, deodorant and Cotillion cologne. CMV $10. each.

1943-48 SUN CREAM
4 oz. clear glass, turquoise cap. OSP 85c, CMV $20. MB, $15. BO.

1960's ATOMIZER - MENS DEODORANT
(Left) Black and red, also came in turquoise. OSP 69c, CMV $4. in box.

1940's-50's ATOMIZER FOR COLOGNES
(Right) Turquoise bulb, 24K gold plated. CMV $5. in box.

1950's-60's AVON ATOMIZER
Red and black, also turquoise and white. OSP 69c, CMV $3. in box.

1954-59 LIQUID ROUGE
(Right) 1/8 oz. gold embossed cap. OSP 69c, CMV $7 MB, $5 BO.

1959-66 LIQUID ROUGE
(Left) 1/4 oz. smooth brass cap, 2 different labels. OSP 89c, CMV $4. MB, $3. BO.

1959 MERRY CHRISTMAS HAND LOTION
Christmas box holds 6 oz. white pearl plastic bottle with blue cap of White Pearl hand lotion. Sold Christmas only. OSP 98c, CMV $10. MB, $6. BO.

1949-58 SUN LOTION
4 oz. bottle with white cap. Montreal label to 1954. CMV $11., Pasadena label 1954-58 OSP $1., CMV $10. BO, $12. MB.

1954 SUN LOTION
2 oz. bottle, white cap. Came in camping kit set only. CMV $22.
1955-57 SUN FOAM
Peach colored can and cap. OSP $1.35, CMV $6. MB, $4. can only.

1958-65 TAN MOISTURIZED SUNTAN LOTION
4 oz. white plastic bottle with brown cap. OSP 98c, CMV $2. BO, $3. MB.
1954-58 HAND LOTION
4 oz. green cap and label. OSP 59c, CMV $2. BO, $4. MB.

1968-74 BRONZE GLORY TANNING OIL
4 oz. brown plastic with yellow cap. OSP $1., CMV 50c.
1972-74 BRONZE GLORY TANNING LOTION
4 oz. yellow plastic with brown cap. OSP $1., CMV 50c.
1967-74 KWICK TAN
4 oz. white, orange and red. OSP $1., CMV 25c.
1973-74 BRONZE GLORY TANNING BUTTER
7 oz. brown can with yellow cap. OSP $1., CMV 50c.

1963-64 HAND LOTION & PUMP
8 oz. gold stripes on bottle, gold and white pump. Also came without gold neck band. OSP $2.50, CMV $8. MB, $3. BO.
1964-65 LOTION LOVELY
8 oz. gold painted label. Came in Wishing, Here's My Heart, Persian Wood, To A Wild Rose. OSP $3. - Somewhere, Topaze, Cotillion, OSP $3.50 - Occur!, Rapture, OSP $4. CMV $7. MB, $3. BO.

1973-76 MOISTURIZED HAND LOTION
10 oz. plastic bottle. OSP $1., CMV 25c.
1965-66 HAND LOTION
4 oz. white and turquoise plastic. OSP 79c, CMV $2.

1965-66 VITA MOIST BODY LOTION
1965-66 RICH MOISTURE BODY LOTION
both 8 oz. white pump on gold top. OSP $3.50, CMV $2. BO each, $5. MB.

1966-70 HAND LOTION
Pink plastic bottle with pink cap, gold lettering. 1966-70, 10 oz. size OSP $1.50, CMV $1. 1966-67, 4 oz. size, OSP 79c, CMV $1.

1956-57 GIFT HAND LOTION
8 oz. bottle with pump dispenser, indented front and back. 1956 box has Christmas tree on it. 1957 box shown. OSP $1.39, CMV $15. in box, $10. bottle only.

1948 HAND LOTION
2 oz. glass bottle with blue cap. Came in 1948 Hair Ribbons Set. CMV $15.

1950 Only HAND LOTION
4 oz. clear glass, turquoise cap and label. OSP 59c, CMV $14. mint.

1950 HAND LOTION
4 oz. pink cap. Same bottle as Cotillion of that period. This was a substitute bottle. Rare. OSP 59c, CMV $15. BO, $20. MB.

1942 Only HAND LOTION ROSE WATER, GLYCERINE & BENZOIN LOTION
6 oz. flat sided bottle. Came in sets only. CMV $40. mint.

1951-54 HAND LOTION
4 oz. pink or white plastic cap, blue and pink label. OSP 59c, CMV $15. in box. $13. bottle only.

1966-69 DEEP CLEAN CLEANSING LOTION FOR DRY SKIN
6 oz. light pink with dark pink cap. OSP $1.25, CMV $1.
1966-69 DEEP CLEAN WASH-OFF CLEANSER FOR NORMAL SKIN
6 oz. white with dark aqua cap. OSP $1.25, CMV $1.
1966-69 DEEP CLEAN WASH-OFF CLEANSER FOR OILY SKIN
6 oz. light peach with dark peach cap. OSP $1.25, CMV $1.
1966-69 DEEP CLEAN CLEANSING LOTION FOR NORMAL SKIN
6 oz. light aqua. OSP $1.25, CMV $1.

1943-50 HAND LOTION
4 oz. clear glass, turquoise cap. OSP 59c, CMV $17. in box, $12.50 bottle only.

1970-76 EVEN TONE
1.5 oz. plastic white cap. OSP $1., CMV 25c.

1960-66 EVEN TONE
1½ oz. plastic bottle, gold lid (1961-62), 1962-66 same bottle with white plastic lid in same shape. OSP $1.35, CMV $1. white cap, $2. gold cap. Also came 1.75 oz. size.

1969 GENTLE LOTION SHAMPOO
8 oz. yellow plastic bottle with white cap. OSP $1., CMV $1.

1975-77 NATURALLY GENTLE CONCENTRATE
6 oz. clear plastic, yellow cap. OSP $2., CMV 25c.

1975-78 HI-LIGHT SHAMPOO FOR OILY HAIR
6.5 oz. clear plastic with white cap. OSP $1., CMV 25c.

1967-73 AEROSOL HAIR CONDITIONER
2 oz. pink, white and gold. 1973 only changed top and added white lid over spray. OSP $3., CMV $1.

1966-75 ULTRA SHEER LOOSE POWDER
1966-74 1¾ oz. white cardboard trimmed in gold. OSP $2.50, CMV 50c.

1973-74 FLUFF FOUNDATION
2 oz. white can with gold. OSP $3.50, CMV 50c.

1968-74 FINISHING GLO
.75 oz. white can trimmed in gold. OSP $2.50, CMV 50c.

1967-74 LIPSTICK
White and gold plastic. OSP $1.75, CMV 50c.

1969-74 ASTRINGENT
4 oz. clear plastic, white cap, green label. OSP $1., CMV 50c.

1969-74 SKIN FRESHENER
4 oz. clear plastic, white cap, pink label. OSP $1., CMV 50c.

1961-76 VITA MOIST BODY LOTION
Yellow plastic, white cap. 1961-64 4 oz. SSP $1., CMV $2. 1966-74 8 oz. SSP $1.50, CMV 50c, 1974-78 16 oz. SSP $2.75, CMV 25c.

1966 Only - GOLD STAIN
Eye Highlight - gold case, came in box with girls pictured on front. OSP $1.75, CMV $2.; Complexion Highlight - cardboard with girls pictured on top and box. OSP $1.75, CMV $3. MB; Fingertip Highlight - clear glass with white cap. Came in box with girls picture. OSP $1.75, CMV $2. MB. Powder Eye Shadow Brush - OSP $1.50, CMV $1.

1968-70 MOUTHWASH & GARGLE
10 oz. bottle with white cap. Came in glass changed to plastic, glass bottle bigger. OSP $1.25, CMV $1. in glass, 50c in plastic.

1968-74 BREATH FRESH
10 oz. bottle with white cap. Came in glass changed to plastic, glass bottle bigger. OSP $1.25, CMV $1. in glass, 50c in plastic.

1962-63 CLEAR-IT SUDS
6 oz. white plastic with clear plastic lid with red on inside white cap. OSP $1.25, CMV $3.

1960-63 CLEAR-IT SHAMPOO
3 oz. white plastic with clear plastic lid with red on inside white cap. Also came in 6 oz. OSP 79c, CMV $2.50.

1966-69 SKIN FRESHENER
4 oz. glass bottles, 3 different color labels and caps. Normal Skin in blue, Astringent Freshener for Oily Skin in peach and Dry Skin in pink. OSP $1.25, CMV $1. each.

1966-69 DEW KISS
Came in 1½ oz. and 3½ or 5 oz. size glass. White cap with label band around cap from 1966-69. CMV $1 1969-76 label is on front of bottle. OSP $1.50, and $3. CMV $1 each. Later issue was plastic bottle.

1967 EYE AND THROAT OIL
1 oz. gold cap. Issued during glass strike in 1967 only. Short Issue. OSP $2.50, CMV $5. BO, $7. MB.

1962 BATH OIL
6 oz. plastic bottles, white caps. Came in 1962 Bath Bouquet set only, in Somewhere, Cotillion, Here's My Heart, Topaze, Persian Wood, Royal Jasmine, Rose Geranium, Royal Pine, Floral and To A Wild Rose. CMV $6.

1978 SMOOTH AS SILK BATH OIL TRIAL SIZE
1 oz. plastic bottle, pink cap. CMV 29c, CMV 30c.

1965-66 AVON DIRT
Gold cap frosted glass bottle is same as Crown Top powder sachet bottle. Front label reads "4A design at top, Avon Dirt - Contains handful of 100% dehydrated mud to be used by clean people". Back label reads "Directions: For people unaccustomed to having dirty hands. Moisten hands lightly and rub on Avon Dirt to a gooey mess. Now you can use Avon Soap to remove Avon Dirt". This is a rare bottle. Only one found to date. If you know what or where it was used, please notify Bud Hastin. No value established.

1960-61 BATH OILS - MISC.
4 oz. white plastic bottle with blue lid. Came in Modern Simplicity Set only in To A Wild Rose, Here's My Heart and Cotillion. CMV $15. each.

1971-75 LADY SHAVE FOAM
4 oz. white and pink can, pink cap. OSP $1., CMV 25c.

1976 LADY SHAVE FOAM
6 oz. white yellow and green, yellow cap. OSP $1., CMV 25c.

1976 LADY SHAVE CREAM
6 oz. white tube, yellow cap. OSP $1., CMV 25c.

1973-76 STEPPING OUT FOOT POWDER SPRAY
7 oz. blue and white with blue cap. OSP $1., CMV 25c.

1971-74 STEPPING OUT SOOTHING LOTION
4 oz. white and blue plastic, blue cap. OSP $1., CMV 25c.

1969-76 STEPPING OUT FOOT CARE CREAM
4 oz. blue jar, white cap. OSP $1., CMV 25c.

1970-76 STEPPING OUT FOOT COMFORT SPRAY
5 oz. blue and white can. Short one rare. OSP $2., CMV for tall 50c, for short $6.

1975-78 MOISTURIZED HAND LOTION
16 oz. yellow or pink plastic bottle with white cap. OSP $2 - CMV 25c.

1975-78 FLAVOR FRESH MOUTHWASH
14 oz. plastic bottle with white cap. OSP $1., CMV 25c.

1960-62 HI LIGHT SHAMPOO FOR OILY HAIR
6 oz. white plastic, clear plastic cap. Also came for Normal or Dry Hair. OSP $1.19, CMV $3. MB, $2. BO.

1957-60 DEEP CLEAN CLEANSING CREAM
6 oz. white with gold lettering, aqua cap. OSP $1.39, CMV $3. mint.

1964-76 AVON CURL SET
8 oz. plastic with aqua lid. OSP $1.50, CMV 25c.

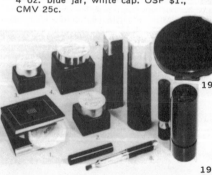

1971-78 FASHION GROUP
All items are black with gold caps and trim. Compact, Contour Cream, Cremelucent Foundation, Hi Lite Cream, 1976 issue round jar, Blushing Stick, Under Make Up Moisture Veil, Blushstick and Lipstick, Creamy Rouge compact. Moisture Droplets, Toning Cream or Creme of Blush.

1975-76 LIQUID LUCENT FOUNDATION
CMV 50c each.

1974-78 NATURALLY GENTLE CREME RINSE
8 oz. plastic with yellow cap and plunger. OSP $2., CMV 25c.

1974-82 NATURALLY GENTLE SHAMPOO
8 oz. or 16 oz. plastic with yellow cap. OSP $3., CMV 25c.

1965-74 PROTECTIVE HAND LOTION
7.75 oz. light green with white cap. OSP $1., CMV 50c.

1973 SPECIAL COMPLEXION GRAINS
4.5 oz. pink, white and gold. OSP $1., CMV $1.

1971-75 AMERICAN SPORTSTER SUPERSTICK
White tube, blue and red design. OSP $2.50, CMV 50c.

1971-73 SHOWERING SOAP SHAMPOO
White plastic bottle, blue and red design, blue cap. OSP $2.50, CMV $1.50.

OUTDOOR SHIELD
White plastic compact with blue and red design. OSP $2.50, CMV $1.

SKIN COMFORT GEL
White plastic tube, red and blue design. OSP $2.50, CMV 75c.

1968-74 BUBBLE BATH
8 oz. white plastic with white cap. 1972 Christmas box. OSP $2., CMV 25c. CMV $3. mint with box shown.

1973 SUMMER DEW MOISTURIZING BODY CREME
5 oz. white with pink and blue design. SSP $4., CMV $2. MB, $1. BO.

1973 SUMMER DEW MOISTURIZING BODY FLUFF
4 oz. white with pink and blue design. SSP $4., CMV $2. MB, $1. BO.

1974-76 TWICE BRIGHT TOOTH POLISH
2.75 oz. white plastic, blue lid. OSP $1., CMV 25c.

1970-74 CLEANER & CONDITIONER FOR FALSE EYELASHES
.75 oz. white plastic. OSP $1., CMV 50c.

1971-73 EYE MAKE UP SEALER
.5 oz. white plastic. OSP $1., CMV 50c.

1973-76 BLUSHLUCENT LIQUID ROUGE
.25 oz. white plastic with gold cap. OSP $1., CMV 25c.

1973-76 ESSENCE OF BALSAM HAIR SPRAY
7 oz. light green with green cap. OSP $2., CMV 25c.

ESSENCE OF BALSAM HAIR SPRAY FOR HEATED ROLLERS
7 oz. green with white cap. OSP $2., CMV 25c.

ESSENCE OF BALSAM LOTION SHAMPOO
8 oz. green with white lid. OSP $2., CMV 25c.

ESSENCE OF BALSAM LOTION CONDITIONER
8 oz. yellow with white lid. OSP $2., CMV 25c.

1973-77 LOTION CONDITIONER
8 oz., yellow with white lid. OSP $2., CMV 25c.

1976-78 EVEN TONE MAKE-UP
Off white, plastic. Choice of Dewy Make-Up or Matt in light, medium or heavy coverage. OSP light and medium, $1.50 each. OSP heavy cover, $2. each, CMV 25c each.

1973-74 ULTRA SHEER FLUFF FOUNDATION
2 oz. white and gold can, white cap. OSP $2., CMV 25c.

1967-73 FINISHING GLO
.75 oz. white and gold. OSP $2.75, CMV 50c.

1971-74 TRANSPARENT FACE TINT
1.5 oz. white tube, white cap. OSP $2., CMV 50c.

1971-75 FROSTY OR TRANSPARENT GEL BLUSH
.5 oz. white and gold tube with white cap. (Frosty sold only 1975) OSP $1., CMV 25c.

1974-78 PERFECT BALANCE PEACH COLORED OR WHITE
4 oz. Tissue-Off Cream. OSP $2., CMV 25c; 6 oz. Toning Freshener, OSP $2, CMV 25c; 4.5 oz. Cleansing Grains, OSP $1., CMV 25c; 6 oz. Toning Astringent, OSP $2., CMV 25c; 4 oz. Wash-Off Lotion, OSP $2., CMV 25c; 3 oz. Night Time Moisturizer, OSP $2., CMV 25c; 2.5 oz. Night Creme, OSP $2., CMV 25c; .75 oz. Eye Cream, OSP $2, CMV 25c.

1975-78 NATURAL SHEEN HAIR DRESS & CONDITIONER
3 oz. brown and white tube. OSP $2., CMV 25c.

1975-76 NATURAL SHEEN AEROSOL HAIR GLOSSER
7 oz. brown and white can. OSP $3., CMV 50c.

1975-76 PERFECT CARE BODY LOTION DRY ASHY SKIN
6 oz. brown and blue plastic bottle. OSP $3., CMV 50c.

1975-76 SHADES OF BEAUTY LIQUID FOUNDATION
1.5 oz. brown and white plastic bottle. OSP $2., CMV 50c.

1975-76 SHADES OF BEAUTY CREAMY BLUSH
.25 oz. brown and white tube. OSP $2., CMV 25c.

1970-78 PROTEM PRODUCTS
Back Row — 7 oz. Hair Spray, OSP $2., CMV 25c; 12 oz. Conditioner, OSP $4., CMV 25c; 6 oz. Cream Rinse, OSP $2., CMV 25c; 6 oz. Hair Set, OSP $2., CMV 25c; 6 oz. Conditioner (new style cap), OSP $2., CMV 25c; 6 oz. Conditioner (old style cap) OSP $2., CMV 25c.
Front Row — 1970-73 Hair Gloss, OSP $1., CMV 75c; 6 oz. Creme Shampoo (old style lid), OSP $2., CMV 25c; 3 oz. Dandruff Shampoo, OSP $1., CMV 25c; 3 oz. Super Rich Conditioner, OSP $1., CMV 25c.

1976-78 DELICATE BEAUTY SKIN CARE SAMPLE
GENTLE WHIPPED NIGHT CREAM
CMV 25c each.
GENTLE FRESHENER
5 oz. turquoise and white. OSP $2., CMV 50c.
GENTLE LOTION CLEANSER
4 oz. turquoise and white. OSP $2., CMV 50c.
GENTLE WHIPPED NIGHTCREME
3 oz. turquoise and white. OSP $3., CMV 50c.
SAMPLE GENTLE LOTION CLEANSER
CMV 25c each.

1975-78 CLEARLY GENTLE WHITE AND BLUE
7 oz. Nursery Spray, OSP $1., CMV 25c; 4 oz. Ointment, OSP $1., CMV 25c; 10 oz. Lotion, OSP $1., CMV 25c; 3 oz. Soap, OSP 50c, CMV 50c, 10 oz. Liquid Cleanser, OSP $1., CMV 25c.

ULTRA SHEER - White & Gold
1972-74 UNDER MAKEUP MOISTURIZER SAMPLES
Box of 10, CMV 50c.
UNDER MAKEUP MOISTURIZER
2 oz. Came in mauve, apricot, aqua, untinted. SSP $3., CMV $1.
ULTRA SHEER PRESSED POWDER
5 oz. mirrored compact with lamb's wool applicator. SSP $3., CMV $1.
ULTRA SHEER LIP GLOSS POT
.10 oz. white plastic with gold Avon on lid. Choice of 3 colors. SSP $1., CMV 50c MB.
ROUND COMPACT
.5 oz. SSP $3., CMV $1.
1971 SHEER COMPANIONS
White plastic case held white and gold lipstick and compact. SSP $5., CMV $6. MB.

1975-80 HI-LIGHT SHAMPOO FOR NORMAL HAIR
6.5 oz. plastic with white cap. OSP $1., CMV 25c.

1972-76 SHAMPOO FOR COLOR TREATED HAIR
8 oz. clear plastic with white cap. 1971 had outline of girls head on front. OSP $1., CMV 25c.

1970-75 SUPER HI-LIGHT SHAMPOO
12 oz. clear plastic white cap. OSP $1., CMV 25c.

1967 Only - NON-TEAR SHAMPOO
12 oz. white and pink with pink cap. OSP $1.50, CMV $2.

1072-76 RESILIENT HAIR CARE
Yellow and black with yellow caps. 4 oz. Hair Texturizer, OSP $2., CMV 25c; 8 oz. Creme Rinse, OSP $2., CMV 25c; 8 oz. Lotion Shampoo, OSP $3., CMV 25c; 7 oz. Hair Spray, OSP $1.50, CMV 25c.

1973-76 HONEY GIRL
4.7 oz. yellow with yellow plunger. OSP $1., CMV 25c.

1973 RESILIENT CREME RINSE SAMPLE
1 oz. yellow tube. CMV $1.

1970's (early) PROFESSIONAL HAIR CARE PRODUCTS
Used in Avon beauty salons only, not sold.
HAIR SPRAY
13 oz. pink, blue and white can. CMV $5.
INSTANT LOTION CONDITIONER
16 oz. frosted plastic bottle, orange letters. CMV $4.
SHAMPOO FOR DRY HAIR
16 oz. plastic bottle. CMV $4.
HAIR NET
8 oz. plastic bottle. Oily hair, green letters; Normal hair, purple letters. CMV $3. each.
BEAUTY SALONS RAIN HAT
Pink and white case holds clear plastic rain bonnet. Used in Avon beauty salons only, not sold. CMV $3.

1972 FASHION GROUP CUSTOM FOUNDATION KIT

Gold and black cardboard with black plastic tubes. .25 oz. Cremelucent Foundation, .25 oz Hi-Lite Cream, .25 oz. Contour Creme. OSP $4.50, CMV $4. MB.

1973 DEW KISS DECANTER
(Left) 4 oz. clear glass with gold cap. SSP $3., CMV $3. MB.

1974 DEW KISS DECANTER
(Center) 4 oz. clear glass with gold cap. SSP $2.50, CMV $2. MB, $1. BO.

1960-66 DEW KISS
(Right) 1½ oz. pink lid, gold string with pink and gold tag, with 4A design. OSP $1.25, CMV $5. MB, $3. bottle with tag.

1966-67 ULTRA SHEER LIQUID FOUNDATION
1 oz. gold top, embossed bottle. OSP $2.25, CMV $2.

1968-74 ULTRA SHEER NATURAL VEIL
1 oz. embossed bottle, same as Liquid Foundation only name changed. OSP $2.25, CMV 50c.

1965-72 EYE & THROAT OIL
1 oz. gold cap, painted label. OSP $2.50, CMV $1.

1973-75 FASHION GROUP BODY MAKEUP

2 oz. gold can, black lid. Black applicator with sponge. OSP $3., CMV $3. MB.

1975-79 CREME HAIR RINSE
12 oz. white plastic bottle with white cap. OSP $1., CMV 25c.

1975-79 BUBBLE BATH FOR CHILDREN
12 oz. white plastic bottle with white cap. OSP $2., CMV 25c.

1975-84 NON-TEAR SHAMPOO
12 oz. white plastic bottle, white cap. OSP $2., CMV 25c.

1974-76 FOAMING BATH OIL
6 and 12 oz. plastic bottle with cap colored to match fragrance. Came in Charisma, Moonwind, Sonnet, Bird of Paradise, Field Flowers, Cotillion, or Timeless. OSP $4.50 for 6 oz. and $7.50 for 12 oz. 1977 Imperial Gardens was sold. CMV 50c.

1973-84 CARE DEEPLY HAND CREAM
4 oz. white and black tube. OSP $1., CMV 25c.

1975-84 CARE DEEPLY LIP BALM
White and black, black cap. OSP $1., CMV 25c. Also with sunscreen 4 different.

1974-84 CARE DEEPLY LOTION
16 oz. white plastic with white cap. SSP $2.50, CMV 50c.

1974-84 CARE DEEPLY HAND CREAM
6 oz. black and white. OSP $1.50, CMV 25c.

1971 Only - PRIMA NATURA PRODUCTS
All items are white with gold letters.

NIGHT VEIL CONCENTRATE
2½ oz., OSP $6.

THERMAL FACIAL
3 oz., OSP $6.50, came with cloth mask.

CLEANSING FORMULA
4 oz., OSP $5.50

MOISTURIZING FRESHENER
4 oz., OSP $3.50.

TONING FRESHENER
4 oz., OSP $3.50.

EYE CREAM CONCENTRATE
.75 oz., OSP $4.
CMV all items above $1. BO, $1.50 MB

CREME OF SOAP
5 oz. with white spatula. OSP $4.50, CMV $2.50 MB, $1.50 BO.

1972-75 EAU DE COOL
6 oz. light blue glass, silver cap. OSP $5., CMV $2. MB, $1. BO.

1970-76 CLEAR SKIN CLEANSING GRAINS
4.5 oz. white, silver and blue cardboard. OSP $1.75, CMV 50c. Other pictured with label upside down, CMV $5.

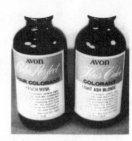

1971-72 COLOR PERFECT HAIR COLOR
2 oz. brown glass with white cap and Avon on bottle. CMV $1.50.
1969 HAIR COLOR COLORANT
2 oz. brown glass with white cap. Has 4A on cap. No Avon on bottom. CMV $5.

1970-72 BREATH FRESH CONCENTRATED MOUTHWASH
1 oz. glass bottle with white cap. OSP $1.75, CMV 50c BO, $1.50 MB.

1975-78 FLAVOR FRESH MOUTHWASH (Backward label)
14 oz. plastic with embossed star on back side of bottle. Should be on front side. Factory mistake. OSP $1., CMV $8.

1977-80 FIRM & NATURAL HAIR SPRAY
(Left) 6 oz. non-aerosol plastic pump spray. OSP $2.29, CMV 25c.
1977-80 KEEP CLEAR ANTI-DANDRUFF SHAMPOO
(Left center) 7 oz. plastic bottle. OSP $2.29, CMV 25c.
1977-80 KEEP CLEAR ANTI-DANDRUFF SHAMPOO SAMPLE
(Right center) 2 oz. plastic bottle. OSP 25c, CMV 25c.
1977-80 ON DUTY DEODORANT
(Right) 4 oz. non-aerosol pump spray in plastic bottle. OSP $2.49, CMV 25c.

1970-80 CLEAR SKIN PRODUCTS
1970-76 labels are silver and blue, silver caps. 1977-80 labels changed to dark and light blue with dark blue caps.
SHAMPOO CONCENTRATE - 4 oz., blue cap.
CLEANSING GRAINS - 4½ oz.
BAR OF SOAP - 3 oz.
LIQUID MAKEUP - 2 oz., silver cap.
COVER STICK - 4 oz.
LOTION - 6 oz.
ASTRINGENT - Silver cap old, blue cap new issue. CMV 50c each.
1971-72 FACIAL MASK - 3 oz., silver cap old, blue cap new issue.
CREAM CLEANSER - 5 oz. silver cap.
ASTRINGENT - 12 oz., silver cap old, blue cap new issue.
CLEANSING GEL - 6 oz. blue cap
OIL FREE BLOTTING CREAM - .65 oz. tube. CMV 50c each.

1978 MOISTURE SECRET PRODUCTS TRIAL SIZE
All are pink plastic and introductive size in 1.7 oz. tube. Enriched Creme-gel Cleanser, 1 oz. tube Enriched Freshener, and ½ oz. tube of Enriched Daytime Moisturizer. All with PMN and .47 oz. jar of Enriched Night Concentrate. CMV 50c.

1969-71 ANTISEPTIC POWDER
3½ oz. cardboard container, plastic shaker top. OSP 89c, CMV $1.
1969-71 ANTISEPTIC CREAM
1.75 oz. plastic tube, blue cap. OSP 89c, CMV $1.

1978 HI-LIGHT SHAMPOO 1/3 EXTRA
8.7 oz. plastic bottles with 1/3 extra free on top. Came in normal, oily, and dry hair shampoo. SSP 99c, CMV 25c.

1969-72 LIQUID EYELINER
.25 oz. bottle. OSP $2., CMV $1. MB.

1976-78 BODY SPLASH
8 oz. plastic bottle. Came in Field Flowers, Honeysuckle, Hawaiian White Ginger, Apple Blossom, Roses Roses, and new in 1978 Sun Blossoms. Each came in a different color container and cap. SSP $2.50, CMV 50c each.

1978-80 CLEAR SKIN MEDICATED LIQUID CLEANSER
10 fl. oz. plastic white bottle, blue cap. OSP $2.49, CMV 25c.
1978-80 CLEAR SKIN MEDICATED ASTRINGENT
12 fl. oz. white plastic bottle, blue cap. OSP $2.99, CMV 25c.
1978-80 CLEAR SKIN MEDICATED LOTION
4 fl. oz. white plastic bottle, blue cap. OSP $1.89, CMV 25c.
1978-80 CLEAR SKIN MEDICATED CLEANSER PLUS
3 oz. white tube, blue cap. OSP $1.29, CMV 25c.
1978-80 CLEAR SKIN MEDICATED SOAP
3 oz. bar. OSP 99c, CMV 60c.

1971 HAIR BEAUTY PACK
1.25 oz. tube used in Avon beauty salons. CMV $3.
1971 COFFEE CUP HOLDER
Used in Avon beauty salons. White plastic. CMV $3.

1977-78 DELICATE BEAUTY
2 oz. glass bottle liquid makeup. Gold cap. OSP $5., CMV 25c.

1971 HAIR DRESSING AND CONDITIONER
11 oz. pink spray can and cap. CMV $5.
1971 SHAMPOO FOR COLOR TREATED HAIR
12 oz. pink plastic bottle, white cap. CMV $4.
1971 SETTING LOTION
16 oz. plastic bottle. CMV $4.
1971 HAIR THICKENER
16 oz. plastic bottle. CMV $4. All of these items used only in Avon beauty salons. Not sold.

1977-80 SUNNY MORN SHAMPOO
8 oz. plastic bottle in different colors. Came in Hyacinth, Jonquil, Lilac, Strawberry and Clover fragrances. OSP $2.29, CMV 25c.
1977-80 SUNNY MORN HAIR CONDITIONER
8 oz. plastic oil free conditioner. OSP $2.29, CMV 25c.

1975-78 COUNTRY CUPBOARD BUBBLING BATH FOAM
6 oz. plastic bottle. Came in Green Apple, Peach or Strawberry. OSP $4.50, CMV 25c.
1975-78 COUNTRY CUPBOARD PERFUMED TALC
5 oz. cardboard container. Came in Green Apple, Peach or Strawberry. OSP $2.50, CMV 25c.

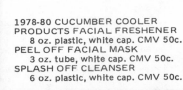

1978-80 CUCUMBER COOLER PRODUCTS FACIAL FRESHENER
8 oz. plastic, white cap. CMV 50c.
PEEL OFF FACIAL MASK
3 oz. tube, white cap. CMV 50c.
SPLASH OFF CLEANSER
6 oz. plastic, white cap. CMV 50c.

1978-79 GOOD & GLOSSY ROLL-ON LIP GLOSS
.33 oz. clear glass, white caps. One with blue band around cap and blue letters. One with pink band and white letters. One with green band and white letters. SSP 82c each, CMV 50c each.

1978-80 FRIVOLIE PRODUCTS
All are green and yellow.
SPARKLING BODY SPLASH
8 oz. plastic. CMV 50c.
BUBBLING BUBBLE BATH
8 oz. plastic, CMV 50c.
TANTALIZING TALC
3.5 oz. cardboard and plastic. CMV 50c.
COLOGNE ICE
1 oz. plastic. CMV 50c.

1978-79 DEW KISS PRODUCTS
Frosted or pink plastic containers.
DEW KISS SAMPLE — (Left) CMV 25c.
LIP DEW - (Center left) CMV 25c.
UNDER MAKEUP MOISTURIZING CREAM - (Center right) 3 oz. CMV 25c.
UNDER MAKEUP MOISTURIZING LOTION - (right) Gold or pink cap. Came in 5 oz., 3.5 oz. or 1.5 oz. size. CMV 25c each.

1978 KEEP CLEAR ANTI-DANDRUFF SHAMPOO
8 oz. white plastic bottle, blue cap. OSP 89c, CMV 25c. Also came with back label on both sides with front label missing, factory mistake. CMV $8.

1979-80 ALL OVER FACE COLOR
1 oz. plastic, gold cap. CMV 25c.
1979 CREME NAIL ENAMEL
White cap in special color up box. CMV 25c.
1970's CREME HAIR RINSE
6 or 12 oz. size pink plastic, pink 4A cap. CMV 50c.

1978-81 NEW VITALITY PRODUCTS
CONDITIONING SETTING LOTION
8 oz. plastic, pump top. CMV 50c.
EXTRA BODY CONDITIONER
8 oz. plastic, yellow cap. CMV 50c.
BLOW DRY CONDITIONER
8 oz. plastic, pump top. CMV 50c.
CONDITIONING SHAMPOO
8 oz. plastic, yellow cap. CMV 50c.
HOT CONDITIONING TREATMENT
Box holds 3 plastic tubes. CMV $1. MB.

1977 SUNNY MORN SHAMPOO DOUBLE STAMP LABEL
8 oz. plastic bottle. Label has been stamped 4 times at factory by mistake. CMV $8.

1979-80 MOISTURE GARDEN PRODUCTS
BODY LOTION
10 oz. plastic, CMV 25c. 1st issue with 50c off companion bottle, CMV 50c.
PUMP DISPENSER
For body lotion. CMV 50c.
FACIAL LOTION
4 oz. plastic bottle, not shown. CMV 25c.
HAND CREAM
4 oz. plastic jar, not shown CMV 25c.
1979 MOISTURE GARDEN FLOWER GARDEN
Avon box holds planter and packet of seeds. Box came with white outside sleeve. CMV $1. MB.

1978-80 FEELING FRESH PRODUCTS
1978 FEELING FRESH COOLER BAG
White and blue zipper bag given to Avon Reps only, CMV $4.
BODY SPLASH WITH MOISTURIZERS
8 oz. plastic. CMV 50c.
DEODORANT BODY POWDER WITH BAKING SODA
8 oz. plastic. CMV 50c.
FOOT COMFORT SPRAY
3 oz. metal can. CMV 50c.
ROLL-ON DEODORANT
2 oz. plastic. CMV 50c.
1979-80 FEELIN' FRESH AEROSOL DEODORANT
4 oz. white can and cap. Blue and green letters. Ozone safe formula. SSP $1.59, CMV 25c.

1979-80 ON DUTY ROLL-ON DEODORANT
(Left) 2 oz. black and blue plastic, blue cap. Anti-stain, quick drying. SSP $1., CMV 25c.

1979-80 ON DUTY AEROSOL DEODORANT
(Center) 4 oz. black can. Ozone safe formula. SSP $1.59, CMV 25c.

1979-80 DRI 'N DELICATE AEROSOL DEODORANT
(Right) 4 oz. pink and white can, white cap. Ozone safe formula. SSP $1.59, CMV 25c.

1982-83 ULTRA TOUCH NAIL CARE PRODUCTS
.5 oz. clear glass bottles with tall brown caps in brown boxes. Choice of Nail Fortifier, Quick Nail Dry, Super Base Coat, Shiny Top Coat. Brown tube of Cuticle Remover and white handled Avon nail file in pink case.

HOT OIL TREATMENT
Box of 8 packets

CUTICLE & NAIL CONDITIONING CREAM
1 oz. tube. SSP $1.50 each product, CMV 25c each.

1982-83 SUNSATIONS MAKEUP
Sun Sheer Lip Gloss, Sun Sheer Nail Enamel, Sun Sheer Face Color, Sun Sheer Eye Shadow. CMV all products 25c each.

1982-84 CHECK POINT DEODORANT
(left) 2 oz. size in red, blue or green. SSP $2 - CMV 25c ea.

1983-84 SAHARA DRY DEODORANT
(right) 1.5 oz. plastic, tan top, white bottom. SSP $1.50 - CMV 25c.

1982-83 EVEN TONE PRODUCTS
Soft Matte Makeup Medium Cover, Dewy Makeup Light to Medium Cover, Finishing Face Loose Powder with puff, Dewy Makeup Ultra Cover, Bronze Beauty Makeup. All products CMV 25c, powder CMV $1.

1982-83 GENTLE WAVES SOFT PERM
Box holds 3.75 oz. bottle of Waving Lotion, 3.75 oz. bottle of Neutralizer, Foamer Application bottle, 100 end papers and instruction sheet. SSP $4., CMV $4. MB.

1982-83 GENTLE WAVE CURLERS
Box holds 2 different size curlers. Box of 50 SSP $4., CMV $4. MB.

1982-83 GENTLE WAVE HAIR MIST
6 oz. blue spray bottle, CMV 50c.

1981-83 ACCOLADE PRODUCTS
Complete Cleansing Complex, Facial Toning Rinse, Night Treatment, Daytime Moisture Support. CMV all products 25c.

1981-82 SALON SYSTEM PRODUCTS
7 oz. plastic bottles, brown caps. Choice of Freshening Shampoo, Freshening Detangler, Balanced Shampoo, Balanced Conditioner, Moisture Rich Shampoo, Moisture Rich Conditioner and 5 oz. tube of Moisture Rich Pack. SSP $3. each, CMV 25c each.

1982-83 CARE DEEPLY LOTION FOR DRY SKIN
10 oz. plastic. White bottle is Extra Creamy Lotion for Dry Skin, and peach color bottle is same with Cocoa Butter. SSP $2.50, CMV 25c each.

1982-83 CLEAR SKIN 2 PRODUCTS
Blue and white basic colors.
ASTRINGENT CLEANSING LOTION
8 oz. bottle
CLEANSING SCRUB - 2.5 oz. tube.
5% BPO LOTION - 1 oz. bottle.
TINTED BLEMISH CREAM - 1 oz. tube
ANTIBACTERIAL CLEANSING CAKE
SOAP - 2.5 oz. bar. CMV all products
25c each. CMV soap, $1 mint.

1982 NAIL ACCENT TOP SHIELD
.5 oz. yellow cap, pink lettering.
Came in set only, no box. CMV $1.
1982 NAIL ACCENTS
Same as above only came with 3
sheets of stick on nail decals. SSP $3
CMV $3 set.

1979-81 VITAMIN SAMPLE DEMO
CMV $10. MB.

1981-82 LUSCIOUS BUBBLES
(Left to right)
3.5 oz. pink plastic bottles.
FOAMING CREAMY CLEANSER
SUPER BUBBLE BATH
SSP $1.50, CMV 25c each, no boxes.
1981 HENNA RICH TRIAL SIZE
1 oz. each plastic. Shampoo or
Conditioner. SSP 70c, CMV 25c
each, no box.

1982-83 MOMENTUM PRODUCTS
CELL ENERGIZING FORMULA
2 oz. lavender plastic bottle. SSP $5.,
CMV 25c MB.
CELL ENERGIZING FORMULA
SAMPLES
Package of 10 samples with sample
cards. CMV, pkg. of 10 mint, 50c.

1980-81 BEAUTY PLAN PRODUCTS
CREAMY COMPLEXION BAR SOAP
CMV $1.50
OIL CONTROL COMPLEXION BAR
SOAP - CMV $1.50
OIL FREE MOISTURE LOTION
3 oz. plastic bottle, CMV 25c.
MOISTURE FULL CREAM - 3 oz. jar.
CMV 50c.
BEAUTY PLAN BAG - 6¼"x 8¼" size.
Sold 1 campaign only, CMV $3.
Sample of each product 10 to a box.
CMV 25c per box.

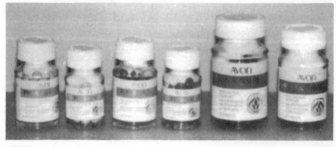

1979-81 PROPER BALANCE
VITAMINS
3 different bottles, 60 and 100 size.
Proper balance for the whole family.
CMV $10. MB, for Womens Vitality,
CMV $10. MB, for Dieters Support,
CMV $10. MB.

1980-83 BEAUTY FLUID
3 oz. bottle, black cap. SSP $4.,
CMV 50c MB. 1983 only short issue
in 4.5 oz. bottle. CMV $1 MB.

1981 SUMMERTIME COOLER
Short issue. Blue and white plastic
cooler. 10½"x 7"x 6½". SSP $3.,
CMV $3. mint.

1980-81 VITA MIGHTS FOR KIDS
Vitamins for kids, bottle of 100
tablets. CMV $20. MB.

1979-81 VITAMINS SAMPLES
3 different vitamins on sample cards.
CMV $5. each.

1960's NAIL CLIPPER
Avon on nail clippers. We have no
information on this. Rare. CMV $5.

1982-83 NEW VITALITY PRODUCTS
7 oz. plastic bottles with NPD. 4 different. SSP $2.50, CMV 25c each.

1981-82 TWICE FRESH MOUTHWASH
10 oz. frosted plastic, white cap. SSP $1.80, CMV 25c.
1981-82 CHILDRENS LIQUID CLEANSER REFILL
8 oz. white plastic, green cap. SSP $3., CMV 50c.

1981 SUMMERTIME PILLOW TOTE
Blue and white plastic beach bag. Says Avon on it. Can be blown up to make a pillow. SSP $1.40, CMV $1.50 mint.

1980-83 ACTIVE AID PRODUCTS
All are white with blue trim.
MEDICATED SKIN COMFORT LOTION - 8 oz. plastic.
ANTISEPTIC FIRST AID SPRAY
3 oz. metal can.
ANTISEPTIC FIRST AID CREAM
1.5 oz. tube.
MEDICATED PROTECTIVE SHIELD
1.5 oz. tube. SSP $1.60, to $2. each. CMV 50c each, no boxes.

1981 PRETTY PORTABLES
White with pink caps and multi color design. Sold one time only. Ultra Talc, Hand Cream, and Bubble Bath in 2 oz. plastic bottle. SSP 70c, CMV $1. each, no box.

1980-81 SPORTIN' TOTE
Tan nylon, 12"x 14"x 4". SSP $7., CMV $7. In Avon bag.

1981-82 AMERICAN BATH FOAM
2 oz. plastic, beige top
1981-82 ORIENTAL BATH FOAM
2 oz. plastic, green top.
1981-82 SCANDINAVIAN BATH FOAM
2 oz. plastic, blue cap.   SSP $4.
each, CMV 50c.

1980-82 TIME CONTROL TEMPORARY WRINKLE SMOOTHER
.75 oz. plastic bottle, gold cap. SSP $6., CMV 25c MB.
1980-82 ULTRA WEAR NAIL ENAMEL
.5 oz. clear glass, tall square top cap. SSP $2., CMV 25c MB.

1980-83 RICH MOISTURE PRODUCTS
FACIAL LOTION - 4 oz. bottle short issue.
BODY LOTION - 8 or 16 oz. bottle.
FACE CREAM - 3.5 or 6 oz. jar. CMV 50c each, all are turquoise in color.
1980-83 VITA MOIST PRODUCTS
Yellow and white, brown trim.
BODY LOTION - 8 or 16 oz.
HAND CREAM - 3.75 or 6 oz. tubes.
FACE CREAM - 3.5 or 7 oz. jar. CMV 50c each.

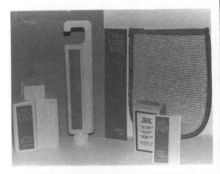

1982-83 BODY TONICS PRODUCTS
All are light green
EMOLLIENT BATH BEADS WITH MINERALS
5 oz. plastic bottle. SSP $3., CMV 25c.
EMOLLIENT CLEANSER WITH MINERALS
5 oz. tube like plastic bottle. SSP $3., CMV 25c.
FRICTION MITT
Green and white scrub mitt. Does not say Avon. SSP $6., CMV 50c mint.
EMOLLIENT CLEANSER WITH MINERALS SAMPLES
Box of 10 samples, CMV 25c, box of 10.

1980-81 REFLECTIONS COLLECTIONS
All in silver and gray boxes.
DAZZLE DUST HIGHLIGHTING POWDER
Small plastic jar. SSP $4., CMV 50c MB.
REFLECTIVE LIPSTICK
Pearl and silver tube. SSP $4.50, CMV $1. MB.
REFLECTIVE NAIL GLAZE
.5 oz. bottle, square top cap. SSP $2.30, CMV 50c MB.
SOFT REFLECTIONS BODY GLOW
1.5 oz. plastic bottle. SSP $3.50, CMV 25c MB.

1980 NUMBER 1 COLOR PRODUCTS
Special No. 1 box with:
COLORCREME MOISTURE LIPSTICK
Pink and gold, SSP $1.25, CMV $1. MB.
COLORCREME WATERPROOF MASCARA
Pink and gold, white cap. SSP $1.25, CMV $1. MB.
AVON NUMBER ONE NAIL ENAMEL
No. 1 on bottle, tall square top cap. SSP $1.25, CMV $1.25 MB.

1980-82 CLEAN & LIVELY
(Left to right)
OIL FREE CONDITIONER - green cap.
OIL CONTROL SHAMPOO
Yellow cap. 7 oz. plastic bottles. SSP each $1.90, CMV 25c.
1980-82 LUSCIOUS BUBBLES
Foaming Creamy Cleanser
Super Bubble Bath
7 oz. each, plastic bottles. SSP $3. each, CMV 25c each.
1980-82 BODY BONUS
Conditioner with added body. Shampoo with added body.
7 oz. plastic bottles. SSP $2.20 each, CMV 25c.

1981-83 HENNA RICH
Shampoo and conditioner. 8 oz. plastic bottles. SSP $2. each, CMV 25c.

1980-82 SUN SEEKERS TANNING BUTTER
Brown plastic jar. SSP $2.80, CMV 25c.
1980-83 SUN SEEKERS LOTIONS
5 different 4 oz. plastic bottles, same shape. Ultra Sunsafe Lotion, Sunsafe Lotion, Tanning Oil and Tanning Lotion, SSP $3.50 each, CMV 25c each.

1980-83 ENVIRA PRODUCTS
Conditioning Cleansing Cream, 3.75 oz. jar. All Night Conditioning Cream, 3.75 oz. jar. Clarifying Toner, 5 oz. Protective Moisturizing Lotion, 2 oz. CMV 50c each.

1982-83 PIZAZZ PRODUCTS
Stay Put Eyeshadow, Oil Inhibiting Blush, Oil Inhibiting Foundation, Super Long Smudge Proof Mascara, Shine Up Lip Tint. All products CMV 25c each.

1981-83 FANCY FEET PRODUCTS
Double Action Cream, 3 oz. tube. Double Action Spray, 4 oz. can. Double Action Talc, 3.5 oz. size. Double Action Brush. All are blue in color. SSP $2. to $3. each, CMV 25c each.

1980-82 SHOWER SCAPE COLLECTION
All are blue and white.
MOISTURE MIST
2.8 oz. can.
SHOWER BRUSH
SHOWER GEL
6 oz. tube.
SMOOTH TALC
5 oz. CMV each 25c. Brush $1.

1981 WINTER TUCK-INS
Matching set, green and white, no boxes. Winter Glow Soap, Rich Moisture Hand Cream. Winter Glow Powder Sachet. SSP $1.25 each, CMV $1.25 each.

1982-83 ENVIRA PRODUCTS
Gentle Eye Color, Soft Eye Definer, Conditioning Mascara, Pure Color Blush, Pure Color Lipstick, Conditioning Make Up. CMV all products 25c.

SKIN-SO-SOFT

SEE 1984 SUPPLEMENT IN BACK OF BOOK FOR
MORE SKIN-SO-SOFT

1968-78 SATIN TALC
(Left) 3 oz. size. 2 different labels as shown. OSP $2., CMV 50c each.
1977-78 SKIN-SO-SOFT TRIAL SIZE
(Right) 1 oz. plastic bottle, white lid. OSP 25c, CMV 25c.

1965-67 SKIN-SO-SOFT AFTER SHOWER FOAM
(Left) 4 oz. white spray can with turquoise cap. OSP $2.25, CMV $1.
1965-74 SKIN-SO-SOFT SOAP
(Inside Left) 3 oz. bar. OSP 49c, CMV $1. mint.
1964-69 SKIN-SO-SOFT
(Inside Right) 8 oz. glass bottle with three S's on side. Turquoise cap. OSP $4., CMV $1.
1961-69 SKIN-SO-SOFT
(Right) 4 oz. glass bottle with three S's on side. Turquoise cap. OSP $2.25, CMV $1.

1979-80 SKIN-SO-SOFT TRIAL SIZE
(Left) 1 oz. plastic bottle, blue cap. CMV 25c.
1979-80 SKIN-SO-SOFT LIGHT BOUQUET
(Right) 16 oz. plastic bottle, blue cap. SSP $5.99, CMV 25c. All plastic bottle Skin-So-Soft products. 8 oz. size issued 1978. CMV 25c each.

1966-67 SKIN-SO-SOFT
(Left) 1 oz. gold cap with painted leaf. Came in set of three only. Unforgettable, Rapture, Occur!, Somewhere, Topaze, Cotillion, Here's My Heart, To A Wild Rose, Wishing. CMV $3. MB - $2. BO.
1969 SKIN-SO-SOFT
(Right) 1 oz. gold cap & paper label. Came in Unforgettable, Rapture, Occur!, Somewhere, Topaze, Cotillion, To A Wild Rose & Here's My Heart. OSP $1.50 each, CMV $4. MB - $3. BO.

1969-78 SKIN-SO-SOFT
(left) 4 oz. in clear or frosted bottle with turquoise cap. OSP $3., CMV 25c.
1969-78 SKIN-SO-SOFT
(Center) 8 oz. clear plastic bottle with turquoise cap. OSP $5., CMV 25c.
1972-78 SKIN-SO-SOFT
(Right) 16 oz. clear plastic bottle with turquoise cap. OSP $8.50, CMV 25c.

SKIN-SO-SOFT PRODUCTS
White & gold with aqua lids.
1973-78 SKIN SOFTENER
(Left) 5 oz. plastic jar. OSP $4.50, CMV 25c.
1960's BATH OIL SAMPLE
(Inside Left) CMV 50c.
1973-77 SATIN POWDER SPRAY
(Left Center) 7 oz. can. OSP $4.50, CMV 50c.
1970's BATH OIL SAMPLE
(Center) CMV 25c.
SATIN TALC
(Center Right)
1974-78 EMOLLIENT SHOWER GEL
(Inside Right) 6 oz. OSP $4., CMV 25c.
1970's EMOLLIENT SHOWER GEL SAMPLE
(Right) CMV 25c.

1967 SKIN-SO-SOFT
(Left) 4 oz. white cap. This bottle has no S embossed on side. Issued during glass strike. OSP $2.25, CMV $10.
1969-70 SKIN-SO-SOFT SCENTED BATH OIL
(Right) 2 oz. clear glass bottom, clear plastic top. This top is the same as the clear Just II. Came in Charisma, Brocade, Rapture, Unforgettable, Occur!, Here's My Heart, Cotillion, To A Wild Rose & Regence. OSP $2.50, CMV $4. MB - $3. BO.

1970's SKIN-SO-SOFT SAMPLES
Box of 10 packets, marked not for resale. CMV $1. MB.

1980 SMOOTH AS SILK SKIN SOFTENER
(Left) 5 oz. pink plastic. CMV 25c.
1980 SKIN-SO-SOFT SKIN SOFTENER
(Right) 5 oz. blue plastic. CMV 25c.

1970 SKIN-SO-SOFT
(Left) Clear glass container holds 2 oz. Skin-So-Soft, gold cap. Comes in Bird of Paradise, Elusive, Charisma, Brocade, Unforgettable, Field Flowers, Occur!, Rapture & To A Wild Rose. OSP $2.50, CMV $2.

1971-72 SKIN-SO-SOFT "2 OZ."
(Right) 2 oz. 7 layer glass bottle with gold cap. 4½" high. Came in Bird of Paradise, Elusive, Charisma, Brocade, To A Wild Rose. OSP $2.50, CMV $2. BO - $3. MB.

1967 SKIN-SO-SOFT COMPLIMENTS
Box holds 3 oz. box of Satin Talc & 2 bars of SSS soap. OSP $2.50, CMV $9. MB.

1964-65 BATH MATES
Box holds 4 oz. bottle Skin-So-Soft bath oil & 2 cakes of soap. OSP $3.23, CMV $11. MB.

1966-67 BATH LUXURY
Box holds 4 oz. bottle of Skin-So-Soft & pink bath sponge. Came with 2 different sponges. Coarse as shown & fine grain. OSP $4.50, CMV $11. MB.

1966 FRAGRANCE TRIO
Box holds 3 bottles of Skin-So-Soft, 1 oz. each, gold cap. In choice of Unforgettable, Rapture, Occur!, Somewhere, Topaze, Cotillion, Here's My Heart, To A Wild Rose & Wishing. OSP $4.50, CMV $12. MB.

1968 SKIN-SO-SOFT SMOOTHIES
Box holds 4 oz. bottle of Skin-So-Soft & 3 oz. Satin Talc. OSP $3.50, CMV $8. MB.

1965 SKIN-SO-SOFT DISH & SOAP
Blue & white plastic soap dish with white bar of SSS soap. OSP $1.50, CMV $10. MB - soap & dish $8. - dish only $3.

1965 SHOWER MATES
Green & white box holds 4 oz. can of after shower foam & 2 bars of SSS soap. OSP $3.20, CMV $11. MB.

BATH SALTS — MISC.

1931-33 BATH SALTS
(Right) 10 oz. ribbed glass bottle with blue lid, silver label. 2 different labels. OSP 75c, CMV $60. MB, $40. BO mint.

1933-37 BATH SALTS
(Left) 8½ oz. ribbed glass jar with dark blue cap. Came in Ariel & Vernafleur from 1933-37, Pine & Jasmine from 1935-37. OSP 63c each, CMV $60. MB - $40. BO mint.

1954-57 BATH SALTS
8 oz. bottle with turquoise cap and label. Came in Jasmine and Pine. OSP 89c each. CMV $20. MB, $15. BO.

1943-45 BATH SALTS
5 oz. red and white paper containers. Came in Attention, Jasmine, Pine, Vernafleur. OSP 69c each. CMV $25. each mint, $30. MB.

1929-30 BATH SALTS
10 oz. bottle with metal lid, silver and blue label. Ribbed glass sides. OSP 75c - CMV $60 BO, $75 MB.

BEAUTY DUST, POWDERS, TALC — MISC.

1933-37 BATH SALTS SAMPLE
Ribbed glass bottle with blue cap. Came in Ariel, Vernafleur. CMV $60., Pine and Jasmine CMV $55. each.

1945-48 DUSTING POWDER
6 oz. blue and white cardboard with ladies face on lid. Also contained Apple Blossom Beauty Dust. OSP $1.35, CMV $25.

1936-49 DUSTING POWDER
13 oz. turquoise and beige can with "A" on top. 1st (1936-39) issue had CPC on bottom. CMV $30. 1940-49 Avon Products label only. OSP $1.39, CMV $20., $25. MB. There are at least 3 different varieties of the 1936-49 metal dusting powder. One has a deeply indented bottom, shining silver, with CPC on it, another has a slightly indented shiny gold bottom, no CPC, and another has a slightly indented dull silver bottom, no CPC on it.

1930-34 DUSTING POWDER
(Left) 8 oz. blue and silver square can. OSP $1.35, CMV $40. MB, $30. can only mint.

1926-29 DUSTING POWDER
(Right) Gold metal can with black stripes. Came in Daphne, Vernafleur, Trailing Arbutus, California Rose, Baby Powder and Super Rite Talcum. OSP $1., CMV $50. MB, $40. can only.

1935-36 DUSTING POWDER
13 oz. metal gold colored can. Came in Bath Ensemble Set only. CMV $35. mint.

1935-36 DUSTING POWDER
Same as gold can only general issue was silver and blue can. OSP $1.20, CMV $30. can only mint. $40. MB.

1944 BEAUTY DUST CHRISTMAS BOX
Special issue Christmas box. Holds feather design paper container of beauty dust. OSP $1.10, CMV $27. MB as shown, beauty dust only mint, $22.

1936 BATH SALTS
8½ or 9 oz. glass jars with turquoise lids from 1936-44, small paper label. 9 oz. jars from 1943-53 came in Ariel, 1936-44 CMV $30. Pine 1936-44 then 46 to 53 CMV $25. Vernafleur 1936-44 CMV $35 and Jasmine 1936-44 then 46-48 CMV $25. Attention 1943-44 then 46-48 OSP each 63c, CMV $25. Add $5. for box. See attention Fragrance for regular issue box.

1943-46 DUSTING POWDER
13 oz. paper box, turquoise and ivory. OSP $1.39, CMV $35. MB, $30. box only mint.

1943 DUSTING POWDER CHRISTMAS BOX
Outer box special issue for Christmas. Holds square cardboard beauty dust. CMV $50. MB as shown.

1965 BEAUTY DUST REFILL
White outer box holds colorful inner box with plain beauty dust refill. Came in choice of Persian Wood, Cotillion, To A Wild Rose, Somewhere, Topaze, Occur!, Here's My Heart, and Rapture. OSP $2.98, CMV $7. as shown MB.

1940-41 DUSTING POWDER CHRISTMAS BOX
Special issue blue and white Christmas box holds regular issue metal can of dusting powder. OSP $1., CMV $35. MB as shown.

1930-36 DUSTING POWDER REFILL
Gray box holds plain paper wrapped box of powder. OSP 59c, CMV $25. MB.

1930-36 FACE POWDER
Silver and blue paper box came in Ariel and Vernafleur. OSP 78c, CMV $16. in box. $12. container only mint.

1943-44 DUSTING POWDER
Turquoise and white paper box. OSP $1.39, CMV $35., $40. MB.

1936-49 DUSTING POWDER REFILL
Round cardboard container. Came in Jasmine or Avon dusting powder. OSP 89c, CMV $15. MB, Add $5. for CPC label.

(Left to Right)
1942-48 BEAUTY DUST
6 oz. blue feather design cardboard. Came in Avon Beauty Dust and Apple Blossom. OSP $1.19, CMV $22., $25. MB.
1942-48 FACE POWDER
1¾ oz. blue feather design cardboard. OSP 89c. CMV $8. mint. $12. MB.
1946-48 HEAVENLIGHT FACE POWDER
2½ oz. same feather design paper box. OSP 89c, CMV $8., $12. MB.
1942-49 ROUGE
Blue feather design, paper container on right. OSP 55c, CMV $5., $7. MB.
1942-46 FEATHER DESIGN LIPSTICK
Blue plastic top and bottom with cardboard sides. Also came with red plastic top and bottom. OSP 59c, CMV $5., $8. MB.

1941 DUSTING POWDER MOTHERS DAY BOX
Special issue lavender box with white lace holds regular issue dusting powder. Sold during Mothers day. OSP $1., CMV $35. MB as shown.

1966-68 BEAUTY DUST DEMO
White box, came in choice of beauty dust refill and different fragrance empty container. Both came boxed. Used by Reps C10, 1966. CMV $11. MB.

1955-57 SHEER MIST FACE POWDER
Turquoise cardboard with white and pink flowers and gold 4A design on lid. OSP $1.10, CMV $4., $5. MB.

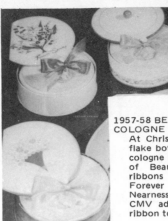

1957-58 BEAUTY DUST WITH COLOGNE
At Christmas only a 5/8 dram snow flake bottle with white round cap of cologne was given free with purchase of Beauty Dust. Matching neck ribbons on each bottle. Cotillion, Forever Spring, To A Wild Rose, Nearness, Elegante, Bright Night. CMV add $9. for each bottle with ribbon to price of Beauty Dust.

1936-39 FACE POWDER
3" diameter, turquoise and cream container, cardboard. Came in Cotillion, Ariel or Vernafleur fragrance. Choice of natural, rose, peach, Rachel No. 1, Rachel No. 2, orchre, orchre-rose and suntan shades. OSP 78c, CMV $10., $13. MB.

1956 BEAUTY DUST WITH COLOGNE
At Christmas only a 5/8 dram bottle with white flat cap and neck ribbon came in Beauty Dust. Elegante with red ribbon, Nearness, lavender ribbon, Cotillion, and To A Wild Rose, pink ribbons, Forever Spring, purple ribbon, Quaintance, blue ribbon. Each ribbon has gold edge. Add $12. to each Beauty Dust if bottle has ribbon.

1958-59 SHEER MIST FACE POWDER
2½ oz. white cardboard box with pink rose on lid and pink rim around edge. OSP $1.10, CMV $1. box only, $3. MB.

1960-63 FACE POWDER
Same design as Sheer Mist only has plastic lid, no pink rim. OSP $1.25, CMV $1., $1.50 MB.

1963-67 FASHION FINISH FACE POWDER
1½ oz. white plastic box. OSP $2.25, CMV 50c.

1976 FINISHING FACE POWDER EVEN TONE
1½ oz. pink plastic box. Same as 1969-75 white box. OSP $3., CMV 50c.

1953-55 BEAUTY DUST WITH COLOGNE
At Christmas only a 5/8 dram bottle of cologne with silk ribbon came in Beauty Dust in Quaintance, To A Wild Rose, both pink and white. Also blue container Golden Promise, Forever Spring and Cotillion. OSP $1.75 each, CMV add $12. to price of Beauty Dust if bottle has ribbon and $10. without ribbon.

1943-46 ELITE FOOT POWDER
Maroon and cream colored paper box. 2.75 oz. Black screw off octagonal cap. OSP 43c, CMV $25. mint.

1943-46 ELITE FOOT POWDER
2.75 oz. maroon and white victory paper box. Flat punch out top with paper lift off lid. OSP 43c, CMV $25. mint.

1936-48 ELITE POWDER
Large family size on left, turquoise and white can. OSP $1.19, CMV $25. $30. MB.

1936-54 ELITE POWDER
2.9 oz. or 3 oz. size on right, turquoise and white can, 2 different boxes. OSP 43c, CMV $10. CO, $12. MB. Add $3. for CPC label.

1930-32 TALCUM POWDER
Silver and blue can came in regular and family size. OSP 50c, CMV $35., $40. MB. 1 lb. family size OSP $1., CMV $35., $45. MB.

1944 HEAVENLIGHT FACE POWDER
General issue feather design paper box. Shown in 1944 pink design box. 2½ oz. contents. Powder only sold in 1944-48. CMV $12. MB as shown. Powder box only $8.

1932-36 SMOKER'S TOOTH POWDER
Green can OSP 51c, CMV $35. MB, $25. can only.

1943-46 ELITE POWDER
Turquoise and white paper boxes in family size. OSP $1.19, CMV $30. Regular size OSP 43c, CMV $20. Three different caps, plastic cap, punch out top and punch out top with paper top and bottom cover. Same CMV.

1936-49 TOOTH POWDER
Box holds 2¼ oz. turquoise and white can. Silver slide open cap. OSP 49c, CMV $10., $15. MB.

1931-36 ELITE POWDER
Silver and blue can with blue cap is general issue in regular size on right. OSP 37c, CMV $25. Family size 1 lb. can on left OSP $1.04, CMV $30. Add $5. MB.

1934-35 ELITE POWDER
Same design and shape cans. Came in sets only in gold and blue cans. CMV small size $35. Large family size $35. add $5. each MB.

1944-46 SMOKER'S TOOTH POWDER
Turquoise and white paper container. Plastic cap. OSP 57c, CMV $23. mint.

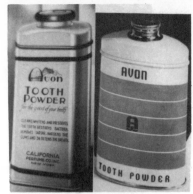

SMOKERS TOOTH POWDER SAMPLES

(Left) 1936-40 Small ¼ oz. turquoise and white can. CPC label, turquoise sifter cap. CMV $35. mint.

(Right) 1940-49 Same can only has chrome lift off cap. CMV $30. mint.

(Center) Same can, has small chrome cap, CMV $30.

1930-36 TOOTH POWDER

(Left) Green metal can. OSP 35c, CMV $30. MB, $25. can only mint.

1936-50 TOOTH POWDER

(Right) Turquoise and white metal can, silver cap. OSP 36c, CMV $14. in box, $10. can only.

1943-46 ELITE POWDER

2.75 oz. or 3 oz. paper box. OSP 43c, CMV $18. mint.

1943-46 TOOTH POWDER

3 oz. paper box. OSP 39c, CMV $20. mint.

1943-46 SMOKER'S TOOTH POWDER

3½ oz. paper box with metal top and bottom. OSP 59c, CMV $20. mint. All are turquoise and white.

(Left to Right)

1936-49 SMOKER'S TOOTH POWDER Metal cap, 3½ oz. turquoise and white can. OSP 36c, CMV $16., $18. MB.

1950-54 SMOKER'S TOOTH POWDER 3½ oz. turquoise and white can. turquoise tilt cap. OSP 57c, CMV $14., $16. MB.

1946-50 SMOKER'S TOOTH POWDER 3½ oz. turquoise and white can, turquoise plastic cap. OSP 57c, CMV $14., $16. MB.

1949 Only - AMMONIATED TOOTH POWDER

3 oz. turquoise can and tilt cap. This can with this style cap was a very short issue. OSP 49c, CMV $15. MB, $13. can only mint.

1958-66 AQUA DENT

7 oz. green color can with white cap. OSP 79c, CMV $3., $4. MB.

1943-46 TOOTH POWDER

Flat metal top, paper side container. 3 oz. size. Turquoise and white. OSP 39c, CMV $25. MB, $20. can only mint.

1949-55 AMMONIATED TOOTH POWDER

3 oz. turquoise and white can with turquoise lid. OSP 49c, CMV $10., $13. MB.

1943-46 SMOKER'S TOOTH POWDER "PAPER"

(Left) Maroon and cream paper sides, tin top and bottom. OSP 36c, CMV $20. mint, $25. MB.

1943-46 TALC FOR MEN "PAPER"

(Right) Maroon and cream paper container. Metal screw on cap in black or maroon. OSP 37c, CMV $20. mint.

1936-49 TALC FOR MEN
Maroon and cream colored can with maroon cap. OSP 37c, CMV $15. in box, $12. can only.

1938-49 SMOKER'S TOOTH POWDER
Maroon and cream colored can. Came in Men's Sets only. CMV $16. mint.

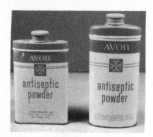

1956-62 ANTISEPTIC POWDER
(Left) 3 oz. gray and white can, red cap. OSP 59c, CMV $2.

1962-64 ANTISEPTIC POWDER
(Right) 3 oz. gray and white can, red cap. OSP 69c, CMV $1.50.

1965-68 ANTISEPTIC POWDER
Same as 1962-64 can only 2¾ oz. size. OSP 69c, CMV $1.

1970-71 POWDER PUFFERY BEAUTY DUST
5 oz. white plastic base with pink puff in Charisma, Brocade, Cotillion and To A Wild Rose. OSP $5., CMV $3., $5. MB.

1963 SACHET PILLOWS
Green and white holder contains powder sachet pillow. Came 6 to a pack. OSP 50c, CMV for set of 6, $7. mint.

1960-61 BEAUTY DUST
3 oz. white plastic bottle, has paper label or painted label, turquoise cap. This came in Modern Simplicity Set only. Came in Cotillion, To A Wild Rose and Here's My Heart. CMV $15.

1965 BATH BOUQUET TALC
1½ oz. green paper box. Came in Bath Bouquet Set only in all fragrances of that set. CMV $8. mint.

1973-76 HEAVY DUTY POWDERED HAND CLEANSER
10 oz. blue, white, pink and black cardboard with plastic top and bottom. OSP $2.25, CMV $1.

1960-70's POWDER PUFF COMPACT REFILLS
2 different puffs and package for compacts. CMV $3. each mint.

1966-68 PAT 'N POWDER MITT
Lace mitt contains beauty dust in Occur!, Rapture, and Unforgettable. OSp $2.50, CMV $3. MB.

1940-50's DUSTING POWDER PUFF
Envelope holds Avon puff. Rare. CMV $10.

1940's TRIM TONE COSMETIC STOCKING
Beige with gold band, box turquoise. OSP $1.50, CMV $25. MB.

1940's POWDER PAK PUFFS REFILL
Envelope holds 2 compact puff refills.
CMV $5. mint.
1960's POWDER PUFF REFILLS
Envelope holds 2 puff refills. CMV
$3.

COLOGNES — MISC.
SEE 1984 SUPPLEMENT IN BACK OF BOOK FOR MORE MISC. COLOGNES

1940-41 REFRESHING COLOGNE
4 oz. bottle with turquoise cap and label. Turquoise box. OSP 52c, CMV $35. MB, $30. bottle only.

1967-68 GOLD CAP ROCKER COLOGNE
½ oz. gold round cap. Came in Brocade, Regence, Unforgettable, Rapture, Occur!, Somewhere, Topaze, Cotillion, Here's My Heart, To A Wild Rose, Persian Wood and Wishing. OSP $1.25, CMV $2. each BO, $3.50 MB.
1959-62 FLAT TOP ROCKER COLOGNE
½ oz. flat plastic cap. Came in Persian Wood, Here's My Heart, Cotillion, To A Wild Rose, Topaze, Somewhere, Regence, Bright Night and Nearness. OSP $1. each, CMV $4. BO, $6. MB. Add $1. for Nearness and Bright Night.

1931-36 HEADACHE COLOGNE
4 oz. ribbed glass bottle with dark blue cap and silver label. OSP 75c, CMV $50. bottle only, $60. MB.

1936-40 INHALANT COLOGNE
4 oz. bottle with turquoise cap and label. Turquoise and white box. OSP 52c, CMV $35. MB, $30. BO.

1973-75 DEMI COLOGNE
½ oz. clear glass, gold cap. Came in Imperial Garden, Patchwork, Sonnet, Moonwind, Roses Roses, Field Flowers, Bird of Paradise, Charisma, Unforgettable, Topaze, Occur!, Here's my Heart. SSP $1., CMV $1. MB.
1962-63 FAN ROCKER
½ oz. cologne, gold cap with neck cord. Came in To A Wild Rose, Here's My Heart, Persian Wood, Cotillion, Somewhere, Topaze. OSP $1., CMV $3. BO, $4. BO with cord, $6. MB.

1977-78 COLOGNE MINIATURE FOR MEN
(Left) ½ oz. Came in Clint, Everest or Wild Country. Smoked glass, gray cap. SSP 88c, CMV $1. MB.
1977 CHRISTMAS CANDLE COLOGNE DECANTER
(Center) 1 oz. green glass. Came in Charisma, Sweet Honesty, Topaze or Moonwind. SSP $1.29, CMV $1.50 BO, $2. MB.
1977 FRAGRANCE FACETTES
(Right) ½ oz. colognes. Came in Moonwind, Charisma, Topaze, Occur, Unforgettable, Here's My Heart, Cotillion, Sweet Honesty, Sonnet or Bird of Paradise, with gold cap. SSP $1., CMV $1. MB.

1975-77 COLOGNE
2 oz. clear glass with gold cap. Name of cologne on side in gold. Came in Moonwind, Charisma, Topaze, Sonnet. OSP $4., CMV 50c.
1975-76 DEMI-COLOGNE
Pepper Mill Shape. ½ oz. clear glass with gold cap. Holds Sonnet, Moonwind, Charisma, Patchwork, Somewhere, Topaze, Occur!, Cotillion. OSP $2., CMV $1.

1976-79 COLOGNE PETITE
(Left) ½ oz. Came in Charisma, Moonwind, Topaze, Here's My Heart, Unforgettable, Sweet Honesty, Cotillion, Occur!, Persian Wood, Regence, Rapture and Brocade. Gold cap. SSP 99c, CMV 50c.

1977-78 ULTRA COLOGNE
(Center and right) .33 oz. Came in Unspoken, Emprise, Ariane, Timeless, Candid. Came with silver or gold caps. SSP $1.50, CMV 50c MB.

1977-78 COLOGNE ½ OZ.
.5 oz. Came in Field Flowers, Honeysuckle, Hawaiian White Ginger, Apple Blossom, Raining Violets, Roses Roses, Lily of The Valley. Different fragrances came with different colored caps. OSP $2., CMV $1. each, $1.50 MB.

1966-70 COLOGNE SILK
3 oz. frosted glass bottle, gold cap, colored neck labels. Came in Here's My Heart, To A Wild Rose, Somewhere, Topaze, Cotillion, Unforgettable, Rapture, Occur!. OSP $3.50, CMV $2. BO, $3.50 MB.

1968-69 BUD VASE COLOGNE
4 oz. gold neck trim, colored paper label in Here's My Heart, To A Wild Rose, Somewhere, Topaze, Cotillion. OSP $4; Unforgettable, Rapture, Occur! OSP $5., CMV $3. BO, $5. MB.

1962-63 REFRESHING HOURS COLOGNE
2½ oz. gold cap, front side of bottle is flat, trimmed in gold. Came in Somewhere, Topaze, Cotillion, Here's My Heart, Persian Wood, To A Wild Rose Cologne. Came in Refreshing Hours Set only. CMV $8. mint.

1970-71 MINUETTE COLOGNE
5 oz. clear glass cologne bottle with gold cap. Came in Bird of Paradise, Elusive, Charisma, Brocade, Regence, Unforgettable, Rapture, Occur!, Somewhere, Topaze, To A Wild Rose, Cotillion and Here's My Heart. OSP $1.50, CMV $2. BO, $3. MB.

1966 COLOGNE ½ OZ.
Has embossed leaves in glass, gold cap. Came in Unforgettable, Rapture, Occur!, Somewhere, Topaze, Cotillion, Here's My Heart, To A Wild Rose or Wishing. Came in red and gold box in Renaissance Trio only. CMV $5. MB, $3. BO.

1964-66 ½ OZ. HEART SHAPED COLOGNE
Left is gold band on plastic cap. Came in Unforgettable, Rapture, Occur!, Cotillion, Somewhere, Topaze, Here's My Heart, Persian Wood, To A Wild Rose, and Wishing. OSP $1.25, CMV $5. MB, $3. BO.
HEART SHAPED EAU DE COLOGNE (Foreign)
(Right) No gold band around plastic cap. CMV $8.

1953-55 ½ OZ. COLOGNE
½ oz. size with white cap & painted label. Came in Cupids Bow, Fragrance Tie Ins, Fragrance Rainbow & Special Date Set only. Came in Forever Spring, Cotillion, Quaintance & To A Wild Rose. CMV $10. each. Bright Night, CMV $14. each mint.

1962-63 BATH CLASSIC
1½ oz. clear glass with gold design & gold cap. Came in Bath Classic Set only. Came in Somewhere, Cotillion, Topaze, Here's My Heart, Persian Wood & To A Wild Rose. CMV $10. BO mint.

1956 POWDER BOX COLOGNE
1/16 oz. Came in Beauty Dust only with ribbons attached. In Cotillion, Forever Spring, Golden Promise, To A Wild Rose & Quaintance. CMV $11. BO - $13. mint with ribbon.

1969-75 DAZZLING PERFUME
(Left) 1/8 oz. gold cap. Came in Unforgettable, Rapture, Occur! OSP $3.25; Somewhere, Topaze, Cotillion, Here's My Heart, To A Wild Rose, OSP $2.75; Charisma, Brocade, Regence, Bird of Paradise, Elusive & Moonwind, OSP $3.75, CMV $1. - $2. MB.

1969-70 MINUETTE COLOGNE
(Inside Left) ½ oz. gold cap. Elusive, Charisma, Brocade, Regence, Unforgettable, Rapture, Somewhere, Topaze, Occur!, Cotillion. OSP $1.50, CMV $1. - $2. MB.

1968-69 FRAGRANCES FLING COLOGNE
(Inside Right) ½ oz. gold cap. Came in Charisma, Brocade, Regence, Occur!, Unforgettable, Rapture, Somewhere, Topaze, Cotillion, Here's My Heart, To A Wild Rose, Wishing, Persian Wood. OSP $4., CMV $2. - $4. MB.

1969-76 PERFUME ROLLETTE
(Right) Unforgettable, Rapture, Occur!, OSP $2.50; Somewhere, Topaze, Cotillion, Here's My Heart, To A Wild Rose, OSP $2.; .33 oz. with gold 4A design on cap. CMV 50c - $1. MB.

1968 COLOGNE RIVIERA
(Left) 4 oz. silver cap & silver on bottle. Unscrew bottom of bottle & reverse metal to make stand for bottle. Came in Brocade & Regence. OSP $6., CMV $5. BO - $7. MB.

1967-68 COLOGNE CLASSIC
(Center) 4 oz. spiral bottle with gold cap, came in Here's My Heart, To A Wild Rose. OSP $3.50; Somewhere, Topaze, Cotillion, OSP $4.; Unforgettable, Rapture, Occur!, OSP $5., CMV $3. BO - $5. MB.

1969 GIFT COLOGNE
(Right) 4 oz. gold cap. Came in Topaze, To A Wild Rose, Somewhere, Here's My Heart, Cotillion & Rapture. OSP $4., CMV $3. BO - $5. MB.

1958 COIN FAN BOTTLES
½ oz. clear glass with turquoise caps. Box pink & gold. Came either cologne or lotion sachet, choice of To A Wild Rose, Cotillion, Nearness, Forever Spring, Bright Night, Elegante, Here's My Heart & Persian Wood. Came in Wishing Coin Set only. CMV $3. BO each - $8. MB.

1956 FRAGRANCE COLOGNES
(Left) 3 dram bottle with white painted label and cap. Came in Fragrance Rainbow set only in Nearness, Cotillion, Bright Night & To A Wild Rose. CMV $15. mint.

1953-55 BEAUTY DUST COLOGNE
(Right) 5/8 dram bottle with no label & flat white or round white cap. Came in Beauty Dust at Christmas only. Each had a silk neck ribbon with gold edge. Quaintance, blue ribbon; To A Wild Rose, pink ribbon; Forever Spring, purple ribbon; Cotillion, pink ribbon; Nearness, pink ribbon; Elegante, red ribbon. CMV with ribbon $12. - bottle only $8.

1957 Only ½ OZ. GEMS IN CRYSTAL COLOGNES
½ oz. bottle in 2 different shapes. Both came with pointed & flat top plastic caps. Each came in To A Wild Rose, Cotillion, Bright Night, Nearness. Each has matching tops and labels. All came in Gems in Crystal Set only. CMV $15. flat cap - $18. pointed cap.

343

1979-80 PURSE CONCENTRE
.33 oz. clear glass, gold tone cap. Comes in Here's My Heart, Unforgettable, Sonnet, Bird of Paradise, Occur!, Cotillion. SSP $1.50, CMV $1. MB.

1957-58 SNOW FLAKE COLOGNE
1/8 oz. round white caps. Came in Beauty Dust only in Cotillion, Forever Spring, To A Wild Rose, Nearness, Elegante & Bright Night. No labels on bottles. CMV $9. each. Flat top bottle came in all Beauty Dust at Christmas 1963. CMV $8. each.

1978-79 ULTRA COLOGNE .33 OZ.
.33 oz. clear glass. Came in gold & silver caps in Timeless, Ariane, Tempo, Candid, Emprise, Unspoken. Each comes with different color bands on caps & different boxes. SSP $1.50, CMV $1. MB.

1979 ANNIVERSARY COLOGNE PETITE
(Left) .5 oz. clear glass, gold cap, special box. Comes in Regence, Persian Wood, Rapture or Brocade. SSP $1.25, CMV $1. MB.
1979-80 COLOGNE CLASSIQUE
(Center) .5 oz. clear glass, gold cap. Comes in 11 fragrances. SSP $1.25, CMV $1. MB.
1979-80 PURSE CONCENTRE
(Right) .33 oz. octagonal shaped bottle. Different color stripe on cap for 9 different fragrances. SSP $1.50, CMV $1. MB.

1966-69 COLOGNE GEMS
1 oz. clear glass with flat plastic top. Came in Cotillion, Rapture, Unforgettable, Somewhere, Occur!, Topaze, Here's My Heart & To A Wild Rose. OSP $1.75, CMV $2. BO - $4. MB.

1980-82 SILKEN SCENTS COLOGNE
1.7 oz. clear glass. Sold with Silken Scents Scarf Set. CMV $4. MB.

1980 CRYSTAL DROP COLOGNE
(Left) Red Xmas box, .5 oz. clear glass, gold top. Choice of Moonwind, Charisma, Topaze, Occur!, Sweet Honesty, Zany, Sportif or Country Breeze. SSP $1.10, CMV $1. MB.
1980-81 ULTRA COLOGNE .33 OZ.
(Right) .33 oz. clear glass, gold or silver caps. Choice of Tempo, Candid, Timeless, Ariane, Emprise, Unspoken, Tasha & Foxfire. SSP $2., CMV $1. MB.

1981-82 ULTRA COLOGNE MINI SPRAY
Gold box holds .33 oz. gold, red decor. Choice of Timeless, Candid, Ariane, Tasha, Foxfire, Odyssey. SSP $4., CMV $1. MB.

1981 ULTRA SHIMMER COLOGNE DECANTER
(Left) .75 oz. octagonal shape clear glass, gold cap. Choice of Timeless, Foxfire, Tasha, Odyssey. In gold box dated 1981. SSP $4., CMV $4. MB.
1981-82 CLASSIC MINIATURE COLOGNE
(Inside Left) Small .33 oz. clear glass, gold cap. Choice of Tasha, Foxfire, Odyssey, Candid, Timeless, Unspoken, Ariane, Emprise. In gold box dated 1981. SSP $1.30, CMV $1.30 MB.
1981-82 FLUTED PETITE COLOGNE
(Inside Right) .5 oz. clear glass, gold cap, 4" tall. Choice of Moonwind, Topaze, Charisma, Occur!, Sweet Honesty, Zany or Country Breeze. SSP $1.25, CMV $1.25 MB.
1981 CHRISTMAS CHARMER COLOGNE
(Right) .33 oz. clear glass, red cap. Came with Country Charmer Candlestick. Zany or Charisma. CMV $2. BO.

1973 FRAGRANCE FACETS
.5 oz. gold cap. Came in Brocade & all fragrances. OSP $1.50, CMV $1.50 MB.

1956-58 COLOGNE STICK
White plastic with colored cap. Gold, white & red paper ornament package. Christmas only in 1957-58. Came in Nearness, Elegante, Bright Night, OSP $1.50; To A Wild Rose, Forever Spring, Cotillion, OSP $1.25, CMV stick only $6. - In package $20.

1952-56 COLOGNE STICK
Turquoise plastic cologne stick came in Golden Promise, Cotillion, Quaintance, Forever Spring & To A Wild Rose. 1956 only Nearness & Bright Night came in white plastic of same design. OSP $1.50, CMV each $10.

1956-58 COLOGNE STICK
White plastic with colored caps. Came in Nearness, Bright Night, OSP $1.50; Cotillion, Quaintance, To A Wild Rose, Forever Spring, OSP $1.25. Came in blue, white & gold paper ornament at Christmas only. CMV in ornament $20. - stick only $6.

SEE 1984 SUPPLEMENT IN BACK OF BOOK FOR MORE COLOGNE SPRAYS

COLOGNE MIST, SPRAYS – MISC.

COLOGNE & COLOGNE MIST SPECIAL ISSUE BOXES
Each was sold with choice of fragrance on a short selling period.
1968 COLOGNE
(Left) CMV $2. box.
1969 COLOGNE
(Inside Left) CMV $2. box.
1974 COLOGNE MIST
(Inside Right) CMV $1. box.
1971 COLOGNE MIST
(Right) CMV $1. box.

1962-64 CRYSTAL GLORY
(Left) Does not say Spray Essence on cap. Plastic gold top & base. 1 oz. refillable bottle. Came in Topaze, Somewhere, Cotillion, Here's My Heart, Persian Wood, To A Wild Rose. OSP $4.50 - $5., CMV $10. BO - $12. MB.
1962-64 CRYSTAL GLORY SPRAY ESSENCE
Gold top & base. Same fragrances as above. OSP $4.50 - $5., CMV $8. BO - $10. MB.
1962 SILVER TOP CRYSTAL GLORY SPRAY ESSENCE
Metal on top & base is silver instead of gold. Rare. Same fragrances as above. OSP $4.50 - $5., CMV $30.
1962-64 CRYSTAL GLORY REFILL
(Right) 1 oz. spray bottle fits inside Crystal Glory bottle. Came in all fragrances above. OSP $2., CMV $6. MB.

1953-54 COLOGNE STICKS CHRISTMAS PACKAGING
(Left) Green & red on white cardboard, pink ribbon in top. CMV $18. MB.
1952 Only COLOGNE STICK CHRISTMAS PACKAGING
(Right) Red & white candy striped cardboard, red ribbon top. CMV $18. MB.

COLOGNE MIST SPECIAL ISSUE BOXES
Each came in choice of fragrance & was sold for a short period.
1975 COLOGNE MIST
(Left)
1975 COLOGNE MIST
(Inside Left)
1976 COLOGNE MIST
(Inside Right)
1978 ULTRA COLOGNE SPRAY
(Right)
Add $1. to CMV of each bottle for each box shown.

1969-70 COLOGNE MIST
(Left) 2 oz. gold cap, frosted glass. Came in Charisma, Brocade, Elusive & Regence. OSP $4.25, CMV $2.
1969-71 SPRAY ESSENCE
(Right) 1¼ oz. gold cap, ribbed glass. Came in Charisma, Brocade, Regence. OSP $4.50, CMV $2.

1970-76 PURSE SPRAY ESSENCE
(Left) ¼ oz. glass bottle with gold cap in Elusive, Charisma, Brocade, Regence, Unforgettable, Rapture, Occur!, Somewhere, Topaze, Cotillion, Bird of Paradise & Hana Gasa. OSP $3.50, CMV $1. MB.

1971-75 COLOGNE MIST
(Right) 2 oz. silver top. Came in Bird of Paradise, Hana Gasa, Elusive, Charisma, Brocade & Regence. OSP $4.25, CMV $1.

1975-76 CARNATION COLOGNE MIST
(Left) 2 oz. clear glass, gold cap. OSP $3., CMV 50c.

1975-76 COLOGNE MIST
(Inside Left) 1 oz. clear glass, gold cap, white neck label. Came in Sonnet, Bird of Paradise, Moonwind, Charisma, Field Flowers or Roses Roses. OSP $2., CMV 50c.

1974-75 COLOGNE MIST
(Inside Right) 2 oz. clear glass, gold cap. Came in Imperial Garden, Sonnet, Charisma or Moonwind. OSP $4., CMV 50c.

1975-76 COLOGNE MIST
(Right) 2 oz. clear glass, gold cap. Came in Occur!, Topaze, Unforgettable, Here's My Heart, Cotillion, To A Wild Rose, Field Flowers, Regence, Brocade, Bird of Paradise. OSP $4., CMV $1.

1968-72 COLOGNE MIST
(Left) 2 oz. gold cap, gold & white band. Came in Here's My Heart, Topaze, To A Wild Rose, Somewhere, Cotillion, Occur!, Roses Roses & Unforgettable. OSP $2.50, CMV $1.

1963-66 COLOGNE MIST
(Right) Embossed bottles with gold plastic caps, came with black & gold paper label and green & gold cloth type label and green & white paper label. Held 2 oz. of Occur!, Somewhere, Topaze, Cotillion, Persian Wood, Here's My Heart & To A Wild Rose. OSP $2.50, CMV $5. each MB - $3. BO.

1966-68 COLOGNE MIST
(Left) 2 oz. gold cap with 4A design on cap. Came in Here's My Heart, To A Wild Rose, OSP $2.25; Somewhere, Topaze, Cotillion, OSP $2.50; Unforgettable, Rapture, Occur!, OSP $3., CMV $1. BO - $2. MB each.

1966-67 SPRAY ESSENCE
(Right) 1¼ oz. plastic coated glass with gold cap. Came in Here's My Heart, To A Wild Rose, Wishing, OSP $3.50; Somewhere, Topaze, Cotillion, OSP $3.75; Unforgettable, Rapture, Occur!, OSP $4., CMV $2. BO - $3. MB.

1959-66 SPRAY ESSENCE
(Left) 1 oz. black plastic coated, gold & blue lid. Came in Cotillion, To A Wild Rose, Bright Night, Nearness, OSP $3.; Persian Wood, Here's My Heart, OSP $3.25; Somewhere 1962-66, OSP $3.50; Rapture, Occur! 1965-66, OSP $4., CMV $2. BO - $5. MB.

1957-59 ESSENCE DE FLEURS
(Right) 1 oz. black plastic coated, gold & blue lid. Came in Nearness, Elegante, To A Wild Rose, Cotillion, Bright Night & Forever Spring. OSP $3., CMV $4. BO - $7. MB.

1972 DECORATOR COLOGNE MIST
4 oz. plastic coated bottle in color to match fragrance. Long gold cap with top matching fragrance color. Came in Moonwind (deep blue), Charisma (crimson red), Bird of Paradise (pale blue) & Field Flowers (spring green). SSP $5., CMV $4. BO - $6. MB.

1967-70 SPRAY ESSENCE
1¼ oz. All had gold caps. Eight different fragrances with 8 different colored bands around neck. Unforgettable, Rapture, Occur!, OSP $4.; Somewhere, Topaze, Cotillion, OSP $3.75; Here's My Heart, To A Wild Rose, OSP $3.50. CMV $2. BO - $3.50 MB.

1979-80 COLOGNE SPRAY 1.8 OZ.
1.8 oz. clear glass, gold & silver caps with matching neck bands, boxes & label. Comes with Moonwind, Charisma, Sonnet, Topaze, Here's My Heart, Bird of Paradise, Cotillion, Occur! & Unforgettable. SSP $4., CMV 25c each.

SACHETS, CREAM — MISC.

1958 CREAM SACHET CHRISTMAS BOX
Special issue blue & gold box came with choice of cream sachet in To A Wild Rose, Cotillion, Forever Spring, Nearness, Bright Night, Elegante. OSP $1.50 each. See jar in each fragrance line and add $5. for this box.

CREAM SACHET BOXES
Special short issue boxes came with cream sachets in several fragrances. Left to Right: 1956, 1964, 1958, 1954; CMV see bottle in each fragrance line & add $5. each for these boxes.

1973-75 CREAM SACHET JARS
Clear ribbed glass jar with colored border on lid & colored flower to match fragrance. .66 oz. came in Gardenia, Violet & Carnation. SSP $1.25, CMV $1. each.

1960 CREAM SACHET DECOR
Ribbed clear plastic with removable bottom, sold for 50c at Xmas with purchase of cream sachet in Bright Night, Nearness, Cotillion, To A Wild Rose, Persian Wood & Here's My Heart. CMV $8., holder only $12. MB.

1958 CREAM SACHET
.3 oz. white glass jar. Turquoise flower lid. Came in 1958 Wishing Trio set. Pink & gold box. CMV $5. jar only - $10. MB.

1957 CREAM SACHET CHRISTMAS BOX
Special issue box at Christmas. Pink & white, came in choice of Cotillion, Nearness, Forever Spring, Bright Night, To A Wild Rose, Elegante cream sachet. OSP $1.50. See bottle in each fragrance line and add $6. for this box.

1957 CREAM SACHET
(Left) White jar with green, yellow or pink lid. Came in Cotillion, To A Wild Rose, Bright Night & Nearness. Came in Rainbow Set. CMV $8. each.

1956 CREAM SACHET PETITES
(Right) Plastic cream sachet came in Cotillion, Bright Night, Nearness, To A Wild Rose. Came in Cream Sachet Petites Sets only. 4 different colors. CMV $10. each MB.

1974-76 MAGNOLIA CREAM SACHET
(Left) .66 oz. clear embossed glass with white lid and pink & yellow on flower. OSP $1.25, CMV $1.

1974-77 MAGNOLIA DEMI STICK
(Inside Left) .19 oz. white with floral colored center. OSP $1.25, CMV $1.

1974-76 HYACINTH CREAM SACHET
(Inside Right) .66 oz. clear embossed glass with pink flowers on lid. OSP $1.25, CMV $1.

1974-77 HYACINTH DEMI STICK
(Right) .19 oz. white with pink flowers. OSP $1.25, CMV $1.

1969 SCENTIMENTS CREAM SACHET
½ oz. clear glass jar, gold lid, 4A design on lid. Came in Scentiments Set only in Unforgettable, Rapture, Occur!, Somewhere, Topaze or Cotillion. CMV $4. mint.

SACHETS, POWDER — MISC.

1936-38 POWDER SACHET
1¼ or 2 oz. ribbed glass bottle with turquoise cap & label. Came in Ariel 1936-38, CMV $24.; Cotillion 1937-38, CMV $20.; Marionette 1938 only, CMV $24.; Jardin D'Amour 1936-38 or Jardin Sachet, CMV $22. OSP each $1.04. All prices are mint only. Add $4. MB.

1930-32 POWDER SACHET
(Left) Clear glass bottle with brass cap & silver & blue label. Came in Ariel, OSP 78c; & Jardin D'Amour, OSP $1.04, CMV $60. each mint.

1934-36 POWDER SACHET
(Right) 1¼ oz. ribbed glass bottle with dark blue cap & silver & blue label. Came in Jardin D'Amour, OSP $1.04; & Ariel, OSP 78c, CMV $28. each mint - $33. MB.

1939-48 POWDER SACHET
1¼ oz. glass bottle with turquoise cap & label. Came in Jardin D'Amour 1939-40, CMV $20.; Ariel 1939-42, CMV $20.; Cotillion 1939-46, CMV $12.; Garden of Love, turquoise or black cap, 1940-46, CMV $18.; Attention 1942-48, CMV $15.; Marionette 1939-46, CMV $17. OSP $1.04 each. Add $3. MB.

1973-75 TURN-OF-CENTURY POWDER SACHET SHAKER
(Left) 1.25 oz. clear glass with gold cap. Came in Roses Roses, Charisma, Unforgettable. OSP $4.50, CMV $3.50 MB - $2. BO.

1972-73 POWDER SACHET SHAKER
(Right) 3½" high, 1.25 oz. white glass jar with gold cap. Came in Moonwind, OSP $5.; Bird of Paradise, Unforgettable, Field Flowers, SSP $3. CMV $3. BO - $5. MB.

1965-66 CROWN TOP POWDER SACHET
.9 oz. frosted bottle with gold cap. Came in perfume pillowette set in Rapture, Wishing, Occur!, Lavender, Somewhere, Topaze, Cotillion, Here's My Heart, To A Wild Rose. CMV $8. BO - $10. MB.

1969-70 POWDER SACHET
(Left) 1½ oz. painted red over clear glass, red neck bow with silver lid. Comes in Cotillion, Charisma, Unforgettable & To A Wild Rose. OSP $4.50, CMV $6. in box - $5. bottle only.

1970-71 POWDER SACHET
(Right) Crystal-like glass bottle holds 1¼ oz. of powder sachet in Elusive, Charisma, Unforgettable & Topaze. OSP $4., CMV $3. BO - $4. MB.

1944-45 POWDER SACHET
1¼ oz. pink paper sachet boxes. Came in Attention, Garden of Love, Cotillion, Marionette. Pink plastic flower on lid. OSP $1.15 each, CMV $18. each - $20. MB.

1952 Only POWDER SACHET CHRISTMAS BOX
Special issue red & green box for all powder sachets at Christmas. Came in Cotillion, Golden Promise, Quaintance & Flowertime. See bottle in each fragrance line & add $5. for this box.

1958 POWDER SACHET CHRISTMAS BOX
Special issue pink & white box came with powder sachet in choice of To A Wild Rose, Cotillion, Forever Spring, Nearness, Bright Night, Elegante. OSP $1.50 each. See jars in each fragrance line for CMV & add $5. for this box.

1952 VALENTINE GIFT SACHET
Short issue box in red & white. Came in Flowertime, Golden Promise, Cotillion & Quaintance. Cotillion came in same design, different shaped box. Add $7. CMV to price of each bottle for this box.

1957 POWDER SACHET CHRISTMAS BOX
Pyramid shaped box in pink, green, blue & white. Came in To A Wild Rose, Forever Spring, Cotillion, Nearness, Bright Night & Elegante powder sachet. Short issue - RARE. OSP $1.50 each. See bottle in each fragrance line & add $6. for this box mint.

1963 POWDER SACHET CHRISTMAS BOX
(Left) Short issue box came in 6 fragrances at Christmas. Add $4. to CMV of bottle for this box.

1965 POWDER SACHET CHRISTMAS BOX
(Right) High top boot design box was short issue. Came in 8 fragrances. Add $4. to CMV of bottle for this box.

1956 POWDER SACHET CHRISTMAS BOX
Special issue Christmas box came with choice of 6 fragrances. Add $5. to CMV of bottle for this box.

PERFUMED TALCS — MISC.
SEE 1984 SUPPLEMENT IN BACK OF BOOK FOR MORE PERFUMED TALCS

1959 PERFUMED TALC CHRISTMAS BOX
Short issue box in choice of 6 fragrances of talcs. Add $4. CMV for this box to price of talc, MB.

PERFUMED TALC SPECIAL ISSUE CHRISTMAS BOXES
(Left to Right) 1966 Christmas, 1967 Christmas, 1969 Christmas, 1970 Christmas. Each came in choice of talc. Add $2. each box to CMV of the talc it holds, MB.

1958 PERFUMED TALC CHRISTMAS BOX
Special issue Christmas box for perfumed talc in choice of To A Wild Rose, Cotillion, Nearness & Forever Spring. OSP 69c each. Check fragrance line for MB CMV on talc & add $5. for this box.

1959-60 FLORAL PERFUMED TALC
Lavender & white can. Matching box. OSP 69c, CMV $5. can only - $7. MB.

TOILET WATERS — MISC.

1940 Only TOILET WATER
(Left) 2 oz. plastic caps, blue & gold label with tulip. Came in Cotillion, Vernafleur, Lily of the Valley, White Rose, Lilac, Trailing Arbutus, Marionette, Lilac Vegetal. OSP 78c, CMV $35. BO mint - $40. MB.

1940-46 TOILET WATER
(Center) 2 oz. gold ribbed cap & gold label. Also came with plastic caps. Came in Cotillion, Jasmine, Marionette, Lilac, Lily of the Valley, Trailing Arbutus, Apple Blossom, Sonnet & Attention. OSP $1.04, CMV $30. BO mint - $35. MB.

1935-40 TOILET WATER
(Right) 2 oz. gold cap with A on top of cap. Blue & gold tulip label. CPC on back of label. Came in same as 1st toilet water on left. OSP 78c, CMV $35. BO mint - $40. MB.

PERFUMES — MISC.
SEE 1984 SUPPLEMENT IN BACK OF BOOK FOR MORE PERFUMES

1933-34 TOILET WATER
2 oz. ribbed bottle came in Trailing Arbutus, Vernafleur, Lily of the Valley, White Rose, Lilac Vegetal. Black or blue cap. OSP 75c, CMV $50. bottle only mint - $60. MB.

1934-39 - ¼ OZ. TULIP PERFUME
Glass stopper, gold label with tulip. Came in Lucy Hays, Topaze, Jardin D'Amour, Bolero, Cotillion, Ariel, Narcissus, Rose, Lily of the Valley, Trailing Arbutus, Gardenia, Sweet Pea, Marionette, Courtship. OSP $1.04, CMV $75. BO - $90. MB.

1931-34 GIFT ATOMIZER PERFUME
1 oz. red glass bottle with screw on metal top & white squeeze bulb. Came in Atomizer Set No. 6 only. Does not say Avon or CPC. Also comes in green glass. CMV $85.

1934-39 - 2 DRAM TULIP PERFUME
¼ oz. or 2 drams, gold cap & label with tulip. CPC on back of label & Avon on bottom of bottle. Came with 2 different labels as shown. Came in Jardin D'Amour, Bolero, Cotillion, Ariel, Narcissus, Rose, Lily of the Valley, Trailing Arbutus, Gardenia, Sweet Pea, Marionette, Courtship, Lucy Hays, Topaze. OSP 78c, CMV $65. MB - $55. BO mint.

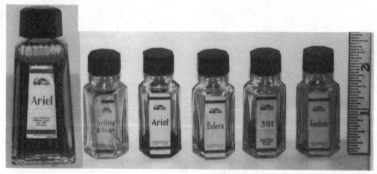

1933-36 RIBBED PERFUME
(Left) ½ oz. ribbed glass bottle with black octagonal cap & gold label. Came in Gold Box set in Bolero, 391, Gardenia, Ariel, Vernafleur. CMV $45. mint.

1933-36 PERFUMES
(Right) Small six sided bottle with silver label & black caps. Came in Ariel, Bolero, Gardenia, Trailing Arbutus, 391, Vernafleur. Came in Little Folks set & Handkerchief set. CMV $45. mint.

1934-39 - 7 DRAM TULIP PERFUME
Glass stoppered bottle, gold label with tulip. Came in Jardin D'Amour, Bolero, Cotillion, Ariel, Narcissus, Rose, Lily of the Valley, Trailing Arbutus, Gardenia, Sweet Pea, Marionette, Topaze, Courtship, Lucy Hays. OSP $2., CMV $125. MB - $100. BO.

1934-39 - 7 DRAM TULIP PERFUME
Glass stopper, gold label with tulip. Came in Lucy Hays, Topaze, Jardin D'Amour, Bolero, Cotillion, Ariel, Narcissus, Rose, Lily of the Valley, Trailing Arbutus, Gardenia, Sweet Pea, Marionette, Courtship. OSP $2.60, CMV $125. In box - bottle only $100. mint.

1931-33 - 391 PERFUME
(Left) Silver & blue box holds 1 oz. glass stopper. Blue ribbon on neck. OSP $2.60, CMV bottle only $125. - in box $150.

1931-33 - 391 PERFUME FLACONETTE
(Center) Small embossed bottle with glass stopper with long dabber. Brass cap with 391 on it. OSP $1.30, CMV $85. BO - $95. MB.

1933-36 - 391 PERFUME
(Right) ½ oz. ribbed glass bottle with black octagonal cap. Came in Gold Box set. CMV $45. mint.

1950 PERFUMES
5/8 dram each. Quaintance, Cotillion, Golden Promise, Luscious. Green, blue, pink & yellow caps. Came in Avon Blossoms set. CMV $12. each mint.

1940-42 MISC. 1/8 OZ. PERFUME
(Left) 1 dram or 1/8 oz. gold cap & label. Came in Cotillion, Ballad, Gardenia, Garden of Love, Apple Blossom, Marionette, Trailing Arbutus, Lily of the Valley, Sweet Pea. CMV $25. BO mint - $35 MB.

1940-44 MISC. 1/8 OZ. PERFUME
(Right) Gold metal or plastic caps & gold label. Came in Garden of Love, Gardenia, Marionette, Sweet Pea, Lily of the Valley, Trailing Arbutus, Ballad, Courtship, Apple Blossom, Cotillion. OSP 75c, CMV $25. BO mint - $30. MB.

1941 VALENTINE'S DAY PERFUME
1/8 oz. clear glass bottle with gold cap with Ballad perfume. Box red & white. Came in several fragrances. CMV $75. MB.

1946-50 - 1/8 OZ: PERFUME OR 1 DRAM
Gold box, gold label. Some have metal gold caps. Came in Crimson Carnation, Lily of the Valley, Gardenia, Cotillion, Golden Promise, Garden of Love, Ballad, Quaintance, Flowertime. OSP $1., CMV $20, - Crimson Carnation $30. Add $5. each MB. Also came in Gold Box set of 1947-49.

1946-50 PERFUME
(Left) 1/8 oz. clear glass, gold cap, painted label. Available in Crimson Carnation, Lily of the Valley, Gardenia, Cotillion, Golden Promise, Garden of Love, Ballad, Quaintance, Flowertime. OSP $1., CMV $20. BO - $25. MB.

1954 Only 5/8 DRAM PERFUME
(Right) Came in 1954 House of Charms set only. Blue caps, pink, blue & white label. Came in Cotillion, Quaintance, To A Wild Rose, Golden Promise, Lily of the Valley. Rare. CMV $22. each.

1951-53 PERFUMES 5/8 DRAM
Bottle with pink, yellow, green or blue caps came in Cotillion, Quaintance, Forever Spring, Golden Promise, Luscious, Lily of the Valley. Came in 1952-53 House of Charm, 1951 Always Sweet Set & Sweet As Honey Beehive Set. CMV $12. each, mint.

1937-46 PERFUME
1/8 oz. bottle on right has flower on label with 3 branches on each side. Came in sets only in Gardenia, Cotillion, CMV $14.; Narcissus, Trailing Arbutus, Sweet Pea, CMV $17. each. White, blue, red, green or yellow plastic caps. 2 dram size or ¼ oz. on left came in 1939-40 Gold Box sets & Little Folks sets in same fragrances and caps. CMV $25. each.

PERFUMES FOR SIZE COMPARISON ONLY
(Left to Right) 2 dram or ¼ oz., 1/8 oz. or 1 dram, 5/8 dram, 5/8 dram.

1946 Only 1/8 OZ. PERFUME
(Left) 1/8 oz. plastic cap. Came in Gardenia, Cotillion, Garden of Love, Lily of the Valley, Trailing Arbutus, Sweet Pea. OSP 75c, CMV $25. BO - $30. MB each mint.

1941-46 - 1/8 OZ. PERFUME
(Right) 1/8 oz. size, white paper label, gold metal caps & plastic caps. Came in Gardenia, Sweet Pea, Courtship, Apple Blossom, Cotillion, Trailing Arbutus, Lily of the Valley, Garden of Love, Marionette. OSP 75c, CMV $25. BO - $30. MB.

1946-53 - 1/8 OZ. PERFUME
(Left) Flower on label, plastic cap. Came in Trailing Arbutus, Cotillion, Crimson Carnation, Quaintance, Lily of the Valley, Gardenia, Garden of Love, Sweet Pea. Came in Fair Lady, Your Charms & Hair Ribbons sets. CMV each $15. - Crimson Carnation & Sweet Pea, CMV $25. mint. Same label came on 5/8 dram size "smaller bottle" but has no size on label. Same CMV.

1941-45 - 1/8 OZ. PERFUMES
(Right) 1/8 oz., 2 different flat gold caps & also plastic caps. White paper label. Came in Courtship, Sweet Pea, Lily of the Valley, Trailing Arbutus, Marionette, American Ideal, Apple Blossom, Cotillion, Ballad, Gardenia, Garden of Love. OSP $1., CMV bottle only $30. mint - $40. MB.

1944 Only FLORAL PERFUMES
3 dram gold cap & label. Came in yellow feather design box in Trailing Arbutus, Gardenia, Sweet Pea, Lily of the Valley, Cotillion. OSP $2.50, CMV $90. MB - bottle only $60. mint.

1940-44 BOUQUET PERFUMES
3 dram, glass stopper, box is gold base & orange lid. Came in Garden of Love, Apple Blossom, Marionette, Courtship, Cotillion. Gold neck tag. OSP $2.50 each, CMV $100. BO mint - $135. MB.

1946-47 MISC. FLORAL PERFUMES
Blue & white box holds 3 dram bottle with plastic cap. Came in Crimson Carnation, Gardenia, Lily of the Valley. OSP $3.75, CMV $75. in box - bottle only $50. - Crimson Carnation, CMV $100. MB, $60. BO.

1940-42 FLORAL PERFUME
3/8 oz. gold cap & label in gold speckled box. Came in Sweet Pea, Gardenia, Trailing Arbutus, Lily of the Valley. OSP $1.50, CMV $50. BO mint - $80. MB.

1944-45 FLORAL PERFUMES
3 dram gold cap & labels. Came in yellow feather design box in Trailing Arbutus, Cotillion, Gardenia, Sweet Pea, Lily of the Valley, Marionette. 2 different boxes. OSP $1.65 - CMV $60 bottle only mint with tag - $90 MB.

1945-47 BOUQUET PERFUMES
Blue, pink & white box holds 3 dram glass stoppered bottle with gold neck tag. Came in Courtship, Cotillion, Garden of Love. OSP $3., CMV $125. MB - $100. BO.

1944 Only BOUQUET PERFUMES
Blue & pink box holds 3 dram perfume, glass stopper. Came in Marionette, Cotillion, Garden of Love. Gold neck tags. OSP $3., CMV $140. MB - $100. BO with tag.

1963-71 - 1 OZ. HEART PERFUME
Gold box, 4A insignia on glass stopper. Gold neck tag. Came in Unforgettable & Occur!, OSP $25.; Somewhere, Topaze, Cotillion, OSP $20.; Here's My Heart, Persian Wood, Rapture, To A Wild Rose, OSP $17.50, CMV $35. BO - $60. MB.

1955-59 PERFUMES "1 DRAM"
Clear smooth glass, gold scroll cap with felt like wrapper. Nearness, gray; Bright Night, black; Elegante, maroon; To A Wild Rose, pink; Forever Spring, green; Cotillion, gold. Simulated grain leather. Luscious, 1st issue 1950, tan; Here's My Heart, blue. OSP $2.25, CMV $14. each in wrapper mint, $8. BO, $17.50 MB.

1955 CHRISTMAS PERFUME
1 dram, gold cap in red, white, blue and gold Christmas box. Came in To A Wild Rose, Cotillion, Forever Spring, Golden Promise, Luscious, and Quaintance. OSP $1.75, CMV $25. MB.

1959-63 ROCKER PERFUME
White box holds 1 oz. bottle with flat glass stopper with 4A on top. Gold cord criscrossed bottle with white tag label. Came in Here's My Heart, Persian Wood, OSP $17.50; To A Wild Rose, Bright Night, Nearness, OSP $15.; Cotillion, OSP $20.; CMV in box $65. - bottle only with tag $50. CMV Nearness & Bright Night $80. in box - $65. bottle with tag.

1953-54 PERFUME
Green and pink fold out box holds 1 dram ribbed glass bottle with gold scroll cap. Came in To A Wild Rose, Cotillion, Forever Spring, Quaintance, Golden Promise, Luscious, Ballad. OSP $1.75, CMV $25. MB as shown.

1953 VALENTINE PERFUMES
1 dram ribbed perfume came in To A Wild Rose, Forever Spring, OSP $1.75; Cotillion, Golden Promise, Quaintance, OSP $1.50. CMV $25. MB as shown.

1950-55 PERFUMES "1 DRAM"
Ribbed bottles with gold caps came in Cotillion, Quaintance, Ballad, Golden Promise, Gardenia, Lily of The Valley, Forever Spring and To A Wild Rose. OSP $1.50, CMV $12. MB, $8. BO.

1951-52 WITH LOVE PERFUMES
(Left) Pink heart box opens to 1 dram ribbed bottle and cap in Lily of The Valley, To A Wild Rose, Luscious, Quaintance, Golden Promise, Cotillion, Ballad, Flowertime, Gardenia. OSP $1.75, CMV $25. MB as shown.

1951 CHRISTMAS BELL PERFUME
(Right) Gold bell box holds 1 dram, ribbed bottle and cap in Forever Spring, To A Wild Rose, Luscious, Cotillion, Flowertime, Quaintance, Golden Promise, Ballad, Gardenia and Lily of The Valley. OSP $1.60, CMV $25. MB as shown.

1958 ONE DRAM GIFT PERFUME
1 oz. smooth clear glass bottle, cap either smooth or embossed. Box is blue, white and gold. Choice of Elegante, Nearness, Bright Night, Forever Spring, To A Wild Rose or Cotillion. OSP $2., CMV $20. MB as shown, $8. BO. Nearness and Bright Night, $10. BO.

1971 PERFUME HALF OUNCE
½ oz. bottle with clear plastic top in a pink and gold box. Came in Somewhere, Topaze, Cotillion, Unforgettable, Rapture, Occur!. OSP $12.50; Regence, Brocade, Charisma, Elusive, OSP $15., CMV $16. MB, as shown, $6. BO.

1964-65 ONE DRAM PERFUME GOLD BOX
(Center) 4A embossed gold box. Ribbed bottle, gold cap. Came in Somewhere, Topaze, Cotillion, Here's My Heart, Persian Wood, To A Wild Rose, Wishing, Occur!, Rapture, and Unforgettable. On left, same bottle sold in regular issue box. 1962-66. OSP $2.25 to $2.50, CMV $8. MB in gold box. 1965 Christmas special issue box on right. CMV $9. MB, CMV regular issue box $4. BO, $5. MB.

1959-60 TOP STYLE CHRISTMAS PERFUME
Sold only at Christmas time in box shown. Came in all regular fragrances of Top Style perfume. OSP $2.50, CMV $15. MB in this box only.

1966-67 PERFUME FLACON
(Left) 1 dram, gold ribbed cap, ribbed glass. Came in Here's My Heart, Wishing, To A Wild Rose, Somewhere, Topaze, Cotillion, Unforgettable, Regence, Rapture, Occur!. OSP $2.50, CMV $2. BO, $4. MB.

1959-62 TOP STYLE PERFUME
(Right) Shown with general issue box. 1 dram size, gold cap. Came in Topaze, Persian Wood, Here's My Heart, To A Wild Rose, Cotillion, Bright Night and Nearness. OSP $2.50, CMV $5. BO, $7. MB.

1961 GOLDEN GIFT PERFUME
Blue, gold and green box holds 1 dram top style perfume. Came in Cotillion, To A Wild Rose, Nearness, Bright Night, Somewhere, Here's My Heart, Persian Wood, Topaze. OSP $2.25, CMV $13. MB.

1965-69 PERFUME ROLLETTES
.33 oz. glass bottles available in Somewhere, Topaze, Cotillion, Here's My Heart, To A Wild Rose, Wishing, Regence, Occur!, Rapture, Unforgettable, Brocade and Charisma. Issued in carnival glass or clear ribbed glass. OSP $1.75 to $3. CMV clear, $2. MB, $1. BO; CMV carnival $7. BO, $9. MB. Box pictured is 1966 Christmas box. Add $2. extra for this box.

1963-65 PERFUME CREME ROLLETTE
4A embossed bottles with gold caps. Came in Here's My Heart, Persian Wood, To A Wild Rose. OSP $2.; Cotillion, Somewhere, Topaze, and Wishing, $1.75; Occur! and Rapture, OSP $2.50. CMV $5. MB, rollette only $3. mint.

1969-72 ½ OZ. PERFUME
(Left) Pink box holds jewel like clear glass bottle 4" high. Comes in Elusive, Charisma, Brocade, Regence. OSP $15. Unforgettable, Rapture, Occur!, Somewhere, Topaze, Cotillion. OSP $12.50, CMV $13. MB, $6. BO.

1966-69 PERFUME
(Right) ½ oz. gold cap, metal leaves around base. White and gold box. Came in Unforgettable, Rapture, Occur!. OSP $12.50; Somewhere, Topaze, Cotillion, OSP $11.; Here's My Heart, To A Wild Rose, Wishing, OSP $10., CMV $16.50 MB, $9. BO.

1951-53 PERFUME "1 DRAM"
Vertical ribbed bottle and ribbed gold cap with scroll on cap. Came in Cotillion, Golden Promise, Quaintance, To A Wild Rose, Forever Spring. OSP $1.75, CMV $14. MB, $12. BO mint.

1972-75 PERFUME PENDANT
Gold with 2 simulated half pearls, 32" chain. Came in Sonnet or Moonwind perfume. OSP $10., CMV $10. MB. Pendant only $5.

1971-72 GOLDEN MOMENTS PENDANT PERFUME
Antiqued brass pendant on 32" gold chain. Holds 1/8 oz. perfume in Moonwind, OSP $15., Bird of Paradice, Elusive, Charisma, OSP $14. CMV pendant on chain only $10. mint, $16. MB.

1970 PERFUME PENDANT
Gold pendant with ruby teardrop, holds 1 dram liquid perfume. Comes in Charisma, Elusive, Brocade and Regence. OSP $14., CMV $15. MB, $10 pendant only mint.

1973-74 SCENTIMENT PERFUME ROLLETTE
(Left) .33 oz. white base with blue bird and pink flowers, gold trim and cap. Holds Moonwind, Patchwork, Sonnet. SSP $2.50, CMV $3. BO, $4. MB.

1974 SCENTIMENT PURSE SPRAY ESSENCE
(Right) .25 oz. blue plastic coated bottom, white and pink bird design on paper label with gold cap. Came in Field Flowers, Bird of Paradise or Charisma. SSP $3., CMV $4. BO, $6. MB.

PERFUME OILS

1969-73 PERFUME OIL
(Left) ½ oz. gold caps. Came in Elusive, Rapture, Hana Gasa, Charisma, Brocade, Moonwind, Regence, and Bird of Paradise. OSP $6.; Unforgettable and Occur!, OSP $5. CMV $2., $3. MB.

1965 BULLET PERFUME OIL
(Right) 5/8 dram, gold top. Came in Wishing, Somewhere, Occur!, Rapture, To A Wild Rose, Topaze, Unforgettable, Here's My Heart, Cotillion. Came in Fragrance Ornaments Set only. CMV $10. with holder, $6. BO.

1966 PERFUME OIL PETITES (PIN CUSHION) 5/8 dram, clear bottle, gold cap and label. Came in Pin Cushion Set only. Came in Somewhere, Wishing, Occur!, Rapture, Topaze, To A Wild Rose, Here's My Heart, Unforgettable, Cotillion. CMV $10. each mint.

1964-65 JEWEL PERFUME OIL
(Left) 5/8 dram, gold cap. Perfume Oil came in Jewel Collectton only. Came in Cotillion, Topaze, Persian Wood, Here's My Heart, To A Wild Rose. CMV $6. each mint.

FOREIGN JEWEL EAU DE COLOGNE
(Right) ½ oz. gold cap. CMV $20.

SEE 1984 SUPPLEMENT IN BACK OF BOOK FOR MORE PRODUCTS

COMPACTS & LIPSTICKS — MISC.

ALL ITEMS PRICES EMPTY — MINT
See 6 and 16 for Grading Examples on Mint Condition.

1931-33 FAN COMPACT
Silver and blue metal compact. OSP $2 - CMV $30 mint, $40 MB.

1930-32 COMPACT
Silver metal compact in single size. OSP $1.35, double size OSP $1.85. CMV $30 each, $40 MB.

1937-39 NAIL WHITE & NAIL CUTICLE CREAM
Both turquoise and white small metal cans. Came in Manicure Set only. CMV $7. each mint.

1932-33 COMPACT
Octaganal shaped blue and gold. Avon lid shown closed and open. Came in 1932-33 Vanity Set only. CMV $30. mint.

1930-36 SINGLE ROUGE COMPACT
Blue and silver metal compact. OSP 52c - CMV $20, $25 MB.

1930-33 EYE LASH CREAM
Blue compact with mirror, same as above rouge compacts. OSP $1.. CMV $20 - $25 MB.

1931-33 TRIPLE COMPACT
Blue and silver metal compact. Avon on lid. OSP $1.30 - CMV $35, $40 MB.

1931-36 NAIL WHITE & NAIL CREAM
Both small silver and blue or gold and blue cans. Came in Manicure Sets only. CMV $8. each mint.

1933-36 MASCARA COMPACT
Blue and silver metal compact. OSP $1.04 - CMV $30 mint, $35 MB.

1934-36 DOUBLE COMPACT
Blue and silver compact and puffs. OSP $1.75 - CMV $30 mint, $35 MB.

1934-36 COMPACT REFILLS
Avon on small and large size, blue and silver puff with refill cake. Came in gray box. CMV $4. each.

1930-36 DRESSING TABLE ROUGE
Silver and blue paper box. OSP 47c, CMV $12. mint, $16. MB.

1932-36 LIPSTICK
Blue and silver metal tube. OSP 52c, CMV $20, $25 MB.

1930-36 CREAM ROUGE COMPACT
Blue metal compact as above. OSP 75c - CMV $20, $25 MB.

1936-42 FACE POWDER SAMPLE
Cream colored metal can. Came in Verna Fleur, Ariel in 5 shades. CMV $5., CPC label, $8. Add $2. MB.

1936-42 DRESSING TABLE ROUGE
Turquoise and gold cardboard with turquoise and white box. Came in 5 shades. OSP 47c, CMV $5., $8. MB. Add $2. for CPC label.

1936-42 POWDER ROUGE REFILL
Turquoise and white box. Refill fits double compact. OSP 52c, CMV $6. MB.

1936-42 CREAM ROUGE COMPACT
Turquoise and gold metal case. OSP 78c, CMV $7., $9. MB.

1936-42 SINGLE ROUGE COMPACT
Turquoise and gold metal case. OSP 52c, CMV $7., $9. MB.

(Left to right back row)
1960-66 COMPACT DELUXE & LIPSTICK DELUXE
Silver and gold. OSP Compact $3.50, CMV $5., $6. MB, OSP Lipstick $1.35, CMV $3., $4. MB.

1971-73 ENCORE COMPACT & LIPSTICK
Green ribbed plastic, gold 4A design on top. OSP Compact $3.50, CMV $2. OSP Lipstick $1.35, CMV $1., $2. MB.

1971-73 SIMPLICITY COMPACT
(Front) Pink plastic gold design. OSP $2.75, CMV $1., $2. MB.

1949-52 MASCARA
Gold metal case. OSP $1., CMV $8. MB, $5. case only.

1942-46 LIPSTICK - PLASTIC
Blue feather design plastic lipstick. OSP 52c, CMV $8. MB, lipstick only $4.

1936-41 MASCARA COMPACT
Turquoise and gold. OSP $1.04, CMV $12., $15. MB.

1936-41 LIPSTICK
Turquoise and gold. OSP 52c, CMV $8. mint, $10. MB.

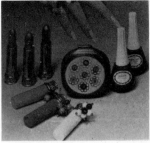

1969 RING FLING
Plastic tube of lipstick with beaded ring to match. White top lipstick, white and black beads. Lime green top, lime green and green beads. Blue top, dark blue and light blue beads. Pink top, dark pink and light pink beads. Yellow top, red and yellow beads. Orange top, yellow and orange beads. OSP $3.49, CMV $6. with rings, MB.

1969 SWING FLING COMPACT
.5 oz. dark pink with colored design. OSP $2., CMV $2.50, $4. MB.

1969 ENAMEL FLING
.5 oz. clear glass, white cap. OSP $1., CMV $1., $1.50 MB.

1968 FESTIVE FANCY LIPSTICK & COMPACT
(Top Left) Green plastic with white flowers. OSP compact $3., CMV $2., Lipstick OSP $1.75, CMV $1.

1971-72 LIPSTICK-A-LA-MODE
(Top Right) White plastic, top holds glace, bottom lipstick. OSP $4.50, CMV $1.

1967-73 FASHION LIPSTICK & COMPACT
(Lower Left) Brown plastic with gold trim. OSP lipstick $1.35, CMV 50c. OSP compact $2.25, CMV 75c.

1968-71 ENCORE COMPACT & LIPSTICK
(Lower Right) Gray with gold trim. OSP lipstick $1.25, CMV 75c. OSP compact $2., CMV $1.50.

1969 CAPTIVATORS COMPACT & LIPSTICK
Leopard, Zebra and Tiger design plastic compacts. OSP $3.50, CMV $4., $5. MB each. Matching lipsticks, OSP $1.75, CMV $2., $3. MB.

357

1969-78 LIP DEW
Gold and white case. OSP $1., CMV 50c

1970-71 LIP MAKER
Pink and red. OSP $1., CMV 50c.

1971-75 LIP FOUNDATION
Red, purple and white case. OSP $1., CMV 50c.

1968-73 QUICK COVER
Tan and brown case. OSP $1., CMV 50c.

1970-74 HIDE 'N LITE
White with green and gray stripes. OSP $1., CMV 25c.

1973 Only SUN SAFE STICK
Gold, tan and white. OSP 89c, CMV 25c.

1974-78 ABOUT TOWN LIPSTICK
Brown and gold. OSP $3., CMV 25c.

1969 RING FLING LIPSTICK
Plastic top, white, black, lime green, blue, pink or yellow. OSP $2., CMV $1., $2. MB.

1966-74 ULTRA SHEER LIPSTICK
White plastic. OSP $1., CMV 50c.

1972-73 ENCORE LIPSTICK
Clear plastic. OSP $1., CMV 75c.

1973-78 WINDSOR LIPSTICK
Dark blue plastic. OSP $2., CMV 25c.

1968-71 ENCORE LIPSTICK
Gray and gold plastic. OSP $1., CMV $1.

1956-59 CHAP CHECK
(Left) Small white plastic tube, red cap. OSP 25c, CMV $3. mint.

1960-73 CHAP CHECK
(Center) Is same color as above only longer tube. OSP 39c, CMV $1.

1951-55 CHAP CHECK
(Right) Small turquoise and white plastic tube. 1/10 oz. size. OSP 25c, CMV $4. mint.

1970-71 DELUXE LIPSTICK
Carved ivory design. OSP $2., CMV $3., $5. MB.

1965-67 LIPSTICK REFILLABLE
Gold metal case. Held Encore Lipstick. OSP $2., CMV $3., $4. MB.

1966-74 ULTRA SHEER
White plastic. OSP $1., CMV $1., $2. MB.

1960-61 FASHION LIPSTICK
White and pink plastic. OSP 98c, CMV $2., $3. MB.

1967-72 FASHION LIPSTICK
Tortoiseshell case. OSP $1., CMV $1., $2. MB.

1964-66 FASHION CASE CAMEO LIPSTICK
White plastic with cameo on lid. OSP 98c, CMV $3., $4. MB.

1943-45 CHAP STICK
Olive green metal case. Lipstick Anti-Chap and Sunburn Protective Hot Climate. Avon Products, Inc., New York on label. Given to G.I.'s in World War II in first aid kit. CMV $25. mint.

1980 LIP BALMS

DIPLOMA
Short issue. Came in autograph hound stuffed animal. CMV $1.50.

1981 SMOOTH DAYS AHEAD
1981 Calendar. SSP 69c, CMV 75c. Issued in 1980.

CANDY CANE
Came in red or green. SSP $1., CMV $1.

1973-74 SUNNY LIP GLEAMER
Clear pink top, white plastic tube. OSP $1., CMV 50c.

1973-74 COLOR MAGIC
White case with colorful butterfly. OSP $1., CMV 50c.

1973-75 LOOKING PRETTY MIRRORED LIPSTICK
Green plastic. OSP $2., CMV $1.

1972-73 POP TOP LIPSTICK
Turquoise plastic, gold design. OSP $1.50, CMV 50c.

1973-75 POP TOP LIPSTICK
Brown plastic, gold design. OSP $1.50, CMV 50c.

1956-57 FASHION CASE LIPSTICK
Clear plastic base with black cap. OSP 79c, CMV $5. mint, $7. MB.

1936 LIPSTICK SAMPLES
Turquoise and brass metal sample. CMV 50c mint each.

1978 LIPSTICK CASE
2 different green plastic cases with mirror inside lid. Holds lipstick. Sold 1 campaign only. 1 case is square bottom and one is round bottom. OSP $1., CMV $1.50.

1979-80 COLOR CREME MOISTURE LIPSTICK
Blue and silver, clear plastic top. SSP $1.79, CMV 50c MB.

1981-82 COLOR CREME MOISTURE LIPSTICK
Blue and silver bottom, clear plastic cap. SSP $2.30, CMV 50c MB.

1982 BAZOOKA LIP BALM
Red, white and blue. Red cap. SSP $1., CMV $1.

1982 JELLY BEAN LIP BALM
Red cap, jelly bean design. SSP $1., CMV $1.

1967 FLOWER PRINT COMPACT & LIPSTICK
4 compacts with matching lipsticks. Designs are Sunflower, Daisy, Poppy, and Carnation. Compacts OSP $2.50, CMV $3., $5. MB. Lipsticks OSP $1.50, CMV $2., $3. MB. Also came in flower print nail polish. See Misc. Bottles.

1954 JEWELED LIPSTICK
Gold Christmas box holds gold lipstick with jewel on top. OSP $1.75, CMV $15. In box shown.
1954-56 JEWELED LIPSTICK
Gold lipstick with white jewel on top. OSP $1.75, CMV lipstick only $5., $8. MB.

1970-71 EMPRESS LIPSTICK
Green, blue and gold lipstick. OSP $3., CMV $2., $3. MB.
1970-71 EMPRESS COMPACT
Green, blue and gold compact. OSP $7.50, CMV $4., $5. MB.

1968-69 JEWELED LIPSTICK
Gold lipstick with simulated diamond. OSP $6., CMV $5., $6. MB.
1968-69 JEWELED COMPACT
Gold powder compact with simulated diamonds. OSP $10., CMV $12. MB. Compact only $8.50.

1967-69 COMPACT & LIPSTICK DELUXE
Gold compacts OSP $5.50 each. CMV $6., $8. MB. Gold lipstick OSP $2., CMV $3., $5. MB.

1970 PETIT POINT LIPSTICK
Black, pink and green floral lipstick and box. CMV $3. MB.
1979 ABOUT TOWN TRIAL OFFER LIPSTICK
Box came with Candid lipstick. Made in Spain on label. OSP 79c, CMV $1. MB.

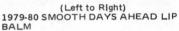

(Left to Right)
1979-80 SMOOTH DAYS AHEAD LIP BALM
White, blue and red calendar on side CMV 50c.
1968 FESTIVE FANCY DEMI STICK
Green and gold matching box. CMV $1., $1.50 MB,
1960's LIPSTICK
Black and white. CMV $1., $2. MB.
1958-61 TOP STYLE LIPSTICK
Brass. CMV $4., $5. MB.

(Left to Right)
1948-58 DELUXE LIPSTICK
Gold metal case. OSP 95c, CMV $3., $5. MB.
1962-63 FASHION LIPSTICK
Black metal case. OSP 98c, CMV $3., $4. MB.
1967-68 ENCORE LIPSTICK
Gold and white plastic. OSP $1., CMV $1.50 MB.
1968-69 GADABOUTS
Black and white or yellow and white plastic. OSP 99c, CMV $1.50 each MB.
1957-60 FASHION CASE LIPSTICK
White metal. OSP 89c, CMV $3., $4. MB.
1968 ULTRA SHEER LIPSTICK
White plastic, gold base. OSP 99c, CMV $1.

1978-79 POLISH GOLD COLLECTION
Each comes in gold and white box. All 3 pieces sold for $6.50 for the set. Nail Enamel, Gold Lipstick, Creamy Powder Eye Shadow. CMV 25c each, 50c MB. Lipstick $1., $2. MB.

1982 COOL MILLION LIP BALM
Green and white. SSP $1.40, CMV $1.

1982 WEATHER BARRIER LIP BALM
SSP $1., CMV $1.

1981 BEARING GIFTS LIP BALM
Red and green, CMV $1.

1979-80 FLAVOR SAVERS LIP GLOSS
All in different colors. Strawberry, lime, chocolate, cherry, orange and grape. SSP $1. each, CMV 50c each.

1975 FRUIT STIX PERFUMED DEMI STICK
.19 oz. Available in apple, (pink and red) lemon (yellow and gold) or strawberry (pink and red) OSP $1., CMV $1., $1.50 MB.

1940's ROUGE PUFFS REFILLS
(Left) Avon package holds 3 small turquoise rouge double compact puffs. CMV $3., package mint.

1940's POWDER COMPACT PUFFS REFILLS
(Right) Avon package holds 2 turquoise puff refills. CMV $3. package mint.

1943-44 FACE POWDER COMPACT
Feather design cardboard compact with mirror inside. 3½" across. CMV $20., $25. MB.

1943-49 MASCARA
Blue and white feather design paper box. OSP 69c, CMV $14. mint, $17. MB.

1942-49 FACE POWDER SAMPLE
Blue and white feather design, metal case, or paper box in 1943-46. CMV $4. mint.

1943-45 HEAVENLIGHT COMPACT
Blue plastic or metal with white feather, came in rouge or face powder. Rouge is smaller. OSP 59c, CMV $8., $10. MB.

1945-49 EYE SHADOW
Blue plastic compact with white feather. Same as 1943 Rouge feather compact above. OSP 79c, CMV $7., $9. MB.

1936-42 COMPACTS
Single compact. OSP $1.25. Double compact. OSP $1.75. Both turquoise and gold metal. CMV $15., $20. MB.

1941-48 NAIL WHITE PENCIL
White plastic pencil in turquoise box. OSP 29c. Avon on pencil, CMV $2., pencil only $5. MB.

1916-20 CPC EYEBROW PENCILS
Metal tubes. OSP 30c, CMV $15. each, $25. MB.

1944 LIPSTICK REFILL
Foil wrapped lipstick in plastic case, for metal or paper case. came in green and white box. 2 different boxes. Some are white top, green bottom as shown or reversed. CMV $10. each MB.

1941-48 MASCARA COMPACT
Gold metal, bamboo design. Sold 1942-43 then 1946-48. OSP $1.19, CMV $12., $15. in box.

1941-48 BAMBOO LIPSTICK
Gold metal bamboo design. OSP 79c, CMV $6., $8. MB.

1941-48 BAMBOO SINGLE ROUGE COMPACT
Gold metal bamboo design. OSP 79c, CMV $7., $9. MB.

1941-48 BAMBOO CREAM ROUGE COMPACT
Gold metal bamboo design. OSP 69c, CMV $7., $9. MB.

1941-49 BAMBOO COMPACT
Gold metal, bamboo design. OSP $2.35 for double size, $1.75 for single size in same design. Sold 1942-43 then 1946-49. CMV $15. each mint, $20. each MB.

1949-57 ROUGE COMPACT
Small gold embossed cream compact. OSP 79c, Larger cake rouge compact in same design. OSP 89c. CMV each $9.. in box, $7. compact only.

1949-56 EYE SHADOW
Same gold case design as 1949 rouge compacts above. OSP 79c, CMV $7., $9. MB.

1930-41 BLACKHEAD REMOVER
Made of metal. Came in CPC Avon envelope. OSP 15c, CMV $7. mint in envelope only.

1951-55 POWDER PAK COMPACT
Turquoise plastic with white scroll design. Not 4A. OSP $1.10, CMV $3.

1964-66 PLATINUM ROSE COMPLEXION HIGHLIGHT
Tan and white box. OSP $1.35, CMV $1.

1949-52 GAY LOOK
Gold deluxe compact and lipstick in black taffeta snap shut case. OSP $5., CMV $15. mint.

1953-56 GAY LOOK
Black covered metal case holds same as above. OSP $5.75, CMV $15. mint.

1949-56 DELUXE COMPACT
Gold compact. OSP $3.95, CMV $10. MB, $8. compact only mint.

1952-58 MASCARA COMPACT
Turquoise plastic. OSP $1., CMV $5. Also came in white plastic, CMV $4.

1954-58 CREAM MASCARA
Turquoise plastic container holds mascara tube and brush. OSP 69c, CMV $5. Later issue came in pink tube and holder. CMV $4.

1955-57 POWDER PAK PLAQUE
(Left) Turquoise powder refill. OSP 69c, CMV $3. 1958-60 Same only pink. OSP 69c, CMV $2.

1949-55 POWDER PAK
(Center) Gold and turquoise card. board powder box. OSP 95c, CMV $3., $4. MB.

1955-57 POWDER PAK (Not shown)
Gold and turquoise cardboard powder box. Face powder same design only bigger box. 4A emblem on lid. OSP 95c, CMV $3.

1955-57 POWDER PAK COMPACT
(Right) Turquoise and white compact with 4A design. OSP $1.10, CMV $2., $3. MB.

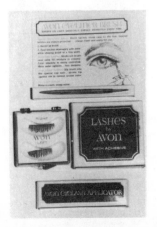

Left to Right - Top to Right

1966-72 ULTRA SHEER POWDER
White plastic. 1¾ oz. OSP $2.50, CMV $1.

1967-69 FINISHING FACE POWDER
Pink and brown box 2½ oz. OSP $1.50, CMV $2. mint, $3. MB.

1950-55 DRESSING TABLE ROUGE
Turquoise and gold cardboard 1/3 oz. size. OSP 69c, CMV $3., $4. MB.

1949-55 FACE POWDER
Turquoise cardboard 2½ oz. size. OSP 89c, CMV $5., $7. MB.

1968-74 EYEBROW BRUSH-A-LINE
Tortoise colored plastic with gold trim. SSP $1., CMV 25c.

1974 ABOUT TOWN COMPACT
Tortoise colored plastic with gold design. SSP $3., CMV $1.

1968-70 GLACE FASHION COMPACT
.12 oz. brown compact, gold top. OSP $2., CMV $1., $2. MB.

1973-75 AVONSHIRE BLUE PERFUME GLACE COMPACT
.12 oz. blue and white plastic. Available in Moonwind, Charisma or Elusive. OSP $2.50, CMV $2. MB.

1969-74 EYE LINER BRUSH
Brown plastic. OSP $1., CMV 50c.

1969-75 FALSE LASHES
Choice of black or brown. Came in brown and white case. OSP $4., CMV $2. MB.

1969-73 EYELASH APPLICATOR
Gold toned. OSP $1., CMV 50c MB.

1970-71 COLOR EYES QUARTETTE
(Left) Black and gold compact. OSP $5.50, CMV $2., $3. MB.

1969-71 SPARKLING CREAM SHADOW COLLECTION
Brown compact with raised gold flower design. OSP $3.50, CMV $2., $3. MB.

1967-68 APPLIQUE LIPSTICK
Gold case with pop-up mirror and lipstick inside. Two different designs. OSP $3.50, CMV $4., $5. MB.

1967-68 IMPERIAL COMPACT
(Top) Gold compact. OSP $7., CMV $6., $7. MB.

1966-68 COMPETITE COMPACT
(Bottom) Basketweave style compact. OSP $4.50, CMV $4., $5. MB.

1960-63 CURL 'N COLOR MASCARA
Gold metal tube, with Avon embossed on it. OSP $2., CMV $2.50.

1957-66 EYE SHADOW STICK
Same type gold tube as Curl 'N Color Mascara. OSP $1., CMV $2.

1966 FASHION AWARD COMPACT
Pink marbleized plastic case. OSP $1.75, CMV $3., $4. MB.

1958-61 TOP STYLE COMPACT
All gold compact with 4A in center of gold mesh lid. OSP $3.50, CMV $6., $7. MB.

1961-63 FASHION COMPACT
Black bottom and gold lid. OSP $2., CMV $4., $5. MB.

1963-65 POWDER-PAK COMPACT
(Left) Pink plastic. OSP $1.50, CMV $2. - $3. MB.

1970-71 BLUSHMAKER COMPACT
(Right) Green with gold, also has green handle brush. OSP $5., CMV $2. - $3. MB.

1973 Only DESIGNER'S ACCENT COMPACT
(Bottom) Pink with pink & dark pink design. Called Accent in Mauve. Sold for 3 campaigns only. OSP $1.50, CMV $2. - $3. MB.

1963-65 PETTI PAT COMPACT
(Left) White plastic compact with pink design. OSP $1.10, CMV $2.

1963-65 CAKE ROUGE
(Right) Small white plastic compact. OSP $1.50, CMV $2. MB.

1966-67 DRESSING TABLE FACE POWDER
(Front row) All pink plastic. OSP $1.25, CMV $2., $4. MB.
Second row left to right
White plastic compact with 4A design. CMV $1.50.

1972-75 FASHION LACE COMPACT
White plastic with cut out design. OSP $3.50, CMV $1.

1972-74 FASHION LACE LIPSTICK
White plastic with cut out design. OSP $1.50, CMV 50c.

1966-67 BLUSHMATES
Maroon plastic case holds white compact & make-up brush. OSP Avon blush $5.50 - Sparkling blush $6, CMV $10.

1965-66 IMPERIAL JEWEL COMPACT
Gold compact with rhinestone clasp with 4A design. OSP $6., CMV $8. $10. MB.

1968-69 GADABOUTS COMPACT
Black and white plastic compact. Also had yellow and white compact. Each had matching lipsticks. OSP compact $1.50, CMV $2., $4. MB.

1962-65 GOLDEN HIGHLIGHT CREME FOR EYES
Clear plastic. OSP $1.25, CMV $2. - $3. MB.

1965-68 NATURAL BLUSH
(Top Left) White plastic. OSP $1.50, CMV $1.

1966-68 BLUSH
(Top Right) White plastic, brown label. OSP $2., CMV $1.

1970-72 BLUSHING CREAM
(Bottom Left) Pink lid, white bottom. OSP $2., CMV 75c.

1966-68 SPARKLING BLUSH
(Bottom Right) White plastic. OSP $2., CMV $1.

1958-64 POWDER PAK
(Left) Pink plastic box. 7 oz. size. OSP $1.10, CMV $2. - $3. MB.

1957-64 POWDER PAK COMPACT
(Right) Pearl color plastic compact. OSP $1.25, CMV $2. - $3. MB.

1968-70 BLUSHING CREAM
(Left) .25 oz. clear plastic, gold 4A design. OSP $2., CMV 50c.

1971-75 BLUSHING CREAM
(Right) .25 oz. white plastic base, pink top, gold 4A design. OSP $2., CMV 25c.

1961-68 CREAM ROUGE
Clear plastic with 4A design on lid. OSP $1., CMV 50c - $1. MB.

1962-64 EYE SHADOW
Same container as above. Came in Eye Shadow. OSP $1., CMV 50c - $1. MB.

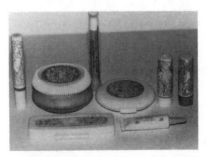

1970-76 CERTAIN LOOK PRODUCTS
MASCARA
(Back Row) OSP $2., CMV 25c.
DEW GLOW
(Back Row) OSP $2.50, CMV 50c.
EYE SHADOW STACK
(Back Row) OSP $1., CMV 50c.
COMPACT
(Back Row) OSP $2., CMV 50c.
LIPSTICK
(Back Row) Has white base. OSP $1., CMV 50c.
LIP BEAMER
(Back Row) Has purple base. OSP $1., CMV 50c.
SHADOW & LINER TRIO
(Front Row) OSP $2., CMV $1.
EYE SHINE
(Front Row) OSP $1., CMV 25c.

1972-76 CERTAIN LOOK PRODUCTS
1972 BLUSH PETITE COMPACT
.19 oz. white with pink & blue picture. Came with brush. SSP $3., CMV $2.

1972 EYE SHINE
.25 oz. white with pink & lavender. SSP $1., CMV 50c.

1972-74 DEW GLOW
2.25 oz. pink frosted glass with white cap & pink & blue picture. SSP $3., CMV $1.50.

1972 LIPSTICK
White with pink & blue picture. SSP $1., CMV $1.50.

1974-76 LONG LASH MASCARA
CMV $1.50.

1974-78 DELICATE BEAUTY
Beige & white design.
AUTOMATIC EYELINER
(Back Row) OSP $3., CMV 25c.
CREAM FOUNDATION
(Back Row) OSP $3., CMV 25c.
AUTOMATIC MASCARA
(Back Row) OSP $2., CMV 25c.
UNDER MAKEUP MOISTURIZER
(Back Row) OSP $3., CMV 25c.
BLUSH STICK
(Back Row) OSP $4., CMV 25c.
LIPSTICK
(Back Row) OSP $1.50, CMV 25c.
PRESSED POWDER COMPACT
(Front Row) OSP $3., CMV 50c.
POWDER SHADOW DUET
(Front Row) OSP $2., CMV 25c.
BLUSHING CREAM
(Front Row) OSP $2., CMV 25c.

1973-74 DIAL A SHADOW
(Left) White & clear plastic holder holds 5 powder eye shadows & applicator. OSP $6., CMV $1. - $2. MB.

1976-78 ABOUT TOWN COMPACT
(Right) Brown plastic with weave design on lid. OSP $3.50, CMV 50c - $1. MB.

1974-75 COMPACT
(Top Left) Black plastic. CMV 50c - $1. MB.

1975-76 BLUSH COMPACT
(Top Right) Brown plastic, gold trim. OSP $3., CMV 50c. - $1. MB.

1976-68 MAKING EYES EYE SHADOW
(Bottom Left) Turquoise plastic case. OSP $1., CMV 25c.

1972-74 TANTALEYES COLLECTION COMPACT
(Bottom Right) Brown case with 2 eye shadows, plus mascara has brush & sponge tip applicator. OSP $3., CMV $1. - $1.50 MB.

1972 OWL MAKEUP
(Top Left) White plastic gold trim. SSP $6., CMV $5. - $8. MB.

1970-71 BUTTERFLY COLLECTION
(Top Right) White plastic, turquoise, pink & gold, tube of 1 lipstick in center. SSP $6., CMV $5. - $8. MB.

1973 HONEY CAT MAKEUP COLLECTION
(Bottom) Brown plastic with sponge tipped application. SSP $7., CMV $5. - $8. MB.

1970 COLOR EYES DUET
(Top Left) OSP $2., CMV $1.

1968-69 SPARKLING CREAM EYE SHADOW
(Top Inside Left) OSP $1.75, CMV $1.

1971-75 EYE GLEAM
(Top Inside Right) OSP $1., CMV 50c.

1967-74 CAKE EYELINER
(Top Right) OSP $1.50, CMV 50c.

1970-76 POWDER SHADOW DUET
(Bottom Left) OSP $2., CMV $1.

1962-65 GOLDEN HIGHLIGHT
(Bottom Inside Left) OSP $1.25, CMV $2.

1960's CREAM ROUGE
(Bottom Inside Right) OSP $1.25, CMV $1.

1973-74 ULTRA SHEER LIP GLOSS POT
(Bottom Right) OSP $2.25, CMV $1.50.

1970's EYEBROW BRUSH-A-LINE
Miscellaneous cases. CMV 50c. each - $1. MB.

1967-73 ULTRA SHEER PRESSED POWDER
(Back Left) White plastic & gold trim. OSP $3., CMV $1.

1969-71 BLUSH COMPACT
(Back Right) Brown plastic with gold trim. Came with a brush. OSP $3., CMV $1.

1972-74 FASHION GROUP COMPACT
(Front Left) Black plastic with gold trim. OSP $4.50, CMV $2.

1970-73 SILVERY POWDER SHADOW COLLECTION
(Front Center) Jade-like, mirrored, with gold trim. OSP $5., CMV $2.

1970-72 LIP TWINS
(Front Right) Jade-like plastic, gold trim, holds 2 lipsticks, mirror on back. SSP $3., CMV $2.

1972-74 CREMESTICK FOUNDATION
(Left) .85 oz. white plastic with gold trim. OSP $2., CMV 50c.

1973-76 MOISTURE STICK
(Inside Left) .7 oz. pink & gold. OSP $1., CMV 25c.

1969-75 GLO GETTER BLUSH STICK
(Center) 1 oz. brown & gold. OSP $1., CMV 50c.

1971-74 GO TOGETHER
(Inside Right) One side is foundation, other side blush. OSP $4., CMV $1.

1976 GREAT BLUSH FROST STICK
(Right) .85 oz. brown plastic. OSP $3., CMV 25c.

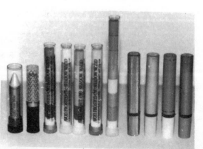

1970's GOLD SATIN EYE BRUSH
(Left) Small eye brush. CMV 50c on card.

1960's EYE SHADOW WAND
(Center) Eight tier eye shadow in packet. CMV 50c.

1971 POWDER PACK REFILL
(Right) Pink box holds metal powder refill. CMV $1. MB.

(Left to Right)

1975-76 EYE SHADOW CRAYON
Black base, clear top. OSP $1., CMV 50c.

1970-74 CRYSTAL SHADOWS
Black base, clear top. OSP $1., CMV 50c.

1971-78 EYE SHADOWS WANDS
Came frosted or velvet. Different years different colors available. OSP $1., CMV 50c.

1962 EYE SHADOW WAND
6 stack up shades. OSP $1.35, CMV $1.

1962-78 MASCARA
Lash Supreme, gold case; Making Eyes, pink case; Sweet Honesty, blue & white; 1976 Making Eyes, turquoise case. OSP $1., CMV 25c each.

1976-78 DELICATE BEAUTY POWDER EYE SHADOW
(Left) Gray plastic. OSP $3.50, CMV 50c.

1976-78 DELICATE BEAUTY TENDER PEACH 100% FRAGRANCE FREE POWDER BLUSH
(Right) Gray plastic. OSP $5., CMV 50c.

1972-73 MIRROR MIRROR
Silver box, holds white plastic reversable mirror. OSP $3.50, CMV $2. - $3. MB.

1977-78 COLORSTICKS FOR EYES & LIPS
(Left) Makeup colors in pencil form. OSP $3.50, CMV 25c.

1977-78 COVER-ALL
(Right) Concealing stick. OSP $3.25, CMV 25c.

1981-82 NO. 1 HIT LIP GLOSS COMPACT
2" record look compact. SSP $5., CMV $3. MB.

1982-83 ACCOLADE MAKEUP PRODUCTS
AUTOMATIC CONCEALING CREAM
SOFT ACCENT BLUSH
NOURISHING FOUNDATION
VERY EMOLLIENT LIPSTICK
ENRICHED POWDER EYE SHADOW
CMV all products 50c each.

1982-83 ORIENTAL CLASSICS DEMI STICK
(Left) Sweet Honesty fragrance. SSP $1.50, CMV 50c.

1982-83 ORIENTAL CLASSICS LIP GLOSS
(Right) Blue pill box holds lip gloss. SSP $1.50, CMV 50c.

1980-82 COLORCREME PRODUCTS
Blue & silver colors.
MOISTURE BLUSH-UP STICK
DAY LONG CREAMY POWDER EYE SHADOW
MOISTURE LIPSTICK SAMPLE BAG
CMV 50c each item.

1980-81 SPUNSILK MAKEUP COLLECTION
SPUN COLOR LIPSTICK
SPUN POWDER EYE SHADOW DUO
SPUN COLOR NAIL ENAMEL
SPUN POWDER BLUSH
SPUN FINISH CREAM MAKEUP
CMV $1. MB.

1970's MISCELLANEOUS EYEBROW PENCILS & MASCARA, EYELINER REFILLS & LIP BRUSH
(Left) CMV 25c each.

1963-65 FASHION LIPSTICK
(Right) Pink flowered plastic case with gold base. OSP 98c, CMV $1.50 - in demonstrator case as shown $5. - lipstick only $1. - $2. MB.

1981-82 OPULENT COLORS COLLECTION
ULTRA WEAR NAIL ENAMEL
Red & gold cap. SSP $2.25.
LASTING CREAMY POWDER BLUSH COMPACT
Red compact. SSP $4.75.
DAY LONG CREAMY POWDER EYE SHADOW
Red compact. SSP $3.75.
COLORCREME MOISTURE LIPSTICK
Red. SSP. $2.75. All come in gold and red boxes. CMV 50c, each item MB.

1980-81 SENSATIONAL EYES COLLECTION BOX
(Left) 4½" wide red plastic box comes with 5 eye shadows. SSP $8., CMV $5. MB.
1980-81 PROFESSIONAL MAKEUP BRUSH COLLECTION
(Right) Red plastic, holds 4 brushes. SSP $11., CMV $8. MB.

1982-83 CHINA FANTASY EYE SHADOW COLLECTION
Box holds black plastic 6 sided box with 5 eye shadows. SSP $7., CMV $3. MB.

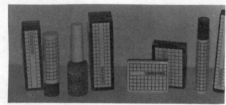

1981-82 COORDINATES PRODUCTS
Black & white check design. All are boxed.
FULL COLOR LIPSTICK
QUICK DRY NAIL ENAMEL
SMOOTH TOUCH EYE SHADOW
ROLL-ON LASH COLOR
SSP $2.29 each, CMV each 50c MB.

SEE 1984 SUPPLEMENT IN BACK OF BOOK FOR MORE JARS

CREAM JARS — MISC.

1930-34 VIOLET NUTRI CREAM
(Left) White jar, metal lid, silver & blue label. 2 & 4 oz. size. OSP 78c on 4 oz. & 52c for 2 oz., CMV $40. in box - $35. jar only.
1930-34 CLEANSING CREAM
(Right) 4 oz. white glass ribbed jar with aluminum lid. Silver & blue label. OSP $1., CMV $35. jar only - $40. in box.

1933-36 CREAM JARS - MISC.
Ribbed white glass jar with blue metal caps. Following came in 2 & 4 oz. size. Rose Cold Cream, Violet Nutri Cream; 4 oz. size only in Cleansing Cream; 2 oz. size only in Bleach Cream, Vanishing Cream, Tissue Cream. OSP 78c on 4 oz. & 52c on 2 oz. size, CMV $30. each - $35. MB.

1930-34 ROSE COLD CREAM
(Left) 2 & 4 oz. white glass ribbed jars with aluminum lids. Silver & blue labels. OSP 2 oz. 52c, 4 oz. size 78c, CMV $40. each in box - $30. jar only.
1932-33 BLEACH CREAM
(Right) 3 oz. frosted glass jar, metal lid, silver & blue label. OSP 78c, CMV $50. - $55. MB.

1939 Only ROSE COLD CREAM BOX
2 oz. white glass jar, turquoise lid in special short issue design box. CPC on box. OSP 10c, CMV $20. MB as shown.

1939 Only CREAM DEODORANT
White glass jar, turquoise lid. OSP 37c. This jar is Rare. CMV $16. MB - $12. jar only, mint.

1941 ROSE COLD CREAM SPECIAL ISSUE BOX
Special issue rose color box with girls face on side. Came with regular issue middle size jar of Rose Cold Cream for 10c with regular order. CMV $17.50 MB as shown.

1936-55 CREAM JARS - MISC
This style bottle was sold from 1935-55. Came in Tissue Cream, Rose Cold Cream, Special Formula Cream, Foundation Cream, Violet Protective Cream, All-Purpose Cream, Bleach Cream, Cleansing Cream, Night Cream, Violet Nutri Cream, Complexion Cream, Vanishing Cream, Super Rich Cream, 1947 Special Dry Skin Cream, 1948 Facial Mask Cream. White glass jars came in small, medium & large size with turquoise metal caps. Paper caps were used 1943-46. OSP 52c to 89c, CMV $4. each. Add $3. each for turquoise paper caps. CMV with CPC labels on jar or box 1936-39 $8. jar only - $12. CPC label on box mint.

1954-55 ANTISEPTIC CREAM
3½ oz. large size jar only. OSP $89c, CMV $4. - $5. MB.

1954-59 CREAM DEODORANT
White glass jar, turquoise lid. OSP 49c, CMV $4. in box - $2.50 jar only.

1940 Only ROSE COLD CREAM BOX
1¾ oz. jar if Rose Cold Cream came in special issue box for Reps to use as demonstrator only. Cost Reps 10c. CMV $17.50 MB as shown.

1942 ROSE COLD CREAM SPECIAL ISSUE BOX
Special issue blue & pink rosebud box holds regular issue large size jar of Rose Cold Cream. OSP 49c, CMV $17.50 MB as shown.

1946 Only COLOR PICK-UP CREAM
7/8 oz. white glass jar, turquoise lid. OSP 89c, CMV $15. mint - $18. MB.

1930-34 TISSUE CREAM
(Left) Ribbed white glass, metal lid, silver & blue label. 2 oz. size. OSP 75c, CMV $35. - $40. MB.

1931 VANISHING CREAM
(Right) 2 oz. white glass jar with aluminum lid. Silver & blue label. OSP 52c, CMV $40. in box - $35. jar only.

1946-47 COLOR PICK-UP CREAM
Painted over twin tone lid. 1-7/8 oz. white glass jar with green lid. OSP 89c, CMV $12. - $15. MB.

1946-50 COLOR PICK-UP LIQUID
(Left) 1 oz. clear glass bottle with turquoise cap. OSP 89c, CMV $8. - $11. MB.

1946-54 COLOR PICK-UP CREAM
(Right) 1-7/8 oz. white glass jar with turquoise lid. OSP 89c, CMV $6. - $10. MB. Also came 1 oz. jar. Same lid & jar.

1943-46 TWIN TONE MAKE-UP CREAM
(Left) 1-7/8 oz. white jar, turquoise paper lid & metal lid. OSP 89c, CMV metal lid $9. - paper lid $12.

1943-46 TWIN TONE MAKE-UP CREAM
(Right) 7/8 oz. white glass jar, turquoise paper lid. OSP $89c, CMV $10. - $14. MB.

1945 Only HAND CREAM
3½ oz. clear glass jar, turquoise lid. Rare. CMV $25. - $30. MB.

1957-60 RICH MOISTURE CREAM
In 3½ & 2 oz. turquoise jars with 4A on white lids. OSP 2 oz. $1.50 - 3 oz. $2.50, CMV $3. MB - $2. jar only, mint.

1955-57 CREAM CAKE
(Left) Avon in center of pink lid, white glass bottom. OSP 95c, CMV $3. - $4. MB.

1948-55 CREAM CAKE
(Right) Dove on top of pink lid, white glass bottom. OSP 95c, CMV $4. - $5. MB.

1953 CREME SHAMPOO
4 oz. jar very short issue. RARE. OSP $1., CMV $15. MB - $10. jar only mint.

1961-72 RICH MOISTURE CREAM
(Left) 2 oz. & 3½ oz. turquoise glass jar with 4A on white lid. OSP 3½ oz. $2.50 - 2 oz. $1.50, CMV 25c each. On 1972 jar the 4A design was dropped.

1961-65 HORMONE CREAM
(Right) 2 oz. turquoise glass jar with 4A on white lid. Same as Rich Moisture Cream jar. OSP $2., CMV $1. MB, 50c jar only.

1954 RICH MOISTURE CREAM
(Left) 1½ & 3½ oz. turquoise glass jars with turquoise plastic lids. OSP $1.50, CMV $3. -$4. MB.

1963-66 CREAM FOUNDATION
(Right) 1 oz. white glass jar with white plastic lid with gold center. OSP $1.35, CMV $1.50.

1956 STRAWBERRY COOLER
Frosted glass jar with strawberry on white lid. OSP $1.50, CMV $3. - $5. MB.

1954-57 NAIL BEAUTY
1 oz. white jar with white lid. OSP 59c, CMV $3. - $4. MB.

1936-54 CREAM DEODORANT
1 oz. white glass jar, turquoise lid. OSP 39c, CMV $7. jar only - $10. MB. Add $4. CPC label.

1954-57 RICH MOISTURE CREAM
Turquoise jar & cap in 2 oz. & 3½ oz. size. OSP $1.50 for 2 oz. - $2.50 for 3½ oz. 2 oz. jar came with 2 different size neck & caps. CMV $4. each size MB - $3. jar only.

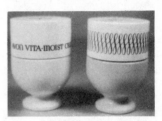

1954-61 AVON CREAMS
(Left & Center) White glass jar with green lid & label. Came in: Hormone Cream, Super Rich Cream, Cleansing Cream & Antiseptic Cream in large & small jars. OSP 89c, CMV $2. each.

1967-69 STAY FAIR NIGHT CREAM
(Right) 2¼ oz. light blue base, blue and white lid. OSP $2., CMV $1.

1967-71 HAIR CONDITIONER
6 oz. white jar, pink metal cap. OSP $2.50, CMV $1.50 - $2.50 MB.

1961-65 COLOR CAKE
(Top) 2 oz. white cap & pink base. OSP $1.95, CMV $1. - $2. MB.

1947-54 CAKE MAKE-UP
(Bottom) 1¾ oz. pink base, white cap. OSP $1., CMV $3. - $4. MB.

1959-61 VITA MOIST CREAM
2 oz. yellow glass jar with white smooth cap. OSP $3., CMV $1.50.

1961-68 VITA MOIST CREAM
1 oz. yellow glass jar with white smooth cap. OSP $1.75, CMV 75c.

1965-69 SUPER RICH CREAM
2¼ oz. pink glass bottom, white & pink cap. OSP $3., CMV 75c.

1969-74 SUPER RICH CREAM
2¼ oz. blue glass jar with white & blue cap. OSP $3., CMV 25c.

1955-57 COLOR PICK-UP CREAM
(Left) White glass jar with pink lid. OSP 95c, CMV $6. each MB - $4. jar only.

1961-65 WHITE VELVET CREAM
(Inside Left) 3½ oz. white glass jar with 4A on turquoise lid. OSP $1.25, CMV $1. - $2. MB.

1963-66 POLISH REMOVER PADS
(Inside Right) White glass jar with red lid, holds 20 pads. OSP 98c, CMV $2. - $3. MB.

1954-58 ANTISEPTIC CREAM
(Right) 3½ oz. white glass jar with gray lid. OSP $1., CMV $2. - $3. MB.

1961-69 VITA MOIST CREAM
2¼ oz. yellow glass jar with white smooth cap. OSP $3., CMV 50c.

1969-72 VITA MOIST CREAM
2.25 oz. yellow glass jar with ribbed white cap. OSP $3., CMV 50c.

1961-69 CREAM SUPREME
2¼ oz. pink glass jar with white cap with gold design around edge. OSP $3., CMV 75c.

1969-72 CREAM SUPREME
2¼ oz. pink glass jar with pink 4A on white ribbed cap. OSP $3., CMV 50c.

1940-50 NAIL & CUTICLE CREAM
(Left) 1 oz. white glass jar, turquoise lid. OSP 43c, CMV $5. - $8. MB.

1951-54 NAIL BEAUTY
(Right) 1 oz. white glass jar, white lid. OSP 49c, CMV $4. - $5. MB.

1965-76 HORMONE CREAM
(Left) 2.25 oz. white glass jar with gold tip on white lid. OSP $1.50, CMV 25c.

1960-74 EYE CREAM
(Right) White glass jar with eye on metal lid. OSP $1.50, CMV 25c.

1974-78 RICH MOISTURE CREAM
(Left) 7 oz. blue plastic with white lid. OSP $4., CMV 25c. Also came in 2 oz. size. CMV 25c.

1972-75 RICH MOISTURE CREAM
(Inside Left) 3.5 oz. blue plastic with white lid. (No lettering on front.) OSP $2., CMV 25c.

1976-78 AVON COLD CREAM
(Inside Right) 3.1 oz. white plastic, blue lid. OSP $1., CMV 25c.

1975-77 VITA MOIST
(Right) 3.5 oz. yellow plastic, white lid. CMV 25c.

1957-63 FRENCH FROSTING
(Left) 1 oz. clear glass jar with pink plastic lid with gold center. OSP $1.25, CMV $2. jar only - $5. in box.

1969-76 COVER PERFECT
(Right) 2 oz. clear glass jar with white, pink & brown striped lid. OSP $2., CMV 50c - $1. MB.

1970 MAKE-UP SETTING PADS
Pink frosted jar, white cap. Has 45 pads per box. OSP $2.75, CMV $5.

1977-78 TANNING BUTTER
1.75 oz. bronze plastic container. OSP $1.49, CMV 25c.

1969-75 UNDER MAKEUP MOISTURIZER
(Left) 2 oz. white milk glass jar, white & gold lid. OSP $3., CMV 25c.

1980-81 NURTURA VANITY JAR
(Center) 4 oz. clear glass jar with tortoise lid. Holds Nurtura Replenishing Cream. SSP $7., CMV $4. MB.

1981 SHINE SHINE LIP GLOSS
(Right) Clear bottom jar, white & pink lid. SSP $2., CMV 50c MB.

1974-76 VITA MOIST CREAM
(Left) 3.5 oz. yellow plastic with white & yellow lid. OSP $2., CMV 25c.

1975-78 VITA MOIST CREAM
(Inside Left) 7 oz. yellow plastic with white & yellow lid. OSP $3., CMV 25c.

1976-77 HORMONE CREAM
(Inside Right) 3.25 oz. white plastic with white & gold lid. OSP $2., CMV 25c.

1970-73 DEEP CLEAN CLEANSING CREAM
(Right) 4 oz. white plastic, blue lid. OSP $1., CMV 50c.

1969-70 STEPPING OUT
4 oz. blue jar, white lid. OSP $2., CMV $1. MB - 50c jar only.

1971-76 STEPPING OUT
Is same only 5 oz. size. Blue jar. OSP $2., CMV 25c.

1973-74 SKIN-SO-SOFT SOFTENER VANITY JAR
(Left) 5 oz. clear glass with antiqued gold lid. SSP $4., CMV $2.50 - $3.50 MB.

1973-75 CREAM SACHET VANITY JAR
(Center) 1 oz. clear glass with antiqued silver lid. Holds Field Flowers, Charisma or Topaze. SSP $3., CMV $2. - $3. MB.

1973 RICH MOISTURE CREAM VANITY JAR
(Right) 5 oz. clear glass with antiqued silver lid. SSP $2.50, CMV $2. - $2.50 MB.

1980-82 PURE ESSENTIALS PRODUCTS
Cream jars in cold cream, all purpose cream, petroleum jelly plus. SSP $1.50 each, CMV 25c each.

SEE 1984 SUPPLEMENT IN BACK OF BOOK FOR MORE BRUSHES

BRUSHES & COMBS — MISC.

1970 BRUSH & COMB VALET
Black brush & comb with copper colored insert. OSP $3., CMV $3.

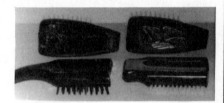

1974-75 OUTDOORSMAN BRUSH & COMB SET
(Back Left) 5" long, brown plastic with decorative panel. Comb is brown. OSP $4., CMV $2. MB.

1975 AMERICAN EAGLE BRUSH & COMB VALET
(Back Right) 5½" long, black plastic with eagle on top. Red & blue shield. OSP $5., CMV $2. MB.

1970-73 CLUB BRUSH
(Front Left) Black with black bristles. OSP $2., CMV $1. MB.

1972 VALET TRIO
(Front Right) Brown plastic with brown comb & silver shoe horn. OSP $3., CMV $2. MB.

1974 FAMILY CLOTHES BRUSH
(Top) 9" long, simulated wood grain, black bristles. OSP $4., CMV $2. MB.

1974-76 CLOTHES BRUSH VALET WITH SHOE HORN
(Middle) 10" long, brown plastic. OSP $2.50, CMV $1.50 MB.

1972-73 SURE WINNER COMB & BRUSH
(Bottom Left) White with blue stripe. OSP $3., CMV $1.50 MB.

1974-76 JACKKNIFE COMB & BRUSH
(Bottom Right) Black & silver with black comb. OSP $4., CMV $3. MB.

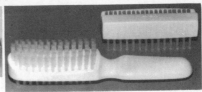

1980-81 PURSEMATES MIRROR & COMB
6" long burgandy suede case has Avon mirror & comb. SSP $5., CMV $3.50 MB.

1977-78 BATH BRUSH
Approx. 15½" long, plastic brush. Came in blue, ivory or yellow. SSP $6.99, CMV $2. each MB.

1970-73 NAIL BRUSH
(Top) White plastic nylon bristles. OSP $1., CMV 50c MB.
1973-76 HAND & NAIL BRUSH
(Bottom) White plastic, nylon bristles (with long handle). OSP $1.88, CMV 50c MB.

1978 COMB & BRUSH VALET
Brown plastic. Deer on top, brown box. SSP $7., CMV $3. MB.

1969-73 COMPLEXION BEAUTY BRUSH
Pink & white box holds white plastic brush. CMV $1. MB.

1982 COLORCASE
Black vinyl case with mirror inside lid. Outer sleeve. CMV $1.

JEWELRY

PLEASE NOTE: Avon Jewelry is not considered a collectable item by most avid collectors & bottle dealers. Most collectors agree that most people buying Avon Jewelry are buying it to wear, not to put in a collection.

Avon Products, Inc., is now the world's largest retailer of costume jewelry and are making vast amounts of jewelry in large volume. Because of these reasons, Avon Jewelry should not be considered collectable at this time as a collectors item. I do not encourage you to buy Avon Jewelry as a collector's investment, as you are sure to never recover your original investment. Buy it only for your personal use as Avon is making some very beautiful pieces of jewelry.

1975-78 PLAQUE CONTROL
(Left Top) 2 brushes, 1 blue, 1 yellow, red or green. OSP $1., CMV $1. MB.
1973-78 TOOTHBRUSH DUO
(Left Second) 2 brushes, 1 brown, 1 white. OSP $1.25, CMV $1.25 MB.
AVON PLAQUE CONTROL
(Left Third) CMV $1.
1972-73 SAF-T-DENT TOOTHBRUSH
(Left Fourth) 1 brush, pink or blue. OSP $1., CMV $1. MB.
1973-76 STIMU-TEX TOOTHBRUSHES
(Left Bottom) 2 brushes, 1 white, 1 blue. OSP $1., CMV $1. MB.
1970-73 DECORATOR TOOTHBRUSH TRIO PAK
(Center) 3 brushes, either 1 of each, yellow, green, pink or all three same color. OSP $1., CMV $1.50 MB.
1965-70 DECORATOR TOOTHBRUSH TRIO PAK
(Right) 3 brushes, choice of pink, yellow or blue box matching color of brushes. OSP $1., CMV $2. MB.

1975-78 JEWELRY DEMO DISPLAY CASE
Case for representatives to demonstrate jewelry. Blue case. CMV $4.

1977-78 JEWELRY CASE
White jewelry case 10½" x 8½" x 2". Dark blue velvet inside. SSP $5., CMV $4. Avon on bottom & outer sleeve.

1978-79 DECORATOR'S JEWELRY CHEST

Wood box sold empty. Lift up lid. Bottom drawer only opens. Bottom gold label says "Avon Decorator's Jewelry Chest 1978 Made in Taiwan" Very short issue. Same box sold in other stores. Must have Avon label on bottom. SSP $6. with a $10. purchase of other Avon products, CMV $30. with Avon label only in box.

1977 - 14K GOLD FILLED JEWELRY DEMO CASE

(Top) Gray leatherette demo case used by Avon Reps to show 14K gold jewelry. Avon on outside. Cost Avon Reps $2.50, CMV $3.50.

1977 JEWELRY WRAP CASE

(Bottom) Blue velvet wrap case, clear plastic inside, Avon tag on inside. Sold for $3.50 with purchase of 2 jewelry items. CMV $2.50.

1920 BABY BOOK
(Left) CMV not established.

1898 CATALOG CPC
(Center) 62 page sales catalog. Only has illustrations, not pictures of products. Book is dated 1898. CMV not established.

1897 CATALOG CPC
(Right) 62 page sales catalog. Book is dated 1897. CMV not established.

SEE 1984 SUPPLEMENT IN BACK OF BOOK FOR MORE PAPER ITEMS

PAPER ITEMS — MISC.

SALES CATALOGS

1916-18 CPC MAIL ORDER CATALOG
(Left) 4½"x 6" gray cover 40 page booklet sent to customers in areas where CPC Reps did not call. Rare. No price established.

1898 CPC CATALOG
(Right) 5"x 7" size blue cover and 64 pages in blue paper. Used by CPC Reps to sell products. Eureka Trade Mark on back cover. Very rare. No price established.

1896 CPC CALLING CARD
(Left) Has list of products on backside and CPC Co., 126 Chambers St., New York on front. CMV $25.

1896 CPC SALES CATALOG
(Right) Small 30 page booklet on products. Contains no pictures. Rare. No price established.

1912 INSTRUCTIONAL MANUAL
(Left) Used by CPC Sales Managers. CMV not established.

1912 CATALOG CPC
(Center) 64 page sales catalog used by Reps. CMV not established.

1909 WOMAN BEAUTIFUL BOOKLET
(Right) Small booklet on massage cream. CMV not established.

CATALOGS CPC

1900 CPC Catalog shown on top left, top right 1898, bottom right 1908 and bottom left is 1915. Each one shows the item sold during that period by CPC and gives prices. 1915 was the last small catalog printed, 1916 they went to the large black hard bound color books. For comparison of size, the 1896 is 4½" wide and 6 5/8" high. No value can be set on this type of book because of their rarity. If you have knowledge of any old CPC catalogs or Outlooks for sale, please contact Bud Hastin, P. O. Box 43690, Las Vegas, NV 89116, as he is always in the market to buy them for information to pass on to you the collector.

1916-29 CPC SALES CATALOG

On bottom is black hard bound CPC Sales Catalog with 32 to 40 color pages. Book is 10½" x 16" in size. The hard bound book was first issued in 1916 in the big size and last used in 1921. Gold lettering on front. 1922 to 1929 the black catalog is soft cover and 34 pages in color. 10"x 14½" in size. These catalogs are usually not dated and very hard to find. CMV range from $25. in very bad condition to $200. for a mint, new condition catalog. Each year a new book was issued.

CATALOGS — AVON 1930-57
Top Row - left to right
1930-36 - 10" x 7" dark blue, silver Avon on cover. CMV $20. to $50. depending on condition.
1936-48 - 7¼"x 10½" size, green cover, gold tulip A. CMV $15. to $40.
1948-54 - 7¼"x 10½", green cover, Avon in gold letters. CMV $10. to $30.
Bottom row - left to right
1954 - A special gold cover catalog for Honor Presidents Award Reps. CMV $20. each.
1954-57 - General issue was green cover, 7½"x 10½", gold Avon and 4A design. CMV $10. to $20.
1956 Honor Award - Red cover catalog, gold Avon and 4A design. CMV $25. Each of these catalogs was made to install or remove pages. The dates given reflect the years that each cover was used. Each catalog was changed each year on the inner pages.
WANTED: If you have any Avon Sales Catalogs for 1941, 43, 44, 45, 47 and wish to sell them, please contact Bud Hastin, P.O. Box 43690, Las Vegas, NV 89116.

1937 POCKET CATALOG
A small fold out leaflet brochure left with the customer to buy Avon products. CMV $25. mint.

CHRISTMAS AVON CATALOGS
Starting in the early 1930's thru 1956, Avon printed a special Christmas Sales Catalog showing many gifts never sold at any other time. These catalogs are rare and hard to find. CMV 1930's $40. each. 1940's, $35. each. 1950's $25. each.
1967 CHRISTMAS CATALOG
In upper right part of picture is special hard bound edition. CMV $15. mint.

1905 -74 OUTLOOK'S
Outlooks were first printed in 1905 and given only to sales Reps. of CPC and Avon. They were to show new items coming out and also show awards they could win. The Outlook was discontinued in 1974 and the name was changed to "Avon Calling". If you have any old Outlooks 1939 or older and want to sell them, please contact Bud Hastin. Outlooks were given for each sales campaign during the year. CMV 1905 to 1930, $5. to $15.; 1930 to 1939 $2. to $5.; 1940 to 49 $1. to $5.; 1950 to 1959 $1. to $4.; 1960 to 1965 $1. to $3.; 1966 to 1969 50c to $1.; 1970 to 1976 10c to 25c each.

1920's - 30's SALES BROCHURES
Fold out sales brochures given to customers by CPC and Avon Representatives. Each one shows all items sold in regular sales catalog. These are rare and in color. Left to right 1926, CMV $50; 1929, CMV $40; 1931-36 same cover as CMV $35.; CMV $25. A 1933 brochure is laid out on bottom to see all the products offered.

1909 DEPOT MANAGERS CONTRACT CPC
Paper agreement between CPC and sales lady. CMV $40. mint.

1913 SALES MANAGERS CONTRACT
Paper agreement for Avon ladies in early 1900's. Signed by D. H. McConnell, founder of Avon. CMV $25.

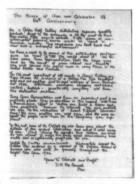

1936 LETTER FROM AVON
Misc. letters from Avon may vary in price depending on the year. Any letters personally signed by D. H. McConnell, founder of Avon in his own handwriting should be worth at least $25. Letter shown is a copy. CMV $15. mint.

1900's CPC D.H. McCONNELL LETTER
On CPC letterhead. Hand written by D. H. McConnell, founder of Avon to his factory workers. CMV for any hand written D. H. McConnell letter dated 1890's to 1930's would be $25. to $50. depending on buyer.

Note that most later years McConnell's signature is rubber stamped and not handwritten.

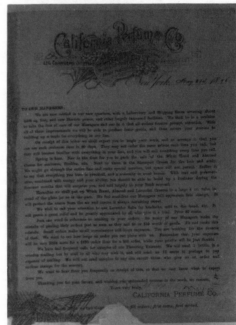

1896 LETTER FROM CPC
On CPC letterhead. Letter to CPC managers. CMV $45.

1912 CPC INK BLOTTER
Used by Reps in early 1900's. CMV $35.

1920 CPC INSTRUCTIONAL MANUAL
14 page booklet used to train early day Avon Reps. Tells them how and what to do to be a sales lady for CPC. No pictures. CMV $25.

EARLY 1900's CPC CHRISTMAS GREETING CARD
1c post card sent out at Christmas time. 126 Chambers Street, New York is the return address. CMV $25.

1910 CPC CALENDAR
9" wide, 12 5/16" high. Printed in 6 colors. Given to all customers with order of 75c or more, CMV $100. mint.

1979-80 CALENDAR — AVON
Large Avon calendar given to customers by Avon Reps. Came in big envelope each year. CMV $1. each mint in envelope.

1926 ORDER BOOK CPC
Order book used by Reps shown with CPC envelope and announcement of new headquarters address in New York. CMV $25. as shown.

1909 CPC CALENDAR
Given only to best CPC customers. CMV $100. mint.

1928 CPC INTRO BOOKLET
(Left) 30 page booklet used by Reps to start selling Avon. CMV $25. mint.
1922 CPC ORDER BOOKLET
(Right) Used by Reps to keep records of their orders. CMV $25 mint.

1940 ORDER BOOK COVER
Dark green cover for order book imprinted with tulip "A" and name of representative. Given for sales during 1940 Founders Campaign. CMV in envelope $20 - book only $15. mint.

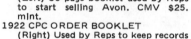

1930 ORDER BOOK CPC AVON
(Left) CMV $15. mint.
1930 CUSTOMER LIST BOOKLET
(Center) 8 pages. CMV $5. mint.
1928 CPC CUSTOMER LIST BOOKLET
(Right) 12 pages. CMV $8. mint.

1960's-70's ORDER BOOK
Misc. Avon Order Books used by Reps. CMV 50c. each.

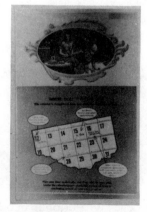

1967 CALENDAR
Avon Calling calendar. CMV $8. mint.

ORDER BOOKS (Left to right)
1933,37,42. Far right 1939 green order book cover. CMV $15. each mint.

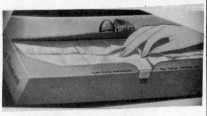

ORDER BOOKS
(Left to Right) 1920's CPC on cover (white cover). CMV $20.
1930's Tulip A design (white cover). CMV $15.
1940's Script A design (blue cover). CMV $10.
1950's 4A design (green cover). CMV $5.
1960's 4A design (white cover). CMV $2.
All must be in new condition for CMV given.

1930's-40's ADDRESS BOOK
(Left) Green leather, gold A design. CMV $10.
1956 HONOR AWARD BOOK COVER
(Center) Red plastic, gold design. CMV $7.50.
1900 JOE JEFFERSON CPC PAD
(Right) 50 sheets, scratch pad. CMV $50 mint.

1932-36 FACIAL TISSUES
Box of 160 tissues. OSP 50c, CMV $30 mint.

1981 ORDER BOOK
(Bottom) Green & white. CMV 50c.
1982 ORDER BOOK
(Top) Pink & white. CMV 50c.

1935 BUSINESS INTRO BOOK
(Left) 20 page booklet on how to be an Avon lady. Used by Reps. CMV $5.
1931 BUSINESS INTRO BOOK
(Right) 17 page booklet on how to be an Avon lady. Used by Reps. CMV $5.

1930-32 CLEANSING TISSUE
Wrapped in cellophane. Package of 135 sheets. OSP 50c, CMV $15. mint.

1930's CPC LADY INTRODUCTION CARD
3½" x 5¼" card used by Reps to introduce themselves to customers. CMV $2.

1937-44 AVON FACIAL TISSUE
Turquoise & white paper box. Rare. OSP 50c, CMV $20. mint.

1926 CALOPAD SANITARY NAPKIN
Cardboard box holds 12 napkins. OSP 50c - CMV $75 MB. Extremely rare.

1960 ORDER BOOK
(Left) CMV $2.
1958 CALL TAG PADS
(Right) Pad of tear off sheets left by Avon lady. CMV $3. pad.

1930's CPC FIVE HUNDRED CLUB CERTIFICATE
Sent to a representative when she completes $500. worth of net business. CMV $20. mint.

1935 BEAUTY SERVICE BOOK
30 page booklet showing how to apply Avon cosmetics. Used by Reps. Came in Avon CPC envelope. CMV $10. mint with envelope.

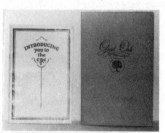

CPC BOOKLET
(Left) Cover says "Introducing You To The CPC". CMV $25.
1945 GREAT OAK BOOKLET
(Right) 20 page, blue cover. Given to reps in 1945. Written by D. H. McConnell, founder of CPC in 1903. Came with letter from Russel Rooks who became President of Avon. Rare. CMV $50. with letter.

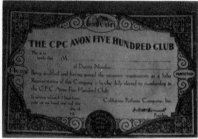

EARLY 1930's CPC AVON FIVE HUNDRED CLUB
Certificate given to representatives for selling $500. worth of Avon products. CMV $15. each, mint.

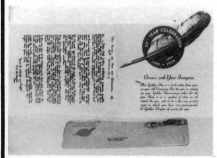

1937 PAVING THE WAY
Booklet used by Reps in 1930's to help train them for better sales. Tulip A on cover. CMV $8.

1930 McCONNELL LETTER BOOK
174 pages of letters from Managers to D. H. McConnell, Avon Founder. Rare. No price established.

1953 PROMISE TO MYSELF BOOKLET
23 page booklet published by Irene Nunemaker & Avon Products, Inc. CMV $10.

1936 - 50TH ANNIVERSARY GOLD QUILL PEN & LETTER
Sent to representatives to announce the 50th year celebration. The circle stands for the "Avon Family Circle", the feather and quill indicated the opportunities to "Feather Your Nests." Comes complete with attached 50th anniversary letter. It folds in center. Did not come separate. CMV complete as pictured $45. mint.

1930's CPC SALES REP CONTRACT
Used to sign up CPC Reps for sales in early 1930's. Came in CPC Avon business envelope. Shown also with Customer List booklet & booklet "Now You are in Business for Yourself." CMV $25. complete as shown.

1934 BEAUTY SERVICE BOOKLET
24 page beauty tip book. CMV $10.

1945 MANAGERS INFORMATION BOOKLET
8¼" x 9" - 18 page booklet for managers to show new Avon Reps for general information on Avon products. The cover of this booklet is the same artwork Avon Products used to make the 1977 National Association of Avon Clubs plate advertised in C26-77 Avon Calling. CMV $15.

1948 HOW TO CONDUCT GOOD SALES MEETINGS BOOKLET
Black leatherette spiral bound. Booklet used by Avon managers. CMV $10.

1959 WEST GERMAN BRANCH OPENING CARD
Card introducing the starting of Avon operations in Hamburg, Germany. CMV $10. mint.

1950's CHRISTMAS CARD
(Left) CMV $1. each.
1970 COASTER FROM AVON
(Right) Different varieties. CMV $1. each.

1950's AD DISPLAYS
Magazine advertising on hardbacks. CMV $15. each.

1960's NOTEBOOK COVERS - MANAGERS
3 different blue plastic binders used by Avon Managers. One is Avon Beauty Notes, Group Meetings and Avon on 3rd one. Small one is red. CMV $3. each.

1964 BEAUTY BOOK
(Left) 128 page book used by reps on beauty counciling. CMV $4.
1967 BEAUTY BOOK
(Right) 140 page book used by reps on beauty counciling. CMV $4.

1961 ROSE STAMPS
Page of 75 rose stamps for Avon Rep use in C-2-1961. Stamps say "Avons 75th Year". CMV $20.

1968 BUSINESS CARD - AVON
CMV $3. box.

1960's-70's CHILDREN'S COLOR BOOKS
Small World, Mickey Mouse, Peanuts, I Wish I Could. CMV $2. each.

1962 MANAGERS SALES MEETING NOTEBOOK
Campaign 15, 16, 17, 18 sales meeting plans. Red with white Christmas tree. CMV $25.

1966 CALENDAR
Quarterly calendar for Sept., Oct., Nov., Dec. showing Avon for the 1966 Christmas selling season. CMV $5.

1963 BEAUTY BOOK
CMV $2.

1978 NAPKIN "SWEET DREAMS"
(Left) White napkin with moon & sunrise scene. CMV $1.
1979 NAPKIN "GETTING BETTER EVERY DAY"
(Right) For President's Club members. White napkin, red letters. CMV $1.
1978 NAPKIN "GROUND BREAKING CEREMONY"
(Bottom) Red napkin from Pasadena branch ground breaking ceremony, April 13, 1978. CMV $1.50.

GREETING CARDS FROM AVON
1977 FATHER'S DAY CARD
(Left) Red & white card. CMV $1.
1977 SEYMOUR KENT CARD
(Center) Red card, came with white lace handkerchief made by Desco. CMV $1.50.
1969 FATHER'S DAY CARD
(Right) Straight 8 on front. CMV $1.50.

1959 CHRISTMAS CARD - CANADA
Avon Christmas card given to customers by reps in Canada. CMV $3.

1970's GREETING CARDS - AVON
Many different cards used by Avon managers & reps for different occasions. CMV about 50c each.

1972 DEEP WOODS ST. REGIS CARD
(Left) Special thank you card for Avon reps from St. Regis Paper Co. CMV $1.
1970's DAVE'S WAITING PICTURE
(Center) Picture of David Mitchell, Chairman of Avon Products. No price established.
1960's SALES CHART
(Right) Green & white paper. CMV $2.

1976 MOTHER'S DAY CARD
Given to customers in Mother's Day orders 1976 by Avon reps. CMV $1.

1970's AUTO HANDBOOK
Red plastic 2 ring instruction manual for employees of Avon with company leased cars. CMV $5.

1978 NOTE CARDS
Box of blank Avon note cards. CMV $4. MB.

1978 IVORY COAST AFRICA 1ST ISSUE AVON CATALOG
47 page catalog given to each Avon manager in U.S. with letter from Avon Products announcing expansion into Africa. CMV $6.

1978 CATALOG - HONG KONG
Avon sales catalog from Hong Kong. CMV $5.

1978 NOTE SET PEOPLE TO PEOPLE
Box with matching outer sleeve with A's on it used by managers. About 100 notes in box & envelopes. CMV $8. MB.

1973 CIRCLE OF EXCELLENCE ITEMS
Given to managers on C of E trip to Bermuda. White plastic airline ticket holder (CMV $10.); menu, program of events, airline menu (CMV $5. each item). Honor Roll Booklet, blue & gold booklet listing all C of E managers for 1973. CMV $10.

1979 RING SIZER PAPER
Blue & white paper Avon ring sizer issued before plastic sizers were delivered. Very short issue to Avon reps, issued C25-79. Size 3 to 9. CMV $1. mint.

1979 TEAM LEADER ORGANIZER
10½" x 12" size light brown binder organizer. Came in white box. Team Leader Organizer on front of binder. CMV $7. MB.

1975 BIRTHDAY CARD - AVON
Birthday cards made only for Avon & sent to reps on their birthday. Avon on back & inside. This type of card has been used for years. CMV $1. each.

1973 PLAN BOOKS FOR MANAGERS CMV $5.

NAPKINS - AVON - 1970's-80's
(Top Left) President's Club "Getting Better Every Day" CMV 50c.
(Top Right) United Way. CMV 50c.
(Bottom Right) "We're Going To Make You Feel Beautiful" CMV 50c.
(Bottom Left) 1978 Ground Breaking Ceremony, Pasadena, California, April 13, 1978. CMV $1.

1970's CARDS FROM AVON
Sent to representatives. CMV $2. each. Many different ones.

1971 PLACE MATS
Four Seasons - Robert Woods signed plastic place mats for Avon. Had choice of one of the four when you bought certain products. CMV $3. each.

1975 HERITAGE ALMANAC
1975 calendar given to District Managers only. Duplicate of 1929 calendar, each page shows different outlook. Limited edition, 2,678 given. CMV $25.

1972 MANAGERS INTRODUCTION BOOK
Turquoise binder holds 25 glossy pages. Managers use to get new Avon ladies to sell Avon. CMV $7.

1976 GEORGE WASHINGTON REPRESENTATIVE GIFT LETTER
Folder (on left) and a copy of a letter George Washington wrote from Mt. Vernon. Given at sales meeting in February. CMV $5.

1982 ULTRA NOTE PAPERS
Choice of 5 different color boxes holds 200 sheets of 4" x 6" note paper. Does not say Avon. SSP $2., CMV $1. mint.

1971 DESIGNERS COLLECTION CHRISTMAS CARDS
Box of 25 Avon Christmas cards, all the same design. Came in 36 different designs. No. 1 shown. OSP $4 to $10. per box. Back of each card marked Avon Products, Inc. & gives the card number. CMV each card 50c to $1.

1971 DESIGNER COLLECTION CHRISTMAS CARD SAMPLE SET
Box of 36 different Avon Christmas cards used by Avon Reps for sales. Short issue. CMV $35 complete set.

1980 ACTIVE WOMAN'S COOKBOOK
80 page cookbook from Avon. CMV $5.

1981 BEAUTY CALENDAR
Given to customers by Avon reps. Comes in 2 different envelopes. CMV $1.

1972-74 CREATIVE NEEDLECRAFT KITS FROM AVON
Embroidery kits included picture, yarn, needle & instructions. Came in many patterns. CMV $8.50 mint set. 29 sets issued. Creative Needlecraft Kits are as follows: American Eagle Pillow, Basket of Strawberries Pillow, Blue Moo Pillow, Floral Sentiments Pillow, Owl Mates Pillow, Spring Violets Pillow, Wild Pheasants Picture, Country Snowscape Picture, Noah's Ark Picture, Starburst Belt, Winter in the Country Picture, Myrtle Turtle Picture, Calico Kate Doll, House Mouse Doll, Owl Picture, Birds & Blossoms Picture, Friends Picture, Piglets & Posies Picture, Burst of Spring Picture, Pals on Parade Picture, Scarlet Tanagers Picture, Thirteen Original Colonies Pillow, Love 'N' Stuff Pillow, Vintage Cars Wall Hanging, Lakescape Picture, Playful Kitten Picture, Tree Owls Wall Hanging, Spinning Wheel & Wild Roses Pillow, First Prize at the Country Fair Pictures.

1981 PRESIDENT'S CELEBRATION LITERATURE
Misc. paper items: menus, name tags, etc. CMV $1. each.
1981 I'VE WON BUTTON
(Center) CMV $1.

1980 ONE TO ONE AVON AD PLAQUE
Ad on hardboard given to Avon managers. Self-standing. CMV $15.

1980 SCENT WITH LOVE POSTALETTES
Lavender box holds 15 sheets note paper with matching seals & 1 packet of Unforgettable sachet. SSP $5., CMV $5. MB.

1980 BOOK COVERS
Plastic book covers from Avon. Used by Managers. CMV $3. each.

1982 VALENTINE FUN KIT
Package of red & white heart gift wrap paper, 1 gift card & 4 gum stickers. Given to Avon customers free. CMV $1. mint package.

1981-82 POCKETS PRODUCTS
Red & blue design.
COLORSTICK FOR EYES
COLORSTICK FOR LIPS
SSP $2.50, CMV each 50c. MB.
POCKETS FRAGRANCED POSTALETTES
Red & blue box has matching 15 postalettes & red seals & packet of Sweet Honesty sachet. SSP $5., CMV $3. MB.
POCKETS POCKET
5½" x 5" blue cotton pocket pouch. SSP $6., CMV $1.
POCKETS KEY HOLDER
Blue denim with red polka dot kerchief inside. SSP $4., CMV $1.

1981 McCALLS TAPESTRY PATTERN COLLECTION
Package of Avon patterns designed by McCall. SSP $1.25, CMV $1.25 mint.

1982 CALENDAR BEAUTIFUL STYLE
Features women's designs from the past. Comes in Avon envelope. CMV $1. mint.

1980 ORDER BOOK COVER
(Left) You Never Looked So Good on cover. CMV 50c.
1980 COLORCREME EYE SHADOW SAMPLE
(Right) Blue & white card. CMV 25c.

1981-82 LOOKING GOOD, FEELING BEAUTIFUL BOOK
Book of beauty by Avon Products. 95 pages, small booklet. SSP 75c, CMV 75c.

1982 ENGINE EARS COLOR TOY
Pop out Easter train from Avon. 12" long. Must be mint. CMV $1. mint.

1971 DESIGNERS COLLECTIONS CHRISTMAS CARD CATALOGUE DEMONSTRATOR
Large spiral bound picture album holds 1 each of 36 different Christmas cards sold by Avon in 1971. CMV $75. complete, mint with all 36 cards, album only, no cards, $45. Never sold to public.

ADVERTISING — AVON

Avon and magazine advertising began in March, 1906, but was rather short lived with only a few California Perfume ads appearing in Good Housekeeping magazine. For the next thirty years the company relied on their representatives and the worth of their products to spread their name and gain new customers.

By 1936 a dramatic change took place in the company's attitude and in April of that year a national advertising campaign was begun. Once again the ever popular Good Housekeeping was used as their advertising vehicle. The first advertisements were black and white and not very impressive in comparison to their competitor's full color, full page layouts. Public response was good enough, however, to continue the series and in 1938 Avon ads began to appear in the Christian Science Monitor as well as Good Housekeeping. The following year Woman's Home Companion was added and so on until by the end of the 1940's Avon ads were appearing in 15 of the nations leading publications.

Along the way, color ads and full page ads, as well as some two page ads were introduced. To date Avon ads have appeared in over 40 different magazines and in 1975 found their way into some metropolitan newspapers.

We do not know how many Avon collectors have already begun to collect the ads, but the number is certain to grow once everyone is aware of their existance. Not only do they reflect the company's public appearance, but they also picture many of Avon's now collectable products.

To date Avon has produced over 500 different magazine advertisements; a spectacular number by any standard. Of these, many were published in as many as 12 magazines at the same time while others were produced for a specific market and appeared in only one publication making them quite naturally difficult to obtain. Other factors involved in valuing ads are the content, number of products shown and their collectability and naturally, age. Other considerations are size, ½ or full page and if it is in color or black and white.

The prices shown here are mainly in relation to age and degree of difficulty to find. The other factors mentioned will cause this price to fluctuate and the value shown should be considered only as a broad guide and by no means a definite price. This "Avon Advertising" section was prepared by Dalene Thomas, 8612 W. Warren Lane, Lakewood, CO 80227. For more information on "Avon Advertising", write to Dalene Thomas, enclosing a self-addressed, stamped envelope, if you wish a reply.

C P

The Sign of Quality

**March 1906
Good Housekeeping Only
CMV $25.00**

This is "Roses"

The new odor- the most delicate, and yet the most fragrant and lasting Perfume made. "Roses" is also exclusive—nothing else like it anywhere. Made of the finest imported French Roses, put up in beautiful glass bottles—price 40 cents per ounce. Try it and get acquainted with the famous

C. P. Toilet Specialties

A line of over 50 different high grade articles used by women of refinement in almost every town in the United States. Sold only by local representatives, never in stores.

Write for name of local representative and the C. P. Book which illustrates and describes the complete line, with many suggestions on Beauty and Health.

A few profitable agencies open for good representatives.

California Perfume Co.

San Francisco   New York   Kansas City

**March 1937
CMV $4.00**

Shop at home
THE AVON WAY

**SAVE TIME
AND MONEY**

exchanged or the full purchase price will be im-
mediately refunded upon
its return to us or to our
Representative.

Avon and Perfection
products are sold only
through our trained rep-
resentatives. If you are
not being served by the representative
of your community a postcard request
will receive prompt attention.

FREE BOOKLET

Let us send you the illustrated booklet "Is You and Your Home." Simply
address your request to California
Perfume Co., 113 Fifth Ave., N.Y.C.

CALIFORNIA PERFUME CO., INC.
AVON PRODUCTS INC., DIV.
Kansas City   New York   Montreal

FULLY GUARANTEED

April 1936
Good Housekeeping Only
CMV $5.00

*Elizabeth Schuller, Red Cross Clubmobile Group Captain, was among
the first Red Cross workers to land in Normandy where she showed great
courage and initiative, and exerted effort beyond the call of duty.*

A tribute to the Red Cross

The Avon Medallion of Honor
has been created in recognition
of the work women are doing in
the service of humanity. Has
award to Miss Schuller is the
first that can truthfully presented by
women of outstanding achievement, who have been chosen by
the following committee of
prominent women:

For outstanding service to the Red Cross and to America by materially
aiding morale on the battlefield, Avon presents the Medallion of Honor for
Women of Achievement to Miss Elizabeth Schuller of Montclair, N. J.

Miss Schuller's devotion to duty is typical of the unstinting contribution
that thousands of Red Cross workers, here and abroad, are making
to alleviate the suffering of others. On all fronts the Red Cross is first
to bring comfort to fighting men and prisoners, and cheer to distressed
civilians. Our efforts at home must not slacken. Give liberally NOW.
KEEP YOUR RED CROSS AT HIS SIDE IN 1945!

Avon
March 1945 Good Housekeeping

COSMETICS • AT RADIO CITY, NEW YORK   Copyright 1944, Avon Products, Inc.

March 1945
CMV $4.00

Perfection
MOTHICIDE

Protect precious woolens and furs with
Perfection Mothicide! Comes in the
form of clean, white crystals. Destroys
both moths and larvae more effectively
than moth balls...offers a more pleas-
ing odor which vanishes quickly when
clothes are aired. A complete selection
of Avon Perfection household and
kitchen products plus fine quality Avon
Cosmetics are available through the
Avon Representative who brings them
direct to your home. Welcome her
when she calls. Enjoy this convenient
shopping service.

Perfection
MOTHICIDE
An AVON Product

Guaranteed by
Good Housekeeping

Radio City   New York

September 1947
CMV $5.00

AVON'S NEW BLUE BLAZER FINDS A YOUNG MAN'S SPIRIT!

AVON CALLING with Blue Blazer, newest additions
to Avon's fine products for men.

AVON FOR MEN
RADIO CITY, NEW YORK

October 1962
CMV $3.50

**January 1960
CMV $3.00**

Women love these new Avon Cosmetics and

Imagine! You can select the newest, the finest, the most beautifully packaged cosmetics in the world *without stirring from your home.* Glamorous make-up in all its intriguing new forms... scientifically formulated creams and lotions for the loving care of your complexion...a wide and wonderful variety of fragrances for you to spray on, splash on, dust on, cream on—you choose these with the help of your Avon Representative.

"AVON CALLING" means a pleasant face-to-face chat with your friendly Avon Representative who brings exciting beauty news to your home.

AVON COSMETICS FOR ALL THE FAMILY ARE BROUGHT TO YOUR HOME BY YOUR AVON REPRESENTATIVE

...men enjoy good grooming with Avon

Look at these new grooming products for men! Handsome, aren't they? And their performance is first-rate. As for the scent, it's nice and crisp. A complete selection for shaving, for protection, for after-shower use...together with excellent hair dressings. Men who care about the impression they make, enjoy using Avon.

AVON
RADIO CITY, NEW YORK

Your Avon Representative is delighted to call at your home. Welcome her and enjoy admiring cosmetics and toiletries the Avon way.

AVON COSMETICS FOR ALL THE FAMILY ARE BROUGHT TO YOUR HOME BY YOUR AVON REPRESENTATIVE

Think how great it would be to find Avon gifts under your tree!

How can you feel sophisticated, romantic, feminine, modern—whenever you wish? Wear an Avon fragrance. Avon has colorful fragrance gifts to hang on a tree, to tuck in a tote, to sit prettily on a dressing table. In one fascinating fragrance form after another! An Avon Representative also brings soothing bath oils, festive lipsticks, exciting makeup—designed in a gay holiday spirit to please everyone you know. Avon gifts are always a joy to give, a joy to receive.

AVON cosmetics
ROCKEFELLER PLAZA, NEW YORK
© 1967 AVON PRODUCTS, INC.

Wear Avon's 12 ways of fragrance for the 12 days of Christmas!

**November 1967
CMV $3.00**

PERFECTION — ALL PRODUCTS

1943-46 PERFECTION SPOTS OUT
9½ oz. glass jar, white metal lid. OSP
45c, CMV $22., $25. MB.
**1943-46 PERFECTION KWICK METAL
POLISH**
11 oz. glass jar with white metal cap.
OSP 39c - CMV $30, $40 MB. Rare.
**1943-46 PERFECTION SILVER
CREAM POLISH**
10½ oz. glass jar with white metal lid.
OSP 49c, CMV $22., $25. MB.

1923 SILVER CREAM POLISH
8 oz. metal can. OSP 30c, CMV $40.
mint. 16 oz. can. OSP 54c, CMV
$45. mint. Add $5. MB.

**1941-52 PERFECTION SILVER
CREAM POLISH**
Green, brown and white. 8 oz. can.
Sold 1941-43 then 1946-52. OSP
49c - CMV $15 mint, $20 MB.

**1931-41 PERFECTION SILVER
CREAM POLISH**
½ lb. brown, orange and white can.
OSP 35c, CMV $25. MB, $20. can
only mint.

1943 SILVER CREAM POLISH
Stick on white and green label over
name of other products on can. Used
during shortage of products during
war. OSP 49c, CMV $25. mint with
label shown.

1925 MOTHICIDE
1 lb. metal can on right. Paper label
around can is in English and French.
OSP $1 - CMV $50 mint. CMV as
shown with spots $20. ½ lb metal can
on left, OSP 50c, CMV $40. mint.

1906 SILVER PLATE POLISH
4 oz. glass bottle with metal cap.
OSP 25c, CMV $100., $115. in box.
1918 CPC SILVER CREAM POLISH
6 oz. jar, metal lid. OSP 30c, CMV
$85. mint.

1925 MOTHICIDE
½ lb. metal can with blue label.
OSP 48c - CMV $50 in box, $40 can
only mint.

1931-41 PERFECTION MOTHICIDE
½ lb. orange, brown and white can. OSP 50c, CMV $25. In box, $17.50 can only mint. Add $5. CPC label.

1923 MOTHICIDE
½ lb. metal can 3¼'' across. Paper label in English and French. OSP 48c. CMV $40 mint.

1954-57 PERFECTION MOTHICIDE
8½ oz. bronze metal can, green top, three different edges on lid. Sold 1954-57. CMV $10. Red metal can sold 1957 only. CMV $12., OSP each 55c. Add $2. MB each.

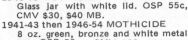
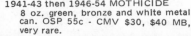

1943-46 MOTHICIDE
Glass jar with white lid. OSP 55c, CMV $30, $40 MB.
1941-43 then 1946-54 MOTHICIDE
8 oz. green, bronze and white metal can. OSP 55c - CMV $30, $40 MB, very rare.

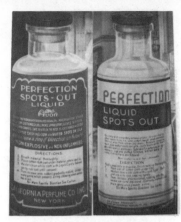

1929 PERFECTION SPOTS OUT LIQUID
(Left) 4 oz. bottle with CPC on black cork stopper and blue label. OSP 50c - CMV $45 MB, $40 BO.

1931-34 PERFECTION LIQUID SPOTS OUT
(Right) 4 oz. size. CPC on cork stopper. OSP 40c, CMV $40. MB, $32.50 BO.

1925-29 LIQUID SPOTS OUT
4 oz. clear glass bottle, black cork cap. blue label. OSP 40c, CMV $50 MB, $45 BO mint.

1934-41 LIQUID SPOTS OUT
4 oz. bottle. Orange, brown and white label. Black cap. OSP 40c, CMV $30. MB - $25. BO.

1946-58 LIQUID SPOTS OUT
4 oz. bottle, green smooth or threaded cap. 2 different labels. One box brown and one box bronze. OSP 50c, CMV in box $20., bottle only $15.

1920 SPOTS OUT
Metal can. OSP 33c, CMV $50. can only mint. $65. MB.

1923 SPOTS OUT
8 oz. metal can. OSP 33c, CMV $40. mint. 16 oz. can not shown, OSP 59c, CMV $45. mint. Add $10. each MB.

1931-41 SPOTS OUT
½ lb. orange, brown and white can. OSP 40c, CMV $25. MB. $20. can only mint.

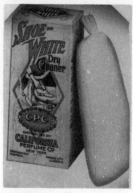

1915 SHOE WHITE
Box holds 5 oz. sack of Shoe White Powder. OSP 25c - CMV $75 MB.

1920 SHOE WHITE
Green box holds 5 oz. sack of powder. OSP 25c - CMV $75 MB.

1931-35 PERFECTION LIQUID SHOE WHITE
(Right) Box holds 4 oz. bottle with cork stopper. Brown, orange and white label. OSP 50c, CMV $25., $30. MB.

1928-30 LIQUID SHOE WHITE
(Left) 4 oz. glass bottle with cork stopper. OSP 35c, CMV $50. MB, $45. BO mint.

1941-43 SPOTS OUT
8 oz. green, brown and white can. Sold 1941-43 then 1946-48. OSP 45c - CMV $20, $25 MB.

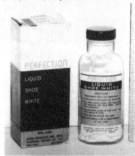

1935-41 PERFECTION LIQUID SHOE WHITE
Box holds 4 oz. bottle with brown cap. Brown, orange and white label. OSP 50c, CMV $25., $30. MB.

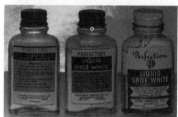

1935-41 LIQUID SHOE WHITE SAMPLE
(Left) ½ oz. black cap. CPC on label. CMV $40. Also with Avon Products label only and white cap. CMV $25.

1935-41 LIQUID SHOE WHITE SAMPLE
(Center) Same as above, different label. CMV $40.

1941-57 LIQUID SHOE WHITE
(Right) ¾ oz. white cap, green and brown label. CMV $35.

1922 KWICK CLEANING POLISH SAMPLE
Small sample can issued for one month on introduction of this product. Rare. CMV $75.

1941-57 PERFECTION LIQUID SHOE WHITE
4 oz. green smooth or threaded cap. Two different labels. OSP 37c, CMV $10. bottle only, $12.50 in box.

1922 KWICK CLEANING POLISH
8 oz. metal can, brown label. OSP 24c, CMV $50 MB, $40 can only mint. Also came in 16 oz. can. OSP 45c - CMV $55 MB, $45 can only mint.

1925 KWICK METAL POLISH
½ lb. metal can with brown label. OSP 24c CMV $45 in box, $35 can only mint.

1931-41 PERFECTION KWICK METAL POLISH
½ lb. orange, brown and white can. OSP 35c, CMV $25. MB, $20. can only mint.

1954-57 KWICK METAL POLISH
Green and brown 13 oz. can on right. Two different lids. OSP 55c, CMV $30 mint.

1941-48 KWICK METAL POLISH
8 oz. green, brown and white can. Sold 1941-43 then 1946-48. OSP 39c. CMV $25, $30 MB.

1938-41 LAUNDRY CRYSTALS PERFUMED
Brown, orange, and white paper sides, tin top and bottom. Top cut out to be used as bank. Held 13 crystals. Came with Avon and CPC labels. OSP 27c - CMV $25 Avon label, $30 CPC label.

1931-34 POWDERED CLEANER
Red, white and blue. 16 oz. can. OSP 35c - CMV $60. mint, $75. MB.

1941-48 PERFECTION LAUNDRY CRYSTALS PERFUMED
Green, brown and white can with green lid holds 13 crystals. Metal top and bottom and paper sides. Sold 1941-46. All metal sold 1946-48. OSP 29c, CMV $20. mint each.

1943-46 PERFECTION LAUNDRY CRYSTALS PERFUMED
All cardboard wartime packaging. CMV $25. mint. Also came with white top and bottom.

1928-31 POWDERED CLEANER
12 oz. blue box. OSP 25c, CMV $60. mint, $75. MB.

1941-48 PERFECTION PREPARED STARCH
8 oz. brown, green and white can. Two different labels. Shiny top or painted top. OSP 39c - CMV $20 mint, $25 MB. 1943-46 had paper sides, CMV $20 mint.

1931-36 PERFECTION LAUNDRY CRYSTALS
Brown, orange and white paper box. OSP 25c, CMV $30. MB.

1934-36 LAUNDRY CRYSTALS PERFUMED
(Right) Brown, white and orange box holds 13 white crystals. OSP 25c, CMV $30. mint.

1934-41 PERFECTION POWDERED CLEANER
16 oz. orange, brown and white can. Two different labels. Cardboard sides, metal top and bottom. OSP 35c, CMV $25. MB, $20. can only mint.

1906 CARPET RENOVATOR
Box holds 1 bar of soap. SSP 35c, CMV $70 MB.

1915-20 CARPET RENOVATOR SOAP
Paper box with one bar carpet soap, 2 different boxes shown. First issued about 1893. OSP 35c - CMV $60 each mint.

1928-31 AVON POWDERED CLEANER SAMPLE
Small blue, orange and white paper box. 3 oz. size sample. CPC on lable. Rare. CMV $75 mint.

1943-46 POWDERED CLEANER
16 oz. paper can, green, bronze and white. OSP 39c, CMV $15. mint, $20. MB.

1941-43 then 1946-57 POWDERED CLEANER
16 oz. paper sides with metal top and bottom. Green, Bronze and white. OSP 39c, CMV $10., $12. MB. Five different labels.

1933-36 PERFECTION AUTO POLISH
1 pt. brown, orange and white can. Two different labels. OSP 75c, CMV $35, $30 can only mint. Rare.

1930-33 AUTO LUSTRE
(Left) Blue 1 pt. can. OSP 75c, CMV can only $65 mint, $75 MB.

1930-33 AUTO LUSTRE SAMPLE
(Right) 1 oz. blue metal can. Rare. CMV $75.

1931-41 PERFECTION PREPARED STARCH
6 oz. brown, orange and white can. Sold 1931-36. CMV $25., $30. MB. Same can in 8 oz. size sold 1936-41, two different labels as shown. CMV $20., $25. MB.

1912 FURNITURE POLISH
8 oz. - ½ pint bottle, cork stopper, clear glass. OSP 50c - CMV $100, $125 in box.

1915 FURNITURE POLISH
(Left) 8 oz. clear glass bottle, cork stopper. CMV $85. BO mint, $100. MB. Same label is on rare amber bottle.

1943-46 PERFECTION FURNITURE POLISH
(Right) 12 oz. bottle, metal cap. Two different labels. Green and white label, and green, white and bronze. CMV green and white add $5. OSP 69c - CMV $22, $25 MB.

1925 FURNITURE POLISH
12 oz. metal can with blue label on right. OSP 48c. Same as above only in 32 oz. on left, blue metal can. OSP $1.20. Back side labels in French on both cans. CMV $55 can only mint, $65 MB each.

1904 FURNITURE POLISH
8 oz. glass bottle. This bottle may be dark amber glass or clear. Eureka trade mark on neck label. Cork stopper. OSP 50c, CMV $100. BO mint, $135. MB.

1936-41 PERFECTION FURNITURE POLISH
12 and 32 oz. brown, orange and white can. Three different labels. OSP 75c and $1.35, CMV $15., $20. MB. CMV 32 oz. size $20. - $25. MB.

1931-36 PERFECTION FURNITURE POLISH
12 oz. brown, orange and white can. OSP 75c - CMV $20, $25 MB.

1944 Only - FURNITURE POLISH
12 oz. bottle, black cap. OSP 79c, CMV $40. BO - $45. MB.

1916 FURNITURE POLISH
12 oz. metal can with green label. OSP 50c, CMV $75. in box, $65. can only mint. Also came in qt. size. OSP $1.20, ½ gal. size. OSP $2.25, CMV $75. mint.

1915 FURNITURE POLISH
8 oz. amber glass, cork stopper. Very rare. CMV $150. bottle only mint, $175. MB.

1906 CPC FURNITURE POLISH
(Right center) 8 oz. bottle with cork stopper. Came as round or square bottle, same label. OSP 50c, CMV $100., $125. MB.

1912 FURNITURE POLISH
(Left) 8 oz. bottle, cork stopper, label also reads for automobile bodies. OSP 50c, CMV $125. MB, $100. BO mint.

1941-48 PERFECTION MACHINE OIL
3 oz. brown, green and white can. Sold 1941-43 then 1946-48. OSP 29c, CMV $15. MB, $10. can only.

1931-41 PERFECTION OLIVE OIL
1 pt. orange, brown and white can. Two different labels. OSP $1.35, CMV $30. in box, $25. can only mint.

1895 OLIVE OIL
8 oz. glass bottle with cork stopper. OSP 50c, CMV $75. bottle only, $85. in box. Also came in 1 pt, 1 qt., ½ gal., and 1 gal. size. CMV $100 rare.

1905 OLIVE OIL
16 oz. bottle. OSP $1.25, CMV $75. mint, rare.

1923 SUPREME HUILE D'OLIVE OIL
Green and yellow can in 1 pt. size. OSP $1.35, CMV $45. MB. $35. can only mint. Also came in qt. size can. OSP $2.50, CMV $60 MB, $50 can only mint.

1915 OLIVE OIL
8 oz. glass bottle with cork stopper. OSP 50c, CMV $85. in box, $75. bottle only mint. Also came in 16 oz., 1 qt, ½ gal., 1 gal. size. CMV $100, $125 MB, rare.

1915 BAKING POWDER
16 oz. container. OSP 25c, CMV $60. MB, $45. container only mint. Also came in 1 lb. and 5 lb. size. CMV $60 mint.

1943-46 PERFECTION MACHINE OIL
3 oz. smooth side glass, metal cap. OSP 29c, CMV $20. BO, $25. MB.

1945 MACHINE OIL "RIBBED SIDE"
Short issue 3 oz. ribbed sided bottle, metal cap. OSP 29c. Came in two different boxes as shown. CMV $25. BO, $30. MB.

1936-41 BAKING POWDER SAMPLE
Orange, brown and white 1 oz. can, 2¼" high. Two different size samples. Rare. CMV $40. mint each.

1941 FURNITURE POLISH
All green, bronze and white metal can. 12 oz. can 1941-43 then 1946-48. OSP 69c, CMV $12., $15. MB. 16 oz. can 1948-51, OSP 79c, CMV $12. 32 oz. can 1941-43, OSP $1.29, CMV $15. Add $5. MB.

1931-41 PERFECTION MACHINE OIL
3 oz. brown, orange and white can. Two different labels. OSP 26c, CMV $18. in box, $12.50 can only mint.

1943-46 BAKING POWDER
16 oz. paper container used during the war. OSP 45c - CMV $35 mint.

1941 PERFECTION SAMPLES
Sample size each. Perfection flavor sample came 20 in a box for 50c. Baking powder came 16 for 50c. CMV flavoring bottle, $20. each. Baking powder, $40. each.

1940's PERFECTION MEASURING CUP
Metal cup.

1940's PERFECTION PIE PAN
9" pie pan with removable bottom. Center of pan says "Trade Mark Perfection Patented". We believe both items were sold by Perfection Stove Co. and not by Perfection of Avon Products. No value established.

1933-41 PERFECTION MENDING CEMENT
Brown, orange and white tube. OSP 25c, CMV $12. in box. Tube only $10 mint.

1941-48 PERFECTION MENDING CEMENT
White, green and brown tube. OSP 29c, CMV $12 in box, $10 tube only mint.

1941-43-46-48 PERFECTION BAKING POWDER
16 oz. red and white can, cardboard sides, metal top or all metal can and top. OSP 45c - CMV $20 mint, $25 MB.

PERFECTION CAKE PAN
Tin pan marked "Perfection" We believe this was sold by Perfection Stove Co. and not by Perfection of Avon Products. If you have information on this please write to Bud Hastin.

1906 BAKING POWDER
½ and 1 lb. can. OSP. 25c, and 45c, CMV $75. mint.

1906-15 BAKING POWDER
5 lb. container, paper label, metal can. OSP 25c - 1 lb. CMV $60 mint. Pictured next to 1923-30 1 lb. can, for size comparison.

1923-30 PERFECTION BAKING POWDER
(Left) 1 lb. can. Also came in ½ lb. and 5 lb. sizes. OSP 45c - CMV $50 mint, $55 MB.

1931-41 PERFECTION BAKING POWDER
(Right) 1 lb. orange, brown and white can. OSP 45c, CMV $25., $30. MB. Add $5. CPC label.

1918 CPC EASYDAY OR SIMPLEX AUTOMATIC CLOTHES WASHER
Made of pure zinc. Washer is 11" high and 9" in diameter. Has Easyday name at top and Pat. July 4, 1916. OSP $2., CMV $100.

1918 CPC MARVEL ELECTRIC SILVER CLEANER
Metal plate has Marvel name and Pat. Jan. 11, 1910. OSP 75c, CMV $50.

1905-08 FLAVORING EXTRACT
(Left) 8 and 16 oz. bottle, glass stopper. Came in all flavors listed under smaller bottles of 1893 Flavoring Extracts. OSP $1., CMV $150. BO mint - $175. MB.

1900-12 FLAVORING EXTRACTS
(Right) 2 oz. bottle shown is same shape as 4 oz. bottle. Paper label. Came in almond, banana, blood orange, celery, cinnamon, cloves, lemon, nutmeg, onion, orange, peach, pear, peppermint, pineapple, pistachio, quince, jamaica ginger, rasberry, rose, strawberry, vanilla and wintergreen. OSP 25c, and 45c, CMV $100. MB, $85. BO mint. Also came in 16 oz., 1 qt., ½ gal., and 1 gal. CMV $125. BO, $150. MB.

1908 EXTRACT OF LEMON
16 oz. glass stopper. OSP $3.25, CMV $150. BO mint, $175. MB.

1908 FRUIT FLAVORING
2 oz. embossed Fruit California Perfume Co. Flavors. Had paper label on reverse side. CMV $35. BO, $100. mint with paper label, $125. MB. Some came with reversed "A" in California. Add $5. for reverse "A".

1910 VANILLA TONKA AND VANILLIN FLAVOR EXTRACT
2 or 4 oz. glass bottle, cork stopper. Comes in 17 flavors. OSP 50c & 90c - CMV $100 mint, $125 MB.

1908 FLAVORING EXTRACTS
Came in 1, 2, 4 and 8 oz. sizes with cork stoppers. Also came in 1 pt. and 1 qt. with glass stoppers. Flavors are almond, banana, celery, cinnamon, jamaica ginger, lemon, maple, nutmeg, orange, onion, peppermint, pineapple, pistachio, rasberry, rose, strawberry, vanilla, tonka and vanillin, vanilla pure and wintergreen. The 2 oz. bottles are embossed "California Perfume Co. Fruit Flavors" on back side, paper label on front. OSP 1 oz. 25c, 2 oz. 45c, 4 oz. 90c, 8 oz. $1.75, 16 oz. $3.25. CMV each $100 mint with label, CMV $125. embossed bottle with no label $25. CMV 1 pt. and 1 qt. size $125. BO $150. MB with label and glass stopper.

1898 EXTRACTS — FRUIT FLAVORING
2 oz. clear glass. Fruit Flavors California Perfume Co. embossed on backside. Pineapple and wintergreen or rose. Cork stopper. OSP 25c, CMV $110. BO mint, $130. MB.

1915 ROOT BEER EXTRACT
2 oz. cork stopper, clear glass. Very rare. OSP 45c, CMV $100. mint, $125. MB.

1915 SAVORY COLORING
3 oz. clear glass bottle, cork stopper. 3 oz. size is rare. OSP 25c, CMV $75. with mint label, $90. MB.

1908 FOOD COLORING
2 and 4 oz. bottles with cork stoppers, and paper labels. Came in coffee, violet, lilac, orange, chocolate, red, green, and lemon. OSP 25c and 45c, CMV $75. bottle with label, $90. in box.

1920 PERFECTION CONCENTRATED COLORING
½ oz. bottles with cork stopper. Came in blue, brown, green and yellow. Came in Coloring Set only. 2 oz. bottle of red. All yellow labels and same shape. CMV $60. each mint.

1915 HARMLESS RED COLORING
2 oz. clear glass, cork stopper. OSP 25c, CMV $75. mint with label, $90. MB.

1923-30 PERFECTION CONCENTRATED FLAVORING EXTRACT
2, 4, and 8 oz. sizes, and 1 pt. and 1 qt. Came in flavors of lemon, vanilla tonka, almond, orange, peppermint, wintergreen, strawberry, pure vanilla. Cork stoppers. Yellow labels. OSP 39c to $4.45. CMV $60. MB, $45. BO with mint labels.

1908 VEGETABLE COLORING
2 oz. clear glass. Front white paper label. Embossed Fruit Flavors on back side. OSP 45c, CMV $100. mint, $125. MB.

1920-30 PERFECTION CONCENTRATED COLORING
(right) 2 oz. No coloring listed on label. Cork stopper. OSP 33c, CMV $45. BO mint, $55. MB.
1900 VEGETABLE COLOR SAMPLE
(left) Small clear glass vial with cork stopper. CMV $50. mint.

1923-30 PERFECTION FLAVORING EXTRACT
2 oz. clear glass bottle, cork stopper. Lemon, orange, grape, cherry, rasberry, loganberry. CMV $45., $50. MB.

1915 SAVORY COLORING
8 oz. clear glass. Cork stopper. Rare in 8 oz. size. CMV $125 mint - $150. MB.

1910 VANILLA TONKA & VANILLIN FLAVOR SAMPLE
(Left) Small sample bottle, clear glass, cork stopper. CMV $100. mint, $125. MB.
1906 "EXTRACT CONCENTRATED" VANILLA EXTRACT
(Right) 2 and 4 oz. glass bottle with cork stopper. OSP 50c and 90c, CMV $100. - $125 MB.

1923-30 SAVORY COLORING
(Left) 2 and 3 oz. bottle with yellow labels and brown letters, cork stoppers. Came in red, yellow, blue, brown, and green. Also came with brown. label and yellow letters. OSP 33c, and 59c, CMV each with mint label $45., $55. MB. ½ oz. bottle came in Coloring Set only. CMV same as above.
1931-34 PERFECTION SAVORY COLORING
(Right) 4 oz. cork stopper. CPC label. OSP 35c, CMV $35. MB, $30. BO.

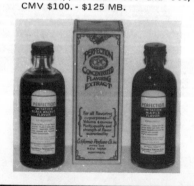

1923-30 CONCENTRATED FLAVORING EXTRACT
8 oz. size with handle. Same label as 1923-30 extracts. This bottle is very rare with handle. Label in poor condition. CMV $75. mint.

1934-41 FLAVORING EXTRACT
8 oz. bottle plus cap. Came in vanilla, tonka, lemon, almond, orange, peppermint, wintergreen, pure vanilla, black walnut and maple. OSP $1.45, CMV $35 MB, $25 BO.

1934-41 PERFECTION EXTRACT
Metal caps on ½ oz. 2, 4, and 8 oz. bottles. Flavors are vanilla tonka, lemon, almond, orange, peppermint, wintergreen, pure vanilla, black walnut, maple. OSP 2 oz. size 50c, 4 oz. size 75c, and 8 oz. size OSP $1.45. CMV each 2 oz. and 4 oz. $12.50 each; 8 oz. size $20.; CMV each ½ oz. size $12.

1941-48 SAVOURY COLORING
4 oz. bottle with the word Savoury spelled different. Regular spelling is Savory. OSP 39c, CMV $15. BO mint, $17. MB.

1939-41 PERFECTION IMITATION VANILLIAN COUMARIN VANILLA AND TONKA SAMPLE
¼ oz. size bottle. Metal cap. CMV $25. mint.

1934-39 VANILLA TONKA ¼ OZ. SAMPLE
(Right) ¼ oz. size, 2 3/8" high, metal cap. On right shown next to ½ oz. size, on left that came in food flavor sets. CMV $25. ¼ oz. size sample mint. CMV ½ oz. size $15. mint.

1934-41 PERFECTION COLORING
½ oz. size in green, yellow, blue and brown. Came in Coloring Set. CMV $15. each. 2 oz. size in same colors plus red. OSP 25c, CMV $17., 4 oz. size in savory coloring OSP 35c. All have metal caps. CMV $17. Add $3. each MB.

1939-41 IMITATION VANILLIN COUMARIN VANILLA AND TONKA FLAVOR
4 oz. red cap. CMV $15. mint.

1941-48 FOOD COLORING
Red plastic caps. Savory coloring came in 4 oz. bottle. OSP 39c, red, yellow, blue, brown and green came in 2 oz. bottles. OSP 29c, all but red and savory coloring came in ½ oz. bottles in coloring set. CMV $12. each size, $15. each MB.

1937 VANILLA TONKA VANILLIN SPECIAL ISSUE BOX
Regular issue 2 oz. bottle came in special issue box for 15c with regular order. CMV $25. MB as shown.

1941-48 PERFECTION FLAVORING EXTRACTS
Vanilla and lemon came in 2 and 4 oz. sizes. 2 oz. size only in maple, black walnut, orange, peppermint, almond, wintergreen. All have red plastic caps. OSP 49c, 2 oz., and 89c 4 oz. CMV $9. each ½ oz. size came in Extract Set only. CMV $12., $15. MB.

1895-1920 HARMLESS COLORING SET
Set of eight ½ oz. bottles with cork stoppers. Came in wood box. Lemon, chocolate, lilac, coffee, orange, red, violet and green. OSP 50c, CMV $400. set MB or $45. each bottle.

1909 FOOD FLAVORING DEMONSTRATOR SET
Black leather covered wood case holds 24 1 oz. bottles of food flavoring. OSP to Reps was $2., CMV mint with all labels, $2,000. complete.

1900 FOOD FLAVORING DEMONSTRATOR SET
Straw covered wood case holds 20 bottles of food flavoring extracts. CMV complete set mint $1,600.

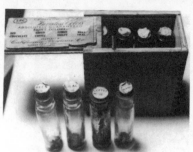

1910-15 HARMLESS COLORS SET
Wood box, slide open lid, holds 8 ½ oz. bottles with cork stoppers. Red, chocolate, green, coffee, lemon, velvet, orange, lilac. Labels on top of corks only. OSP 50c, CMV $350. MB.

1915 HARMLESS COLORS SET
Wood box with slide open lid, paper label on top. Holds eight ½ oz. bottles with cork stoppers. Paper labels on top of cork and front of bottles also. Came in chocolate, lemon, green, red, coffee, violet, lilac and orange. OSP 50c, CMV $350. MB.

1920 HARMLESS COLORS SET
Cardboard box holds eight ½ oz. bottles with cork stoppers. Red, chocolate, green, coffee, lemon, velvet, orange, lilac. OSP 50c, CMV $300. MB.

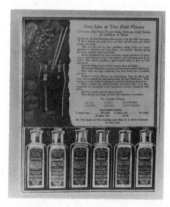

1923 FRUIT FLAVORS BROCHURE
Introducing new line of CPC Perfection fruit flavors. 1 page. CMV $20.

1912 FLAVORING EXTRACT SET
Black leather grain case with double handles and snaps. Holds 20 one ounce bottles of food flavor extract. Used by Reps to show products. CMV $1,800. complete set mint.

1920-30 PERFECTION COLORING SET
Bottles of green, yellow, blue, brown in ½ oz. size. Red in 2 oz. size. All have cork stoppers. Came with CPC Cook Booklet. OSP 74c, CMV $250.

1930's FOOD COLORING DIRECTIONS
Came in Perfection Food Coloring sets. CPC on back. CMV $15 mint.

1934-41 PERFECTION COLORING SET
Orange, brown and white metal cans hold four ½ oz. bottles in blue, yellow, brown and green coloring and 2 oz. bottle of red. All have metal caps. Came with Perfection Cook Booklet. OSP 85c, CMV $75. MB. Can only $15. mint.

1930-34 PERFECTION COLORING SET
Brown and orange paper box. Red coloring in 2 oz. size, brown, blue, yellow, green coloring in ½ oz. size. All have cork stoppers. OSP 85c, CMV $160. MB, Box only $20. mint.

1930's CAKE CHEST PRODUCT BOX
CPC box with list of all contents that came in Perfection Cake Chest. CMV $10. box only.

1941-48 PERFECTION FLAVORING SET
Red, white and bronze can holds 2 oz. bottle of vanilla, ½ oz. bottle of maple, black walnut, almond and lemon. All have red plastic caps. OSP $1.15, CMV $60. complete set mint. Set came with Avon Recipe Booklet in can. Add $10. for Recipe Booklet. Can only $12. mint.

1941-48 PERFECTION COLORING SET
Orange, brown and white can holds 2 oz. red coloring and ½ oz. each of yellow, brown, blue and green coloring, red plastic cap. OSP 98c, CMV $65. MB. Set came with Avon Recipe Booklet. Add $10. for Recipe Booklet. Can only $15. mint. This set also came in 1934-41 can. Only can is marked Avon and not CPC. Came with red caps and 1941-48 labels. CMV $70. MB. Same set came 1942 only with matching caps to color content. Rare. CMV $85. set MB.

1930-34 PERFECTION FLAVORING EXTRACT SET
In orange, brown and white can, has 2 oz. vanilla and ½ oz. each of almond, lemon, peppermint, and wintergreen extract. All have cork stoppers. OSP $1., CMV $125. Can only $15. mint.

1934-41 PERFECTION FLAVORING EXTRACT SET
Orange, brown and white metal can holds four ½ oz. bottles in wintergreen, peppermint, almond and lemon, and a 2 oz. bottle of maple. All have metal caps. Came with Perfection Cook Booklet. CMV booklet only $12., OSP $1., CMV $75. MB can only $15. mint.

1930's 1940's PERFECTION RECIPE BOOKS
Came in food coloring or flavoring sets. At least four different booklets. CMV $12. each mint.
1920 far right - CMV $25.

1941-42 PERFECTION CAKE CHEST
Brown and red designed cake chest has coloring set in can, 2 oz. bottles of lemon and almond extract, 2 oz. bottles of maple and black walnut flavoring, and 4 oz. bottle of vanilla. All bottles have red plastic caps. Can of baking powder, recipe book, cake chest is same as 1938 to 1941. Avon Perfection in bottom of cake pan. OSP $3.95, CMV set complete $110. MB. Chest only $35. mint.

1933-38 PERFECTION CAKE CHEST
Blue and gold cake pan 10½" in diameter contains Perfection coloring set, metal caps. Can of Perfection baking powder. Bottles contain lemon, maple, black walnut, almond and vanilla flavoring and recipe book. Avon Perfection in bottom of cake pan. OSP $3.50, CMV set complete $135, chest only $50 mint.

1923 NO ALCOHOL FLAVORS IN TUBES
Lemon and vanilla only in small and large size tubes. OSP 24c and 45c. CMV $30. in box mint, tube only $20. mint.

1938-41 PERFECTION CAKE CHEST
Gold, red, brown, black cake chest. Contains can of baking powder, coloring set of 4 oz. vanilla extract. 2 oz. each of lemon and almond extract, 2 oz. each of black walnut and maple flavors. All have metal caps, recipe book. Avon Perfection in bottom of cake pan. OSP $3.50, CMV set complete $135. MB - chest only $35. mint.

1920 FLAVORING EXTRACT SET
Box holds two 2 oz. bottles and four 1 oz. bottles of any flavor desired. 1, 2, and 4 oz. bottles shown. OSP $1.90, CMV $450. set mint in box.

1914 FOOD FLAVORING SET
Box holds 2 oz. bottle of vanilla tonka, a 2 oz. bottle of lemon, and four 1 oz. bottles of any other flavor. OSP $1., CMV $450. for set.

SEE 1984 SUPPLEMENT IN BACK OF BOOK FOR MORE IN THIS SECTION

SAMPLES & DEMONSTRATOR KITS

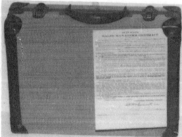

1920-21 NO ALCOHOL FLAVORING SET
Set came with five small tubes and one large tube. Choice of vanilla, lemon, pineapple, banana, maple, almond, orange, strawberry, jamaica ginger, peppermint, nutmeg, wintergreen, cinnamon, rose, celery, onion, pistachio and rasberry. OSP $2., CMV $200. MB.

1921 NO ALCOHOL FLAVOR IN TUBES
Metal tubes came small and large size, available in flavors as set. OSP small tube 30c, large tube 55c. CMV small tube $30., large tube $30.

DELIVERY BAGS
(Left) 1929 Black leatherette, CMV $30. (Middle) 1948 Black leatherette front opening lays flat, CMV $20. (Right) 1942 Black leatherette, CMV $20.

1913 CPC SALES MANAGERS DEMO BAG
Leather bound straw bag used by early day Avon ladies to show their products. Measures 14" wide, 4" deep, 10" high. Does not say CPC on case. CMV $75. mint. Also came with CPC Products label inside lid. Same design case only size is 17" x 11¼" x 4" deep. CMV $100.

1937 DEMO BAG
Simulated ostrich leather holds Avon sales catalog & room for 4 demo packages. Used by Avon Reps. CMV $35. bag only mint.

1935 PORTFOLIO BAG AWARD
Red two tone brown leather bag with suede inside. Came with matching key case, billfold, change purse, 2 way mirror. Given to top 77 Reps in U.S. for top sales during Mr. McConnell birthday celebration. CMV $75. complete.

1953 SALES BAG
Black bag used by Avon reps in early 50's. CMV $22. mint.

1970's DELIVERY BAG
White, blue & green design used by Avon ladies. CMV $6.

1941-43 DELIVERY BAG
Black imitation leather waterproof bag used by Reps to deliver Avon products. Base of bag measures 15½" long, 7" wide, 10" high and has a 21 inch zipper. Cost a Rep $1.49. CMV $15. mint.

1960's (early) BEAUTY SHOWCASE BAG
(Right) Two tones blue with black trim. Used by Reps. CMV $6.
1960's (late) BEAUTY SHOWCASE BAG
(Left) Two toned blue & blue trim. Used by Reps. CMV $5.

1960's DELIVERY BAG
Used by Avon Reps. CMV $25.

1944 DELIVERY BAG PRIZE
Black waterproof bag, zipper top, metal buttons on bottom to set on. Given to Reps for placing order of $150. or more. Used to deliver Avon products. CMV $15. mint.

1960's DELIVERY BAG
Two toned blue, silver 4A emblem under handle. CMV $6.

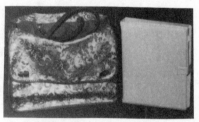

1970's BEAUTY SHOWCASE BAG
Blue & green vinyl came with blue plastic holder for samples. CMV $10. for both or $5. each.

1977 COLORWORKS SHOULDER BAG
Given to customers who bought all 5 Colorworks products. Sold to Reps for $2.50 as a demo. Tan canvas bag with red, yellow and green strap. Measures 8½" x 10". CMV $3.

1950's DELIVERY BAG
Black leatherette. CMV $17. mint.

1970 REPRESENTATIVES DEMO BAG
White background with bright colored flowers. Silver 4A emblem under handle. CMV $6. mint.

1976 DELIVERY BAG
(Left) Blue brocade bag used by Avon Reps to make delivery of Avon products. CMV $3.

1976 BEAUTY SHOWCASE DEMO BAG
(Right) Used by Avon Reps to carry Avon demonstrations products. Matching blue brocade. CMV $3.

1940 REPRESENTATIVE DEMO KIT
Box holds jars of cleansing cream, night cream, foundation cream & bottle of skin freshener. OSP $1., CMV $50. MB.

1947 SHAMPOO DEMO KIT
Box holds 2 bottles of soapless & liquid shampoo. For Reps only. CMV $50. Mint.

1942 Only DEMONSTRATOR KIT
Box holds jar of cream deodorant & 1 bar of Lemonol soap. CMV $45. MB.

1953 HAND CARE DEMONSTRATOR KIT
Box holds 2 bottles of nail polish, 1 tube of hand cream, jar of nail beauty. CMV $40. MB.

1953 PACK UP YOUR SKIN TROUBLES DEMONSTRATOR KIT
Cardboard carrying case holds jars of cleansing cream & tissue cream & 4 oz. bottle of astringent. CMV $50. MB.

1936 MAKE-UP TRIO DEMO KIT
Brown box holds 1¾ oz. box of Ariel Suntan Face Powder, turquoise & gold rouge compact in Crusader red & matching lipstick in Crusader red. Came with fold out display card. CMV $60. MB.

1948 REPRESENTATIVE DEMONSTRATOR KIT
Black leather kit. CMV $90. mint.

1980-81 BEAUTY SHOWCASE DEMO BAG
Used by Reps to show Avon products. CMV $5.

1956-60 BEAUTY COUNSELOR DEMO KIT SAMPLES
(Front row left to right) White plastic jars with turquoise caps. Came in Vita Moist Cream, Strawberry Cooler, Rich Moisture Cream. CMV $6. each. (Back row left to right) Skin Freshener, clear glass, white cap, $10; Deep Clean Cleansing Cream, white plastic, gold lettering, white cap, CMV $6.; rouge, clear glass, white cap, CMV $6. each.

1956 SKIN CARE DEMONSTRATOR
Plastic case holds plastic bottle of Deep Clean Cleansing Cream, 1 oz. glass bottle of Skin Freshener, 2 white jars of Rich Moisture & Hormone Cream & plastic spoon. CMV $37.50 MB.

1952 SKIN CARE DEMO KIT
Flip open display box holds 1 jar each of Cleansing Cream and Night Cream and a bottle of Skin Freshener. Used by Reps to show products. CMV $35. MB.

1940's FACIAL DEMO KIT
Green lid box with pink base holds white glass jars of cleansing cream, night cream, foundation cream & 4 oz. bottle of skin freshener. All have turquoise caps. Used by Reps to demonstrate facial products. CMV $45. MB.

1951 CLEANSING CREAM DEMONSTRATOR KIT
Demo box holds 2 white glass jars with turquoise lids of Cleansing Creams & 1 jar of Night Cream. Used by Reps to show products. CMV $25. MB. Comes in 2 different boxes.

1946 DEMONSTRATOR KIT
Box holds tube of toothpaste & hand cream & bottle of antiseptic. CMV $45.

1949 DEMONSTRATOR KIT
Demo box holds tubes of hand cream and creme shampoo and jar of perfumed deodorant. Used by Reps to show products. CMV $35. MB.

1947 CLEANSING CREAM DEMO KIT
Box with lady's face on lid holds tube of liquifying & fluffy cleansing cream. Pink tubes, 2¼ oz. each. Tubes were never sold to public. For Reps only. CMV Rare $45. MB.

1948 HAND LOTION & HAND CREAM DEMO KIT
Demo box holds tubes of hand cream & 4 oz. bottle of hand lotion. Not sold. Used by Reps to sell products. CMV $30. MB.

1948 SKIN CARE DEMO KIT
Demo box holds blue 2¼ oz. tube of Fluffy Cleansing Cream, 4 oz. bottle of Skin Freshener & tube of Special Dry Skin Cream. Not sold to public. Used by Reps as demonstrator. CMV $55. MB.

1949 DENTAL DEMO KIT
Box holds tube of Ammoniated toothpaste and can of Ammoniated tooth powder. Not sold to public. Used by Reps to show products. CMV $40. MB.

1942 CLEANING CREAM DEMONSTRATOR KIT
Box holds jar & 3 sample tubes of cleansing cream. CMV $35. MB.

1940-41 PERFUME DEMO KIT
Green & gold box holds three 1 dram bottles with colored caps. Perfume samples set used by Representatives. Came in Marionette, Garden of Love, Cotillion & Gardenia. OSP 30c, CMV $67.50 MB.

1964 PERFUME SAMPLE
Small 1/8 oz. bottle came in Occur!, Somewhere, Cotillion, Topaze, Here's My Heart, Persian Wood, To A Wild Rose. CMV $8. each.

1942 FACIAL DEMONSTRATOR KIT
Box holds 3 tubes of night cream, jar of night cream, foundation cream & 4 oz. bottle of skin freshener. OSP 69c, CMV $50. MB.

1932 PERFUME SAMPLE
Very small glass vial with cork stopper in envelope. Came in Gardenia, Jardin D'Amour, Bolero, Cotillion, Ariel, Narcissus, Rose, Lily of the Valley, Sweet Pea, Trailing Arbutus. CPC on package. CMV $18. each in envelope mint.

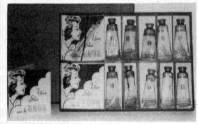

1951 BIRTHDAY CAKE
Blue & white box holds foam cake with five 1 dram ribbed perfumes. To A Wild Rose, Golden Promise, Cotillion, Quaintance & Flowertime. This was a demonstrator kit, for Reps. CMV $90. cake & bottles only mint - $125. MB.

1940's CLEANSING CREAM SAMPLE SET
Box holds 10 turquoise 1/4 oz. sample tubes of cleansing cream. Also came with 2 stacks of Your Skin Can Be Beautiful pamphlets. CMV $35. MB.

1940 GARDEN OF LOVE PERFUME SAMPLE
Small bottle with metal cap in sample envelope. Also came in Ballad, Trailing Arbutus, Cotillion, Gardenia, Merriment, Sweet Pea, Courtship, Lily of the Valley, Jardin D'Amour. CMV $18. each in envelope only. Add $2. for CPC on envelope.

1947-50 PERFUME SAMPLES
Small sample tubes with glass vials of perfume inside. Gardenia, Lily of the Valley, Crimson Carnation, Luscious, Garden of Love, Ballad, Quaintance & Golden Promise. CMV $20. each with vials. Here's My Heart, Flowertime, Quaintance & Cotillion came in pink or blue tubes. CMV $15. each mint.

1938 HAND CREAM SAMPLES
Box of 24. 1/4 oz. turquoise & white tubes. CMV $3. each tube - mint complete $100.
1938 CLEANSING CREAM SAMPLES
Same box as hand cream samples. Box of 24. 1/4 oz. tubes. CMV $3. each tube mint - complete set $100.

1962 - 76th ANNIVERSARY CELEBRATION DEMO KIT
Pink cardboard box holds 2 oz. Cotillion cologne, Cotillion cream sachet, 2 oz. perfumed deodorant, 6 oz. Rosiest Spray Sachet, Silver Notes Eye Shadow & Hi Light Shampoo. CMV $30.

1974 PERFECT BALANCE MANAGER'S DEMO KIT
Contained Tissue-Off cleansing cream, Toning Freshener, night cream, Wash-Off cleansing lotion, Toning astringent, night time moisturizer. CMV $35. MB.

1965 MANAGER'S DEMO KIT
White box holds eye & face make-up. CMV $55. MB.

1970 PRIMA NATURA PRODUCTS INTRODUCTION DEMO KIT FOR MANAGERS ONLY
White Avon embossed box holds Creme of Soap, Night Veil Concentrate, Toning Freshener, Moisturizing Freshener. CMV $25.

1979 MAKE-UP DEMO CASE
Large tan vinyl case. CMV $10. MB.

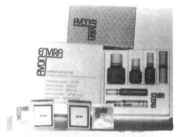

1979-80 ENVIRA MAKE-UP DEMO KIT & PRODUCTS
Pink lid box with outer sleeve & white plastic inner base holds 1 each of Envira Products which are also sold separate: Conditioning Make-up, CMV 25c; Pure Color Blush, CMV 25c; Gentle Eye Color, CMV 25c; Pure Color Lipstick, CMV 25c; Soft Eye Definer, CMV 25c; Conditioning Mascara, CMV 25c. CMV complete set in demo box, mint, $7.50.
SAMPLES CONDITIONING MAKE-UP
Box of 10. CMV 25c.
SAMPLES OF PURE COLOR BLUSH
Box of 10. CMV 25c.

1979 FRESH LOOK MAKE-UP DEMO KIT
Used by Reps only. Peach color box. CMV $5. MB.

1963 - 77th ANNIVERSARY DEMO SET
Demo kit for Avon Reps on 77th Anniversary. Top of box has rose in left corner & says "Celebrating Avon's 77th Anniversary." Box holds 2 oz. cologne mist with 4A's embossed on side, jar of cream foundation, 4 oz. skin-so-soft & petti pat compact. CMV $35. MB.

1980 MOISTURE SECRET KIT
Outer sleeve holds white and pink plastic case. 4 small pink plastic containers of creams. SSP $3.50, CMV $3.50 MB.

1970 REP'S DEMO & ORDER CASE
Blue plastic snap shut case. Has order pad & fragrance samples & color brochures. CMV $10. mint.

1982 ACCOLADE DEMO KIT
Carmel color plastic case holds Accolade products for Avon managers. CMV $40. mint.

1980 TIME CONTROL DEMO KIT
Black & pink box & sleeve has small white hour glass & .75 oz. plastic bottles of Time Control. Plus 6 more bottles in box. Used by Reps as demo kit. CMV $8. MB.

1977 FASHION MAKEUP GROUP COLLECTION
Demo kit used by Reps to sell Fashion Makeup products. Box is black & gold with white base. Outside sleeve. Cost Rep $5.47, CMV $5.50 MB complete.

1980 BEAUTY FLUID SAMPLE KIT
Given to President's Club member Reps. Box has outer sleeve. Silver & brown box & sleeve. Holds 3 oz. bottle of beauty fluid & pack of tissues. CMV $12. MB.

1976 CANDID MANAGER'S DISPLAY
Orange plastic display for Avon managers to display new Candid products. Base holds 7 Candid lipsticks, 6 eye colors, 2 mascaras, 3 cheek colors & three 1½ oz. bottles of makeup. CMV complete set full in box $45. - empty items 25c each - base only $15.

1978 MOISTURE SECRET SKIN CARE KIT
White & pink plastic kit holds pink plastic tubes of Moisture Secret Enriched Cremegel Cleanser, Enriched Freshener & Enriched Daytime Moisturizer. All with PMB and pink plastic jar of Enriched Night Concentre. All are trial size. Came with outer sleeve over kit. SSP $2.50, CMV $4. MB.

1977 COLORWORKS DEMO KIT
Silver & white box with outer sleeve holds Oil Free Liquid Makeup, Oil Free Cheekblush, Supershine Lip Gloss, Lasting Color Eye Shadow & Lashes, Lashes Mascara. Used by Avon Reps to sell new Colorworks products. Rep cost $4.50, CMV $5. MB complete.

1975-78 JEWELRY DISPLAY CASE
Blue case won by Avon Reps for meeting sales achievement goal. Avon on case. Was also sold for $4. to Reps for demo case. Case came empty. Measures 10½" x 8½" x 2". Avon on lid and outer sleever. CMV $5. in sleeve.

1976 C-17 MAKING EYES DISPLAY
Plastic base used by managers to display new turquoise color eye makeup products. Base holds 12 powder eye shadows, 5 cream eye shadows, 2 eye shadow wands, 3 mascaras, 3 brow & liner pencils. CMV $45. MB as shown full. Products 25c each empty. CMV base only $15.

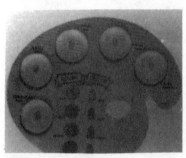

1936 REPRESENTATIVE DEMO CASE
Black case with metal mirror in lid. Handle is on opposite side of lid opening. Inner shelf is dark blue & lifts out of case. Storage area under shelf. Case came complete with 1936 sales catalog, ¼ oz. glass stopper perfume in Cotillion, metal cap ¼ oz. perfume in Gardenia, blue & silver lipstick & rouge compact, silver box of face powder, ribbed glass bottle of skin freshener (2 oz.), astringent (2 oz.), Lotus Cream (4 oz.), Rosewater Glycerin & Benzoin (4 oz.). All with black caps. 2 oz. jars of vanishing cream & tissue cream & 4 oz. jars of cleansing cream. CMV $1,000. MB complete set.

1941 DEMO KIT - CHRISTMAS
For Representatives only. CMV complete $350.

1957 FACE POWDER DEMONSTRATOR PALETTE
Turquoise board holds 10 samples with clear plastic tops. CMV $22. mint.

1930's REPRESENTATIVE DEMO CASE
Black case held sets & demo products & catalog. No price established. Case only $75. mint.

1938 FACE POWDER DEMONSTRATOR PALETTE
Board holds 5 samples in Ariel & Vernafleur. CMV $32. mint.

1943 GIFT DISPLAY ENSEMBLE DEMO
A special hand carrying box used by Reps at Christmas time to show Christmas sales items & sets. To determine price of this kit, look up each set & get their price, then add $25. for this demo box.

1959-60 BEAUTY COUNSELOR DEMO KIT
Black shoulder bag with outside pocket holds removable turquoise & white plastic inner case with Avon & 4A design on lid containing 3 white plastic jars with turquoise lids holding .46 oz. of Rich Moisture Cream, Vita Moist Cream & Strawberry Cooler, 1 oz. glass bottle sample of Skin Freshener, 1¼ oz. white plastic sample bottle Deep Clean Cleansing Cream, 17 sample bottles of Liquid Powder, 5 liquid rouge samples in small bottles, 45 gold metal lipstick samples & 16 plastic shaker powder samples. CMV $200. complete.

1942 GIFT DISPLAY ENSEMBLE DEMO
A special hand carrying box used by Reps at Christmas time. Came with several sets to show customers. To determine price of this kit, look up each set & get price. Then add $25. for the demo box.

FACE POWDER DEMONSTRATOR PALETTES
1946-49 HEAVENLIGHT
(Left) Blue board holds 9 feather design samples. CMV $27.
1949-54 FACE POWDER PALETTE
(Right) Turquoise board holds 8 to 10 samples. CMV $22.
1954-55 FACE POWDER PALETTE
(Bottom) Turquoise board holds 10 samples. CMV $22.

1942 FACE POWDER DEMONSTRATOR PALETTE
Board holds 8 paper box samples. CMV $32. mint.

1946 HEAVENLIGHT FACE POWDER SAMPLE PALETTE
Each pink sample has Heavenlight written across each top. CMV $30.

1940 FACE POWDER DEMONSTRATOR PALETTE
Board holds 8 metal samples. CMV $32. mint.

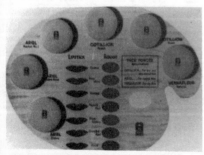

1940 FACE POWDER DEMONSTRATOR PALETTE
Board holds 6 metal samples in Ariel, Cotillion & Vernafleur. CMV $30.

1950's FACE POWDER PALETTE DEMONSTRATOR
Board holds 10 sample powders. Came in pink envelope. Used by Reps. Same palette came in different envelopes. CMV $22. with envelopes.

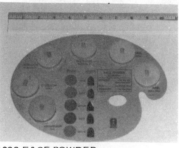

1939 FACE POWDER DEMONSTRATOR PALETTE
Board holds 6 different face powder samples with tulip A on lid in Cotillion, Ariel or Vernafleur. CMV $30. mint.

1940's HEAVENLIGHT FACE POWDER SAMPLE
Blue metal case, white feather on lid. CMV $2. mint.

1949-55 FACE POWDER SAMPLES
(Left) Green metal samples. CMV $1 each mint.

1930-36 FACE POWDER SAMPLE
(Right) Small silver can, came in Ariel or Vernafleur. CMV $2 mint.

1942 FACE POWDER SAMPLE SET
Box holds 30 metal face powder samples. OSP 50c, CMV $45. set MB - $1. each sample. Also came with CPC Avon label. CMV $65. set MB.

1946-49 HEAVENLIGHT FACE POWDER SAMPLES
Box holds 30 feather design samples. OSP 50c, CMV $35. MB. Samples came both in cardboard & tin.

1940's FACE POWDER SAMPLE BOX
Light green box holds 30 plain blue face powder samples. Avon on back. CMV $25. box complete mint.

1942 FACE POWDER SAMPLES
Box holds 30 blue feather design samples. CMV $42. MB.

1949-55 CREAM CAKE SAMPLES
Holds 6 shades of cream cake. CMV $8. mint.

1940-1950's FACE POWDER SAMPLES
Avon envelope holds 10 sample packets of face powder. CMV $3. mint.

1949-50 FACE POWDER DEMO SAMPLES
Pink & white feather box holds 50 demo packets of face powder. Used by reps. Packets are different. Was not sold to public. CMV $15. MB.

1940 DEMONSTRATOR KIT
Box with gold Avon seal on lid holds lipstick sample box, face power palette, box of face powder & 30 cotton puffs. CMV complete set $75. MB.

1942 LIPSTICK DEMONSTRATOR CASE
Box holds 30 turquoise plastic or metal samples or 30 brass bamboo samples. CMV $40. MB. Lady's face on top of box.

1960 FRAGRANCE SAMPLES - WOMEN'S
(Top) Pink & gold box holds ten 1 dram bottles, white caps. CMV $12.
1949-early 1950's LIPSTICK JEWEL ETCHED SAMPLES
(Bottom) Box holds 30 metal lipstick samples. CMV $30.

LIPSTICK SAMPLES
(Left) 1947 red box holds 30 brass samples. Also came 2 boxes in a plain carton from Avon. CMV $30. CMV $60. box of 2 sets.
(Right) 1951 white plastic tray holds 30 brass lipstick samples. CMV $25.

1952 LIPSTICK DEMONSTRATOR
Box holds 4 full size gold embossed lipsticks & 1 refill. Used early to mid 50's. CMV $30. MB.

1940 LIPSTICK DEMONSTRATOR
Box holds 30 metal lipstick samples, with cards. CMV $35. MB with all 30 cards.

1936-40 NEW CUSTOMER KIT
Turquoise box holds 30 turquoise metal lipstick samples with 30 sample cards. CMV $45. set MB with all cards.

409

1950's LIPSTICK PACKS
Two different packs of 10 brass lipsticks. CMV $6. complets pack or 50 sample pack, brass. CMV $15. complete.

EARLY 1950's COLOGNE DEMONSTRATOR SET
1 dram bottles of Cotillion, Quaintance, Forever Spring, Golden Promise & To A Wild Rose. In green & gold box. Came in 5 & 6 bottle sets. CMV $17. MB.

1960 NOSE GAY LIPSTICK DEMO KIT
White foam, pink ribbon & flowers. Holds 4 white lipsticks. Came only in plum, orange, peach & cherry blossom. Made up like flower bouquet. CMV $65. mint.

1940 LIPSTICK SAMPLE
Gold metal case on display card. Came in 2 different size & style cards as shown. CMV $1. on card - lipstick only 25c.

1938 LIPSTICK SAMPLE
Same card as 1940 card only came with turquoise metal lipstick sample. CMV $1. on card, mint.

1971-72 CUSTOM CONDITIONER
(Left) ¾ oz. bottle with white cap. Used in Avon beauty shops for professional use only. CMV $10.

1971-72 NEW DIMENSION EXTRA & REGULAR
(Right) ¾ oz. glass bottle. Used in Avon beauty shops for professional use only. Top of bottle must be broken to use contents. CMV $10.

1960 EYE SHADOW DEMONSTRATOR CARD
Six gold metal eye shadow tubes. CMV $12. mint.

1961 LIPSTICK DEMONSTRATOR
A demonstrator piece sold to representatives for $1.35. Black plastic base with clear lucite dome. Came with silver deluxe lipstick with 4A on top (wrong lipstick shown in case). CMV $22. MB.

1960's CLEAR 'N' COVER SAMPLE
(Left) CMV $1.

1960 LUMINOUS CREAM EYE SHADOW
(Right) CMV $1.

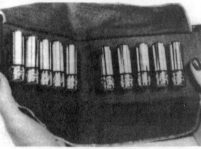

1949 LIPSTICK DEMONSTRATOR KIT
Black flannel roll-up kit holds 10 gold full size lipsticks. CMV $30. mint.

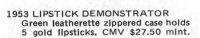

1978 LIPSTICK DEMO
Demo card holds turtle shell lipstick. CMV $2. mint on card.

1953 LIPSTICK DEMONSTRATOR
Green leatherette zippered case holds 5 gold lipsticks. CMV $27.50 mint.

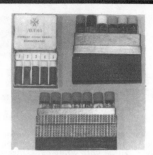

1977 COLORSTICK PENCIL SAMPLER
Plastic base with sleeve lid holds color chart & 5 Colorstick pencils & brown plastic 2 hole pencil sharpener, marked Avon. Used by Reps to sell Colorstick products. Rep cost $3.99, CMV $4. MB complete.

MEN'S AFTER SHAVE SAMPLES
Two on left are 1960's. Box red & silver, bottles have red caps. CMV $10. MB. Two on right are late 60's & early 70's. Box is red woven design & black, bottles have red caps. Came with 2 different outer sleeves as shown on top. CMV $6. each MB.

1956 HARMONY ROUGE SAMPLES
(Left) 5 sample bottles. CMV $15.
1950 COLOGNE SAMPLES
(Right) Green box holds 6 samples, colored lids. CMV $12. MB.
1968 COLOGNE SAMPLES
(Bottom) Green box with woven design holds 7 samples, all have yellow caps. CMV $5. MB.

1956 COLOGNE DEMONSTRATOR SET
1 dram bottles of To A Wild Rose, Forever Spring, Bright Night, Nearness, Elegante & Cotillion. All different color caps, in pink & gold box. CMV $15. MB. Also came out in Canada in all white caps. CMV $15. MB.

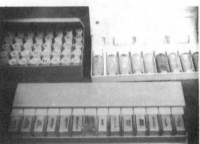

1960's-70's LIPSTICK SAMPLES
(Top Left) Turquoise plastic box holds 40 white plastic lipstick samples. CMV 10c each sample or $5. MB complete.
1967 LIQUID POWDER SAMPLES
(Top Right) Box of 12 samples, clear plastic top. CMV $8. MB.
1958 POWDER SAMPLES
(Bottom) 14 samples, square container. CMV $10. MB.

1960's FOUNDATION DEMONSTRATORS
Clear glass bottles with white plastic lids. (Top to bottom) 12 bottle set, only 6 showing; 12 bottle set; 10 bottles set. Front row 8 bottle set. CMV all sets $5. MB.

1968 BATH FRESHENER SAMPLES
(Left) Colored caps, 7 samples. CMV $6. MB.
1968 COLOGNE SAMPLES
(Right) 14 samples, white caps. CMV $7. MB.

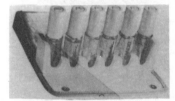

1978-83 FRAGRANCE DEMO KIT
Plastic demo kit holds 6 sample bottles of Avon fragrance. CMV $2.

1965 FRAGRANCE COLOGNE SAMPLES
Pink & gold box holds 10 cologne samples with white caps. CMV $7. MB.

1957 NAIL POLISH DEMONSTRATOR
Six ½ dram bottles with white caps. CMV $20. MB.

1973 FOUNDATION MAKEUP DEMO
Box holds 7 bottles with white caps. Used by Reps only. CMV $3. MB.

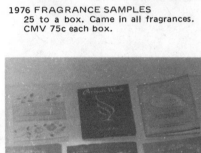

1977 FOUNDATION MAKEUP DEMO
(Left) Box holds 7 Even-Tone foundation tubes with white caps. Marked not for resale on back. CMV $2. MB.

1978 COLORCREME MOISTURE LIPSTICKS DEMO SET
(Right) Fruit basket design box holds 15 small white plastic sample lipsticks & 1 full size lipstick in silver & blue tube. Box came with outer sleeve. CMV $2. MB.

1976 FRAGRANCE SAMPLES
25 to a box. Came in all fragrances. CMV 75c each box.

1978 SAMPLE & DEMO PRODUCTS
1977-78 Lipstick samples, pack of 10 white plastic lipstick samples. CMV 25c a pack.

1976-78 Ring Sizer - white plastic Avon marked ring sizes. Used by Reps to sell Avon rings. 3 different. CMV 25c.

1977-78 FRAGRANCE SAMPLE DEMO KIT
(Front) Blue plastic, white inside has plastic tray with room for 38 sample 1/8 oz. bottles of both women's & men's fragrances. CMV $2. case.

1963 TRIBUTE AFTER SHAVE SAMPLES
(Left) Box of 10. CMV $5.

1965 OCCUR! CREAM SACHET SAMPLES
(Center) Box of 30. CMV each $5.

1961 CREAM HAIR DRESS SAMPLES
(Right) Box of 30 tubes. CMV $5. MB - each tube 25c.

1950's POWDER SACHET PACKETS
Came in all fragrances, 10 in an envelope. CMV $1. each or $7. for packet of 10 mint.

1950's FLAVOR BUDS TOOTHPASTE SAMPLE
Red & white box with foil tear off samples. CMV $7. MB.

1970's RICH MOISTURE CREAM SAMPLES
(Left) 10 packets. CMV 25c. box.

1970's FASHION GROUP SAMPLES
(Right) Box of 10 packets. CMV 25c. box.

1949 TISSUE DEMONSTRATOR
Small packet of Avon tissues for demonstrators. CMV $12. mint.

1972-77 RING SIZER
Pink plastic Avon ring sizer for Reps to sell Avon rings in correct size. CMV $1.

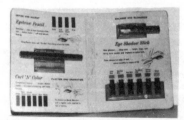

1937-44 FACIAL TISSUES SAMPLES
Beige & green paper wrapper. CMV $10. mint.

1979-80 SAMPLE TRIAL SIZE PRODUCTS
Bottles are all plastic. (Left to Right) Smooth as Silk Bath oil, 1 oz., CMV 25c.; Bubble Bath, 1 oz., CMV 25c; New Vitality Extra Body Conditioner, 2 oz., CMV 25c; Rich Moistur Hand Cream, 1/2 oz., CMV 25c; Nurtura Replenishing Cream, box of 10 samples, CMV 25c; Care Deeply Lotion for Problem Dry Skin, 2 oz., CMV 25c.

1960 NEW BEAUTY FOR EYES DEMO
Cardboard card opens up with 6 brass lipstick samples, brass eye shadow stick, eyebrow pencil & curl 'n' color. Used by Reps. CMV $12.50 mint.

1964 EYE SHADOW TRY-ONS
Demo paper container with 50 match samples, double sided. CMV $6. mint. Eye Shadow Try-Ons also came with 15 match samples. CMV $5. mint.

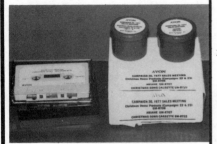

1970's FILM STRIP DEMO KITS
Used at sales meetings by managers to show & tell about new products & training programs. Kits contain 2 film strips & cassette tapes. Many different kinds. CMV $10. each.

SEE 1984 SUPPLEMENT IN BACK OF BOOK FOR MORE SPRAY CANS

SPRAY CANS — MISC.
ALL ITEMS PRICED MINT

1954-57 AVON NET HAIR SPRAY
Green & white can, white caps. Came in 5 oz. size. OSP $1.25, & 11 oz. size, OSP $2.; CMV $7. MB - $6. each can only.

1958-68 KLEAN AIR
12 oz. spray can. 1958-63 came in Mint with blue cap, CMV $2.; Bouquet 1958-63 with pink cap, CMV $2.; 1961-67 Citrus, orange cap, CMV $1.; Meadow Fresh 1961-67 in pink cap, CMV $1.; Pine 1961-67 in green cap, CMV $1.; Spice 1962-67, brown cap, CMV $1.; Sudden Spring 1966-68, turquoise cap, CMV 75c; Indoor Garden 1964-67, yellow cap, CMV $1. OSP $1.89 each.

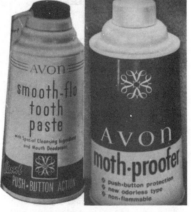

1959-61 SMOOTH-FLO TOOTHPASTE
(Left) 5½ oz. white, red & gray metal can, red cap. OSP 89c, CMV $4. can only - $5. MB.
1956-60 MOTH PROOFER
(Right) 12 oz. red & white spray can, white cap. OSP $1.89, CMV $4.
1968-72 MOTH PROOFER
11 oz. red & white spray can with white cap. OSP $1.89, CMV $1.

1974-76 ORIENTAL IRIS
(Left) 7 oz. white can, lavender flowers & cap. SSP $2., CMV 25c.
1976-78 COUNTRY MEADOWS ROOM FRESHENER
(Right) 7 oz. green can & cap. OSP $1.49, CMV 25c regular can. Pictured with rare upside down label. CMV $8.

1957-58 AVON NET HAIR SPRAY
White & pink spray can came in 5 & 11 oz. sizes. OSP $1.25 & $2., CMV $5. each.
1958-60 AVON NET FOR FINE HAIR
5 oz. blue & white can & cap. OSP $1.25, CMV $5.
1959-64 AVON NET REGULAR
5 oz. pink & white can & cap. OSP $1.25, CMV $4.
1956 LATHER FOAM SHAMPOO
Green can & cap, short issue. OSP $1.29, CMV $6. mint.

1958-73 SPRAY SACHET
Box holds 6 oz. can of spray sachet in Lavender, 1958-72 with lavender cap, CMV 50c; 1961-72 Rosiest, pink cap, CMV 50c; Sunny Morning 1961-63, blue cap, CMV $4.; Bayberry 1963-72, green cap, CMV 50c; Carnation 1964-68, red cap, CMV $2.; Ribbons 'N' Lace 1967-72, pink cap, CMV 50c; 1969-72 Potpourri, red cap, CMV 50c; 1970-72 Sheer Fancy, green cap, CMV 50c; 1971-72 Lemon Verbena, light green cap, CMV 50c. OSP $1.50 - $2. each.

1965-67 WARDROBE FRESHENER FOR MEN
(Left) 6 oz. brown can, black cap. OSP $2., CMV $4. MB - $3. can only.

1967-68 WARDROBE FRESHENER
(Center) 6 oz. purple & gold can, white cap. OSP $2., CMV $3. can only - $4. MB.

1968-78 WARDROBE FRESHENER
(right) 6 or 7 oz. red, black & gold with black cap. OSP $1 - CMV 25c.

1977-78 GENTLE RAIN ROOM FRESHENER
(Left) 7 oz. blue spray can, blue top. OSP $1.49, CMV 50c.

1978 BURST OF SPRING ROOM FRESHENER
(Center) 7 oz. yellow and green can, yellow top. OSP $1.49, CMV 50c.

1971-73 ENAMEL SET SPRAY
(Right) 7 oz. white can, red cap, red design. OSP $1., CMV 50c.

1973-78 ROOM FRESHENERS
1973-78 SCOTTISH HEATHER
Can with pink cap. CMV 50c.

1973-78 SWISS SNOWDROPS
Can with dark green cap. CMV 50c.

1973-74 WASSAIL BOWL
Can with red cap. CMV 75c.

1973-78 EVERGREEN
Can with green cap. CMV 50c.

1973-76 DUTCH TULIP
Can with pink cap. CMV 50c.
OSP $2. all scents.

1971-74 MATTER MINITS MASQUE
(Left) 3.75 oz. yellow, brown & white with yellow cap. OSP $1.50, CMV 50c.

1974-75 AEROSOL HAIR CONDITIONER
(Inside Left) 2 oz. pink, white & gold with white cap. OSP $2., CMV 25c.

1970-72 ASSURA SPRAY
(Inside Right) 3 oz. blue & white can, white cap. OSP $1., CMV $1.

1973-74 ASSURA SPRAY
(Right) 3 oz. blue & white can, white cap (powder spray) or green & white with green cap (dry mist). OSP $1., CMV 50c.

1971-73 INSTANT COOL
(Left) 4 oz. white & blue can, white cap. OSP $2., CMV $1.50.

1968-70 HAIR SPRAY (Unscented)
(Center) 7 oz. white & gold with pink cap. OSP $1., CMV $2.

1975-79 ON DUTY DEODORANT
(Right) 7 oz. black & white with black cap. OSP $1., CMV 25c. Also came with upside down label. CMV $8. 1979-80 came in 4 oz. can. Same CMV.

1979-80 HELLO SPRING ROOM FRESHENER
(Left) 7 oz. white can, green cap. SSP $1.11 no box, CMV 25c. Also came with upside down label. CMV $8.

1979-80 HAIR SPRAY FULL CONTROL
(Center) 6 oz. brown can & cap. SSP $1.79, CMV 25c.

1979-80 HAIR SPRAY FIRM & NATURAL
(Right) 6 oz. green & white can & green cap. SSP $1.79, CMV 25c.

1956-58 KLEAN AIR
(Left) 12 oz. blue & white spray can with white cap. Mint scented. OSP $1.89, CMV $5. mint. Also came 3 oz. pink & white. Same shape can. CMV $7.

1970-73 KLEAN AIR
(Right) 12 oz. citrus blossoms can with yellow green cap. OSP $1.98, CMV $1. 12 oz. Mountain Mist can with turquoise cap. OSP $1.98, CMV $1.

1968 KLEAN AIR CONCENTRATE
3 oz. Citrus, green can; Sudden Spring, yellow can; Jamaican Waterfall, pink can. OSP $1.69, CMV $1. each.

1965-68 BEAUTIFACIAL
3.75 oz. metal can. OSP $2.50, CMV $2.

1982-83 COOL CONFIDENCE SPRAY DEODORANT
(Left) 4 oz. lavender can. SSP $2.30, CMV 25c.

1982-83 COOL CONFIDENCE ROLL-ON DEODORANT
(Center) 2 oz. lavender plastic. SSP 95c, CMV 25c.

1982-83 TINGLE FRESH COOLING AFTER BATH SPRAY
(Right) 4 oz. blue & white can. SSP $3.50, CMV 50c.

1974-78 NORMANDY ROSE
With upside down label in any scent. CMV $8., regular issue CMV 25c.

1974-78 ROOM FRESHENERS
Yellow & white can, yellow cap. Pink, green & white can, light pink cap. Lavender & white can, lavender cap. Red & green can, red cap. OSP $1.50, CMV 25c.

1974-77 BAYBERRY
OSP $1., CMV 25c.

1971-74 MEADOW FRESH
12 oz. yellow & green, yellow cap. OSP $1.50, CMV 75c. Also came 3 oz. size. CMV $1.

1971-74 JAMAICAN WATERFALL
12 oz. pink & white with pink cap. OSP $1.50, CMV 75c. Also came 3 oz. size. CMV $1.

1971-76 SURFACE DISINFECTANT
White 12 oz. can, white cap. OSP $1.50, CMV $1.

1970-74 ROOM FRESHENERS
1970-72 Country Strawberry can with red cap, CMV $1.; 1970-73 Green Apple can with green cap, CMV $1.; 1972-74 Hawaiian Pineapple can with yellow cap, CMV $1.; 1972-73 Fresh Melon can with yellow-green cap, CMV $1.; 1973-74 Really Raspberry can with red cap, CMV $1.; 1970-72 Tangy Tangerine can with orange cap, CMV $1. OSP all scents $2.

1982-83 CEDAR CLOSET WARDROBE FRESHENER
(Left) Beige & brown 7 oz. spray can. SSP $2., CMV 25c.

1981-83 EVERGREEN ROOM FRESHENER
(Center) Green & gold 7 oz. can. SSP $1.60, CMV 50c mint.

1980-83 MISTLETOE & HOLLY ROOM FRESHENER
(Right) 7 oz. red & green can. SSP $1.60, CMV 50c. mint.

TEST BOTTLES & COMPS

Test bottles have been removed from this book only to discourage the theft of test bottles from the factory that make them for Avon. Test bottles and comps are still considered very collectable, but we will no longer print pictures or prices on them in this book.

Continued on page 416 . . .

The following definition of test bottles is "A very limited run by one to seven glass factories in 'flint' (clear) or colored glass samples. The size, shape or features may vary somewhat. Avon decides the final color to be used; the unused and discarded colors may be rejects, oddities, facimilies of issue - and coveted sample or TEST bottle." Avon Test Bottles are not sold by the Avon Representative. They are a very limited run of bottles made at the factory to check the color, size, glass thickness and shape of an Avon bottle before it goes into production. Usually no more than 1,000 test bottles are made of any one item and in most cases only a few dozen to a few hundred are made in test samples. In most cases the test bottle is run off in a different color than the regular production model is. Sometimes it will be run in more than one color as a test to see which looks the best. Test bottles are not supposed to be taken from the factory and are supposed to be destroyed when the test bottles are perfected as to Avon desires. They are hard to find and most test bottles come from New Jersey and Ohio where the test bottles are tested. Because of the very limited production of test bottles and the fact they are hard to find, the prices sometimes command a high price. WARNING! WHAT TODAY MAY BE A VALUABLE TEST BOTTLE, MAY BE TOMORROW REGULAR ISSUE.

Avon more and more is using the same bottle over the years in a different color, which often will be the same as the original test bottle. When this happens, unless you can see the definite difference, the price of the test bottle will not be worth any more than the regular issue.

Many bottles are being painted over clear glass or white milk glass by Avon. Always unscrew the cap to see what color of glass your bottle actually is.

You also have to be aware that Avon is selling all over the world in the same bottle, only the color will change in several different countries. Use the foreign bottle section to help you identify bottles in a different color.

COMPS are the artist's model, made up and painted to see what the item will look like before the production mold is made. Comps are also used to photograph for Avon Catalogs. Some are made of solid lucite, plastic and other materials different from the production model. Comps are extremely rare and most are made one of a kind.

Avon Products since 1977, has been giving the National Association of Avon Clubs one each of about 40 different comps each year at the big Annual N.A.A.C. Collectors Convention. Each comp given comes with a letter signed by an Avon Vice President stating that the comp is one of a kind and was never sold by Avon Products. These comps are either auctioned off or sold by raffle and bring prices from $150.00 up to $500.00. You will have to contact members of the more than 150 Avon Collectors clubs around the U.S. to find comps. The CMV varies widely so be sure you get the letter from Avon with it as it will be of little value without the letter to prove it is an original comp.

Avon test bottles are a very exciting part of Avon collecting, but we suggest you use caution in buying them at big prices until you know what you are getting. WARNING! Many items are issued in other countries in the same color as a U.S. test bottle which destroys the value of the U.S. test bottle.

The following is a list of some of the comps given by Avon Products at the Annual N.A.A.C. Collectors Convention. If no price is quoted, the price range is from $150.00 to $500.00, depending on the buyer. Be sure to get the letter from Avon with a comp. Please read introduction to this section to better understand what a comp is.

Bed of Nails Comb/Carton
Conair[R] 1200 Blow Dryer Decanter/Carton
Dingo[R] Boot Decanter/Carton
Avon Flowerfrost Collection Sherbert Glass & Hostess Soaps/Carton
Fuzzy Bunny Cologne Decanter/Carton
Gentlemen's Talc
"Heart and Diamond" Convertible Candlestick/Carton
It All Adds Up! Decanter
Moisture Garden Rosewater & Glycerin Body Lotion, Hand Cream and Facial Lotion
On the Mark After Shave Decanter
Peek-A-Mouse Christmas Stocking and Cologne Decanter/Carton
Quaker State Avon Heavy Duty Powdered Hand Cleanser Decanter
Sweet Pickles Outraged Octopus Toothbrush Holder, Brushes/Carton
Sweet Pickles Fearless Fish Sponge Mask, Soap/Carton - CMV $150. with letter
Sweet Pickles Yakety Yak Sponge, Soap/Carton - CMV $200. with letter
Sweet Pickles Zany Zebra Hair Brush/Carton
Sweet Pickles Puzzles
Sweet Tooth Terrier Cologne Decanter/Carton
Tubbo The Hippo Soap Dish and Soap/Carton
Weekend Decision Maker/Carton - CMV $150. with letter
Duster D. Duckling - CMV $200. with letter
1876 Centennial Express - CMV $300. with letter.

There are many more very rare comps given out by Avon Products to the National Association of Avon Collectors each year at the Annual Avon Collectors Convention. Always make sure you get the letter from Avon Products with every comp. or don't buy it.

SEE 1984 SUPPLEMENT IN BACK OF THIS BOOK FOR MORE FOREIGN AVONS

FOREIGN AVONS

PONY DECANTER SHORT - GERMAN
120 cc After Shave, emerald green glass CMV $16. in box. More common issue is greenish brown, CMV $12. MB.

SHORT PONY AFTER SHAVE — CANADA
Emerald green on left - CMV $10. 1973 Light amber - Canada, CMV $6. Dark amber - Australian CMV $100.
UNICORN COLOGNE
Canada - CMV $10. - Mexico is Her Prettiness - CMV $20.

1972 PONY POST IMPERATOR FOREIGN
(Left) Green glass pony post 9'' tall. 2-7/16'' wide across the base. Came with gold cap and nose ring. CMV $25.
1974 UNICORN — FOREIGN
(Right) Emerald green glass, silver cap. Held cologne. Rare. Same size as Canada, clear. CMV $150. green glass.

1978 CHATEAU D'AVON, CHAMPAGNE - EUROPE
(Left) 30 ml size green glass bottle. Came in green box. CMV $7.
1979 ARIETE PONY POST - MEXICO
(Right) 5¼'' high dark amber glass, gold cap. Brass ring. Brown box. CMV $6.

1976 STANLEY STEAMER — MEXICO
(Left) 158 ml, light green glass. Black seats and caps. CMV $12.50.
1975 PACKARD ROADSTER — EUROPE
(Right) 175 ml. medium amber glass, as the U.S. Porsche car only different

1979-80 BUGATTI, 1927, EUROPE
195 ml. black glass, cream colored plastic top. CMV $10. MB.
1979 BUGATTI, FATHERS DAY CARD
Grey, Avon marked card. CMV $4.

1975 DUNE BUGGY — MEXICO
148 ml. size. Green glass, Black cap. Came in after shave CMV $12.

1973 PONY POST — MEXICO
Shiny gold, painted over clear glass bottle. This bottle is same as American clear glass Pony Post only Mexican bottle has mold number on bottom. Mexico came both with & without Avon in bottom where U.S. clear Pony Post never had Avon in bottom. CMV $25. MB - $20. BO. mint.

1972 ELECTRIC CHARGER — MEXICO
Clear glass, red cap & red bottom label. Came in After Shave. CMV $32.

1976-77 PONY DECANTER — JAPAN
(Left) 118 ml. size light amber glass. Appears green when full of after shave. CMV $13. Pony also came in dark green glass from Japan. CMV $14. Light green glass from Mexico, CMV $11. Light amber from Australia, CMV $11. and light green from Australia, CMV $10.
1976 BUTTERFLY POMANDER — EUROPE
(Right) Pink plastic. CMV $6. MB.

1975 MG CAR DECANTER
England, Spain & Germany. Green glass. CMV $14. MB.

1977 RALLY CAR — EUROPE
60 ml. size cobalt blue color. Same as the U.S. Porsche car only different color. CMV $11.

1977 VOLKSWAGEN — MEXICO
(Left) 120 ml. black painted over clear glass. Holds after shave. CMV $8.

1973 RADIO — CANADA
(Center) 5 oz. amber glass, gold cap. Holds after shave. Gold front decal has 600 on station number. CMV $5.

1977 CAPE COD WIND GOBLET & CANDLE — EUROPE
(Right) Light purple glass, Avon on bottom. CMV $8.

1975 COUPE AFTER SHAVE — MEXICO
(Left) Same as the Sterling 6 in U.S. CMV $12. MB.

1970 SKITTLE BOWLING PIN — GERMAN
(Right) 120 cc white glass bottle holds after shave. Red neck stripes & label. CMV $12. MB.

1974-75 MINI BIKE — SPAIN
(Left) 120 cc green glass holds after shave. CMV $13.

1974-75 BOOK END COLOGNE FOREIGN
(Center) 2 0z. dark amber glass, paper label. Sold in Europe, Australia. CMV $11. Mexico issued in green glass, paper label. CMV $14.

1974-75 1st EDITION BOOK — FOREIGN
(Right) 60 ml. size, amber glass, Painted label, CMV $10.

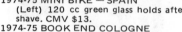

1977 CRYSTALSONG BELL — MEXICO & EUROPE
(Left) 118 ml. light green glass, clear plastic handle. CMV $12.

1977 SUPER CYCLE — MEXICO
(Right) 118 ml. light green glass and cap. CMV $12.50.

(Left to Right)
1980 SOCCER PLAYER DECANTER — MEXICO
90 ml. green glass with light green plastic top. CMV $12.50. MB.

1980 FORD PICKUP — 1973 MEXICO
148 ml. emerald green glass with green plastic pickup bed & decals. CMV $10. MB.

1980 PONY POST MINIATURE — MEXICO
45 ml. dark amber glass. CMV $6. MB.

1980 EL TORO BULL — MEXICO
130 ml. dark amber glass with white plastic horns. CMV $8.50. MB.

1976-77 RACING MOTORBIKE — EUROPE
100 ml. size black glass, black cap. Looks purple next to bright light. CMV $18. MB.

1976 SEIGE CANNON — EUROPE
(Left) 60 ml. size amber glass. After shave. CMV $10. MB.

1976 ROCKET 022 — EUROPE
(Right) 120 ml. size black glass. Gold cap. CMV $12. MB.

1969 PIPE DREAM — EUROPE
177 cc size dark amber glass. Came in gold & maroon box without the plastic base stand. Avon cosmetics label on bottom. Same size as U.S. CMV $32.50. MB.

1976 ANGLER DECANTER — CANADIAN
Darker blue glass than American. CMV $8.

1972 WINE SERVER
After Shave - Mexican green, CMV $25. After Shave - Mexican clear. CMV $30. (flat caps). Cologne - Canadian green,. CMV $20. (round cap).

(Left to Right)
1977 BLOOD HOUND PIPE — ENGLAND
150 ml. white milk glass, back cap, silver band, came in after shave. CMV $10.

1978 PONY EXPRESS RIDER PIPE — MEXICO
88 ml. dark amber glass, white and gold handle. CMV $10.

1976 CORN COB PIPE — MEXICO
90 cc dark amber glass, black and gold cap. CMV $10.

1975 PIPE FULL PIPE — MEXICO
60 ml. light green glass, black and silver cap. CMV $10.

1966 HIGH SOCIETY ORB EUROPE
237 cc, clear glass, red letters & gold crown cap. Red felt neck band. Bottle same as our Royal Orb, only painted letters on front say "Avon High Society 237 ccm" CMV $75. mint.

CAPTAINS CHOICE AFTER SHAVE CANADA
(Left) Emerald green glass, CMV $10.
TOUCH-DOWN AFTER SHAVE — MEXICO
(Right) Dull silver on blue glass. This bottle is easy to duplicate with silver paint. Use caution. CMV $15. mint.

1970 PERFUME AWARD — GERMAN
(Left) Falconette Perfume given to German Avon ladies in red Avon box. CMV $25. MB.

1970 FALCON AFTER SHAVE — GERMANY
(Right) 150 cc amber glass bottle, gold falcon head cap. CMV $32. MB.

1960's VIKING HORN — EUROPE
205 cc. dark amber glass. Foreign label on bottom. Goldtone top & horn tip. CMV $22.50

1978 ELEY GRAND PRIX — EUROPE
(Left) 60 ml. red plastic, gold cap. CMV $5. Holds after shave.

1978 SOCCER FOOTBALL — MEXICO
(Center) Yellowish tan plastic bottle. CMV $5. Issued in Europe 1979 rust color. CMV $5.

1978 SPICY AFTER SHAVE LOTION
(Right) 15 ml. clear glass, black cap. DMV $5.

1976 NEW WORLD — EUROPE
180 ml. size clear glass. Silver cap. Blue letters on cap. After shave. CMV $4. MB.

1976 HAWK — EUROPE
150 ml. size clear glass, gold cap. After shave. CMV $10. MB.

1980 HAWK — JAPAN
Same size & shape as Europe Hawk only has Japanese writing on bottle. CMV $15. MB.

1975 OIL LANTER — MEXICO, FOREIGN
(Left) Green glass, silver cap. After shave. CMV $8.

1976 SUPER SHAVER — FOREIGN
(center) 112 ml. size green glass - grey plastic top. After shave. CMV $8.

1976 VIOLIN — MEXICO, SPAIN
(Right) 88 ml. size clear glass, gold cap. Cologne. CMV $15.

1976 CRUZEIRO — BRAZIL
115 ml. size clear glass bottle. Gold cap. Brazil on one side and 1949-1 Cruzeiro on the other side. Came in after shave. CMV $17.

419

1971-72 FOREIGN CHESS PIECE SHAVE LOTION
150 cc, gold cap, white painted bottle over clear glass. CMV $11. MB. - $9. BO.

(Left to Right)
1977 ZODIAC HOROSCOPE — MEXICO
Cobalt blue glass, gold caps. Blue and gold labels. Came in all 12 zodiac signs in choice of Charisma or Wild Country. CMV $8. each.
1977 CHRISTMAS SURPRISE BOOT — CANADA
1 oz. green glass, red cap. Different from U.S. issue, CMV $3.
1975 AFTER SHAVE — EUROPE
30 ml. clear glass with yucky green cap. CMV $5.
1975 - 1/2 OZ. COLOGNE — CANADA
Clear glass, black cap. CMV $3.

1976 EXCALIBUR — MEXICO
(Left) Clear glass, gold cap. Blue painted label on front of bottle and black and gold neck label. CMV $10.
1975 LEATHER BOOT — MEXICO
(Center) Dark amber glass and cream color cap, plastic. Cologne for men. CMV $10.
1977 LEATHER BOOT — MEXICO
(Right) Dark amber glass and gold plastic cap. Cologne for men. CMV $8.

STRUCTURED COLOGNE — MEXICO
(Left) Clear glass, clear plastic top. CMV $5.
EDICION DE LUJO BOOK — MEXICO
(Right) Same as 1st Edition Book. CMV $10.

(Left to Right)
1979 NOBLE PRINCE DECANTER — EUROPE
90 ml. dark amber glass shown with American issue on left for size comparison, CMV $10. MB.
1979-80 CHAMPAGNE DECANTER — MEXICO
58 ml. green glass with gold plastic top. CMV $6. MB.
1978 CHAMPAGNE DECANTER — EUROPE
30 ml. green glass with plastic gold top. CMV $5. MB.
1978 CHAMPAGNE DECANTER — AUSTRALIA
30 ml. green glass with gold plastic cap. CMV $5. MB.

1973 BOOT — MEXICO
Dark brown amber boot on left pictured with American boot on right which is much lighter. Gold cap and bottom spanish label. CMV $15.

(Left to Right)
1976 BARBER POLE — CANADA
3 oz. white glass and red painted stripes. Came in after shave. White cap. CMV $5.
1976 BARBER POLE — MEXICO
88 ml. size clear glass painted gray or white with paper stripe label. White cap. CMV $8. each.
1977 CPC ANNIVERSARY KEEPSAKE — EUROPE
15 ml. clear glass, black cap. CMV $5. Back of bottle is embossed "Avon Anniversary Keepsake" U.S. issue says 90th on back. CMV $8. MB. Rare issue with clear plastic cap, CMV $10.
1976 COLOGNE — CANADA
(Far Right) .5 oz. clear glass, white cap. CMV $3.

1979 ST. BERNARD — SPAIN
(Left) 150 ml. dark amber glass. Brown plastic neck strap with beige plastic keg around neck. Bottle is same size issued in U.S. keg & strap are different. CMV $15. MB.
1972 ST. BERNARD — GERMANY
(Right) 100 ml. dark amber glass. Silver keg and neck strap. Smaller than U.S. & Spain bottle. CMV $18.

1972 BOOT — SPAIN
(Left) 236 cc amber bottle, gold cap. Leather Cologne. CMV $10.
1972-76 ELECTRIC PRE-SHAVE — SPAIN
120 cc clear glass bottle with white cap & label. CMV $5.

COLONIA — MEXICO
(Left) 4A design on black cap. CMV $9.

1974-76 COLONIA — MEXICO
(Right) CMV $5.

1971 EMPERATOR SHAVE LOTION — ENGLAND
(Left) 150 cc size, clear ribbed bottle blue & silver neck band & cap. CMV $10. - $14. MB.

1970's TALC DEODORANT — EUROPE
(Right) 85 g. white and blue paper container with plastic top and bottom, CMV $2.

1976 VICTORIAN FASHION FIGURINE - BRAZIL
Base is white milk glass with white plastic top. CMV $35.

1976 COURTING LAMP — MEXICO
Blue paint over clear glass base. Blue ribbon, white shade top. Lighter blue than one from England. CMV $16.

1976 PINK COURTING LAMP — BRAZIL
Pink painted glass bottom. Pink ribbon on white glass top. 140 ml. CMV $50.

1977 NOVIA BRIDAL MOMENTS — MEXICO
(Right) 147 ml. dull white paint over clear glass, white plastic top. Came all white. CMV $12. Some are showing up with painted flowers on cap. It is very easy to paint this so don't pay a big price for one that someone has probably painted the flowers to get more money out of. CMV $14. with painted flowers. Pictured in Mexican Avon catalog all white.

1980 ENCHANTED ISLES DECANTER — AUSTRALIA, MEXICO
(Left) 60 ml. clear glass with gold top. CMV $7. MB.

1980 SPANISH SENORITA — AUSTRALIA, MEXICO
(Center) 115 ml. clear glass painted red & white with pink plastic top. CMV $12.

1980 LITTLE BURRO — AUSTRALIA
(Right) 25 ml. light smoked glass with plastic cap, straw hat & red flower. CMV $7.

1974 COFFEE MILL COLOGNE — CANADA
(Left) Cream color milk glass, 5 oz. size. Same as U.S. issue only no gold trim. CMV $7.

1976 SECRETAIRE — SPAIN
(Center) Light pink milk glass, gold cap. Holds cologne. CMV $10.

1974 FLOWER MAIDEN — CANADA
(Right) 4 oz dull yellow frosted paint over clear glass. Plain white plastic cap. U.S. issue has painted flower on cap. CMV $10.

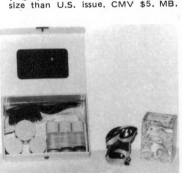

1979 FRAGRANT KEY — EUROPE
(Left) Same as U.S. issue of 1967 only does not have 4A design on cap. Different label on box. CMV $8. MB.

1979 ROSE POINT BELL — AUSTRALIA
(center) 115 ml. size clear glass coated light pink. No date on bottom CMV $10.

1980 LADY'S GLOVE POMANDER — EUROPE
(Right) Lavender plastic, smaller in size than U.S. issue. CMV $5. MB.

1979 TRAVEL KIT — JAPAN
(Left) White plastic case, Avon on clasp & 4A design on lid holds Avon comb, brush, 3 plastic jars & 3 plastic bottles. All are marked Avon. CMV $20.

1980 PRECIOUS RABBIT — EUROPE
(Right) 30 ml. size goldtone over clear glass. CMV $10. MB.

1976 PRECIOUS RABBIT — MEXICO
30 ml. size. Smaller than U.S. gold plastic head. CMV $10. MB.

COLOGNE BELLS — FOREIGN
15cc each. One has gold & clear plastic handle. CMV $30. - Right-gold cap & neck tassel. CMV $35.

1976 RECOLLECTIONS CRUET — EUROPE
(Left) Amethyst color glass cruet and stopper. CMV $10.

1976 RECOLLECTION CANDLE STICK COLOGNE — EUROPE
(Center) 150 ml. size amethyst color glass. CMV $10.

1976 FRAGRANCE HOURS CLOCK — EUROPE
(Right) 180 cc size olive color glass. Cologne. CMV $12.

1971 KEEPSAKE CREAM SACHET — ENGLAND
(Left) Lavender frosted glass bottom gold tree top. CMV $11.

1971 FRAGRANCED LANTERN — ENGLAND
(Right) 30 cc Lantern shaped cologne bottle, gold cap. CMV $12. MB. Also came in 30 cc Skin So Soft, gold cap. CMV $10. MB.

1975 CHIMNEY LAMP — CANADA
2 oz. clear glass, plain frosted top shade. Holds cologne. CMV $6. MB.

1972 COURTING LAMP - YELLOW — GERMAN
(Left) 150 ml yellow glass bottom with white glass top. Holds cologne. Yellow box CMV $20. in box. Also came in blue as U.S. Also in green - Mexico. CMV $25. in green glass.

1972 SKIN SO SOFT MINIATURE — GERMAN
(Right) 30 ml crown shaped bottle, gold cap. CMV $5. MB.

1978-79 LA BELLE TELEPHONE — BRAZIL
Small white milk glass base with gold toned plastic top. CMV $30. MB.

1976 PRECIOUS BELLS — EUROPE
(Left) 30 ml. clear glass, gold cap. Cologne. CMV $8. MB.

1976 ROYAL SWAN — EUROPE
(Right) 30 ml. size clear glass, gold cap. Cologne. CMV $12.50. MB.

1977 COMMEMORATION CROWN — EUROPE
(Left) 30 ml. size clear glass different from U.S. crown. Gold cap. Came in cologne. Sold from Queens Coronation Celebration. CMV $7. MB.

1976 SUN BURST COLOGNE — MEXICO
(Right) 14.5 ml. size clear glass, gold cap. Came in cologne. CMV $7.

1975 PETITE TELEPHONE — EUROPE
30 ml. clear glass. One plastic cap is ivory and one is peach ivory color. CMV $10. each MB.

1968 KEYNOTE — EUROPE
7 cc. clear glass key, gold cap. Bottle is same as U.S. only has foreign label on bottle & box. Different from 1979 Fragrant Key. CMV $25. MB.

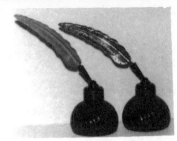

**1977 PLUMIERE (INK WELL) —
MEXICO**
(Left) 175 ml. dark amber glass, tan
plastic feather pen, black cap. CMV
$10.
1978 INKWELL — EUROPE
(Right) 180 ml. dark amber glass,
black cap, gold feather pen. CMV
$10.

(Left to Right)
**1978 - 1886 PERFUME ON
ROLLETTE — GERMANY**
Clear glass, red cap. CMV $5.
**1977 - 1886 EAU DE COLOGNE —
EUROPE**
1886 embossed on clear bottle,
red cap. CMV $8.
**1978 - 1886 EAU DE COLOGNE
SPRAY — GERMANY**
50 g. clear glass, red cap. CMV $11.
**1976-1886 EAU DE COLOGNE —
EUROPE**
100 ml. 1886 embossed on clear
glass, red cap. CMV $9.

**1980 TREE MOUSE DECANTER —
MEXICO**
(Left) 18 g. dark amber glass with
gold mouse. CMV $5. MB.
**1980 BOSTONIAN GLASS 1876
CANDLE — MEXICO**
(Center) Dark cobalt blue glass.
CMV $10. MB.
1980 LITTLE BURRO — MEXICO
(Right) Dark amber glass with straw
hat and pink flower. 28 ml. CMV
$5.50 MB.

**1980 CHURCH MOUSE DECANTER —
EUROPE**
(Left) white milk glass with pink
and white plastic head & cloth
veil. CMV $10. MB.
**1980 CHURCH MOUSE DECANTER —
MEXICO**
Same as above only clear glass
painted white. CMV $7. MB.
**1980 SEASON SONG BIRDBATH —
EUROPE**
(Center) 30 ml. frosted glass with
plastic top & blue bird. CMV $7. MB.
**1980 PETITE TELEPHONE —
EUROPE**
(Right) 30 ml. clear glass painted
gold with gold plastic top. CMV $10.
MB.

1980 BLUE EYED CAT — MEXICO
(Left) 45 ml. white milk glass. CMV
$6. MB.
1980 CHRISTMAS ANGEL — MEXICO
(Center) 2.8 ml. clear glass with
white plastic head. CMV $5. MB.
1980 LOVE BIRD — MEXICO
(Right) Frosted glass with gold cap.
43 ml. CMV $7.00 MB.

**1973 FUNNY FLOWER POT —
ENGLAND**
120 ml yellow painted glass bottle
with green plastic flower pot lid with
green, pink, blue & yellow plastic
flowers. Holds cologne. CMV $15.
MB.

**1973-76 BATH SEAONS —
ENGLAND — SPAIN**
(Left) 90 ml white glass bottle with
pink ribbon, red & green strawberry
design. Holds strawberry cream bath
foam. CMV $7. MB.
**1973 - ENGLAND — FLORAL
DEMI CUPS**
((Right) 90 ml white glass cup,
white metal lid with pink cap. Red &
green flower design. Holds bath oil.
CMV $11. MB.

**1972 SEA TREASURE DECANTER —
MEXICO**
Clear glass bottle with gold cap.
CMV $12. MB.

(Left to Right)
**1977 FROSTED COLOGNE —
JAPAN**
59 ml. frosted glass, clear top. Same
as ours just two bottles in 1965,
CMV $10.
1974 HOBNAIL BELL — MEXICO
58 ml frosted glass, gold handle.
Belt on bottom. CMV $11.
1977 ANGEL — EUROPE
30 ml. clear glass, gold cap. CMV
$6.50
1974 BELL COLOGNE — EUROPE
25 cc size. Same as our 1968 U.S.
Bell on right only smaller in size.
CMV $8.

424

(Left to Right)

1977 FIGA FIST — BRAZIL
55 cm. dark amber glass and matching plastic fist cap. CMV $32.50.

1980 HEARTH LAMP COLOGNE DECANTER — BRAZIL
Light green glass with green & white plastic shade & cloth daisies. 235 cm CMV $25. MB.

1980 LITTLE DUTCH KETTLE — BRAZIL
150 cm. clear glass painted grey. Blue flowers & blue cap. CMV $20. MB.

1980 PRECIOUS RABBIT — BRAZIL
Clear glass with white plastic head. CMV $20. MB.

1979 HOSPITALITY BELLS — MEXICO, EUROPE
Mexico came in dark blue glass with silver handle. CMV $8.50 MB. European came in deep cobalt blue glass with silver handle. CMV $10. MB.

1979 ANNIVERSARY KEEPSAKE — EUROPE
Came with pink atomizer. CMV $12.50. MB.

(Left to Right)

1980 TIMELESS PUMP SPRAY COLOGNE — EUROPE
50 ml. clear glass with gold top & decal. CMV $6. MB.

1980 FRAGRANCE BELLE — EUROPE
15 ml. clear glass with gold top. CMV $5. MB.

1980 ROSE BOTTLE — MEXICO
Clear glass with gold top. CMV $7. MB.

1980 V.S.O.P. DECANTER — EUROPE
30 ml. green glass with black top. CMV $6. MB.

1975 SNOWMAN DECANTER — CANADA, AUSTRALIA
(Left) 1 oz. white glass, pink cap. Holds cologne CMV $5. MB.

1975 CIRCUS TALC — CANADA
(Center) Cardboard sides, white plastic top & bottom. CMV $2.

1975 SPRING PROMISE COLOGNE MIST — CANADA
(Right) 3 oz. lavender plastic coated over clear glass bottle, matching plastic top. CMV $5.

(Left to Right)

1977 FLIGHT TO BEAUTY — MEXICO
Pale blue painted over clear glass, white plastic dove top. CMV $7.

1978 GOOD LUCK ELEPHANT — MEXICO
43 ml. clear glass, silver cap. CMV $8.50

1977 MINIATURE LOCION — MEXICO
57 g. clear glass, gold flower cap. CMV $6.

1978 KOFFEE KLATCH — MEXICO
148 g. blue painted over clear glass. Yellow plastic cap. CMV $8.50.

1975-77 FRAGRANCE HOURS FOREIGN
(Left) 180cc light amber glass, gold cap. Holds cologne. CMV $12.50

1977 SPANISH FIGURINE
(Right) Pink plastic cap. Red & white frosted painted base over clear glass. CMV $12. each MB. Spanish figurine pictured is from Spain. Also came from Mexico with dull red paint and Australia with shiny red paint. CMV $10.

(Left to Right)

1979 SANTA CLAUS — MEXICO
(Left) 29 ml. all clear glass with red cap. U.S. had painted face. CMV $5. MB.

1980 BIRD OF SPLENDOUR — EUROPE
(Center) 75 ml. clear glass with gold plastic top. CMV $10. MB.

1980 BIRD OF PARADISE — MEXICO
(Right) 43 ml. dark blue glass with darker blue plastic head. CMV $6.50. MB. Also issued in Spain with lighter blue plastic head. CMV $8.50. MB.

1972 ROCKER COLOGNE — EUROPE
1/2 oz. gold indented top, pink or white label. 2 different labels. CMV $9. each, MB.

1976 BATH TREASURE SNAIL — EUROPE
90 ml. size. Clear glass, gold cap. Shown next to the larger U.S. snail. CMV $11.

1974 SERENADE IN BLUE DEMI-CUP — MEXICO
(Left) White glass, blue decal and cap. CMV $11.

1978 PERFUMED SKIN SOFTENER — JAPAN
(Center) White glass and gold cap. CMV $8.

1978 COCKER SPANIEL — MEXICO
(Right) 42 ml. white glass and cap. CMV $8.

(Left to Right)
1977 TEDDY BEARS — EUROPE
22 ml. clear glass, gold cap. CMV $6. U.S. issue frosted glass. Mexico - 50 ml. frosted glass, frosted head. CMV $15. Mexico - 50 ml. dark brown frosted glass and matching head. CMV $18. Spain - 50 ml. lighter brown frosted glass and matching head. CMV $20.

1978 MINUETTE — MEXICO
(Left) 88 g. size white glass, green painted neck band. CMV $7.

1977 RENAISSANCE CANDLE — AUSTRALIA
(Center) Blue glass with cameo lady on side. CMV $20.

1978 JARRA PERSA — MEXICO
180 g. clear glass cream lotion. Blue and pink and green front label. CMV $9.

1979 GIVING DECANTER — EUROPE
(Left) 60 ml., clear glass, flower gift card on front of box. CMV $6.50. MB.

1979 CARD, MOTHERS DAY — EUROPE
(Right) Pink flowered card in envelope. CMV $3.

1977 LOOKING GLASS — FOREIGN, MEXICO
(Left) Gold handle, dark amber glass. Mirror in center. 43 ml. size. CMV $8.50. MB'

1976 KITTEN PETITE — MEXICO
(Right) Green glass ball, white cat cap. CMV $8.50. MB.

1980 ROYAL CROWN — MEXICO
28 ml. clear glass, gold cap. Glass design different from others issued. CMV $5.50 MB.

1976 COLOGNE BODY SILK — MEXICO
Clear glass with gold top. 77g. CMV $6. MB.

1980 POPLOVE LIPSTICKS — MEXICO
Plastic tube came in 3 shades. CMV $2.50 each MB.

1978 BOW BOTTLE — JAPAN, EUROPE & AUSTRALIA
(Left) 30 ml. clear glass, gold cap. Cologne. CMV $7.

1976 PRECIOUS SWAN — CANADA
(Center) 4 ml. clear glass, gold cap. CMV $8.

1977 PRECIOUS DOE — MEXICO
(Right) 13 ml. frosted glass, frosted head cap. CMV $8.

(Left to Right)
1977 SCREW DRIVER — MEXICO
Clear glass - silver top on left. U.S. issue on right. CMV $8.

1974 STRAWBERRIES & CREAM BATH FOAM — EUROPE
120 cc. white milk glass, red top. Strawberries are smaller than the U.S. issue on right. CMV $6.50.

1977 GIFT COLOGNE FOR MENT — EUROPE
30 ml. clear glass, blue cap. Smaller than U.S. issue on right. CMV $5.

1972 EVENING LIGHT PERFUME — GERMAN
Box holds small perfume bottle in pink hang on carton. CMV $16. MB.

1970 FALCONETTE PERFUME — GERMAN
1 dram bottle in gold and white box. CMV $8. MB.

BATH SEASONS — ENGLAND
(Left) 90 mm white glass with dark flowers. CMV $10.

1978 LANTERN COLOGNE — ENGLAND
(Center Left) 15 mm clear glass, gold cap. CMV $8. Also issued in Canada, CMV $3.

LAVENDER BATH OIL — ENGLAND
(Center Right) 150 mm white plastic, lavender ribbon and label. CMV $8.

1974-75 BLUE NILE DECANTER — CANADA
(Right) 6 oz. blue glass and cap. gold neck band. Holds Foaming Bath Oil. OSP $4.75, CMV $8.

1975 COLOGNE PETITE — CANADA
½ oz. clear glass, gold cap. Came in all fragrances. CMV $4. MB.
PINEAPPLE COLOGNE DECANTER — CANADA
3 oz. clear glass, comes in Field Flowers, Hana Gasa, Bird of Paradise, Elusive and Charisma cologne. CMV $5. MB. Also sold in Mexico under name of Colonia Magnifiscents. CMV $10. MB.

1974 LOTION LUXURY — AUSTRALIA
Came in all fragrances. CMV $8.
1971 BATH SEASONS — GERMAN
90 cc white glass bottles trimmed in green (Honeysuckle), blue (Lily of The Valley), red (Strawberry), lavender (Lilac). Each holds bath foam. CMV $11.

1976 BATH SEASONS — EUROPE
90 ml. white glass. Bubble bath. White cap. Blue painted band around neck. CMV $7. MB.
1976 SWIRL PITCHER — EUROPE
150 ml. clear glass swirl bottle and cap. CMV $7. MB.

1972 FRAGRANCE ORNAMENT — CANADA
5/8 dram bullet perfume bottle, gold cap. In paper ornament. CMV $14. MB.
1973 CHRISTMAS ORNAMENT — ENGLAND
Paper ornament holds small bottle of perfume, frosted cap. CMV $15. MB.

1969 LOTION LUXURY — FOREIGN
Clear glass bottle and stopper. CMV $10., $12. MB.

1973 SKIN SO SOFT BATH CAPSULES GERMAN
Blue box holds glass jar of gold bath capsules, blue neck tag on gold cord. CMV $15. MB.
1968 CREAM BODY LOTION — EUROPE
177 cc bottle with gold cap. Same as U.S. 1964 Skin So Soft. CMV $12., $15. MB.

1974 GRAPE BUD VASE — EUROPE
(Left) 180 ml. purple glass holds perfumed bath oil. CMV $8.
1977 EMERALD BUD VASE — AUSTRALIA
(Center Left) 85 ml. emerald green glass holds cologne. CMV $8.
1978 CREAM LOTION — JAPAN
(Center Right) 150 ml. clear glass, gold cap. CMV $10.
1976 EAU DE COLOGNE — EUROPE
(Right) 50 ml. clear glass with white cap. Came in many fragrances. CMV $8.

1976 NOVA BUD VASE — SPAIN
(Left) 100 cc green glass and top. CMV $12.
1973 NOVA BUD VASE — ENGLAND
(Center) 100 cc purple glass and cap. CMV $12.
U.S. ISSUE
(Right) was called Sea Green Bud Vase. It is shown to show size.

CREAM LOTION — CANADA
5¼ oz. clear glass bottle with gold cap. CMV $10.
SKIN SO SOFT BATH CAPSULES — CANADA
Blue glass jar and lid. Made in Belguim in bottom of jar. Blue and silver neck label. CMV $12.
SKIN SO SOFT DECANTER — CANADA
6 oz. clear glass bottle holds bath oil. Silver top fits over white cap. CMV $10.

1964 SKIN SO SOFT BATH CAPSULES — CANADA
Tall glass jar, green, red and yellow capsules. CMV $22.50 MB.

1976 PACKY THE ELEPHANT — MEXICO
90 ml yellow plastic white cap. CMV $6.

1975 PIGS — EUROPE
150 ml pink plastic bottle and cap. CMV $7.

1978 LEO THE LION — MEXICO
290 ml yellow plastic, pink hat. CMV $6.50.

1973 LITTLE PIGGY NON TEAR SHAMPOO — CANADA
150 cc pink plastic. CMV $6.

1973 MAZE GAME - AMAZING CLOWN — CANADA
6 oz. green plastic, pink lid. Clown on face. CMV $6.

1975 MR. BUNNY — EUROPE
(Left) 90 ml white plastic, blue hat. CMV $6. It has an orange and green carrot.

1976 MR. BUNNY — SPAIN
(Center Left) 90 cc size, all white plastic, blue hat. CMV $6.

1977 PINK ELEPHANT — EUROPE
(Center Right) 150 ml pink plastic, dark pink cap. CMV $6.

1976 ELFY THE ELEPHANT — MEXICO
(Right) 150 g pink plastic and cap. CMV $7.

1970 ANDY CAPP — ENGLAND
Black and white plastic with green hat. Holds body powder. CMV $125. BO mint, $185. MB.

1972 THE RACER SPORTS TALC — EUROPE
Orange plastic bottle, white cap. CMV $8. MB.

1976 RABBIT — MEXICO
(Left) 68 g. size. White plastic green hat, lotion. CMV $6. MB.

1976 PERFUMED TALC — MEXICO
(Right) Tin can, gold and white. CMV $4.

1972 CLOWN BUBBLE BATH — EUROPE
120 ml plastic bottles, pink whistle cap. CMV $7. MB.

1972 FIREMAN SHAMPOO — EUROPE
120 ml plastic bottles. Orange whistle cap. CMV $7. MB.

1972 BROTHER & SISTER BUBBLE BATH — EUROPE
120 ml plastic bottle with blue flower cap and came with paper doll cut-outs and color booklet. CMV $7. MB.

1977 CHESHIRE CAT SOAP AND SPONGE — AUSTRALIA
Cat soap and sponge in pink and white. CMV $8. MB.

1974 TUB TALK — AUSTRALIA
Yellow box holds red plastic telephone with light blue base and cap. Holds shampoo for children. CMV $9. MB. Reissued 1979 in yellow bottle with blue cap and handle. CMV $7. MB.

1979 RING RING PHONE — MEXICO
Same as Tub Talk only in blue plastic with yellow cap and holder. CMV $6. MB.

1977 RULER COMB — EUROPE
Yellow plastic comb in metrics. CMV $4. MB.

1976 WORLD BANK — EUROPE
300 ml size blue plastic globe with stick-on colored countries. It is larger than the U.S. issue on right. CMV $11. MB.

**1979-80 SHAMPOO FOR CHILDREN —
MEXICO**
90 ml white, orange and red plastic
with orange whistle top. CMV $5.
MB.

**1979-80 MADAME GUS PERFUME
GLACE — MEXICO**
.7 g. green and purple plastic pin and
perfume glace. CMV $4.50 MB.

1979-80 LOVE LOCKET — MEXICO
Green, yellow and pink plastic. Solid
perfume container. Comes with pink
necklace. CMV $5. MB.

**1979-80 PRETTY PEACH SOLID
PERFUME — MEXICO**
.7 g. peach and green colored plastic
solid perfume container. CMV $5.
MB.

**1979-80 ICE CREAM COMB FOR
CHILDREN — MEXICO**
Tan plastic with vanilla colored ice
cream and red cherry. CMV $4. MB.

**1972-73 SMALL WORLD HAND
CREAM — CANADA**
2.25 oz. green and white tube, pink
cap. OSP $1.10, CMV $7. MB.

**1975-76 FLOWER TALK HAND
CREAM — CANADA**
60 ml (2.25 oz.) white flowered
tube and cap. Canada. OSP $2.,
CMV $2.50 MB.

**1980 MOISTURE SECRET SET —
EUROPE**
White vinyl case contains skin care
products in light tan packaging. Same
set in U.S. was pink packaging. CMV
$8. MB.

1980 FISH BUBBLE BATH — EUROPE
400 ml, plastic fish container with
white top. Holds pink bubble bath.
CMV $6.

1980 GOLF BALL — EUROPE
45 ml. green, yellow and white plastic. ½ size of U.S. issue. CMV $6.50
MB.

**1976 HIGHWAY BRUSH & COMB —
AUSTRALIA**
(Left) Brown plastic. CMV $5. MB.

1976 AUSSIE BEAR — AUSTRALIA
(Center Left) Red, white and blue
brush and white comb. CMV $5.
MB.

**1976 VALET BRUSH & COMB —
CANADA**
(Center Right) Brown plastic, gold
leaf on top. CMV $3.50 MB.

**1977 FORST LORD BRUSH &
COMB — AUSTRALIA**
(Right) Brown and gold plastic. CMV
$3.50 MB.

CANDLE SET — CANADA
Red box holds wood candle holder
with red scented candle. CMV $9.
MB.

WEATHER OR NOT — CANADA
5 oz. dark amber glass, plain gold
cap. CMV $10. MB.

**1973 WILD COUNTRY AFTER SHAVE
BRAZIL**
(Left) 105 cm. Red plastic, green
Cap. CMV $10.

1976 ELEPHANT IN A TUB
(Center) Box holds pink elephant
soap and blue plastic tub brush. CMV
$6. MB.

1974 FOOTBALL BOOT — BRAZIL
(Right) 85 cm. Black and white
plastic boot after shave. CMV $12.

**1968 CANDLE, RED GLASS —
ENGLAND**
Dark red glass candle on left not
coated as in American red candle on
right. Both same size. Avon in
bottom of glass. CMV for red glass
only, $50.

**1972 FESTIVE CANDLE — ENGLAND,
AUSTRALIA, GERMAN**
Wooden candle holder does not say
Avon. Perfumed candle not marked.
Must be in box. CMV $9.

**1973 MODERNE CANDLE —
ENGLAND**
Silver based candle holder marked
Avon. Red candle wrapped in Avon
paper. CMV $8. MB.

1969 FROSTED CANDLE — FOREIGN
Frosted glass. CMV $22.50.

1972 PERFUMED PAIR — EUROPE
Matching talc and soap. All fragrances. CMV $12. MB.

1976 PERFUMED PAIR SET — EUROPE
Different color boxes hold matching perfumed talc can and soap. CMV $11. each set.

1975 FRAGRANCE FANCY SET — CANADA
Box holds perfumed talc and perfume rollette. CMV $6.

1975 SIDE BY SIDE SET — CANADA
Box holds bar of soap and ½ oz. cologne. CMV $8.

1979 PERFUMED PAIR SETS — EUROPE
Box holds talc and soap. Container and product different color and design for each fragrance. Timeless, Ariane, Lily of The Valley, Honeysuckle, Unspoken, Moonwind. Moonwind and Unspoken have two different package designs. CMV $9. each MB.

1975 PERFUMED PAIR — CANADA
Box holds can of perfumed talc and bar of matching soap. Came in all fragrances. CMV $9. MB.

1969 FRAGRANCE FLING SET — FOREIGN
15 cc cologne and green soap. CMV $17. MB.

1973 DOUBLETTE SET — EUROPE
Yellow box holds yellow flower shaped soap and 25cc cologne. CMV $14. MB.

1973 SNOW DRIPS SET — CANADA
Box holds cologne and soap. CMV $10 MB.

1972 GIFTABLES SET — CANADA
Box holds cologne and soap. CMV $10. MB.

1972 SIDE BY SIDE SET — GERMAN
Blue box holds soap and 15 ml cologne bottle. CMV $13. MB.

1971 SIDE BY SIDE BAMBOO SET — GERMAN
Blue and green box holds green bar of soap and frosted 15 cc cologne with silver cap. CMV $15. MB.

1975 ELEGANCE GIFT SET — SOUTH AMERICA
Light green and white box with clear lid holds cologne spray and perfumed talc. CMV $25. MB.

(Left to Right)

1974 PERFUMED PAIR — EUROPE
Came in 4 fragrances with different color on each one. Box holds bar of soap and perfumed talc in metal can. CMV $12. each MB.

1975 PERFUMED PAIR — EUROPE
4 different fragrances in different colors with matching talc and bar of soap. CMV $12. each MB.

1977 PERFUMED PAIR — EUROPE
4 different fragrances in different colors with matching metal talc and bar of soap. CMV $10. each MB.

1973 SIDE BY SIDE — ENGLAND
Light green box holds yellow soap and bottle of cologne, gold cap. CMV $12. MB.

**1974 PERFUMED TALC SET —
CANADA**
Box holds 3 metal talc cans. CMV
$12. MB.

1976 MERRY TINTS SET — EUROPE
Box holds nail enamel and 1 blue lipstick. CMV $10.

**1975 FRAGRANCE FAVORITES —
CANADA**
Box holds cream sachet and per-
fumed talc. CMV $7.50 MB.

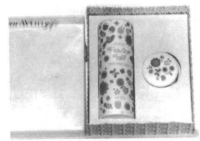

**1975 FLOWER TALK GIFT SET —
SOUTH AMERICA**
Blue, gold and white box with clear
lid. Holds perfumed talc and cream
sachet. CMV $22.50 MB.

**1977 SKIN SO SOFT SMOOTHIES —
AUSTRALIA**
(Left) Gold and blue box holds 85 g
Satin talc and 100 ml plastic bottle
of Skin So Soft, bath oil. CMV $8.
MB.

**1976 SKIN SO SOFT SMOOTHIES —
AUSTRALIA**
(Right) Blue and gold box holds 85 g
Satin talc and 100 ml plastic bottle
of Skin So Soft bath oil. CMV $10
MB.

1974 ELEGANTE SET — MEXICO
Yellow and gold box holds cologne
and perfume rollette. CMV $20. MB.

1976 SIDE BY SIDE SET — FOREIGN
Box holds 15 ml clear glass bottle
cologne, gold cap, 1 bar soap. CMV
$9. MB.

**1975 FRAGRANCE FANCY —
CANADA**
Box holds perfumed talc and per-
fume rollette. CMV $7.50 MB.

1972 BABY BRUSH AND COMB SET
White brush and comb in box. CMV
$5.

**1972 HAIR CARE PORTABLES SET —
CANADA**
Box holds Chic 'N' Sure hair spray
can and Avon brush. CMV $5.

1976 FRAGRANCE TWINS — EUROPE
Box holds cream sachet and bar of
soap. CMV $9.

**1978 PRETTY PEACH PRINCESS
GIFT SET — AUSTRALIA**
Pink box holds 100 g. white plastic
Pretty Peach Talc and yellow glass
cream sachet. CMV $12. MB.

1978 SWEET VIOLETS GIFT SET
Box holds Sweet Violets Talc and
cream sachet. CMV $10 MB.

**1975 RICH MOISTURE DOUBLE
CANADA**
Pink and white box holds 2 pink and
white tubes of rich moisture hand
cream in French and English. CMV
$7.

1977 PERFUMED PAIR — MEXICO
Pink and white box holds matching
48 g metal talc and 13 ml bottle of
cologne. Came in Elegante pictured
and Somewhere and Charisma. CMV
$8. MB.

1979 DELMONICO DUET — JAPAN
Blue box holds blue compact and blue lipstick. CMV $17. MB.

1979 DELMONICO COMPACT AND LIPSTICK — JAPAN
Blue plastic compact and lipstick holder. Came with blue velvet pouch. CMV $14. MB.

1979 EMPRESS DELUXE GIFT SET — JAPAN, AUSTRALIA
Box holds bone style, flower embossed lipstick and compact, with brass trim. CMV $18. MB Japan, CMV $12. MB Australia.

1979 GIFT SET FOR MEN — MEXICO
(Left) 48 g. plastic talc, brown and white, and 45 ml. clear glass cologne with brown cap. CMV $10. MB.

1979 PERFUMED PAIR — MEXICO
(Right) Clear glass petite perfume with red top and 48 g. talc in flowered cardboard container. CMV $8. MB.

(Left to Right)
1976 PERFUMED PAIR — CANADA
Box holds perfumed soap and metal talc in choice of fragrances. CMV $8. MB.

1977 BOUQUET OF PANSIES SOAP — AUSTRALIA
Blue box holds white bar with flowered decal. CMV $4.50. MB.

1978 PERFUMED SOAP BARS — EUROPE
Large bars in Lavender, Lilac and Lily of The Valley. CMV $4. each, mint.

1979 MOONWIND GIFT SET — JAPAN
Blue box holds 4 bars Moonwind soap and 70 ml bottle Moonwind cologne. CMV $25. MB.

1975 PRETTY PEACH GIFT SET — SOUTH AMERICA
Pink box with clear top holds Pretty Peach Talc and Cream Sachet. CMV $22.50 MB.

1976 LAVENDER SOAPS — EUROPE
(Left) Red Christmas box holds 3 lavender soaps. CMV $12. MB.

1975 OCCUR! SOAPS — SPAIN
(Center) Black box holds 3 yucky colored bars. CMV $12. MB.

1975 AVONSHIRE BLUE SOAPS — AUSTRALIA
(Right) Blue box holds 3 bars, blue, in angel shape. CMV $12. MB.

1980 CHIC SELECTED SUMMER FRUIT SET — EUROPE
Box holds nail polish, lipstick and wand style eye shadow. CMV $12. MB.

1980 FASHION MAKE-UP GROUP SET — EUROPE
Box holds eye shadow, 60 ml. creme-lucent foundation, mascara and lipstick. CMV $16. MB.

1980 EMPRISE GIFT SET — AUSTRALIA
Black, gold and white box holds 18 g. Ultra creme perfume, 100 g. perfumed talc, and 50 ml. Ultra cologne spray. CMV $20. MB.

1980 GENESIS GIFT SET — AUSTRALIA
Brown and gold box holds 50 ml. Ultra cologne spray, same as U.S. Timeless, and 9 ml. Ultra perfume concentrate. CMV $20. MB.

1978 SONNET SOAP — JAPAN
White box holds 6 pink soaps. CMV $14. MB. Also came in Moonwind, 6 to a box CMV $15. MB.

1979 FRAGRANCE DUET SETS — EUROPE
Box holds soap and perfume rollette. Each fragrance has different color design and bottle. Elegance, green; Ariane, pink; Timeless, tan; Unspoken, blue; Moonwind, blue; Charisma, red. CMV $8. MB.

**1972 DECORATOR SOAP EGGS —
CANADA**
(Left) 6 eggs shaped soaps, 2 blue,
2 yellow, 2 pink. CMV $7. MB.
**1973 HAWAIIAN WHITE GINGER
SOAP CANADA**
(Right) 3 white soaps. CMV $6. MB.

1975 QUACK A. DOODLE — CANADA
Bar of soap with white and orange
rubber duck. CMV $6.50 MB.

**1978 ORCHARD FLOWERS SOAPS —
EUROPE**
(Left) Yellow and gray box holds 3
yellow soaps. CMV $8.50 MB.
1973 JUMBO SOAP TRIO — CANADA
3 blue elephant soaps. CMV $10. MB.

(Left to Right)
**1975 LAVENDER COLOGNE —
SPAIN**
50cc white milk glass, purple painted
flowers, white cap. Came without
neck ribbon. CMV $5. MB.
**1975 LAVENDER PERFUMED SOAPS
— SPAIN**
Box of 3 long lavender bars. CMV
$12. MB.
**1974 LAVENDER DUO SET —
EUROPE**
Box holds 1 lavender bar of soap and
50 ml milk glass lavender cologne
with neck ribbon. CMV $14.
**1976 LAVENDER PERFUMED SOAPS
— AUSTRALIA**
Box holds 3 square lavender soaps.
CMV $10. MB.

1973 TIMOTHY TIGER — GERMANY
Yellow plastic soap dish. CMV $13.
MB.

**1975 SHUT OUT SOAP & SPONGE
CANADA**
Box holds orange Avon sponge &
white hockey puck soap. CMV $7.50.
MB.

1973 SNOWBIRDS SOAP - CANADA
3 blue soaps. CMV $7. MB.

1974 STERLING SIX SOAP — MEXICO
Box holds 2 yellow car embossed
bars. CMV $16. MB.

**1969 BATH FLOWER SOAP &
SPONGE ENGLAND**
Box holds bar of soap & flowered
sponge. CMV $20. MB.

**1975 RECOLLECTIONS SOAP —
EUROPE**
(Left) Yellow girl soap in green box.
CMV $7. MB.
**1976 CHILDRENS NOVELTY SOAP
SET — EUROPE**
(Right) Box holds 3 small hippo
soaps in green, pink, and orange.
CMV $7. MB.

**1974 PHINIAS T. FROG SOAP &
SPONGE — CANADA**
Green frog sponge and yellow-green
and orange wrapped soap. CMV $7.
MB.

1972-73 LITTLE PRO SOAP & SPONGE — CANADA
Left hand sponge light orange & white ball soap. Green box from Canada. OSP $4., CMV $9. MB.

1976 HIGH BUTTON SHOE SOAP — ENGLAND & EUROPE
Pink boot soap. CMV $10. MB.

1979 NATURE BEAUTIFUL SOAPS — CANADA
(Left) Box holds 2 bars with fruit decals only. CMV $5. MB.

1979 NATURE BOUNTIFUL SOAP — CANADA
(Center) Holds 1 decal soap. CMV $3. MB.

1979 WINTER SCAPE SOAP — CANADA
(Right) Holds 1 Currier & Ives decal soap. CMV $3. MB.

1979 SUMMER BUTTERFLIES SOAPS — JAPAN
(Left) Holds 3 butterfly bars. CMV $18. MB.

1979 TOUCH OF BEAUTY SOAPS — JAPAN
(Right) Holds 2 pink flower embossed bars. CMV $10. MB.

1977 GARDEN GIRL SOAP — CANADA
4 oz. bar. Garden Girl - 1 was light yellow in Field Flowers and one was lilac and lavendar in color. CMV $5. each, MB.

1976 OSIDOS BEAR SOAPS — MEXICO
(Left) Box holds 3 yellow bears. CMV $12.50. MB.

1978 TEDDY BEAR COLOGNE — BRAZIL
(Right) 20 cm dark amber glass, gold ring around neck. CMV $20. MB.

1972 HER PRETTINESS SPONGE MITT & SOAP — CANADA
Pink & yellow sponge & bar of soap. CMV $8. MB.

1975 TUBBY TIGERS SOAP SET CANADA
2 small orange tiger soaps. CMV $7. MB.

1975 HAWAIIAN WHITE GINGER — CANADA PERFUMED TALC
(Left) 2.75 oz. can, pink cap. CMV $2.

1975 PERFUMED SOAPS
(Right) Box holds 3 bars. CMV $6.50.

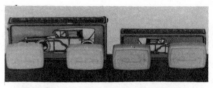

1975 GRAND TOURER SOAPS — EUROPE
Silver & black box in 2 different sizes. Holds 2 car embossed bars of the same size. CMV $13. MB. each set.

1979 PANSY SOAP SET — JAPAN
(Left) Blue box holds 3 decaled bars. CMV $18. MB.

1979 LOVE BIRD SOAPS — JAPAN
(Right) Pink & white box holds 6 pink heart shaped bars. CMV $18. MB.

1980 PERFUMED SOAPS — EUROPE
Single bars, boxed. Came in Timeless, Ariane, Emprise, and Unspoken. CMV $3. each. MB.

(Left to Right)
1976 SOCCER FOOTBALL SOAP ON A ROPE — EUROPE
White soap and rope. CMV $7. MB.
1977 HARVEY THE RABBIT SOAP ON A ROPE — EUROPE
Yellow rabbit soap, white rope. CMV $7. MB.
1978 BIG SHOT SOAP ON A ROPE — EUROPE, AUSTRALIA
Brownish gray soap on white rope. CMV $7. MB.
1978 HAPPY HIPPO SOAP ON A ROPE — CANADA
Hippo on white rope. CMV $5. MB.
1978 LORD LEO SOAP ON A ROPE — EUROPE, AUSTRALIA
Tanish grey lion soap on white rope. CMV $7. MB.

(Left to Right)
1977 PEEK A BOO SOAP — EUROPE
Yellow chick soap. CMV $6. MB.
1978 FRAGRANCE BELL SOAP — FOREIGN
Pink bell soap from Canada - CMV $4. MB. - Red bell soap from Europe - CMV $6. MB.
1977 CHILDREN'S NOVELTY WALRUS SOAP — EUROPE
Green walrus soap. CMV $6. MB.
1977 CHEERFUL CHIMPY SOAP — EUROPE
Orange monkey soap. CMV $6. MB.
1977 GOLDEN CARRIAGE SOAP— EUROPE
Yellow carriage soap. CMV $6. MB.

1979 A TOKEN A LOVE SOAP — AUSTRALIA
(Left) White bar with pink center. CMV $6.50. MB.
1979 ORCHARD FLOWERS SOAPS — EUROPE
(Center) Gray box holds 3 yellow flower embossed soaps. CMV $7. MB.
1978 PIRATE PETE SOAP ON A ROPE — EUROPE
(Right) Yellow soap with orange rope. CMV $5. MB.

1977 PERSIAN KITTEN SOAP — CANADA
White soap in purple box. OSP $4., CMV $4. MB.

(Left to Right)
1976 ERIC THE BRAVE SOAP — EUROPE
Blue soap. CMV $8.
1976 HUGGY BEAR SOAP — EUROPE
Tan color soap. CMV $8. MB.
1976 WINTER RIDE SOAP — EUROPE.
Pink Soap. CMV $8. MB.
1976 BIG IN A BONNET SOAP — EUROPE
4.9 oz. pink pig soap. CMV $8. MB.

1976 WYNKEN, BLYNKEN & NOD SOAP - CANADA
Box holds pink, yellow & blue soaps. CMV $5. MB.

1969-70 SOAPS ON A ROPE — FOREIGN
Each yellow soap, left to right. HARRY THE HOUND, HAPPY COW, RUFUS THE SQUIRREL. CMV $16. each MB.

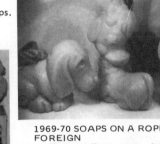

1976 OLAND SOAP ON A ROPE - AUSTRALIA
(Left) Tan soap on white rope. CMV $6. MB.
1974 IMPERIAL GARDENS SOAP ON A ROPE - CANADA
(Inside Left) White soap on orange rope. CMV $5. MB.
1976 SURE WINNER SKI BOOT SOAP ON A ROPE - CANADA
(Inside Right) Blue soap, white rope. CMV $6 MB.
1977 PARISIENNE BELL SOAP - SPAIN
(Right) Pink lady bust soap. CMV $8. MB.

1979 SOUTH SEAS SOAPS — EUROPE
(Left) Box holds 3 green fish shaped soaps. CMV $6. MB.
1979 LEMON SOAP TRIO — EUROPE
(Right) Holds 3 yellow lemon shaped soaps. CMV $6. MB.

1972 SOAPS — EUROPE
Came in all fragrances. CMV $5. each. MB.

(Left to right)

1975 ST. BERNARD SOAP — EUROPE
White soap. Blue & green box. CMV $10. MB. - $8. soap only.

1975 BO BO SOAP — EUROPE
Yellow elephant soap. Blue & yellow soap. CMV $10. MB. $8. soap only.

1975 HIGH FLYER SOAP ON A ROPE — EUROPE
Yellow soap. White rope. Yellow soap & box. CMV $10. MB. $8. soap only.

1975 PERSIAN KITTEN SOAP — EUROPE
White cat soap, blue box. CMV $10. MB. $8. soap only.

1974 CHEEKY CHAPPIE SOAP-ON-A-ROPE — EUROPE
Light green soap on white rope. CMV $11. MB. Reissued 1979 in Australia under the name of Cheeky Charlie. CMV $7. MB.

1974 DUTCH SHOE SOAP — SPAIN
Blue soap and box. CMV $12. MB, $10. soap only. Also sold in Canada.

1974 LADY SLIPPER SOAP — SPAIN, ENGLAND
Lavender soap and box. CMV $12. MB, $10. soap only.

1974 REGENCE — CANADA
PERFUMED TALC
2.75 oz. green metal can, gold cap. CMV $2.

SAVON PERFUMED SOAP
Box holds 3 green bars. CMV $6.

PERFUME SOAP
3 oz. plain wrapper. 3 oz. green floral wrapper. CMV $3. each.

1974 TOUCH OF BEAUTY SOAPS — SPAIN
Gold and pink box holds 2 white bars. CMV $11. MB.

1974 FOUR SEASONS SOAP SET — EUROPE
Box holds 4 bars of orange, blue, yellow, and green soap. CMV $11. MB.

1974 ELEGANTE PERFUMED SOAPS EUROPE
Green box holds 3 embossed aqua bars. CMV $13. MB.

1972 MOLLY MOUSE SOAP — EUROPE
(Left) Blue mouse soap on white rope. CMV $12. MB.

1972 MR. FROG SOAP — EUROPE
(Right) Green soap on pink or white rope. CMV $12. MB.

1972 CAMEO SOAP-ON-A-ROPE — CANADA
Pink soap, white rope. CMV $5. MB.

1973 MINERAL SPRINGS SOAP-ON-A-ROPE — CANADA
Beige soap, white rope. CMV $5. MB.

1972 LILAC SOAP — EUROPE
Blue box holds lilac soap with blue ribbon. CMV $10. MB.

1972 STRAWBERRY FAIR SOAP — EUROPE
Strawberry soap in yellow basket and ribbon. CMV $9. MB.

1975 FRAGRANCE BELL SOAP — EUROPE
Dark pink soap and box. CMV $11. MB.

1975 LITTLE GIRL BLUE SOAP — EUROPE
Blue soap, white and blue box. CMV $12. MB.

1975 KNIGHT IN ARMOR — EUROPE
White soap, black and yellow box. CMV $17. MB.

1974 AVON SOAP GEMS — FOREIGN
Orange, yellow and green soaps. CMV $12. MB.

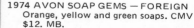

1979 FIELD FLOWERS SOAPS — JAPAN
Green box holds 2 pink, 2 green, and 2 yellow soaps. CMV $18. MB.

1979-80 TOUCH OF ROSES SOAPS — JAPAN
Red box holds 6 pink rose shaped bars. CMV $18. MB.

1972 JUMBO SOAP SET — EUROPE
Blue, tan and pink elephant soap CMV $11. MB.

1972 TOP DOG SOAP — EUROPE
Tan colored soap on white rope. CMV $11. MB.

1972 DECORATOR SOAP
(Left) Gold box holds 5 oz. white bar. CMV $4. MB.

1976 SKIN SO SOFT SOAP-ON-A-ROPE — CANADA
(Center) Turquoise soap with white rope. CMV $5. MB.

1975 CAMEO SOAP SET
(Right) Blue box holds 4 white cameo soaps. CMV $6.50 MB. Also came in white box with blue trim. CMV $11.

1979-80 WINTER SONG SOAPS — EUROPE & CANADA
Cardinal box holds 2 white bird decal bars. CMV $6. MB Europe. CMV $5. MB Canada.

1979-80 LADY SLIPPER SOAPS — EUROPE
Box holds 2 white, 2 pink slipper bars. CMV $8. MB.

1969 WHITE GINGER SOAP FOREIGN
Beige soap came in fancy box. CMV $12. MB.

1973 BOUTIQUE SOAP SET — EUROPE
Box holds 2 green bars and 2 lavender bars. CMV $8. MB.

1973 ROSE BLOSSOMS SOAP — EUROPE & SPAIN
Box is pink, holds 4 flower embossed bars. CMV $8. MB.

1973 FASHION BOOT HOSTESS SOAP — ENGLAND
Soap is blue with lavender bow. CMV $9. MB.

CANADA
Soap is same only no bow. Boxes are different labels. CMV $7. MB.

SOAPS — SINGLE BARS

FROM EUROPE
Aqua soap, Elegance, Nearness and Dr. Zabriskies soap. CMV $3. each bar.

FROM CANADA
Clear Skin, Regence, Moonwind, Scent of Roses, Hawaiian White Giner, Charisma, Rich Moisture Soap, and Blue Lotus. CMV $2. each bar.

FROM SPAIN
Perfumed Deodorant Soap, Deluxe Toilette Soap, Charisma, Topaze, Regence in Brocade package. CMV $4. each bar.

FROM AUSTRALIA
Occur!. CMV $4.

1978 PERFUMED SOAPS — JAPAN
Three different colored bars in own box in Bird of Paradise, Charisma and Unforgettable. CMV $7. each.

1975 ROSE BLOSSOMS SOAPS — MEXICO
Pink box holds 4 white bars. CMV $10. MB.

1975 FLEUR D'AVON — SPAIN
Pink, white and green box holds 3 flower soaps. CMV $12. MB.

1976 PERFUMED FLOWER SOAPS — MEXICO
Green box holds 4 gray flower soaps. CMV $12.50 MB.

1975 UNFORGETTABLE SOAPS — SPAIN
Orange box holds 3 orange bars. 4A design embossed in center of soaps. CMV $10. MB.

1977 CHRISTMAS ORNAMENT — MEXICO
Pink and green hang-up card holds eye shadow wand. CMV $10. mint.

1974 CHRISTMAS ORNAMENT — EUROPE
Small diamond shaped bottle, gold cap. Came in green and gold hang-on holder. CMV $10. MB.

1977 SKIN SO SOFT SOAPS — CANADA
(Left) Gray box holds three SSS white bars. CMV $5. MB.

1976 SKIN SO SOFT SOAPS — CANADA
(Center) Winter scene box holds 3 white bars of SSS soap. CMV $5. MB.

1976 PINE TREE GIFT SOAPS — CANADA
(Right) Green box holds 3 green tree soaps. CMV $6.50 MB.

1975 BUTTERFLY SOAP SET — SPAIN
(Left) Box holds 4 bars in yellow, orange, turquoise, and lavender butterflies, CMV $12. MB.

1975 SAVONS PERFUMED SOAPS — CANADA
(Center) Matching boxes came with 3 bars of Lavender, Lily of The Valley, green, Honeysuckle, yellow, and Apple Blossom in pink. CMV $5. each set.

1976 BUTTERFLY SOAPS — CANADA
(Right) Box holds 3 yellow bars. CMV $7. MB.

1974 LOVE SOAPS — MEXICO
Love box holds 4 yellow bars. CMV $22.50 MB.

1975 APPLE BLOSSOMS SOAP SET — CANADA
Green and white box holds 4 flower shaped soaps. CMV $6. MB.

1975 HOSTESS SOAP SET — CANADA
Green and pink box holds 2 pink bars and 2 green bars. CMV $6. MB.

1976 HONEYSUCKLE PERFUMED SOAPS — AUSTRALIA
(Left) Box holds 3 yellow bars. Also came in Lilac with 3 pink bars. CMV $8. each MB.

1978 TOPAZE SOAP — AUSTRALIA
(Center) Yellow box holds 3 Topaze yellow bars. CMV $8. MB.

1975 TOPAZE SOAP COLUMN — SPAIN
(Right) Yellow box holds 3 yellow column bars in plastic holder. CMV $13. MB.

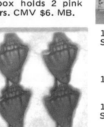

1978 COUNTRY PEACH SOAPS — EUROPE
Box holds 3 long bars. Also came in strawberry. CMV $7. each MB.

1977 COUNTRY CUPBOARD SOAPS — AUSTRALIA
Box holds 3 square bars in peach in pink, or strawberry in red, soaps. CMV $9. each MB.

1976 COUNTRY CUPBOARD SOAPS — CANADA
Box holds 3 long bars. Came in strawberry and peach. CMV $7. MB.

1975 GIFT OF THE SEA — CANADA
Peralessen soap dish and 4 pink sea shell soaps. CMV $9. MB.

1975 CAMEO SOAP SET — CANADA
Brown box, 3 bars. CMV $6. MB.

1975 TOUCH OF ROSES SOAP-ON-A-ROPE
Pink rose soap, white rope. CMV $5. MB.

1975 PERFUMED SOAPS — SPAIN
Flowered boxes came with 3 bars in Lilac, Hyacinth, Magnolia. CMV $11. each MB.

1975 SOMEWHERE SOAP — SPAIN
Box holds 3 pink S soaps. CMV $11. MB.

1975 NEARNESS PERFUMED SOAPS SPAIN
White and gold box holds 3 pink ribbed soaps. CMV $12. MB.

1977 LOVEBIRDS SOAP SET — AUSTRALIA
Box holds 3 pink bird embossed soaps. CMV $9. MB.

1975 WILD COUNTRY SADDLE KIT — CANADA
Box holds all brown plastic kit with box containing 6 oz. Wild Country After Shave and 7 oz. Spray Talc. CMV $20.

STACK PACK SET—FOREIGN
Bronze box holds bar of soap and 50 cc bottle of shave lotion. CMV $16. MB.

1977 IMPERIAL GARDEN SOAP-ON-A-ROPE — CANADA
Orange rope, white bar. CMV $4.

1973 INTERNATIONAL MEN'S SET — ENGLAND
Green and white box holds 50 ml size bottle with green cap. Holds After Shave Lotion and 1 white bar World embossed soap. CMV $13. MB.

1979 THE TRAVELLER SET — AUSTRALIA
Brown box holds one 100 ml light brown plastic Tai Winds after shave and one dark brown 75 ml squeeze spray deodorant. CMV $6.50 MB.

1979-80 LEATHER AFTER SHAVE — MEXICO
118 ml. clear glass with brown top and label. CMV $5. MB.

1979-80 LEATHER TALC — MEXICO
100 g. cardboard container. CMV $3. MB'

1969 GENTLEMAN'S COLLECTION — FOREIGN
Red and silver box holds bar of soap and 6 cc bottle of shave lotion with copper cap. CMV $16. MB.

1972 CARTE BLANCHE MEN'S GIFT SET — CANADA
Box holds Carte Blanche After Shave and Soap-On-A-Rope. CMV $16.

1976 DAILY DOUBLE SET — AUSTRALIA
(Left) Brown and white box holds choice of mens fragrance with 100 g talc and 150 ml plastic after shave. Blend 7 pictured. CMV $12. MB.

1977 GENTLEMANS COLLECTION SET — AUSTRALIA
(Right) Box holds choice of mens fragrance in 100 g. talc and 150 ml. plastic bottle of after shave. Windjammer pictured. CMV $12.

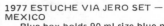

1972 GENTLEMEN'S COLLECTION SET — ENGLAND
Box holds 50 cc bottle, brown cap, bar of soap. CMV $13. MB.

1977 ESTUCHE VIA JERO SET — MEXICO
Blue box holds 90 ml size blue plastic bottle, gold caps in after shave and deodorant or brown box with brown bottles and gold caps. CMV $10 each set.

BLUE BLAZER — MEXICO
Dark blue glass, 2 different paper labels. Cologne and After Shave, red caps. CMV $18. each.

BLUE BLAZER — EUROPE
Soap-On-A-Rope. CMV $5., Talc can, CMV $5., Talc cardboard, CMV $5., Spray Deodorant, CMV $5., After Shave Lotion, 170 cc clear glass bottle, large red round cap. CMV $15.

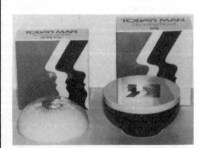

1975 BLUE BLAZER AFTER SHAVE— FOREIGN
Clear glass. Left - English, right - Spain,(cut out label). CMV $10 each.
1978 BLUE BLAZER COLOGNE — SPAIN
Same as center bottle. Clear glass. CMV $10.

1973 TODAYS MAN — EUROPE
Shaving bowl refill, in box. CMV $4. MB. Other box holds black and gray plastic soap bowl. CMV $7. MB.

1973 TODAYS MAN — EUROPE
Mens Products came in spray deodorant. CMV $6.
CLEAR HAIR DRESS
CMV $5.
HAIR GROOM SPRAY
CMV $6.
FOAM SHAVE CREAM
CMV $5.
LATHER SHAVE CREAM
CMV $5.
ELECTRIC PRE-SHAVE LOTION
CMV $10.
SHAVING BRUSH
(Not shown) CMV $5.

(Left to Right)
1977 TODAYS MAN HAIR TONIC — JAPAN
117 ml. clear plastic bottle, black cap. CMV $6.
1977 TODAYS MAN DEODORANTE — MEXICO
60 ml. clear glass bottle, black cap. CMV $3.
1977 TODAYS MAN ROLL ON DEODORANT — EUROPE
60 ml. white plastic bottle, black cap. CMV $4.
1977 TODAYS MAN SHAVING BRUSH — EUROPE
Black and white plastic handle. CMV $4.
1977 TODAYS MAN SHAMPOO SHOWER SOAP-ON-A-ROPE AUSTRALIA
White soap and rope. CMV $6.

1973-76 ELECTRIC PRE—SHAVE — FOREIGN
4 oz. bottle, clear glass, black cap. England. White cap, Australian. CMV $6. each MB.

1978 TODAYS MAN PRODUCTS — JAPAN
Each is brown and cream color plastic in After Shave 120 ml. bottle, 1/5 g. tube of Hair Gel, 115 gr. tube of Hair Dress, 115 tube Skin Conditioner, 180 ml. bottle Hair Tonic, 180 ml. bottle Hair Liquid, 120 ml. milky Lotion. CMV $4.50 each.
1977 CARTE BLANCHE — CANADA
Spray Talc, metal can, green paper label and cap. CMV $2.50.
CARTE BLANCHE AFTER SHAVE BALM TUBE
3 oz. green and white tube. CMV $1.50.

(Left to Right)
1976 IMPERATOR PRODUCTS — EUROPE
ELECTRIC PRE SHAVE
180 ml. silver top, blue 4A cap. CMV $8.
COLOGNE AFTER SHAVE
Both 120 ml. blue decal labels and 4A caps. CMV $6. each.
SOAP SET FOR MEN
Blue and silver box holds 2 white bars with 4A embossed centers. CMV $12. MB.

1973 FOUNDATION FOAM — CANADA
Pink can, CMV $1.
1973 TRIBUTE AEROSOL DEODORANT FOR MEN
Blue and silver can. CMV $2.
1973 TRIBUTE CREAM HAIR DRESS
Blue and silver tube. CMV $2.
1973 ISLAND LIME AEROSOL DEODORANT
Green and yellow can. CMV $2.

1978 SPICY AFTER SHAVE — JAPAN
120 ml. light amber glass, black cap. CMV $10.

1978 SPICY COLOGNE — JAPAN
120 ml. light amber glass, black cap. CMV $10.

1978 SPICY AFTER SHAVE LOTION— MEXICO
117 ml dark amber glass, black cap, brown and black label. CMV $6.

1978 SPICY COLOGNE — MEXICO
117 ml. dark amber glass, black cap. Gold and black label. CMV $6.

1977 SPICY AFTER SHAVE LOTION— EUROPE
(Left) 120 ml. clear glass, black cap. CMV $4.50.

1978 SPICY AFTER SHAVE LOTION— CANADA
(Center) 4 oz. clear glass, black cap. CMV $2.50.

1978 SPICY AFTER SHAVE — CANADA
(Right) 150 ml. frosted plastic, black cap. CMV $2.

(Left to Right)

1976 WINDJAMMER RUBDOWN COOLER — CANADA
10 oz. plastic bottle, blue and gold cap. CMV $3.

1977 WINDJAMMER AFTER SHAVE - EUROPE
120 ml. light blue glass, blue paper front label. Indented all blue cap. CMV $8.

1978 EVEREST AFTER SHAVE - CANADA
4.9 oz. plastic bottle, blue cap. Painted white label in French and English. CMV $3.

1978 ENDEAVOUR SOAP ON A ROPE - EUROPE
Blue soap on a white rope. CMV $5. MB.

1978 ENDEAVOUR AFTER SHAVE— EUROPE
150 ml. clear glass, blue cap. CMV $6.

1978 AFTER SHAVES — AUSTRALIA
Each is 150 ml. plastic bottle with Blend 7, brown cap; Windjammer, blue cap. CMV $4. each. Bay Rum, tan cap; Leather, red cap; Island Lime, green cap. CMV $5. each.

1976 HAIR TONIC SPICY — JAPAN
118 ml. size, real dark green glass, black cap. Japanese label on back. CMV $10. MB.

1976 SUMMER LOTION — JAPAN
130 ml. clear plastic bottle, white cap. Japanese label on back. CMV $6. MB.

1975 WINDJAMMER — MEXICO
Colonia Para Caballeros. Dark purple glass, painted label. CMV $25.

WINDJAMMER COLOGNE
Left - Mexico, light blue glass, painted label. CMV $10. Right - Canadian, painted label (address on front). CMV $4.

1976 WINDJAMMER — AUSTRALIA
Shower Soap-On-A-Rope, in blue box. CMV $8. MB.

AEROSOL SPRAY DEODORANT
4 oz. blue metal can and cap. CMV $5.

1975 NEW WORLD TALC — FOREIGN
(Left) White plastic container with blue paper label. CMV $4.

1975 NEW WORLD TALC — FOREIGN
(Center) Blue metal can, white cap. CMV $6.

1977 PYRENEES COLOGNIA — SPAIN
(Right) 150 ml. clear glass, blue cap. CMV $7. MB.

(Left to Right)

1976 NEW WORLD AFTER SHAVE — MEXICO
After shave with light blue cap and cologne in light blue cap. Both clear glass. CMV $5. each.

1977 NEW WORLD SPRAY TALC — AUSTRALIA
Blue metal can. CMV $3.50.

1977 NEW WORLD SHOWER SOAP — AUSTRALIA
Blue bar on blue rope. CMV $6.

1977 NEW WORLD AFTER SHAVE — AUSTRALIA
175 ml clear glass, silver cap. CMV $8.

1976 SPICY — FOREIGN
Talc - Canada, 2.75 oz. metal can. CMV $1. Spray Deodorant - Europe, 81 cc, white plastic bottle, brown cap, CMV $2. Savon Sur Corde Soap-On-A-Rope - Canada, tan soap, white rope, CMV $5.

FOREIGN AVONS

1970's CARTE BLANCHE — CANADA
6 oz. After Shave, silver cap, clear glass. CMV $6. 5 oz. Soap-On-A-Rope, CMV $4. 2 oz. Gentlemen's Selection, silver cap, clear glass. CMV $4.

(Left to Right)
1977 HUD — FOREIGN
After Shave in 15 ml size. CMV $5. After Shave in 100 ml size. CMV $8. Talc, gray and white 100 g. size, CMV $4.

1980 AFTER SHAVES — EUROPE
All are 75 ml. size plastic bottles. Hud, grey with silver cap; Tai Winds, green with gold cap; Wild Country, brown with silver cap; Windjammer, blue with gold cap. CMV $3.50 each.

(Left to Right)
1976 MENS COLOGNE — EUROPE
60 ml. clear glass, indented sides. Black cap. CMV $4.
1975 TORERO AFTER SHAVE — EUROPE
120 cc clear glass, black cap. Pink label. CMV $6.
1978 BLEND 7 HAIR TONIC — JAPAN
150 ml clear glass, brown cap. CMV $9.
1978 BLEND 7 AFTER SHAVE — JAPAN
150 ml. clear glass, brown cap. CMV $9.
1976 BLEND GOLD — CANADA
Amber glass bottle with gold 7 painted on front. Brown cap. CMV $4.

(Left to Right)
1980 CLINT PRODUCTS — JAPAN
COLOGNE
120 ml. size. CMV $8. MB.
HAIR TONIC
150 ml. size. CMV $9. MB.
HAIR LIQUID
150 ml. size. CMV $9. MB.
AFTER SHAVE
120 ml. size. CMV $8. MB.
1980 CLINT PRODUCTS — MEXICO
TALC
100 g. size. CMV $3. MB.
DEODORANT
90 ml. size. CMV $2.50 MB.

(Left to Right)
1976 SQUEEZE SPRAY DEODORANT — EUROPE
81 ml. Torero, red plastic with black cap. CMV $4.
1978 SQUEEZE SPRAY DEODORANT — MEXICO
90 ml. Tai Winds, light green plastic with dark green cap. CMV $2.50.
1976 SQUEEZE SPRAY DEODORANT — EUROPE
90 ml. Wild Country, white plastic with brown cap. CMV $3.
1977 SQUEEZE SPRAY DEODORANT — MEXICO
90 ml. Wild Country, white plastic with brown cap. CMV $2.50.
1978 SQUEEZE SPRAY DEODORANT — MEXICO
80 ml. Spicy, white and borwn plastic with brown cap. CMV $2.50.
1973 SQUEEZE SPRAY DEODORANT — BRAZIL
105 ml. brown bottle with dark brown cap. CMV $10.

1978 LLAMA SPORT — MEXICO
TALCO
100 g. metal can. CMV $4.
LOCION JUVENILE
120 ml. size, clear glass orange cap. CMV $5.
DESODORANTE
90 ml. white plastic, orange cap. CMV $4.

1980 WINDJAMMER AFTER SHAVE — EUROPE
30 ml. clear glass with navy blue top. CMV $5. MB.
1980 CLINT AFTER SHAVE — MEXICO
1.5 ml. clear glass bottle with blue top and red writing. CMV $5. MB.
1980 EVEREST AFTER SHAVE — MEXICO
1.5 ml. clear glass with dark blue top. CMV $5. MB.

(Left to Right)
1970 COLOGNE — MEXICO
Green and white plastic bottle, silver soccer ball cap. CMV $8.
1970 DEODORANTE — MEXICO
Same as cologne above. CMV $8.
1976 LEATHER AFTER SHAVE — MEXICO
Clear glass, red label, black cap. CMV $6.
1975 AFTER SHAVE AND COLOGNE — MEXICO
After shave in black cap and cologne in gold cap. CMV $8. each.

1980 AFTER SHAVES — EUROPE
(Left to Right) All 50 ml. size in Tai Winds, Wild Country, and Nexus. CMV $5. each MB. Windjammer and Spicy on far right 100 ml. size are from Australia. CMV $5. each MB.

(Left to Right)

**1976 CAVALIER AFTER SHAVE —
MEXICO**
120 ml. clear glass black cap and pink
and black label. Also came in cologne.
CMV $6. each.
**1976 CAVALIER SQUEEZE
DEODORANT — MEXICO**
9 ml. pink and black plastic bottle.
CMV $3.
1978 OSLO — MEXICO, SPAIN
168 ml. clear glass, brown marbleized cap. Came in after shave or
cologne. CMV $6. each.
**1978 OSLO SQUEEZE
DEODORANTE — MEXICO**
90 ml. cream color and brown plastic
bottle. CMV $3.

**1975 COLOGNES FOR MEN —
FOREIGN**
60 cc bottles, flat on face side, gold
caps. Windjammer & Spicy fragrance.
CMV $3. each.

**1972 ORIGINAL AFTER SHAVE —
SPAIN**
118 cc. bottle, red cap, white label.
CMV $8. MB.
1973 OLOF COLOGNE — SPAIN
120 cc bottle with brown cap with
silver "O" on top. CMV $7. MB.

**1976 BLUE BLAZER TALC —
EUROPE**
(Left) 100 g. blue metal can, red cap.
CMV $5.
1965 BAY RUM TALC — CANADA
(Left Center) 2.6 oz. green metal can,
black cap. CMV $20.
1976 TAI WINDS TALC — EUROPE
(Right Center) 100 g. green metal
can, white cap. CMV $6.50.
1974 EXCALIBUR TALC — EUROPE
(Right) 100 g. black cardboard side,
plastic top and bottom. CMV $6.

1971 LOCION PARA — MEXICO
Green and red box holds 4 oz. bottle,
red cap, green and red label. Came in
After shave or cologne. CMV $5.
each MB.

**1975 AEROSOL DEODORANT —
EUROPE**
(Left two) 71 g. size metal cans in
Windjammer, blue; and Tai Winds in
green. CMV $4. each.
**1978 DEODORANT SQUEEZE
BOTTLE — MEXICO**
(Right four) Plastic bottle in Blend
7, Squeeze Spray Deodorant, Deso-
dorante Perfumado, and Desodorante
Pulveizador. CMV $2.50 each.

1970 DESODORANTE — FOREIGN
2 oz. clear glass bottle, white caps.
Red and black label. CMV $4. MB.

1973 AFTER SHAVE — SPAIN
60 cc. blue labels and silver caps.
Blue Blazer, Windjammer, Excalibur
and Wild Country. CMV $4. each MB.
**1973 AVON STEEL AFTER SHAVE —
EUROPE**
90 cc. blue glass bottle, silver cap.
CMV $5. in box.

**1977 TAI WINDS MINIATURE —
EUROPE**
15 ml. size green glass and cap. CMV
$5. MB.
**1976 ENDEAVOUR MINIATURE —
EUROPE**
15 ml. size clear glass, blue cap. CMV
$5. MB.
**1976 WILD COUNTRY MINIATURE —
EUROPE**
15 ml. size clear glass, brown cap.
CMV $5. MB.
**1976 WINDJAMMER MINIATURE —
EUROPE**
15 ml. size blue glass and cap. CMV
$5. MB.

**1972 AMBER AFTER SHAVE —
GERMANY, MEXICO**
50 ml. amber bottle came in Imperator, light blue label; Windjammer,
dark blue label and Oland, tan label.
Spicy is brown label, Blue Blazer in
blue, Wild Country in black label,
Deep Woods, orange label; Windjammer in light blue lable with black
cap. All other caps are silver. CMV
$7.50 each MB.

1973 HAIR TONIC — EUROPE
180 ml. bottle with oil, orange label;
without oil, green label. Both black
caps. CMV $6. each MB.

TALC'S FROM MEXICO

1975 WINDJAMMER
CMV $8.

1975 CARRIAGE TALC
Green, CMV $6.

1977 BLEND 7,
Spicy, Blue Blazer, Deep Woods, Cavalier, New World, Tai Winds, Oslo, Wild Country. CMV $4. each.

1978 TALCS — CANADA
Two on top left are Christmas issues in Foligere (red) and Hawaiian White Ginger. CMV $3. each. Regular issues are Sonnet, Unspoken, Come Summer, Foligere (green), Sweet Honesty, Flower Talk, Apple Blossom, Topaze, Roses Roses, Imperial Garden, Emprise. 5 mens talcs are 2.75 oz. with cardboard sides, paper labels, plastic tops. CMV $2. each.

PERFUMED TALCS — EUROPE
Each is 100 g. size. 1974 issued metal can, plastic top. CMV $5. each. 1976 issued cardboard sides, plastic top and bottom. CMV $4. each. 1978 issued in all plastic with painted label sides. CMV $3. each. Came in Lily of The Valley, Honeysuckle, Her World, Nearness, Lavender, Lilac.

1978 PERFUMED TALCS — AUSTRALIA
100 g. white plastic with paper band labels. Came in Bird of Paradise, Honeysuckle, Sweet Honesty, Violet, Topaze, Elusive, Lemon Velvet, Unspoken, Bouquet of Roses, Occur!, Unforgettable, Charisma, Somewhere, Sweet Violets, Country Cupboard Peach, Country Cupboard Strawberry, Happy Jungle, Pretty Peach. CMV $3. each.

1976 & OLDER TALCS
100 g. cardboards as pictured in Sonnet. All came this way. CMV $4. each.

1978 PERFUMED TALCS — JAPAN
100 g. cardboard or plastic sides. Three on right are from Japan. Gardenia, Violet, Lilac. Came in all fragrances. CMV $6. each.

1978 TALCS FROM MEXICO
All metal cans in Timeless, childrens talc, with white or blue top; Moonwind, Charisma, and Sweet Honesty on top row. Bottom row left to right: 1974 Regence and Charisma in bright colored cans. CMV $6. each. 1978 issue in Jasmin, Raining Violets, Blue Lotus, Bird of Paradise, Dia Fresco, and Nearness. CMV $4. each on all 1978 talcs.

1977 PERFUMED TALCS — EUROPE
200 g. metal cans. Came in Roses Roses, Charisma, Timeless, Moonwind, Foligere, Lilac, Lily of The Valley, Honeysuckle, Unspoken, Promise of Heaven. CMV $5. each.

1978 PERFUMED TALCS — EUROPE
100 g. metal cans in Nearness, Timeless, Sweet Honesty, Roses Roses, Charisma, Moonwind, Promise of Heaven, Country Peach, Country Strawberry, Come Summer. CMV $3. each.

1975 PERFUME TALCS — EUROPE
100 g. metal can in Elegance (green) and Brocade in gold. CMV $4. each.

1978 TALC'S FOR MEN— AUSTRALIA, EUROPE
100 g. size plastic with painted or paper label. Older issue in cardboard sides. Came in Blend 7, 2 different; Spicy, 3 different; Tai Winds, 2 different; Endeavour; Everest; Wild Country, 3 different; Clint; Oland; Windjammer; Deep Woods; Blue Blazer. CMV $3. each.

1976 TALCS FROM CANADA
2.75 oz. metal cans, Mens came in Tai Winds, Deep Woods, Oland, Wild Country. Womens came in Lilac, Silk & Honey, Happy Jungle Talc, Roses Roses, Charisma. Here's My Heart Topaze, Unforgettable. CMV $3. each.

PERFUMED TALC — CANADA
In Brocade, Elusive, Charisma, Somewhere. CMV each $2.
PERFUMED SOAPS
In Brocade, Elusive, Charisma, Somewhere. CMV each $2.50.

FOREIGN NEARNESS PERFUMED TALC
Blue can from Canada. CMV $15.

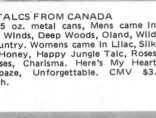

1967 PERFUMED TALC — CANADA
2.75 oz. each in Honeysuckle, Cotillion, Rapture, To A Wild Rose, Wishing. CMV $2.
1976 PERFUMED SOAP
Single wrapped bars in To A Wild Rose, Topaze, Here's My Heart. Also came in other fragrances. CMV $3. each.

1976 ANTISEPTIC POWDER — CANADA
2.75 oz. metal can, white cap. CMV $2.
1975 SPICY TALC FOR MEN
2.75 oz. metal can, black cap. CMV $2.
1975 BLUE LOTUS PERFUMED TALC
2.75 oz. metal can, lavender cap. CMV $2.

1973 MINERAL ISLE SOAP-ON-A-ROPE — ENGLAND
CMV $5. MB.
1973 MINERAL ISLE SAMPLES — ENGLAND
Box holds 5 sample packets of bath crystals. CMV $1. per packet.

1981-82 REDOUTE' ROSE COLLECTION — EUROPE
CARE DEEPLY HAND LOTION
White milk glass, painted rose label. Comes with pump dispenser. CMV $10. MB.
SOAP
Box of two decorator bars. CMV $10. MB.
TOILET WATER
Clear glass with painted rose label. CMV $8. MB.
BUBBLE BATH
White plastic bottle, green cap. CMV $5. MB.
POMANDER
White ceramic container. CMV $10. MB.

1976 MEXICO TALCS
All metal cans, plastic tops. Talco Desodorante, Bravo Talco, Desodorante Para, Caballeros. To A Wild Rose Talco Perfumado, Rapture Talco Perfumado, Occur! Talco Perfumado. CMV $4. each.

1973 PERFUMED BODY POWDERS — EUROPE
Somewhere, pink; Elegance, green; Rapture, blue; Occur!, black; Unforgettable, orange; Topaze, yellow. All are plastic bottles. CMV $7. each.

1975 BEAUTY DUST — CANADA
5 oz. white plastic, gold base band. CMV $5.
CREAM SACHET
.66 oz. white glass bottom with white plastic top and gold band. CMV $2.50.
COLOGNE MIST
3 oz. white plastic coated bottle, white plastic cap, gold band. CMV $7.

1975 ROSE GERANIO PERFUMED TALC — MEXICO
Pink metal shaker can. CMV $4.
CREAM SACHET
Rose frosted jar with gold cap. CMV $4. MB.

1978 ELEGANTE — MEXICO
In the Topaze containers used in U.S. Left to right is cream sachet. CMV $4. Perfumed Skin Softener. CMV $4.
1972 CREAM LOTION
CMV $8.
1978 COLOGNE MIST
CMV $8. All are yellow containers.

1972 PRETTY PEACH — EUROPE
Soap-On-A-Rope. CMV $10. MB. Talc - CMV $7.; Hand Cream - CMV $2.50; Cream Sachet - CMV $5. MB.

1972 PRETTY PEACH — EUROPE
Bubble Bath, Shampoo, Cologne. All CMV $9. MB.

1976 FOLIGERE — GERMANY
150 cc. green plastic bottle. CMV $4.
1976 FOLIGERE SOAP — GERMANY
Green box holds green soap. CMV $5. MB.

1979—80 SKIN SILK PRODUCTS — JAPAN
120 ml. clear glass, with pink caps. Comes in lotion or creme. CMV $8. each.
SAMPLE SIZE OF LOTION AND CREME
In frosted glass, pink caps. CMV $5. each.
1980 SPONGE, COSMETIC — JAPAN
Small yellow sponge in white vinyl case. CMV $3.50.

(Left to Right)
1974 DAISY TALCO PERFUMADO
White plastic bottle. CMV $6.
1974 PRETTY PEACH TALCO
Metal can, plastic top. CMV $6.
1978 PRETTY PEACH COLOGNE — MEXICO
57 ml clear glass peach cap. No leaf. CMV $5.
1978 PRETTY PEACH CREAM LOTION — MEXICO
118 g. peach plastic, peach cap, no leaf. CMV $4.
1974 CHIPPY TALCO
Metal can, plastic top. CMV $5.

1974 PETTI-PAT—GERMANY
Perfume Glace. CMV $10. MB. Lipstick. CMV $3. MB. Both are gold and black with pink flowers.

1976 GOLDEN NILE — EUROPE COLOGNE MIST
85 g. size. CMV $8.
PERFUMED SOAPS
3 bars. CMV $7.

1977 GOLDEN NILE — EUROPE
Cream sachet, gold cap. CMV $2. MB.
PERFUMED TALC
Gold can. CMV $3. MB.
1976 LAVENDER EAU DE COLOGNE — EUROPE
120 ml. size clear glass, black cap. CMV $5. MB.

WISHING EAU DE COLOGNE MIST — FOREIGN
3 oz. white plastic coated, gold four leaf clover on gold string in place of wishing bone. CMV $10.
WISHING CREAM SACHET — FOREIGN
White glass with gold four leaf clover on lid. CMV $6.

**1978 GENESIS PRODUCTS —
AUSTRALIA**
Same design as U.S. Timeless.
PERFUMETTE
9 ml. amber glass, gold cap. CMV $4.
COLOGNE SPRAY
Amber glass, gold cap. CMV $8.
PERFUMED POWDER MIST
200 g. metal can. CMV $5.
PERFUMED SOAPS
Box of three tan bars. CMV $7.
FOAMING BATH OIL
200 ml. plastic. CMV $5.
ULTRA CREAM PERFUME
19 g. amber glass, gold cap. CMV $5.

1978 DAISIES — MEXICO
CREAM LOTION
118 ml. size, turquoise plastic, white
cap. CMV $4.
COLOGNE
2 oz. clear glass, smaller than U.S.
size. CMV $4.
TALC
100 g. size, green metal can. CMV $4.
PERFUME GLACE
White with yellow center. CMV
$4.50.

1974 HANA GASA — CANADA
PERFUMED TALC
2.75 oz. yellow can and cap. CMV
$2.
1974 PERFUMED SOAP
Single wrapped bar. CMV $3.50
1974 GIFT NOTES
15 yellow sheets 5¾x 8'' with 18
seals wrapped in plastic. CMV $4.

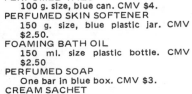

**1976 PROMISE OF HEAVEN —
EUROPE**
SOAP
Blue box of three bars. CMV $7.
PERFUMED TALC
200 g. size, blue can. CMV $6.
PERFUMED TALC
100 g. size, blue can. CMV $4.
PERFUMED SKIN SOFTENER
150 g. size, blue plastic jar. CMV
$2.50.
FOAMING BATH OIL
150 ml. size plastic bottle. CMV
$2.50
PERFUMED SOAP
One bar in blue box. CMV $3.
CREAM SACHET
19 g. size in blue glass. CMV $4.
COLOGNE MIST
85 g. size. CMV $8.

1978 TIMELESS — MEXICO
All are clear glass,gold caps. U.S.
issue is amber glass.
ULTRA PERFUME ROLLETTE
CMV $4.
ULTRA COLOGNE SPLASH
58 ml. size. CMV $6.
ULTRA COLOGNE SPRAY
57 ml. size. CMV $8.
ULTRA CREAM PERFUME
CMV $4.50.

**1972-75 CLASSIC COLLECTION —
CANADA**
7 oz. Perfumed Powder Mist, CMV
50c; Cream Sachet. CMV $2.50 MB;
Cologne Mist, CMV $4. MB; Beauty
Dust, CMV $7.50 MB; Foaming
Bath Oil, CMV $2. MB.; Perfumed
Talc, CMV 50c.

1980 REGENCE PRODUCTS — JAPAN
Elegant packaging, all have gold caps.
White plastic Avon tray. CMV $12.
Cleansing Cream, plastic; Toning
Freshener, glass; Skin Lotion, glass;
Milky Lotion, glass; Massage Cream,
glass; Peal Off Pack, plastic. All
products CMV $10. MB.

1979-80 CHIC PRODUCTS — EUROPE
Same as Candid in U.S. Foaming
Shower Gel, Perfumed Talc, Purse
Spray, two different colognes, Body
Satin, Luxury Foam Bath. All pro-
ducts. CMV $3.50 MB. Vanity mirror
CMV $6. MB.

**1979-80 CANDID PRODUCTS —
JAPAN**
Scarf, signed S. M. Kent. CMV $6.
Face Paper and Tissue Paper, vinyl
case, CMV $8. Pressed Powder Com-
pact, plastic, CMV $6.

1980 FIRST FLOWERS PRODUCTS — EUROPE

Green and white flower daisy design, on all products. 60 ml. Eau De Cologne, CMV $4. MB. Hair Brush, CMV $4. MB. Perfume Glace, white and yellow plastic, CMV $5. MB. Soap, three white daisy bars, CMV $6.50 MB. Perfumed Talc, CMV $3.50 MB. Hand Cream, CMV $2. MB.

1960 KAVON HERE'S MY HEART PERFUMED TALC — EUROPE

Kavon Cosmetics. Blue tin powder can. Early name used by Avon Cosmetics in Europe. RARE! Kavon name was used only a short time. CMV $20.

1960 KAVON PERSIAN WOOD EAU DE COLOGNE — EUROPE

4 oz. glass bottle, gold cap. RARE! Kavon name used only a short time, then changed to Avon Cosmetics. CMV $20.

1974 MOONWIND — CANADA
HAND & BODY CREAM LOTION
8 oz. blue plastic bottle, blue cap. CMV $4.

PERFUMED TALC
2.75 oz. blue metal can, blue cap. CMV $2.

MOONWIND TRAY
Blue plastic with silver band and center design. CMV $12.50 MB.

1980 DELICATE DAISIES SET — AUSTRALIA

Green and white daisy flower design. Box holds 50 ml. clear glass cologne with painted on daisies, and 100 g. perfumed talc. CMV $10. MB.

1980 DAISIES PERFUME ROLLETTE — MEXICO

8.5 g. clear glass with green and white daisy design, plastic top. CMV $3.50 MB.

1980 DAISIES HAND CREAM — MEXICO

43 g. green and white plastic daisy design tube. CMV $2. MB.

1980 STYLE PRODUCTS — EUROPE

Left to right. Same as U.S. Tempo.

COLOGNE
30 ml. size. CMV $6.50 MB.

PERFUMED TALC
100 g. CMV $3. MB.

SOLID PERFUME
5.5 g. CMV $4.50 MB.

ROLLETTE
10 ml. CMV $4. MB.

1973 BROCADE — ENGLAND
BEAUTY DUST
CMV $10.

DEMI STICK
CMV $3.

CREAM SACHET
CMV $5.

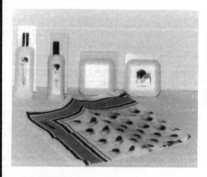

1980 SUNSEEKER PRODUCTS — JAPAN

Sunseeker scarf, orange, grey and white. CMV $8. Make-up Creme, white plastic; Foundation, blue plastic; Color Control Cake, white pearl compact. All products CMV $6. MB.

1974 BIRD OF PARADISE TRAY — CANADA

Turquoise plastic with gold band. CMV $5.

PERFUMED SOAP
3 oz. bar. CMV $2.

PERFUMED TALC
2.75 oz. turquoise metal can and blue cap. CMV $2.

GIFT NOTES
15 sheets 5¾ x "8" with 18 seals. Sealed in plastic, CMV $4.

(Left to Right)

1976 DEVOTEE CREAM LOTION — MEXICO
59 g. clear glass, gold cap. CMV $5.

1977 COLOGNE — JAPAN
59 ml. clear glass, gold pointed cap. CMV $8.

1978 ARISTECRATICO COLOGNE — MEXICO
43 ml. clear glass, clear plastic cap. CMV $5.

1976 LOCION CAPILAR — MEXICO
120 ml. clear glass, red cap and label. CMV $8.

1978 COLOGNE SPRAY — JAPAN
70 ml. clear glass, red painted band around gold cap. CMV $10.

1978 COLOGNE SPRAY — EUROPE
57 g. clear glass, gold cap. CMV $6.

1978 PERFUME CONCENTRATE SPRAY — JAPAN
12 ml. black and gold metal container. CMV $8.

1976 LEMON VELVET — CANADA
2.75 oz. Perfumed Talc, yellow metal can, green cap. CMV $2.
1976 HAND CREAM — CANADA
3 oz. yellow tube, green cap. CMV $2.
1975 PERFUMED TALC — AUSTRALIA
3½ oz. yellow and green cardboard container with plastic shaker top. CMV $4.

1972 BLUE PETAL — ENGLAND
Perfumed Talc in paper container. CMV $4. MB.
CREAM SACHET
Lavender frosted glass and lid. CMV $5. MB.

1969 COLOGNE — FOREIGN
(Left) Ribbed glass bottles with 4A insignia on plastic cap. CMV $15.
1970 LOCION CREAM — MEXICO
(Center) Embossed rose bottle, gold cap. CMV $7.
1972 COLOGNE SPRAY — MEXICO
(Right) Clear glass, silver cap with 4A on top. CMV $6.

1973 YOUNG ROMANTICS — EUROPE
180 cc. white plastic bottle, lavender cap. Holds bath oil. CMV $10.; 118 cc. clear glass bottle, lavender cap, holds cologne. CMV $10.

1974 FIELD FLOWERS TRAY — CANADA
Light green plastic tray with gold edge and Field Flowers decal in center. CMV $5.
PERFUMED TALC
2.75 oz. metal can with green cap. CMV $2.
GIFT NOTES
15 sheets 5¾ x "8" with 18 seals, sealed in plastic. CMV $4.

1978 COLOGNES — MEXICO
Each is 58 ml. size. Charisma, red paint over clear glass; Moonwind in cobalt blue, CMV $6.50 each. All rest are clear glass in Somewhere, Raining Violets, Sweet Honesty, CMV $5. each. To A Wild Rose and Sonnet, CMV $6.50 each.
1978 TO A WILD ROSE LOCION CREAM — MEXICO
White glass, pink cap. CMV $5.

1976 COLOGNES — FOREIGN
½ oz. each. Left to right: black cap, white cap and silver cap. Two on left are from Canada and right is Europe. CMV $3. Canada, $3. Europe.

1980 SKIN FRESHENER — JAPAN
180 ml. clear glass with gold top. CMV $10. MB.
1980 SKIN FRESHENER — JAPAN
180 ml. clear glass with silver top. CMV $10. MB.
1980 SKIN SILK — JAPAN
180 ml. clear glass with gold top. CMV $12. MB.
1980 SUMMER LOTION — JAPAN
180 ml. clear glass with clear plastic top. CMV $10. MB.
1980 VANITY JAR — JAPAN
140 g. clear glass with gold cap. CMV $10. MB. Also issued in Europe. Same jar with silver cap. CMV $10. MB.

1977 FLOWER TALK — CANADA
All are white with flower design. Cream Sachet, CMV $1.50; Hand Cream, CMV $2.; Perfumed Talc, CMV $2.; Soap-On-A-Rope, pink soap and white rope. CMV $5. MB.

1973 LOTION LUXURY — ENGLAND
Clear glass bottle, gold cap. CMV $7. MB.
1973 BUD VASE EAU DE COLOGNE— ENGLAND
Clear glass bottle and cap. Holds 150 ml. cologne. CMV $9. MB.

COLOGNES — FOREIGN
½ oz. clear glass bottles, Canadian on left, English center two (gold and black caps) Canadian on right. CMV $5. each MB.

1973 EAU DE PARFUME — ENGLAND
15 ml. glass bottle, gold flat cap as shown. Reissued in 1976 with gold flat top cap. CMV $8. each MB.

1973 EAU DE DOLOGNE — ENGLAND
15 ml size, clear glass, gold cap. CMV $6. MB.

HAWAIIAN WHITE GINGER — MEXICO
CMV $7.
ELEGANTE COLOGNE — MEXICO
CMV $6.

1976 COOL EAU D'AVON ROLL ON — EUROPE
Octaganal shaped blue glass bottle with silver 4A design cap. CMV $4. MB.
1976 COOL EAU D'AVON — EUROPE
60 cc. blue glass bottle with silver 4A design cap. CMV $4. MB.
1977 COOL EAU DE COLOGNE SPRAY — EUROPE
57 g. light blue glass bottle, blue paper neck label. Clear and silver plastic cap. CMV $5.
1975 EAU DE COOL — CANADA
6 oz. CMV $3. MB.

(Left to Right)
1978 COLOGNES — MEXICO
Roses Roses, 58 ml. frosted glass, tall gold cap. CMV $6.50. Roses Roses, 58 ml. clear glass, tall off white cap. CMV $5.50. All rest are 57 or 58 ml. clear glass in Rapture, Here's My Heart. CMV $6.50 or Bird of Paradise, Unforgettable, CMV $5. each.

(Left to Right)
1977 PURSE PERFUME SPRAY — EUROPE
Blue plastic coated over clear glass, gold cap and flower paper front decal. CMV $6.
1977 PERFUME ON ROLLETTE — EUROPE
10 ml. white milk glass, painted flower design, gold cap. CMV $6.
1974 PATTERNS PERFUME ON ROLLETTE — EUROPE
White milk glass, black cap and painted design. Gold band around neck. CMV $5.
1974 PATTERNS CREAM SACHET — EUROPE
White milk glass, black cap and painted design. CMV $5.
1978 PERFUME ROLLETTE — MEXICO
Charisma is red paint over clear glass and Moonwind is cobalt blue glass. CMV $4.50 each.

1974 COLOGNE — CANADA
2 oz. clear glass bottle with light gold cap. Came in Hawaiian White Ginger, Blue Lotus, Honeysuckle, Lilac. CMV $4. MB.

1978 ROCKER COLOGNE — EUROPE
(Left) 15 ml. gold cap, red label. CMV $5.
1978 PARFUME CONCENTRE — EUROPE
(Center Left) 15 ml. clear glass, gold cap. CMV $8.
1978 EAU DE PARFUME — EUROPE
(Center) 15 ml. clear glass, gold cap. Embossed flowers around center. CMV $6.
1977 ROSETTE COLOGNE — CANADA
(Center Right) ½ oz. white cap, clear glass. Different flowers than Europe bottle on left side. CMV $4.
1975 BUTTER CHURN COLOGNE — CANADA
(Right) 1½ oz. clear glass, gold cap. CMV $6.

PICTURESQUE COLOGNE — GERMAN
(Left) 20 cc. swirl glass bottle with gold cap. CMV $10. MB.
DIAMOND COLOGNE — GERMAN
(Center Left) 25cc. ribbed glass bottle, gold cap. CMV $10. MB.
BEAUTEMP COLOGNE — GERMAN
(Center Right) 15 ml bottle with gold cap. CMV $5. MB.
1972 EUROPEAN BELL — GERMAN
(Right) 15 ml bottle, tall gold cap. CMV $10. MB.

(Left to Right)

1975 NILE BLUE BATH URN — EUROPE
180 ml deep cobalt blue glass. Holds perfumed bath oil. CMV $12.

1977 AGUA DE COLONIA (After Bath Freshener) — SPAIN
Large 470 ml. frosted glass, white painted on label and design. White cap. CMV $8.

1978 SPRING PROMISE PRODUCTS — MEXICO
Talc in pink metal can, CMV $4. Cologne, 58 ml., pink cap, CMV $5. Perfume Rollette, pink cap, CMV $3.

1978 COLOGNE MIST — CANADA
2 oz. each, all have gold caps with 11 different color bands around cap. Moonwind came with silver and blue cap. 11 different fragrances. CMV $3.50 each.

(Left to Right)
1978 SPLASH COLOGNE
2 on left are Europe, 60 ml. clear glass and 2 different size gold caps. CMV $5. each; Center, 70 ml. from Japan, CMV $8.; 4th is Australia in 60 ml. size, CMV $4.; Right is Canada, black cap, 57 ml. size. CMV $2.50. Gold caps on all but Canada.

1974 FRAGRANCED SKIN SO SOFT — EUROPE
60 cc. blue and white front label, gold cap. CMV $5.

1977 IMPERIAL BOOT—MEXICO
54 ml. clear glass boot, gold cap. Side buttons are smaller than U.S. issue. Came in cologne. CMV $5.

1976 TOQUE DE AMOR CREAM LOTION — BRAZIL
10 cm. clear glass, white painted label and white beaded cap. Same as old Here's My Heart U.S. bottles. CMV $10.

1960's NOTION DE ESTRELAS COLOGNE — BRAZIL
Same as old U.S. Bright Night bottle. Clear gold speckeled cap different from U.S. issue. Spanish neck tag on gold string. CMV $15.

(Left to Right)

1978 COLOGNE — AUSTRALIA
15 ml. gold tall cap. CMV $4.

1976 TEARDROP COLOGNE — AUSTRALIA
15 ml. tall round gold cap. CMV $4.

1977 COLOGNE — JAPAN
15 ml short bottle, gold cap. CMV $8.

1977 EAU DE COLOGNE — EUROPE, JAPAN
30 ml. square glass bottle, flat top, gold round cap. CMV $6. for Europe, $8. for Japan. Europe label on bottom, Japan on back.

1977 CORONET COLOGNE — AUSTRALIA
30 ml. clear glass, round gold cap. CMV $6.

1975-78 PETITE COLOGNE — EUROPE
15 ml. clear glass, silver or gold cap. CMV $4.

(Left to Right)
1978 COLOGNE MIST
Five on left are from MExico in Here's My Heart, blue band; Sweet Honesty, light pink band; Rapture, dark blue; Somewhere dark pink; Unforgettable in orange. CMV $5. each.

1978 ELEGANCE SPRAY COLOGNE — EUROPE (far right)
80 ml. clear glass painted green, green and gold cap. CMV $7.

1973 BROCADE SPRAY COLOGNE — EUROPE
Sandy brown plastic coated base, gold brocade cap. CMV $8.

1978 PERFUME ROLLETTE — CANADA
9 ml. clear ribbed bottles. Each has different color cap. 12 different fragrances. CMV $2.50 each.

1977 COLOGNE MIST — FOREIGN
12 different pictured from Canada, Europe, and Australia. CMV $3. each from Canada, $5. each on rest.

1978 CREAM SACHET — CANADA
19 g. ribbed glass bottom. Different colored tops with gold bands. in 9 different fragrances. CMV $2.50 each.

(Left to Right)
1974 COLOGNES —BRAZIL
OCTAGANAL COLOGNE
Clear glass, gold cap, 55 ml. CMV $10.

CHARISMA COLOGNE
Red paint over clear glass. red and gold cap. 55 ml. CMV $5.

MOONWIND COLOGNE
Blue glass, silver cap. 55 ml. CMV $5.

COLD EAU D'AVON
Clear glass, silver cap. 55 ml. CMV $8.

ROSA SILVESTRE COLOGNE
White paint over clear glass, pink cap. 55 ml. CMV $7.

1977 PERFUME ROLLETTE'S — FOREIGN
19 different pictured from Europe, Mexico, Canada and Australia. All are glass. CMV $3.

1972 COLONIA IMPERIO —
MEXICO
Ribbed glass bottle, gold ribbed cap.
CMV $6. each.
KAVON TOPAZE CREAM BODY
LOTION — GERMAN
CMV $22.50

(Left to Right)
1976 THE CREAMERY — CANADA
6 oz. frosted glass, gold cap. Label in
French and English. CMV $4.
1978 FIJAPELO PARA NINOS (Hair
Cream) — MEXICO
177 ml. white plastic, green cap. Deer
on label. CMV $3.
1978 SHAMPOO — MEXICO
177 ml. white plastic, pink cap.
Rabbit on front. CMV $3.
1978 BABY ACEITE — MEXICO
170 ml. white plastic, blue cap. CMV
$3.
1978 BABY TALCO — MEXICO
230 g. white metal can, blue cap.
CMV $6.
1978 BABY SHAMPOO — MEXICO
177 g. white plastic, blue cap. CMV
$3.
1978 BABY UNGUENTO — MEXICO
58 g. white tube, blue cap. CMV $2.

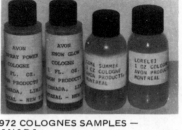

1972 COLOGNES SAMPLES —
CANADA
1 oz. plastic bottle of cologne test
samples, black caps, paper labels.
CMV $4. each.

1974 SKIN-SO-SOFT — CANADA
PERFUMED BATH OIL
2 oz. bottle, gold cap, bottom
label only. CMV $4.
BEAUTY DUST
5 oz. white plastic base with turquoise top. CMV $7.
PERFUMED SOAP SET
Box holds 3 white bars. CMV $6. MB.

1977 BUBBLE BATH SAMPLE —
CANADA
(Left) 40 ml. pink plastic bottle,
white cap. CMV $1.
1977 SKIN-SO-SOFT BATH OIL
SAMPLE — CANADA
(Center) 40 ml. clear plastic bottle.
Turquoise cap. CMV $1.
1973 HAPPY JUNGLE TALC —
CANADA
(Right) 2.75 oz. metal can, green and
orange, orange cap. CMV $2.

(Left to Right)
1977 TRAVEL LITE — CANADA
Beige plastic bottles, brown caps in
deodorant, after shave, and shampoo
shower soap. Labels in French and
English. CMV $2.
1972 GENTLEMEN'S SELECTION
COLOGNE — CANADA
1.76 oz. black caps. Also came in
after shave. CMV $5.
1977 SPECIAL PRESENTATION
COLOGNE FOR MEN — MEXICO
48 ml. clear glass, silver cap. CMV
$4.50
1977 CREAM SACHET — MEXICO
Frosted glass base, gold edge cap with
different color tops in Rosa Geranio,
Jasmin, Hawaiian White Ginger. CMV
$4. each.
1972 CHARISMA CREAM SACHET —
EUROPE
Red paint over clear glass, red and
gold cap. CMV $4.50.
1977 SONNET PERFUME
ROLLETTE — MEXICO
White dull paint over clear glass, gold
and white cap. CMV $5.

1978 DEMI STICKS — FOREIGN
(Left) Colored centers with white
caps. Each different from U.S. issues.
CMV $2.50 each.
1977 PERFECT BEAUTY SAMPLES —
EUROPE
(Right) Small beige color plastic bottle 2" high. Came in daytime moisturizer and cleansing lotion, skin
freshener. Used as samples only for
Avon Reps in Europe. CMV $5. each.

(Left to Right)
1977 MIRROR MIRROR —
AUSTRALIA
Bright plastic double mirror and base
came in orange, red, blue or lime
green plastic. CMV $5. each MB.
1977 MINI BRUSH
To match each mirror. CMV $2.
each MB.
1977 PURSE POMANDER — EUROPE
Blue plastic in blue box. Came with
white string. CMV $4. MB.
1975 OWL POMANDER — EUROPE
Blue plastic, white string. CMV $5.

1976 BUBBLE BATH — CANADA
8 oz. plastic, pink cap. CMV $2.
1976 PERFUMED BATH OILS —
EUROPE, AUSTRALIA
All are plastic with different color
caps. Some are 106 ml. and some 115
ml. size. Came in Violets, 115 ml;
Lily of The Valley, 106 ml; Lilac,
115 ml; Honeysuckle, 106 and 115
ml. size; Carnation 115 ml. CMV $3.
each.
1976 CARNATION FOAMING BATH
OIL — CANADA
8 oz. plastic, red letters and cap.
CMV $2.
1974 ROSA GERANIO BATH
FRESHENER — MEXICO
8 oz. clear glass bottle, pink cap. Also
came in Madreselva with yellow cap.
CMV $4.

(Left to Right)
**1978 BLUE BAY BUBBLE BATH —
EUROPE**
Blue plastic bottle, white caps in
200 ml. and 480 ml. size. CMV $3.
small and $4. large.
1978 SETTING LOTION — EUROPE
180 ml. plastic bottles in Firm Hold,
yellow bottle and Normal Hold, blue
bottle. CMV $3. each.
**1977 INVIGORATE BATH GEL —
AUSTRALIA**
Came in 200 ml blue and white
plastic bottle. CMV $3. and 100 g. blue
and white plastic tube. CMV $2.
**1978 RICH MOISTURE HAND
LOTION — EUROPE**
120 ml. blue green, white cap. CMV
$2.

**1977 BABY BRUSH & COMB SET —
CANADA**
Blue box holds small white plastic
comb and brush with Avon on both.
CMV $5.
**1977 NON TEAR SHAMPOO —
CANADA**
8 oz. clear plastic bottle, white
cap. CMV $2.
1977 BABY POWDER — CANADA
5 oz. white metal can, blue cap.
CMV $2.

**1972 SKIN SO SOFT BODY LOTION —
GERMANY**
180 cc. frosted glass bottle with pink
cap. CMV $5. MB.
1972 SKIN SILK DAY CREAM
66 cc. frosted glass jar with pink lid.
CMV $4. MB.

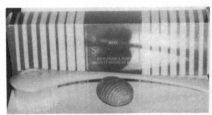

(Left to Right)
1978 AGUA DE COLONIA — MEXICO
300 and 180 ml. size plastic bottles,
blue green caps. CMV $5. big, $4.
small.
**1978 GLYCERINE HAND LOTION
WITH SILICONE — AUSTRALIA**
250 ml. green plastic bottle, white
cap. CMV $4.
**1978 GLYCERINE HAND CREAM —
AUSTRALIA**
115 g. green and white tube. CMV
$3.
**1978 SILICONE CREAM LOTION —
MEXICO**
120 g. green plastic bottle, white cap.
CMV $3.
**1976 SONNET EMOLLIENT
FRESHENER — CANADA**
6 oz. white plastic, gold cap. CMV $3.

**1975 MISS LOLLY POP TALCO
PERFUMADO — MEXICO**
Metal shaker top can. CMV $5.
1978 BABY LOCION — MEXICO
White plastic bottle with blue cap.
CMV $3.
1975 FLUFF PUFF SET — MEXICO
Box holds pearl white puff and can
of Talco Perfumado. CMV $12.

**1974 SILK & HONEY BATH BRUSH &
SOAP SET — CANADA**
Box holds long brush, has Avon on
Handle. 1 bar of soap. CMV $9.

1976 CANADIAN SAMPLE CASE
Dark blue plastic case holds 40
sample bottles. CMV $12.50.

**1978 EMPRESS DELUXE COMPACT —
FOREIGN**
White plastic flower design case.
CMV $6. MB.
1977 PERFUME GLACE
White plastic flower designed case.
CMV $5. MB.
1975 NOBLESSE COLOGNE
Box holds ½ oz. bottle same as U.S.
1966 ½ oz. cologne. Came in all
fragrances. CMV $5. MB.
**1975 CLEAN BOWLED SOAP ON A
ROPE — AUSTRALIA**
Red soap, white rope. CMV $12. MB.

(Left to Right)
1978 BABY SHAMPOO — AUSTRALIA
175 ml. blue plastic, white cap. CMV
$2.
1978 BABY OIL — AUSTRALIA
175 ml. white plastic, blue cap. CMV
$2.
**1975 HARD WORK POWDERED
HAND CLEANER — SPAIN**
250 g. blue & white plastic. CMV $3.
1974 BLUE LOTUS — BRAZIL
180 cm. clear glass, lavender cap.
CMV $3.
1970 WISHING TALC — BRAZIL
CMV $5.
1970 BALLAD TALC — BRAZIL
CMV $6.
**1970 ROSA SILVESTRE TALC —
BRAZIL**
CMV $5.

1972 RING FLING — EUROPE
Lipsticks & matching rings. Green, yellow, white, orange, pink, turquoise. CMV set $6. each MB.

1970's AVON SAMPLES — EUROPE
AVON FRAGRANCES — SPAIN
(Top Left) Pink & gold box, 8 small bottles, white caps. CMV $7.
AVON FRAGRANCES — GERMAN
(Top Right) Blue & gold box holds 14 small bottles, white caps. CMV $7.
AVON FOR MEN — GERMAN
(Bottom Left) Red & black box holds 8 small bottles, red caps. CMV $7.
MADE-UP DEMO — GERMAN
(Bottom Right) Pink box, clear plastic lid holds 11 white cap bottles. CMV $7.

CREAM BODY LOTION — EUROPE
(Left & Inside Left) 120 ml. plastic bottle, white cap. Came in all fragrances. CMV $3. MB.
1972 HAND LOTION — EUROPE
(Inside Right) 120 cc. pink plastic bottle & cap. CMV $2.50 in box.
1973 DEW KISS — EUROPE
(Right) 45 cc. clear glass bottle, pink neck tag & cap. CMV $5. in box.

1969 SKIN-SO-SOFT — FOREIGN
CMV $7.

(Left to Right)
1973 HONEYSUCKLE BODY POWDER — EUROPE
Yellow plastic, orange cap. CMV $7.
1973 HAWAIIAN WHITE GINGER BODY POWDER — EUROPE
Turquoise plastic, white cap. CMV $7.
1973 TOPAZE BATH OIL — EUROPE
Yellow plastic and cap. CMV $7.
1973 WISHING CREAM BODY LOTION — EUROPE
4.1 oz. white plastic, gold string and wishbone. CMV $7.
1973 WISHING SPRAY EAU DE COLOGNE — EUROPE
white plastic coated bottle. Came with four leaf clover around neck. CMV $10.
1978 CREAM LOTION — MEXICO
75 g. pink plastic bottle, white cap. CMV $3.
1978 HAND CREAM — MEXICO
Light orange and white tube. CMV $2.

1980 SAMPLES — JAPAN
COLOGNE SAMPLES
Package of five. CMV $5.
LIQUID MAKE-UP
Package of seven. CMV $8.
ACCOLADE
Night cream. CMV $5. MB.
NIGHT CREAM
Box of five packets. CMV $5.

1978 SKIN-SO-SOFT — FOREIGN
SMOOTHING CREAM
CMV $4.
SATIN TALC
2.75 oz. can. CMV $3.
SOAP DISH & SOAP
Turquoise soap dish and bar of soap. CMV $6. mint.

1977 SKIN-SO-SOFT — EUROPE
120 cc. plastic bottle, turquoise cap holds bath oil. CMV $2. Turquoise and white metal can holds Satin Talc. CMV $5. MB.

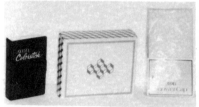

1979 COLORSTICK CASE — JAPAN
Brown vinyl. CMV $5.
1979 SKIN SILK PADS — JAPAN
Box of cotton pads. CMV $4.
1979 SHOWER CAP — JAPAN
Pink plastic shower cap with Avon printed on it. CMV $4.

1973 VITA MOIST HAND COSMETIC— ENGLAND
100 cc. white and green plastic bottle, gold cap with Avon on lid. CMV $5.

1979 BUBBLE BATH, TRIAL SIZE — CANADA
40 ml. pink plastic, white cap. CMV $1. full.
1979 SKIN-SO-SOFT TRIAL SIZE — CANADA
40 ml. clear plastic, turquoise cap. CMV $1. full.

1980 LIPSLICKER, EYESLICKER COMPACTS — EUROPE
Came in blue or pink plastic. CMV $6. MB.

1980 FASHION MAKE-UP GROUP — JAPAN
White plastic compacts in Creamy Cake or Creamy color. CMV $6. MB.

(Left to Right)

1977 HAIR CREME — MEXICO
57 g. size, red plastic. CMV $4.

1977 HAIR LOTION — MEXICO
Clear glass, CMV $5.

1980 CREME SILICONE LOTION — MEXICO
120 g. size green plastic. CMV $3.50.

1980 SWEET HONESTY COLOGNE — MEXICO
57 ml. size clear glass, pink cap. CMV $6.

1980 SPRING PROMISE COLOGNE — MEXICO
58 ml. size clear glass with lavender cap. CMV $6.50

1980 COLOGNE SPRAY — EUROPE
27 g. clear glass, gold cap, different color neckbands for different fragrances. CMV $7.

1980 COOL EAU DE AVON — EUROPE
50 ml. size blue glass, silver cap. CMV $7.

1980 COLOGNE SPRAY — JAPAN
70 ml. clear glass, gold cap, different color neckbands for different fragrances. CMV $9.

1980 PERFUME ROLLETTE — JAPAN
10 ml. size clear glass, gold cap. Different color neckband for each fragrance. CMV $5.

1978 VANITY JARS — JAPAN
Clear glass bottom, one has yellow cap, and one has white cap. One is 140 g. and 130 g. size. CMV $12. each.

1978 CALAMINE LOTION — JAPAN
120 ml. size frosted glass, white cap. CMV $7.

1980 SAMPLES — JAPAN
TUBE SAMPLES
CMV $2. each.

AFTER SHAVE SAMPLES
CMV $5. each.
CREAM SAMPLES
Assorted. CMV $4. each.

1975 EMERALD ELEGANCE — CANADA
Box holds 6 oz. green glass jar and lid with Mineral Springs bath crystals. CMV $5. MB.

1979-80 CARE DEEPLY SET — JAPAN
Green box holds 2 white tubes hand cream. CMV $7. MB.

1979-80 BEAUTY DUST — JAPAN
Brown turtle shell, plastic with gold trim. CMV $22. MB.

1979-80 PURSE SPRAY COLOGNE — JAPAN
12 ml. gold container. CMV $10. MB.

1979-80 CHIC ULTRA PURSE SPRAY — JAPAN
12 ml. black and gold case. CMV $10. MB.

1979-80 MAKE-UP SPONGE — JAPAN
Beige top, burgundy plastic base. CMV $15. MB.

1978 SPRING PROMISE PRODUCTS — CANADA
All are pink and white labels are in French and English.
FRAGRANCE SAMPLE
10 in a box. CMV $1. box.
PERFUMED POWDER MIST
CMV $3.50
PERFUMED SKIN SOFTENER
Plastic CMV $3.50
SHADOW COLLECTION COMPACT
CMV $6.
CREAM SACHET
CMV $2.50
PERFUME ROLLETTE
CMV $3.

(Left to Right - all from Japan)

1978 DEEP CLEAN
177 ml. plastic bottle in cleansing lotion in pink, wash off cleanser for oily skin beige, for normal skin blue and white. CMV $5.

1978 HAIR TONIC FOR WOMEN
180 ml. green plastic bottle. CMV $5.

1978 RINSE
300 ml. pink plastic for dry hair and green for normal hair. CMV $5. each.

1978 SKIN FRESHENER
118 ml. clear glass, blue cap on for normal skin and pink cap on for dry skin. CMV $5. each.

1978 ASTRINGENT FRESHENER FOR OILY SKIN
118 ml. clear glass, peach cap. CMV $5.

1978 SKIN SILK DAY CREAM —
AUSTRALIA
175 g. pink plastic jars and lid. CMV
$3. In 2¼ oz. frosted glass jar, pink
lid, CMV $4.
1978 SKIN SILK MILD SKIN
FRESHENER — AUSTRALIA
175 ml. pink frosted plastic bottle
and cap. CMV $4.50.
1978 SKIN CARE PRODUCTS —
JAPAN
Three different products in 120 ml.
Two are clear glass and one frosted.
Pink caps. CMV $8. each.
1978 SKIN SILK DAY CREAM —
JAPAN
64 g. frosted glass jar, pink cap. CMV
$8.
1977 SKIN BEAUTY DAY CREAM —
CANADA
60 ml. pink plastic jar and lid. CMV
$2. Also in 2.25 oz. frosted glass
jar, pink lid with label on lid. CMV
$3.
1977 HORMONE CREAM — CANADA
60 ml. white plastic jar and lid. Label
on lid. CMV $2.
1976 STRAWBERRY COOLER —
SPAIN
1972 SKIN BEAUTY DAY CREAM —
EUROPE
Frosted glass jar, pink cap with no
writing on lid. CMV $4.

1982 SWISS EMBROIDERY
HANDKERCHIEF & SACHET PILLOW
SET — EUROPE
CMV $8. MB.

1970 AVON DICE GAME — EUROPE
2 page paper game given at Christmas, 1970 with purchase. CMV $5.

1971 COLOR BOOK, AVON —
EUROPE
Red cover. Given with purchase at
Christmas, 1971. CMV $5.

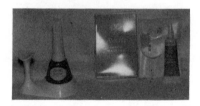

1975 NAIL POLISH & STAND —
GERMANY, MEXICO
White plastic stand holds nail polish.
Gold box issued in Australia in white,
pink or blue plastic base. CMV $5.
each.
CREAM MASCARA — SPAIN
Pink box holds small pink tube and
brush in white plastic case. CMV $4.
MB.

1974 AVON CARD GAME — EUROPE
Envelope holds two fold out sheets.
Punch out card games. Given at
Christmas with purchase. CMV $5.

1976 COLOR BOOKS — CANADA
Issued in 4th quarter 1976 in Canada.
One printed in English and one in
French. Given free to customers.
CMV $2.50 each.

1977 STATIONARY PERFUMED —
AUSTRALIA
Folders on boxes came with sachet,
envelopes and writing paper. Choice
of Unspoken (CMV $6. MB), Petal of
Roses, Petal of Violets and Whispers
of Lavender. CMV $5. each.

SEE 1984 SUPPLEMENT IN BACK OF BOOK FOR
MORE FOREIGN AWARDS

AWARDS — FOREIGN

1982 SILVER CIRCLE
PRESENTATION DAY AWARD -
AUSTRALIA
Figurine given to Australian Reps for
meeting sales goals. CMV $60.

1978 ALBEE AWARD - ENGLAND
Blue & pink figurine of 1st CPC Avon
sales lady of 1886. Given to top 10
Reps in each district in England. Bottom says "Florence Albee created
exclusively for Avon 1886-1978
Made in England" CMV $400 MB.

1979 FOUR SEASONS AWARD DOLLS - CANADA
Four ceramic dolls of each season in white, blue & beige. Won by Reps. for sales achievement. Made only for Avon but does not say Avon on bottom. "Rex Made in Spain" on bottom. Plain cardboard box. CMV $75. set of 4.

1976 PEWTER GOBLETS AWARDS - ENGLAND
Silver pewter goblets came in 3 sizes & were given to Reps for reaching sales goals in 3 steps. Small CMV $27.50 MB; middle CMV $42.50 MB; large CMV $62.50 MB. Each came in blue & silver box. 4A design on side of each goblet. They are about 3-4-5 inches in height.

1978 PRESIDENT'S CLUB KEY CHAIN - CANADA
(Left) Clear plastic on gold ring. 4A design. Given to each President's Club Rep. CMV $10.
1976 MANAGER'S 90th ANNIVERSARY PIN - CANADA
(Right) Sterling silver with 90th on front. Given to Avon managers. CMV $25.

1982 TEDDY BEAR CANDLE AWARD - CANADA
(Left) Tan & red bear with white candle & "We're Going All Out To Win" flag on candle. Given to each Team Leader. CMV $25. mint.
1981 TEDDY BEAR CLOCK AWARD - CANADA
(Right) Smoke lucite battery operated clock. Given to Team Leaders at August jamboree. CMV $45.

1976 ROSE STEMWARE - CANADA
Given to Reps for meeting sales goals. Each has Avon rose in design. Set consists of: Step 1, 4-5 oz. wine glasses, CMV $15. set; Step 2, 4-6 oz. long stem parfait glasses with parfait spoons (spoons say stainless Korea on back), CMV $25. set; President's Club, Step 2, 4-20 oz. long stem goblets, CMV $35. set. CMV complete set $75.

1959-61 KVON I.D. PIN - GERMAN
(Left) Used 3 years only & name was changed to Avon. Gold & black with 5 pearls. Very rare. CMV $75.
SILVER DOOR KNOCKER PIN - EUROPE
Silver Door Knocker pin with black center. 4A design. Came on turquoise Avon card. CMV $20. on card.

1979 TEDDY BEAR TEAM LEADER - CANADA
Stuffed teddy bear with French & English Avon tag. Given to Canada Team Leaders. CMV $35.

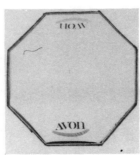

1979 SMILE UMBRELLA, TEAM LEADER - CANADA
White nylon umbrella, red plastic handle. Avon in red. Given to Team Leaders in Canada. CMV $30. mint.

1980 TEDDY BEAR AWARD FOREIGN
(Left) French Canadian red shirt. CMV $40.
(Right) Australian stuffed teddy bear award in blue shirt. CMV $50.

1972 - 4A OLYMPIC I.D. PIN - GERMANY
Gold color tin stick pin given to German Avon Reps during Olympics in 1972. CMV $25. mint.

1978 DIAMOND STICK PIN - CANADA
Gold pin with .07 point diamond given to Reps for selling $5,000 in Avon in 6 months. Came in brown velvet box. CMV $75. MB.

1970's AWARD PINS — CANADA
(Left) Moonwind pin, Sterling silver. CMV $20.
(Center) 1977 A Key Pin, goldtone key pin. CMV $10.
(Right) 1978 Candid Pin, brass. CMV $10. Each of these pins were given to Avon Reps in Canada.

1977 CHARM BRACELET AWARD - GERMANY
Sterling silver bracelet with possible 8 charms awarded to top selling Reps in Germany. CMV not established.

1977 UNSPOKEN AWARD JEWELRY - AUSTRALIA
Sterling silver with blue synthetic aquamarine stones. Earrings, ring & necklace. Each came in blue Avon boxes. CMV $75. set MB.

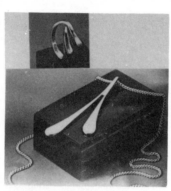

1977 RING AWARD - GERMANY
(Top) Sterling silver ring given to top selling reps in Germany. CMV not established.

1977 NECKLACE WISHBONE AWARD - GERMANY
(Bottom) Sterling silver wishbone necklace given to top selling Reps in Germany. CMV not established.

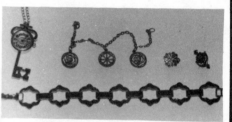

AWARDS - GERMANY
1978 BRACELET
Goldtone marked Avon. Red & black enamel. For high sales. CMV $16.
1979 WATCH KEY AWARD
Goldtone watch & chain. Given to Reps for getting new Reps. Avon on back of case. CMV $55.
1979 DOOR KNOCKER
Goldtone, small 4A design in center. CMV $10.
1978 - 4A PIN
Silvertone metal. 4A pin given to Reps. CMV $16.50.
1978 CHARM BRACELET
Gold chain & 3 charms with pearl, sapphire & diamond in center. Given for top sales. CMV not established.

1979 GEMEM'S AWARDS - AUSTRALIA
Necklace with amber color stone. Goldtone. Avon on back. Given to Reps. CMV $20. MB. Ring - goldtone, amber color stone. Came in tan felt box. CMV $25. MB.

1978 ARIANE NECKLACE PENDANT - CANADA
Given to all Reps in Canada. Dated 1978. CMV $8.

1980 HEART LOCKET MANAGER'S AWARD - CANADA
(Left) Goldtone locket with tiny diamond chip. Backside inscribed "You're the Heart of Avon". Given to managers only. CMV $35. MB.

1980 AVON PIN MANAGERS - CANADA
(Right) Goldtone Avon pin with red enamel center of heart shaped O. Given to managers only. CMV $25. MB.

1978 CUSTOMER COUNT DOOR KNOCKER PIN AWARDS - CANADA
Given to Reps for calling on customers. Door Knocker design. Pins came with 50, 75 & 100 on pins. 3 different. CMV 50, $15.; 75, $20.; 100, $25.

1978 DIAMOND "A" PENDANT NECKLACE - CANADA
10K gold "A" pin with small diamond. Given to 10 top Reps in each division. Came in Keyes brown & gold box. CMV $75. MB.

1972 BIRD OF PARADISE AWARD PIN - CANADA
Gift to Representatives for meeting sales goal of Bird of Paradise products. CMV $20. MB.

1972 - 4A PIN - EUROPE
Sterling silver pin with blue stone in center. Given to Avon Reps in Europe. CMV $15. pin only - $25. MB.

1977 A KEY PIN - CANADA
Small gold in color pin given to Reps for customer list. Blue box. CMV $10. MB.

1975 CHARM BRACELET AWARD - ENGLAND
Sterling silver bracelet holds 6 silver charms given to Reps for top sales. CMV $150.

1977 NO. 1 PENDANT AWARD - CANADA
Gold No. 1 given to all Reps in the winning district of each division for top sales in their division. CMV $12. MB.

1969 PRESIDENT'S CAMPAIGN TEAM AWARD - CANADA
Sterling silver pendant on 18" silver chain. Back side says "President 1969" and front has 4A design. Given to all Reps on winning team for top sales. CMV $25 MB.

1969 PRESIDENT'S CAMPAIGN NATIONAL WINNER LOCKET AWARD - CANADA
Sterling silver locket 1" x ¾" size on 18" silver chain. Given to winning team in each division for top sales. 4A design on front. CMV $40 MB.

1973 - 4A OLYMPIC PIN - EUROPE
Goldtone stick pin. Given to Reps in Europe during 1973 Olympic Games. CMV $40.

1977 EMPRISE PENDANT AWARD - CANADA
10K gold & black "e" pendant given to Rep selling most Emprise products in her district. CMV $40. MB.

1975 TIMELESS AWARDS - CANADA
(Left) Earrings. Gold color, brown center stone. Avon on back. Given to Reps for top sales. CMV $12. MB.
TIMELESS NECKLACE
(Right) Same as earrings. On a long chain. CMV $12. MB.

1969 PRESIDENT'S CAMPAIGN AWARD - CANADA
Sterling silver earrings, brooch and bracelet given to Reps for reaching higher sales goals. 4A design on each piece. CMV earrings $25 MB Brooch, $25 MB, bracelet, $35 MB.

1981 CANDID NECKLACE AWARD - SPAIN
Goldtone and orange metal. Came in tan felt Avon bag. Given to Avon Reps in Spain. CMV $70.

1979 MANAGER COIN PURSE KEY CHAIN AWARD - FOREIGN
Brass cage coin purse given to Avon managers in Hong Kong. Avon on front of cage. Rare. CMV $50.

1979 CHRISTMAS PLATE TEAM LEADER GIFT - CANADA
Blue green pottery plate given to Team Leaders at Christmas 1979. Came with card shown from Avon. CMV $75.

1967 PRESIDENT'S AWARD PLATE - CANADA
Metal plate, 13¼ inches. CMV $75.

1970 ANNIVERSARY AWARD PLATE - CANADA
Made of aluminum, given to Reps in C-9-1970. CMV $27.50.

1973 AWARD BRACELET - FOREIGN
(Left) Gold chain, first charm with pearl, second charm rose with ruby set. Charms are size of U.S. dime. Awarded for sales goals. CMV $35. each.
1972 MANAGER'S KEY CHAIN - GERMANY
(Right) Made of Sterling silver. Has 4A design on front side. Only 60 were given to Avon managers in Germany for year end conference. CMV $160.

1972 PRESIDENT'S CLUB PLATE - CANADA
Given to all President's Club members. CMV $25. MB.

1977 SILVER JUBILEE PLATE - ENGLAND
8-7/8" diameter silver plated plate given to 506 Avon Reps in England, for top sales in their zone in C7-77. Front of plate has the Royal Coat of Arms & Queen Elizabeth II. Silver Jubilee 1952-1977. On back side it has "A Limited Edition Exclusively Created for Avon Representatives". Silver plated plate by Pepper & Hope. Comes in beautiful blue satin lined box. RARE., CMV $150. MB.

1977 SILVER JUBILEE PLATE - ENGLAND

In celebrating the 25th anniversary of Queen Elizabeth. Given to Reps for selling 33 pounds (about $50. U.S.) of Avon products in C7-77. CMV $75. MB.

1978 SMILE ORDER BOOK COVER - CANADA

(Left) White plastic and French & English order book inside. CMV $3.

1977 CURRIER & IVES AWARD PLATE - CANADA

(Right) Given to Reps for sales. Back side is printed in French & English. CMV $9. MB.

1978 SPRING PROMISE DISH AWARDS - MEXICO

Won for top sales by Mexican Avon reps. Came in 4 steps.
Step 1: gravy boat, salt & pepper shaker, toothpick holder. CMV $15.
Step 2: creamer & sugar holder. CMV $15.
Step 3: plate & butterdish. CMV $20.
Step 4: bowl, coffee pot & bud vase. CMV $25.
Made of ceramic by Munoz. All items complete set, CMV $100.

1976 PONTESA DISHES AWARD - SPAIN

Set of 4 bowls about 5'' across, made by Pontesa & given to Reps in Spain for top sales. Dark pink in color. CMV $15. MB. Also came set of 5 bowls & large matching serving bowl for meeting higher sales goals. CMV $30. set MB. Gold.

1979 CURRIER & IVES AWARDS - EUROPE

Collection made in Bavaria for Avon.
Step 1: Sweets plate, bowl, sugar bowl, cream jug set, cup & saucer. Choice of 1 item for 100 points on above. CMV $30. each piece.
Step 2: Choice of 1 for 200 points. Milk jug, biscuit plate or butterdish. CMV $35. each item.
Step 3: Choice of 1 for 400 points in sales. Cake stand, coffee pot & tea pot. CMV $40. each item.

BELL GIFT
(Bottom Left) Given to Reps at Christmas 1979. CMV $30. MB.

POSY VASE
(Bottom Right) Given to Reps for placing an order in C1 and C2-79. CMV $20.

1971 MOONWIND AWARDS - CANADA

Blue glass, silver overlay candy dish. Cream & sugar & tray. CMV $25. - jam set $30.

1976-77-78 GENI CHRISTMAS PLATES - CANADA

Each is 9'' size. Front of plates are same as Avon plates only back is marked Geni Products. CMV $25. MB each.

1974 PROMISE OF HEAVEN TEA SET AWARD - ENGLAND

21 piece fine English Bone China made only for Avon. Given to top Rep in each zone. CMV $160. complete set.

SILVER CIRCLE AWARDS - EUROPE
1979 COFFEE CUP - GERMANY

(Left) White china with 4A design on cup. Used by employees at Avon plant. CMV $25.

1979 CANDY DISH

(Center) With silver plated base. 1979 in bottom of glass. CMV $35.

1978 CANDY DISH

(Right) Lead crystal dish. Does not say Avon. CMV $25.

1979 - 10th ANNIVERSARY HEART OF AVON AWARD - JAPAN
(Left) Box holds white porcelain heart with flower design, bottom says "Heart of Avon Exclusively made for Avon Lady". CMV $45. MB.

1979 BELL CHRISTMAS GIFT - ENGLAND
(Right) White porcelain bell with Currier & Ives design, not marked Avon. White & blue box says "Happy Christmas from Avon". CMV $30. MB.

1977 CANDY DISH AWARD - GERMANY
White porcelain with pink flowers. Bottom Avon label made only for Avon. Given to German Avon Reps. CMV $30.

1967 PRESIDENT'S AWARD SPOON HOLDER - CANADA
Gold & turquoise spoon holder. Holds 12 spoons from Oneida Silver with crest of each province on each spoon & 1 for Canada crest. Top says 1867-1967 on one side & Avon President's Award 1967 on other side. Awarded to President's Club Reps only. CMV $125. complete, mint.

1979 SMILE COFFEE CUP AWARD - CANADA
Set of 6 given to Reps for signing up new Reps in Canada. Came in plain cardboard box. CMV $30. set of 6 MB - $5. each cup.

1979 PRESIDENT'S CLUB CHRISTMAS GIFT - CANADA
(Left) Plastic tree ornament with Noel scene, gold sticker on bottom says Avon's President's Club Gift, 1979. CMV $17.50 MB.

1979 CHRISTMAS GIFT FOR REPS - CANADA
(Right) Fostoria nut bowl with 4A design on bottom. In red & pink Noel box. Came with card from W. E. Griffin, Jr. President of Avon, Canada. CMV $12. MB.

1979 AUSTRALIAN AWARDS
ARIANE NOTE PAD
Red velvet. CMV $15.
ARIANE INCH
In black bag. CMV $10.
SERENITY CLOCK AWARD
Small white plastic clock made in Germany by Jerger. Has blue serenity flowers on face. CMV $25.
PRESIDENT'S CLUB SILVER PLATED COVERED DISH
Top flips open, glass dish inside. Given to Reps. "Avon President's Club" inscribed on top. CMV $55.

1979 REPRESENTATIVE CHRISTMAS GIFT - AUSTRALIA
Squatty glass decanter says Avon 1979 on bottom. Avon thank you tag around neck. CMV $25. MB.

1980 CHRISTMAS ORNAMENT GIFT - CANADA
Red plastic bulb with Avon sticker on bottom given to President's Club Reps at Christmas. In red Avon box. Comes with 1980 Avon card. CMV $15. MB.

1973 CREAM & SUGAR AWARD - ENGLAND
White porcelain with green, pink, blue flowers on side. Given to Reps in England. Does not say Avon. Came in plain box. CMV $10. set.

1974 PROMISE OF HEAVEN AWARDS - ENGLAND
First step for selling 7 cream sachets won the 9" high white porcelain vase. CMV $22.50. Second step for selling 15 cream sachets won the white clock, 3½" high x 3¼" wide. CMV $25. Third step for selling 25 cream sachets won the blue, white & gold electric lamp. CMV $50.

1980 PEN SET PRESIDENT'S CLUB - CANADA
(Left) Clear & white plastic. 1980 4A pin embedded in plastic base. "President's Club 1980" on pen. Came in green & gold box & Avon card. CMV $25. MB.

1977 TERRITORY RECORD COVER - CANADA
(Right) Blue plastic with gold door knocker. CMV $2.

FIELD FLOWERS DESK SET - CANADA
Given to Reps. CMV $20. MB.

1975 CHRISTMAS GIFT COLOGNE - CANADA
Given to all Reps in Canada at Christmas 1975. Box has outside sleeve that says in English & French "Especially for you from Avon." CMV $17. as shown with sleeve, MB.

1973 - 87th ANNIVERSARY AWARD CLOCK - CANADA
(Left) White plastic with roses. Made by Phinney Walker, Germany. CMV $10.

PRESIDENT'S CLUB ORDER BOOK COVER - CANADA
Winter scene on front. CMV $5.

1978 WATCH AVON AWARD - GERMANY
17 jewel date watch with 4A design on face. Leather strap. Given to Avon reps in Germany. Avon on back. CMV $80. mint.

1974 CHRISTMAS GIFT COLOGNE - CANADA
3 oz. bottle of cologne never sold to public, given to all Reps at Christmas 1974 in Canada. Red lined gold box. Outside sleeve says in French & English "A Gift to You from Avon." CMV $22.50 MB as shown.

1973 MOONWIND CLOCK AWARD - GERMANY
(Left) Given to German Avon Reps for top sales. Blue & silver. Moonwind on clock face. CMV $40.

1967 DESK PEN SET AWARD - CANADA
(Right) Black pen. Clear plastic base with 4A design & British Columbia crest on base with 50c Canadian coin inside clear base. Only 1 per district given to Reps only. CMV $30.

1978 PRESIDENT'S CLUB WATCH - CANADA
Gruen watch in black case & box with President's Club on face of watch in English & French & 4A design. Won for $5,000. in sales in 9 campaigns. CMV $125 MB.

1971 CHRISTMAS GIFT - GERMANY
Blue & silver box holds ribbed glass perfume rollette, silver cap in Moonwind. Given to Avon Reps at Christmas 1971. CMV $22.50 MB.

1977 TIMELESS GIFT SET AWARD - CANADA
Gold box given to Avon Reps in Canada for sales of Timeless products. Outside sleeve came in English & French. CMV $22.50 MB.

1979 PRESIDENT'S CLUB BATHROOM SET AWARD - CANADA
Beige plastic set consists of trinket box, cotton box, tissue box & beauty box with mirror. Given for best increase in sales. Designed by M. H. in Italy. CMV $65. set MB.

1981 ROSE STICK PIN CHRISTMAS GIFT - CANADA
Real preserved rose given to Canadian Avon Reps. Comes in red and white box with description of rose. CMV $20. MB.

1979 SILK ROSE PRESIDENTS CLUB GIFT - CANADA
Blown glass vial 7" high with red silk rose given to all Presidents Club in Canada. Came in gold box. Came with card from R.J. Fairholm, Avon Products. CMV $15.

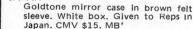

1980 TRY ME MIRROR AWARD — JAPAN
Goldtone mirror case in brown felt sleeve. White box. Given to Reps in Japan. CMV $15. MB'

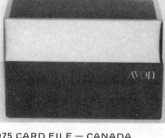

1975 CARD FILE — CANADA
For Avon ladies, green and gold. Field Flowers. CMV $7.

1974 PROMISE OF HEAVEN ORDER BOOK — ENGLAND
White plastic order book cover used by Avon Reps. CMV $10. Each piece is decorated in Promise of Heaven design.

1978 TEAM LEADER ORGANIZER — CANADA
Blue plastic, for Reps in Canada. CMV $5.

SMILE PRODUCTS — ENGLAND
1979 SMILE TOTE BAG
Plastic coated cloth bag. Smile on backside. CMV $7.50.
SMILE BALOONS
CMV 50c.
1979 SMILE WITH AVON BUTTON
CMV $2.
1979 OPERATION SMILE TAPE & FILM SET
Cassette and film used by managers at sales meeting. CMV $10. MB.

1979 SHOPPING BAGS — JAPAN
Plastic coated paper bags. Came in blue, pink and green. CMV $5. as a set.

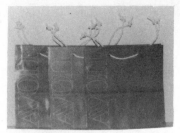

1979 CATALOG FOLDER — MEXICO
Blue vinyl folder used by Reps. CMV $5.
1980 CALENDAR — EUROPE
Foldout Avon calendar. CMV $4.

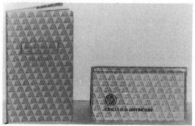

1979 DIARY, JEWEL PIN CLUB — JAPAN
Vinyl covered Avon diary given to Japanese Reps. CMV $15.
1979 CIRCLE OF EXCELLENCE ORDER BOOK COVER — MEXICO
Vinyl covered order book. Name on front Circulo de Distincion. CMV $5.

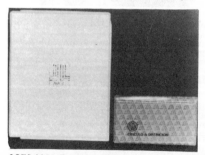

1979 MAKE-UP BINDER — JAPAN
White plastic 2 ring binder marked Avon. CMV $10.
1979 CIRCLE OF DISTINCTION ORDER BOOK COVER — MEXICO
Tan plastic cover. Same as our Presidents Club in U.S. CMV $10.

1978 CRUISING HAT — CANADA
White and black hat. Given to each team leader in Canada. CMV $5.
1979 SMILE HAT — CANADA
White, red and black hat given to team leader in Canada. CMV $5.

1972 JEWELRY CASE AWARDS — CANADA
Given to Reps on meeting sales goals on introduction of Avon Jewelry in Canada. Avon rose inside lid on both. 1st level is ring case, CMV $12., 2nd level is Jewel case, CMV $17.50.

1980 MANAGERS BLAZER — CANADA
Maroon blazer with gold tone Avon buttons and 4A gold emblem on pocket. Given to managers for meeting appointment goals. Modeled by Ruth Hershberger. CMV $150.

1981 KIMONO MANAGERS AWARD — JAPAN
Red and black. Given to managers in Japan. Very rare. Front and back side modeled by Dwight Young. CMV $100.

1972 JEWELRY CASE AWARDS — CANADA
Given to Presidents Club members only for sales goals on introduction of Avon Jewelry in Canada. 1st level award was travel case, CMV $16. 2nd level award was Deluxe Jewelry Case, on bottom of picture. Avon rose inside of lid. CMV $22.50.

1981 SWEATER AWARD — CANADA
White sweater. Avon in red. Given to managers on in Canada. CMV $25.
1981 SCARF & TOQUE SET AWARD-CANADA
Red and white stocking cap and scarf. both marked Avon. Given to Reps for new recommendation. CMV $25. set or $12.50 each.
1981 MITTENS AWARD — CANADA
Red and white. CMV $10. Modeled by Vera Young.

1975 CAPUCCI SCARF
Brown and rust color silk scarf given to Reps in Germany for sales. Came in color matching envelope. CMV $10.

1973 REP. CHRISTMAS GIFT — CANADA
Tan and white card holds tan silk A scarf given to all Canada Reps. at Christmas. CMV $20. mint in card. Scarf only, $12.

1978-79 4A TOWEL AWARDS — CANADA

Reps. could win 1st level 4A face cloth, CMV $5. MB; 2nd hand towels, CMV $7. MB; 3rd bath towels, CMV $10. MB each; 4th bath sheets, CMV $20. MB each. Each came in white or brown. Each had 4A design on towel and came in Avon box. Boxes have French on one side and English on other.

1979 SMILE NECK SCARF — CANADA

Red and white, black letters. Made in Canada. Given to managers only. CMV $25.

1977 AWARDS — GERMANY
CLUTCH
Gray and brown. A all over it. Came with calculator. CMV $32.50 with calculator.
1978 ARIANE INCH
Silver tone dated 1978, has red plastic dabber. In red bag. CMV $15.
1977 SCARF AND PURSE
Brown and tan. CMV $12. scarf, CMV $20. purse.

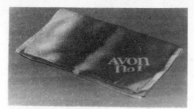

1979 AVON NUMBER 1 SCARF AWARD — ENGLAND
Given to top Reps. in England. CMV $15.

1978 TOWEL AWARDS — GERMANY
Rust and beige color towels with doves on towels. Tag says "Made in Belgium by Santens for Avon". Large and small towel. CMV $10. small, CMV $15. large.

1977 RECOMMENDATION PRIZE — GERMANY
Terrycloth, plastic lined bags. Green or pink with 4A design. CMV $7. each.

1978 CANDID AWARDS — CANADA
Candid Scarf, Step 1. CMV $6.; Candid Scarf Clip. Sept 2, CMV $9.; Candid Umbrella, Step 3, CMV $22.50.

1979 LIVE, LAUGH, LOVE TEMPO AWARDS — CANADA
Beige and red design. Level 1 - terry hat, CMV $5.; Level 2 - Lounger, CMV $20.; Level 3 - terry warm-up, CMV $30.

1976 SIGNATURE COLLECTION AWARDS — CANADA
Scarf, clutch purse, hand bag and large tote bag not shown, size 16½" x 14½". Each is brown and tan canvas. CMV complete set is $45. 1976 Order Book also shown. Inside cover says Avon's 90th Anniversary Sales Achievement Award. CMV $4.

1976 TIMELESS AWARD SET — SPAIN
Set given to Reps. in Spain for selling Timeless cologne mist. Set consists of leather overnight case, leather manicure set, travel clock made by Blessing and Avon on face, in leather case, and leather jewelry case. CMV $80. complete set.

1978 TRAVEL BAG AWARD — CANADA
Beige canvas, navy trim bag given to winning team Reps for sales in C14-78. CMV $5.

**1979 COLOGNE TEST SET —
ENGLAND**
White box has 5 samples. CMV $20
MB.
1979 AWARD BAG — ENGLAND
Suede hand tote bag. Avon tag. CMV
$12.

**1974 SALES ACHIEVEMENT AWARD
BAGS — CANADA**
Tan canvas with brown leather trim.
Given to Reps for top sales. Clutch,
handbag, medium tote and large tote.
All 4 as set, CMV $45.

**1978 RECORD CHRISTMAS GIFT —
CANADA**
Record album given to all Canadian
Avon Reps at Christmas. Record is
marked "Avon Presents A Christmas
Concert by Boston Pops". CMV $8.
mint.

**1978 CANDID AWARD BAG —
MEXICO**
Given to Mexican Avon Reps. for top
sales. CMV $15.

**1979 SMILE BEACH BALL —
ENGLAND**
Given to Reps. in England. Orange
and white plastic. CMV $5.

1979 CALENDAR — JAPAN
CMV $5.
1980 CALENDAR — JAPAN
CMV $5.

1974 PEN & PENCIL SET — CANADA
Black and red Papermate pen box
holds 2 pens with 4A inscribed.
Given to Presidents Club Reps. CMV
$35. set MB.

1978 SMILE PEN AWARD — CANADA
White and black pen with black silk
ribbon. Given to Reps. for selling
$400. in Avon in C6-C7 in 1978.
Came in white Avon box. CMV $12
MB.

1981 CHRISTMAS GIFT — CANADA
Embroidered rayon and silk picture
of Mrs Albee, 1st Avon lady. French
and English Avon label on back. Giv-
en to team leaders. CMV $50. MB
only.

**1979 PARKER PEN PRESIDENTS
CLUB — CANADA**
Blue and gold box holds Parker 75
Pen inscribed on side (Presidents
Club 1979). CMV $25. MB.

1976 SALES BAG — EUROPE
Gray bag, brown A design. Used by
Avon Reps. in Germany for deliver-
-ies. CMV $20.

1972 ADVENT AVON CALENDAR — GERMAN
Given to Reps for getting a new Rep. for Avon. CMV $5.

1972 CALENDAR — GERMAN
Cloth roll up calendar, says Avon on bottom. CMV $10.

1973 AVON CALENDAR — GERMAN
Cloth roll up calendar, does not say Avon on it. CMV $10. Both were given to Reps. for sending in orders in C-1.

1976 CHRISTMAS CARD GIFT — CANADA
Brown and beige card, 1st issue from Avon. Given to all reps at Christmas. 4A design on white card. Winter scene on inside. CMV $5.

1975 AVON CHRISTMAS CARDS — GERMANY
Avon on inside and 4A design on front. CMV $2.

1979 CHRISTMAS CARD AND WRAPPING PAPER — EUROPE
Card, CMV $3., wrapping paper, CMV $4.

1977 CHRISTMAS CARD GIFT — CANADA
2nd issue gold fold out large card with Sugar Bush scene inside. 4A design on outside of card and envelope. Given to all Reps at Christmas. CMV $4.

1970 COLORING BOOK — EUROPE
CMV $5.

1968 CHARISMA PORTFOLIO — CANADA
Avon Christmas Award on cover Order Book, pencil. Date pads. CMV $8.

1971 REPS. CHRISTMAS GIFT — CANADA
Green Seasons Greetings envelope holds four 8"c 10" size pictures to frame with a letter from Canada's Avon President. Given to all Reps at Christmas. CMV $20. complete, mint.

1978 CHRISTMAS AVON CARD — GERMANY
Gray card, Avon '78 on inside. CMV $2. in envelope.

1972 REP. CHRISTMAS GIFT — CANADA
Green box holds Christmas card with black and red rose print on inside to be cut out and put in small gold picture frame. "Made in Austria" on back. Inside card says "from Avon" and signed by Avon President from Canada. Given to all Canadian Avon Reps. at Christmas. CMV $20. MB.

TUBES — MISC.

SEE 1984 SUPPLEMENT IN BACK OF BOOK FOR MORE TUBES

1979 CALENDAR — JAPAN
Shows make-up products and described in Japanese. CMV $8.

1904 WITCH HAZEL CREAM
OSP 2 oz. tube 25c, 6 oz. tube 50c, CMV $50 MB, $45 tube only mint.

1904 ALMOND CREAM BALM
OSP 2 oz. tube 25c, 6 oz. tube 50c, CMV $50 MB, $45 tube only mint.

1908 WITCH HAZEL CREAM
2 & 6 oz. size tubes. OSP 25c & 50c CMV $50 each MB, $40 tube only mint.

1908 ALMOND CREAM BALM
2 & 6 oz. size tubes OSP 25c & 50c, CMV $50 each MB, $40 tube only.

1914 MENTHOL WITCH HAZEL
OSP 25c, CMV $45 MB, $40 tube only mint.

1914 WITCH HAZEL CREAM
Small & large tube. OSP 25c & 50c, CMV $45 MB, $40 tube only mint.

1923 WITCH HAZEL CREAM
Large & small green tube. OSP 30c & 59c, CMV $40 MB, $35 tube only mint.

1909 MENTHOL WITCH HAZEL CREAM
2 oz. tube-1st issue. OSP 25c, CMV $45, $50 MB.

1925 BAYBERRY SHAVING CREAM SAMPLE
Small sample tube in sample box. Comes with instruction sheet. CMV $70 MB.

1923 MENTHOL WITCH HAZEL CREAM
Green tube. OSP 33c, CMV $35, MB, tube only mint $30.

1930-36 MENTHOL WITCH HAZEL CREAM
Green & black tube. OSP 50c. CMV $20, MB $15 tube only mint.

1930-36 WITCH HAZEL CREAM
Green & black tube OSP 75c. CMV $20 MB, $15 tube only mint.

1910-ALMOND CREAM BALM
Tube came in 2 sizes. OSP 25c & 50c, CMV $45 MB, $40 tube only mint.

1923-COLD CREAM TUBE
Large & small tube. OSP 23c & 45c, CMV $30 tube only mint, $40 MB.

1980 TAKE ALONG HAND CREAM
1 oz. tube in Vita Moist red design, or Rich Moisture blue design. SSP 88c, CMV 50c each.

1959-CREME SHAMPOO
2.4 oz. yellow tube & turquoise cap. Yellow & blue box. OSP 69c, CMV $5., MB $3. tube only.

1960-62 CREME SHAMPOO WITH LANOLIN
Green & white box holds yellow tube with turquoise cap., OSP 69c, CMV $6 MB.

1925 WITCH HAZEL CREAM SAMPLE
Green tube, says on back "Not for sale Sample" CMV $45 MB, $40 tube only mint.

1936-44 WITCH HAZEL CREAM
Turquoise & white tube OSP 52c, CMV $15, MB tube only mint $12.

1936-44 MENTHOL WITCH HAZEL CREAM
Maroon & ivory colored tube. OSP 37c, CMV $20 MB tube only, mint $15.

1908-ALMOND CREAM BALM
Metal tube. OSP 50c, CMV $45, mint, $55 MB.

1948-50 AMBER CREAM SHAMPOO OR AMBER GEL
Turquoise & white tube with blue cap. OSP 59c, CMV $8., MB $4. tube only.

1955-60 CREME SHAMPOO
Green and white tube. CMV $10., MB $6. tube only.

1949-58-CREME SHAMPOO
(Top) Green tube with blue or white cap. OSP 59c, CMV mint tube only $5., $8. MB.

1954-55 CREME SHAMPOO
(Bottom) Greent tube with white OSP 59c, CMV $8., MB Mint tube only $6.

1936-42 SEN-DEN-TAL
(Left) Turquoise & white tube. OSP 36c, CMV $20 MB tube only mint $15.
1933-36 SEN-DEN-TAL
(Right) Green tube of tooth paste. OSP 35c - CMV $25 MB, $20 tube only mint.

1923-BAYBERRY SHAVE CREAM
Green tube. OSP 33c - CMV $40 MB $35 tube only mint.
1923-SHAMPOO CREAM
Yellow tube, osp 48c - CMV $40 MB $35 tube only mint.
1936-49-SHAVING CREAM
Maroon & ivory tube. OSP 36c, CMV $20 Mb tube only mint $15.

1923 BAYBERRY SHAVING CREAM
Green, tube, came in Gentlemens Shaving Set CMV $35 - Mint $40 MB.
1923 STYPTIC PENCIL
White pencil. OSP 10c - CMV $10, $15 MB.
1936-49 BRUSHLESS SHAVING CREAM
Maroon & ivory tube. OSP 41c, CMV $20. MB, $15. tube only mint.

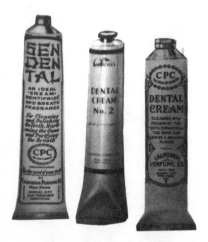

1921-33 SEN-DEN-TAL
Yellow tube. OSP 47c, CMV $35 in box. $30 tube only mint, also came in small sample tube. CMV $35 mint.
1932-36 -DENTAL CREAM NO. 2
Green tube. OSP 35c, CMV $25 MB.
Tube only mint $20.
1915-33-DENTAL CREAM
OSP 23c, 1915-23 tube was pink, 1923-33 tube was light blue. CMV pink tube mint $40, blue tube mint $35. Add $5 for box.

1912 DENTAL CREAM
Metal tube, Paper label. OSP 25c, CMV $50. Mint, $75. MB.

1930-36-BAYBERRY SHAVING CREAM
Green tube. OSP 35c, CMV $25 MB, $20 tube only mint.
1935-36 BRUSHLESS SHAVING CREAM
Green & black tube. OSP 51c, CMV $25 MB, $20 tube only mint.

1931-36 HAIR DRESS
(Left) Silver tube. OSP 37c, CMV $25 MB, $20 tube only mint.

1936-49 HAIR DRESS
(Center) Maroon & ivory colored tube. OSP 37c, CMV $20 MB, Tube only $15 mint.

1962-65 CREAM HAIR DRESS
(Right) 4 oz. white tube. Red cap. Stage coach on tube. OSP 89c, CMV $4., $6. MB.

1925 STYPTIC PENCIL
White stick in CPC box. Came in Humidor Set box in French and English. CMV $25 MB.

1934 HAND CREAM CHRISTMAS BOX
(Left) Green & Red box, short issue, holds silver tube of hand cream. OSP 10c with regular order, CMV $18. MB as shown.

1934-HAND CREAM
(Right) Regular issue, gray box holds silver tube of hand cream, OSP 52c, CMV $12., tube only mint $15. MB.

1934-36 HAND CREAM INTRODUCTORY
Blue & silver tube. OSP 52c, CMV $25 MB as shown, $20 tube only mint.

1935 HAND CREAM CHRISTMAS BOX
Silver tube of hand cream came in special issue Christmas box for 10c with regular order. CMV $17.50 MB as shown. Same box came with Tulip 'A' tube of Hand Cream on right in 1936. CMV $15. MB.

1943 HAND CREAM NEW YEAR BOX
Regular issue tube of hand cream. Came in special short issue Flower designed box. RARE. OSP 15c, CMV $17. MB as shown.

1941 HAND CREAM SPECIAL ISSUE BOX
Special issue flowered box holds regular issue tube of hand cream. Sold for 10c with regular order. CMV $15. MB as shown.

1938 HAND CREAM
10c with each order, Feb. 1938 bells on box, CMV $17.50 MB as shown.

1939 HAND CREAM SPECIAL ISSUE BOX
Short issue box came with regular issue, tube of hand cream for 10c with regular order, CMV $17.50 MB as shown.

1940's-50's TOOTH BRUSH
Turquoise and white box with Tulip A holds 1 Avon tooth brush. OSP 50c, CMV $3.50 MB.

1935-36-TOOTHPASTE
Red, white and green tube. OSP 23c CMV $17.50 MB as shown. Tube only mint $12.

1953 67th ANNIVERSARY HAND CREAM DUO
Box holds two 2½ oz. tubes of hand cream. OSP $1.10, CMV $20. MB.

1953 Only-MERRY CHRISTMAS HAND CREAM DUO
2 turquoise & white metal tubes of hand cream in Merry Christmas box. OSP $1.10, CMV $20. MB.

1940 HAND CREAM SPECIAL ISSUE BOX
Special issue box is rose and white color. Has hand and flower on box with tulip A in flower. Sold for 10c. Holds regular issue hand cream tube. CMV $16. MB as shown.

1953 HAND CREAM DUO
Box holds 2 tubes 2½ oz. size of hand cream. Turquoise & white, OSP $1.18, CMV $18.50 MB.

1956 Only-FOR BEAUTIFUL HANDS
Blue flowered box holds 2 tubes of 2¾ oz. hand cream. OSP $1.10, CMV $16. MB.

1956 HAIR BEAUTY
Blue box holds two 2 oz. tubes creme shampoo. OSP $1.29, CMV $17.50 MB.

1942 HAND CREAM SPECIAL ISSUE BOX
Special issue box with flower design holds regular issue tube of hand cream. OSP 10c, CMV $16. MB as Shown.

1974 CARE DEEPLY HAND CREAM
2 tubes 4 oz. in pink, blue, orange & Purple box. OSP $2., CMV $3. MB.

1954 FOR BEAUTIFUL HANDS
2½ oz. Turquoise and white tubes with hand cream, turquoise caps. One tube with "Lanolin added" other regular issue. Box bouquet red roses. OSP $1.10, CMV $17. MB.
In 1955 same box came with 2 tubes of hand cream like in the 1954 Merry Christmas Hand Cream Duo. CMV $17. MB.

1954 DOUBLY YOURS
Rose box holds 2 tubes of Avon Hand Cream. OSP $1.18, CMV $17. MB.

1956 Only-MERRY CHRISTMAS TWIN FAVORITES
Green & red box holds 2 tubes of hand cream. OSP $1.18, CMV $18. MB.

1964-HAND CREAM CHRISTMAS PACKAGING
Special Christmas boxes in pink, blue and white, came with choice of green tube of 3 oz. hand cream, 4 oz. white plastic bottle of hand lotion, pink and white 3¾ oz. tube of moisturized hand cream and 2¼ oz. turquoise and white tube of Silicone Glove. OSP 79c or 2 for $1.29. CMV $3. each MB.

1960 Only-CHRISTMAS TREASURE BOX
Red and green box holds turquoise tube of hand cream. OSP 69c, CMV $7. MB as shown. Tube only $2. mint.

1958-59 MERRY CHRISTMAS GIFT BOXES
Special issue gift box came with choice of Moisturized Hand Cream-pink and white tube. OSP 79c, Avon Hand Cream-Turquoise tube, OSP 59c, Silicone Formula Hand Cream-white tube, OSP 98c, CMV $10. MB as shown each.

1936-CLEANSING CREAM SAMPLE
(Left) ¼ oz. tube, black or turquoise cap., CMV $6., CPC label add $4.
1957-CLEANSING CREAM
(Right) 2½ oz. white tube with gray band, turquoise lettering. OSP 59c, CMV $3., $4. MB.

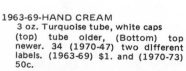

1962-71 ROSEMINT FACIAL MASK
3 oz. pink and white tube. OSP $1., CMV $1.50 MB.

1954 MERRY CHRISTMAS HAND CREAM DUO
Red & white box holds two green tubes of Avon Hand Cream. OSP $1.10, CMV $17. MB.

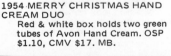

1963-69-HAND CREAM
3 oz. Turquoise tube, white caps (top) tube older, (Bottom) top newer. 34 (1970-47) two different labels. (1963-69) $1. and (1970-73) 50c.

1963 Only-MOISTURIZED HAND CREAM CHRISTMAS BOX
3¾ oz. pink and white tube pictured with special issue Christmas box. OSP 89c, CMV $3. MB Tube only sold 1957-67, CMV tube only $1.

1963 Only- SILICONE GLOVE CHRISTMAS BOX
(Right) 2¼ oz. turquoise and white tube in special issue Christmas box. OSP 79c, CMV $3. MB Tube only sold 1960-69, CMV tube only $1.

1955-62 HAND CREAM
(Left) Turquoise tube and cap. Flat cap sold 1955-57 2½ oz. tube. Tall cap sold 1957-62 2.65 oz., OSP 59c. CMV $3. Flat cap MB. Tube only $2. flat cap mint $1. less on tall cap tube.

1937-54 HAND CREAM
(Right) 2½ oz. turquoise and white tube, OSP 52c, CMV $8. MB, tube only mint $4.

1936-39 PORE CREAM
(Left) Turquoise & white tube. OSP 78c, CMV $20 MB, $15 tube only mint.

1930-36 PORE CREAM
(Right) Silver & blue tube, OSP 78c CMV $25 MB, $20 tube only mint.

1954 Only-HAND CREAM WITH LANOLIN
2½ oz. tube. OSP 59c, CMV $12. MB $10. tube only mint.

1940-43 SPECIAL FORMULA CREAM
Turquoise & white tube. OSP 78c, CMV $12. MB tube only mint $9.

1966-68 HAND CREAM FOR MEN DOUBLE PAK
Box holds 2 black & orange tubes. OSP $2.50, CMV tubes $2. ea. set, $8. MB.

1947 FLUFFY CLEANSING CREAM
1947 LIQUEFYING CLEANSING CREAM
Both tubes are pink 2¼ oz. Came in 1947 Cleansing Cream Demo Kit only. Was never sold to public. Very rare. CMV $20 each.

1955 FALL BAZAAR GIFT BOX
Special issue Christmas box holds 2 turquoise tubes of hand cream. OSP 89c, CMV $17. MB.

1931-36 ROSE COLD CREAM SAMPLE
Small silver and blue sample tube, black cap. CMV $10 mint.

1948 NIGHT CREAM
1948 SPECIAL DRY SKIN CREAM
Both tubes are blue 2¼ oz. size. Came in 1948 Skin Care Demo Kit. Was never sold to public. Very rare. CMV each $20 mint full.

1938 TOOTH PASTE SPECIAL ISSUE BOX
Short issue box holds regular issue tooth paste. Cost 10c with regular order. CMV $17.50 MB as shown.

1937 TOOTH PASTE SPECIAL ISSUE BOX
Regular issue tooth paste came in special issue box for 10c with regular order. CMV $17.50 MB as shown.

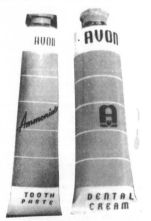

1949-55 AMMONIATED TOOTH-PASTE
Green & white tube. OSP 49c, CMV $8. MB, $5. tube only mint.
1936-44 DENTAL CREAM
Turquoise & white tube. OSP 26c, CMV $10. MB, $7. tube only mint.

1931-34 DEPILATORY
Silver tube. OSP 75c, CMV $17.50 MB, $12. tube only mint.
1948-53 DENTAL CREAM
Red cap, red, white, & blue tube. OSP 43c, CMV $6. MB tube only mint $4.

1940 TOOTHPASTE
Special Box, OSP 10c with good order from Rep. in Sept. 1940. CMV $18. MB as shown.

1939 TOOTHPASTE-SPECIAL BOX
OSP 10c with good order October 1939 CMV $18. MB as shown.

1933-36 DENTAL CREAM
(Left) Green tube. OSP 25c, CMV $20 MB, $15 tube only mint.
1936-48 TOOTHPASTE NO. 2
(Center) Turquoise and white tube. OSP 23c, CMV tube only $10. Mint $15. MB.
1936-48 TOOTHPASTE
(Right) Turquoise and white tube. OSP 23c, CMV $12. MB, tube only mint $7.

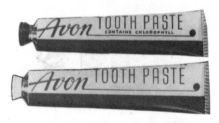

1953-56 CHLOROPHYL TOOTHPASTE
Green & white tube, green cap. OSP 49c, CMV $8. MB, tube only mint $5.
1953-56 TOOTHPASTE
Blue & white tube, white cap. OSP 49c, CMV $8. MB, tube only mint $5. Also came in ¾ oz. sample tube. CMV $5. mint.

1941-50 SMOKER'S TOOTHPASTE
Maroon & cream colored tube. OSP 39c, CMV $18 MB, $15 tube only mint.

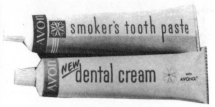

1957-67 SMOKER'S TOOTHPASTE
Red & white & grey tube. White cap.
OSP 50c, CMV $2.50 MB, $1. tube
only mint.

1957-63 DENTAL CREAM WITH AVONOL
Red, white & gray tube, white cap.
OSP 50c, CMV $3. MB, Tube only
$1.

1971-74 BRONZE GLORY TANNING GEL
3 oz. brown plastic tube yellow cap
OSP $1., CMV 50c.

1965-76 SUN SAFE
4oz. white, yellow with peach cap.
OSP $1., CMV 50c.

1975-78 BRONZE GLORY KWICK TAN
5.5 oz. brown plastic, brown cap.
OSP $1., CMV 50c.

1975-78 BRONZE GLORY SUN SAFE
5.5 oz. white plastic with white cap.
OSP $1., CMV 50c.

LEFT TO RIGHT
1968-77 CUTICLE REMOVER
OSP $1., CMV 50c.

1968-77 CUTICLE CONDITIONER
3 different issued. Wording on
labels different. OSP $1., CMV 50c

1973-76 NAIL BUFFING CREAM
.25 oz. tube white and red. OSP
$1., CMV 50c.

1955-60 NAIL BEAUTY
1 oz. tube white & red cap. OSP
59c, CMV $3. mint.

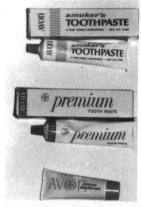

1964-67 SMOKER'S TOOTHPASTE
5 oz. white tube, blue cap. OSP 79c
CMV $1.50 MB.

1964-66 PREMIUM TOOTHPASTE
5 oz. white tube, red cap. OSP 89c
CMV $1.50 MB.

1964-67 CREAM DEODORANT
OSP 69c, CMV $1.50, $2. MB.

1957-61 SILICONE FORMULA CREAM
White tube, small turquoise cap. OSP
98c, CMV $2. MB, mint tube only
$1.

1957-67 MOISTURIZED HAND CREAM
Pink & white tube, small white cap.
OSP 79c, CMV $2. MB, tube only $1.
mint.

1977-79 CUTICLE CONDITIONER & CUTICLE REMOVER
1 oz. tube. CMV 25c ea.

1965-67 FOUNDATION SUPREME FOR EXTRA DRY SKIN
1½ oz. plastic tube, came in 11
shades. OSP $1.50, CMV $1.

1982 SOFTNESS TO GO SKIN SOFT-ENER
1 oz. gray flowered tube, white,
yellow, green, pink or blue cap.
SSP 95c, CMV 25c.

1981-82 TWICE BRIGHT TOOTH PASTE
5 oz. white, green & blue tube. SSP
$1.30, CMV 50c MB.

1962-68 CUTICLE REMOVER
1 oz. white plastic tube, red cap.
OPS 69c, CMV $2., $3. MB.

1962-68 NAIL BEAUTY
1 oz. white plastic tube, red or white
cap. OSP 69c - CMV $2, $3 MB.

LEFT TO RIGHT
(CHECK ALL DATES)
1969 SATIN SUPREME CREME FOUNDATION
1 1/8 oz. lavender tube & cap. Came
in 8 shades. OSP $1.50, CMV $1.

1968-69 HIDE 'N' LITE
.75 oz. tube, beige cap. 1968 came
with gold cap. OSP $1.50, CMV $1.

1965 TONE 'N' TINT
2 oz. tube, rose color cap. OSP
$1.50, CMV $2. MB.

1970 SATIN SUPREME
1 1/8 oz. tube, white or lavender cap.
CMV $1.

1968 ULTRA COVER
2.1 oz. tube, blue cap. Came in 8
shades, OSP $1.75, CMV $1.

1968-69 TONE 'N' TINT
Pink tube & cap. 2 oz. Came in 8
shades, OSP $1.50, CMV $1.

1957-60 ANTISEPTIC CREAM
1¾ oz. tube white & red & grey with
red cap. OSP 69c, CMV $3. mint, $4.
MB.

1968-75 RICH MOISTURE HAND CREAM
3.75 oz. or 6 oz. pink and white with pink cap. OSP 3.75 oz $1., CMV 25c OSP 6 oz $2., CMV 25c. 1976-78 Color changed to aqua same design.

1970-78 SILICONE GLOVE
4.5 oz. or 2.25 oz. white & aqua tube with aqua cap. OSP 2.25 oz. $1., CMV 25c, OSP 4.5 oz. $2., CMV 25c.

LEFT TO RIGHT
1977-78 BATH GELEE
4 oz. tube came in Roses, Roses, Honeysuckle, Apple Blossom or Strawberry. OSP $3.50, CMV 25c.

1977-78 FRESH STRAWBERRY PEEL OFF FACIAL MASK
3 oz. tube, white cap. OSP $3., CMV 25c.

1977-78 LEMON FACIAL MASK
3 oz. plastic tube. OSP $3., CMV 25c

1976-78 CUCUMBER COOLER FACIAL MASK
3 oz. plastic tube. OSP $3., CMV 25c

1977-78 NATURAL EARTH FACIAL MASK
3 oz. plastic tube, OSP $3., CMV 25c

1977-78 MOISTURE WORKS FACIAL MASK
3 oz. plastic tube, OSP $3., CMV 25c.

LEFT TO RIGHT
1970's PROTEM LOTION SHAMPOO SAMPLE
1 oz. pink tube OSP 49c, CMV 50c

1970's PROTEM HAIR CONDITIONER SAMPLE
1 oz. pink tube. OSP 49c, CMV 50c.

1967-72 SHEEN HAIR DRESSING
2 oz. pink, white & gold with white cap OSP $1., CMV $1.

1975-77 HI LIGHT DANDRUFF SHAMPOO
4 oz blue & white plastic tube, white cap. OSP $1., CMV 50c.

1975-78 HI LIGHT 60 SECOND HAIR CONDITIONER
6 oz. yellow plastic, white cap. OSP $1., CMV 50c.

1975-77 HI LIGHT HAIR SETTING GEL
6 oz. pink & white, white cap. OSP $1.00, CMV 50c.

1970-75 DANDRUFF GEL SHAMPOO
3 oz. clear plastic white cap. OSP $1., CMV 50c.

1969-74 DEEP CLEAN CREAM
4 oz. white tube blue cap. OSP $1. CMV 50c.

1969-76 FASHION LEGS
6 oz. white tube brown or white cap. OSP $2., CMV 50c.

1970's FASHION LEGS SAMPLE
1 oz. white tube brown cap. OSP 49c, CMV 50c.

1974-78 VITA MOIST HAND CREAM
6 oz. yellow & white tube, white cap. OSP $1., CMV 25c.

1978-79 KEEP CLEAR ANTI-DANDRUFF CREAM SHAMPOO
7 oz. tube, white & blue, blue cap. SSP $1.69, CMV 25c.

1979-80 RIPE AVOCADO CONDITIONING MASK
3 oz. yellow & green tube. SSP $1.50, CMV 25c.

1975 THE GLISTENERS
Cheek color-pink tube & cap. Lip color-red tube & cap. Eye color-blue tube & cap. OSP $1., CMV 75c ea.

1974-77 SOFTSHINE LIP COLOR
2 oz. pink, red & white with white cap. OSP $1., CMV 50c.

1976-78 REAL ROUGE CREME FLUFF
.25 oz. pink and red, with red cap. OSP $1., CMV 50c.

1969-75 LOOK BRONZE
2 oz. brown & white tube with bronze cap. OSP $2., CMV 50c.

1964-66 FOUNDATION SUPREME
1½ oz. white tube, gold cap. OSP $1.35, CMV $1. mint.

1973 RESILIENT CREME RINSE FOR ADDED BODY-SAMPLE
1 oz. yellow plastic tube. CMV $1.50

1973 ESSENCE OF BALSAM HAIR CONDITIONER SAMPLE
1 oz. yellow plastic tube. CMV $1.50.

1982-83 NEW VITALITY HOT CONDITIONING TREATMENT PLUS NPD
Box of three .75 oz. tubes. SSP $2.50, CMV $1. MB.

1975-76-ESSENCE OF CAMOMILE
4 oz. white tube, green cap. OSP $1., CMV 50c.

1973-76-PEACH SUPREME
3 oz. white tube with orange cap. OSP $1., CMV 50c.

1974-76-ORANGE FRESH
2 oz. white tube orange cap. OSP $1., CMV 50c.

1968-77-FRESH AND GLOW
3½ oz. white tube, red cap. OSP $1., CMV 50c.

1967-74-NEW YOU MASQUE
2 oz. white tube, red cap. OSP $1., CMV 50c.

1973-76-HERBAL SCENTED MASK
2 oz. white tube, green cap. also came in light brown tube. OSP $1. CMV 50c.

1975-TWO TO-GO FOUNDATION & BLUSH
Pink and white. OSP $2., CMV 75c.

1981-82-PEEL OFF FACIAL MASK
Small .75 oz. tubes. Cucumber Cooler-Blue, Aloe Smooth-Green, Fresh Strawberry-Red. SSP 80c Ea., CMV 25c ea. No boxes.

1980 -SANTA'S HELPER HAND CREAM & LIP BALM
Lip balm is green, red & white. Care deeply hand cream is Red, White & Green, 1.5 oz. tube. Sold together with no box. SSP $2.50, CMV $3. Mint Set.

1980-82-ALOE SMOOTH PEEL OFF MASK
Yellow & green tube 3 oz. SSP $1.75, CMV 25c.

1980-81-PAINT BOX BRIGHTS
3 colors for eyes & 3 colors for lips. Small .25 oz. Tubes, 6 different. SSP $1.30, CMV 50c ea.

1981-82 HOT STUFF
Tanarifics Tanning lotions. 3.75 oz. Yellow tube. SSP $2., CMV 50c.

1981-82 COOL IT
Tanarifics Tanning lotion 3.75 oz. blue tube. SSP $2., CMV 50c.

1981-SOFT AS ROSES HAND CREAM
3 different 1 oz. tubes in Pink-Rich moisture cream, moisture Garden Hand Cream in Blue & Vita Moist Hand Cream in Yellow flowers & cap. SSP 99c ea., CMV 50c ea.

1975-78-MAKING EYES CREAM EYE SHADOW
.25 oz. light blue with turquoise lettering. OSP $1., CMV 25c.

1964-76-NATURAL RADIANCE
.25 oz. clear plastic tube gold cap. OSP $2., CMV 50c.

1970-73 FLOWING CREAM EYE SHADOW
.25 oz. clear plastic tube, gold cap. OSP $1., CMV 50c.

1973-75 FLOWING CREAM EYE SHADOW
.25 oz. white plastic tube with gold cap. OSP $1., CMV 50c.

1982-83-FRESH AS NATURE MASK
3 different tubes, 1.5 oz. size, rose, Almond or Mineral clay mask. SSP $2., CMV 25c ea.

NEW Drexyl Dragon Decorating Body Soap

1981-DREXYL DRAGON DECORATING BODY SOAP
3 different color dragon design tubes. Red, Blue or Yellow. SSP $3. ea., CMV 50c ea.

1981-82-FRESH TAKES
Small plastic tubes in Lip Reviver-in box, Cool Lift Moisturizer, Cool Lift Hand Cream. SSP $1. ea., CMV 25c ea.

1981-FRUIT FOR ALL HAND CREAM & LIP BALM
Lip balm & 1.5 oz. matching tube of hand cream in strawberry, grape or orange. SSP $2. set each. CMV $2. each set.

TOOTH TABLETS

1936-40 TOOTH TABLET
Aluminum lid on white glass bottom. Avon Tulip "A" on lid. OSP 36c, CMV $55. mint, $75. MB.

1934-36 TOOTH TABLET
Aluminum lid on white glass bottom. OSP 36c, CMV $60., $80. MB.

1921-23 TOOTH TABLET
(Left) Aluminum lid & clear glass bottom. OSP 25c, CMV $60. mint.
1923-34 TOOTH TABLET
(Right) Aluminum lid with white glass bottom. OSP 36c, CMV $55. mint. Both have same lid, different bottoms. Add $20. each in MB.

1906-1921 TOOTH TABLET
Painted metal top with clear glass bottom embossed with Calif. Tooth Tablet in glass. 2 different boxes. 1906 to 1921 lid is painted just under New York with Food & Drug Act 1906. OSP 25c, CMV $70. mint, $90. MB each.

1896-1905 CALIFORNIA TOOTH TABLET
Blue and white painted metal lid. Clear glass bottom has embossed California Tooth Tablet, Most Perfect Dentifrice. OSP 25c, CMV $85. mint, $110. MB.

FRAGRANCE JARS

1923-33 AMERICAN BEAUTY FRAGRANCE JAR
(Far Left) - Clear glass jar & lid. Red ribbon around neck. OSP, $2.95, CMV, $100.00.
1914-23 LAVENDER FRAGRANCE JAR
3 different sizes. Left - 5½" high, 3" wide base. Center - 5 7/8" high,

3" wide base. Right - 7" high, 3 9/16" wide base. It also came 5 3/8" high and 3" wide base. OSP $2.50 each, CMV $125 each size. One on far right is 1st issue. Add $25 MB each.

1934-43 AMERICAN BEAUTY FRAGRANCE JAR
6 oz. glass jar and stopper. Red tassel around neck. OSP $2.75, CMV $40. jar only mint. $55. with tassel MB.
1936-54 FRAGRANCE JAR LIQUID
6 oz. green cap and label. OSP $1.39, CMV $20., $25. MB.

1946 FRAGRANCE JAR
Made of pink ceramic, white flower on pink lid. Very short issue. Does not say "Avon" on it. Also came with white, blue and green flowers on lid. OSP $2.75, CMV $80. MB. Jar only mint $60. Also came with white flowers on white lid.

1948-57 ROSE FRAGRANCE JAR
6 oz. 1st issue came out with clear rose shaped glass stopper. 1949 issue had frosted rose glass stopper. Both had red silk neck ribbon. OSP $3.50. CMV $32.50 clear stopper, $22.50 with frosted stopper. Add $10. MB each.

1948 ROSE FRAGRANCE JAR TEST
Dark amber glass. Was not sold. Test bottle at factory. CMV $100.

1948-57 ROSE FRAGRANCE JAR SET
Box contains one 6 oz. fragrance jar liquid. One 3 oz. fragrance jar cubes. One 8 oz. empty fragrance jar. CMV $85. set MB.

1923 AMERICAN BEAUTY FRAGRANCE JAR CUBES
4 oz. can. OSP 48c, CMV $45. mint. Front and back view shown.

1921 FRAGRANCE JAR LIQUID
(Left) 4 oz. cork stopper, brown label. OSP 96c, CMV $100, $115. MB.
1925 AMERICAN BEAUTY FRAGRANCE JAR LIQUID
4 oz. bottle, brown label, metal cap. OSP 96c - CMV $85 MB, $75 BO.

1943-49 FRAGRANCE JAR CUBES
3 oz. jar. OSP 85c, CMV $25., $35. MB.

1934-36 FRAGRANCE JAR LIQUID
6 oz. bottle, aluminum cap. Silver and blue label. OSP $1.75, CMV $40. mint, $45. MB.
1955-57 FRAGRANCE JAR LIQUID
7 oz. white cap, gray label. OSP $1.39. CMV $15., $20. MB.

AMERICAN IDEAL

1911 AMERICAN IDEAL PERFUMES
Introductory size glass stoppered bottle with green neck ribbon and pink paper label with ladies face, in green box. OSP 60c, CMV $150. MB, $100. BO mint.

1914 AMERICAN IDEAL INTRODUCTION LETTER
Given to customers on trial size bottle of perfume. CMV $20.

1910 AMERICAN IDEAL PERFUME "INTRODUCTORY SIZE"
Glass stopper in round screw on wood box, gold label. OSP 75c, CMV $110. BO. Bottle in wood box, $225. mint.

1913 Only - AMERICAN IDEAL PERFUME
(Right) Introductory size octaganal shaped glass stoppered bottle fits in wood box with screw on wood lid, paper label with ladies face. OSP 75c, CMV $110. mint, $225. MB. Both came with neck ribbons.

1911 AMERICAN IDEAL PERFUME
1 and 2 oz. size bottles, glass stopper. Ladies face on paper label in green box. OSP $2.50 and $4.75. CMV $150. MB, $125. BO mint each.

1941 AMERICAN IDEAL
1/8 oz. clear glass bottle, gold cap. Gold and blue label. OSP 75c, CMV $35. BO, $55. MB.

1917 AMERICAN IDEAL PERFUME
Glass stoppered bottle came in green box. 1 and 2 oz. size, gold neck and front label. Green neck ribbon. OSP $2.50 and $4.75. CMV $175. MB, $135. BO.

1917 AMERICAN IDEAL PERFUME
½ oz. glass stoppered bottle, green box, gold label on front and neck. Green neck ribbon. OSP 75c, CMV $125. MB, $100. BO mint.

1919 AMERICAN IDEAL PERFUME
1 oz. with frosted flower embossed glass stopper. Green label. OSP $2.40, CMV $125., $150 MB.

1908 AMERICAN IDEAL PERFUME
Glass stoppered bottle came in 1 and 2 oz. size. Velvet lined wood box. Neck ribbon on bottle, gold front and neck label. OSP $2. and $3.75. CMV $200. MB, $150. BO.

1925 AMERICAN IDEAL PERFUME
1 oz. bottle with wide flat glass stopper. Green neck ribbon and gold and green label. OSP $2.40, CMV $150. MB, $125. BO mint.

1910 AMERICAN IDEAL PERFUME
Wood case with dark velvet lining holds 1 oz. glass stoppered bottle with green and gold label with ladies face. Neck ribbon matches inside of box. OSP $2., CMV $200. MB, $150. BO mint.

1930-33 AMERICAN IDEAL PERFUME
1 oz. clear glass bottle with frosted glass stopper. In silver box. Label on top of bottle. OSP $2.40, CMV $135, MB, $100. BO.

1925 AMERICAN IDEAL PERFUME
Flaconette size embossed bottle with brass cap over long dabber glass stopper. OSP $1.10, CMV $90. BO, $110. MB.

1910 AMERICAN IDEAL SACHET
Box holds ribbed sided bottle with brass cap and ladies face on green and gold label. OSP 50c, CMV $125. MB, $100. BO mint.

1941 Only - AMERICAN IDEAL PERFUME

3 dram glass stopper, paper neck tag. Name was changed to Apple Blossom in 1941. OSP $2.25, CMV $120. BO with tag, $150. MB.

1923 AMERICAN IDEAL POWDER SACHET

(Right) Glass bottle, brass cap, green label. OSP $1.20, CMV $95. BO mint - $115. MB.

1908 AMERICAN IDEAL SACHET

Glass bottle with metal cap.. 2 piece gold label. OSP 50c, CMV $105. BO mint, $125. MB.

1911 AMERICAN IDEAL TALCUM

Pink can with gold top. OSP 35c, CMV $75., $100. MB.

1917 AMERICAN IDEAL TALCUM POWDER

3½ oz. glass jar, gold metal lid and gold label. OSP 75c, CMV $90. BO, $115. MB.

1920 AMERICAN IDEAL COMPACT

Contains face powder or rouge. Brass container with mirror on lid. OSP 59c, CMV $50 MB, compact only $40 mint.

1911 AMERICAN IDEAL TOILET SOAP

Pink and gold metal can holds 1 bar of soap wrapped in same design as can. OSP 50c, CMV can only $60., with wrapped soap $85. mint.

1911 AMERICAN IDEAL POWDER SACHET

Large size sachet bottle with brass cap and lady on paper label. OSP $1., CMV $95. BO Mint $115. MB.

1923 AMERICAN IDEAL FACE POWDER

Green and gold box with green and gold label. OSP 96c, CMV $45 in box, $40 powder box only mint.

1923 AMERICAN IDEAL SOAP

One bar toilet soap in white paper with gold label. OSP 48c, CMV $50. mint.

1921 AMERICAN IDEAL DOUBLE COMPACT

Contains face powder and rouge. Made of solid brass. OSP $1.17, CMV $55 MB. Compact only $45 mint.

1923-28 AMERICAN IDEAL TALCUM

3½ oz. glass jar, brass cap, gold and green label. OSP 72c, CMV $90. BO mint, $115. MB.

1915 AMERICAN IDEAL FACE POWDER
Green and gold box. OSP 75c, CMV $55 MB, powder box only $50 mint.

1922 AMERICAN IDEAL FACE POWDER
Green box holds green and gold paper container. OSP 96c, CMV $40 $50. MB.

1928 AMERICAN IDEAL TALCUM
Frosted glass bottle with brass lid, gold & green label. OSP 75c, CMV $75. MB - $70. BO.

1925 AMERICAN IDEAL FACE POWDER
Green & gold box. OSP 96c, CMV $40 mint, $50 MB.

1923 AMERICAN IDEAL CREAM DELUXE
White glass jar with CPC on metal lid. Gold & green label. OSP 96c, CMV $55. MB - $40. jar only mint.

1929 AMERICAN IDEAL PERFUME
1 oz. glass stoppered bottle in green satin lined box. Paper label on top of bottle. OSP $2.40, CMV $135. MB - $100. BO mint.

1920 AMERICAN IDEAL TOILET SOAP
White box, green label. OSP 48c, CMV $55. MB.

1925 AMERICAN IDEAL TOILET SOAP
Green box holds 2 bars. OSP 96c, CMV $75 MB.

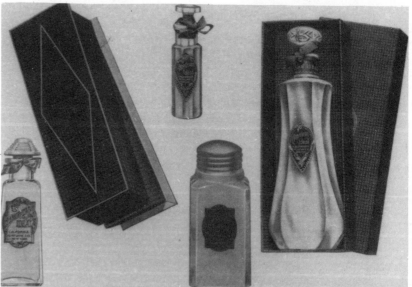

(Left to Right)
1919 AMERICAN IDEAL PERFUME
1 & 2 oz. glass bottle with glass stopper, green & gold label, green box, green neck ribbon. OSP $2.40 & $4.65, CMV $150. MB - $125. BO.

1923 AMERICAN IDEAL PERFUME
Introductory size bottle. Glass bottle & stopper. Green label & neck ribbon. OSP 75c, CMV in green box $135. BO, $110. mint. Also came with octagonal glass stopper set in cork

with long glass dabber. Same CMV.
1919 AMERICAN IDEAL SACHET POWDER
Glass bottle with brass cap, green label. OSP $1.20, CMV $90. BO - $110. MB.

1923 AMERICAN IDEAL TOILET WATER
2 & 4 oz. glass stoppered bottle with green front & neck label & neck ribbon. Green box. OSP $1.50 & $2.85, CMV $140. MB - $115. BO mint.

1929 AMERICAN IDEAL LIPSTICK
CPC on green metal tube. OSP $1..
CMV $25 tube only, $35 MB.

1919 AMERICAN IDEAL SET
Green silk lined box holds 1 oz. glass stoppered American Ideal perfume, powder sachet, bottle of talcum powder & toilet soap. All have green labels. OSP set $5.50, CMV $425. MB.

1923 AMERICAN IDEAL THREESOME
Green box contains 2 oz. toilet water, bottle of sachet & glass bottle of talc. Green & gold label. OSP $3.95, CMV $325. MB.

1925 AMERICAN IDEAL FOURSOME SET
Green box holds 1 oz. bottle with glass stopper of perfume, glass bottle of talcum, green box of face powder & white jar of vanishing cream. OSP $6.50, CMV $350. MB.

1911 AMERICAN IDEAL BOX C SET
Flip top box holds glass stoppered perfume & powder sachet. OSP 50c, CMV $275. MB.

1911 AMERICAN IDEAL SET
Large fancy box with green lining holds American Ideal talcum powder, powder sachet, 1 oz. glass stoppered perfume & bar of toilet soap in pink soap can. OSP $4., CMV $450. MB.

ARIEL

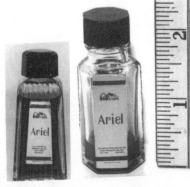

1933-36 ARIEL PERFUME "RIBBED"
(Left) ½ oz. ribbed glass bottle with black octagonal cap & gold label. Came in Gold Box Set. CMV $45. mint.

1933-36 ARIEL PERFUME
(Right) Small six sided octagonal shaped bottle with black octagonal cap. Came in Little Folks set and Handkerchief set. Has silver label. CMV $45. mint.

1930 ARIEL PERFUME
(Right) 1 oz. glass stoppered bottle with small silver label. Silver box. OSP $2.50, CMV $110. BO - $140. MB.

1930 ARIEL PERFUME FLACONETTE
(Left) Brass cap over glass stoppered embossed bottle. OSP 84c, CMV $90. BO mint - $115. MB.

1930 ARIEL PERFUME
1 oz. glass stoppered bottle, large silver & blue label. Came in silver box. OSP $2.50, CMV $105. BO mint - $135. MB.

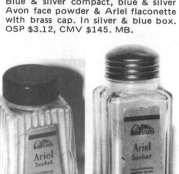

1933-37 ARIEL BATH SALTS
8½ oz. ribbed glass, navy blue cap. Silver & blue label. OSP 63c, CMV $60. MB - $40. BO mint.

1929-30 ARIEL BATH SALTS
10 oz. clear glass with chrome cap, silver & blue label. CMV $60. BO - $75. MB.

1932-33 ARIEL THREESOME
Blue & silver compact, blue & silver Avon face powder & Ariel flaconette with brass cap. In silver & blue box. OSP $3.12, CMV $145. MB.

1930-35 ARIEL TOILET WATER
2 oz. glass stoppered bottle, small label on top of bottle. Came in silver & blue box. OSP $1.75, CMV $100. BO - $130. MB.

1932-36 ARIEL POWDER SACHET
(Left) 1¼ oz. ribbed glass. Dark blue cap. OSP 78c, CMV $28. - $33. MB.

1930-32 ARIEL SACHET
(Right) Metal cap, silver & blue label. OSP 78c, CMV $60. mint - $75. MB.

1931-33 ARIEL SET NO. 2
Silver & blue box holds silver & blue fan compact & silver box of Ariel face powder. OSP $2.50, CMV $65. MB.

1933-37 ARIEL BATH SALTS SAMPLE
Small ribbed glass bottle with dark blue or black octagonal shaped cap. Silver label. CMV $60. mint.

1930-36 ARIEL FACE POWDER
Silver & blue round box in special issue 1935 red Christmas box. OSP 78c, CMV $12. container only mint - $16. MB as shown in Christmas box - or $13. in regular issue box on left.

DAPHNE

1931-36 DAPHNE TALCUM
Silver and blue can with blue cap. OSP 35c, CMV $25., $30. MB. Same can in gold color. CMV $35. Silver and blue can in large 1 Lb. family size, OSP $1., CMV $30. can only. $40. MB.

DAPHNE TALCUM
Silver can in 2 special boxes. 49 Year box on left 1935 & 50th Year box on right 1936. OSP 20c, CMV mint & boxed only in either box $50. each. Also came in gold can in 50th year box. CMV $60. MB.

1940 ONLY DAPHNE TALC MAY POLE BOX
Yellow box with dancing girls around May Pole holds regular issue 2.75 oz. Daphne Talc. can. Sold in May 1940 for 10c with regular order from Avon lady. CMV $30. MB as shown.

1933-36 DAPHNE TALCUM
(Left) Metal can came in sets only. CMV $35. mint.

1943-46 DAPHNE TALCUM
(Right) Turquoise & white paper box. No top cover, bottom cover, cap only. Family size. OSP $1.19, CMV $30. MB.

1938 Only - DAPHNE TALC 52nd ANNIVERSARY
Turquoise & white can in special box sold for 10c during 52nd anniversary campaign. CMV $32.50 in box shown.

1936-43 then 1946-50 DAPHNE TALCUM
(Right) 2.75 oz. turquoise & white can, turquoise cap. OSP 37c, CMV $12., MB $15.

1936-43 then 1946-50 DAPHNE TALCUM
(Left) 14.5 Turquoise and white can, turquoise cap. OSP $1.19, CMV $20. MB $25.

1944-46 DAPHNE TALCUM
Turquoise and white paper container. Plastic cap. OSP 39c, CMV $20. mint.

1943 DAPHNE TALCUM CHRISTMAS BOX
Pale blue and pink outer box issued only at Christmas 1943 with cardboard large size talc with top & bottom cover caps. OSP 98c, CMV $40. MB as shown. Talc only $30. mint.

1940-41 DAPHNE TALCUM CHRISTMAS PACKAGE
Outer sleeve fits over short issue blue Christmas box with white Christmas tree. Holds large size 14.5 oz. metal talc turquoise and white can of Daphne Talcum. Can only sold 1936-50. OSP 89c, CMV $40. MB as shown.

1925 DAPHNE PERFUME
1 and 2 oz. glass bottle with flat glass stopper. Bottle and top of stopper have embossed flowers. Came in green and gold box, gold label and green neck ribbons. OSP $1.95 and $3.45, CMV $125. BO $160. MB.

1937 Only - 51st ANNIVERSARY DAPHNE TALCUM
Special box was given to Avon customers with any purchase. CMV $30. MB as shown.

1925 DAPHNE GLYCERINE SOAP
Green box & wrapping with gold labels. Two bars of soap. OSP 72c, CMV $75 MB.

1916 DAPHNE PERFUME
1 & 2 oz. bottles shown with frosted glass stoppers. Also came in ½ oz. size. Each Came in green box. OSP $1., $1.90 & $3.50, CMV $110. BO, $135. MB.

1922 DAPHNE POWDER SACHET
Brass cap, green and gold square label. OSP 96c, CMV $90. BO mint, $115. MB.

1925-30 DAPHNE PERFUME
Clear glass, brass cap, box is brown, yellow & green, Came in Jack & Jill Jungle Jinks Set. CMV $70. MB.

1917 DAPHNE FACE POWDER VANITY COMPACT
Green box, came in white, pink and brunette tints. OSP 75c, CMV $40. MB. Same box also came in Daphne Rouge. Same CMV, $30. compact only mint.

1917 DAPHNE DOUBLE VANITY COMPACT
Contained face powder & rouge. Green compact with mirror on lid. OSP $1, CMV $55, $45 compact only mint.

1917 DAPHNE VANITY COMPACT
Face powder, came in white, pink & brunette. Green compact with mirror on lid. OSP 50c, CMV $40. MB, $30. compact only mint.

1923 DAPHNE TOILET WATER
Green box holds 2.or 4 oz. size bottle with frosted glass stopper, gold front & neck label, green neck ribbon. OSP $1.20 & $2.25, CMV $100. BO, $125. MB. Came with 2 different glass stoppers set in cork as pictured & outer box. CMV for both boxes $140. MB.

1922 DAPHNE PERFUME
¼ oz. vial given to customers for each $5. order in March 1922. CMV $150. MB, $125. BO mint.

1925 DAPHNE DERMA CREAM
White glass jar ½'' thick green lid. Came in Septette Gift box. CMV $40. mint.

1925 DAPHNE CERATE
½'' thick white glass jar, green lid. Came in Septette gift box. CMV $40. mint. Also came in large size jar.

1920 DAPHNE POWDER SACHET
Brass cap & gold label. OSP 96c, CMV $90. mint, $110. MB.

1926 DAPHNE CERATE
½" thick white glass jar, solid green lid says Daphne CPC Cerate on top. Also came in Daphne Derma Cream. Came in Septette gift box set. CMV $35. ea. mint.

1923 DAPHNE TALCUM POWDER
4 oz. green can, brass cap. OSP 48c, CMV $75. MB, $65. can only.

1923 DAPHNE ROLLING MASSAGE CREAM
White glass jar with CPC on metal lid, gold label. OSP 69c, CMV $45., $50. MB.

1923 DAPHNE CERATE
White glass jar with CPC on metal lid, gold label. Small & large size jars. OSP 72c & $1.35. CMV $45., $50. MB.

1923 DAPHNE DUPLEX COMPACT
Green compact & puffs, mirror on lid. OSP 98c - CMV $40, $50 MB.

1929 DAPHNE CREAMS
Square white glass jars with ribbed sides & CPC on aluminum lids & gold labels. Came in Daphne Cerate, Daphne Derma Cream & Daphne Rolling Massage Cream, OSP 75c CMV $50. ea. MB, $40. jar only.

1925 DAPHNE BATH SALTS
Ribbed glass jar with brass lid, gold label. OSP 98c, CMV $75. MB, $65. BO.

1925 DAPHNE LIPSTICK & EYEBROW PENCIL
2-1/8" metal lipstick has embossed name & CPC on side. OSP 39c, CMV $25 mint, $30 MB Gold Eyebrow pencil OSP 29c, CMV $20 mint, $25 MB.

1926 DAPHNE CREAMS
Large & small size glass jars with gold and green labels and green lids. Came in Daphne Derma Cream & Daphne Rolling Massage Cream. Came in large size jars only. OSP 72c, CMV $50. ea. MB, $45. jar only.

1919 DAPHNE LIPSTICK
Metal case. Daphne on case. OSP 50c, CMV $30. mint.

1923 DAPHNE THREESOME
Green box contains 2 oz. toilet water, bottle of sachet & can of talc. OSP $3.20, CMV $300. MB.

1918 DAPHNE SET
Green box holds Daphne Perfume in 1 oz. glass stoppered bottle, green box of Daphne Face Powder & green box of Daphne rouge. OSP $3.50, CMV $210. MB.

1925 DAPHNE SEPTETTE GIFT BOX
Green box holds jar of Derma Cream, jar of Cerate, green box of face powder, rouge compact, can of talcum, 1 oz. bottle of toilet water & flaconette of perfume. All in Daphne fragrance. OSP $2.95, CMV $450. MB.

MISSION GARDEN

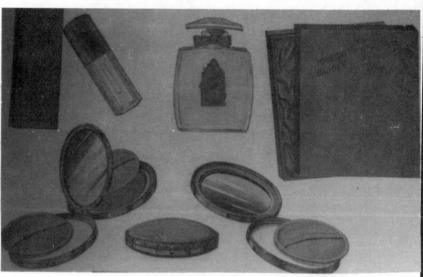

1922-25 MISSION GARDEN PERFUME
1½ oz. bohemian glass bottle with frosted sides & frosted glass stopper. Satin lined tan box. OSP $4.95, CMV $200. MB, $150. BO mint.

1925 MISSION GARDEN PERFUME
Flaconette size, gold box, embossed glass bottle with glass stopper. Brass cap over stopper. OSP $1.20, CMV $95. BO, $115. MB.

1925 MISSION GARDEN PERFUME
1 oz. glass bottle, flat embossed glass stopper. Satin lined gold box. OSP $2.85, CMV $110. BO, $140. MB. Also came in 2 oz. size, $150. MB.

1925 MISSION GARDEN COMPACT
Mission Garden CPC on edge of compact. Embossed brass case in single or double compact. OSP 98c and $1.48, CMV $55 each MB, $40 compact only.

1922 MISSION GARDEN TOILET WATER
2 & 4 oz. glass bottle with frosted glass stopper. Gold label on front & neck. OSP $2.25 & $4.35, CMV $125. BO, $150. MB.

1922 MISSION GARDEN SACHET POWDER
Glass bottle with brass cap & gold label. OSP $1.75, CMV $90. BO $110. MB.

1926 MISSION GARDEN FLACONETTE
Glass tube of perfume in brass case. Sold at Easter time. OSP 98c, CMV $90.. Tube in case only $70.

1923 MISSION GARDEN TALC SET
2 cans of Mission Garden Talc was a gift set to CPC employees. Red and gold silk lined box. CMV $200. MB.

1925 MISSION GARDEN TALC
4 oz. red & gold can, brass cap. Came in Mission Garden Threesome Set only. CMV $75. mint.

1922 MISSION GARDEN DOUBLE COMPACT
Contains face powder & rouge. Made of solid brass. OSP $1.45, CMV $45, $55 MB.

1922 MISSION GARDEN FLACONETTE
Brass tubes and cap with gold label on the tube. Holds clear glass vial with blue stripes and steel cap, glass stopper. OSP 98c, CMV $90. mint as shown.

1925 MISSION GARDEN THREESOME
Satin lined gold box holds 1 oz. Mission Garden Perfume, Talc & gold compact. OSP $7., CMV $300. MB.

NARCISSUS

1931-34 NARCISSUS PERFUME
1 oz. glass stoppered bottle came in silver & blue box, label on top of bottle. Same as 1929 perfume only box is changed. OSP $2.25, CMV $110. BO, $140. MB.

1929-30 NARCISSUS PERFUME
1 oz. glass stoppered bottle. Came in silver, blue & gold box. Blue label on top of bottle. OSP $2.20, CMV $110. BO, $160. MB.

1925 NARCISSUS PERFUME
1 oz. glass bottle with frosted embossed glass stopper. Bottle in blue & gold box, blue label & neck ribbon. OSP $2.19, CMV $110. BO mint, $150. MB.

1925 NARCISSUS PERFUME FLACONETTE
Embossed bottle with glass stopper with long glass dobber under brass cap. OSP 84c, CMV $95. BO mint, $115. MB.

NATOMA

1914-17 NATOMA ROLLING MASSAGE CREAM
Glass stoppered jar with front & neck label. OSP 50c, CMV $150. Mint, $175. MB.

1914-15 NATOMA ROSE PERFUME
½ oz. glass stoppered bottle with front & neck label. Green ribbon, green snap shut box. OSP 40c, CMV $150. MB, $125. BO.

1916 NATOMA ROSE PERFUME
(Left) ½ oz. glass stoppered bottle, green ribbon on neck, green neck & front label. Green box. OSP 40c, CMV $110. BO mint, $135. MB.

1914-21 NATOMA ROSE PERFUME
(Right) 1 oz. clear glass, glass stopper, green label. OSP $1.40, CMV $150. MB, $125. BO mint.

1913 NATOMA ROSE ART OF MASSAGE BOOKLET
10 page booklet on giving a massage with Natoma Massage Cream. CMV $20.

1915 NATOMA ROSE PERFUME
1 oz. glass stopper bottle, green front and neck label. Green neck ribbon in green felt box. OSP 40c, CMV $110. BO mint, $135. MB.

1911 NATOMA MASSAGE CREAM
1st issue glass jar, cork lid stopper. Side, neck & lid labels. OSP 75c, CMV $125. - $150. MB.

1915 NATOMA ROSE PERFUME
1 oz. bottle, glass stoppered, front and neck label. OSP 60c, CMV $110. BO mint, $135. MB.

1918-21 NATOMA ROLLING MASSAGE CREAM
Metal screw on lid, green paper label. OSP 75c, CMV $125, $150 MB.

1914-21 NATOMA ROSE PERFUME
Green box, holds 1, 2 or 4 oz. size glass stoppered bottle with green front & neck label with green neck ribbon. OSP $1.40, $2.75 & $5.25, CMV $175. MB, $150. BO.

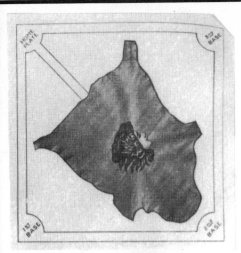

1913 NATOMA LEATHER TABLE COVER
Full size sheep skin leather cover with Natoma Indian head or male Indian head in center. Laid out like a baseball field. Given to Reps for meeting sales goals. CMV $350.

1911 NATOMA TALCUM POWDER
3½ oz. metal can. Brass cap. Label and cap a little different from 1915. issue. OSP 25c, CMV $125. MB as shown. Can only mint, $100.

1915 NATOMA TALCUM POWDER
(Left) 2" tall Brass top. Came in 1915 Juvenile Set only. CMV $150. Also came 3½ oz. regular size on right. OSP 33c, CMV $100. mint.

1914-21 NATOMA ROSE TALCUM
4 oz. green can with pink roses, brass cap. 3 different. 1 has green sifter cap. one brass cap and one has flowers painted on top of can and brass cap. CMV flower top can $90, $110 MB. OSP 25c - CMV $80 mint, $95 MB.

SEE 1984 SUPPLEMENT IN BACK OF THIS BOOK FOR MORE PRODUCTS IN THIS SECTION

TRAILING ARBUTUS

1923 TRAILING ARBUTUS PERFUME
(Left) 2 oz. glass stoppered bottle. Basket design front label and neck label. OSP $2.10, CMV $125. BO mint, $150. MB.

1933-36 TRAILING ARBUTUS PERFUME
(Right) Small 6 sided octagonal bottle and black cap came in Little Folks Set and Handkerchief set. Silver label, came with CPC or CPC Avon Products, Inc. division label. CMV $45. mint.

1928-29 TRAILING ARBUTUS PERFUME
Came in 1 & 2 oz. glass stoppered bottle with blue label. Blue box. OSP $1.20 & $2.10, CMV $150., MB $115. BO.

1915 TRAILING ARBUTUS PERFUME
Fancy embossed box holds glass stoppered bottle with front & neck label. Came in 1, 2 & 4 oz. size. OSP $1.10, $2.10, $ 4., CMV $175. MB $140. BO mint.

1923 Only - TRAILING ARBUTUS PERFUME
  1 oz. travelers bottle, gold labels. Metal cap over glass stopper. Short issue. OSP 78c, CMV $150., $175. MB.

1930 TRAILING ARBUTUS PERFUME
  ½ oz. bottle with frosted glass stopper, silver label. CMV $95. mint.

1941-45 TRAILING ARBUTUS PERFUME
  1/8 oz. bottle, white paper label, brass cap. OSP $1., CMV $35. BO mint, $40. MB.

1928-29 TRAILING ARBUTUS ROUGE
  Blue box. OSP 40c, CMV $35 in box. Rouge only $30 mint.

1928-29 TRAILING ARBUTUS FACE POWDER
  Blue & pink box. OSP 35c, CMV $45 in box. $35 powder box only mint.

1940-42 TRAILING ARBUTUS PERFUME
  3/8 oz. bottle, gold octagonal cap. Gold speckled box. OSP $1.50, CMV $60. BO mint, $85. MB.

1933-34 TRAILING ARBUTUS TOILET WATER
  2 oz. ribbed glass, black cap. Silver label. OSP 75c, CMV $50. BO mint. $60. MB.

1915 TRAILING ARBUTUS TOILET WATER
  2 oz. clear glass bottle with blue & gold front & neck label. Metal crown stopper set in cork. OSP 35c, CMV $140 BO mint, $155 MB.

1915 TRAILING ARBUTUS SACHET
  Brass cap, flowered label, clear glass, 2 different labels. OSP 60c, CMV $90. BO mint each, $115. MB.

1926 TRAILING ARBUTUS PERFUME FLACON
  Frosted ribbed glass with long glass stopper under CPC embossed brass cap. Front paper label. OSP 59c, CMV $90. mint with brass cap and label, $110. MB.

1918 TRAILING ARBUTUS TALCUM REFILL CAN
  1 lb. metal can with brass finish. Front paper label. CMV $75. mint in new condition.

1925 TRAILING ARBUTUS FACE POWDER
  Blue box. OSP 33c, CMV $50 MB, $40 powder box only mint.

1925 TRAILING ARBUTUS VEGETABLE OIL SOAP SAMPLE
  Small 2" X 1 1/8" size sample bar. CMV $50. Mint.

1925 TRAILING ARBUTUS COLD CREAM SAMPLE
Small sample tube in box marked sample. Came with CPC instruction sheet. CMV $60. MB $40. tube only mint.

1914 TRAILING ARBUTUS TALCUM POWDER
4 oz. blue can. 1914-17 can had brass sifter cap with grooved edge. CMV $85. MB, $70. can only. 1917-29 can came with removable brass cap. OSP 33c, CMV $75. MB, $60. can only. Both came with 'The Story of Itallian Talc' in box. 2 different labels on can. With the top section of can all gold, rare - $100.

1925 TRAILING ARBUTUS BATH POWDER
Blue 1 lb. size can with brass cap. This label says only "Trailing Arbutus Bath Powder". OSP 89c, CMV $85. MB, $70. can only mint.

1920 TRAILING ARBUTUS TALCUM POWDER
16 oz. Blue can, brass cap. OSP 89c, CMV $85. MB, $70. can only mint.

1925 TRAILING ARBUTUS VEGETABLE OIL SOAP
Blue box holds 3 embossed soap bars. OSP 39c, CMV $90 MB.

1925-30 TRAILING ARBUTUS COLD CREAM CAN
Came in Jack & Jill Jungle Set, gold can with blue and pink lid. Box is brown, yellow and green. Also came in plain brown CPC box. CMV $40. MB.

1925 TRAILING ARBUTUS PERFUME
1 and 2 oz. sizes. Ribbed bottle with glass stopper. Came in blue box. Front and neck label. OSP $1.17, and $2.10, CMV $115. BO $140. MB.

1925 TRAILING ARBUTUS POWDER SACHET
Brass cap and blue label. OSP 72c, CMV $90. BO mint, $110. MB.

1925 TRAILING ARBUTUS TOILET WATER
2 and 4 oz. sizes. Ribbed bottle with metal and cork cap. OSP 59c, and $1.08, CMV $80. BO. $100. MB,

1925-29 TRAILING ARBUTUS BATH POWDER
4¾ oz. blue can and cap. OSP 35c, CMV $75. MB, $60. can only mint.

1925-29 TRAILING ARBUTUS BATH POWDER
1 lb. size blue can with brass cap. OSP 89c, 2 different labels on front and top of can. This can says only "Bath Powder". CMV $85. MB, $70. can only mint.

1914 TRAILING ARBUTUS TALCUM POWDER SAMPLE
Small blue sample can, gold cap. Front of box in English and back side in French. CMV $85. mint, $105. MB.

1925 TRAILING ARBUTUS CREAMS
Large and small white glass jars of Cold Cream and Vanishing Cream. CPC on blue or plain aluminum metal lids. OSP 33c and 59c, CMV $55. ea. MB, Jar only $45. mint.

1925 TRAILING ARBUTUS COLD CREAM TUBE
Large and small size. Blue tubes. OSP 23c and 45c, CMV $35 MB, tube only $30 mint.

1928-29 TRAILING ARBUTUS CREAMS
Large & small round white glass jars with CPC on blue lids. Came in cold cream & vanishing cream. OSP 33c & 59c, CMV $55. MB, Jar only $45. each.

1923 BRILLANTINE
A hair dressing with Trailing Arbutus perfume scent. Glass bottle with frosted glass stopper. Blue front & neck label. OSP 39c, CMV $105. BO mint, $130. MB.

1915 TRAILING ARBUTUS GIFT BOX
Red, green & pink box contains Trailing Arbutus talcum can, powder sachet & 4 oz. toilet water. OSP $1.25, CMV $350.

1923 TRAILING ARBUTUS THREESOME
Blue box contains 2 oz. bottle of toilet water, 4 oz. can of talcum & bottle of sachet powder. OSP $1.85, CMV $300. MB.

1925 TRAILING ARBUTUS SEXTETTE SET
Large blue box holds white glass jar of Trailing Arbutus Cold Cream & Vanishing Cream. Both have blue lids. Blue can of Talcum Powder, blue box of Face Powder & 2 bars of Vegetable Oil Soap. OSP $1.59, CMV $325. MB.

1925 TRAILING ARBUTUS SEXTETTE BOX
Box only showing label in center of box. CMV box only $20. mint.

VERNAFLEUR
ALL CPC'S MUST BE NEW MINT
CONDITION FOR CMV

1928-29 TRAILING ARBUTUS SEXTETTE GIFT BOX
Blue box holds 2 bars Vegetable Oil Soap, Cold Cream jar & Vanishing Cream jar, box of Face Powder & can of Talcum Powder. All are trimmed in blue & have Trailing Arbutus labels. OSP $1.60, CMV $310. MB.

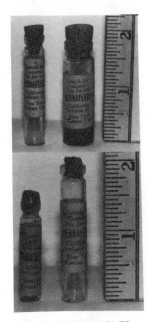

1923 VERNAFLEUR SAMPLES
3 different small glass vials with cork stoppers. One is 1½" the other is 2" high & the fat one is 1¾" high. Not for sale on label. CMV $75. each mint.

1925 VERNAFLEUR PERFUME FLACON
(Left) Brass cap over glass stopper with long glass dabber. OSP 69c. CMV $90. - $110. MB.

1933-36 VERNAFLEUR PERFUME
(Right) 2¼" tall - six sided bottle with black octogonal cap. Silver label, Came in sets, only. CMV $45. mint.

1928 ATOMIZER PERFUME
2 oz., 5¾" tall. Green frosted bottle with gold plated top. Came in Vernafleur Perfume. Is not marked Avon or CPC. OSP $2.50, CMV $80. BO. mint, $110. MB.

1928 VERNAFLEUR TOILET WATER
4 oz. Ribbed glass — CPC brass crown top, front & neck label. OSP $1.35., CMV $90. BO. mint, $110. MB.

1928 VERNAFLEUR PERFUME
1 oz. ribbed clear glass bottle, frosted glass stopper, front label, neck ribbon. OSP $1.17., CMV $110. BO. mint, $135. MB.

1931-33 VERNAFLEUR PERFUME
1 oz. bottle with plastic sealed cork stopper, silver and blue label. Silver box. CMV $70. BO. mint, $100. MB.

1946 VERNAFLEUR BATH SALTS
9 oz. jar, turquoise lid. Short issue. Special blue & white label, OSP 63c, CMV $40. - $55. MB. See Bath Salts Misc. section for regular issue.

1927-29 VERNAFLEUR BATH SALTS
Clear glass, brass cap. Sent to Representatives to give to each customer that orders $2. worth of merchandise. Representative must attain $45. in customer sales on January 1927 order. Offer expired Jan. 31, 1927. (Not a sample) Rare. CMV $150. mint. $175. MB as shown with paper.

1923 VERNAFLEUR PERFUME EXTRACT
¼ oz. glass bottle with glass stopper. Neck label & ribbon. OSP 48c, CMV $100. MB. - $80. BO.

1923 VERNAFLEUR ADHERENT POWDER
Gray metal can. OSP 48c, CMV $45. MB, $35. can only.

1923 VERNAFLEUR PERFUME
Gray box holds 1 oz. ribbed glass bottle with frosted glass stopper. Front & neck label. Green ribbon on neck. OSP 1 oz. size $1.44., 2 oz. size $2.70, CMV $110. BO. - $135. MB.

1923 VERNAFLEUR TOILET WATER
2 & 4 oz. glass bottle with metal & cork shaker cap. OSP 74c & $1.35, CMV $110. MB - $90. BO. mint.

1925 VERNAFLEUR TOILET WATER
2 & 4 oz. Ribbed glass bottle with metal & cork cap. OSP 74c & $1.35, CMV $85. BO. - $100. MB.

1922 VERNATALC
4 oz. can of Talc Powder. Gray. OSP 30c, CMV $60. MB. Can only $50.

1923 VERNAFLEUR TISSUE CREAM
White glass jar with ribs on sides. CPC on metal lid. Large & small size jars. OSP 48c & 89c, CMV $45. MB. Jar only $35.

1923 VERNAFLEUR NUTRI CREAM
Large & small white glass jar with ribs on sides. CPC on metal lid. OSP 48c & 89c, CMV $45. MB, $35. Jar only.

1925 VERNAFLEUR BATH SALTS
10 oz. glass bottle with brass lid, ribbed glass sides. OSP 75c, CMV $85. MB, $70. jar only, mint.

1925 VERNAFLEUR PERFUME FLACON
Flaconette size frosted ribbed bottle with glass stopper, brass cap over stopper. Small front label. CPC on cap. Comes in yellow & green box. OSP 70c, CMV $90. with cap, $110. MB.

1928 VERNAFLEUR TISSUE CREAM
Small & Large size white glass jar with ribbed sides. Came with or without CPC on aluminum lid. OSP 50c & 90c, CMV $55 MB, $40 jar only.

1928 VERNAFLEUR PERFUME
1 oz. glass stoppered bottle, blue, yellow & black box. OSP $1.45, CMV $150. MB, $110. BO. mint.

1928 VERNAFLEUR COMPACT
Silver compact with Vernafleur on lid. Single & double compact. OSP $1 & $1.50, CMV $45 MB, $35 compact only mint.

1928 VERNA TALC
4 oz. multi-colored can, brass cap. OSP $1.15, CMV $75. mint, $90. MB.

1928 VERNAFLEUR NUTRI CREME
Large & small white glass jar with ribbed sides. CPC on aluminum lid. OSP 50c & 90c, CMV $50. MB, $40. jar only mint.

1928-31 VERNAFLEUR TOILET SOAP
Box holds 3 bars of soap in blue paper. OSP 75c - CMV $90.

1925 VERNAFLEUR FACE POWDER
Blue, yellow & black metal can. OSP 48c, CMV $40. MB, $30. can only mint. This was also called Vernafleur Adherent Powder.

1928 VERNAFLEUR FACE POWDER SAMPLE
Adherent Powder sample. Came several in a box. OSP 48c per box of samples. CMV not established.

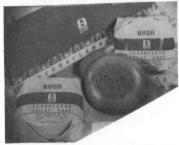

1936-39 VERNAFLEUR TOILET SOAP
Turquoise & white box & wrapping holds 3 violet colored bars. OSP 77c, CMV $55. MB.

1925-28 VERNAFLEUR TOILET SOAP
Gray box & wrapping holds 3 bars. OSP 69c - CMV $85 MB.

1929 CHRISTMAS CHEER
Red, white & blue boxes of Vernafleur Sachet Powder. Came in sets of 4 boxes. OSP $1.20, CMV $40 each box.

1925 VERNAFLEUR NUTRI-CREME SAMPLE
(Left) Multi-colored tube, says on back side "not for Sale Sample." CMV $50 MB, $40 tube.

1925 VERNAFLEUR FACE POWDER SAMPLE
(Right) 1½" small paper box used as sample. CMV $45 mint.

1931-36 VERNAFLEUR TOILET SOAP
Lavender in color, in white wrapper. Box of 3 bars. OSP 75c, CMV $60. MB.

1933 ATOMIZER GIFT SET
Blue box with green & red holly leaves holds 1 oz. bottle of Vernafleur perfume with small silver label & 1 oz. red glass bottle with spray atomizer. OSP $2.86., CMV $185. MB.

499

1929 VERNAFLEUR BATH SET
Black & gold box holds bottle of Vernafleur Bath Salts, Dusting powder in gold & Black striped can & 1 bar of Vernafleur Toilet Soap. OSP $3.50., CMV $225. MB.

1928 VERNAFLEUR THREESOME GIFT BOX
Gray box holds 2 oz. bottle of Vernafleur Toilet Water, jar of Vanishing Cream & can of Face Powder. OSP $2.10, CMV $190. MB.

1929 VERNAFLEUR QUINTETTE SET
Blue, black & gold box holds Vernafleur Tissue Cream & Nutri-Cream. Face Powder, Talc & Flaconette of Perfume. OSP $2.25., CMV $325. MB.

VIOLET
SEE MISCELLANEOUS CPC JARS FOR OTHER VIOLET PRODUCTS.

1893 VIOLET ALMOND MEAL
8 oz. glass jar with metal lid. OSP 50c, CMV $140 MB, $120 jar only mint.

1915 VIOLET TOILET WATER
(Left) 2 oz. bottle, metal crown stopper in cork, front & neck label. OSP 35c, CMV $100. BO. mint, $125. MB.
1915 VIOLET TOILET WATER
(Center) ¼ oz. clear glass, cork stopper. Came only in 1915 Juvenile Set. Rare, CMV $125. mint.
1915 VIOLET PERFUME
(Right) Front & neck label, glass crown stopper in cork. OSP 50c, CMV $175. mint.

1908 VIOLET ALMOND MEAL
(Left) 8 oz. Glass jar with metal lid. OSP 50c, CMV $100. jar only mint, $120. MB. 1910 issue same only Eureka Trade Mark in place of CP at top of label.
1915 VIOLET PERFUME
1 oz. size, cork stopper. Used with spray atomizer. Came in 1915 Violet Gift Box H set only. CMV $100. mint.

1923 VIOLET TALCUM
(Left) 3-1/3 oz. Violet & green colored can, brass cap. OSP 23c, CMV $75. mint, $90. MB.
1916 VIOLET TOILET WATER
(Right) 2 oz. bottle with metal crown pour cap in cork. Colorful front and neck label. OSP 35c, CMV $100. BO mint., $125. MB.

1912 VIOLET ALMOND MEAL
(Right) Glass jar with metal shaker lid. Came 3½ oz. & 3¾ oz. size. Two different labels. OSP 50c, CMV $90., $115. MB.

1915 VIOLET GIFT SET H
Green, white & purple box contains bottle of Violet Talcum, 1 oz. Perfume bottle with cork stopper & Atomizer, Violet Powder Sachet. OSP $1.35, CMV $400. MB.

1923 VIOLET ALMOND MEAL
4 oz. sifter top metal can. 2 different labels. OSP 48c, CMV $60, $75 MB.

1907 VIOLET ALMOND MEAL
8 oz. Clear glass — metal shaker top. OSP 50c, CMV $105 jar only mint, $130. MB.

1912 VIOLET NUTRI-CREME
(Left) Small & large size white glass jars with aluminum lid. OSP 50c & 90c, CMV $55. each MB. $45. jar only mint.

1923 VIOLET NUTRI-CREME
(Right) Large & small white glass jars with CPC on metal lid. OSP 49c, & 89c, CMV $45. each, $55. MB.

1915 VIOLET TALCUM POWDER
(Left) 3½ oz. Glass jar, OSP 25c, CMV $110. MB. - $90. BO.

1908 VIOLET TALCUM POWDER
(Right) 3½ oz. Glass jar with metal Cap has 2 variations of labels. OSP 25c, CMV $110. Jar only mint $135 MB.

1923 VIOLET THREESOME SET
Contains 2 oz. bottle of Toilet Water, 3 & 1/3 oz. can of Talcum & bottle of Sachet Powder in violet colored box. OSP $1.40., CMV $325. MB.

BABY ITEMS — CPC
SEE 1984 SUPPLEMENT IN BACK OF BOOK FOR MORE CPC BABY ITEMS

1923 BABY SET
Yellow box contains 2 oz. bottle of Toilet Water, bar of Baby Soap & can of Baby Powder. OSP 99c, CMV $200 MB — CMV Toilet water only $95. mint.

1910 VIOLET NUTRI-CREME
White glass jar, aluminum lid. Paper label all around jar. Bottom pat. Dec. 9, 1890. OSP 50c, CMV $50. mint - $60. MB.

1898 BABY POWDER
Metal can. Eureka Trade Mark on label. OSP 25c, CMV $110. mint, $135. MB.

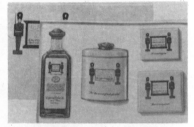

1905 BABY POWDER
(Left) Metal can lift off cap 1905. 1906 cap has sifter top, CP in center of Trade Mark. 1910 same can sifter cap a little different and Eureka trade mark in place of CP.

1912-16 BABY POWDER
(Right) Metal can. OSP 25c, CMV $80 mint, $100 MB.

1916 BABY POWDER
(Top) Blue & pink can. OSP 25c, CMV $90 MB. - $75 can only, mint.

1916 BABY SET
(Bottom) Baby set box holds can of baby Powder as pictured above, without box, bar of Baby Soap & 2 oz. bottle of Violet Toilet Water. OSP 75c, CMV $300 MB.

1925 BABY SET
Yellow box holds 4 oz. bottle of Supreme Olive Oil, 4 oz. yellow can of Baby Powder, yellow box of Boric Acid & 5 oz. yellow cake of genuine imported Castile Soap. OSP $1.78 - CMV $250 MB.

1925 SUPREME OLIVE OIL FOR BABY'S
4 oz. bottle with yellow label & cork stopper. Came in Baby Set only. CMV $85. mint.

1925 CASTILE SOAP FOR BABY'S
5 oz. cake wrapped in yellow paper. Came in Baby Set only. CMV $45 mint.

1925 BORIC ACID FOR BABY
Yellow Box with soldiers on top. OSP 33c, CMV $35.

1923 BABY POWDER
4 oz. Yellow can. OSP 29c, CMV $50 MB, can only CPC $50.

BAY RUM
ALSO SEE AVON BAY RUM SECTION. ALL BOTTLES PRICED MINT. SEE PAGE 6 & 16 FOR GRADING.

1898 BAY RUM
4 oz. clear glass square bottle. Glass stopper. Colored label. OSP 40c, CMV $175., $200. MB.

1896 BAY RUM
(Left) 4 oz. glass stoppered bottle. OSP 40c, CMV $150. Also came in 8 & 16 oz. size with glass stoppers. OSP 75c & $1.25, CMV $150. each. BO $200. MB.

1905 BAY RUM
(Right) 16 oz. size glass stopper. OSP $1.25, CMV $150. mint, BO $200. MB.

1905 CALIFORNIA BABY SOAP
4 oz. white embossed bar in wrapping. OSP 15c, CMV $75 MB.

1930-36 BAY RUM
8 oz. clear glass bottle, black cap, green & black label. OSP 89c, CMV $40. BO mint, $50. MB.

1908 BAY RUM
(Left) 4 oz. glass stoppered bottle. OSP 40c, CMV $135., BO $160. MB. Also came in 8 & 16 oz. size glass stoppered bottles. CMV $140. ea. mint. $165. MB.

1912 BAY RUM
(Right) 4 oz. glass stoppered bottle. Also came in 8 & 16 oz. size glass stoppered bottles. OSP 40c, CMV $140. ea. mint, $165. MB.

1927 BAY RUM
4 oz. metal & cork CPC embossed stopper. Front & neck label. Also came in 8 "shown on right" & 16 oz. size with cork stopper. OSP 50c, CMV $100 BO 4 oz., $120 8 & 16 oz. Add $25 for box, mint.

1929 BAY RUM
(Left) 16 oz. size with metal cap. OSP $1.44 - CMV $95 BO, $110 MB.

1923 BAY RUM
(Right) 4 oz. bottle, metal shaker cap in cork. OSP 47c, CMV $95 MB $85 BO. Also came in 8 oz. OSP 84c, 32 oz. $2.40, CMV $95 BO each, $110. MB.

LEFT TO RIGHT

1915 BAY RUM
4 oz. with crown metal & cork stopper. OSP 25c, CMV $125. mint. $150. MB.

1921 BAY RUM
4 oz. front & neck label. Cork stopper. OSP 47c, CMV $175. MB, $125. BO.

1898 BAY RUM
4 oz. cork stopper. 126 Chambers St. on label where CPC started. Very rare. CMV $175. - $200. MB.

1920 BAY RUM
4 oz. clear glass bottle, glass stopper. CMV $110. mint, $135. MB.

1912 BAY RUM
16 oz. clear glass, cork stopper. RARE. CMV $150., $175. MB.

1930-36 BAY RUM
4 oz. Ribbed glass bottle with black cap & green label. OSP 50c, CMV $50. MB, $45. BO. Also came in 16 oz. size OSP 89c, CMV $50. BO $60. MB

CPC BOTTLES — MISC.
SEE 1984 SUPPLEMENT IN BACK OF BOOK FOR MORE CPC BOTTLES

1915 BENZOIN LOTION
(Left) 2 oz. size, metal crown stopper in cork. Flowered label. OSP 75c. Also came in 4 oz. size at $1.50. CMV $100. each mint - $125. MB.

1923 BENZOIN LOTION
(Right) 2 oz. bottle with metal & cork stopper. OSP 59c, CMV $75. - $100. MB.

1925 BENZOIN LOTION
(Left) 2 oz. ribbed glass bottle with metal & cork stopper, blue & gold label. OSP 59c, CMV $65. BO - $85. MB.

1896 LAIT VIRGINAL
(Right) 2 oz. size, ribbed glass bottle has ribbed glass stopper set in cork. OSP 65c, CMV $150. mint - $175. MB.

1896 FACE LOTION
(Left) Glass bottle with cork stopper. OSP $1., CMV $110. - $135. MB.

1908 FACE LOTION
(Right) Glass bottle, cork stopper, front & neck label. OSP $1., CMV $110. - $135. MB.

1918 FACE LOTION
(Left) 6 oz. glass bottle has cork stopper, green front & neck label. Came with small sponge tied to neck. OSP $1, CMV $80, $100 MB.

1923 FACE LOTION
(Right) 6 oz. glass bottle, blue label, cork stopper. OSP 97c, CMV $80 $100. MB.

1900 LAIT VIRGINAL
2 oz., cork stopper. OSP 60c, CMV $100. - $125. MB.

1929-30 CUTICLE REMOVER OR SOFTENER
(Left) ½ oz. bottle with brown label & cork stopper with glass dabber. Also came in Boudoir Set. OSP 35c, CMV $60. BO - $75. MB.

1924 CUTRANE
(Center) Glass bottle with cork stopper with camel hair brush on stopper. Gold & black label. OSP 30c, CMV $60. BO mint - $75. MB.

1920 LIQUID FACE POWDER
(Right) 6 oz. clear glass, cork stopper. Has green front & neck label. OSP 97c, CMV $80 mint BO, $100 MB.

1912 FACE LOTION
(Left) 6 oz. clear glass bottle, cork stopper. Front & neck label. Came in white & pink shades. OSP $1., CMV $100. BO - $125. MB.

1914 LIQUID SHAMPOO
(Right) 6 oz. glass bottle with metal cap. OSP 35c, CMV $95. BO - $120. MB.

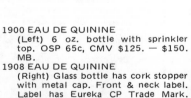

1923 LIQUID SHAMPOO
6 oz. front & neck label. Metal shaker cap in cork, OSP 48c, CMV $85 $100. MB.

1900 EAU DE QUININE
(Left) 6 oz. bottle with sprinkler top. OSP 65c, CMV $125. — $150. MB.

1908 EAU DE QUININE
(Right) Glass bottle has cork stopper with metal cap. Front & neck label. Label has Eureka CP Trade Mark. OSP 65c, CMV $125. — $150. MB.

1905 EAU DE QUININE HAIR TONIC
Glass stopper in cork. Eureka Trade Mark on neck label. OSP 65c, CMV $125. — $150. MB.

1896 WITCH HAZEL
(Left) 4 & 8 oz. bottles came with sprinkler top. OSP 25c & 45c, CMV $100. Pint bottle came with glass stopper. OSP 75c, CMV $150. mint — $200. MB.

1905 WITCH HAZEL
(Right) 16 oz. size, glass stopper. OSP 75c, CMV $150. mint — $200. MB.

1915 WITCH HAZEL
(Left) 4 oz. glass bottle with cork stopper. OSP 25c, CMV $90. 8 & 16 oz. size with glass stopper. OSP 45c & 75c, CMV $125. each mint — $145. MB.

1924 WITCH HAZEL
(Center & Right) 4 oz. clear glass bottle, cork stopper. Front and neck label. 3 different labels, 2 shown. OSP 39c, CMV $75. BO. mint — $90. MB.

1915 EAU DE QUININE
(Left) 6 oz. glass bottle with metal crown & cork cap. OSP 65c, CMV $100. BO. — $125. MB.

1923 EAU DE QUININE
(Right) 6 oz. glass bottle, metal shaker cap in cork. OSP 69c, CMV $90. BO. — $110. MB.

1908 WITCH HAZEL
(Left) 16 oz. size glass stopper. OSP 75c, CMV $150. mint — $200. MB.

1908 WITCH HAZEL
(Right) Came in 4, 8 & 16 oz. bottles with glass stopper. Eureka Trade Mark on label. OSP 25c, 45c & 75c, CMV $150. mint — $200. MB.

1920 WITCH HAZEL
(Left) 16 oz. clear glass, cork stopper Front label. Rare. OSP 75c — CMV $135. Mint — $160. MB. Also came in 8 oz. size with metal crown & cork stopper. OSP 45c CMV, $100. Mint $125. MB.

1930 ONLY WITCH HAZEL
(Right) 4 oz. ribbed glass bottle, black cap. green label. Rare, CMV $75. —$85. MB.

1923 WITCH HAZEL
(Left) 4 oz. bottle with cork stopper, green front & neck label. OSP 39c, CMV $75. Also came in 8, 16 & 32 oz. size. OSP 69c, $1.20 & $2.25. CMV each, $75. mint, add $25. MB each.

1925 WITCH HAZEL
(Right) 4 oz. bottle with cork stopper, green label on front & neck. OSP 39c, CMV $65. Also came in 8 & 16 oz. size. OSP 69c & $1.20. CMV each $75. mint, add $25. MB each.

1910 WITCH HAZEL
16 oz. clear glass, glass stopper. OSP 75c, CMV $150. — $175. MB.

1908 TOOTH WASH
(Left) Glass bottle has cork stopper with metal crown top. Eureka Trade Mark on neck label. OSP 25c, CMV $140. MB — $115. MB.

1915 TOOTH WASH
(Right) Glass bottle with metal & cork cap. Back side of bottle is embossed California Tooth Wash. OSP 25c, CMV $100. with label mint. Embossed bottle only $25. — $125. MB.

1923 ROSE WATER, GLYCERINE & BENZOIN
(Left) 6 oz. clear glass bottle. Glass stopper set in cork. Print front & neck label. OSP 60c, CMV $100. — $125. MB.

1924-25 ROSE WATER, GLYCERINE & BENZOIN
(Right) 6 oz. bottle with cork stopper. Front and neck label. This was a very short issue bottle. OSP 60c, CMV $100. BO. — $125. MB.

1924 ROSE WATER, GLYCERINE & BENZOIN SAMPLE
Glass bottle, cork stopper, CMV $75 MB, $60 BO mint.

1917 LOTUS CREAM SAMPLE
Blue and white box holds ½ oz. sample bottle with cork stopper. Blue label. CMV $80 MB, $65 BO. mint.

1925 ROSE WATER GLYCERINE AND BENZOIN SAMPLE
Small sample bottle on 1st introduction of this product in January 1925. Rare. CMV $75, $85 MB.

1921 TOOTH WASH
(Left) 2 oz. glass bottle, brass & cork stopper. OSP 25c, CMV $100., $125. MB.

1923 TOOTH WASH
(Right) 2 oz. glass bottle, metal and cork cap. Front and neck label. OSP 33c, CMV $85., $110. MB.

1929 ONLY ROSE WATER, GLYCERINE & BENZOIN
(Left) 4 oz. clear glass ribbed bottle with black cap. Bottle came from Avon with small sample pink label marked not for resale. Bottle with this label rare. CMV $100. mint BO.

1926 ROSE WATER GLYCERINE & BENZOIN
(Right) 4 oz. ribbed bottle with cork stopper, front & neck label. OSP 50c - CMV $75 mint, $90 MB.

1917 LOTUS CREAM
12 oz. bottle has glass stopper, OSP $1.23, CMV $150.; 4 oz. bottle has cork stopper, OSP 48c, CMV $120. Add $25. MB each, both have front & neck labels. Also came in 1 quart, ½ & 1 gallon size.

1925 LOTUS CREAM
4 oz. ribbed bottle with cork stopper, front & neck label. OSP 48c, CMV $75 BO mint, $90 MB.

1931-36 HAIR TONIC EAU DE QUININE
(Left) Ribbed glass bottle with black cap & silver label. OSP 90c, CMV $40. bottle only - $45. in box. Also came in 16 oz. size. OSP $1.75, CMV $50. BO mint - $55. MB.

1928 NULODOR
(right) Bottle has clear stopper, front & neck label. OSP 35c CMV $100 mint. Rare.

1914 NAIL BLEACH
2 oz. round bottle with glass stopper, front paper label. 2 different labels shown. OSP 25c, CMV $90. BO - $110. MB each.

1929 Only GERTRUDE RECORDON'S PEACH LOTION
Clear glass. Box states "This merchandise sent free for demonstration purposes or personal use. It must not be sold." CMV $90 MB.

1916 NAIL BLEACH
2 oz. glass stopper, square bottle. Rare. OSP 25c, CMV $125. BO - $150. MB.

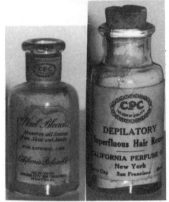

1912 NAIL BLEACH - 1 OZ.
(Left) 1 oz. bottle, cork stopper. OSP 25c, CMV $100. - $115. MB.

1915 DEPILATORY
(Right) 1 oz. bottle with cork stopper. OSP 50c, CMV $90. - $110. MB.

1908 ROUGE
Rouge powder can. CMV $50, $70 MB.

LIQUID ROUGE
Bottle, CMV $100, $125 MB. OSP each 25c. Eureka trademark on both labels and CP in center of early label instead of Eureka.

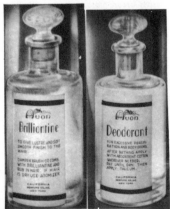

1930 Only BRILLIANTINE
(Left) 2 oz. bottle with frosted glass stopper in cork. Silver label. OSP 50c, CMV $75. mint - $95. MB.

1930 Only DEODORANT
(Right) 2 oz. bottle with corked frosted glass stopper. OSP 50c, CMV $75. - $95. MB.

1914 ROSE POMADE
(Left) White glass jar. Top & side label. OSP 25c, CMV $65.

1912 NAIL BLEACH - 2 OZ.
(Right) 2 oz. clear glass round bottle, cork stopper, front & neck label. OSP 25c, CMV $95. BO - $110. MB.

1916 ROUGE
(left) Rough. OSP 25c, CMV $45, $60 MB.

1916 LIQUID ROUGE
(Right) Glass bottle, cork stopper. OSP 25c, CMV $80. BO - $100. MB.

1905 SHAVING SOAP
(Left) 1 bar of soap. OSP 20c, CMV $50. in wrapper, mint.

1923 BAYBERRY SHAVING STICK
(Right) Three piece nickel metal container holds shaving soap. OSP 33c, CMV $45. mint.

1915 SHAVING CREAM STICK
Gold or silvertone metal can. Came with soap stick, CPC on lid. OSP 25c, CMV $55. MB - $40. can only mint.

CPC JARS

1915 AUTOMASSAGE SHAVING BRUSH
Automassage on handle. Rubber center of brush as shown. This was not made for CPC but sold by CPC on a special offer with CPC shaving powder. OSP 25c, CMV $50. MB - $30. brush only.

1890's LAVENDER SALTS
(Left) Teal green glass, octagonal shaped bottle. Ground glass stopper. Rare. OSP 35c, CMV $275. - $300. MB.

1890's LAVENDER SALTS - METAL TOP
(Right) Emerald green glass, glass stopper with screw on metal top. Rare. OSP 35c, CMV $275. - $300. MB.

1893 LAVENDER SALTS
(Left) Emerald green glass bottle with green glass stopper with leather liner. OSP 35c, CMV $200. mint - $225. MB.

1915 LAVENDER SALTS
(Right) Glass stoppered bottle. OSP 35c, CMV $115. mint - $140. MB.

1923 LAVENDER SALTS
Glass stoppered bottle, front & neck label. OSP 49c, CMV $110. mint - $135. MB.

1910 LAVENDER SALTS
Emerald green glass. Same label only 1 bottle is 1/8'' bigger than the other. Green glass stoppers set in rubber. OSP 35c, CMV $250. each mint - $275. MB.

1896 MASSAGE CREAM
Glass jar with glass stopper. OSP 75c, CMV $150 mint, $175 MB.

1912 LAVENDER SALTS
(Left) Glass stoppered bottle. OSP 35c, CMV $110. - $135. MB.

1908 LAVENDER SALTS
(Right) Green glass bottle has green glass stopper with rubber base. OSP 35c, CMV $160. mint - $185. MB.

1926-30 LEMONOL CLEANSING CREAM
Frosted glass jar with brass lid. OSP 50c - CMV $75 MB, $65 jar only.

1896 SHAMPOO CREAM
4 oz. glass jar. Man's picture, washing his hair on lid. Rare. OSP 35c, CMV $115. - $140. MB.

1923 DERMOL MASSAGE CREAM
(Left) White glass jar with ribbed sides. CPC on metal lid. OSP 96c, CMV $50. - $60. MB.

1926 VIOLET NUTRI-CREME
(Right) White glass jar with flowered label. OSP 89c, CMV $50. - $60. MB.

1916 MASSAGE CREAM
Glass jar has glass stopper, green ribbon, on neck. OSP 50c, CMV $125 mint, $145 MB.

1896 SHAMPOO CREAM
4 oz. white glass jar, metal lid. OSP 35c - CMV $90, $110 MB.

1905 SHAMPOO CREAM
4 oz. white glass jar. OSP 35c, CMV $85. jar only mint - $105. MB.

1920-23 DERMOL MASSAGE CREAM
Glass jar with metal screw on lid. OSP 96c - CMV $75 mint, $90 MB.

1908 TOOTH POWDER
White glass bottle with metal cap. OSP 25c, CMV $110. mint - $130. MB.

1908 SHAMPOO CREAM
4 oz. white glass jar with metal lid. OSP 35c, CMV $75. jar only, $95. MB.

1912 SHAMPOO CREAM
4 oz. white glass jar, metal lid, with or without CPC on lid. Early issue 1912 has Eureka trademark on box - 1915 one does not. OSP 35c, CMV $80 jar only $95 MB for Eureka trademark, $10 less without.

1923-30 - 4 OZ. BANDOLINE HAIR DRESSING
Tall 4 oz. clear glass with cork stopper. Comes with neck label to be mint. OSP 45c, CMV $65. BO mint - $80. MB.

1908 BANDOLINE
2 oz. glass bottle, cork stopper. OSP 25c, CMV $110. MB - $90. BO.

1915 SHAMPOO CREAM SAMPLE
Small 1" size aluminum round bottom container. Rare. CMV $50. mint.

1923-30 BANDOLINE HAIR DRESSING
(Left) 2 oz. yellow label & cork stopper, clear glass jar. OSP 24c, CMV $60. mint - $75. MB.

1923-30 BANDOLINE HAIR DRESSING
(Right) 4 oz. size. Glass bottle, cork stopper, front & neck label. OSP 45c, CMV $65. BO - $80. MB.

1896 COLD CREAM
White glass jar with metal lid. Eureka trademark on label. OSP 25c, CMV $90. mint - $110. MB.

1915 COLD CREAMS
Large & small white glass jars with CPC on metal lid. OSP 25c & 45c, CMV $75. MB each - $60. jar only, mint.

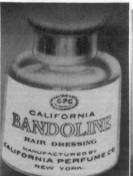

1915 BANDOLINE
(Left) Glass bottle with cork stopper. OSP 25c, CMV $75. mint - $90. MB.

1930-35 BANDOLINE
(Right) Frosted glass bottle with blue wrapped cork stopper. OSP 37c, CMV $55. BO - $65. MB.

1926 COLD CREAM
White glass jar with CPC on aluminum lid. OSP 63c - CMV $50 mint, $65 MB.

1908 CALIFORNIA COLD CREAM
2 oz. white glass jar with metal lid. OSP 25c, CMV $95. MB - $80. jar only mint.

1912 CPC COLD CREAM
Large white glass jar with metal lid. OSP 45c, CMV $60. jar only - $75. MB.

CPC PERFUMES — MISC.

1917 TRAVELERS PERFUME 1 OZ.
1 oz. octagonal shaped bottle with glass stopper & screw on nickle lid. OSP 90c, CMV $135., BO mint, $160. MB.

1896 TO 1914 PERFUMES

The following list of perfumes were sold by CPC from 1896 to 1914. Use this list to identify misc. perfumes.

The regular line of CP Floral extracts consists of thirty odors, in the following range of prices and sizes:

Roses		
Lily of the Valley		
White Rose		
Violet		
White Lilac		
Sweet Peas		
Hyacinth		
Heliotrope	1 ounce bottle	$ .60
Carnation	2 ounce bottle	1.10
Bouquet Marie	4 ounce bottle	2.00
New Mown Hay		
Marie Stewart	½ pint bottle	3.75
Rose Geranium	1 pint bottle	7.00
Stephanotis		
Ylang Ylang		
Jack Rose		
Tube Rose		
Treffle		
California Bouquet		

Crab Apple Blossom	1 ounce bottle	$ .75
Trailing Arbutus	2 ounce bottle	1.40
Frangipanni	4 ounce bottle	2.75
May Blossom	½ pint bottle	5.25
Jockey Club	1 pint bottle	10.00
White Heliotrope		

Lou Lillie	1 ounce bottle	$ .50
Musk	2 ounce bottle	.90
Golf Club	4 ounce bottle	1.75
Venetian Carnation	½ pint bottle	3.25
Golf Violet	1 pint bottle	6.00

1915 TO 1921 PERFUMES

The very extensive CPC line gives a wide range of selection, and among the 27 different odors there is sure to be one or more to satisfy the most fastidious and exacting.

The prices are according to the cost of production and the value of the goods offered. All perfumes are in attractive bottles, put up in beautiful lithographed boxes, as illustrated.

Concentrated Floral Odors
Triple Extracts

Violet		
White Rose		
Carnation		
Heliotrope		
Lily of the Valley	1 ounce bottle	.50
White Lilac	2 ounce bottle	.90
Hyacinth	4 ounce bottle	1.75
California Bouquet	½ pint bottle	3.25
Roses	1 pint bottle	6.00
New Mown Hay		
Sweet Pea		
Treffle		
Rose Geranium		
Jack Rose		

Quadruple Extracts

Crab Apple Blossom	1 ounce bottle	$ .60
Trailing Arbutus	2 ounce bottle	1.10
Jockey Club	4 ounce bottle	2.00
Honeysuckle	½ pint bottle	3.75
White Heliotrope	1 pint bottle	7.00

Extra Concentrated Odors

Natoma Rose	1 ounce bottle	.75
Venetian Carnation	2 ounce bottle	1.40
Golf Violet	4 ounce bottle	2.75
Musk	½ pint bottle	5.25
	1 pint bottle	10.00

1898 PERFUME REPRODUCTION
1 oz. size, glass stopper, neck ribbons. White Rose, Lily of the Valley, Violet, Heliotrope. All different labels. OSP 25c - CMV $100 each mint. All bottles shown are Avon Products reproductions.

1900-1923 TRAVELER'S PERFUME
½ oz. size. Metal cap over glass stopper. Gold label. Bottle is octagonally shaped. Came in all fragrances of 1896-1908. Red flowered box. OSP 50c, CMV $125. BO mint. $150. MB. Also came in 1 oz. size on left. RARE. CMV $150.-$175. MB.

1930-35 PERFUME FLACONETTE
(Left) Embossed clear glass stopper, brass cap over glass stopper. Avon on cap. Came in all perfumes of 1930-35. OSP $1.10, CMV $90. each mint. $110. MB.

1900 ROSE PERFUME SAMPLE
(Right) ½ oz. size, cork stopper. Came in all fragrances of 1900. CMV $125. mint.

1923 PERFUME FLACONETTE
Octagonal shaped bottle with long glass stopper, neck label. Came with & without brass cap with CPC on cap. Came in Daphne, Crab Apple, Vernafleur, Trailing Arbutus, White Rose, Carnation, Violet, White Lilac, Heliotrope, Roses, Lily of the Valley. OSP 49c, CMV with brass cap $90. without cap $75. - $110. MB.

1928 PERFUME SPRAY ATOMIZER
1 is green opaque over clear glass & 1 is green painted over clear, gold plated top. CMV $90. each.

1926 PERFUME FLACONETTE
Frosted ribbed glass bottle with long glass stopper. Small paper label on front. Came with brass cap with CPC on cap. Came in Crab Apple, Daphne, Trailing Arbutus, Vernafleur, American Ideal, Carnation, Heliotrop, White Rose, Violet, Lily of the Valley. OSP 59c, CMV with brass cap $90., $70. BO, $110. MB.

1925 PERFUME FLACONETTE
Flaconette size embossed glass bottle with glass stopper. Brass cap over stopper. Came in Mission Garden, American Ideal, Narcissus, Daphne, Jardin D' Amour. OSP $1.10, CMV $90. BO, mint with brass cap. $120. MB. The cap has fragrance on it.

1918 WHITE ROSE PERFUME
2 oz. size, RARE, cork stopper. Front & neck label with neck ribbon. OSP $1., CMV $125. mint.

1898 PERFUME REPRODUCTION
1 oz. size, glass stopper, neck ribbons. Hyacinth, Crab Apple Blossom, Sweet Pea, Carnation. All different labels. OSP 25c, CMV $100. ea. mint. All bottles shown are Avon Products reproductions.

1918 PERFUME
½ oz. bottle with crown glass stopper set in cork. Front & neck label. Came in all fragrances of 1918. OSP 50c, CMV $100. BO mint, $125. MB.

1908 LITTLE FOLKS PERFUMES
2" high small bottles with cork stoppers came in early 1900's Little Folks gift sets. Came in Heliotrope, Rose, Carnation, and Violet. Front labels and neck ribbons. CMV $75. each mint.

1918 CPC PERFUME
(Left) ½ oz. glass & cork stopper. Came in 1918 Gift Box A Set. CMV $110. mint.
1919 ½ OZ. PERFUME
(Right) ½ oz. glass crowned shaped stopper in cork. Came in all 1919 fragrances. OSP 75c, CMV $100. mint, $125. MB.

1915 - ½ OZ. PERFUME
(Left) ½ oz. bottle with glass stopper set in cork. Front and neck label. Came in Violet, White Rose, Carnation, White Lilac, Heliotrope, Lily of the Valley. Two different stoppers as shown on left. OSP 25c, CMV $110., $135. MB.
1 OZ EXTRA CONCENTRATED PERFUMES
(Right) 1 oz. size, front and neck label. Came in Golf Violet, Musk, Crab Apple Blossom, Natoma, Rose, Venetian Carnation. OSP 75c, CMV $175. MB, $135. BO.

1925-32 LITTLE FOLKS PERFUME
(Left) ½ oz. bottle with brass screw on cap. Came in 1925 Little Folks Set only. Came in Violet, Carnation, Heliotrope, White Lilac, Daphne, Vernafleur, Trailing Arbutus. CMV $65. ea. mint.
1896 LITTLE FOLKS PERFUME
(Right) 2" high. Came in 1896 & 1906 Little Folks Set only in Rose, or White Rose, Heliotrope, Violet, & carnation. Cork stopper. CMV $75. ea. mint.

1915 LITTLE FOLKS PERFUME
(Left) Small gem size bottle with front label & ribbon on neck. Cork stopper. Came in 1915 Little Folks Set only. Came in Carnation, Violet, White Rose, Heliotrope. CMV $75. ea. mint.
1910 LITTLE FOLKS PERFUME
(Right) 2" high, cork stopper. Came in Little Folks Set only from 1910 to 1915. Both bottles pictured came in same fragrances. CMV $75. mint.

1900 FRENCH PERFUMES
(Left) ¼ oz. bottle with glass stopper. Came in Le Perfume Des Roses, L' Odeur de Violette, Peau d'Espagne. OSP 25c, CMV $125. BO, $150. MB.
1896 FRENCH PERFUMES
(Right) ¼ oz. glass bottle, cork stopper. Came in Le Perfume Des Roses, L'Odeur de Violette, Peau d'Espagne. OSP 25c, CMV $125. BO mint - $150. MB.

1900 FRENCH PERFUMES
(Left) Trial size ¼ oz. on left. 2 oz. size on right. Cork stoppers. CMV $125. BO trial size mint, CMV $200. 2 oz. size mint, add $25. MB.

1916 FRENCH PERFUMES
(Right) 2 different embossed glass bottles. Cork stoppers. Trial size. OSP 25c, CMV $125. BO mint, $150. MB.

1908 PERFUME
(Left) 1 oz. glass stopper, gold label. Eureka Trade Mark on label. Came in all fragrances of 1908. CMV $180. MB $150. BO Mint. Also came in several different glass stoppers. 2 different shown on left.

1906-1918 PERFUME
(Right 4 oz. glass stoppered bottle, gold embossed front and neck label. Came in all perfumes of the period. See list on front of this section. OSP $2.75, CMV $150. BO, $200. MB.

1918 PERFUME & ATOMIZER
1 oz. bottle with atomizer came in black box. Bottle has cork stopper & green front & neck label. Came in all fragrances of 1918, including American Ideal & Daphne. OSP $1.50, CMV $150. MB with atomizer. $100. BO mint.

1923 PERFUMES
½ oz. bottle with crown glass stopper set in cork. Front & neck label. Crab Apple, Blossom, White Rose, Trailing Arbutus, Rose Carnation, Heliotorpe, Violet, White Lilac, & Lily of the Valley. Came in red box 2 Different Bottles as shown. OSP 59c, CMV $110. BO, $135. MB.

1900 VIOLET PERFUME
Eureka Trade Mark. Neck ribbon, neck label is plain. CMV $165. BO mint.

1908 JOCKEY CLUB PERFUME
Green front and neck label and green neck ribbon. OSP 50c, CMV $100. mint, $130. MB.

1906 PERFUMES
1 oz. round bottles came in Atomizer Perfume Set with cork stopper. Came in all fragrances of 1908. CMV $110. ea. mint.

1896 PERFUME
1 oz. octagonal shaped bottle, front & neck label with Eureka Trade Mark. Came in Atomizer Perfume Set with cork stopper. Came in all fragrances of 1896. CMV $165. mint.

1896 EXTRACT ROSE GERANIUM PERFUME
1 oz. glass stopper, paper label. OSP 40c, CMV $200. mint.

1908 ATOMIZER PERFUME
(Left) 1 oz. 6 sided bottle with cork stopper. Green neck & front label. Came in all fragrances of 1908. Came only in CPC Atomizer Sets. Used with Spray Atomizer. OSP 50c, CMV $100. mint.

1914 ATOMIZER PERFUME
(Right) 1 oz. bottle with green & gold front & neck label, cork stopper. Came in 1918 Atomizer Box Set only. Used with Spray Atomizer. Came in all 1918 perfumes. OSP 50c, CMV $100. BO mint.

1906 CPC PERFUME
1 oz. perfume, gold front & neck label. Came in all 1906 perfumes. CMV $200. MB, $150. BO.

1908 WHITE ROSE PERFUME
2 oz. Extract of White Rose perfume. Neck ribbon & glass stopper. OSP 90c, CMV $150. BO mint. $200. MB.

1915-20 CUT GLASS PERFUME
2 oz. bottle with cut glass stopper. 2 different labels in embossed gold. White leatherette box. Came in Trailing Arbutus & Crab Apple Blossom. OSP $2.25, CMV $200. $250. MB. Octagonal label on bottom is 1911 issue. Same CMV.

1905 FRENCH PERFUME
Glass stoppered bottle came in ½, 1, 2 & 4 oz. sizes in these fragrances: Le Perfume des Roses, L'Odeur de Violette, & Peau d'Espagne. 1 oz. size pictured. OSP 25c to $3.75 CMV $165. BO, $215. MB.

1906 CHRISTMAS BOX NO. 5 PERFUME
(Left) White leather covered box holds 3 oz. glass stoppered perfume. OSP $1.50 CMV $175. BO mint, $225. MB.

1896 MUSK PERFUME
(Right) 1 oz. size, glass stoppered. Came in all fragrances. CMV $100. mint. $125. MB.

1905 CHRISTMAS PERFUME
2 oz. glass stopper perfume. OSP 75c, CMV $150. BO, $200. MB.

1896 PEAU D' ESPAGNE PERFUME
(Left) 4" high flaconette size, cork stopper. CPC French perfume. OSP 25c, CMV $160. mint. $180. MB.

1910 CRAB APPLE BLOSSOM PERFUME
(Center) 1 oz. glass stopper, front & neck label. CPC on label. CMV $110. mint, $135. MB.

1896 WHITE ROSE PERFUME
(Right) 1 oz. glass stopper. Bottom part of label is missing on bottle shown. OSP 40c, CMV $150. BO, $200. MB.

1896·EXTRACT PERFUMES
(Left) 2 oz. round glass stopper. New York, Chicago, San Francisco on label. Came in all fragrances in 1908. OSP 90c to $1.40, CMV $150. BO $200. MB.

1896-1908 FRENCH PERFUME
(Right) ½ oz. bottle with glass stopper. Eureka Trade Mark in center of label. Came in Le Perfume des Roses, Peau d'Espagne, L'Odeur de Violette. OSP 55c, CMV $150. BO, $200. MB.

1908 PERFUME "FLORAL EXTRACTS"
1 oz. glass stoppered bottle with Eureka CP Trade Mark on label. Came in all 1908 perfumes. OSP 50c, CMV $150. BO, $200. MB. Also came in 2, 4, 8 & 16 oz. bottles. CMV same as 1 oz. size.

1908 1 OZ. PERFUMES
1 oz. glass stoppered bottle. Eureka Trade Mark on label. In gray flowered box. Came in all fragrances of 1908. OSP 50c to 75c, CMV each $200. MB., $150. BO. Each fragrance came with different flower on label. Heliotrope on left and Crab Apple Blossom on right.

1915 PERFUME
(Left) 1 oz. clear glass bottle with glass stopper. Came in all 1915 fragrances. OSP 75c, CMV $150. mint - $175. MB.

1905 CRAB APPLE BLOSSOM
(Right) 1 oz. clear glass bottle, glass stopper, label has CPC Eureka Trade Mark. Came in all 1908 fragrances. Bottle came with different shaped stopper also. OSP 50c - 75c CMV $150. BO, $200. MB.

1923 PERFUMES
1 & 2 oz. bottle in same shape & design with glass stopper. Front & neck label with gold basket design. Beige box. Came in Carnation, Roses, Heliotrope, Violet, White Lilac, Lily of the Valley, Crab Apple Blossom, Trailing Arbutus, White Rose. OSP $1.17 & $2.10, CMV $135. BO, $170. MB. Also came in 4 oz. size.

1905 EXTRACT PERFUMES
1 oz. glass stopper, white paper label. Came in all fragrances of 1896. OSP 50c, CMV $200. MB, $175. BO mint.

1922 CPC PERFUME SAMPLE SET
Black carrying case with "California Perfume Co." on front. 4 glass flaconette with gold cap & fits into gold case. CMV $350. MB, $75. each flaconette.

1905 PERFUMES 8OZ.
(Left) 8 oz. glass stoppered bottle. Came in California Bouquet. shown, Violet, White Rose, Carnation, Heliotrope, Lily of the Valley, White Lilac, Hyacinth, Roses, New Mown Hay, Sweet Pea, Treffle, Rose Geranium, Jack Rose, front paper label and also came with neck label. OSP $3.25 ea., CMV $175. ea. BO, $225. MB.

1923 PERFUME
(Right) 1 oz. glass stoppered bottle is ribbed. Came in Carnation, Crab Apple Blossom, Heliotrope, Lily of the Valley, Violet & White Rose. Front & neck label. OSP $1.17, CMV $135. BO, $160. MB.

1916 CPC PERFUME
3 different glass stoppers shown. 1 & 2 oz. sizes. OSP 50c, CMV $135. BO mint, $175. MB.

1916 2 OZ. PERFUME
2 oz. glass stopper either faceted or round. Front & neck label. Came in all fragrances of 1915. OSP $1.10, CMV $200. MB, $150. BO.

1908 PERFUMES
The 6 glass stoppered 1 oz. bottles shown on left came in California Bouquet, Carnation, Heliotrope, Hyacinth, Lily of the Valley, New Mown Hay, Rose Geranium, Sweet Pea, Treffle, Violet, White Lilac, & White Rose. OSP 50c, CMV $150. BO, $195. MB.

1931 PERFUME SAMPLE SET
Four 3 dram ribbed & frosted glass bottles with clear ribbed stoppers. Black carrying case. Came in Daphne, Trailing Arbutus, Vernafleur, American Ideal, Crab Apple, Carnation, Heliotrope, White Rose, Violet & Lily of the Valley. CMV set $315. mint. Came with card on proper way to demonstrate perfumes. Add $10. for card.

1931 PERFUME SAMPLE SET-SILVER LABELS
Same CPC black case & bottles, only has very rare silver & blue labels on bottles. CMV $400. set, mint.

1923 CPC PERFUME SAMPLE SET
Black box holds 4 glass stoppered perfume samples. Box has California Perfume Co. on front, 3 dram size. Each has neck labels. Labels read Daphne, Vernafleur, American Ideal, Trailing Arbutus or Roses. CMV $75. ea. bottle. $335. Set MB.

1908 APPLE BLOSSOM PERFUME
(Left) 1 oz. glass stopper. Special Christmas box. OSP 70c, CMV $225. MB.

1908 HELIOTROPE PERFUME
(Right) 1 oz. glass stopper. Special Christmas box. OSP 70c, CMV $225. MB.

1910 FRENCH PERFUMES
Bottle on left is 1 oz., center is ¼ oz. trial size, right is ½ oz. size. Each has glass stopper. Came in L' Odeur De Violette, Le Parfume Des Roses & Peau De' Espagne. Also came in 2 & 4 oz. size. OSP 25c, 55c, $1., $1.90 & $3.75. CMV bottle ½ oz. size to 4 oz. $150. BO each, ¼ oz. size $125. BO. Add $25. for box.

1905 PERFUME CHRISTMAS BOX 4 OZ.
Fancy flowered box holds 4 oz. glass stoppered bottle. Front & neck label. OSP $1.50, CMV $175. - $225. MB.

1905 PERFUME CHRISTMAS BOX 8 OZ.
Embossed paper box, satin lined. Holds 8 oz. glass stoppered bottle with neck ribbon. OSP $3.50, CMV $200. - $275. MB.

1905 PERFUME CHRISTMAS BOX 4 OZ.
Embossed paper box, satin lined. Holds 4 oz. glass stoppered bottle with neck ribbon. OSP $2., CMV $175. - $250. MB.

CPC TOILET WATER

1910 WHITE ROSE WATER
4 oz. clear glass stopper. Eureka trademark on label. OSP 35c, CMV $150. mint - $190. MB.

1905 FLORIDA WATER
(Left) 1½ oz. size, glass crown & cork stopper. OSP 35c, CMV $175. mint - $200 MB.

1896 EAU DE COLOGNE FOR THE TOILET
(Right) 2 oz. ribbed glass bottle. Front & neck label with Eureka trademark. Glass stopper in cork. OSP 35c, CMV $175. BO mint - $210. MB.

1906 TOILET WATERS
(Left) 2 oz. clear ribbed glass bottle & glass corked stopper. Pure food act 1906 on label. Came in Violet Water, White Rose, Lavender Water, Florida Water, California Sweet Cologne & Eau de Cologne. OSP 35c, CMV $175. mint - $210. MB.

1896 TOILET WATERS
(Right) 2 oz. ribbed glass bottle, glass stopper in cork. Front & neck label has Eureke trademark. Came in California Sweet Cologne, Violet Water, White Rose, Lavender Water & Florida Water. OSP 35c, CMV $175. BO - $210. MB.

1908 TOILET WATERS
(Left) 2, 4, 8 & 16 oz. sizes. Glass stoppered bottle. Came in Violet, White Rose, Lavender, Florida, California Sweet Cologne & Eau De Cologne. Bottle shown in 2 oz. size. OSP each 35c, 65c, $1.25 & $2., CMV each $150. BO - $200. MB.

1910 LAVENDER WATER
(Right) 2 oz. glass stoppered bottle with Eureka trademark on label. Also came in Violet, White Rose, Florida Water, California Sweet Cologne & Eau De Cologne. Also came in 4 & 8 oz. & 1 pint sizes with glass stopper. OSP 35c, CMV $150. BO mint - $190. MB.

1916 TOILET WATER
4 oz. bottle with metal & cork stopper. Came in red & gold box. Came in California Sweet Cologne, Carnation, Eau De Cologne, Florida Water, Lavender Water, Trailing Arbutus, Violet, White Lilac, White Rose & Crab Apple Blossom. OSP 65c - CMV $120 BO, $150 MB.

1922-25 TOILET WATERS
Came in 2, 4 & 8 oz. sizes in Violet, Vernafleur, Lavender, White Lilac, Lily of the Valley, Carnation, White Rose, Trailing Arbutus, Crab Apple Blossom & Eau De Cologne. 2 & 4 oz. size same as pictured. Front & neck labels. Metal crown stopper in cork. OSP 59c, $1.08 & $1.95, CMV $90. BO - $115. MB.

1896 TRIPLE EXTRACT TOILET WATER
(Left) 4 oz. & 8 oz. size glass stopper, label has Eureke trademark. Came in Violet Water, White Rose, Lavender Water, Florida Water, Eau De Cologne, California Sweet Cologne. OSP each 65c, CMV $200 MB - $150. BO mint.

1900 FLORIDA WATER
(Right) 2 oz. bottle, glass stopper. OSP 35c, CMV $175. mint - $210. MB.

1910 TOILET WATER
8 oz. bottle with glass stopper. Front & neck label. Came in all fragrances of 1916 in Toilet Waters. OSP $1.25, CMV $175. BO mint - $225. MB.

1910 TOILET WATER
2 oz. bottle with metal pour cap in cork, 1916 up. California Sweet Cologne, Lait Virgital, Eau De Cologne, Trailing Arbutus, White Rose, Violet, White Lilac, Lavender Water, Florida Water, Crab Apple Blossom & Carnation. Front & neck label, in 2 styles. OSP 35c, CMV $115. BO - Mint $140. MB. Also came with brass crown and cork stopper in 1910.

1910 TOILET WATER
2 oz. size with metal crown cork stopper. Came in either of 2 labels shown in Carnation, Florida Water, Trailing Arbutus, White Lilac, White Rose, Violet, Lavender Water, Eau De Cologne, California Sweet Cologne. OSP 35c, CMV $115. each BO - $140. MB.

1928-29 LILAC VEGETAL
(Left) 2 oz. ribbed glass bottle with crown metal top in cork. Pink front & neck label. This bottle with CPC on front label came in Humidor Shaving Set only. CMV $80. - $100. MB.

1925-30 LILAC VEGETAL
(Right) 2 oz. ribbed glass bottle with metal stopper in cork. Pink front & neck label. OSP 59c. Also came in 4 oz. size. OSP $1.08, CMV $80. BO - $100. MB.

1923-29 TOILET WATER
(left) 2 or 4 oz. metal crown cork stopper, ribbed bottle, front & neck label. Came in Lily of the Valley, Violet, White Rose, Carnation, Crab Apple Blossom. OSP 59c - CMV $80 each mint, $100 MB.

1923 BABY TOILET WATER
(Right) 2 & 4 oz. size bottles. Red soldier on front label, blue neck label. Brass & cork stopper. OSP 48c & 89c - CMV $95 BO, $110 MB.

1898 EAU DE COLOGNE REPRODUCTION
(Left) 4 oz. size, glass stopper. Came in all Toilet Waters of 1890. OSP 65c, CMV $125. mint.

1898 PERFUME REPRODUCTION
(Center) 1 oz. size, glass stopper, neck ribbon. Came in all fragrances of 1890. OSP 25c, CMV $110. mint.

1898 TOILET WATER REPRODUCTION
(Right) 2 & 4 oz. size, glass stopper. Came in all fragrances of 1890's. Front & neck labels. OSP 65c, CMV $125. mint.

1890's FLORIDA WATER REPRODUCTION
2 & 4 oz. size, glass stopper, front & neck labels. CMV $100. each mint. Bottles shown are Avon Products reproductions.

CPC POWDERS

1905 SWEET COLOGNE REPRODUCTION
2 & 4 oz. size, front & neck labels, cork stopper. OSP 35c & 65c, CMV $150. each MB - $125. BO each mint. bottles shown are Avon Products reproductions.

1915 Only TOOTH POWDER
(Left) Small metal can came in 1915 Juvenile Set. CMV $75. mint.

1908 TOOTH POWDER
(Right) Metal can. OSP 25c, CMV $60. MB - $50. can only mint.

1925 PYROX TOOTH POWDER
(Left) Blue metal can. OSP 24c, CMV $55 MB, $40 can only mint.

1923 CALIFORNIA ROSE TALCUM
(Right) 4. oz. pink can with brass cap. OSP 33c - CMV $75, $90 MB.

1915 ELITE POWDER
Glass jar, metal sifter lid in CPC box. OSP 25c, CMV $80. BO mint - $95. MB.

1923 ELITE POWDER
(Left & Center) 1 lb. blue can with English & French label. 2 different brass caps & narrow & wide blue band around top. OSP 89c, CMV $65 each, $75 MB.

1923 ELITE POWDER REGULAR ISSUE
(Right) Pictured for size comparison.

1907 ROSE TALCUM POWDER ANTISEPTIC
Metal can with brass sifter cap. OSP 25c - CMV $90 mint, $110 MB.

1916 SWEET SIXTEEN FACE POWDER
(Left) Yellow, pink & green box. OSP 25c, CMV $45. mint.

1916 CALIFORNIA NAIL POWDER
(Right) Paper sides. Came bright green or beige in color. OSP 25c, CMV $40 mint.

1919 ELITE FOOT POWDER
Paper side round container. Sold for 25c each after WWI from the Army & Navy kits. Rare. CMV $75. - $100. MB.

1921 CALIFORNIA ROSE TALCUM
3½ oz. glass jar with brass cap. OSP 33c, CMV $85. jar only - $105. MB.

1911 ELITE POWDER
(Left) Glass jar with aluminum lid. OSP 25c, CMV $80. mint - $100. MB.

1923 ELITE POWDER
(Right) Blue metal can with sifter cap. OSP 24c, CMV $60. MB - $45. can only mint. Came in 2 different sifter caps & 2 variations in labels. Same CMV.

1919 WHITE LILAC TALCUM
(Left) 4 oz. blue metal can, blue sifter cap. OSP 24c, CMV $70. mint - $85. MB.

1917 WHITE LILAC TALCUM
(Right) 4 oz. paper box, purple in color. OSP 25c - CMV $60 mint, $80 MB.

1920 WHITE LILAC TALCUM
   4 oz. blue metal can with brass take off cap. Box came with paper on the Story of Italian Talc. OSP 24c, CMV $65. can only mint - $80. MB as shown.

1924-29 RADIANT NAIL POWDER
   (Left) Small gold & black can. All 3 pieces came in 1924 Manicure Set. CMV $35.

1924-29 CUTI CREME OR NAIL CREAM
   (Center) Small gold & black can. CMV $20. - $30.

1924-29 NAIL WHITE
   (Center Top) Small gold & black can. CMV $20. - $30. MB.

1914 DEPILATORY
   A metal can of hair remover. OSP 50c - CMV $65 MB, $55 mint. Came with brass lift off cap.

1918 SMOKERS TOOTH POWDER
   (Left) 2¾ oz. bottle with metal & cork stopper also comes with metal crown stopper. OSP 50c, CMV $105. BO - $130. MB.

1920 SMOKERS TOOTH POWDER
   (Right) 2¾ oz. metal & cork stopper. OSP 50c, CMV $105. BO - $130. MB.

1910 CALIFORNIA BATH POWDER
   Gold, white & green can. Came with sifter cap & take off cap. OSP 25c, CMV $65. - $80. MB.

1906 HYGIENE FACE POWDER
   Leatherette box trimmed in gold. OSP 50c - CMV $75 mint.

   (From the Onstot Collection)
1925-33 SMOKERS TOOTH POWDER
   4 oz. cream colored can. Label in French & English. OSP 50c, CMV $70. MB - $50. can only mint.

1918 HYGIENE FACE POWDER
   Green, gold & red powder box. OSP 50c - CMV $75 mint.

1923 RADIANT NAIL POWDER
   (Left) Blue & pink can. 2 different Labels. OSP 24c - CMV $50 mint each, $65 MB.

1915 SHAVING POWDER
   (Right) 2 oz. metal can. OSP 25c, CMV $55 mint, $65 MB.

1897 POWDER BOXES
2 different design aluminum powder cans with puffs. Does not say CPC on them but shown is old CPC literature. CMV not established.

1928-29 CPC BODY POWDER
Yellow, black & maroon colored metal can. CPC New York, Montreal on bottom. Came in Trailing Arbutus, Daphne & Baby Powder. OSP $1.19, CMV $60. mint - $75. MB.

1890's SACHET POWDER
Heliotrope violet or white rose sachet in box. Metal cap. OSP 25c, CMV $110. MB. - $90. BO. mint.

1890's - 1915 SWEET SIXTEEN FACE POWDER
(Left) Paper box. OSP 25c, CMV $55. mint.

1915 HYGIENE FACE POWDER
(Right) Green paper box. OSP 50c, CMV $50. mint.

1920 POWDER CAN REFILL
1 lb. gold tone can. Came in several fragrances as a refill. CMV $75. in new condition.

1905 POWDER SACHET
(Left) Round glass bottle, aluminum lid. Came in Violet, Lilac, Rose, White Rose & Heliotrope. Came in sets only. CMV $100. BO. mint.

1890's-1912 POWDER SACHET
(Right) Clear glass, gold cap, front label. Came in French Odors of Le Parfume de Roses, L'Odour de Violette, Peau D'Espagne. OSP 25c, CMV $110. MB. - $90. BO. mint.

POWDER SACHETS — MISC.
ALL CPC'S MUST BE IN NEW
MINT CONDITION FOR CMV
SEE 1984 SUPPLEMENT IN BACK OF BOOK FOR
MORE SACHETS

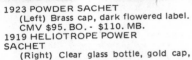

1890's-1912 POWDER SACHET
Silver or gold cap on glass bottle with front label. Came in Lilac, Rose, White Rose, Violet, Heliotrope. OSP 25c, CMV $110. MB. - $90. BO. mint. Each one has different label.

1923 POWDER SACHET
(Left) Brass cap, dark flowered label. CMV $95. BO. - $110. MB.

1919 HELIOTROPE POWER SACHET
(Right) Clear glass bottle, gold cap, label yellow with lavender flowers and green leaves. Came in other fragrances. Rare. CMV $110. BO., $125. MB. Both bottles came in Carnation, Heliotrope, White Rose, Violet, White Lilac.

1890's SACHET POWDER ENVELOPE
Eureka Trade Mark on label. Envelope contains powder in Violet, White Rose, Heliotrope. OSP 25c, CMV $45 per envelope mint.

1922-25 POWDER SACHET
Large & small bottles with brass caps. Came in Carnation, Heliotrope, Violet, White Rose & Trailing Arbutus. OSP 49c, & 72c, CMV $100. BO. - $115. MB each size.

1915 POWDER SACHET
Gold cap, paper label on glass bottle. Came in Carnation, White Rose, Violet, White Lilac & Heliotrope. 2 different - Boxes & labels as shown. OSP 25c, CMV $90. mint BO - $110. MB.

1908 SACHET POWDER ENVELOPES
Came in Violet, White Rose, & Heliotrope. OSP 25c - CMV $40 mint.

1916 FACE POWDER LEAVES
Small book of 72 sheets of scented paper. Came in Rose, White, Rachel. OSP 20c - CMV $40 mint.

CPC SAMPLE CASES

EARLY 1900's SAMPLE CASE
Plain wood box with brass handle. CMV $100. mint with CPC price list. Case was used by CPC Reps to sell products.

1920 CPC SALES CASE
Black case with red velvet lining. California Perfume Co. on chrome handle. Used by Reps to show products. Case measures 14½" long x 8" wide, 3½" high. CMV $100. mint.

1915 CPC SAMPLE CASE
Straw basket weave case & leather handle & trim. Measures 11 x 17. The large CPC black catalogs fit inside perfectly. A CPC label is inside lid stating all contents that came in sample case. CMV $100. with CPC label.

CPC SETS

WARNING!! Grading condition is paramount on sets.
CMV can vary 50% to 75% on grade.
Refer to page 6 and 16 on Grading.

EARLY 1900's SAMPLE CASE
Plain wood box with leather handle. Red felt lining, printed paper price list inside lid. CMV $75. mint with list.

1900 SAMPLE CASE
Black leather covered case with leather strap. Case came with CPC list of all products glued inside lid of case. Case was carried by CPC Reps to show products. CMV. Case mint full of products, $1,500. Case only mint $100. with list.

1915 CALIFORNIA IDEAL HAIR TREATMENT SET
Box holds 4 oz. glass stoppered Bay Rum White Jar of Shampoo Cream, 6 oz. Eau De Quinine. All products in set came in separate boxes in set with pamphlet on the 3 products. OSP $1.35., CMV $500. MB. as shown.

1896 ATOMIZER SET
Box holds atomizer & three 1 oz. bottles with cork stoppers. 2 bottles are round & center bottle is octagonal shape. Each has front & neck labels. OSP $1.35., CMV $425. MB. completed set. Came in all fragrances of 1896.

1908 ATOMIZER BOX SET
Three 1 oz. bottles with cork stoppers & atomizer. Came in all fragrances of 1915. Green box. Each bottle has green front & neck labels. OSP $1.50., CMV $350. MB. complete set.

1915 ONLY — JUVENILE SET
Box holds miniature size cans of Natoma Talcum Powder, Tooth Powder, small bottle of Violet Water with cork stopper & small cake of Savona Bouquet Soap. Each item is about 2" high. OSP 50c., CMV $425. MB.

1906 ATOMIZER SET
Box holds three 1 oz. bottles of perfume with cork stoppers & atomizer. Came in all fragrances of 1908. OSP $1.50., CMV $375.00. MB.

1925-30 JACK & JILL JUNGLE JINKS SET
Brown decorated box holds 1 can Superite Trailing Arbutus Talcum, 1 bottle of Daphne Perfume, 1 cake of Apple Blossom soap, 1 can Trailing Arbutus Cold Cream, 1 tube Sen-Den-Tal Cream, 1 imported juvenile size tooth brush. OSP $1.50., CMV $310. MB metal box only $65. mint.

1900 MANICURE SET
Box holds bottle of Nail Bleach with glass stopper, CMV $100. White jar of Rose Pomade, CMV $50. & paper box of Nail Powder, CMV $35. OSP each 25c, OSP complete set 65c, CP on center of labels. Replaced with Eureka Trade Mark in 1910. CMV set $225. MB.

1912 MANICURE SET
Gray box contains buffer, scissors, file, Nail Bleach, Nail Powder & Rose Pomade. OSP $3., CMV $250. MB.

1929 CPC ATOMIZER SET
Black box with green liner & gold tone lid holds green glass, lift off lid jar & 2 oz. green glass spray atomizer bottle. Both have gold tone lids. Does not say CPC on it or box. CMV not established.

1909 BOX A SET
Holly green, red & gold box holds two ½ oz. perfumes with glass stoppers. OSP 50c, CMV $300. MB.

1916 MANICURE SET
(Left) Box holds glass stoppered bottle of Nail Bleach, jar of Rose Pomade and paper container of Nail Powder. OSP 65c, CMV complete set $235. MB.

1914 NAIL POWDER
(Right) Paper box. OSP 25c, CMV $35. mint.

1924-30 MANICURE SET BOX
Gold and black stripped metal can. CMV $25., metal box only, mint.

1924-30 LOVELY HANDS BOOKLET
Came in Manicure Set Shown. CMV $10. booklet only mint.

1920 MANICURE SET
CPC box holds Rose Pomade jar, 1 oz. bottle of Nail Bleach, cork stopper & can of Radiant Nail Powder. OSP 65c, CMV $235. MB.

1915 GIFT BOX A
Same pattern as Holly Pattern set. Green & red holly box. Two ½ oz. glass stoppered perfumes in choice of Violet, White Rose, Carnation, White Lilac, Heliotrope & Lily of the Valley. OSP 50c, CMV $285. MB.

1929 ONLY — GERTRUDE RECORDON'S FACIAL TREATMENT SET
4 oz. bottle of astringent with cork stopper, $75. 4 oz. bottle of peach lotion with cork stopper, $75. Ribbed white glass jar with CPC on metal lid each in cleansing cream & skin food. Each jar $45. OSP $4., CMV complete set $275. MB.

1923 MANICURE SET
White box holds can of Radiant Nail Powder, bottle of Nail Bleach with glass stopper, orange wood stick & jar of Rose Pomade. OSP 72c, CMV $250. MB.

1924-28 MANICURE SET
Gold & black striped metal can holds gold & black can of Radiant Nail Powder, 1 can each of Nail White & Cuti-cream & bottle of Cutrain with cork stopper. OSP $1.20, CMV $165. MB.

1929-30 BOUDOIR MANICURE SET
Same set as 1924 Manicure Set with name changed and has bottle of Cuticle Softener or Cuticle Remover, & small can of Nail Cream, Nail White & Radiant Nail Powder. All in same design. OSP $1.20 - CMV $165 MB. Set came with Lovely Hands Booklet.

1928-29 GERTRUDE RECORDON'S INTRODUCTORY FACIAL TREATMENT SET
Box holds white jars of Gertrude Recordon's cleansing cream & skin food. CMV each jar $50. 2 bottles with cork stoppers of peach lotion & astringent. CMV each bottle $50. & roll of facial tissues. CMV set mint $275. MB.

1921 HOLLY PATTERN BOX A
Set has two ½ oz. glass & cork stoppered perfume bottles. Came in Carnation, Lily of the Valley, Violet, White Rose, White Lilac & Heliotrope. OSP 50c, CMV $275. set MB.

1918 GIFT BOX NO. 3
Box holds 2 half ounce bottles of perfume. Crown glass stopper set in cork. Came in all fragrances of 1917-18 period. CMV $275. MB.

1910 HOLLY SET
Holly design box holds 2 half ounce bottles with glass & cork stoppers. Gold front & neck labels. Choice of Violet, White Rose, White Lilac, Carnation, Heliotrope, Lily of the Valley perfume. OSP 50c, CMV $300. MB.

1912 HOLLY SET
Holly pattern design box holds 2-½ oz. size glass & cork stopper bottles. OSP 50c, CMV $275. MB.

1906 CHRISTMAS BOX SET NO. 4
Box holds Hygiene Face Powder, Savona soap & glass stoppered perfume. Box is 6¾'' square. OSP $1. CMV $300. MB.

1913 MEMORIES THAT LINGER SET
3 glass stoppered perfumes in book shaped box. Box is 8 x 5½ inches. Violet, White Rose & Carnation Perfume. OSP $2., CMV $425. MB.

1906 CHRISTMAS BOX SET NO. 3
Roses on box, 2 perfumes, glass stoppered. Gold labels. Box is 5 ¼ x 4 ¾ inches. OSP 65c, CMV $300. MB.

1906 CHRISTMAS BOX SET NO. 2
Babies on box, 2 glass stoppered perfumes. Gold labels. OSP 50c, CMV $300. MB.

1926-30 DRESSING TABLE VANITY SET
Orange & gold two-section box has brass lipstick & eyebrow pencil & rouge compact in top half of box & bottom half is full of Jardin D'Amour or Ariel Face Powder OSP $2.25, CMV $110. MB.

1915 GIFT BOX NO. 2
Box holds ½ oz. perfume with glass & cork stopper & powder sachet in Carnation, White Lilac, Heliotrope, Violet & White Rose. OSP 50c, CMV $250. MB.

1905 CHRISTMAS SET NO. 4
Fancy box holds 1 oz. glass stoppered bottle of perfume, Round bottle of Powder Sachet, screw on cap & 1 wrapped bar of Savona Bouquet soap. OSP $1., CMV $400.

1905 PERFUME SET NO. 2
Lithographed box holds 2 crown shaped glass stoppered in cork bottles. Front & neck labels. OSP 50c, CMV $350. MB.

1922 GIFT BOX NO. 2
½ oz. bottle of perfume & bottle of sachet. Came in Violet, White Rose, Carnation, Heliotrope & White Lilac, OSP 97c, CMV $235. MB.

1905 PERFUME SET NO. 5
Holly Christmas Box holds two 1 oz. glass stoppered bottles. OSP $1., CMV $350.

1915 GIFT BOX NO. 2
Yellow & purple box holds ½ oz. perfume & powder sachet. Choice of Carnation, Heliotrope, White Lilac, Violet & White Rose. OSP 50c per set. Set $275. MB.

LITTLE FOLKS SETS

SEE 1984 SUPPLEMENT IN BACK OF THIS BOOK FOR MORE SETS.

1911 LITTLE FOLKS SET
4 small bottles of Violet, Carnation, White Rose or Rose & Heliotrope perfume. Birds & kids on lid & edge of box. OSP 40c, CMV $350. MB.

1905 LITTLE FOLKS SET
Boy & girl with dog inside lid of box. Four gem sized perfume bottles of Violet, Carnation, White Rose & Heliotrope. Bottles had cork stoppers & ribbons on neck. Flower on labels. Box size is 5½" x 3¼". OSP 40c, CMV $400. for set, mint - $75. each bottle.

1908 LITTLE FOLKS SET
Four gem sized bottles of perfume came in Violet, Carnation, Rose & Heliotrope. Cork stoppers. Same bottles & labels as 1905 Little Folks Set. OSP 50c, CMV $75. each bottle - $350. for set, mint.

1912 LITTLE FOLKS SET
Same box as 1911 set only different labels. Birds & kids on lid. OSP 40c, CMV $350. MB.

1915-23 LITTLE FOLKS SET
Contains 4 gem bottles of perfume with Violet, Carnation, White Rose & Heliotrope. OSP 50c, CMV $75. each bottle - $350. for set, MB.

1923-32 LITTLE FOLKS SET
Blue box contains four gem size bottles of Floral perfumes in Daphne, Vernafleur, Trailing Arbutus & Carnation, Violet, Heliotrope or White Lilac. All have brass caps. OSP 69c, CMV $300 for set, mint - $65. each bottle.

1937-39 LITTLE FOLKS SET
Fancy box has four bottles of perfume in Gardenia, Cotillion, Narcissus & Trailing Arbutus. 2 dram size. OSP 94c, CMV $130. MB - each bottle $25.

1932-36 LITTLE FOLKS SET
Four small bottles, choice of Ariel, Vernafleur, Gardenia or Bolero, 391 & Trailing Arbutus perfume with black caps, silver labels. OSP 90c, CMV $175. MB - $190. MB with outer turquoise box as shown.

1932 Only LITTLE FOLKS SET
Same box as 1923-32 Little Folks Set. Holds 4 octagonal shaped bottles. Silver labels, black caps. Came in Ariel, Bolero, Gardenia & Trailing Arbutus. OSP 90c, CMV $250. set MB.

1930-33 HUMIDOR SHAVING SET
Gold & black metal box holds 4 oz. ribbed glass Bay Rum, 2 oz. ribbed glass Lilac Vegetal (black cap), styptic pencil, green tubes of Bayberry shaving cream & Menthol Witch Hazel cream & green can Talc for Men. OSP $2.50, CMV $240. MB.

CPC MEN'S SETS

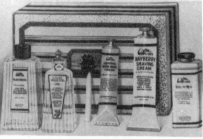

1928-30 HUMIDOR SHAVING SET BOX
Metal gold striped box only. Measures 9¼" wide x 5¾" x 3" deep. Does not say CPC on box. Picture of ship on lid. CMV box only mint $40.

1928-29 HUMIDOR SHAVING SET
Gold & black metal box holds 4 oz. bottle Bay Rum, 2 oz. bottle Lilac Vegetal, styptic pencil, green tube Menthol Witch Hazel cream, green tube Bayberry shave cream & can of either White Lilac talcum or Avon Talc for Men. OSP $2.25, CMV $325. complete set MB.

1930 "early" Only HUMIDOR SHAVING SET
Gold & black metal box holds 4 oz. ribbed bottle of Bay Rum, 2 oz. bottle of Lilac Vegetal with crown cork stopper, styptic pencil, green tubes of Menthol Witch Hazel cream & Bayberry shaving cream & green can of Talc for Men. OSP $2.50, CMV $285. MB.

1925-29 HUMIDOR SHAVING SET BOX
Maroon & gold metal box only. Measures 9¼" wide x 5¾" x 3" deep. Bottom says Metal Packaging Corp. of New York. CMV box only mint $40.

1925-28 HUMIDOR SHAVING SET
Wood grained box trimmed in gold & black holds 2 oz. bottle of Lilac Vegetal, 4 oz. bottle of Bay Rum, blue can of White Lilac talcum, Trailing Arbutus cold cream, tube of Menthol Witch Hazel cream, Bayberry shave cream tube & styptic pencil. OSP $1.95, CMV $335. MB.

1917 GENTLEMEN'S SHAVING SET
Brown box holds cream shaving stick, Menthol Witch Hazel cream tube, 50 sheet shaving pad, 2 oz. bottle of White Lilac toilet water, styptic pencil, 4 oz. bottle of genuine Bay Rum with glass stopper & box of White Lilac talcum or jar of Violet talcum. OSP $1.50, CMV $400. MB complete set.

1919 GENTLEMEN'S SHAVING SET
Box contains blue can of White Lilac talcum, green tube of Menthol Witch Hazel cream, can of cream shaving stick, 4 oz. Bay Rum with cork stopper, styptic pencil, 2 oz. bottle of White Lilac toilet water & 50 sheet shaving pad. OSP $2.25, CMV $400. MB.

1918 ARMY & NAVY KIT
Heavy cardboard box holds 2 bars of peroxide toilet soap, styptic pencil, Elite foot powder, cream shaving stick, dental cream. OSP $1.25, CMV $250 MB.

1923 GENTLEMEN'S SHAVING SET
Box contains Bayberry shave cream tube, White Lilac talcum, White Lilac toilet water, styptic pencil, Bay Rum, Menthol Witch Hazel & shaving pad. OSP $1.95, CMV $335. MB.

1915 GENTLEMAN'S SHAVING SET
Box holds glass bottle of Violet talcum powder, can of cream shaving stick, tube of Menthol Witch Hazel cream, styptic pencil, 4 oz. glass stoppered bottle of Bay Rum, 2 oz. White Lilac toilet water & 50 sheet shaving pad. OSP $1.50, CMV $435. MB.

AWARDS & REPRESENTATIVES GIFTS

SEE WOMEN'S FRAGRANCE LINES FOR ADDITIONAL AWARDS

WARNING: All Avon Awards with gold or silver content should be bought and sold with caution.

Unless it is marked 10K, 12K, 14K or marked "Solid Gold", it is described as gold for color only. For it to be real gold, it must be marked 10K, 12K or 14K ONLY.

For it to be real silver, it must be marked Sterling or Solid Silver. Trays and goblets must be marked Sterling to be of any real metal value. Silver plate is of very little value in silver content.

If you have real solid gold or sterling silver awards, it would be best to ask someone who is buying the metal what they would pay for it. This is the true value of the metal. A jewelers appraisal is not worth the paper it is written on. It is a quote below what he would sell it for and the real value is the wholesale price of what he will pay for it.

With the exploding up and down prices on gold, silver and diamonds, we suggest you check on the value before you buy or sell such items. Prices can change from day to day. All prices quoted reflect the collectors value plus the gold price of $500. per ounce.

1968 MANAGERS DIAMOND RING
¼ carat art carved 58 faceted diamond set in a gold 4A design mounting. Given to managers for achievement of sales goals for several quarters. CMV $475. mint.

1978 PRESIDENT'S CLUB RING "LADY'S"
(Left) Gold plated sterling 4A ring with red simulated ruby. Stone comes in several different shades. Given to all female President's Club Reps. CMV $35. MB.

1978 MANAGERS 4A RING
(Right) Silver 4A ring with high grade ruby stone given to 4 managers in Atlanta branch for best planning. CMV price not established.

1961 MANAGERS DIAMOND PIN
Gold 4A pin same as Representatives except has an "M" made of 11 diamonds. CMV $125. MB.

1961-76 DIAMOND 4A PIN
Larger than other 4A pins; set with diamond. Given for selling $3,000. at customer price in an 18 campaign period. In 1974-76 you had to sell $4,500. in 13 campaigns. CMV $50. MB.

1963-76 SAPPHIRE 4A PIN
Same as pearl pin, 7/8" dia. set with a genuine sapphire. Awarded for reaching $2,000. in customer sales price in a 9 campaign period. In 1974-76 you had to sell $3,500. in 13 campaigns. CMV $30. MB.

1963-70 PEARL 4A PIN
10 kt. gold in a 4A design with pearl in center. Awarded for reaching $1,000 in customer price sales in a 9 campaign period. 5/8" diameter. CMV $20. MB.

(Continued at top of column 2)

1973-76 RUBY 4A PIN
10 kt. gold with ruby in center. Awarded for selling $2,500. in customer price sales in 6 month period to become eligible for President's Club Membership. CMV $15.

1961 MANAGERS DIAMOND 4A PIN
4A diamond pin with diamond crown guard. Given to managers reaching a special quota in 1961. CMV $175.

1971 CIRCLE OF EXCELLENCE RING
Same as pin only ring. CMV $275. mint.

1969 CIRCLE OF EXCELLENCE PIN
4A gold pin circled with pearls and diamonds in center. Managers only pin has a logo on back and can also be worn as a pendant. CMV $250.

1910-25 CPC IDENTIFICATION PIN
Given to all Representatives to identify them as official company Representatives. Says CPC 1886 on face. CMV $90. mint.

1910-15 CPC IDENTIFICATION HONOR PIN
Given to Representatives for selling $250. in merchandise. CMV $90. mint. Both pins are solid gold.

1900 CPC I.D. PIN
Solid gold I.D. pin given to early day Reps. to show they worked for the CPC company. This is the 1st I.D. pin ever given by the CPC. CMV $150.

1929-38 CPC AVON I.D. PIN
(Top) Given to all Reps to show they work for Avon and the CPC. Silver pin with blue enamel. "California Perfume Co., Inc., "Avon" on face of pin. This pin is larger in size than the 1938-45 I.D. pins. This pin came in two different ways. The A and V on Avon is close together on one and wide apart on the others. CMV $45. mint.

1929-38 I.D. HONOR AWARD PIN
(Bottom) Gold filled with dark blue enamel. Given to Reps for $250. in sales. "CPC — AVON — HONOR" on face of pin. CMV $55. mint.

1964 QUEENS AWARD PIN
Gold colored metal 1¼" across. Given to each member of the winning team during the 78th Anniversary for top sales. CMV $20.

1938-45 IDENTIFICATION PIN
Silver with aqua enamel. Given to all Representatives for identification. "Avon Products, Inc., Avon" on face of pin. CMV $30 mint.

1938-45 HONOR I.D. PIN "GOLD"
Gold plated with aqua enamel Given for $250. in sales. "Avon Products, Inc., Avon Honor" on face of pin. CMV $35. mint.

1938-45 I.D. HONOR PIN & CASE "SILVER"
(Left) Silver with aqua enamel. Given to all Representatives for identification. "Avon Products, Inc., Avon Honor on face of pin. CMV $30.

1945-61 FIELD MANAGER'S I.D. PIN & GUARD
(Right) Same design as the jeweled pin but has no printing. The "M" guard is smooth gold. CMV $55.

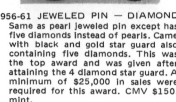

1956-61 JEWELED PIN — DIAMOND
Same as pearl jeweled pin except has five diamonds instead of pearls. Came with black and gold star guard also containing five diamonds. This was the top award and was given after attaining the 4 diamond star guard. A minimum of $25,000 in sales were required for this award. CMV $150. mint.

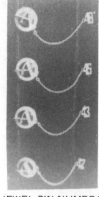

1945-56 JEWEL PIN NUMERAL GUARDS
Smooth gold numerals given for additional sales in multiples of $1,000. starting with No. 2. There was no No. 1. These are made to attach to the jewel pin. Highest numeral known is 115. The higher the number the more valuable. CMV $8. on numbers 2 to 10. $12. on 11 to 20. $14. on 21 to 30. $18. on 31 to 40 $20. on 41 to 75. $25. each on 76 up.

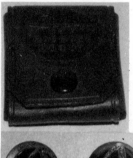

1945-61 JEWELED PIN PEARL — HIGHEST HONOR CASE
10K gold with black enamel background. 5 oriental pearls are set in the A. Came in black highest award case above. Given for sales if $1000. CMV $30. pin, $40 in case.

1945-51 IDENTIFICATION PIN
Gold pin with black background. "A" has scroll design rather than jewels. Edges are plain, no writing. Given to Representatives for $1,000. in sales. CMV $20.

1945-61 CITY MANAGERS I.D. PIN & PEARL GUARD
Given to all City Managers. Pin has 5 pearls. Guard is set with 11 seed pearls. CMV $75. mint.

1977 HEART DIAMOND A PIN
14k gold heart shape pin with 12 small diamonds. Can also be used as a pendant on chain. Came in gray felt box with white outer box. Only 1 given in each division for top Rep. Rare. CMV $400. mint.

1936 50th ANNIVERSARY PIN
Red circle with gold feather. Given to every representative who made a house to house sales trip of her area. CMV $55. mint.

1945-61 JEWELED PIN — HIGHEST HONOR — "PEARL"
10k gold with black enamel background, 5 oriental pearls are set in the A. Given for sales of $1,000. CMV $30.

1956-61 STAR GUARDS
Raised star on round gold metal pin. Given for each $5,000. in sales in any 12 month period. Four guards could be won, each had an additional diamond. Made to wear with the jeweled pin. CMV $15. one diamond. Add $12.50 for each additional diamond.

1969 CHARM BRACELET AWARD
22 kt. gold finish, double-link bracelet with safety chain & 5 charms. Each charm given for progressively higher sales. CMV $7. ea. charm, plus bracelet.

1976-78 A PIN AWARD
Given to Reps. for selling $1,500. in Avon in a 13 campaign period. Came in blue lined box. CMV $5. MB or red lined box CMV $7. MB.

1971-76 GOLDEN ACHIEVEMENT AWARD

Bracelet & 1st charm awarded for $5,500. total sales in 6 month period. Each succeeding charm awarded for $5,500. within each subsequent 6 month period. First charm 2 joined 4A design with green stone. Second charm - Avon Rose with red stone. Third charm - The First Lady with a genuine topaze. Fourth charm - The "World of Avon" set with a genuine aquamarine. Fifth charm - "The Doorknocker" with a genuine amethyst. Sixth charm - jeweled "A" with a genuine sapphire. Seventh charm - the "Key" with a genuine garnet. Eighth charm - Great Oak. (Above order of charms correct) CMV $35. each charm. Charm No. 8 $50.

1963-65 MANAGERS CHARM BRACELET

One charm was given each quarter for 3 years making a total of 12 charms possible. These were won by attaining certain sales increases which increased with each quarter making the later charms very difficult to get. For this reason past the eighth quarter are very hard to find. the bracelet charms are 10 kt. gold. Only four bracelets were won with all 12 charms. A total of 6191 individual charms were given to 1445 managers. The last four charms are like the one pictured in center of bracelet. No. 9 has Rubys, No. 10 Sapphire, No. 11, Emerald & No. 12 Diamond. Each one had 4 stones. CMV 1st 8 charms $45. ea. plus bracelet No. 9 & 10 $60. each. No. 11, 12, $75. ea. CMV all 12 charms $800. mint.

1965 GOLDEN CIRCLE CHARM BRACELET AWARD

22 kt. gold finish double-link bracelet with safety chain and 5 gold charms. Each charm given for progressively higher sales. CMV $7. each charm, plus bracelet $7. Came in an Avon box.

1972-79 CIRCLE OF EXCELLENCE CHARM BRACELET

10K gold bracelet & gold charm with 3 diamonds & 4A design. Black & gold Avon box. Green inside. Given to managers only. CMV $250. MB. Also came charm with 4 diamonds last charm. CMV $300. MB.

1978 PRESIDENT'S CLUB RING FOR MEN

Gold plated sterling silver 4A ring with ruby stone. Given to male Avon Reps. for selling $6000 worth of Avon in 1 year period. Came in plain blue velvet ring box. CMV $200. MB.

1959 CHARM BRACELET - SILVER

Only 2 districts won in each branch. This was a test bracelet & very few were given for sales achievement. CMV $185. mint with all 6 charms.

1982 ALBEE RING AWARD

Gold plated sterling silver. Given to Reps for meeting sales goals. CMV $85 MB.

1977 PRESIDENT'S CELEBRATION DIAMOND RING AWARD

14K gold ring with 8 small diamonds in center. Given to managers in Pasadena branch for largest increase in sales. Only 20 rings given in this branch. Does not say Avon. CMV not established.

1978 SMOKY QUARTZ RING - MANAGERS

Smoky quartz stone, 14K gold mounting marked Avon. Given to managers in C26-78 for best activity event in Atlanta branch. CMV not established.

1977 PRESIDENT'S CELEBRATION STAR AWARD

Sterling silver star & chain with small diamond made by Tiffany. Was given to winning district manager in division. CMV not established.

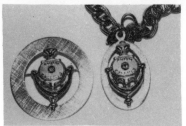

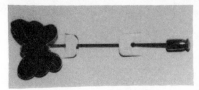

1981 BUTTERFLY PIN AWARD
Gold tone enameled stick pin given to Reps. Does not say Avon. CMV $5.

1974 MANAGERS ACHIEVEMENT AWARD PIN & CHARM BRACELET
1 given to top sales manager in each division. Brush sterling silver with blue sapphire in center of Avon Door Knocker. CMV $70. - $75. MB each.

1974 DIVISION MANAGERS ACHIEVEMENT CUFF LINKS AWARD
Same as award pin on left, only are cuff links. Given to male Division Managers - CMV $85. set. Mint.

1980 IDENTIFICATION PIN AUSTRALIA
Gold toned door knocker pin. CMV $10.

1980 AVON REPRESENTATIVE STICK PIN
Blue & gold. (Says Avon Representative) CMV $20.

1978 HEART STICK PIN AWARD
Sterling silver heart pin made by Tiffany & Co. with Avon products slip. Given to managers only, during President's Celebration. Does not say Avon. Must be in box with Tiffany & Co. Avon card. CMV $30. MB.

1964 SILVER DOOR KNOCKER PIN
Given to all managers in conjunction with the door knocker award program. CMV $25., $30 MB.

1964-83 GOLD DOORKNOCKER PIN
Came on green or white cards. CMV $10 on card. CMV pin only $7. Also came in blue box with white sleeve. Same CMV.

1981 DOOR KNOCKER DIAMOND PIN
Gold with small diamond. Given to managers. Came in Tan box. CMV $60. MB.

1979 ACORN STICK PIN AWARD
Sterling silver acorn pin from Tiffany & Co. given to managers. Came with small card with great oak & Tiffany card for Avon products. CMV $35. MB.

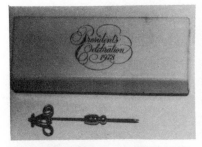

1981 DON'T KNOCK ME DOORKNOCKER NECKLACE AWARD
Gold tone door knocker with simulated diamond. Given to Reps. Comes in "Jo Anne Jewels" box. Made only for Avon. CMV $15. MB.

1966 DOOR KNOCKER EARRINGS
Gold tone earrings. Avon Calling on them. CMV $32.50 pr. MB.

1978 PRESIDENT'S CELEBRATION "A" PIN AWARD
White box holds "A" sterling silver pin given to President's Club Reps. only. CMV $12.50 MB.

AN OPEN LETTER TO ALL AVON REPS.

Do you want to increase the number of Avon collectors in the world? This would greatly increase your sales, too, you know! Try to find out your customer's various interests and those of her children and husband, too! For example:

Mrs. Smith loves animals - bring every animal decanter to her attention as they appear on the market. Sell her the first one and she'll likely buy more, or all, that come! Mr. Smith is a sports fan! Point out what a smart collection he could have on a neat shelf in his den. Young Johnny would love the majestic elephant, or that dinosaur decanter and teenager Sue really "digs" the "Fried Egg" or "Hamburger" compacts.

All these people have a good chance of ending up being a collector! So what does that really mean? Well it means that your collectables will maintain their value and the market will grow steadily. Avon Reps. will have good steady sales. Collectors will have a wider and wider circle of ever growing and interested folk to swap and shop with.

Show your own collection to friends, help to stir the interest of others. Believe me, it will pay off in the end!!

Most important of all, don't forget to carry a copy of Hastin's Avon Collectors Encyclopedia to show your customers. Show them the color pages on "How collectors display their Avons." By showing this book to your customers, you can help create new collectors and you will profit 10 fold, as collectors will buy many more Avon products from you. Be sure to point out information on the Avon Times - Avon Club which they can enjoy right from their own living room. Tell them about the free advertising to over 4000 members to buy, sell or trade Avons. Remember, if you help educate your customers on Avon Collecting you will profit greatly in larger future sales.

For more information on the Avon Times, write or send $12.00 for 1 full year subscription in U.S. or $15.00 U.S. Funds in Canada to: Avon Times - Box 9868 - Kansas City, Missouri 64134.

1980-81 PRESIDENT'S CLUB PIN AWARD
Gold tone pin given to President's Club Members only. Comes in Blue Avon box. Given in 1980 & 1981. CMV $15 MB.

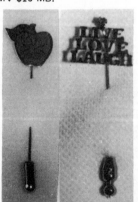

1971 EMPLOYEES GIFT KEY CHAIN
Blue box with gray flannel bag holds gold horseshoe with Avon on one side and You're in Demand on back side of charm. CMV $20. MB.

1977 APPLE STICK PIN
Red apple with 4A design 1977 & P.C. for President's Club on green Leaf. Pin is gold tone color. Given to winning team in each district for highest sales. CMV $15.

1978 LIVE-LOVE-LAUGH DIAMOND PIN AWARD
14K gold with 2 point diamond. Given to Avon managers for reaching appointment goal for August conference. CMV $30. MB.

1968 ANNIVERSARY CAMPAIGN KEY CHAIN
(Left) Silver charm and key chain. CMV $22.50

1972 CIRCLE OF EXCELLENCE KEY CHAIN
(Right) Silver charm and chain with 4A design on one side and Mexico 1972. This was given by Mexico Avon branch to Circle of Excellence Award winning managers for the year 1971. Trip was made in 1972 for the approximately 185 winning managers. CMV $55. mint.

1980 PRESIDENT'S CELEBRATION MEN'S AWARD KEY CHAIN
Sterling silver with oak tree on one side & inscribed on other. Given to men Reps. only for top sales. CMV $100. MB.

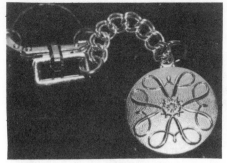

1976-77 SALES ACHIEVEMENT KEY CHAIN
Silver tone key chain. 4A emblem on front & back marked "Avon Sales Achievement Award C/23/76, C/9/77." In special Sales Achievement Award Avon box. CMV $11. MB.

1973-75 4A KEY RING AWARD
Gold lucite key ring in green or red lined box. CMV $10. MB each.

1970'S 5 YEAR SERVICE AWARD KEY RING
Sterling silver - 4A design on front Comes in Blue felt Tiffany bag & box. CMV $25.

1968 ANNIVERSARY CAMPAIGN HONOR AWARD KEY CHAIN
White Avon box holds gold & silver double key ring. Made by Swank. CMV $17.50 MB.

1975 BOCA OR BUST MANAGERS KEY CHAIN
Silver 4A design, CMV $15. MB.

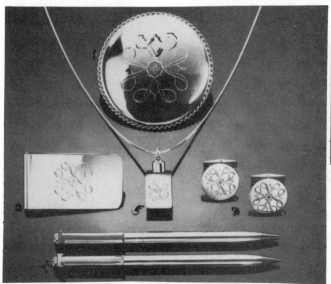

1980 - 10 YEAR SERVICE AWARDS
5 different gifts. All of sterling silver. All marked with 4A design. Each comes in Tiffany & Co. box. Given to Avon managers & all Avon Employees for 10 years service. They had their choice of Pen & Pencil set with T clip's, 3 inch purse mirror, Cuff Links 7/8" diameter, & Small 1¼" high silver flask that opens, on sterling silver chain 23½" long. CMV each item or set. $40 MB. Flask $60, pen set $50 MB.

1967 DISTINGUISHED MANAGEMENT AWARD
Sterling silver key chain with raised 4A design set in brushed finish area. Given to top manager in each division. CMV $35. MB, $27.50 chain only.

1964 LUCKY 7 PIN
Gold tone pin with simulated pearl in center. Given to each representative who sent in a certain size order. CMV $10., $13. MB.

1966 GOOD LUCK BRACELET
Gold double link bracelet with gold charm. Good luck & four leaf clover on the front. Back is plain. Not marked Avon. CMV $12., $15. MB.

1956 MANAGERS BRACELET
Bracelet give to top selling city & district managers during President's campaign 1956. CMV $100 MB.

1978 "KEY CHAIN" DISTRICT MANAGER SAFE DRIVER AWARD
Large brass key chain has "4A" on one side & "Avon District Manager Safe Driver Award 1978" on other side. Came in white & green box. 4A on box lid. Came also with Avon card shown. CMV $10. MB.

1953 AWARD BRACELET
1953 on back of sterling silver heart shaped charm. CMV $40 MB.

1969-70 AVON ATTENDANCE CHARM
1969 AD on one round charm & 1970 Heart shape AD on the other. Both gold tone & chain. CMV $17 ea.

1961 BELL BRACELET AWARD
Silver bracelet & bell that rings. Avon not on bell. CMV $20.

1964 BELL AWARDS
Gold bell earrings. Christmas sales award. CMV $20. Gold bell charm bracelet. Christmas sales award. CMV $30.

1979 KEY CHAIN "THANKS AMERICA" AWARD
Team leader white box holds silver tone heart key chain "Thanks America for making us number one" Back side says "Avon loves team leaders." CMV $12.50 MB.

1951 FIGURE 8 CHARM BRACELET
Sterling silver bracelet with 2 skates attached. Given to representatives for interviewing 120 Avon customers during the figure 8 campaign 3-1951. Made only for Avon. CMV $45.

1979 DREAM CHARM MANAGERS NECKLACE
Gold tone necklace & 3 charms of orchid, butterfly & sea shell. Given to Avon managers at 1979 Dream Conference. Does not say Avon on charms. Came in maroon satin bag with pink tie string. CMV $25. mint in bag.

1975 FIRST AVON LADY PENDANT AWARD
Silver toned with scroll 'A' design around glass insert. On the presentation card it starts "Congratulations! We're happy to present you with this exclusive award. Designed especially for you. It's symbolic of the personal service upon which Avon was founded and which has guided us throughout the years" CMV $25. - $30. MB.

1977 TLC NECKLACE AWARD
Given to Team Leaders. 14K gold. CMV $25.

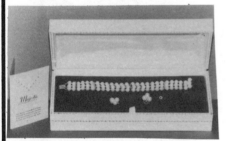

1960 MANAGERS CHRISTMAS GIFT
Pearl bracelet with small diamonds & matching earrings. Given to Avon managers at Christmas about 1960. Does not say Avon. Made by Majestic. CMV $300. MB.

1977 MANAGERS GIFT DIAMOND LOOP
Diamond Loop necklace given to managers in special gold bar type box., on introduction of Avons new 14K gold filled jewelry. CMV $30. MB as pictured.

1966 HONOR AWARD CAMEO PERFUME GLACE NECKLACE
Blue & white set trimmed in gold. CMV $18., $22.50 MB.

1974 PRESIDENTS CELEBRATION AWARD
14 kt. gold necklace with 3 point diamond. Given to 10 top representatives in each of the 81 winning districts for outstanding sales during this presidents celebration. CMV $60. MB.

1978 SMILE PENDANT AWARD
Red and gold pendant, given to all Avon Team Leaders. Back side says Avon, Team Leader, March 1978. CMV $10. MB. Also given to District Managers with D.M. on back. CMV $15. Both came in red box with Avon sleeve. Smile Pendant also given to Division managers at conference. Back says "N.Y. March, 78, Avon". Red box comes with plain white sleeve. CMV $30. MB.

1975 SUNNY STAR AWARD NECKLACE
Given to managers on introduction to Sunny Star necklace. This is the same one that sold only it has Aug. 1975 engraved on it. It can easily be duplicated so a price above the cost from Avon should not be paid. Brass star & chain. CMV $10. MB.

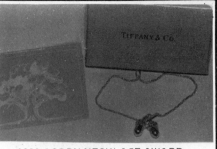

1978 EARRINGS - TEAM LEADER CHRISTMAS GIFT
10K solid gold with small diamond chip. Given to team leaders at Christmas, 1978. Came in Avon box. CMV $40. MB.

1980 ACORN NECKLACE AWARD
Sterling Silver Acorn Pendent & necklace. Comes with great oak card & Tiffany Box in velvet pouch. Given to managers only. CMV $80 MB with card.

1979 PRESIDENT'S CELEBRATION DIAMOND HEART LOCKET AWARD
Given to top 20 Reps. in each district during President's Celebration. Inscribed on back "President's Club 1979" CMV $20. MB. Same given to district managers only has DM inscribed on back also. CMV $30. MB.

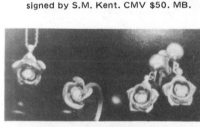

1978 VALENTINE HEART PENDANT AWARD
14K gold heart. Does not say Avon. Only 2500 were given to Reps. at sales meetings. Must have C3-78 brochure with heart to prove its from Avon. CMV $25. with brochure.

1982 TEAM LEADER TEDDY BEAR AWARD
Sterling silver bear with moveable arms & sterling silver chain. From Tiffany. Approx. ½ inch high. Marked T.L. on back of bear. CMV $30. MB.

1978 "YOU'RE PRECIOUS TO US" PENDANT MANAGERS GIFT
14K gold filled with real pearl & small diamond. Gold box says "You're Precious to Us" on lid. Given to Avon managers. Must be in box as described. Came with card signed by S.M. Kent. CMV $50. MB.

1982 SILVER CIRCLE CELEBRATION NECKLACE AWARD, ENGLAND
Blue box holds clear crystal pendant on sterling silver chain. Marked Avon Given to Silver Circle Reps. CMV $40. MB. Also shown with silver Circle Celebration Banquet Menu. CMV $5.

1971 - 85th ANNIVERSARY AWARD JEWELRY
22 Kt. gold plated sterling silver necklace, ring & earrings. Each shaped like a rose with diamond in center. Necklace was for representatives not in the presidents club, and the earrings for the presidents club members only. Two diamond rings were given in each district by a drawing. One was given to a presidents club member the other to a non-member. Ring also available in prize catalog for 2400 points. CMV necklace $35. - $40. MB, Ring $80. - $85. MB, Earrings $35. - $40. MB.

1979 CHRISTMAS GIFT - REPS.
Sterling silver goldtone chain with 10K gold charm with 2 small diamonds. Came in black felt box. Back is marked District managers 1979 - CMV $65., Team Leaders 1979 - CMV $50.

1979 HEART NO. 1 PENDANT AWARD
14K gold heart with small diamond given to 1 top Rep. in each division. In Avon blue velvet box. CMV $125. MB.

1971 85th ANNIVERSARY PINS
22 Kt. gold plated sterling silver pin with diamond. Small pin for representative not in president club, representatives only. Given for meeting sales goal in C-12-71. CMV small pin $15. - $20. MB. Large pin $20. - $25. MB.

1968 ANNIVERSARY AWARD ROSE PIN
Victory luncheon July 9, 1968. Gold rose pin with ruby stone in Avon box. CMV $27.50 MB only.

1971 MOONWIND AWARD PIN
Sterling silver pin given to Reps. for meeting sales goals. CMV $22.50.

1968 "G" CLEF MANAGERS PIN
Gold in color. Awarded to managers. CMV $15. pin only, $20. MB.

1965 AWARD PIN
White plastic on blue background with silver or gold frame. CMV $25. in box. $15. pin only.

1979 SHELL SALES LEADER AWARD
Sterling silver shell comes in Tiffany felt bag & box. Given to managers. CMV $125. MB.

1967 - 81st ANNIVERSARY PINS
Sterling silver pins came in 12 different flowers. Representatives who met their personal prize goal for this anniversary campaign had their choice of one of these 12 flowers. Carnation, Violet, Daffodil, Daisy, Lily of the Valley, Rose, Lily, Gladiolus, Aster, Calendula, Chrysanthemum, and Jonquil. CMV Rose $15., $25. MB. Calendula $30., $40. MB; all others $20., $30. MB.

1969 SALES ACHIEVEMENT AWARD
Large gold Charisma design pin came in black Avon box. CMV $20. MB.

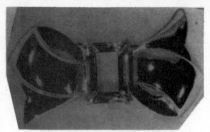

1968 SHELL JEWELRY
(Left) Given for recommending someone as a representative. For each name representatives could choose either the pin or earrings. For 2 or more names you got the set. CMV $12. Set.

1955 NEARNESS MANAGERS PIN
(Right) Gold shell pin with pearl. CMV $35.

1944 Only - AWARD PIN
Hand made sterling silver pin with roses & lilies, given to Reps. for selling $300. to $400. during Christmas campaign. CMV $50, $60 MB.

1944 BOW PIN AWARD
Lapel pin is gold plate with center stone of synthetic aquamarine. Given to Reps. for selling over $300. in 1 campaign. CMV $30, $45 MB.

1962 KEY PIN AWARD
(Top) Gold key, surprise gift for activity. CMV $10.

1961 AWARD EARRINGS
(Bottom) Gold star design. Avon is not on them. CMV $15. MB pair.

1943 MANAGERS AWARD PIN
Gold plated lapel pin with hand set stones, cost Avon $25. in 1943. Only 2 were given to the 2 top selling managers in U.S. during loyality campaign, March 2-22, 1943. CMV $125.

1942 BOWKNOT AWARD PIN
Gold pin with sequins shaped like bow. Given to representatives for selling $100. to $150. in one campaign. CMV $40, $50 MB.

1970 - 5 YEAR SERVICE PIN
For Avon plant employees, not Reps. Gold circle with 4A emblem & blue stone. CMV $30. - MB $25. pin only.

1951 CLOVER TIME PIN
Given to representatives for calling on 120 customers in one campaign. Made by Coro. Pin is outlined with imitation seed pearls & dotted with aquamarine stones for color. Does not say Avon. Came with certificate from Avon in Coro box. CMV $40. MB - $25. Pin only.

1942 VICTORY PIN AWARD
Sterling silver wing pin with red, white and blue center. Given to Reps. during Acres of Diamonds campaign 1942 for getting new customers. CMV $70, $80 MB.

1955 RED ROBIN PIN
Sterling silver pins made by Cora Company. Does not say Avon on it. Given in pairs for getting 12 new customers. CMV $25. - $30. MB

1979 EIFFEL TOWER MANAGERS PIN
Small gold tone tie tack type pin given to managers on Paris trip. Does not say Avon. In plain blue box. Pin is 1 1/8" high. CMV $15.

1980 ROYAL RIBBON TAC PIN AWARD
Sterling silver with yellow, red, white, or blue enamel. Given to managers for recruiting new Reps. CMV - Yellow $15. Red $20. White $25. Blue $30. MB each.

1977 TOP FIFTY PIN AWARD
Gold tone pin has top 50 & 4A design with red background. Given to top 50 Reps. in division for sales. CMV $16.

1978 TOP FIFTY PIN AWARD
Same as 1977 pin only has red rose with green leaves. CMV $12.50.

1979 FLAG PIN AWARD
Gold tone red, white and blue enamel lapel pin. Given to Circle of Excellence winners in Paris trip. Came in red velvet Avon ring box. CMV $50. MB.

1976 MANAGERS PANELIST PIN
Gold tone name pin. Marked "Nat. District Managers Panelist" CMV $15. Given each year.

1982 AVON'S BEST PIN AWARD
Small brass pin says "Avon's Best, Morton Grove." With 4A design. Given to managers for Atlanta conference. CMV $20.

1981 UNICORN PIN AWARD
Brass unicorn lapel pin given to managers at August conference 1981. Back inscribed Conference 81. Avon box says For Display Only - not for resale. CMV $20. MB. Same pin given to Team Leaders. CMV with TL on back $10. Pin also sold to public only plain no marking on back. No CMV.

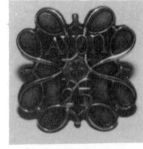

1980 SHOOTING STAR PIN - MANAGERS
Gold tone pin in brown box with outer sleeve. Given to managers. CMV $30. MB. Also came as tie tack for men. CMV $35. MB.

1981 TELEPHONE TIE TAC AWARD
Gold tone telephone Tie Tac. Given to Reps. CMV $10.

1970 - 25 YEAR SERVICE AWARD PIN
1/10 yellow 10K gold 4A pin with 25 on it. Was for 25 years service. Was never issued. Very Rare. CMV $150.

1980 C OF E PIN
Small pin says C of E 1980. CMV $10.

1979 C OF E WINNERS PIN
Blue Enamel on gold tone pin. CMV $20.

1981 SELL A THON TIE TAC
Red, white & blue tie tac pin. Given to all Reps. at sales meeting. CMV $2.

1980 CABLE CAR STICK PIN
Gold tone, sterling silver cable car stick pin given to Avon managers on trip to San Francisco. Does not say Avon. CMV $15.

1979 AVON PIN - DIVISION MANAGER
Gold tone pin with red enamel filled heart shaped O given to division managers only. CMV $25. MB - in red box.

1979 AVON PIN - REPS
Gold tone pin same as above only does not have red heart. CMV $10. MB - in white box.

1979 AVON PIN - DISTRICT MANAGERS
Same gold tone pin as reps. above only DM inscribed on back. CMV $15. MB - in white box.

1979 MONEY CLIP TEAM LEADER AWARD
Green & white lined black & brass box holds 12K gold filled money clip with solid 10K gold emblem with 2 small diamonds on top. Awarded to male team leaders. Rare. "Team Leader 1979" on back. CMV $125. MB. Also given to male managers with D.M. on back. CMV $150. MB.

1979 AVON NO. 1 PIN - HOLLAND
Gold tone pin given to Zone Avon Managers in Holland. CMV $50.

1963 - 1500 PIN
(Top) Given to reps. for $1,500. in sales in one campaign. CMV $20.

1969-70 TEAM CAPTAIN PIN
(Bottom) Torch pin says T C -69-70. CMV $20.

AVON STAR PIN
(Left) CMV $60. If you have any information on what year or what this pin was given for, please write Bud Hastin and tell him.

1938 SERVICE AWARD
(Right) Bronze medallion hangs from aqua colored bar with Avon in gold. Given to representatives for outstanding improvement in sales. CMV $50. mint.

1963 MONEY CLIP
(Left) 10K gold filled. Back says Pathways of Achievement 1963. 4A design on front and initials. CMV $75. MB.

1969 MONEY CLIP
(Center) Black and gold box holds 10K gold filled 4A design on front with initials. Back says Management Conference Atlanta, Georgia November 1969, CMV $75 MB.

1960 MONEY CLIP
(Right) 10K gold filled. Small 4A design on face and initials. Nothing on back. CMV $75.

1945 MEDALLION OF HONOR
Made of solid gold, it is 1 7/8 inches long & 1 3/8 inches wide. Woman on the front is raised. Back side is engraved to person & date. Came with award scroll. Medal can be worn on a ribbon or brooch. This medal was given to women only in 1945 during World War II both military & civilian for service to their country above and beyond the call of duty. Very few medals were given out. CMV medal $500., Scroll $50.

1970's 4A TIE CLIP SERVICE AWARD
Gold tone with 4A design. Given to Avon employees. CMV $25.

1975 TOP SALES MEDALLION
Gold colored metal medallion. Avon lady carrying case. Italy at bottom of foot. No Avon on it. Given to Avon Reps. for top sales and touring Springdale plant. 2 different designs. One star & one round. CMV $17, $22.50 MB each.

1931-37 STAR REPRESENTATIVE GOLD MEDALLION
10 kt. gold filled medal. Given to representatives for selling $1,000. worth of Avon in any 12 month period. CMV $150. - $165. MB.

1978 KEY RING 5 YEAR SERVICE AWARD
1/10 10K gold 4A symbol key ring given to Avon plant employees for 5 years service. Started in 1978. CMV $17.50.

1930-31 GOLD STAR REPRESENT-ATIVE MEDAL - CPC
Highest honor given to Representatives that achieved the goal of $1000. in sales from January to January. If goal reached second year a second gold star is engraved, and so on. Made of gold. CMV $275. MB.

1960 ANNIVERSARY PRINCESS BRACELET
Awarded for increased sales. Bracelet with diamond. Bracelet with emerald, Bracelet with ruby or topaze. 14K gold. CMV $260. each MB.

1968 SWEATER GUARD AWARD
6" gold chain with 4A design clips on each end. Given as general managers honor award to each representative of the winning team in each district. CMV $25. - $30. MB.

1962 SERVICE AWARD CHARM
22 kt. gold finish slightly larger than a quarter, given to all representatives who sold 50 or more customers during campaign 6. CMV $18.

1969 PRESIDENTS COURT CHARM
22 kt. gold finish charm. Given to all representatives of the team in each district. CMV $20.

1937-45 STAR REPRESENTATIVE GOLD MEDALLION
10 kt. gold filled medal, given to representatives for selling $1,000. worth of Avon in any 12 month period. CMV $50. - $60. in Black Highest Award box shown.

LOYAL SERVICE AWARD - 15 YEAR
Solid 10K gold. 4A emblem on front. Avon 15 years loyal service on back. Given to employees of Avon. Came on 10K gold wrist chain. CMV $150.

1966 TOUR GUIDE JACKET GUARDS
Silver color aluminum with 4A design. Used by Avon plant tour guides. CMV $32.50.

1978 - 4A BLUE ENAMEL PIN
Gold tone & blue enamel pin. Comes in Avon box. No information on what it's for. CMV $12. MB.

1967 RETIREMENT PIN
Gold disk with raised 4A design hanging from a golden bow. Given to retiring representatives with 10 years or more of service. CMV $50.

1966 4A MENS CUFF LINKS
Silver links with 4A design. Given to plant & office employees only. CMV $35. pr.

1969 TIE TAC AWARD
Small 1/10 10K gold tie tac given to Avon Male Executive with blue sapphire in center. Came in Avon Box. CMV $50 MB.

15 YEAR SERVICE CUFF LINKS
4A design on face and Avon 15 years Loyal Service on back with persons initials. Given to Avon male executives after 15 years service with Avon. Made of solid 10K gold. CMV $300. pair mint. Also came 30 year Service. Same cuff links. Same CMV.

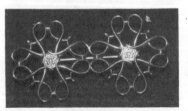

1960'S - 1970'S 4A DOUBLE STICK PIN AWARD
10K gold double 4A stick pin. We have no information on what it is. Please contact Bud Hastin if you know. Comes in Avon box. CMV $75. MB.

1965-68 DISTINGUISHED MANAGEMENT AWARD EARRINGS
4A design clip-on earrings. CMV $35. pair MB.

1973 TOUR GUIDE JACKET GUARDS
Gold metal with pressed flower in center of 4A. Used by Avon plant tour guides. CMV $25.

1962 DEDICATED TO SERVICE AWARD
1886-1962 4A design told tone. CMV $20.

1980 GREAT OAK NO. 1 MEDALLION AWARD
Small medal - Avon Oak Tree on one side, Pasadena No. 1 - 1980 4A design on other side. CMV $12.

1970'S CIRCLE OF EXCELLENCE PIN
Gold tone - 4A design and C of E Managers only. CMV $20.

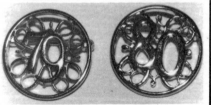

1979-80 PRESIDENT'S CLUB LADY'S PINS
Gold colored 4A pin - 79 in middle is 1st of an annual 4A year pin given to President's Club Reps. for meeting sales goal for that year. CMV $10. each year.

1980-81 PRESIDENT'S CLUB MEN'S TIE TAC
Small gold tone 4A - 81 on face. Given to male President's Club members. CMV $15., $17.50 MB.

1979-80 PRESIDENT'S CLUB MEN'S PIN AWARD
Gold tone 4A design & 79 on one & 80 on the other. Given to all male President's Club members. Smaller than lady's pin. CMV $20. MB 79 pin, CMV $15. MB 80 pin.

1965 AVON HAWAIIAN HOLIDAY CHARM AWARD
14K gold given to 7 avon managers in Hawaii in 1965. Each manager had their initials put on back. CMV $150.

1976 CHARM "DAY TO REMEMBER" AWARD
Small gold tone charm marked "A Day to Remember - C21-76" Came in blue Avon box. CMV $15. MB.

1980 PRESIDENT'S CELEBRATION NECKLACE
Gold tone charm with Great Oak on one side & The President's Celebration 1980 on other side. Given to top Reps. in each district. CMV $25. MB. Same charm in silver tone given to 10 top winning district Reps. CMV $40. MB.

1980 PRESIDENT'S CELEBRATION GREAT OAK MANAGER CHARM AWARD
Sterling silver cut out great oak tree charm. Comes with oak tree card in Avon box. Given to top managers in each district. CMV $100. MB. 1 top manager in each division won a cut out silver oak charm with sapphire around edge. CMV $150. MB. 1 top manager in each branch won same charm only with Ruby's around edge CMV $200. MB. The top manager in the U.S. won same cut out oak charm with a diamond. Very Rare. CMV not established.

1980 DISTRICT MANAGERS CHARM BRACELET
Sterling silver chain & heart shaped charm says "DM 1980". Came in Tiffany & Co. Box. Given to District Managers at September conference. CMV $75.

1980 SALES LEADERSHIP AWARD
Gold tone & black face. Says "Outstanding Sales Leadership" 5th Qtr. 1979-80 Avon. Came with red neck velvet ribbon. CMV $40.

1981 PRESIDENT'S CELEBRATION SALES ACHIEVEMENT MEDAL
(Left) Dated Dec. 11, 1981 on back side. Only 1 given to each branch. Put on red, white and blue ribbon. CMV $150.

1976 PRESIDENT'S CAMPAIGN KEY CHAIN
(Right) Chrome & white with red letters. Given to President's Club Reps. CMV $20.

1976 - 90th ANNIVERSARY BICENTENNIAL PENDANT AWARD
Brass coin & chain given to Reps. for selling $285. worth of Avon in 2 campaigns. Front & back view shown. CMV $15. MB.

1964 HAPPY ANNIVERSARY NECKLACE
For 38 years as a representative. October 1964. CMV $35.

1977 SALES ACHIEVEMENT AWARD PENDANT
1" gold pendant with 18" chain. Says 1977 Avon Sales Achievement Award & 4A design on other side. Came in white Avon box. Given to top 10% of sales Reps. in each division. CMV $20. MB. Same pendant slightly larger - came in Blue box. CMV $25. MB.

1980 RUNNING CIRCUIT AVON MEDAL
2¼" medal has red, white and blue ribbon & medal says "Avon International Running Circuit." Given to people who ran in Avon Running Circuit. CMV $50.

1975 AVON SALES ACHIEVEMENT AWARD BRACELET
Given for sales. Avon on one side and sales achievement on the other. Sterling. CMV $15. - $20. MB.

1979 SALES ACHIEVEMENT AWARD
Solid bronze with Oak Tree on front with "District Manager Quarterly Sales Achievement Award - Avon" 4A symbol on back. Given to managers only. CMV $50.

1974 TEAM LEADER PIN
(Right) Gold raised letters & rim. Given to team leaders. CMV $7. - $9. MB.

1975 TEAM LEADER PIN
(Left) Gold with indented letters. Given to team leaders. CMV $7., $9. MB.

1968 FIELD OPERATIONS AWARD
Solid brass, Avon 4A emblem on front. Field operations seminar on back. Given to managers in Pasadena branch in Better Way program. CMV $55.

1960 GOLF LEAGUE CHARM
1960 on back. Front has Avon League with 4A design & golfer. Solid brass. Given to Avon plant employees, Pasadena branch, for playing golf tournament. CMV $40.

1981 PRESIDENT'S CLUB MEN'S POCKET WATCH AWARD
Gold tone Swiss made 17 jewel watch. Avon on face of watch, metal face cover. Given to male President's Club members. CMV $150 MB.

548

1980 PRESIDENT'S CLUB 1981 WATCH WOMEN'S
(left) gold tone 17 jewel watch on chain. Back says "President's Club 81". CMV $50 MB.

1980 PRESIDENT'S CLUB 1981 MEN'S WATCH
(right) gold tone pocket watch on chain given to male President's Club Reps. Inscribed on back "President's Club 1981". CMV $125 MB. No face cover, CMV $125 MB.

1977 TEAM LEADER WATCH
Given to all Avon team leaders for Christmas 1977. 2 different. (left) for women, (right) for men. The cases are different and the difference in size of winding stem. Very few of the mens watches given. CMV for womens $40 MB. CMV for mens $125 MB.

1977 MANAGERS WATCH
Avon watch same as team leader watch only face says Avon in place of Team Leader & 4A symbol that rotates instead of Avon. Came in male & female size watch as above. CMV $75 MB.

1970 PENDANT WATCH AWARD
Gold tone watch on neck chain given to 6 Reps. in each district for top sales. Made by Sheffield. Also sold in stores. 9,000 watches given by Avon. CMV $20.

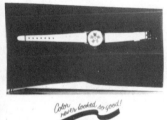

1968 AVON MANAGERS ACHIEVEMENT CLOCK
Box with 4A design & outer Avon sleeve. Clock set in top of brushed gold hour glass inscribed on bottom "1968 Avon Managers Achievement". CMV $100 clock only. $135 MB with outer sleeve.

1979 COLOR UP WATCH AWARD
Le Jour Time Co. watch in gold tone case, white strap. Back side says "For the most colorful time of your life". Came in white box, sleeve & blue felt wrap. Given to Reps for customers served. CMV $35 MB.

1969 DIVISION MANAGERS AWARD CLOCK
Sterling silver Seth Thomas electric clock. 4" square face, bottom says, "Divisional Managers Tribute 1969". CMV $125 mint.

1974 PRESIDENT'S CLUB MEMBERS WATCH
Awarded to club members. Gold watch & hands with black strap. Box blue & white. CMV $42.50 MB.

1979 WATCH STICK PIN, MANAGERS
(left) Gold tone 4A design on face. Given to managers. CMV $75.

1978 FIELD SUPPORT PENDANT AWARD
(right) 1/20 12K gold filled. Back is dated "1978 Field Support Manager". Given to managers. CMV $30.

1978 NAT. DISTRICT MANAGER PANELIST PIN
(bottom) Gold tone. Given to managers. CMV $10.

549

1977 OUTSTANDING SALES MANAGEMENT CLOCK AWARD

Relide 15 jewel Swiss sold brass clock. Inscribed on top "In Recognition of Outstanding Sales Management - Third Quarter 1977". Given to No. 1 Avon manager in each division. CMV $125.

1977 HOURS FOR EXCELLENCE CLOCK AWARD

Gold label on top of Bulova travel alarm. Does not say Avon. Given to Reps. CMV $15 MB.

1977 LIBERTY CLOCK AWARD

Given to managers for 1 million dollar sales increase. Gold tone clock by Bulova. Inside slide clock cover says "To a Million Dollar Baby (name of manager) Division $1,000,000 Sales Increase 1977". Came in Bulova Americana Collection. CMV $125.

1980 ROSE ANNIVERSARY PITCHER AWARD

9" tall clear glass with engraved rose. Given to Reps. for selling $800 in C14-15 1980. CMV $25 MB.

1976 PRESIDENT'S CELEBRATION AWARD CLOCK

Gold plastic & metal Westclock. 4 red roses on face. Was not made only for Avon. CMV $12.

1968 DIARY CLOCK

Made by Seth Thomas. Gold, back opens & says "Avon Award", CMV $40.

1980 ROSE ANNIVERSARY GOBLETS AWARD

6½" high with engraved rose. Set of 4 for selling $400 in C14-15 1980. CMV $15 set of 4.

1971 ANTIQUE CAR GLASSES

Eight different glasses picturing Stanley Steamer, Silver Duesenberg, Gold Cadillac, Sterling Six, Electric Charger, Packard Roadster, Touring T & Straight Eight. Selling 10 Avon cars won a set of 4 glasses. Selling 15 Avon cars won a set of 8 glasses. CMV set of 4 $12, set of 8 $27.50 MB.

1971 ANTIQUE CAR PITCHER

Reps. won this by having one person they recommended as representative appointed. Also available in prize catalog for 1,400 points. 2 different pitchers. Rare one has silver Duesenberg & Stanley Steamer on it. CMV $35, $40 MB. Most of them have Straight Eight & Packard Roadster decal on it. CMV $25, $30 MB.

1974 PRESIDENT'S CELEBRATION CLOCK AWARD

Solid brass clock with "President's Celebration 1974" on face. Clock made by Relide, 15 jewels. Given to Avon managers. Came in plain box & pink felt bag. CMV $200 mint.

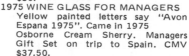

1980 ROSE ANNIVERSARY LUNCHEON PLATES AWARD
Set of 4 clear glass 8" plates with engraved rose in center. Given to Reps. for selling $600 in C14-15 1980. CMV $20 set of 4 plates.

1977 1st DIVISION GLASS AWARD
Lead crystal champagne glass given to No. 1 division Avon managers. CMV $30.

1975 WINE GLASS FOR MANAGERS
Yellow painted letters say "Avon Espana 1975". Came in 1975 Osborne Cream Sherry. Managers Gift Set on trip to Spain. CMV $37.50.

1981 GREAT AMERICAN SELLA-THON CHAMPAGNE GLASS
Given to team leaders and managers. December 1981 on trip to Hawaii. CMV $15.

1975 AVON LADY STEMWARE GLASSES AWARDS
C-20 1975. Set of 6, 10 oz. & 6, 6 oz. glasses with 1st Avon Lady design. 1 set given to all Reps. in the winning district for top sales. CMV set $50 MB.

1974 PASADENA BRANCH WINE GLASS
No. 1 in sales. 429 given. "19 Avon 74 Pasadena Branch" on glasses. CMV $15.

1974 CIRCLE OF EXCELLENCE GLASS
Pasadena Branch No. 1 in sales C of E. Made by Fostoria, very thin glass. Only 30 given to managers. "C of E 1974" on side of glass. CMV $60. Same glass also came in 1973. Same CMV.

1979 CIRCLE OF EXCELLENCE WINE GLASS
Given to managers. Glass embossed "C of E 1979". Came in sets of 2 glasses. CMV $25 each glass.

1980 CIRCLE OF EXCELLENCE CHAMPAGNE GLASS
"C of E 1980" embossed on glass. Given to managers only in sets of 2 glasses. CMV $25 each glass.

1970 INITIAL GLASS AWARD
Campaign 12 & 13, 1970. Reps. won the glasses and President's Club members won the goblets with initial of their choice for reaching sales goals in each campaign. The coasters were won by both for reaching sales goals both campaigns. CMV on coasters $3, glasses $3, goblets $4 each.

1981 ULTRA CRYSTAL EVENT GLASS AWARD
Tiffany & Co. box holds 2 engraved glasses. Given to Reps. who met sales goal by drawing for winner at sales meeting. CMV $50 set MB.

1977 TEAM ACHIEVEMENT AWARD
Goblet given in 1st and 3rd quarters to top team in each district. Came in white embossed Avon box. CMV $20 each quarter. MB.

1952 SUGAR & CREAMER AWARD
Sterling silver base and glass tops. Given to Avon Reps. in 1952. White and silver striped box. Made by Fina. CMV $55 set MB.

1971 AVON CHRISTMAS GLASS
(left) Given to Reps. at special Christmas meeting. Glass tumbler with red printing. "Holiday Greetings from Avon, December 1971". CMV $12.

1971 ANTIQUE RENAULT CAR GLASS
(right) Some set come with this Renault car in set. Rare. CMV $15.

1970 GIVE N GAIN PRIZE
10¾" high, 4" in diameter. A rose, butterfly and lady bug are etched in glass. Given to Avon ladies as prize. This was also sold in stores to public. Came in plain box with Avon stamped on it. Made by Abilities. CMV $25 MB.

1952 CANDY DISH SET AWARD
Sterling silver base by Fina. Glass screw on tops. Given to Avon Reps. in 1952. Came in plain white box. CMV $55.

1980 CRYSTAL CANDLE HOLDERS
10" high clear crystal. Given to Reps. for 30 years continuous service. Base is inscribed "30th Avon Anniversary". CMV $125 pair.

1972 PEOPLE WHO LIKE PEOPLE PRIZE PROGRAM AWARDS
3rd level prize is a set of 8 10 oz. crystal and silver glasses. Won by Reps. for meeting 3rd level sales goals. Was not made only for Avon. CMV $25 set MB.

1971 FRONT PAGE TUMBLERS
14 oz. tumblers with Reps. name printed on "front page" of glass. Given for having a person reccommended as a Rep. appointed. CMV $25 set of 8 MB.

1978 YOU MAKE ME SMILE GLASSES AWARDS
Set of 6 glasses made only for Avon given to Avon Reps. for signing up a new Avon lady. CMV $12 set MB.

1956 CRYSTAL SALAD BOWL AWARD
7½" cut glass with silverplate edge. Comes with serving fork & spoon & card from Avon. Given to Reps. during 70th Anniversary Celebration in 1956. Made by Fina. CMV $55 complete.

1972 PEOPLE WHO LIKE PEOPLE PRIZE PROGRAM AWARDS
4th level prize is a 9" diameter & 6" high silver base and trim crystal footed fruit bowl. Won by Reps. for meeting 4th & final level sales goals. Was not made only for Avon. CMV $25 MB.

1972 PEOPLE WHO LIKE PEOPLE PRIZE PROGRAM AWARDS
2nd level prize is a 12¾" chip 'n dip serving set of crystal & silver timmed. It comes with a 5" matching dip bowl in the center. Won by Reps. for meeting 2nd level sales goals. Was not made only for Avon. CMV $15 MB.

1909-1912 CPC SALES MANAGERS GIFT
4" x 4" size, pressed crystal glass jar with Rogers Silver Plate lid. Given to each Rep. selling $50 in sales in December 1909 & 1912. The silver lid has an embossed floral design. CMV $200 mint.

1971 SCALLOPED SERVING DISH & SPOON PRIZE
Pressed glass nut dish given to Reps. for meeting sales goals. Also available in local stores. CMV $7 MB.

1972 PEOPLE WHO LIKE PEOPLE PRIZE PROGRAM AWARDS
1st level prize. Walnut base with silver handle holds 3 crystal with silver trim 6 oz. bowls. Won by Reps. for meeting sales goals. Was not made only for Avon. CMV $15 MB.

1973 TIC TAC TOE APPLE SALAD SET AWARD
(left) 3 piece set, 10" clear glass apple bowl with William Rogers silver plated fork & spoon. Won for prize goal. Must be in Avon box with card. CMV $10 MB.

1973 DIVIDED APPLE RELISH SET
(right) 3 piece set, 6" divided clear glass bowl with William Rogers silver plated fork & spoon. This bowl won by President's Club members only for prize goal. These items must be in the box with outlook and card, as they were not made only for Avon. CMV $15 MB.

1973 AMERICAN HERITAGE AWARDS
Set of glass crystal edged with silver. Given to Reps. in C-11, 1973. Consists of 10 7/8" relish dish. CMV $20 MB. Fruit bowl 7 1/8" high and 7 7/8" across. CMV $20 MB. Water pitcher CMV $20 MB. Products were not made only for Avon.

1978 MILLION DOLLAR INCREASE GOBLET
(left) Silver plated goblet given to all managers in top division for 1 million dollar increase in sales. CMV $25.

1977 PORT O'CALL CANDY DISH & BAR
(right) China dish by Ilmoges - France & bar of French candy given to managers for meeting appointment goal. Box has gold label "Meet me at the lamp post, Port O'Call Pasadena". CMV $10 MB.

1977 SALES EXCELLENCE AWARD CUP
6½" high pewter cup. "4A design, Avon Sales Excellence Award 1977" on side of cup. Given to top 2% of sales Reps. in each division. CMV $40 MB.

1969 CHRISTMAS CUP
White glass mug. Avon on bottom. Given to district managers for Christmas. CMV $30.

1975 OSBORNE CREAM SHERRY MANAGERS GIFT SET

Wine cask on box lid. Box holds 2 wine glasses with "Avon Espana 1975" painted in yellow, bottle of Osborne Cream Sherry with special label "Especially bottled for the 1974 members of the Circle of Excellence". This set was given to each manager on their C of E trip to Madrid, Spain. Only 200 sets given out. CMV $130 set mint full.

1982 COFFEE MUG AWARD — CANADA

Set of two ceramic coffee mugs given as a bonus for recommendations by Canadian Avon Reps. CMV $10.

1979 SPRINGDALE FOUNDERS CLUB COFFEE CUP AWARD

(top) White glass cup given to all Plant employees who had worked from 1965 to 1979. Red letters. CMV $15.

1979 COLOR UP AMERICA PEN

(bottom) White, black & silver pen on brown leather neck cord. Given to managers. CMV $10.

1975 GOBLET — CIRCLE OF EXCELLENCE AWARD

(left) 7½" high sterling silver goblet. Given to C of E managers who went to Madrid, Spain 1975. Base says "Circle of Excellence, Madrid, 1975" CMV $60.

1976 TEAM LEADER MUG AWARD

(right) White glass mug. CMV $17.50.

1977 SALES ACHIEVEMENT MUG AWARD

Pink rose on side and Sales Achievement 4th Quarter 1977 on other side. CMV $10.

1978 ACHIEVEMENT AWARD MUG

"1st Quarter, 1978" on white ceramic mug given to team getting most new Avon ladies to sign up. CMV $10.

1977 PROSPECT COFFEE JAR & CUP AWARD

Clear glass jar with green painted design on front says "1886 - Avon 1977". Filled with coffee beans. CMV $20 jar only. Coffee cup - came with jar in white box as set. Has Avon district manager 1977 on cup & other writings. CMV $15 cup only Both given to Avon managers only.

1977 MERRY CHRISTMAS MUG

Short glass mug with green lettering on front. CMV $8.

1970's CIRCLE OF EXCELLENCE MUG

Pewter mug inscribed C of E Avon on front. CMV $32.50.

1966 AWARD COMPACT
(left) Sterling silver compact. Engraved on back "National Champion, President's Campaign, 1966". CMV $17.

1960 AVON SUGAR BOWL CLUB
(right) Awarded to sales ladies for getting new customers. CMV $60.

1977-78 CURRIER & IVES COLLECTION AWARD
Made only for Avon & stamped on bottom. Given to Avon Reps. for meeting sales goals. 1st set - Dinner bell, CMV $6.50 MB.
2nd step - Butter dish, CMV $12 MB.
3rd step - Water pitcher 6½" high. CMV $17.50 MB.
4th step - Cake plate 9½" diam. CMV $32.50 MB. Add $10 each piece for bottom writing printed backwards.

1978 CIRCLE OF EXCELLENCE MUG AWARD
Avon C of E District No. 1978 in red letters. Given to Reps. in winning districts. CMV $25.

1981-82 CURRIER & IVES 5 PIECE PLACE SETTING AWARD
Each set has dinner plate, salad plate, cup & saucer, and soup bowl. Given to Avon Reps. for signing up 1 new Avon Rep. CMV $25 set of 5 pieces.
1977-81 Same set only marked 1977-81 on bottom of each piece in set. Only 300 sets got out in Newark Branch. CMV with 77-81 bottom date $100 MB set.

1972 MIKASA CHINA SET
Candle holders & sugar/creamer set for reaching first prize goal. CMV $5 each MB. Beverage server for reaching second goal. CMV $10 MB. Eight cups & saucers for reaching third goal (to be won by President's Club members only). CMV $4. For each cup & saucer set. These items must be in Avon boxes with card or outlook as this set was not made just for Avon.

1953 QUEEN ELIZABETH CUP & SAUCER
Avon 67th Anniversary celebration coincided with Queen Elizabeth Coronation. Awarded at a banquet for top organization. CMV $80 mint.

1977-78 CURRIER & IVES TEA SET
Set consists of plate, tea pot, sugar bowl & creamer. Avon Products, Inc. on bottom of each piece. Awarded to Avon Reps. for Distinguished Sales Achievement 1977. Plate - 1st step. CMV $6.50.
Sugar bowl & creamer - 2nd step. CMV $12.
Tea pot - 3rd step. CMV $17.50.
Cup & saucer - 4th step. Saucer 1st issue marked 1977 on bottom 1978 issue has no date. Add $2 each piece for 1977 date. CMV $35 set of 4. Add $10 if writing on bottom is printed backwards for each piece.

1982 CURRIER & IVES SUGAR & CREAMER AWARD
Set given to Avon Reps. for signing up 1 new Avon Rep. CMV $15 set.

1972 SILVER CANDLELIGHT SET GIFT
Given to Reps. as a gift. Does not say Avon on set & was not made only for Avon. Can be bought in stores. Set has punch bowl & 2 goblets with silver rim. Box has Avon mailing label. CMV $35 in Avon box.

1974 SPIRIT OF '76 CROCK SET AWARDS
(Left) Multipurpose Pitcher - earned for $150 in sales. CMV $7 MB.
(Center) Bean Pot Casserole - earned for $200 in sales. CMV $14 MB.
(Right) Goodies Jar - earned for $300 in sales. CMV $18 MB.

1972 SALAD SET GIFT
Given to Reps. as gift. Does not say Avon and was not made only for Avon. Can be bought in stores. Came in plain box with Avon mailing label. Set has large salad bowl & 4 small ones & silver plated spoon & fork. CMV $35 in Avon box.

1976 POSSET POT AWARD
(left) 9'' high stoneware. Bottom reads ''Made in Brazil Exclusively for Avon Products, Inc.''. CMV $25.
1975-77 PITCHER & BOWL RECOMMENDATION PRIZE
(right) Given for recommending someone, if appointed as a Rep. Has Avon on bottom of both pieces. CMV $50 set.

1977 DECORATORS CHOICE PITCHER AND BOWL PRIZE
Ceramic pitcher 10'' high & bowl 15¼'' across. Made only for Avon. Given to Reps. for signing up 1 new Avon Rep. CMV $50.

1973 REPRESENTATIVES AWARD PLATES
Awarded for years of service. First 5, white with colored decals. Two years- Doorknockers CMV $12. Five years - Oak Tree with pink or brown acorns, CMV $18. 5 year ''Factory Mistake Plate'' marked as normal 5th Anniversary plate on back but same as 10th year plate on front. Rare. Add $25 to 5 year plate. Ten years - California Perfume Co. CMV $24. Fifteen years - Rose CMV $30. Twenty years - First Avon Lady CMV $40. Twenty-five years - Sterling silver with message from Avon President. CMV $135. 1981 up issue is silver plate. CMV $60 MB. All Prices are mint & boxed. CMV complete set $250 MB.

1976 BICENTENNIAL PLATES

Blue & white. Given to Reps. that sent in order for campaign 1, 2, 3 totaling $100 or more.
(left) Independence Hall.
(right) Liberty Bell. Made in England. Has inscription on back. CMV $20 Independence Hall; $30 Liberty Bell.

1975 BIRD PLATE AWARDS

Campaign 10, 1975. Available to Reps. for meeting product goals; serving specified number of customers and meeting goals at suggested customer prices. Bluebird was lowest goal, yellow breasted Chat second and Baltimore Oriole last. If total goals attained, Rep. received all three plates. CMV Bluebird, $20 MB, yellow breasted Chat $20 MB, Baltimore Oriole $30 MB.

1974 TENDERNESS COMMEMORATIVE PLATE

9" diameter ceramic plate, pastel blue and greens. Awarded to Reps. for sending in orders for campaign 1, 2, and 3, 1974. Inscription on back in blue letters "Tenderness Commemorative Plate Special Edition, awarded to Reps. in January, 1974". Plate is made by Pontessa Ironstone of Spain. Award plate has Pontessa in red letters. Regular issue Pontessa in blue letters. Plate also sold with no inscription on back. CMV $22 MB. Red letter plate only.

1976-78 WILD FLOWERS AWARD PLATES

Each is 8¾". Southern Wild Flower plate for $195 in sales. Southern & Eastern given for $245 in sales & Southern, Eastern, Northern & Western flower plates for $330 in sales. C-11, 1976. CMV Southern $10 MB. Eastern $15 MB. All 4 plates MB $60 set. Northern & Western $20 each MB. These same plates were reissued by Geni Products, a division of Avon in March, 1978, as awards to their sales reps.

1967 DISTINGUISHED MANAGEMENT AWARD

Glass plate with 4A design on bottom. Came in white box lined in red velvet. CMV $45 plate only. $55 MB.

1971 CHRISTMAS GIFT PLATE
(Top Left) Sent to Reps. at Christmas. Clear glass with frosted First Avon Lady. CMV $17 MB. $12 no box.

1972 CHRISTMAS GIFT PLATE
(Top Right) Sent to every Rep. at Christmas. Clear glass frosted rose. CMV $15 MB. $10 no box.

1973 CHRISTMAS GIFT PLATE
(Bottom Left) Sent to Reps. who had been with company less than 2 years. Clear glass frosted 4A. CMV $15 MB. $10 no box.

1974 CHRISTMAS GIFT PLATE
(Bottom Right) Sent to Reps. at Christmas. Clear glass with frosted Door Knocker. CMV $12 MB. $8 no box.

1978 FOSTORIA LEAD CRYSTAL PLATES AWARD
Given for top sales. 1st four plates won by Reps: Jeweled A, 1st Rep., Door Knocker, great oak tree. CMV $30 set of 4 or $7 each.
President's Club Reps. & District Managers could win 1st 4 plus 4 more: 4A Avon Key, World of Avon Globe, Avon Rose Last. President's Club set had P.C. marked on Rose plate & D.M. marked Jeweled A plate for managers set. CMV $100 D.M. set of 8, CMV $75 P.C. set of 8.

1970 FOSTORIA COIN PLATE AWARD
Does not say Avon. Must be in Avon box. CMV $12 MB.

1973 RECOMMENDATION GIFT SNACK SET
Fostoria lead crystal dish & bowl. Came in set of 4 each. Given to Avon Reps. for signing up new Avon ladies. CMV $15 each setting, $60 for all 8 pieces.

1963 - 77th ANNIVERSARY QUEEN AWARD
Awarded to 10 Reps. in each district that had greatest dollar increase in sales, were crowned Queen & also received Fostoria Crystal serving dish with Avon 4A in bottom. Tiara not marked Avon. Came with Avon Queen certificate - 2 different certificates were given. Also came with 1963 Queen Ribbon. 11¼" bowl. CMV bowl only $50. CMV Tiara with certificate & ribbon $50. CMV complete set MB $100.

1979 LENOX CHINA PRESIDENT'S CLUB BOWL AWARD
White box with gold trim & burgundy inside holds 4A inscribed china bowl. Bottom inscribed "For Avon's Very Best" given to all President's Club members for 1980. Box has Avon outer sleeve. CMV $40 MB, bowl only $30.

1966 NATIONAL CHAMPION AWARD
Glass bowl with 4A design on bottom. CMV $50 MB.

1930's GRAVY BOAT AWARD
CPC Avon on bottom. Given to Reps. for sales award in 1930's. Blue & green flowers on both sides. Gold trim. CMV $75.

1930's COVERED DISH AWARD
White ceramic bowl & lid. Gold trim with green & pink flowers. Bottom is stamped CPCo. Avon under glazing. Given to Avon Reps. for sales. CMV $110 mint.

1980 GREAT SCENT EVENT TRAY AWARD
9½"x 17¾" gold tone mirror tray given to 15 Reps. in each district for selling the most Ultra colognes. Does not say Avon on tray. Came with & must have Great Scent Event card from division manager. CMV $20 with card.

1978 CAKE STAND AWARD
(Front) Given to top 50 Reps. in state. "Avon Division Top 50" inscribed in center. Silver plated. CMV $25.
1979 IMPERIAL DIVISION AWARD TRAY
(Back) Silver plated, inscribed "Avon Imperial Division Top 50, 1979 #29" CMV $25.

1976 50 YEAR SERVICE PLATE
Gold plated plate given to the late Mrs. Bessie O'Neal on July 27, 1976, by David Mitchell, President of Avon Products, for 50 continuous years as an Avon lady. A letter from Avon & Mr. Mitchell came with the plate. The plate is 1 of a kind & priceless. The plate is made by Dirilyte. No value established.

1950's SILVER SERVER AWARD
(top) 11¾"x 18¾" silver plated tray & cover. Marked Avon Wm. Rogers on bottom. No information on why it was given to Reps. CMV $45 mint.
1950's SILVER CREAMER AWARD
(bottom) Avon Wm. Rogers on bottom. Silverplate creamer. No information on this as Avon award. CMV not established.

1950's SILVER TRAY AWARD
Silver tray 13½" long, "Avon - Wm. Rogers" on bottom. Awarded to Avon ladies in 1950's. Write to Bud Hastin if you have any info on this award. CMV $30.

1976 HIGHEST SALES AWARD BOWL
Silver plated fruit bowl was awarded to 10 different Reps. for highest sales in their category. Each bowl is engraved different from the other. The one is engraved with "4A" design. "Highest Percentage Increase Christmas 1976". CMV $25, $30 MB. Not awarded in all branches.

1977 PRESIDENT'S CELEBRATION AWARD BOWL
Over 40,000 were given as awards. 6⅞" silver plated bowl given to Avon Reps. in 2 winning districts in each division for top sales. Inscription in center of bowl "President's Celebration 1977"; on bottom of bowl, "Awarded exclusively to Avon Reps." F.B. Rogers. Came in white box as shown. Red silk rose also given at same time with name tag. CMV Rose only with tag, $5. CMV bowl $25 MB. Bowl did not come with rose.

559

1961 - 75th ANNIVERSARY SALES CHAMPION SILVER TRAY
Awarded to the top Avon district managers for best sales in campaign 9 & 10, 1961. CMV $40.

1975 DIVISIONS SALES WINNER TRAY AWARD
17¾" long x 13" wide silver tray. Inscribed in center 'Awarded to (name of manager) President's Program 1975 Division Sales Winner with Best Wishes, David S. Mitchell'. Given to top district managers in sales. Came in blue felt bag & white box. CMV $150 MB in bag.

1974 88th ANNIVERSARY AWARD BOWL
6" across and 3" high silverplated by Oneida. Paul Revere Silver. Given to top 5 sales Reps. in each district. CMV $22.50 Same bowl given to top 5 President's Club Sales Reps. and their award bowl says "President's Club" over 4A ensignia. CMV $22.50

1963 SILVER SERVER AWARD
12 5/16"x 2" given to the top 4 established Reps. in each district for sales improvement over the previous year. 4A design engraved in the bottom. Small 9" servers were given to 3 newer Reps. for highest sale & 3 for outstanding sales ability. CMV 9" $40, 12" $45.

1977 EL CAMINO DIVISION SUGAR & CREAMER SET AWARD
Silverplated creamer & sugar bowl. Tray is engraved 'Top 10 Sales - El Camino Division Campaigns 10-22, 1977'. Made by Sheridan. CMV $35 set mint.

1977 SALES EXCELLENCE AWARD
Paul Revere, Jostens Pewter 5" bowl C26-76 — C9-77. Awarded to top sales Reps. CMV $22.50 MB.

1961 ACHIEVEMENT AWARD SILVER TRAY
4A design in center of silver tray. CMV $35.

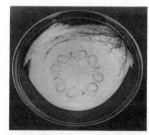

1964 SILVER SERVER
9" diameter. Same as 1963 server except no 12" bowls given and all are gold lined on the inside. CMV $40.

1969 SILVER AWARD BOWL
Silverplate bowl by Fina. Has 4A symbol and Avon in center of bowl. 2 3/4" high and 5" wide at top. Awarded to Avon Reps. CMV $20.

1978 PRESIDENT'S CELEBRATION TRAY AWARD
12" silverplated tray marked 'Awarded Exclusively to Avon Reps.' on back side. Given to 1 winning team Rep. in each division. CMV $35 MB.

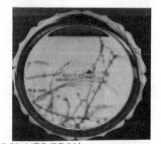

1965 SILVER TRAY
9 7/8"x 1" given to each Rep. from the winning group in each branch during the General Manager's Campaign, engraved "Honor Award - General Manager's Campaign 1965" CMV $35.

1962 PRESIDENT'S AWARD SILVER BOWLS
3 sizes silver bowls. 4A emblem and writing on outside. CMV (left to right) $27.50, $32.50, $37.50.

1956 REPRESENTATIVE AWARD BOWL
Sterling silver Paul Revere Bowl was given to each Rep. in the top selling district in each division during President's Campaign 1956. CMV $45.

1960's CAKE PLATE FOSTORIA COIN GLASS AWARD
Fostoria glass cake plate given to Reps. for sales award. Comes in Avon box. Same piece was sold in local stores. Must be in Avon box as shown. CMV $100 MB.

1964 - 78th ANNIVERSARY FOSTORIA AWARD SET
Box marked Avon Cosmetics holds Fostoria salt & pepper, cruet & glass holding tray. Given to Reps. CMV $45 in Avon box.

1960's COMPOTE TALL
Fostoria coin glass award. Must be in Avon box. Given to Reps for sales award. CMV $65 MB.

1970 FORSTORIA SUGAR & CREAM SET AWARD
From Fostoria glass, box says "Avon Cosmetics". Given to Reps for sales achievement. Design is from the Henry Ford Collection. CMV $30 MB only.

1973 CHINA BELL REP. GIFT
Christmas present to all Reps. that had been with Avon over 2 years. White China with pink roses. CMV $14 MB.

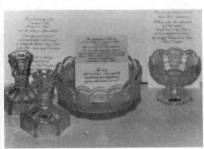

1977 91st ANNIVERSARY COIN GLASS AWARD
Footed compote on right won by Reps. for selling $270 in C8-9-1977. CMV $7 MB. Centerpiece bowl and footed compote won for selling $540 in C8-9-1977. CMV $12 MB. Centerpiece bowl. A pair of candle holders won by President's Club members only with P.C. embossed on bottom. This coin glass was made only for Avon, using Avon emblems in coins and 1886-1977 and the name Avon. Came with card on each piece from Avon and in Avon box. CMV $17 candle holders, MB. District managers received a full set of Coin Glass with D.M. embossed in center of each piece. CMV $75 MB for complete D.M. set.

1961-72 COIN GLASS
Coin glass in Avon boxes only are collectable. The same pieces are available in local stores with both 1886 and 1887 at low prices so get the box. Many pieces available at many different prices starting at $10 up to $100 in Avon box. 1st issue 1961.

1980 TEAM LEADER BELL AWARD
Fostoria bell inscribed "Avon Team Leader Recruit A Thon 1980". Only 1 in each district given. CMV $30.

1968 CARTIER CRYSTAL BELL AWARD
Crystal bell in Cartier bag & box. Signed Val Lambert. Is not marked Avon. Given to one Rep. per district for most recommendations. CMV $65 MB. Bell only $50.

1980 GREAT OAK LAMP AWARD
Electric light in wood base with solid hunk of clear glass with great oak engraved. Given to district managers at yearly conference. CMV $100 mint.

1974 PRESIDENT'S CELEBRATION SILVER CHEST
Silverplated, red lined. Embossed rose on lid. CMV $47.50 MB.

1961 REPRESENTATIVE GIFT CIGARETTE CASE
Silver colored metal case. 4A design & Christmas 1961 on lid. CMV $47.50. Also given to managers in gold tone case. CMV $70.

1936 -50th ANNIVERSARY AWARD LAMP
Made only for Avon "Lalique reproduction" lamp. 22" high, 19" wide shade. Frosted carved glass base. Pink ribbon on shade, clear beads around edge of shade. White painted base. Given only to 50 Reps. for top sales in nation. CMV $300.

1978 SILVER FLOWER BASKET AUGUST CONFERENCE AWARD
Sterling silver basket made by Cartier, hand made. "August Conference 1978" on top of handle. Yellow silk flowers, green leaves. Given to managers only. CMV $100 mint.

1980 TEAM LEADER JEWELRY BOX
Silver tone box with blue felt interior. Mirror inside says "Team Leader - President's Celebration 1980". CMV $20 mint.

1981 BIRTHDAY FLOWER GIFT
White Avon box of artificial flowers comes in 4 different kinds. Given to Avon Reps. on their birthday. Box says "Warm Birthday Wishes - Your Friends at Avon". CMV $5 MB.

1926 ROSE PERFUME LAMP AWARD
Rose colored frosted glass, rose shaped electric lamp with antique green metal base. Top of rose has a small hole to put perfume to scent the air when lamp was burning. Given to only 8 Reps. for top sales. CMV $160.

1980 NATIONAL DISTRICT SALES MANAGER PANEL AWARD
Silverplated card case. Given to top managers only. Made by Reed & Barton. In box & blue bag. CMV $50.

1960's MANAGERS CONFERENCE CORSAGE
Green & gold with red holly has Avon 7 dollar bill attached. Bill says "United States of Avon". Given to managers. CMV $22.

1979 MANAGERS FLOWER BASKET
Basket of silk flowers with Avon tag to managers. In Avon box. CMV $25 MB with tag.
1979 TEAM LEADER FLOWER BASKET
Same flower basket only different box and different tag given to team leaders. CMV $15 MB.

1980 OAK TREE PAPER WEIGHT AWARD
Clear lucite with silver tone 4A design & oak tree. "Pasadena No. 1 - 1980" inscribed inside. Given to managers. CMV $25.

1977 ARIANE NECKLACE & BOUQUET
Wood basket & plastic flowers holds sterling silver necklace with August Conference 1977 on side. Given to Avon managers at August Conference Banquet. Necklace holds sample vial of Ariane perfume. CMV $65 mint.

1966 SOUNDS OF SEASONS MUSIC BOX
Given to managers only. Box holds green & gold Christmas Tree Pin, gold Key & Bell. Came from Cartier in New York. CMV Music box only $65. Complete set $85 MB.

1981 NO. 1 PAPER WEIGHT AWARD — CANADA
Chrome-plated No. 1, gold tone plaque says "You're Number One With Us". Given to Avon managers in Canada. CMV $30.

1978 HUDSON MANOR BUD VASE GIFT
Avon silverplated bud vase & red rose in silver box. Bottom says "Team Leader, August 1978". Made in Italy. Same as regular issue only regular issue does not say Team Leader 1978 on bottom. CMV $25.
1978 MANAGERS BUD VASE GIFT
Same as above only says "August Conference 1978" on bottom instead of Team Leader. CMV $35 MB.

1968 JEWELRY BOX AWARD
10" long x 5" wide brocade & brass music box. Red lined. Given to Reps. for top sales. Does not say Avon. CMV $60 mint.

1978 LIBERTY DIVISION PAPER WEIGHT
Clear lucite has 4A design. "Liberty Division - Two Million Dollar Increase 1978". Given to top managers. CMV $15.
1979 CIRCLE OF EXCELLENCE PINS (lower left) Small blue & gold tone pin says "C of E Winners 1979" Given to top managers. CMV $10.

1980 SALES LEADERSHIP AWARD
Large clear glass emerald diamond shaped paper weight. Engraved "Avon Sales Leadership Award Conference 1980". Tiffany & Co. on bottom. Comes in Tiffany box. Given to managers only. CMV $250 MB.

1970's SHAWNEE DOOR KNOCKER IN LUCITE AWARD
Gold tone door knocker sealed in lucite - has Shawnee in blue. CMV $25.

1980 CIRCLE OF EXCELLENCE CRYSTAL VASE
Given to managers on trip to Spain. Box has "Avon Vase Soliflor". Was not made only for Avon. CMV $40 in Avon box.

1949 PRESIDENT'S CUP AWARD
Sterling silver trophy engraved with top selling team in city & district in each division during President's Campaign during the late 40's & early 50's. Given to managers. CMV $200 mint.

1973 DIVISION COMPETITION AWARD
Clear lucite paper weight given in Springdale branch. CMV $10.

1981 HEAT THERMOMETER AWARD
Clear lucite, black letters & trim, given to managers in 4 test areas only. CMV $25.

1977 SEASONS GREETINGS AVON REPS.
5½" high vase marked on bottom "Seasons Greetings Avon 1977" and has 4A symbol. Given to all Avon Reps. at Christmas 1977 in special box. CMV $12 MB.

1980's - 35th ANNIVERSARY AWARD
Silver plate pitcher engraved on front. Given to Reps. for 35 years service as an Avon Rep. Comes with Avon card. In Avon box from Tiffany & Co. Engraved on side of pitcher "35th Avon Anniversary" CMV $175 MB.

1978 REP. CHRISTMAS GIFT BOWL
Fostoria bowl with 4A design & 1978 on bottom. Given to all Avon Reps. for Christmas 1979. Box shown with red ribbon & gold tag & white & gold plastic bell given to managers. CMV $10 Reps., MB, CMV $15 managers with ribbon.

1979 VALENTINE TEAM LEADER GIFT
3½" across crystal heart shaped glass dish given to all team leaders for Valentines. CMV $12.50 MB.

1966 DIVISION MANAGERS TROPHY
Large pewter trophy given to winning manager in each division. CMV $135.

1977 JUBILEE ANNIVERSARY QUEEN AWARD
Small wood base, gold top for division manager. CMV $10

1975-76 HOOSIER CUSTOMER SERVICE TROPHY
(Left) Given to managers for most customers served. CMV $22.50.

1978 PRESIDENT'S CELEBRATION TROPHY
(Right) Marble base. CMV $15.

1969 KANSAS CITY BRANCH TROPHY
"Number One" national sales increase. CMV $17.

1961 LOVING CUP TROPHY
Gold cup on white base. CMV $20.

1954 BUD VASE AWARD
(Left) 8" tall sterling silver vase awarded to each Rep. in winning district during President's Campaign. CMV $45.

1954-56 PRESIDENT'S TROPHY
(Right) 13 5/8" high, sterling silver trophy was given to top selling city & district managers in each division during President's Campaign each year. Trophy sits on black base. CMV $125.

1972 TRAVELING TROPHY
Gold 4A with first Avon Lady over emblem on walnut base with engraved plate Team Honor Award. CMV $30.

1966 TOP SALES TROPHY
(Left) Small 5" high gold trophy, wood base. C-11-13-1966. CMV $15.

1954 ACHIEVEMENT AWARD TROPHY
(Right) Avon in raised letters on the base of the metal figure. Given to top Reps. in each district. CMV $27.50.

1977 PRESIDENT'S CELEBRATION TROPHY
Inscribed to Top Selling Rep. for President's Celebration. CMV $20.

1978 ADDITION'S AWARD
Black & clear plastic picture cube for recruiting new Reps. CMV $25 MB.

1977 PRESIDENT'S CLUB TROPHY
Gold tone top. CMV $8.

1978 PRESIDENT'S CELEBRATION TROPHY
Given to Reps. for best increase over sales goal. Came with certificate. Marble with wood base. CMV $20.

1982 ROYAL RIBBON TEAM LEADER AWARD TROPHY
Wood base & silver toned cup. 1 given per district. CMV $15.

1978 KEY TO SUCCESS TROPHY AWARD
Trophy floated to each winning manager in division till final winning manager won & kept it. CMV $60.

1965 BEST SUPPORTING PERFORMANCE TROPHY
(Left) This type trophy should not get too high in price as you can still buy the trophies & have brass name plate put on them. CMV $15.

1958-59 ACHIEVEMENT AWARD TROPHY
(Right) This type has Avon in raised letters on the base of the metal figure. These cannot be purchased & should be worth more. CMV $25.

1976 AVON CALLING PEN
(Left) 14K gold filled. Made by Cross. In grey bag and red leather pen holder with rose design in gold. Pen is 5¼" long. Given to Reps. for recommendation prize. CMV $12 MB.

1977 TOP 6 TEAM LEADER TROPHY
(Right) Given for Top 6 Sales in Anniversary Celebration 1977. White marble base, gold statue. Blue plaque. CMV $10.

1978 ANNIVERSARY QUEEN TROPHY
Marble Base. Given to top Rep. in each division for top sales. CMV $15.

1978 QUEEN'S TIARA
Came with Queen's Trophy. Is not marked Avon. No price established.

1954-56 DIVISIONAL SALES CAMPAIGN AWARD
Only 20 black plaques with solid sterling silver rose, were given each year to managers in top selling district in each of the 20 divisions in U.S. CMV $250.

1971 - 3 YEAR WINNER TROPHY
Small wood base, brass plaque that says "Avon 3 Year Winner". Given to Reps. CMV $15.

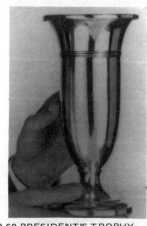

1959-60 PRESIDENT'S TROPHY
Sterling silver trophy given to managers in top selling district in each division. Given late 50's to early 60's. Trophy is inscribed with winning team & year. CMV $125.

1970 STAR SPANGLED MANAGER PLAQUE
Avon-Star Spangled Manager Summer 1970 on face plate. CMV $14.

1974 NATIONAL DISTRICT PANEL PLAQUE
Picture frame plaque - Sara Fleming. Gold & brown. CMV $15.

1971 OUTSTANDING MANAGERS PLAQUE
Wood base with gold plaque. Outstanding managers first quarter. CMV $20.

1979 TEAM LEADER PLAQUE AWARD
Given to team leaders in C of E winning division. CMV $30.

1977 DISTINGUISHED SALES MANAGEMENT PLAQUE AWARD
Solid walnut base holds white ceramic tile center plaque & brass name tag on bottom. Given to top 10 managers in each division. CMV $30.

1978 MILLION DOLLAR CLUB PLAQUE PASADENA BRANCH
Walnut base with red front & gold trim. Presented to district managers for outstanding sales increase. CMV $75.

1977 PRESIDENT'S CELEBRATION PLAQUE
Engraved wood plaque with Cape Cod Water Goblet attached. Given to team leaders with highest sales. CMV $15 mint.

1981 BLUE RIBBON SOCIETY AWARD
Wood & brass plaque. CMV $25.

1980 PRESIDENT'S CELEBRATION GREAT OAK PLAQUE AWARD
Scrimshaw great oak on white plastic center, wood frame. Comes with Avon card. Given to managers only. CMV $35.

1977 MILLION DOLLAR SELECT GROUP AWARD
(Left) Plaque with bag of money on front from Sovereign Division. CMV $75.

1975 OUTSTANDING ACHIEVEMENT AWARD
(Right) Blue velvet on wood plaque, metal wreath with red, white & blue ribbon with 4A pendant with green stone in center. CMV $100.

1971 AWARD PLAQUE
Presented in campaign 1-26, 1971 for increased sales. CMV $10.

1977 TOP 10 DIVISION TROPHY
4½'' high 4A design inside lucite top on wood base & brass plaque. Given to top 10 sales Reps. in each division. Came in plain white box. CMV $40.

1960's HONORABLE MENTION PLAQUE
Green pearlessence plastic base with wood and brass plaque. CMV $12.50.

1943 PICTURE GLASS FRAME PRIZE
Etched glass frame holds 8 x 10 size picture. Given to Reps. for selling over $75 during campaign. CMV $150.

1963 MANAGERS DIPLOMA
Certificate given to new Avon managers during the 1960's. Did not come in frame. CMV $10.

1964 PAUL GREGORY PLAQUE
Silver plaque on black wood. Given to each manager in the winning division. CMV $35.

1981 20 YEAR SILVER PICTURE FRAME AWARD
Sterling silver picture frame from Tiffany & Co. given to Avon Reps. for 20 years service. Bottom of frame engraved "Avon 20 Years", & the initial of person winning frame. Comes in Tiffany felt bag. CMV $100.

1978 TEAM LEADER PICTURE FRAME AWARD
Chrome picture frame marked on top of frame "Made Exclusively for Avon Team Leaders". Given for meeting sales goals. CMV $10 mint.

1965-67 PAUL GREGORY PLAQUE
Black & silver plaque given to winning division of Avon's Paul Gregory Trophy. CMV $30.

1981 CIRCLE OF EXCELLENCE HEART PICTURE FRAME
Silver tone small picture frame with C of E card. Given to C of E managers. CMV $25.

1950 ACHIEVEMENT AWARD
Pink & white with gold. Given for high sales during 64th Anniversary Celebration. This was celebrating new packaging & redesign of Cotillion. This matches packaging for this era. Approx. 10 x 14 inches. CMV $25.

1965 DIVISION CHAMPION PLAQUE
Given for highest sales during general managers campaign 1965. CMV $30.

WHAT IS AVON COLLECTING?

by Connie Clark, Kansas City, MO

Many of you readers may well be familiar with this "strange" hobby, or they may think, as many do, that Avon collectors only collect the cars, the figurines or any of the "pretty" containers. This is true, but only partially.

Avon collecting began in 1968-69 for most. This is when Avon began to promote what is referred to as "figural bottles" or "decanters", in other words, they depict a real object. Such as a duck, a car, a roll of money.

What is surprising is that Avon collecting covers many phases, somewhere, someone, an Avon collector, is trying to find an old metal tube, an old cardboard lipstick or any number of other items, not restricted to "pretty" things.

Avon was originally known as The California Perfume Company which had its beginnings in 1886 (they changed to Avon Products, Inc. in 1929). Collectors, and again we're not talking about all collectors, savor a "CPC" item. You must realize that these items were from the very early days and are very much sought after by collectors - and some of the most expensive. These items very rarely find their way to a garage sale, but many collectors have some very good "fish" tales to tell about their CPC's. The CPC items are attractive, but do not depict an object. They are simply old, and collectors try and find them in the best condition possible.

Avon begins, much like other companies, at the Corporate level. They offer service awards for continued service; this could be a string of pearls for the ladies, cuff-links for the men. Next we have the District Managers who are charged with a certain number of Representatives. They are given sales goals for their districts and when these goals are attained, they are rewarded with awards. The Representatives who make up the district are also given sales goals, and when they are met, they are rewarded with awards. They are also given the opportunity to receive prizes (we call them prizes, because they are not marked with the word Avon). The awards are usually marked in some manner.

As you are probably beginning to wonder or say, "So what?" — well, these are phases of Avon collecting that people do not generally think about . . . but collectors do try and obtain CPC's and Awards. These awards could consist of jewelry, silverware, desk sets, porcelain and many other items. From these Employees, District Managers and Representatives, collectors have added many very fine items to their collections.

We now have seen two phases of Avon collecting. There are still many, many other phases for the Avon collectors; magazine advertising, literature of all kinds, children's toys, fragrance lines, soaps and the list goes on. It must be said that at this point, many collectors have become more selective in their collecting and are beginning to specialize.

It is apparent, or has become so, to many collectors that to collect everything the California Perfume Co. and Avon Products, Inc. ever produced is absolutely non-attainable. Not only is the attainability a deterrent, but also space limitations and monetary considerations. After seeing the many products available, and considering the length of time in existance, it is understandable why collectors are beginning to specialize.

What do we mean by specializing? At a certain point in time, a collector realizes he is running out of space to display his collection, or he tires of certain items and wants to devote his entire collecting energy to one certain phase. This one phase is then the one and only item the collector seeks. However, we do know some collectors who have begun to specialize in several phases.

Let us then take a brief look at what some specialties are, and we'll look at the items that most people do not think of as Avon collectables! These specialties may not be bottles or even produced by Avon and there are several ways collectors will specialize. It could be by collecting everything in one category or in only one category up to a certain period of time. Along with the CPC's and Awards, comes the category of Literature.

Literature is not sold by the Avon Representative or is not particularly "pretty", but it is a desirable collectable to some. Literature is found at most all levels of the Avon organization. The employees have an "in-house" publication, the District Managers have a magazine or booklet printed just for them, and the Representative has the Avon Calling. There are the Outlooks (which are the counterpart of Avon Calling - in past years), the sales brochures, and any other printed or written material such as the sales order books, call back pads, prize catalogs and letterheads/envelopes.

All of these items, depending on the collector who wants them are valuable as a collectable. By valuable, I don't necessarily mean in dollars, but as an Avon item. Don't get me wrong, an old CPC Outlook or early stationery might command a high price, if there is someone willing to pay for it. A lot of collectors use this material for valuable reference material.

Another seldom thought of Avon collectable is the magazine advertising. Avon uses this method of promoting their products. They have been advertising since the very early days and there are collectors who seek this advertising in any shape or form (including T.V. films). Again, this is something Avon does not sell.

Continued on following page . . .

We call collectors who treasure literature paper collectors - and they may very well collect other specialties.

There is one other area of collectables that are not sold to the public, but are sold to Representatives, or given to them for sales aides. These are Samples. The Representatives use these samples to promote their products . . . and some collectors want these for their collections. Some of the older samples are very elaborate and are very much sought after.

The items we have discussed thus far are not items most people bring to mind when speaking of Avon collecting. There are the more common items: cars, figurals, soaps, children's toys, children's soaps, sets, fragrance lines and candles.

As I said above, "common" items. However, in each one of these categories, there are certain items that are not common! Let us, very briefly, look at some of these different categories.

When you speak about Cars and Figurals, you're speaking in the same category. They are items reproduced to look like an object. There are the animals, modes of all kinds of transportation, sports related items, and others. Each of these could be broken down into a specialty. Let us not forget there are also women's figurals . . . the same rule applies here.

Next, we have soaps - does a collector collect only children's soaps, women's soaps or men's soaps? They could collect all three . . . soaps in general. Of course, you have soaps with sponges and soaps with dishes, sets of soaps and only bars of soap.

Mention children's items to some and you're talking about a very hard-to-find specialty. Children have the habit of using these products and toys . . . some of the very old products are almost impossible to find in any kind of good condition.

Throughout the earlier days and especially in the 1930's, 1940's and 1950's, packaging was a great asset to Avon's sales. This is where the gift-set specialty gets into the act. Many collectors like to try and find these gift sets, and the better the condition, the better the price and the more they want them. These gift sets are very attractive and usually contain several items, even if it was only a lipstick and nail polish, the packaging was beautiful. Although they made many sets like the one mentioned above, there were even fancier ones . . . colored net or satin cloth background, with the products laying on top. Take a look at current boxes; they are a work of art in themselves . . . and these older boxes were certainly that!

When we speak of fragrance lines, we're talking about fragrance. Each time a fragrance was introduced, it was distinctive in its looks. For instance, Here's My Heart was blue in color and most of the items were shaped like a heart. Elegante was indeed elegant as it was bright red and had a satin appearance on the boxes. Some collectors like to try and find everything in these different fragrances . . . the specially packaged items. These fragrances were still bottled and sold in many, many other containers - not specially packaged, and that's were we get the various miscellaneous items. Some might try and obtain these miscellaneous items to go with their specially packaged items. And some may try and specialize in several of these old fragrances, cutting back at a certain date.

The glow of a candle is irresistable to some, and here you have candle collectors. Candles in every shape, size and color. Many of them are figurals and many of them can be used for candy after they are holders, most are refillable, some are not.

I am sure I've probably left out someone's very favorite collectable, but this does give you an idea of that Avon collecting consists of. There are still dyed-in-the-wood collectors who will purchase anything with the name Avon on it. They collect, display and are proud of their accomplishments, as all collectors are.

Avon collectors just like to collect . . . but, they also like to share their hobby. This is how Avon clubs came in existence. Yes, there are Avon clubs all over the United States and Canada. These clubs meet each month, and right now, as you read this, there more than likely is an Avon club meeting in progress. Different clubs enjoy different ideas, and one might be playing bingo, another might be presenting a program on awards, still another might be having a giant auction for the members to buy and sell their extra merchandise . . . for we've almost never met a collector who did not need to support his hobby.

From these clubs, in all different locations, sprang a national organization called the National Association of Avon Clubs. It consists, just like the name implies, of Avon clubs. A club may pay their dues, conform to certain criteria set out by the Association, and participate in whatever this Association has to offer. Which is quite a lot: annual conventions (held all over the United States), a chance to purchase unique collectables and the opportunity to join with other collectors to learn and talk about the hobby.

We have just begun to tell you what Avon collecting is all about. There is much more. Intangibles make up a large part of Avon collecting . . . knowledge, friendship, travel, hospitality, competition and challenges. It is truly through these 'intangibles' that Avon collecting has become a major hobby, one that might not be particularly well-known or publicized, but that is gaining momentum day by day, week by week and year by year; as more collectors join the ranks of a very determined hobby and people who make up the hobby.

In summary, there are many, many ways to collect Avon. And there are some we have not mentioned. But, these are the basics and it really doesn't make any difference how an Avon collector collects, or what they collect . . . that it's enjoyed, displayed and shared . . . is the major factor.

1972 TEAM CAPTAIN AWARD
Awarded to all Team Captains in each district. Thick plastic over lettering with gold frame. CMV $12.

1982 ALBEE AWARD
5th in a series given to President's Club members for sales of $7,000 in 1 year. CMV $50.

1961 WOMEN OF ACHIEVEMENT AWARD
(Left) Painted ceramic figure of 1886 sales lady. One given in each district for highest sales. Came with stained walnut base & gold plaque inscribed "Avon Woman of Achievement Award". Printed on bottom of figure "Imported Expressly for Avon Products, Inc. Made in West Germany". CMV $300. $325 MB.

1969 WOMEN OF ACHIEVEMENT AWARD
(Right) White ceramic figure much the same as 1961 model. Base is tall & of white wood with gold trim. Printed on bottom of figure "Imported Expressly for Avon Products, Inc. Made in Western Germany Dresden Art". Brass plaque on base (not shown) says "Presented to.... for Outstanding Contribution to the Better Way". CMV $275. $325 MB.

1977 ARIANE WOMAN PAINTING
25 x 30 inch original oil painting by Szaro. Used by Avon in Avon Catalog C-22, 1977. CMV not established.

1961 LADY OF ACHIEVEMENT TEST
(Right) Pictured on right is smaller size original artwork test figurine for 1961 Lady of Achievement Award. Stands 7" high. Rare. Was not sold or given out by Avon. No price established. Used by factory only.

LEFT TO RIGHT

1978 ALBEE AWARD NO. 1
Porcelain figurine 8½" high in honor of the 1st Avon lady of 1886, Mrs. P.F.E. Albee. Given to top Reps. in sales in each district. Pink umbrella is also porcelain. CMV $125 MB.

1979 ALBEE AWARD NO.2
Hand painted porcelain figurine of the 1st Avon Rep. of 1886. 2nd in a series. Given to President's Club Reps. for outstanding sales. Colors are blue & pink. CMV $100 MB.

1979 ALBEE AWARD — CANADA
Is the same as 1978 Albee issued in U.S. only the bottom printing is in French & English & dated 1979. CMV $125 mint.

1980 ALBEE AWARD NO. 3
3rd in the Albee series. Given to President's Club Reps. only. CMV $100 MB.

1981 ALBEE AWARD NO. 4
4th in the Albee series. Given to President's Club Reps. only. CMV $50 MB.

1973 FIGURINE AWARD
Awarded to each representative in district with greatest total sales increase. Made by Hummel, numbered & says "Made for Avon" on bottom. Figurine 8" sits on white marble base with glass dome. CMV $200. $225 MB.

1980 PRECIOUS MOMENTS CHRISTMAS MOUSE
(Right) Given to Avon Reps. for signing up 2 new Avon Reps. CMV $55 MB.
1980 PRECIOUS MOMENTS DISPLAY POSTER
(Left) Used by managers C18-80. CMV $5 mint.

1976 FIRST LADY PORCELAIN FIGURINE
Blue, white & pink porcelain made in Spain. Given to President's Club members only for outstanding sales in 90th Anniversary celebration. CMV $45 MB.

1982 COLLECTORS CORNER FIGURINE AWARD
Cherished Moments Collection mouse figurine. Given to 25 Reps. for top sales in Campaign 8, 1982 in each district. CMV $40 MB.

1980 PRECIOUS MOMENTS AWARD
Rabbit figurine marked on bottom "President's Club Luncheon 1980". Given to Reps. at President's Club Luncheon only. CMV $20 MB.

1975 LLADRO PORCELAIN LADY DIVISION MANAGER AWARD
12½" lady figurine made by Lladro in Spain. Comes with detachable porcelain umbrella. Given to division managers only. Does not say Avon. Same figurine can also be purchased in fine stores. CMV not established.

1980 PRECIOUS MOMENTS AWARD SET
Set of 3 rabbit figurines given to Reps. for top sales. No. 1 is "Ready for an Avon Day". CMV $25.
No. 2 is "My first call". CMV $35.
No. 3 is "Which shade do you prefer". CMV $60.
Set of 3 CMV $110. Made in Japan only for Avon.

1979 OBELISK COMMUNITY SERVICE AWARD
8¼" clear lucite. 1 given to managers in each division. Has 4A design & message of Ralph Waldo Emerson in center. CMV $50.

573

1978 APPLE PAPER WEIGHT AWARD
Given to divisional managers for top sales. Clear crystal glass apple is engraved "You Made New York Smile", Avon, March 1978, on front side. CMV $100.

1976 HEART TREASURE BOX AWARD
Top sales teams in 252 winning districts won ceramic heart shaped box given in President's Celebration of 1976. Bottom says "Avon President's Celebration 1976". Made in Spain. CMV $30 MB.

1980 LIMOGES FLORAL BOX AWARD
Small white ceramic heart box with blue painted flowers. Given to managers. Does not say Avon. Must have Tiffany card for Avon Products. Was not made only for Avon. CMV $25 MB with card.

1979 PRESIDENT'S CELEBRATION HEART AWARD
Lucite heart marked "You're our number one - Avon 1979 President's Celebration". Made in Taiwan. Comes in white Avon box. CMV $20 MB.

1979 MANAGERS HEART YOU'RE NO. 1"
(Right) Clear lucite, has smaller hole on top & heart is about ¼" smaller. Came in red velvet bag. This one was given to managers only. CMV $30 mint in bag.

1980 HEART PORCELAIN BOX AWARD
Given to managers. Came in Tiffany & Co. box. Small porcelain heart box says "Bernardaud Limoges Made in France. Does not say Avon. CMV $25 in box with card.

1960's MERRY MOODS OF CHRISTMAS ORNAMENT
Dark blue ornament for managers only. Other side says "Avon Presents" with 4A design. CMV $35 mint.

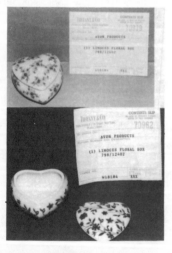

1979 LIMOGES FLORAL HEART BOX AWARD
Small heart shaped ceramic box made by Limoge of France. Given to Avon managers. Must have Tiffany & Co. card as shown for Avon Products. 2 different designs as shown. CMV $30 with card.

1952 CANDLESTICK AWARDS
Sterling silver candlesticks 2½" tall and 2¾" wide at the base. They were given to Reps. for calling on 120 customers during the 66th Avon Anniversary campaign, 1952. Came in nice gift box. The candlesticks were not made just for Avon. Must be in box with Avon card as shown. CMV $60 MB.

1924 FRAGRANCE JAR AWARD
American Beauty fragrance jar hand painted design in blue & gold. Pink & green flowers on lid. Pink ribbon. Given to Reps. for top sales. CMV $350.

1979 REPRESENTATIVE CHRISTMAS GIFT
Ceramic tile picture frame made in Japan. Box says "Happy Holidays Avon 1979". Given to all Avon Reps. at Christmas. CMV $10 MB.

1974 CHRISTMAS ORNAMENTS MUSICAL GIFT SET
Given to Reps. for getting new Reps. Red & gold bell & green & gold ball. Both have music boxes inside. Made by Heinz Deichett, West Germany. Both came in red box as set. CMV $30 each no box; $75 set MB.

1977 MANAGERS CHRISTMAS TREE GIFT
(Left) Hand blown glass Christmas tree in clear, green, red & yellow. Given to Avon managers at Christmas 1977. Does not say Avon. CMV $25.

1978 MANAGERS CHRISTMAS TREE GIFT
(Right) Brass Christmas tree ornament signed by "Bi Jan" on back. Given to Avon managers at Christmas 1978. Came in green box. CMV $20 MB.

1979 "PICTURE FRAME" DREAM AWARD SEPTEMBER CONFERENCE
Ceramic picture frame. White, pink & green flowers with white doves. Center is pink, says "Hold fast to your dreams, For if you do...Tomorrow you'll see More dreams can come true". CMV $15.

1971 CHRISTMAS BELLS — MANAGERS GIFT
Red strap with 5 bells given to Avon managers at Christmas. Came with card with bells on it & "For you from Avon". Must have Avon card. CMV $15 MB.

1981 THE GREAT AMERICAN SELLATHON CHRISTMAS TREE AWARD
Approximately 600 given out at Hawaiian President's Celebration in Hawaii. Has bottom Avon label & green & white gift box. CMV $35.

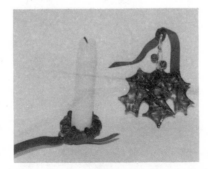

1979 MANAGERS CHRISTMAS GIFT
Blown glass in green leaves & red holly with red velvet ribbon. 2 pieces. Holly leaves ornament & candle holder. Given to managers for Christmas 1979. Does not say Avon. CMV $15 set.

1981 FLOWER BASKET AWARD
Small white ceramic flower basket. CMV $50.

1951 OCTOBER 8 AWARD
1 dram Forever Spring Perfume, smooth gold cap & bottle. Given to each representative sending an order in campaign 12, 1951. CMV $40 MB.

1963 PRESIDENT'S AWARD PERFUME
Clear glass with stopper, silver 4A tag & string. Given to national winners in each division for President's Campaign, 1963. Box silver & white base with clear plastic lid. Bottom label on bottle says "Occur! Perfume Avon Products, Inc. N.Y., N.Y. contains 1 fl. oz.". CMV $200 bottle only. $250 MB with label & tag. Also came in ½ oz. size with gold neck 4A tag. Please write Bud Hastin if you know when and what the ½ oz. size was given for.

1959 GOLDEN SLIPPER AWARD
All gold metal slipper with red stone in toe & clear plastic heel. ½ oz. glass stoppered perfume bottle fits in slipper toe. No Avon name on shoe but has paper label on bottom of bottle saying "73rd Anniversary. Avon Products, Inc." Given to each representative in the winning group of each branch for top sales. CMV $200 slipper & bottle with label. $250 MB.

1950 MANAGERS GIFT PERFUME
(Left) ½ oz. glass stoppered bottle in plastic case. Given to managers to help introduce To A Wild Rose. Paper label on bottom reads "Perfume Avon Products, Inc., Distributor, New York, Montreal, Vol. ½ oz". Came with neck tassel. CMV $250 mint, in plastic case.

1955 PRESIDENT'S AWARD CELEBRATION PERFUME
(Right) ½ oz. perfume, glass stopper. Given to the winning team members for top sales. CMV $100 BO mint. $140 MB.

1978 PERFUME — CIRCLE OF EXCELLENCE
1 oz. glass stopper bottle, made in France. Paper neck tag says "Made Exclusively For You. Circle of Excellence 1978". CMV $100 mint.

1948 PURSE OF GOLD AWARD
Cardboard tube contained 8 samples of Golden Promise. Came in packages shown. Given to each representative sending in an order at the close of campaign 3. CMV $30.

1975 REPRESENTATIVE CHRISTMAS GIFT
Clear glass in blue box. Reproduction of Trailing Arbutus Powder Sachet. CMV $15 MB.

1963 CHRISTMAS GIFT PERFUME
Given to Avon sales ladies for Christmas. The bottle at left is same as the one sealed in gold plastic container with green tassel & red ribbon. 4-10 oz. Christmas gift given to all representatives submitting an order in Dec. 1963. CMV $40 complete. Bottle only $15.

1979 TASHA GO AHEAD AND DREAM MANAGERS GIFT
(Left) 1.8 oz. clear glass, silver neck band. Go Ahead & Dream in gold letters on front of bottle. Bottom label. Given to Avon managers at Christmas conference. CMV $25 MB.

1979 TASHA — TEAM LEADER COLOGNE SPRAY
(Right) 1.8 oz. clear glass. This bottle given to Avon team leaders. Front of bottle has "Team Leader 1979" in gold letters. CMV $12.50 MB.

1978 TEMPO MANAGERS GIFT
(Left) .33 oz. silver over clear glass. Given to district sales managers at August Conference 1978. Came with red felt belt. Splash cologne. Came in beige felt bag & beige string. CMV $15 in bag.

1978 TEMPO SPRAY ATOMIZER GIFT
(Right) Given to Avon Reps. for advanced orders of Tempo fragrance. Silver color container red letters. "Tempo Fall 1978" printed on bottom of case. Came in beige velvet bag, red pull string in special issue box. CMV $10 MB.

1960's AWARD PURSE
Avon marked box holds beige vinyl clutch purse trimmed in brass. Made by St. Thomas. Given to Reps. during President's Campaign. Purse does not say Avon. CMV $9 mint in Avon box.

1975 TRENDSETTER CARRY ALL BAG
Made of tan burlap & brown leatherette Given to managers only. CMV $45.

1975 FOAMING BATH OIL SAMPLE GIFT
Given to President's Club members. ½ oz. bottle, white cap. President's Club label on bottom. Came in introductory envelope. CMV $3.50 in envelope.

1951 PURSE AWARD
Egg shell off white purse with clear plastic closure. Given to Avon Reps. for best sales. Came in Avon box. Purse not marked Avon. Must be in Avon box. CMV $27.50 MB.

1972 CIRCLE OF EXCELLENCE TOTEBAG
About 18" across, black plastic. For trip to Mexico. Aztec calendar design. Given to C of E managers on Mexico trip. CMV $30.

1960 SURPRISE GIFT
Silver and Gold box contained one Deluxe Lipstick. Given as a Christmas Gift to all representatives. CMV $22.50 MB.

1961 ANNIVERSARY CAMPAIGN AWARD PURSE
Same purse with deluxe lipstick & compact as Champagne Mood Set. In Avon award box. CMV $20 MB.

1966 ANNIVERSARY HONOR AWARD PURSE
Red leatherette purse given to Reps. for high sales. 4A design on snap & Avon Anniversary Honor Award in gold letters on purse. Came in Avon box. CMV $15 purse only. $20 MB.

1976 CIRCLE OF EXCELLENCE TOTE BAG
Tan & brown tote bag with C of E on front. Given to Avon managers on Hawaii C of E trip. CMV $16.

1981 CIRCLE OF EXCELLENCE BAG
White canvas bag, red line around bottom. Given to managers in San Francisco C of E trip. CMV $15 mint.
1981 CIRCLE OF EXCELLENCE MAP
Map of San Francisco given to C of E managers on trip. CMV $3.

1981 ATTACHE CASE AWARD
Maroon case with brass corners & black leather handles. Does not say Avon but comes in Avon plastic bag. CMV $10 in Avon bag.

1981 COOLER SEAT AWARD
Yellow nylon insulated cooler seat given to Reps. for selling Avon vitamins in Springdale branch. Has Avon on seat. CMV $15.

1974 FASHION PRIZES
Given to Reps. for meeting sales goals. Blue & white in color. Made only for Avon.
(Bottom) Christian Dior Scarf, 14" x 44". CMV $8.
(Top Right) Sport Tote Bag 10" high 14" wide. CMV $10.
(Top Left) Kadin Hand Bag, blue sail cloth with white vinyl trim. Given to President's Club members only. 8" high, 10" wide. CMV $12.

1980 GREAT OAK BAG AWARD
Canvas bag. CMV $10.

1980 AVON CART AWARD
Canvas wheeled cart collapses to make a hand bag. Given to Reps. for selling $525 in C16-17 1980. CMV $25.

1979 CIRCLE OF EXCELLENCE TOTEBAG
Khaki color bag. Says "Circle of Excellence". Given to top 250 managers. CMV $15.

1980 MONEY ORGANIZER & BALL POINT PEN AWARD
Tan canvas & brown trim, 4A design on side holds "President's Club" insignia pen. Given to President's Club Reps. for selling $325 of products in C16-17 1980. CMV $10.

1975 S.M. KENT COLLECTION AWARDS
Given to Reps. for reaching 4 different levels of selling certain amounts. Robe & handbag were for only President's Club members to win. The scarf was awarded for finding a "hidden customer" in territory. All items have brown or beige A's & signed by S.M. Kent (designer for Avon). CMV clutch $10. CMV Robe $20. CMV Purse $15. CMV Tote $12. CMV Cosmetic $8. CMV Scarf $7. CMV Order Book Cover $5.

1976-78 SUNNY MAKE UP CASE
Blue vinyl reptile grain case with Avon zipper tag. Inside has clear vinyl pockets to hold make up samples. Won by Reps. for signing up a new Avon Rep. and also sold to Reps. CMV $6.

These Sales Mates available later this year.

1978 SALES MATES PRIZES
Will be awarded in 1978 for top sales goals. All are tan vinyl with Avon "A" design. Order book cover & pen CMV $3, Tote bag CMV $7, Sample kit CMV $6, Fragrance Demonstrator CMV $4.

1978 JEWELRY DEMONSTRATOR PRIZE
Tan vinyl with "A" design given to Reps. for selling $600 worth of Avon in 3 campaigns. Measures 13" long and 8" wide. CMV $7.

1953 PORTFOLIO SHOULDER BAG
Light color linen covered shoulder bag to carry Avon order book and samples. Won by Reps. for placing a $100 order. CMV $20 mint.

1965 PRESIDENT'S CAMPAIGN AWARD PURSE
Bone beige coin & bill purse with 4A design on flap. Given to each Rep. in 2 top sales teams in each branch for greatest sales increase over year before period. CMV $15.

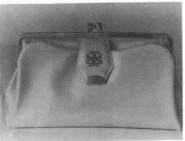

1963 PRESIDENT'S SERVICE AWARD PURSE
Given to all Reps. who called on 35 or more customers during President's Campaign 1963. Egg shell color vinyl coin purse with 4A design on snap. Box says "Avon Fashion First". CMV $20 MB.

1970 PURSE — AVON PLANT TOUR GUIDE
Gray plastic purse with heavy silver chain. 4A silver button on purse. Used by tour guides at Avon Plants. CMV $20.

1977 TOTE BAG
White canvas with black nylon straps. Came from Avon in New York. Was not issued to Reps. in U.S. CMV $25.

1978 SWEET PICKLES BAG GIFT
Green canvas bag given to district managers on introduction of Sweet Pickle products. CMV $12.50 bag only.

1980 TASHA STOWAWAY BAG
Purple shoulder bag given to Reps. Avon tag inside. Pink inside bag. CMV $15. Managers also got the same bag without the brass snap on the outside. Same color inside as outside. CMV $20.

1978 SALES MATES PRIZES PRESIDENT'S CLUB
All are tan & beige in color, covered with "A" design. Umbrella, Beauty Showcase handbag and jewelry demonstrator given to President's Club Reps. for selling $975 worth of Avon in C4-5-6 1978.
CMV Umbrella $20.
CMV Jewelry Demo Case $7.
CMV Handbag $7.

1980 TASHA UMBRELLA "I'M NUMBER ONE"
Tan silk umbrella given Reps. on Flight to Fantasy Trip to Monte Carlo. CMV $30.

1977 ADVERTISING UMBRELLA
White Avon box holds brown plastic handle umbrella. Has the names of Avon & magazines & TV shows Avon advertises on. Given to district managers. CMV $30 MB.

1976 APRIL SHOWERS UMBRELLA GIFT
(Left) Beige canvas, wood handle. Avon in blue letters. Given as recommendation prize. CMV $27.50.

1977 PRESIDENT'S CELEBRATION UMBRELLA
(Center) Marked New York. Given to winning teams. CMV $35.

1980 UMBRELLA & BAG AWARD
Tan & brown Avon bag comes with Avon umbrella. Given to Reps. for selling $425 of products in C16-17 1980. CMV $18.

1970 TOTE BAG & UMBRELLA AWARD
Fawn color leatherette bag & matching coin purse inside. Came with umbrella with tortoise handle. Was not made for Avon only. Must be in Avon box as shown. CMV $20 for all MB.

1980 AVON TENNIS UMBRELLA
Only 50 silver nylon with fine wood handle umbrellas were given to press & promoters of Avon tennis matches. Comes in matching silver pouch. Rare. CMV $125.

1980 AVON TENNIS CLOTHES BAG
Red & white patch on silver & black nylon travel bag. Comes in small carrying pouch. Given to players of Avon tennis matches. CMV $35. Rare.

1980 AVON TENNIS BALLPOINT PEN
Gold tone pen says "Avon Tennis" & has tennis racket on side. Given to Avon tennis match players. Comes in tan suede Avon tennis pouch. CMV $20 mint.

1980 AVON TENNIS WRISTS BANDS
Pair of white cotton wrist bands used by players in Avon tennis matches. CMV $4.

1980 AVON TENNIS HAND TOWEL
White cotton, used by Avon tennis players. CMV $10.

1939 EMPLOYEE GIFT
Blue box with Avon's Suffern Plant on box. Holds Tulip label and gold cap of Cotillion Toilet water. CPC label & Cotillion powder sachet. Rare. CMV $125 MB.

1959 CHRISTMAS CAROL CANDLE SET
Red velvet box with green lining holds 4 red & white angel candles with blue eyes & blond hair. Candles made by Gurley Novelty Co., label on bottom. Outside of box says "An Avon Christmas Carol". Given to Avon managers at Christmas 1959. CMV $130 MB.

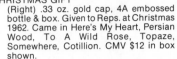

1950's AVON CALLING DOOR BELL
(Left) Used at Avon meetings. Has button on back to ring door bell. CMV $85 mint.

1962 PERFUME CREME ROLLETTE CHRISTMAS GIFT
(Right) .33 oz. gold cap, 4A embossed bottle & box. Given to Reps. at Christmas 1962. Came in Here's My Heart, Persian Wood, To A Wild Rose, Topaze, Somewhere, Cotillion. CMV $12 in box shown.

1944 58th ANNIVERSARY GIFT BOX
Holds heart shaped sachet pillow. Given to all Reps. on Avon's 58th anniversary. CMV $100 MB.

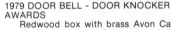

1973's DESK SET PRIZE
Brown plastic came with paper & pen. Given to Reps. for meeting sales goals. CMV $10.

1942 ANNIVERSARY ALBUM AWARD SET
Book type box opens to show 2 satin pillowettes with 56th Anniversary on back of each. One is blue & one pink. Given during Anniversary campaign. CMV $125.

1979 DOOR BELL - DOOR KNOCKER AWARDS
Redwood box with brass Avon Calling door knocker on front, door bell on back side. Given to 5 managers in each division. CMV $75.

1977 INKWELL & PEN SET AWARD
Blue & gold display box holds wood base with old glass ink well & 3 feather quill pens & plastic bottle of ink. Avon card about pen set. Avon brass plaque on base. Given for recruiting new Reps. CMV $45 MB.

1942 56th ANNIVERSARY AWARD
Satin Sachet pillows given to each Rep. who worked her territory for 56 hours during the Anniversary Campaign. Came 2 to a box, in blue & pink. CMV $30 mint.

1972 MANAGER DESK SET AWARD
Has 4A emblem, marble base, 14K gold plated pen. Set made by Cross. CMV $50. $60. MB.

1941 BETSY ROSS RED GIFT SET
Set given to employees of Avon's Suffern Plant as Anniversary campaign gift. Rare. Came with handwritten gift card. CMV $100 MB.

1979 DESK SET ACHIEVEMENT AWARD
Black plastic note pad & pen. Given to district managers for sales achievement. CMV $20 with pen.

1974 88th ANNIVERSARY DESK SET
White marble base. Black pen. Turquoise & silver 4A says "Avon 88th Anniversary". Given to Reps. for selling $125 worth of Avon. CMV $15. $20 MB.

1976 WINNING TEAM DESK SET AWARD
Given for best sales team in district in 1976. White marble base, silver color pen. CMV $8.

1922 DESK VALET — CPC AWARD
Solid bronze. Marked CPC 1922. Awarded to CPC Reps. CMV $100.

1975 LETTER OPENER MANAGER AWARD
Red & black box holds wood handle letter opener. Brass Avon lady insignia & K.C. No. 1, 1975 on handle. CMV $20 MB.

1976 CIRCLE OF EXCELLENCE LETTER OPENER
Given in Indiana only to C of E Reps. Only 25 were given. Brass plaque & door knocker pin is embedded in black plastic handle. CMV $40.

1981 TEDDY BEAR ADDRESS STAMP AWARD
Brown & tan plastic. Says "Avon". Has teddy bear in address imprint. Given to team leaders. CMV $5 MB.

1980 QUICK STAMP ADDRESS AWARD
Made of plastic. Has Avon Reps. name & address on it. Given to Reps. for selling $325 in products in C16-17, 1980. CMV $5.

1967 NAME STAMP AWARD
Won by Reps. for reaching sales goal in campaign 12. Metal stamp has Avon 4A design on stamp. CMV $7.

1972 NAME STAMP
Two-toned blue with name & address. Awarded for entry into President's Club. CMV $4.

1972 STEAK KNIFE & CARVING SET
C-12, 1972. In Avon box. CMV $20 each set MB with sleeve.

1979 SPOON — PRESIDENT'S CLUB AWARD
(Left) Silver plated serving spoon marked "Avon President's Club 1979". Came in Avon box. CMV $10 MB.

1978 CAKE SERVER AWARD
(Right) Silver plated serving spatula. "Avon 92nd Anniversary - President's Club 1978" on spoon. Given to all President's Club members. Special box & card. CMV $10 MB.

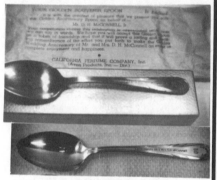

1936 — 50th ANNIVERSARY SPOON
Gold spoon engraved "Compliments Mr. & Mrs. D.H. McConnell - Anniversary 50". The gold on these spoons does not stay very well so many are found silver. CMV in box gold spoon $100 mint. Silver $50 spoon only. Spoon with gold, mint $75.

1915 CPC SPOON "STERLING SILVER"
Sold as a souvenir at the CPC exhibit at the Panama-Pacific International Exposition. Front reads "Palace of Liberal Arts - Panama-Pacific Exposition Tower of Jewels". Back of spoon reads "CPC 1915 Court of Four Seasons". CMV $100 with card shown, $75 spoon only. Was also given to Reps. for selling 12 CPC talcum powders, 1 free for each 12 talcs.

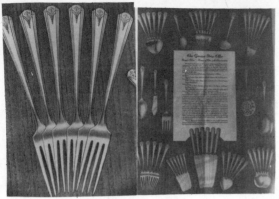

1938 SILVERWARE AWARD
Made only for Avon. Each piece marked on back Simeon L. & George H. Rogers Co. Ltd. X-Tra. Given for meeting sales goal during Avon's 50th Anniversary. 55 piece set. CMV set in box. $125 mint.

1920-30's CPC SILVERWARE
Used in CPC factories for employee eating areas. CPC stamped on back of knife, fork & spoons. CMV $5 each piece.

1977 BLAZER JACKET
Blue blazer with 4A design buttons. Inside label says "Made exclusively for the Avon Representative by Family Fashions". Sold to Avon Reps. Red Avon sewn on patch for pocket. CMV $35.

1969 AVON AWARD SPOONS
6 silver plated demitasse spoons. Each engraved with a design signifying a different fragrance: Occur, Rapture, Unforgettable, Regence, Brocade & Charisma. Each spoon was given in this order for progressively higher sales. A seventh spoon was given to each Rep. in the winning district of each branch. It was engraved "1886-1969" and had a picture of the 1886 Sales Lady. CMV $45 set MB with sleeve or $5 each spoon. 7th spoon $12.50 in silver envelope.

1981 AVON RUNNING RAIN COAT
Shown front & back side. Given to people helping in Avon Running Tournament. Red plastic. Modeled by Vera Young. CMV $10.

1980 MANAGERS CHRISTMAS GIFT
Red & white scarf and mittens given at Christmas time. CMV $30 set.

1981 TOCCARA AWARDS
(Sweater) Dark navy blue with Avon tag. Given for 1st level sales achievement. CMV $10.
(Caftan) Lavender & white with Avon Toccara label. Given to 2nd level sales achievement. Came in shiny silver plastic Toccara bag. CMV $25 in bag.

1980 WINDBREAKER
Blue jacket, red & white trim. Sold to Avon employees in Springdale branch for $15. Modeled by Dwight Young. CMV $15.

1977 CANDID BLAZER & TIE
Off white blazer with CA on left pocket. Given to division managers only. Came in both male & female sizes. Tie is Candid color with CA on it. Very few of these blazers around. Modeled by Dwight Young. CMV Blazer $75. CMV Tie $10.

1982 AVON REP. BIRTHDAY GIFT
Box says "A birthday gift for you". Satin & lace heart pincushion. Comes with Avon card. Given to Reps. on their birthday. CMV $5.

1981 AVON REP. CHRISTMAS GIFT
Red box says "Happy Holidays Avon 1981". Tapestry design address book. Managers book says "District Manager" on front. $15 MB. Reps. same except plain on front. CMV $10 MB.

HOSTESS APRON
Cotton tapestry design apron given to team leaders who met requirements CMV $15.

1979 CIRCLE OF EXCELLENCE TOWEL
Given to top 250 managers. CMV $20.

1972 TOWEL RACK PRIZE AND MILK GLASS SOAP DISH
An exclusive Avon prize. CMV rack, $5. Soap dish $10. White glass dish, 2 white hand towels, gold initials, black & brass stand.

1980 ODYSSEY AWARDS
(Bathrobe) Pink bathrobe given to Reps. for meeting 2nd level sales goals. CMV $25 in Avon bag.
(Nightgown) Pink nightgown matches bathrobe. Given to Reps. for meeting 1st level sales goals. CMV $15 MB.

1981 I'M GOING TO MONTE CARLO MAGNET
(Center) Given to managers. White, red & gold. CMV $4.

1981 VALENTINE SUCKER
(Left) Red heart shaped sucker with red tag. Given to Avon managers. CMV $10.

1981 NUMBER ONE SCARF AWARD
(Right) Given to team leaders. CMV $4.

1976 CIRCLE OF EXCELLENCE BEACH TOWEL
White & brown towel given to managers on C of E Hawaii trip. CMV $20 mint.

1981 TOCCARA PILLOW AWARD
Dark blue satin pillow with Avon card. Given to managers at August Conference. CMV $15 with Avon card.

1982 AVONS BEST BANNER
(Top) Red & white banner. CMV $5.
1982 AVONS BEST SCARF
(Bottom) From Morton Grove branch. Red & white scarf given to managers at Atlanta Conference. CMV $15.

1979 T-SHIRT — AVON RUNNING
Red t-shirt given to each runner in Avon marathon race. CMV $10.

1977 EMPRISE T-SHIRT
Black t-shirt given to Avon managers to introduce Emprise line. CMV $15.

1978 TRAVEL BAG — CIRCLE OF EXCELLENCE
White leatherette bag given to 250 district managers. CMV $50.

1979 COLOR UP AMERICA NECK TIE
(Top left) Given to male managers only. CMV $10.
COLOR UP FLAG
(Center) CMV $2.
COLOR UP HAT
(Bottom) CMV $4.

1979 CIRCLE OF EXCELLENCE AWARDS
Each item given to managers on C of E trip to Paris 1979.
TRAVEL ALARM CLOCK
(Lower right) Plaque on top says "Circle of Excellence 1979". CMV $25.
TOTE BAG
(Upper right) Dark navy blue. Circle of Excellence on front. CMV $15.
CIRCLE OF EXCELLENCE YEAR BOOK
(Center) Blue & gold cover shows all C of E winners. CMV $10.
FRAGRANCE & FASHION BINDER
White plastic. CMV $25 with contents.

1978 TIME OF YOUR LIFE BAG AWARD
Beige canvas bag with red letters given to Reps. on trip to New York. CMV $6.

1978 AVON SMILE HAT
White hat given to Avon collectors at Houston, Texas, 1978 National Association of Avon Club Convention by Avon Products. Modeled by the late Charlie Crawford. CMV $15.

1981 SELLATHON VISOR CAP
(Left) Blue or red. CMV $7.
1981 AVON TENNIS VISOR CAP
(Right) White cap. CMV $7.

1977 HORIZONS CLOTHES BAG GIFT
Given to Avon managers. White plastic bag. CMV $15.

1980 ENVIRA VISOR HAT — AUSTRALIA
Light pink visor hat given to Reps. at the introduction of Envira in Australia. CMV $10.

1981 H-E-A-T BAG AWARD
Canvas bag. CMV $10.
1981 H-E-A-T HAT
White hat. CMV $8.

1978 YOU MAKE ME SMILE LUGGAGE TAG
White platic. CMV $3.

1978 AVON CHAMPIONSHIP TENNIS HAT
White hat, red letters. CMV $7.

1976 MANAGERS BANNER
White silk banner about 8 ft. long, gold braid, pink letters. Used by managers to encourage Reps. to call on new customers. CMV $15.

1961 PRESIDENT'S AWARD BANNER
Small banner given to top sales team in each division. Each winning division had their name on banner. CMV $25.

1979 HARD HAT — CIRCLE OF EXCELLENCE
White plastic hard hat with decal on front saying "Circle of Excellence". Given to managers in Pasadena branch. Hat was not made just for Avon. CMV $10.

1951-52 PRESIDENT'S AWARD PENNANT
Royal blue pennant with gold trim & letters. Given to top selling city & district division managers during early 50's. CMV $45.

1966 OUR BANNER YEAR
Used during district sales meetings. CMV $20. There are many different banners of this type. CMV will range $15 to $20 on most.

1978 BASEBALL CAP
Blue & white Avon Products Inc. hat. Used by plant employees. CMV $12.50.

1970's NECKTIE - AVON 4A
Used by Avon management. Tie has 4A design & is dark blue. Made of Dacron Polyester. CMV $12.50.

1974 PRESIDENT'S CELEBRATION BANNER
Small dark blue felt banner about 18" long, yellow letters & cord. Used by managers. CMV $15.

1979 COLOR UP AWARDS
Blue & red backdrop used at sales meetings "Color Up America". CMV $5.
Color Up Plastic Bag - CMV 50c.
Color Sale Paper Bat - CMV 25c
Color Never Looked So Good On Glasses - set of 6 - CMV $10 set of 6.
Color Up Scarf - CMV $2.
Clutch Bag - CMV $3.
Make Up Bag - CMV $6.
File Folder - CMV $6.
Table Cloth & 4 matching napkins - CMV $15 set.
Colors are red, white & blue striped.

1978 PRESIDENT'S CLUB LUNCHEON BANNER
White canvas, red & gold letters. CMV $20.

1977 AVON CHRISTMAS TABLE CLOTH
4 x 4 ft. blue satin, white letters, used at Christmas dinner 1977 for Avon Reps. in Atlanta branch. CMV $15.

1982 TRAVEL SURVIVAL KIT
(Top) Given to managers March, 1982. CMV $7.
1980 AVON CALLING KEYCHAIN AWARD
(Bottom) Clear lucite with blue letters. Given to Avon Reps. CMV $7.50

1981 GREAT AMERICAN SELLATHON AWARDS
Given to Avon Reps. for meeting top sales goals in C18-81.
T-Shirt - CMV $5.
Calculator - CMV $20.
Coffee Mugs, set of 2 - CMV $15 set.
Drinking glasses, set of 4 - CMV $15 set.
Hot Plate - CMV $20.
Telephone, antique - CMV $100.
Travel beach bag - CMV $15.
Clock - CMV $35.
Directors chair - CMV $35.
Umbrella - CMV $25.
Poncho in bag. CMV $10.
All are red, white & blue decoration.

1979 KEY CHAIN "RECORD BREAKER"
Yellow, green, white or pink plastic. Has 4A design & says "I'm an Avon Record Breaker". Given to reps for getting new reps. CMV $5.

1979 MATCHES — PRESIDENT'S CELEBRATION
Blue foil top box. CMV $2
1970's LUGGAGE TAG
White plastic with gold 4A emblem & The Better Way. CMV $5

1970 LUGGAGE TAG FOR MANAGERS
(left) Black plastic, gold letters & 4A design. Given to Avon managers. CMV $6.
1977 CURRIER & IVES MATCH BOOK
(right) Silk screen Currier & Ives winter scene. Inside says "Merry Christmas and Best Wishes for a Happy New Year". "The Atlanta Management Team". Given to Avon Reps. at 1977 Christmas dinner. CMV $5.

1978 AVON SMILE SALES PROMOTION ITEMS
Are all red and white.
SILK SCARF - $6
BALLOONS - 2 different, 25c each
HAT - paper, $1
THE SMILE STARTS HERE button, $2.
SALES BAG - plastic, large size, $1
OPERATION SMILE LIPS - red paper lips, 50c.
RECORD - Avon Smile - red, small record, $2.

1980 VALENTINE — PRESIDENT'S CLUB
Given to President's Club Reps. Red valentine and white, red and green lace handkerchief. CMV $5 mint in envelope.
1978 KEY CHAIN HEART
Red plastic heart given to managers. CMV $2.

1975 MOISTURE SECRET PRESIDENT'S CLUB GIFT
Sent to President's Club members to introduce Moisture Secret. CMV $6 MB.
1975 I KNOW A SECRET PIN
For President's Club members. Pink pin. CMV $1. $2 on card.

1966 DISTINGUISHED MANAGEMENT AWARD LUGGAGE TAG
Plastic name tag for luggage on white strap. CMV $7.50
1966 POCKET ADDRESS MEMORANDUM
2" x 3" white w/gold lettering. CMV $8

1979 LIVE — LAUGH — LOVE AWARDS
Given to Reps. on cruise to Caribbean Feb. 1979. Silver & Red Menu, CMV $5. Tempo Leather Luggage Tag, CMV $5. Napkin, CMV 50¢. Tempo Leather Wallet for Ladies, CMV $10.

1975 MOISTURE SECRET MANAGERS GIFT SET
Pink box holds pink plastic jars of creme gel 4 oz., enriched freshener 5 oz., and night concentrate 3 oz. C-8-75. CMV $15 set MB.

1975 WHAT'S COOKING RECIPE BOX
Given to Reps. for drawing their name at sales meetings. Avon on the bottom. CMV $5.

LATE 1970's NAME TAGS
3 different stick on name tags used by Reps. CMV 50c each.

1978 TED E. BEAR TEAM LEADER GIFT
Tan teddy bear with red shirt was given to all team leaders at end of year party Nov. 1978. Fold out Teddy Bear card was on each table at party. CMV $4 card, CMV $25 bear mint.

1966 PRESIDENT'S CAMPAIGN COMPACT AWARD
Case marked sterling silver & back marked "Branch Champions President's Campaign 1966". Came in white & gold Avon box in felt bag. CMV $35 in silver case MB.

1980 TEDDY BEAR CANDLE AWARD
Small plastic bear candle holder. Given to Avon Team Leaders. Neck tag says "From Avon with Love". Red candle. CMV $30.

1977 POLLY PROSPECTING BIRD AWARD
Stuffed toy by Possem Trot. Tag has Avon Products on it. Given to Avon managers for recruiting new reps. Came with 2 large cards as shown. CMV $25 with Avon tag. Add $1 each card. Came in Avon mailer tube & letter. CMV $35 MB all.

1981 MONTE CARLO BRASS BOX AWARD
Brass box with burgundy velvet lining. Lid inscribed Casino Monte Carlo. Given to Avon managers eligible to win a free trip to Monte Carlo. CMV $50.

1981 TEDDY BEAR TEAM LEADER GIFT
White ceramic heart shaped box. Given to Team Leaders for 1981 year end party. Can also be bought in Hallmark stores. Does not say Avon. CMV $10. MB

1980 AWARD BANK
Black & gold tin bank. Given to Avon managers in Springdale branch. Special gold label on front says "Fifth National Bank & Trust Co. Springdale Branch. Assets 367 Managers, R. Manning President". Bottom marked "Made in England for Avon". CMV $40.

1962 SALES AWARD SACHET
Cream sachet in blue glass with blue, gold & white lid. Gold metal stand. $12 jar only. $15 in box.

1979 TEDDY AWARD
Black base with plaque. Brown top & bear has red shirt with Avon in white. Given to one Team Leader for recommendation support in each district. CMV $55.

1979 TEDDY BEAR COOKIE JAR AWARD
Tan & red ceramic bear cookie jar. Given to Team Leaders at Christmas. CMV $35.

1981 CABLE CAR MUSIC BOX AWARD
Only 100 given to Circle of Excellence Managers at San Francisco C of E meeting. Was not made for Avon. CMV $35.

1976 CANDID SCARF GIFT
Silk scarf designed by S.M. Kent in Candid folder. Given to Avon President's Club members. CMV $7.

1952 SYMPHONY SCARF
Blue background with pink rose & parts of letters in French. Pure silk. Purchased from store in New York & awarded for selling 36 products in the Prelude to Spring campaign. CMV $30 mint.

1967 PRESIDENTS CAMPAIGN GLACE AWARD
Managers is in script writing with white lined box. CMV $22.50 in box. $18.50 compact only. Representatives is in block writing on Presidents Campaign with blue felt lined box. CMV $10. $12 in box. Both came in Hawaiian White Ginger box.

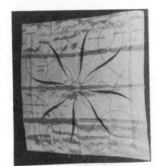

1970 SILK SCARF AWARD
Beige & brown silk scarf. 4A design. Given to Avon reps. CMV $20.

1980 TASHA AWARDS
Monte Carlo scarf, CMV $20.
Tasha picture of the late Princess Grace of Monte Carlo with Tasha card. CMV $20.
Tasha matches - box & book matches, CMV $1 each.
Items were won by reps on Avon trip to Monte Carlo.

1960's AVON CURTAINS
Used to decorate in offices & Avon Plant. CMV $22.50.

1972 AVON SCARF
All silk pink, orange & white scarf with 4 big "A" on it. Avon in corner. Made in Italy. Came in silver box. CMV $12. mint.

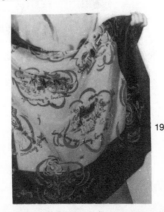

1941 FOUNDERS CAMPAIGN ACHIEVEMENT AWARD SCARF
Blue & white folder holds blue border, white pink & green silk scarf. Shows 1st CPC factory & 1st Avon lady with "The doorway to loveliness" marked under her. Given to reps in 1941. Very rare. CMV $75 in folder mint, $50 scarf only mint.

1950 - 64th ANNIVERSARY SCARF
Silk scarf was made only for Avon. Given to representatives for selling 64 pieces of Avon in campaign 9, 1950. Silk scarf has blue border, white center with sketches in turquoise & rose. Some words on scarf say "Long, long ago"; "A thing of beauty is a joy forever"; "The doorway to loveliness". CMV $50.

1971 4A QUILT
Reversible, ruffled edged, cotton filled comforter in gold, avocado or blue. Given for having a person recommended as a representative appointed. CMV $40.

1969 4A QUILT
Pink quilt with white 4A design. CMV $45.

1977 IT'S NOT YOUR MOTHER'S MAKEUP APRON
Light khaki color and orange plastic apron. Used by Avon managers at sales meetings to introduce colorworks. CMV $5.

1960's WALL PLAQUE
Used at sales meetings. Blue & gold cardboard. CMV $25.

1978 PRESIDENT'S CLUB APRON
Beige & red canvas apron says "I'd rather be selling Avon". Given to all President's Club reps. Modeled by Grace Powers. CMV $10.

1948 AVON APRON
Aqua in color with white center. Avon in center & pictures of Avon products of 1948. Given to Managers only for sales demo. CMV $50 mint.

1970 MOONWIND MANAGERS DISPLAY
Silver and blue cardboard display. CMV $10.

1979 AFTER CONFERENCE MINTS
Pink box of fifty 1979 Susan B. Anthony dollar coins with card for Avon managers for Outstanding Recruiting. CMV $100 MB, with all 1979 coins.

1960's 4A WALL PLAQUE
Used at sales meetings. Large size. CMV $25.

1977 WHAT'S COOKING APRON
Blue apron was won by Reps at sales meeting in drawing for getting new Avon ladies. CMV $7.

1980 JAM GIFT SET AWARD
Set of 16 small jars of jam with front label "Especially for You from Avon". Given to managers. Was not made only for Avon. CMV $10.

1976 VALENTINE GIFT TO REPRESENTATIVES
Whitman Sampler sent to all reps. with Avon card. CMV $3 with card only.

1976 TREND SETTERS ORDER BOOK AWARD
(Left) Yellow plastic with 4A design and Avon Trend Setters on front. Given to Avon Trend Setters Reps. CMV $5.

1977 TEAM LEADER MIRROR GIFT
(Right) Mirror in red plastic, holder with white star and letters. Given to Avon Team Leaders at Avon luncheon, Dec. 1977. CMV $4.

1961-75 YEAR HONOR AWARD ORDER BOOK
Red with gold letters. CMV $8 mint.

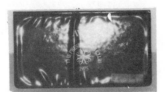

1978 VALENTINE CANDY
Red and gold heart box. Holds 4½ oz. of chocolates by Bartons. Back of box says "This candy heart selected by Avon and packaged especially for you. Given to Avon reps. CMV $5 box only. $10 MB full.

1975 PRESIDENT'S CLUB ORDER BOOK COVER
Blue plastic. CMV $3.

1960 PRESIDENT'S CLUB ORDER BOOK COVER
CMV $7.

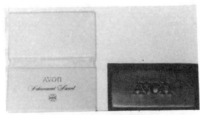

1960's ACHIEVEMENT AWARD ORDER BOOK COVER
(Left) Light blue cover. CMV $7.

1977 ORDER BOOK - CANADA
(Right) Dark blue plastic. Used by reps in Canada. Came with blue and gold pen and order book. CMV $5.

1973 CHECK COVERS
Red & green plastic check book covers given to Reps. CMV $3. each.

1960 GENERAL MANAGERS HONOR AWARD
(Top) Order book cover in blue. CMV $8 mint.

1959 HONOR AWARD ORDER BOOK COVER
(Bottom) Red plastic with gold trim, also had gold pen. CMV $10.

1973 ORDER BOOK COVER
Blue and green design matches delivery bag. Has turquoise and gold pen. Earned for prize points. CMV $5.

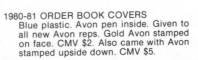

1980-81 ORDER BOOK COVERS
Blue plastic. Avon pen inside. Given to all new Avon reps. Gold Avon stamped on face. CMV $2. Also came with Avon stamped upside down. CMV $5.

1970's CARD CASES AWARDS
President's Club. Pink & turquoise; vinyl. CMV $2.50. Top one Foreign. CMV $5.

1967 BROCADE HONOR AWARD ORDER BOOK COVER
Given to Reps. for calling on customers during introduction of Brocade. Came with Avon pen also. CMV $5. With pen $8.

1978 CUSTOMER SERVICE AWARD
Given to Reps. for calling on 60 customers, "red cover" CMV $4 or 100 customers "gold cover" CMV $6. 2-ring binders were used to put Avon customer addresses in.

1980 CUSTOMER SERVICE AWARD
Leatherette portfolio given to managers; brass corners on outside of maroon cover. CMV $20.

1976-77 ORDER BOOK COVER & PEN
Given to only new Avon Reps. Blue plastic cover and blue and gold pen. CMV $3.

1976 TERRITORY DIRECTORY
Blue plastic 2-ring binder used by Reps. for customers in their territory. CMV $2.

1970's BOOK MATCHES
Gold matches with red Avon rose. Inside says "Welcome your Avon Rep. when she calls". CMV 50c.

1981 PRESIDENT'S CLUB PORTFOLIO
Maroon with President's Club stationery. CMV $5.

1979 UNIVERSITY OF AVON PORTFOLIO
Maroon training portfolio for managers. CMV $10.

1964 PRESIDENTS HONOR AWARD ORDER BOOK COVER
Blue plastic with gold trim. CMV $8.

1966 REGENCE ORDER BOOK HONOR AWARD
Green plastic with gold trim to match Regence packaging. CMV $6.

1977 ARIANE MEMO BOOK
Red cover Memo Book given to Avon Team Leaders when Ariane came out. CMV $7.

1976 MANAGERS PHOTO ALBUM
Given to managers. CMV $20.

1977 PRESIDENTS CELEBRATION ORDER BOOK COVER
Red plastic. CMV $3.

1976 PERSONAL POCKET DIARY
Blue plastic cover with Avon pocket diary and calendar inside. CMV $3.

1980-81 DIVISION MANAGERS GUIDE
1980 red plastic Avon News and 1981 white. Used by managers for training Reps. CMV $10 each.

1980 ALBEE STATIONERY NOTES
Box of 1st Avon lady notes with outer sleeve given to President's Club Reps. CMV $5 MB.

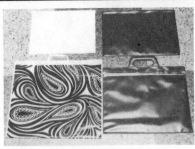

1970's DISTRICT MANAGERS ORGANIZATION GUIDE
Dark blue & gold loose leaf binder, contains guide material. CMV $10.

1970 REPRESENTATIVE CASES
Miscellaneous representatives portfolio cases, plastic. CMV $4 each.

1957 PRESIDENTIAL WINNERS AWARD
Blue felt booklet given to winning district Avon representatives upon touring district Avon plant. CMV $30.

1974 PORTFOLIO
Red plastic, 4A design for Avon Reps. CMV $3.

1961 MANAGERS SALES MEETING NOTE BOOK
Campaign 15, 16, 17, 18 sales meeting plans. Inside front cover says "# so & so of a limited edition for the Management Staff Only". Cover is red satin 12" x 20", comes in white box. For you from Avon on cover. CMV $75 mint.

1980 CHRISTMAS GIFT FOR AVON REPS.
Ceramic base & green note pad holder signed by William Chaney, Avon President. Given to all Avon Sales Reps. at Christmas 1980. CMV $10 MB.

1971 LADY DESK FOLIO
Pink cover holds calendar to be used as a plan guide for sending orders and making appointments. Given for sending a $75 or larger order in. C1-71 CMV $7.50

1952 MANAGER-REPRESENTATIVE INTRODUCTION BOOK
Turquoise & silver booklet. Used by managers to train new Avon Reps. CMV $10.

1977 SUEDE ORDER BOOK COVER AWARD
Brown plastic suede order book cover holds 4 Avon order books. Given to Avon Reps. for reaching sales goals. 1886 Avon lady embossed on front. Was not awarded in all branches. CMV $10.

1965 CELEBRITY AUTOGRAPH BOOK
Not marked Avon. Only in box. CMV $5. $8.50 MB

1976 NOTE PAD TRENDSETTERS
Clear plastic, Avon on top holder. Trendsetter note pads. Given to managers only. CMV $20.

1969-80 CIRCLE OF EXCELLENCE PASSPORT HOLDERS
Given each year. Each marked Circle of Excellence. Given to top managers only for annual C of E trip. Different color each year. CMV $5 each.

CIRCLE OF EXCELLENCE PROGRAM
Given to C of E managers at annual C of E celebration. CMV $5 each year.

1978 TEAM LEADER CARDS
4 different cards given to team leaders, with bears on them. CMV $1 each.

1978 AUGUST CONFERENCE PICTURE HOLDER
Tan cover. Given to managers at August conference. CMV $15.

1970's AVON COSMETICS MARKETING HIGHLIGHT BINDER BOOKLET
Used by managers. CMV $5.

1978 PARIS PICTURE GIFT
French print scene by Bernard Picture Co. given to each manager with French printed Avon Circle of Excellence card & ribbon. CMV $7.50. Must have Avon card as shown.

1979 DATE BOOK
Rust color date book given out by Avon managers. Inside cover says "A gift from your Avon manager". CMV $2.

PENCILS - AVON
1979 Blue Marking Pen - fine point. CMV $1.
1979 Color Up America - red pencil. CMV $1.

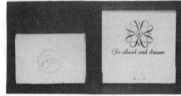

1977-79 CIRCLE OF EXCELLENCE MATCHES
Given to managers on trip to Paris 1979. White, gold letters. Matches are gold heads. CMV $5. Also given in 1977.

1979 GO AHEAD & DREAM MATCHES
White, red letters. Given to managers at September conference. CMV $2 mint.

1980 NICE KRISPIES BOX
Small size cereal box given to team leaders. CMV $6.

1979 CLIP BOARD MANAGERS GIFT
Front says "Thank you for making us number one". Avon on bottom. Given to managers only. Made of Lucite. CMV $10.

1960-70 DIAMOND DECADE HONOR ROLL AWARD
Silver with blue 4A booklet. Given to managers for outstanding service. CMV $12.

1979 CALENDAR - PRESIDENT'S CLUB GIFT
Red felt cover calendar with pages of Avon history on inside. Given to President's Club Reps. only. CMV $4. Also pictured is President's Club luncheon invitation card. Red. CMV 50¢.

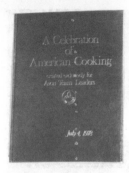

1978 COOK BOOK FOR TEAM LEADERS
Red cover 96 page book given to Team Leaders July 1978. CMV $10 mint.

1978 STEPPIN' OUT KNEE HIGHS OR PANTY HOSE
Knee socks or panty hose given to Reps. for $200 in sales in C14-78. CMV $5 in package.

1978 STEPPIN' OUT ORDER BOOK
Used by Reps. in C14-78. CMV $1.

1977 WHO'S WHO OF AVON DISTRICT MANAGERS
Red cover book with all Circle of Excellence 1976 winners. 72 pages. CMV $17.50.

1979 MENU PRESIDENT'S CELEBRATION
Given to President's Club members at their luncheon celebration. CMV $2.

1971 AVON CALLING PHONE INDEX
Given for sending in order of $75 or more. C1-71. CMV $5.

1980 TASHA FLIGHT TO FANTASY VASE
White porcelain vase given to Reps. on Monte Carlo trip. CMV $40.

1980 TASHA PASSPORT HOLDER
Given to Reps. on Monte Carlo trip, held luggage tag & misc. Tasha paper items, program, etc. CMV $20 for all.

1974 GROW WITH AVON
Avon card with 2 wooden stakes. Many different plants. CMV $3.

1979 PRESIDENT'S CLUB THANK YOU NOTES
White box with outer sleeve. Both has "President's Club, Avon's Very Best" on lid. Holds 25 thank you notes. Given to President's Club Reps. only. CMV $5 MB complete set.

1978 AVONOPOLY
Game used by managers at Avon Rep. sales meeting C12-78. Also came with Avon play money of 25 & 50 green notes. CMV set $12.

1976 AVON FUN DOLLARS
Small green paper play five dollar bill. Used by Reps. at meetings. CMV 50¢

EARLY 1900's CPC SCRATCH PAD
5" square paper pad with 50 sheets. OSP 15¢, CMV $50 mint.

1977 CURRIER & IVES COASTERS
Pack of 6 given to Team Leaders at Christmas. Also given to Reps. for recommendation prize. Marked Avon. CMV $8 pack of 6.

1973 NOTE PAD PRIZE
Gold plastic with 4A design on front. Has 1973 calendar pad and pen inside. Used by Reps. CMV $4.

1978 SPRING GARDEN CLUB FLOWER SEED
7 different flower seed packets made up for Avon, given to Reps. at sales meeting. Packaged by James Vick's Seeds. CMV $1 per pack.

1970 LUCKY WAGON SWEEPSTAKES GIFT
2 white handkerchiefs with monogram in corner with choice of letters. Given for mens car decanter sales C11-70. In dark blue folder with card. CMV $7.

1967 CARD CARRYING CASE PRIZE
Blue plastic with 4A design and says Avon Cosmetics. Given to Reps. for selling $30 over their sales goals. CMV $3.

1965 HANDKERCHIEF GIFT
Pink and white card says "Thank You". Holds white with green and pink design handkerchief given to Reps. for recommendation. CMV $6 mint with card.

1970 LINEN TOWEL CALENDAR
Given to all Reps. for sending in an order in C1-1970. Made only for Avon. Measures 15½" x 28½". CMV $6.50.

1966 PICTURE ALBUM AWARD
White Avon box holds large and small picture album and picture frame in brown and gold. Cover says "For you, from Avon". CMV $45 MB.

1964-65 AVON QUEEN CERTIFICATE
78th & 79th Anniversary Award Certificates. One red and others blue border. Given to top selling Reps. only. CMV $10 each.

1976 AVON CHRISTMAS CARD
Green & gold Christmas card. Inside says "From your Avon Representative". Box of 75 cards given to Avon Reps. for recommendation of new Avon lady. CMV $15 box of 75 mint, or 25¢ each card mint.

1947 PASADENA BRANCH DEDICATION BOOKLET
Gold spiral bound booklet given at opening of Pasadena Branch, Sept. 22-27, 1947. Front says "Avon Serves the Golden West". CMV $25.

1966 PLACE MAT AWARD
Plastic place mat showing Avon Daily Need Products. Given to Reps. for meeting sales. CMV $5.

1945 MANAGERS INTRODUCTION BOOK
Blue cover, 28 page book, used by Avon Managers to sign up new Avon Reps. 11''x 14'' size. Came with clear plastic cover. CMV $35 mint.

1978 BEAUTY & FRAGRANCE CALENDAR
Punch out calendar given to special good customers in C24-77 by Avon Reps. Made only for Avon. CMV $5. Only given in certain states for test marketing.

1975 OUTSTANDING ACHIEVEMENT CERTIFICATE
Given to Reps. for top sales in C20-21 1975. CMV $4.

1972 TEAM HONOR AWARD CERTIFICATE
Given to Reps. on winning teams for sales. CMV $4.

1976 CIRCLE OF EXCELLENCE SCROLL
Given to managers each year with all the Circle of Excellence winners. CMV $3.

1978 MUSIC BOX TEAM AWARD
. Red painted wood music box made in Japan only for Avon. Brass plate on lid says "You Made Avon Smile". Given to winning team for selling most lipsticks. CMV $30.

1969 CUSTOMERS SERVICE FILE
Turquoise paper box holds file envelopes for Avon lady sales. CMV $5.

1961 FILE BOX
(Left) Turquoise cardboard file box with 4A design on lid. CMV $6 mint.
1971 DESIGNERS DREAM SWEEPSTAKES AWARD
(Right) C7-1971. White lace handkerchief with note from Avon for sales accomplishments. CMV $6.50 mint.

1981 HI, I'M BUTTON
Says "I'm going to make you feel beautiful". CMV $2.

1971 JUNE 15 BUTTON PIN
Bright green to remind customers June 15 was Fathers Day. CMV $3.
1970 HELLO 1970 BUTTON PIN
Black background with red, yellow & blue letters & numbers. Given to all representatives to tell the world she welcomes successful seventies. CMV $3.

1970's EARLY TEAM LEADER RIBBON BADGE
Yellow badge and ribbon used by Team Leaders at sales meetings. CMV $5.
1978 I GOT IT PIN
Gray and white pin given to Reps. at Avon sales meetings. Measures 2¼". CMV $1.

1979 ZANY BUTTON
Given to Avon Reps. on introduction of Zany Products. CMV $1.
1979 TEAM LEADER BUTTON
Given to Avon Reps. CMV $1.

1974 I'M THE HEART PIN
Given to Reps. as being the heart of Avon. CMV $2.

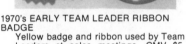
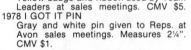

1978 POSTCARD GREATEST HOMECOMING
CMV 50c.
1978 GREATEST HOMECOMING PIN
CMV $1. Both are yellow & blue. Used for President's Celebration.

1977 AVON 91st BUTTON & RIBBON
(left) Red and white button. CMV $1, button; & ribbon $2.
1979 "ASK ME ABOUT THE LOVE OF MY LIFE" BUTTON
(left) White and red button. CMV $1.
1977 LUGGAGE TAG
(right) Round white plastic, back side says "The Magic of Avon". CMV $2.

1946-47 CONFERENCE PIN MANAGERS
On gold braided rope. CMV $50 mint.

BUTTON — PINS
1978 Top Horizon 50 pin. CMV $2.
1976 Say Yes Yes To No No's. CMV $1.
1978 The Smile Starts Here. CMV $1.

1981 AVON COASTERS
Plastic sheet of 8 white plastic coasters. Had to be cut out. Given to managers. CMV $5 for sheet of 8.

1980 AVON CARDS AWARD
(right) Silver faced playing cards say 1980 - Avon New York - Las Vegas. Given to Division Managers at Las Vegas conference for Pasadena Branch CMV $15 MB.

1980 FRISBEE — AVON
(left) White plastic, blue and red letters. CMV $10.

1960 4A NAME PIN
Used by Avon Reps. at meetings. 2½" in diameter. CMV $3.

1977 COLOR WORKS MAKEUP BUTTONS
Given to Reps. for sales meeting attendance. CMV $1.

1981 LOOK A LITE COMPACT AWARD
Lavendar and silver trim. Made only for Avon. Given to Reps. & Managers in blue bag. Card came with it. CMV $15 in bag.

1976 FRISBEES — GIFT TO REPS.
White plastic with red letters. CMV $6. White with red & green letters, CMV $8.

1974 TEAM LEADER BOOK MARK
Gold & red Book Mark. For Avon Reps. use. CMV $8.

1970 PICTURE YOURSELF MIRROR
Two sided mirror with antiqued gold. Awarded for selling 7 body lotions during campaign 7. CMV $7. $9 MB.

1936 FACE POWDER GOLD KEY
9½" long key is gold on one side with large tulip A & Avon. Back side holds silver face powder sample. CMV label. Given to Reps. only. CMV $22.50 mint as shown.

1965 CAMEO VANITY SET PRIZE
Made by Syroco only for Avon. Set consists of Cameo brush, 2 combs, vanity mirror, and hand mirror. Given to Reps. for selling 40 cameo lipsticks or compacts for brush and comb. CMV $7. 76 total for vanity mirror. CMV $13. 100 for hand mirror. CMV $15.

1980 ROYAL RIBBON AWARDS
Given to Reps. for sales achievements. Yellow or red ribbon. CMV $2. White & blue given with certificate. CMV $5 each with certificate. Some dated 1980 and some not.

1976 MANAGERS TOOTHBRUSH
Given to managers. Came in different colors. "Avon" on one side; "Prospecting is a habit, too" on other side. CMV $5.

1977 CHARGE CARD MACHINE
Red plastic, marked Avon. Used by Reps. to take charge cards for Avon Sales. Used only for a short period. CMV $5.

1980 McCONNELL FAMILY REUNION COASTERS
Package of 4 white Fiesta Coasters. Center says "James McConnell Family Reunion 1980". Were given at 1st family reunion of David McConnell ancestors since 1948. Very rare. No price established.

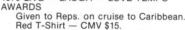

1979 LIVE — LAUGH — LOVE TEMPO AWARDS
Given to Reps. on cruise to Caribbean. Red T-Shirt — CMV $15.
(Left) 1978 Picture Cube — Says "New York - Bermuda - Circle of Excellence" CMV $15.
(Right) Bahamas Stick Pin - In brown felt bag given to Reps. on cruise. Does not say Avon. CMV $2.
(Center) 1979 Cruise Program - Feb. 2-5, 1979. CMV $2.

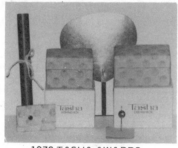

1979 TASHA AWARDS
All are pink and purple.
(center) Wishing box given to Reps. CMV $15 MB.
(right) Dream box with Tasha pin & tray inside given to Managers. CMV $10 MB.
(left) Key Chain. CMV $2.
(back right) Fan. CMV $1.
(back left) Scroll Dream Test. CMV $1. All were given to Reps, except Dream box.

1957 — 71st ANNIVERSARY CAKE
A real cake with 71 on top with Avon card given to managers. Made by Schraffts. CMV $50.

1964-65 AVON DUNCE CAPS
Came in several different colors of plastic. Used at sales meetings. 4A design on top and bottom. CMV $10 each.

1974 WHAT'S COOKING — AVON GIFT
5 yellow plastic scoop, strainer, funnel, egg separator, measurer. Given to Reps. for sales meeting attendance. Made by Geni, a division of Avon. CMV $2 each.

1977 COSMETIC CASE AWARD
(left) Tan and white plastic zipper purse.
1977 PORTABLE PURSE MIRROR AWARD
(right) Matches purse with mirror. Both given to Reps. by Avon. Both came in plastic bags with Avon on them. CMV $3 each. Mint in bag only.

1980 WACKY MONEY BAG
Silver tone bag with red tie string & red $ design. Used at sales meetings. Does not say Avon. CMV $15.

1980 RECORD — HAPPY BIRTHDAY
It's a most unusual day on cover. Given to President's Club Reps. on their birthday. CMV $5 mint.

1979 FLIGHT TO FANTASY RECORD
(left) Given to Reps. in C20-79 to introduce Fantasy fragrance. CMV $3 record and cover mint.

1979 BON APPETIT COOK BOOK
(right) Given to managers on Circle of Excellence trip to Paris. Avon on front. CMV $5.

1979 DOOR KNOCKER RING DISPLAY BOX AWARD
Black ring box with gold tone door knocker on cover. Given to Avon managers. CMV $30 mint.

TRAINING RECORDS — FILM STRIPS
Used by managers to show new products at sales meetings. Box came with record and 1 film strip for each record. Have been used for many years by Avon. No price established because of so many different varieties. CMV record only $2.

1981 TEAM LEADER & MANAGERS CHRISTMAS GIFT
Wood case jewelry box with mirror inside says "Avon Team Leader 1981". CMV $65.
Same thing given to Avon managers only says "Managers 1981". CMV $85.

AVON RECORDS
Christmas Records, given to Reps. at Christmas. CMV $7.50.
Campaign 21, 1974 Sales Meeting record. CMV $3.

1970 AVON CHRISTMAS RECORD
33 1/3 RPM record in blue holder with letter from Avon President Fred Fusse. CMV $7.50.

1982 JEWELRY WRAP AROUND
Cotton jewelry wrap in lavender box. Box says "You deserve something very special". Given to a few Reps. per district. CMV $7.50 MB.

1976 RECOMMENDATION PRIZE
Blue plastic case holds 2 order books and an Avon book calculator made by Arizona. Warranty card says "Made for Avon". Given to Reps. for getting 2 new Avon Reps. CMV $25 mint in working order.

1979 CALCULATOR — COLOR UP AMERICA AWARD

(Left) Avon color never looked so good on face of calculator. Came in Avon leatherette case & matching box. Given to Reps. for sales award. CMV $22.50 MB

1979 COME COLOR WITH US ANNOUNCEMENT

(Right) Inside has crayola & invitation to meeting. CMV $2.

1968 AVON'S SPRING FEVER

Green felt board with 6 tin painted flowers pins. Managers gave a pin to each representative for recommending a new Avon representative. $35 complete card mint. Each pin $4.

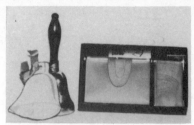

1963 RING THE BELL — MANAGERS GIFT

(Left) 6½" tall brass bell, black handle. Used by Avon managers at sales meetings. Came with red ribbon & 7 bell shaped cards with Avon on each one. Must have Avon bell cards for value. CMV $60.

1976 WALLET & KEY CASE — MANAGERS GIFT

(Right) Leather wallet & key case given to Avon managers with Avon card on top of box. CMV $15.

1971 KEY CASE AWARD

Blue case with large 4A design. CMV $10.

1980 RECOMMENDATION CASIO PRIZE

Casio LC 315 calculator in 4A design black case. CMV $25.

1976 REPRESENTATIVE CHRISTMAS CARD GIFT

White Avon embossed box holds hand screened fold-out glass Christmas card given to all Reps. in 1976. CMV $12 MB.

1970 KEY CASE FLASHLIGHT

Red key case with flashlight inside. Not marked Avon. Made only for Avon. Given to Reps. for meeting sales goals. CMV $5. $8 MB.

1971 DAISY CHAIN JEWELRY & PIN

White and gold earrings, 2 different pins or a daisy topped pen could be chosen by a representative for each person recommended as a representative. Only one gift for each name. CMV $6 each. Daisy display card $7.

1967 KEY CASE AWARD

Blue case with gold 4A emblem. Given to Reps. for reaching sales goal in campaign 12. CMV $10.

1976 15 YEAR PEN SET AWARD
2 Cross 14K gold filled pens engraved "Avon 15 Years" & persons' initials. Both pens are in grey felt bags & pink leather pen holder with gold. 4A pen with red ruby in center & gold rose embossed. CMV $75 MB.

1979 TEDDY BEAR PEN AWARD
Cross chrome pen with small bear marked TL for Team Leader. Avon bear sleeve fits over box. CMV $27.50 MB.

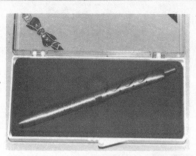

1975 TOP REPRESENTATIVE PEN GIFT
Brass & black design ball point pen. Small size. Came in red velvet lined, plastic display box & gold sleeve. Given for meeting sales goals. CMV $10 MB as shown. Pen only $5.

1980 PRESIDENT'S CLUB CANDIDATES PEN SET AWARD
Red & gold Avon box holds gold tone pen & pencil set. Inscribed on side of pens, "President's Club Candidate". CMV $25 MB.

1969 PEN FOR LEADERSHIP AWARD
Silver, black top with olive leaf on top. Garland Pen. Given to Avon Reps. CMV $15 MB.

1940's AVON PEN AWARD
Yellow & black plastic, "Avon" on clip. Fountain pen on one end, lead pencil on other end. No information. CMV $35.

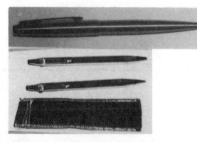

1979 PRESIDENT'S CLUB PEN AWARD
Parker 75 silver & gold pen. Inscribed on side, "President's Club 1979". Comes in blue felt Parker case. CMV $20.

1969 DIVISION MANAGER'S PEN & PENCIL SET AWARD
Sterling silver pens. 4A emblem on pens. Came in blue brocade Cross pen box. Given to managers only. CMV $50 set MB, each pen only $20.

1969 DIVISION MANAGERS TRIBUTE PEN
Silver pen with 4A on clip. Came in blue flannel sleeve & white box. CMV $35 MB.

1970's AVON PENS
Blue & silver "Diamond Quarter 1977". CMV $2.
Red pen says "Get Write to the Point — Sell Avon". CMV $2.

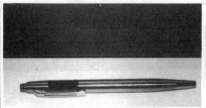

1979 STERLING CLOCK PEN AWARD
Sterling silver pen with digital clock & calendar inside. Inscribed "Number 1 in $ Inc.", plus name of division. Given to managers only. CMV $125 MB.

1950 AWARD PENCIL
Deluxe Eversharp, gold color. Given to Reps. for writing 50 or more orders in campaign 2, 1950. 5 inches long with "Avon Woman of Achievement" on pencil. CMV $40 pencil only, $50 MB.

1972 RAIN HAT
Plastic rain hat in pink & white case. Given at Beauty Salons only. CMV $2.

1974 DING-DONG AVON CALLING PEN
Given at Christmas. Black & white pen. CMV $3.

1960's CHRISTMAS MAGIC PENCIL
White pencils from Avon. CMV $1 each.

1934 CIGARETTE HOLDER AWARD
Made of solid ivory in velvet lined custom made blue & gold box marked "Avon" inside lid. Green & silver center band. CMV $75 MB.

1970 WORLD OF CHRISTMAS — FLOWER PEN AWARD
Small white pen with red, yellow & green holly flower on cap. Given to Avon Reps. CMV $3.50 mint.

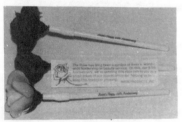

1970 84TH ANNIVERSARY FLOWER PENS
Given for sending in an order C-12 84th anniversary. White barrel with red printing with yellow, pink, red, orange or white rose. CMV $2 each, $3 in cellophane wrapper with card.

1967 WESTERN CHOICE (STEER HORNS) "MANAGERS"
Managers received the steer horns in a special box with "Avon" embossed all over the box. Was used to show at meetings on introduction of Steer Horns. Rare in this box. CMV $35 MB as shown.

1980 RADIO AWARD
Red and white plastic AM-FM Avon radio given 1 to each district manager to give at a drawing. Made by ISIS, in box. CMV $125 MB.

1980 SUGAR 'N SPICE CANDY JAR AWARD
(left) Glass jar full of red candy drops. Yellow neck label. Red Avon sleeve fits over white box. Given to President's Club members. CMV $6 MB.

1980 ULTRA WEAR DEMONSTRATOR
(right) Box holds clear plastic box with steel ball to test Ultra Enamel to customers. Given to Avon Reps. in C10-80. CMV $5 MB.

1980 PRESIDENT'S CELEBRATION CANDLE HOLDERS
Blue candles in clear glass base. "Avon" on bottom label. Given to all Reps. at banquet. CMV $12 pair.

STOCKHOLDER'S GIFTS

1957-1973 STOCKHOLDERS XMAS GIFTS - Stockholders gifts were special packaged Avon items sent to each share holder of Avon Stock at Christmas each year. A special stockholders greeting card was sent with each gift & a stockholders gift is not mint or complete without this card. They were first sent in 1957 & discontinued at Christmas 1973. They are considered quite hard to find.

There are only 2 years of stockholders gifts not shown. If you have any of the following 2 complete sets with card, please contact Bud Hastin. 1957 set had Persian Wood Perfume Mist & Beauty Dust. 1959 set had Topaze Spray Perfume & Cologne Mist. Also listed is After Shower for Men. This could be 1 complete set or 2 different. 1 for men & 1 for women. Also listed for 1960 is 8 oz. Spice After Shave Lotion. This again sounds like 2 different items for 1960. All the other years are pictured & priced.

1958 STOCKHOLDERS GIFT
Satin lined box with large ribbon across lid and stockholders card. Holds Here's My Heart Beauty dust, sachet lotion & Top Style lipstick. CMV $65 MB.

1960 TOPAZE TREASURE STOCK-HOLDERS GIFT
Yellow & gold satin lined box holds Topaze Beauty Dust & 2 oz. cologne. Came with stockholders card. This was a general issue gift that was also sold. CMV $40 MB. $55 MB with stockholders card.

1963 STOCKHOLDERS GIFT
Box opens in center with double lid to show 3 oz. Occur cologne mist & Tribute after shave. Stockholders card. CMV $50 MB.

1965 STOCKHOLDERS GIFT
Box with stockholders card & Just Two set. CMV $80 MB.

1961 STOCKHOLDERS GIFT
Box with stockholders Christmas card, holds Cotillion Beauty Dust, cream sachet & cologne mist. This set is same as 1961-62 Cotillion Debut, only with special card. CMV $60 MB.

1964 STOCKHOLDERS GIFT
White flip open box with 4A design on both sides of lid, holds 4A after shave and Rapture 2 oz. cologne. With stockholders card. CMV $60 MB.

1967 STOCKHOLDERS GIFT
Brown brocade design box holds 1st Edition Book After Shave & Brocade 4 oz. cologne. CMV $40 MB.

1966 REGENCE COLOGNE MIST STOCKHOLDERS GIFT
White, green and gold box. Given to stockholders on introduction of Regence, says "Your introduction to a fragrance masterpiece by Avon". CMV $40 MB.

1968 STOCKHOLDERS GIFT
A special gift given to Avon stockholders. Short pony in Windjammer & Charisma Cologne Mist, set in white foam. Set $32.50 MB.

1962 STOCKHOLDERS GIFT
Flip open box with Avon printed all over lid. Holds Bay Rum jug after shave & skin so soft bud vase. With stockholders card. CMV $65 MB.

1969 STOCKHOLDERS GIFT
Pink foam box holds Elusive Cologne Mist & Perfume Rollette, ribbon around box. CMV $27.50 MB.

1970 STOCKHOLDERS GIFT
Bird of Paradise Cologne Mist in foam box. Gold band around box. Came with card from Avon as Christmas gift to stockholders. CMV $22.50 MB with card only.

1973 IMPERIAL GARDEN'S STOCK-HOLDERS GIFT
Cream sachet in white styrofoam with orange & gold ribbon. Also has card. CMV $18 MB.

STOCKHOLDERS MEETING GIFTS
A special wrapped Avon product is given to each stockholder attending the Annual Avon Stockholders Meeting. Each gift comes with a special card which states "With the compliments of the Board of Directors, Officers and Employees of Avon Products, Inc.". CMV $15 to $20 each mint with card only.

1972 DEEP WOODS STOCKHOLDERS GIFT
Brown foam box shaped like a log, card on top, with brown grograin ribbon and gold sticker, contains Deep Woods Cologne. CMV $25 MB.

1971 STOCKHOLDERS GIFT
White foam box with blue felt band. Contains Moonwind Cologne Mist. CMV $25 MB with card.

NATIONAL ASSOCIATION AVON COLLECTOR'S AVON CLUB BOTTLES & NAAC COLLECTABLES

SOLD ONLY TO MEMBERS
OF NAAC CLUBS

NAAC and club bottle offers not
affiliated with Avon Products, Inc.

CLUB BOTTLES — PLATES — CONVENTION BOTTLES — BELLS

What are they? Where do you get them? Club bottles are made for Avon collectors and are sold thru any of the more than 150 Avon Collectors Clubs throughout the United States and Canada. These clubs are all members of the National Association of Avon Collectors. Club bottles or plates are sold for a period of 60 days only and only the amount sold in that time is made. At the end of the sale period, the order is placed with the factory. It usually takes around 4 months to get them manufactured and shipped to the collector. The resale value of these low issue bottles or plates usually doubles by the time you get them from the factory. Each bottle is numbered with the quantity made. All club bottles are hand painted porcelain of the finest quality. The club bottles are the best bottle investment around today for future value increase. If you do not have an Avon Club in your area belonging to the N:A.A.C. we invite you to join the Avon Times to be eligible to purchase all club bottles as they come out at the lowest possible price. $12.00 yearly dues ($15.00 for Canada, U.S. funds money orders only from Canada). Send to:

AVON TIMES
Box 9868
Kansas City, Missouri 64134

1972 1ST ANNUAL NAAC AVON CLUB BOTTLE
1ST AVON LADY

7" high, hand painted porcelain bottle. Made for Avon Club members only belonging to the National Association of Avon Collectors. 1st NAAC Club bottle issued. Made in image of first CPC saleslady. Each bottle is numbered. Released in June 1972. Total issue was 2870. Bottle made and issued by National Association of Avon Collectors. OSP $10.95, CMV $250. 18 made with red hair & green purse. CMV $700. for a redhead. No registration certificates were issued with the '71 Club Bottle. 4 bottles had blue lettering on bottle. All others had black letters. CMV blue letter bottom $700. Bud Hastin knows the numbers on all red head & blue bottoms. Check before buying. 1972 factory sample of 1st lady sold by mistake. Same as above only no lettering on bottom & neck is flush where cork fits top of bottle. No raised lip for cork as regular production was. Bottle has letter from Bud Hastin as 1 of a kind sample. CMV $500.

1978 NAAC MINI McCONNELL & CPC FACTORY

(Left) Miniature size figurines of the 1886 CPC Factory and Mr. & Mrs. McConnell the founders of Avon. Issued by National Association of Avon Clubs. Only 1200 sets were sold. OSP $16.95 set. Original set came with McConnell & factory 2nd from right. Factory was too large so issued a second smaller factory on left. 1200 small factories made. CMV set with 1 factory & McConnell $35., CMV with both factories in center $55.

1974 NAAC CPC FACTORY CLUB BOTTLE

(Right) 3rd annual Club Bottle issued by the NAAC Clubs in honor of the 1st California Perfume Co. Factory in 1886. Came with a registration card. 4691 bottles were made, the mold was broke at 3rd annual NAAC. Convention June 22, 1974 in Kansas City. OSP $11.95, CMV $55.

1977 NAAC CLUB BOTTLE
1906 AVON LADY

6th annual club bottled issued by the National Association of Avon Clubs. Made of porcelain and hand painted in the image of the 1906 Avon Lady. She stands 7½" high with yellow dress, brown hat and carrying the CPC Avon sales case of the period. Only 5517 were made & sold for $12.95 each. Came with NAAC registration certificate and is numbered on the bottom. CMV $40. - MB 100 sample bottles were given to each NAAC Club and are the same only they are numbered and marked club sample on bottom. CMV $110. Sample bottle.

1976-5th ANNUAL NAAC AVON CLUB BOTTLE

(Left) In the image of the 1896 CPC Avon lady. Blue dress, black bag, and blue feather in hat. Black hair. 5622 were made. Came with registration card and numbered on the bottom. OSP $12.95., CMV $45.

1976 BLOND AVON LADY

(Right) Of the 5622 regular issue 1896 lady, 120 had blond hair. CMV $225. on blond, rare.

1978 NAAC CLUB BOTTLE

7th Annual Club Bottle made in the image of the 1916 CPC Avon lady. She stands 7½" high with a rust colored coat and hat. Brown hair. Only 5022 were made. The bottle is numbered on the bottom and comes with a registration certificate. Made of hand painted porcelain. OSP $13.95, CMV $35. Club Sample was marked on the bottom of 125 club bottles given to each club in the NAAC. Sample bottles are same as regular issue only marked club sample. CMV $105.

1975-4th ANNUAL NAAC CLUB BOTTLE

The modern day Avon Lady is the 1975 Club bottle from the NAAC. Blue hand painted porcelain. Each bottle is numbered on bottom & came with registration card. 6232 were made. OSP $12.45, CMV $40.

1973-2nd NAAC McCONNELL CLUB BOTTLE

2nd annual Club Bottle issued by the NAAC Clubs in honor of Mr. & Mrs. D. H. McConnell founders of Avon. Registration certificate goes with the bottle. 5604 bottles were sold & numbered. OSP $11.95, CMV $80.

1980's NAAC CONVENTION BOTTLES

A series of 11 different Avon ladies dressed in their Sunday best of the 1890's style. To be issued 1 each year & sold only to members of NAAC Avon Collectors Clubs. All are hand painted porcelain, 5½'' high & very limited editions. Each bottle will have the total number sold on the bottom. You can be eligible to buy this beautiful set of bottles by joining the Bud Hastin Avon-Time's or any of the more than 150 NAAC clubs throughout the U.S. & Canada. Their value is sure to increase fast.

1979 NAAC CLUB BOTTLE
1926 AVON LADY

8th annual club bottle. Purple & black. Brown hat & shoes. 4749 were made & numbered on bottom. Came with certificate that says 4725. Actual count is 4749. OSP $14.95. CMV $40. 150 club samples were issued to NAAC Clubs. Bottom is marked club sample. CMV sample $105.

1980 NAAC CLUB BOTTLE
1936 AVON LADY

(Left) 9th annual club bottle. Purple dress, black bag. 7½'' high. 4479 were made & sold, & numbered on the bottom as total sold. Did not come with certificate, bottom cork. OSP $14.95. CMV $30. Same bottle came with blue bag & marked club sample on bottom. 155 club samples were made & given to NAAC clubs. CMV $120, blue bag club sample.

1981 NAAC CLUB BOTTLE
1946 AVON LADY

(Right) 10th annual club bottle. Only 3589 sold and made. Green dress, black bag, cork in bottom. OSP $15.95, CMV $30. 140 sample club bottles made and marked club sample on bottom. CMV $105.

1980 NAAC 1st CONVENTION BOTTLE

Sold only to NAAC club members. 1st in an annual series of NAAC Convention bottles to commemorate the annual NAAC Convention held in Spokane, Washington in 1980. 7½'' high, lavender dress of 1890's style. Hand painted porcelain. This bottle is the only one in the series that the cork is in the head, and 7½'' size. All rest are 5½'' size starting in 1981. The rest of the series will have a cork in the bottom to present a prettier bottle. Only 3593 were made & sold. OSP $14.95, CMV $30.

1982 NAAC 1st CONVENTION BOTTLE RE-ISSUE

Same as 1980 bottle only is 5½'' high to match rest of series in size. Only 1775 reissue bottles made. Reissued bottles sold in 1982. Cork in bottom. OSP $15., CMV $35. 150 club sample bottles were made & marked in the bottom of the 5½'' size. CMV $100.

1982 NAAC CLUB BOTTLE
1956 AVON LADY

(Left) 11th annual club bottle for NAAC club members. 7½'' high, red dress, bottom cork. Only 3000 made & sold. OSP $17, CMV $30. 150 club sample 1956 lady bottles made & marked on bottom. CMV $100. for club sample.

1983 NAAC CLUB BOTTLE
1966 AVON LADY

(Right) 12th annual club bottle. 7½'' high, hand painted porcelain bottle made only for the National Association of Avon Collectors in the image of dress of the 1966 Avon lady. She wears a black & white striped dress. Blue bag. 2,350 made, bottom cork. OSP $18, CMV $35. A new club bottle is issued each year to NAAC members only. 100 club samples made. CMV $100.

1981 NAAC 2nd CONVENTION BOTTLE
Long Beach, CA Convention. 5½" high hand painted porcelain bottle. Yellow & green dress of the 1800's style. Second in a series of 11 bottles of the 1800's style. Only 3128 were made & sold to NAAC club members. SSP $15. CMV $30.

1981 CONVENTION CLUB SAMPLE
140 club sample bottles were made for NAAC clubs. Each marked club sample on bottom & numbered 140 edition. CMV $100. club sample.

1982 NAAC 3rd CONVENTION BOTTLE
(Left) 3rd in a series of 1800's style dress. Blue dress, pink bag & hat trim, blond hair. 5½" high porcelain. Only 2205 bottles were made & sold to NAAC club members only. 1982 NAAC convention was held in Las Vegas, Nevada. SSP $15. CMV $30. Mint. No club samples were made.

1982 NAAC CONVENTION BELL
(Right) 1st issue - only 500 bells made in the same shape as the 1982 convention bottles. Only the dress colors are reversed. Pink dress & blue trim. You had to attend the 11th Annual NAAC Convention in Las Vegas, June 22-27-82 to get a bell. SSP $12, CMV $65.

1975 PLATE - NAAC BOARD MEMBER
(Left) 2" wide gold edge marked board member. Only 7 were issued. This was general issue plate. CMV $130.

1975 PLATE - NAAC BOARD MEMBER
(Right) White plate with small gold edge marked board member. Only 7 were made. This plate was never issued to public. CMV $130. - MB.

1976 3rd ANNUAL NAAC 5 YEAR AVON COLLECTORS PLATE
9 3/8" porcelain plate showing the 1st 4 NAAC club bottles. 1755 were made. OSP $13.95., CMV $35.

1974 NAAC PLATE
1st in an annual series of plates. Clear crystal thumb print plate with blue & red background. Only 790 plates were made. OSP $12.95., CMV $50.

1974 NAAC BOARD MEMBER PLATE
Same as regular issue only have Board Member on plate. CMV $135.

1975 NAAC SAMPLE PLATE
(Left) Sample plate never issued to general public. 84 were made and sent to each Avon Collectors Club in NAAC, numbered on the back. CMV $100. each.

2nd ANNUAL 1975 NAAC PLATE
(Right) General issue plate Mr. & Mrs. McConnell founders of Avon in center, gold 2 inch band around edge. OSP $12.95., CMV $35. - MB.

1977 NAAC 6 YEAR PLATE
1886 Avon lady on plate. Made by AVON Products for the National Association of Avon Clubs. A beautiful china plate. Total of 5000 were made with 1500 gold rimmed, and numbered. CMV $60. MB. 3500 were silver rimmed and not numbered. CMV $32.50. 7 plates marked board member CMV $125. - MB.

1978 NAAC 7 YEAR PLATE

Made by Avon Products for the National Association of Avon Clubs. A beautiful china plate with a decal of the 1906 Avon Sales Lady. Only 5000 were made, OSP $14.95. 2310 were gold rimmed plates, CMV $45. - MB, and 2690 are silved rimmed plates, CMV $35. - MB. 7 made for board members. CMV $125. - MB. Rare issue plate with backward printing on back, CMV $60. - MB.

1980 NAAC PLATE
1916 AVON LADY

Limited edition of 4000. Came with gold edge & number on the back. 2060 made. CMV $30. Or silver edge, 1940 made, & no number $30. MB. Made by Avon Products exclusively for the NAAC. OSP $14.95. 7 plates made marked board members, CMV $125.

1972 NAAC CONVENTION MIRROR

Only 300 made, given at banquet, also some were made with pins instead of mirrors. These were dealers badges, CMV $25. each.

1974 NAAC CONVENTION BANQUET MIRROR

(Left) Yellow and black, mirror on backside. Convention held in Kansas City, Mo. June 22, 1974. CMV $15.

1975 NAAC CONVENTION BANQUET MIRROR

(Right) Blue and black, mirror on back. Convention held in Anaheim, Calif. June 21, 1975. CMV $10. Both were given to each person attending the annual NAAC Avon Convention Banquet.

1979 NAAC PLATE
1896 AVON LADY

Limited edition of 5000. Made by Avon Products exclusively for the NAAC. Came with gold edge & numbered on the back. CMV $37.50. MB, and silver edge & no number. CMV $27.50. MB., OSP $14.95 sold only by NAAC clubs. 7 plates made-marked board members, CMV $125.

1981 NAAC PLATE
1926 AVON LADY

Limited edition of 2000. Gold rim. Marked on back. OSP $20., CMV $35. MB.

1981 NAAC BOARD MEMBER PLATE

Same plate as above only back is marked 1981 board member sample. Only 7 were made this way for NAAC board of directors. CMV $100. MB.

1976-83 NAAC CONVENTION GOBLETS

Different color goblet sold each year at NAAC Convention. 1st year, red, 1976, 276 made. CMV $60. 1977, blue, 560 made. CMV $30. 1978, smoke, 560 made. CMV $20. 1979, clear, 576 made. CMV $15. 1980, purple, 576 made. CMV $15. OSP was $4 to $6 each. 1978-83 a special marked goblet given to each NAAC delegate. CMV $25. Less than 100 delegate goblets made each year. Special marked goblets were made for each 7 NAAC board members. CMV for board member goblet's $100. each year. 1981 - 684 goblets made CMV $15. 1982 — 700 made CMV $15. 1983 - 322 made, CMV $25. 1983 is last year goblets made.

1982 NAAC PLATE

Only 2,000 made and numbered 6th in a series of the 1936 Avon lady. SSP $25., CMV $35.

1976 NAAC CONVENTION BANQUET MIRROR

(Left) 5th annual Avon collectors convention mirror in white with blue letters. Held in Cincinnati, Ohio June 25-27, 1976. Mirror on back. CMV $10.

1977 NAAC CONVENTION BANQUET MIRROR

(Right) 6th annual Avon collectors convention mirror in blue with yellow letters. Mirror on back. Hollywood, Florida, June, 1977. CMV $10.

1978 NAAC CONVENTION BANQUET MIRROR
(Left) Purple with mirror on back. Given to over 500 who attended the Avon Collectors Convention Banquet in Houston, Texas, June 1978, CMV $10.

1979 NAAC CONVENTION BANQUET MIRROR
(Right) White & red, mirror on back. Given to over 500 people attending the annual Avon Collectors Convention Banquet in St. Louis, Mo June 1979. CMV $10.

1980 PRESIDENTS GOLD SET
Set of six different U.S. Presidents Bust, with antique brush gold finish. Only 250 sets made & issued by Bud Hastin Avon Club, OSP $70. set, CMV $130. set MB.

1977 AVON LADY MINI SET NO. 2
1265 sets of 11 miniature Avon ladies of the 1886—1900 period. Issued by the Bud Hastin National Avon Club (now called Avon Times) in 1977. Set came in special display box. Came with numbered registration certificate. Sold only to Bud Hastins National Avon Club members. OSP $60. set, CMV $130. MB.

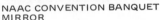

NAAC CONVENTION BANQUET MIRROR
Only 500 of each made for annual NAAC Convention Banquet. 1980 — Spokane, Washington, 1981 — Queen Mary, Long Beach, Ca. 1982 — Las Vegas, Nevada. CMV $10. each.

1976 BICENTENNIAL MINI AVON LADY SET NO. 1
10 exact replicas in 3'' high miniature figurines of the larger NAAC Club bottles. Issued by the Bud Hastin National Avon Club (now called Avon Times). 1775 sets were made and come with a numbered registration certificate. OSP $60. for set of 10. CMV $135. MB.

1978 PRESIDENTS
A set of 6 3'' high bust figurines of the 1st five presidents of the United States, plus Lincoln. Only 1050 sets made. Hand painted porcelain and came with a numbered registration card. Sold only to members of the Bud Hastin National Avon Club. OSP for set of 6 $40., CMV $85.

1978 PRESIDENTS ALL WHITE
Same set as painted presidents above only all white porcelain. Only 150 sets made. OSP $40., CMV $160.

1974 BUD HASTIN NATIONAL AVON CLUB BOTTLE

1st issue Club Bottle by Bud Hastin Avon Club (now called Avon Times) is a 3 piece Avon Family Scene. 3 separate bottles showing the Man, Child & Woman Avon Collectors. 1091 sets sold. OSP $45. per set. Sold in sets only. CMV $145.

1974—75 AVON ENCYCLOPEDIA HARD BOUND COLLECTOR'S EDITION

Only 1000 special limited collectors edition was printed. Blue hard bound cover with gold stamped letters on front. Each is signed and numbered by Bud Hastin. OSP $20., CMV $32.50 mint.

1976—77 AVON ENCYCLOPEDIA HARD BOUND 2nd COLLECTORS EDITION

Only 500 special limited collectors editions were printed. Maroon hard bound cover with gold stamped letters on front. Each book is numbered and signed by Bud Hastin. OSP $20., CMV $30. mint. 6 hard bounds were found with all pages upside down. Each was signed by Bud Hastin as 1 of 6 rare upside down books. Very rare, CMV $40.

1979 AVON ENCYCLOPEDIA HARD BOUND 3rd COLLECTORS EDITION

Only 350 special limited hard bound editions were printed. Blue hard bound covers with gold letters on front. Each book will be signed and numbered by Bud Hastin. OSP $22.50, CMV $30.

1976 AVON ENCYCLOPEDIA COVER SHEET REJECTS

30,000 covers for the 1976 Avon Encyclopedia were printed with the word Encyclopedia spelled Encylopedia. The covers were never used but about 200 sheets were given to collectors with 4 covers and backs printed on a sheet. These sheets are rare. The rest of the covers were destroyed. CMV $15. each sheet.

1976 BUD HASTIN NATIONAL AVON CLUB BOTTLE

2nd issue. Hand painted porcelain made in the image of Mr. Dale Robinson, past director of National Association of Avon Clubs. 1000 bottles made & numbered. OSP $14.95, CMV $40.

1974 GOLD COAST CLUB BOTTLE

Issued in honor of Mr. Bud Hastin for his contribution to the field of Avon collecting. 1st in an annual series. Only 2340 bottles were made. Bottle is 8½" high, white pants, maroon coat, black turtle neck shirt, black shoes. Few were made with white shirt. Rare. OSP $11.95, CMV black shirt $60. CMV white shirt $115.

1977 MINI RED HEAD SET

965 sets of Something Old - Something New made. Issued by Bud Hastins National Avon Club with registration card. 3½" high, 1886 Avon lady on left has green purse and red hair. 1975 Avon lady on right has red hair & Avon Calling is misspelled on base of figurine. OSP $12. set. Sold as set only. CMV $35.

1975 WORLD WIDE JO OLSEN AVON CLUB BOTTLE

(Left) Light blue dress, black hair. 1102 bottles sold. Made in the image of Jo Olsen for her contribution to Avon collecting. OSP $12.95., CMV $40.

1975 GOLD COAST RON PRICE CLUB BOTTLE

(Right) Green suit, brown hair and shoes. Holding book "Testing 1-2-3". 1096 bottles sold. Made in the image of Mr. Ron Price for his contribution to the field of Avon collecting. Mr. Ron price was a member of Board of Directors of the NAAC. Mr. Price passed away in 1977. OSP $12.95., CMV $40.

1976 GOLD COAST MINIS

A set of 3 miniature figurines 3½" high in the image of Bud Hastin, Jo Olsen, and Ron Price. The set sold 914 sets at $18. per set., CMV $40. per set.

1977 CLINT GOLD COAST CLUB BOTTLE

7-5/8" tall. Blue pants, shirt, jacket. Black shoes, brown hair. 1264 made & numbered on the bottom. Came with registration card. 4th Annual Club Bottle. OSP $13.95., CMV $32.50.

NAAC CONVENTION PLATES

Made by Mid-America Avon Club as the official NAAC Convention souvenir plate each year. Very low issue on each. All are etched clear glass & signed by the artist. OSP was $12.95 each. 1975 Orange County, CA - CMV $30. 1977 Hollywood, FL - CMV $30. 1978 Houston, TX - CMV $25. 1979 St. Louis, MO - CMV $25. 1980 Spokane, WASH - CMV $25. 1981 Long Beach, CA - CMV $25. 1982 Las Vegas, NEV - CMV $25.

1983 Wilmington, DE — CMV $25.

1975 CALIFORNIA PERFUME ANNIVERSARY KEEPSAKE MOLD

This is the actual steel mold Avon used to make the 1975 Anniversary Keepsake bottle. Mr. Art Goodwin from Avon Productions, Inc. New York presented this mold cut into 5 separate pieces to the National Association of Avon Clubs at the 4th annual NAAC Convention banquet at Anaheim, Calif. June 19, 1975. The mold was auctioned off bringing several hundred dollars on each piece. This is the 1st time an Avon mold has been destroyed & given to the general public. Very rare. CMV $600. each piece.

1972 MID AMERICA NAAC CONVENTION PLATE

(Left) Clear glass with frosted lettering, 134 were made for the 1st annual NAAC Convention in Kansas City, Kansas, June 1972. This plate was not made until 1975. OSP $12.95, CMV $30.

1973 CENTRAL VALLEY NAAC CONVENTION PLATE

(Right) Clear glass, frosted lettering. 124 were made and sold for 2nd annual NAAC Convention at Sacremento, Calif. This plate was not made until 1975. OSP $12.95., CMV $30.

1974 MID-AMERICAN NAAC CONVENTION PLATE

(Left) Crystal plate with frosted inscription made in honor of the 3rd NAAC Convention by Mid-America Club. 225 were made. OSP $12.95., CMV $30.

1976 QUEEN CITY NAAC CONVENTION PLATE

(Right) Clear glass with frosted letters. OSP $12.95., CMV $25.

1979 ST. LOUIE BLUE PERFUME

Small glass bottle, white cap. Special perfume made & given by Mid-America Avon Club & NAAC at NAAC Convention in St. Louis, June 1979. 231 bottles with registration card & envelope. CMV $20. mint & about 120 bottles only given without envelope & card. CMV $10. BO.

1977 NAAC CONVENTION DELEGATE PLATE

White china plate with the date & place of 6 NAAC Annual Conventions. Given to each NAAC Club delegate attending the convention "85 plates" CMV $50. 7 board member plates were made the same only marked board member. CMV $75.

1976 BETSY ROSS MOLD

(Left) Very rare steel mold given to Avon Collectors at 1976 NAAC Convention. Mold was cut into 5 pieces. Must have a letter from Avon Products stating it is 1 of a kind. CMV $500. with letter.

1976 ANNIVERSARY KEEPSAKE MOLD BASE

(Right) Steel base of Avons anniversary keepsake mold given to National Association of Avon Clubs by Avon Products and auctioned off to Avon collectors. The numbers (17) and 5215 on bottom. CMV $500.

1975 NAAC CONVENTION PLATE

Only 250 made for 4th annual NAAC Convention, Anaheim, Calif. OSP $12.95., CMV $25.

1974-75 NAAC STATIONERY
Blue box with NAAC logo on top. Back of box is signed by all board members of NAAC. Only 214 boxes of stationery made & each is numbered. OSP $7., CMV $20. MB.

1974 NAAC CONVENTION SOUVENIRS
Pin, CMV $2. Each year the mold for the annual NAAC club bottle is broken at the NAAC banquet and distributed to each person attending. 1974 piece of mold and card for NAAC club bottle. Distributed at convention banquet. Overland Park, Kansas, June 22, 1974. CMV $10. 1975 piece of mold and card for NAAC club bottle. Distributed at convention banquet Anaheim, California, June 21, 1975. CMV $10.

1976 BETSY ROSS NAAC CONVENTION SOUVENIR
Given by Avon Products to all collectors touring Avon plant in Springdale, Ohio June 24, 1976. Special NAAC label on bottom. CMV $17.50 with special label.

1975-76 NAAC AVON CHESS BOARD
21½" square plastic chess board made for the Avon chess pieces. Silver & brown checker top with black rim border & back. NAAC logo in center, silver over black. 105 were made for sample to each NAAC club with center gold logo over black. 1,500 are numbered & last 1,000 are not numbered on back. CMV gold logo $200. MB - regular issue silver logo with number $70. MB - black border no number $50. MB. OSP $19.95 MB. Also came brown border with large black logo in center. CMV $40. MB. Last one to be issued had brown border & 4 small logos in center, brown back. CMV $40.

1979 NAAC CONVENTION SOUVENIRS
Each item was sold or given to collectors at annual St. Louis NAAC Convention. Most are very limited & hard to find. Luggage Tag - CMV $2.; pen, brass - CMV $2.; monthly minder Christmas 1980 - CMV $5.; matches, NAAC - CMV 50c.

1975 THE KING II "FOR MEN"
(Left) Special label reads "Souvenir, June 19, 1975 NAAC Tour Monrovia Avon Plant. Given to each male taking the Avon plant tour at NAAC Convention, Monrovia, California. Only 150 bottles have this label. CMV $17.50.
1975 SKIP-A-ROPE "FOR LADIES"
(Right) Same special label given to all ladies on same tour. CMV $17.50.

1976 NAAC FREEDOM DOCUMENTS
Souvenir booklet sold by NAAC at Cincinnati, Ohio, June 20-27, 1976. CMV $5. mint.

1978 NAAC CONVENTION SOUVENIRS
Convention Packet, green plastic. CMV $8. Monthly Minder 1979. CMV $5. Magnifying Glass. CMV $1. All items given or sold at Houston, Texas, 1978 NAAC Convention.

1973 NAAC CONVENTION SOUVENIRS
A few souvenir items were sold at the convention. They are: matchbook, black letters on yellow cover (CMV $1.); a yellow ball point pen, with black lettering (CMV $1.); a green pennant with yellow letters that read "NAAC Convention 73" (CMV $1.50).

1975 NAAC CONVENTION SOUVENIRS

Given to each delegate & board member at NAAC convention in Anaheim, California, June 19, 1975. Blue engraved plastic packet holds package of NAAC stationery, memo pad - blue (250 made CMV $5.), perfumed nips on engraved card (250 made, CMV $5.), and yellow delegate ribbon, Board Member nominee gray ribbon, National Director red ribbon, Chairman purple ribbon, Board Member green ribbon, Historian white ribbon - CMV $10. each ribbon.

1973 CONVENTION DELEGATES RIBBON

(Left) Red ribbon with a red rosette was given to all delegates. Gold printing reads "Official Delegate National Association Avon Clubs Convention Sacramento, California, June 22, 1973" CMV $8.

1973 CONVENTION BOARD MEMBER RIBBON

(Not Shown) Same as the delegate ribbon only in blue instead of red. Board Member replaced the Official Delegate on the ribbon. CMV $15.

1973 CONVENTION NATIONAL CHAIRMAN RIBBON

(Right) Same as the Delegate ribbon only in maroon instead of red. Only one of these ribbons was made. It is owned by Mr. Bud Hastin. No value established.

1972 NAAC CONVENTION SOUVENIR BADGE

(Center) Round, light blue background with first CPC Lady in center. Has pin back. CMV $10.

1973 NAAC CONVENTION SOUVENIR BADGE

(Not Shown) Same except has photo of Mr. & Mrs. McConnell. CMV $5.

1974 NAAC RIBBONS

(Not Shown) All are same CMV as 1973 ribbons.

1977 NAAC CONVENTION SOUVENIRS

Each year at the annual NAAC Avon Collectors Convention a ribbon is given to each club delegate and each board member and alternate delegate. 1976 Cincinnati, Ohio, ribbon has the 1896 Avon lady on the rosette. 1977 ribbon for Hollywood, Florida, has the 1906 Avon lady. Also issued at the convention were book marks in white, green, blue, red; glass ash trays; pocket knife; NAAC pin; blue daily reminder book. We are not going to price these items as very few are around and you can only get them by attending the annual Collectors Convention. Prices will be set by public trading. A marble paper weight given by the Gold Coast Host Club is CMV $15. Piece of 1906 Avon lady club bottle mold & registration card was given. CMV $10. NAAC plastic brief case with logo.

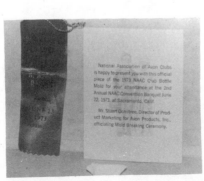

1973 NAAC CONVENTION BANQUET RIBBON

(Left) Blue ribbon, rare. CMV $10.

1973 NAAC CLUB BOTTLE MOLD PIECE

(Right) Piece of mold from 1973 NAAC club bottle & card. CMV $10.

1984 SUPPLEMENT

NAAC CLUB BOTTLES

1983 NAAC 4th CONVENTION BOTTLE
5½" high, bottom cork. Rust & brown color hand painted porcelain. 4th in a series of Avon ladies of the 1890's to commemorate the NAAC Avon Collectors Convention in Wilmington, DE in June 1983. Only 1,875 made. Total number sold marked on bottom. SSP $15., CMV $30. 150 club samples made & marked club sample. 1 of 150 on bottom. CMV $100.

1983 2nd NAAC CONVENTION BELL
Same as 1983 Convention bottle only dress colors are reversed and bottom is open as bell. Bottom label, only 500 made. SSP, $15, CMV $40. Bells created and sold by Bud Hastin.

1984 NAAC 5th CONVENTION BOTTLE
5½" high porcelain bottle, bottom cork. Brown dress, yellow and black umbrella. 1,650 made. 5th in a series of 11 convention bottles to be sold thru NAAC clubs of the Avon ladies of the 1890's for NAAC Avon Collectors 13th Annual Convention in Kansas City, MO June 1984. SSP $15. CMV $30. 100 NAAC Club Samples made and marked Club Sample on bottom. 1 of 100. CMV $100 club samples.

1984 3rd NAAC CONVENTION BELL
Same as 1984 NAAC Convention bottle only dress & umbrella colors reversed & bottom is open as bell. Bottom label. Only 500 made for Kansas City, NAAC Convention. Bells created & sold by Bud Hastin. SSP $16 - CMV $35.

1984 NAAC CLUB BOTTLE 1984 AVON REPRESENTATIVE
13th annual club bottle 7½" high, hand painted porcelain. Gray pants suit, pink blouse, red hair. Brown bag says Avon. Bottom cork. Choice of a white or black representative. Only amount made will be sold. SSP $20, CMV $35. 1985 NAAC clubs will offer the male Rep. bottle.

MEN'S DECANTERS— FIGURINES

1982-83 GENTLEMEN'S REGIMENT COLLECTION
TALC in beige tin can. SSP $5 no box, - CMV $5.
SHAVING MUG AND SOAP
Beige color glass mug and matching bar of soap. SSP $15 - CMV $15 MB.
SHAVING BRUSH
Beige plastic brush. SSP $9 - CMV $9 MB.
AFTER SHAVE DECANTER
4.5 oz. clear glass painted beige. Gold cap. SSP $10 - CMV $10 MB. Fragrance choice was Wild Country or Black Suede.

1983 NAAC PLATE
9" porcelain plate of the 1946 Avon Lady on face. Only 1,125 made. Label on back. SSP $25., CMV $35.

1983 NAAC BOARD MEMBER PLATE
Same as regular issue only back has special label marked "NAAC Board Member Sample." Only 7 made with each board member name on back. CMV $100.

1983 NAAC CONVENTION BANQUET MIRROR
Only 500 small mirrors for the 12th annual Avon Collectors Convention in Wilmington, DE, 1983. CMV $10.

1984 REPORT CARD DAY FIGURINE
3rd in series of Benjamin J. Bearington. Pewter figurines, 2" high. SSP $13 - CMV $8.

1983-84 — 1932 AUBURN BOATTAIL SPEEDSTER
1st in series. Black & red ceramic car figurine. 8½" long. Dated 1983. SSP $29.50 - CMV $20 MB.

1982-83 MINIATURE STEINS
4½" to 5½" high ceramic steins. Choice of Tall Ships, Vintage Cars or Flying Classics. Each numbered and dated 1982. SSP $13 - CMV $13 each MB.

1983 FIRST DAY BACK FIGURINE
1¾" high pewter metal bear figurine. SSP $13 - CMV $8 MB.
1983 HARD AT WORK FIGURINE
2" high pewter metal bear figurine. SSP $13 - CMV $8 MB.

1983-84 SPORTING MINIATURE STEIN
5" tall ceramic stein. Hunting scene on side. SSP $13 - CMV $13 MB.

1983-84 GREAT AMERICAN FOOTBALL STEIN
9" high ceramic stein made in Brazil. Metal flip top. SSP $40 - CMV $30 MB.

1983 ALL AMERICAN SPORTS FAN MUG & POPCORN
5½" high clear glass mug with red, white and blue design. Comes with red and blue cannister of popcorn. SSP $8 - CMV $8 set MB, or $3 mug only.

1982-84 AGE OF THE IRON HORSE STEIN
8½" ceramic stein made in Brazil. Numbered and dated. Metal top. Has train design on side. Sold empty. SSP $40 - CMV $25 MB.

1983-84 WESTERN ROUND UP MINI STEIN
5" high mini ceramic tan and white stein, made in Brazil and numbered on bottom. Cowboys on side. SSP $13 - CMV $13 MB.
1983-84 ENDANGERED SPECIES MINI STEIN
Blue and white 5" mini stein, moose and goat on side. SSP $13 - CMV $13 MB.

1983 BIG SHOT MUG — TEST AREA
Chrome plated brass jigger about 2½ inches high. Comes with or without stick on initials. Sold only in Test Area in midwest. OSP $13 - CMV $25 in white test box.

1983 DAD'S BREW CRACKERS
7'' high paper sides can holds Dad's Crackers. SSP $7 - CMV $7 mint.

1983-84 DUCK SERIES
6 different hand painted metal ducks. 4'' long, 2'' high. SSP $13 each - CMV $10 each MB.
1983-84 DUCK DISPLAY RACK
12½'' long two tier wood rack to display all six duck figurines. SSP $15 - CMV $10 MB.

1982 Only — "ON THE ROAD AGAIN" PRODUCTS
Each green and white with license plates design. Choice of talc, lather shave cream or Anti Perspirant Deodorant in Wild Country fragrance. No boxes. SSP $1 each - CMV $1 each.

WOMEN'S DECANTERS—FIGURINES

1983-84 VICTORIAN COLLECTOR DOLL
8'' high 19th century doll with porcelain head, arms and legs. Comes with metal stand. Fancy box. SSP $24.50 - CMV $24.50 MB.

1983-84 IMAGES OF HOLLYWOOD — SCARLETT O'HARA
1st in a series porcelain figurine, 4½'' high. Vivian Leigh as Scarlett O'Hara SSP $32.50 - CMV $25 MB.
1983 GOOD LUCK BELL
4½'' high porcelain elf on flower bell. SSP $15 - CMV $15 MB.

1984-85 RHETT BUTLER FIGURINE
Clark Gable figurine, 5¾'' high. SSP $32.50 - CMV $25 MB.

1983 MOM'S PRIDE AND JOY PICTURE FRAME
6½"x 2" clear glass MOM frame. SSP $10 - CMV $10 MB.

1983 LOVE MUG JELLY BEANS
3½" high ceramic mug filled with 8 oz. of jelly beans. Some mugs came with Heart on bottom and no date or lettering and some came with heart on bottom and dated 1983 in red letters. SSP $10 - CMV $10 MB.

1983-84 VICTORIANA PICTURE FRAME
4½"x 5¼" size metal frame. Fancy box. SSP $16.50 - CMV $10 MB.

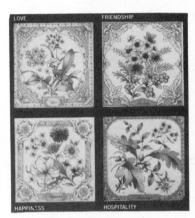

1983 FLORAL EXPRESSIONS CERAMIC TILES
6" square ceramic tiles made in England. Flower design and four different colors. Love, Happiness, Friendship or Hospitality. SSP $10 - CMV $10 MB each.

1982-83 EMERALD ACCENT COLLECTION
DECANTER — 10" high, clear glass, green glass stopper. SSP $15 - CMV $15 MB.
CORDIAL GLASSES — Set of two clear glasses with green glass stems, 4½" high. SSP $13 - CMV $13 MB set.
SERVING TRAY — 11½" long green glass tray. SSP $15 - CMV $15 MB.

1983-84 MEMORIES PORCELAIN MUSIC BOX
White 4¼" long porcelain box with music box in lid. SSP $27.50 - CMV $27.50 MB.

1983 IMAGE OF LOVE PAPERWEIGHT
4" wide clear glass heart, red felt bottom. SSP $10 - CMV $10 MB.

1983 SUMMER FANTASY COLLECTION
TRAY — 12" tin tray, red and green design. SSP $9 - CMV $9 MB.
GLASSES — Set of two. 15 oz. drinking glasses. SSP $10 - CMV $10 MB set.
CANDLE — 3½" high white tin can. Refillable candle. Green and red design. SSP $10 - CMV $10 MB.

1983-84 AMERICAN HEIRLOOM PORCELAIN BOWL
6" across, 4" high porcelain bowl. Plastic stand. Flower design on bowl. SSP $17.50 - CMV $17.50 MB.

1982-84 WISHFUL THOUGHTS FIGURINE
5½" porcelain figurine. 1st issue dated "1982". Blue dress, green base, pink ribbon in hair. SSP $22.50 - CMV $22.50 MB.

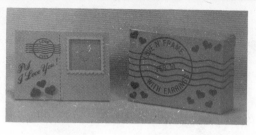

1984 LOVE N' FRAME WITH EARRINGS
Pink box and pink plastic postcard frame and two red heart shaped earrings. SSP $6 - CMV $3 MB.

1982 NATIVITY "THREE WISE MEN"
(left to right) All are white bisque porcelain. The Magi Kaspar, The Magi Melchior, The Magi Balthasar. SSP $19.50 each - CMV $19.50 each MB.

1983-84 MOTHERS DAY FIGURINE "LITTLE THINGS"
(left) 3¾" high hand painted porcelain boy figurine. SSP $18 - CMV $18 MB.

1983-84 MOTHERS DAY FIGURINE "CHERISHED MOMENTS"
(right) 4" high hand painted porcelain girl figurine. SSP $18 - CMV $18 MB.

1982 McCONNELLS CORNER TOWN TREE
6" high ceramic tree, green and white. Dated "Christmas 1982". SSP $12 - CMV $12 MB.

1983 NATIVITY COLLECTION
All are white porcelain
SHEPHERD — 6½" high, SSP $22.50 CMV $22.50 MB.
SHEEP — 4" long. SSP $13.50 - CMV $13.50
SHEPHERD BOY — 4¾" high. SSP $19.50 - CMV $19.50 MB

1982 McCONNELLS CORNER GENERAL STORE
5½" ceramic box, roof lifts off. Dated "Christmas 1982". SSP $24 - CMV $18 MB.

1982 KEEPING THE CHRISTMAS TRADITION
Hand painted procelain figurine dated 1982. 2nd in Christmas Memories Series. SSP $49.50 - CMV $30 MB.

1983 CHRISTMAS PORCELAIN FIGURINE
5½" high hand painted porcelain figurine. Called "Enjoying the Night Before Christmas." Dated Christmas 1983. SSP $52.50 - CMV $35 MB.

1982 COUNTRY CHRISTMAS ORNAMENT & CANDY SET
Box held three red, green and gold ornament boxes with peppermint candy and candy sticks. SSP $9 - CMV $9 MB.

1983 MELVIN P. MERRYMOUSE KEEPSAKE ORNAMENT
2¾" high Santa mouse on sleigh. Dated 1983. Plastic, 2nd in a series. SSP $10 - CMV $10 MB.

1983-84 SANTA'S SEESAW TREE ORNAMENT
Small Santa and elves, plastic ornament. SSP $8 - CMV $8 MB.

1983-84 WINTER FUN "IGLOO" TREE ORNAMENT
White plastic igloo with eskimo family around tree. SSP $8 - CMV $8 MB.

1982 SEASONAL SCENTS FRAGRANCE ORNAMENTS
Three different scented plastic ornaments. Snow flake, blue; sleigh, red; jingle bells, amber. SSP $4 each - CMV $2.50 each MB.

1983 HAPPY HOLIDAYS ORNAMENT
Small brown, red and white plastic Kangaroo tree ornament. SSP $5 - CMV $5 MB.

1982 CHRISTMAS REMEMBRANCE ANGEL
White ceramic angel, gold tassel. Comes in white felt bag. SSP $9 - CMV $9 MB.

1982 NESTLED TOGETHER ORNAMENT
(left) Small nest with two blue birds and red and white hat. SSP $7 - CMV $4 MB.

1982 MELVIN P. MERRYMOUSE ORNAMENT
(center) Small plastic mouse Santa. Back of mirror says Avon Christmas, 1982. SSP $10 - CMV $6 MB.

1982 McCONNELLS CORNER TOWN SHOPPERS
(right) 3" high ceramic figurine. Bottom says Christmas, 1982. SSP $10 - CMV $5 MB.

1983-84 MRS. CLAUS SUGAR BOWL
Red, white and green ceramic sugar bowl. SSP $13 - CMV $13 MB.

1983-84 SANTA CLAUS CREAMER
Red, white and green ceramic creamer. SSP $13 - CMV $13 MB.

1983 SNOWFLAKE ORNAMENT
(left) White porcelain snowflake dated 1983. 2½'' wide on gold tassel SSP $8 - CMV $8 MB.

1983 CAPTURED MOMENTS FRAME ORNAMENT
(right) Green and red plastic wreath. Slide a picture in center. 4'' across. SSP $4 - CMV $4 MB.

1983 PEACE ON EARTH ANGELS ORNAMENT SET
Box holds 5 porcelain angels to hang on Christmas tree. Each angel 2½'' wide. SSP $37.50 - CMV $30 set MB.

1983 BUNNY MATES SALT & PEPPER SHAKERS
Bunny box holds two small ceramic white rabbit shakers. SSP $12 - CMV $12 MB.

1983 CLAUS & COMPANY SANTA'S HELPERS SALT & PEPPER SHAKERS
Red box holds two small green and red ceramic boy and girl salt & pepper shakers. 2½'' high. SSP $10 - CMV $10 MB.

1983 JOLLY JELLY BEANS
4'' high paper cartons with 1.5 oz. of jelly beans. Choice of Rudolph or Santa carton. SSP 90c each - CMV $1 each mint.

1984 PIERRE HAND LOTION DECANTER
8 oz. white glass pig. Cloth Apron on front. Holds Care Deeply Hand Lotion. SSP $10 - CMV $10 MB.

1982-83 STYLISH LADY DECANTER
8 oz. white glass pig with white and pink pump top. Choice of Country Orchard Liquid Cleanser or Moisturizer Hand Lotion. SSP $9 - CMV $9 MB.

1979-80 SWEET DREAMS
1.25 oz. blue frosted over clear glass. White plastic boys head cap. Holds Zany or Somewhere cologne. SSP $5 CMV $5 MB.

1982 CHRISTMAS THIMBLE
(left) White porcelain, dated 1982

1981 CHRISTMAS THIMBLE
(right) Issued in 1982, but dated 1981. SSP $9 each - CMV $5 each MB.

1978-79 SILVER FAWN COLOGNE DECANTER
.5 oz. silver coated over clear glass. Choice of Sweet Honesty or Charisma cologne. SSP $2 - CMV $2 BO, $3 MB.

1983-84 AMERICAN FASHION THIMBLES
All are 2" high, hand painted porcelain, and dated 1983 inside. Boxed in felt bag. (left to right) 1927 blue; 1928 tan; 1923 lavender. SSP $10 each - CMV $10 each, MB. Wood display rack made for 8 thimbles. SSP $13 - CMV $13 MB.

1983 CHRISTMAS THIMBLE
(far right) Small white porcelain thimble with decal. 1983 Christmas in gold. SSP $9 - CMV $9 MB.

1983 AMERICAN FASHION THIMBLE DISPLAY RACK
12½" long mahogany rack with 8 pegs. Can hang on wall or sit on shelf. SSP $13 CMV - $13 MB.

1982 AMERICAN 1890's FASHION THIMBLE
(left) 2" high porcelain, blue.

1982 AMERICAN 1900's FASHION THIMBLE
(right) 2" high porcelain, purple and pink. Both came in gray felt bag & box. SSP $10 each - CMV $10 MB each.

1984-85 AMERICAN FASHION THIMBLE 1942 EDITION
2" high porcelain thimble. 7th in a series of eight. SSP $10 - CMV $10 MB.

1983-84 - 1938 AMERICAN FASHION THIMBLE
2" high hand painted procelain thimble. Blue and white dress, red hair. SSP $10 - CMV $10 MB.

1983 HEART STRINGS DECANTER
(left) .5 oz. red glass with gold cap. Choice of three fragrances. SSP $3 - CMV $3 MB.

1982-83 AUTUMN SCURRY "SQUIRREL"
(center) .5 oz. clear glass squirrel, gold cap. Choice of Moonwind, Topaze or Charisma cologne. SSP $2.25 - CMV $2.25 MB.

1982-83 ULTRA COLLECTION COLOGNE SPRAY
(left) .5 oz. clear glass, black cap. Choice of Timeless, Candid, Ariane, Tasha, Foxfire or Odyssey. SSP $2 - CMV 25c MB.

1982-83 WRITE TOUCH MOUSE
(left) 1 oz. green glass and white plastic mouse with stick on decals. Choice of Sweet Honesty or Charisma cologne. SSP $6 - CMV $6 MB.

1982 FRAGRANCE NOTABLES
(center) .5 oz. clear glass with ribbon design. Red cap and box. Choice of Wild Jasmine, Occur, Moonwind, Charisma, Topaze or Sweet Honesty cologne. SSP $1.50 - CMV $1.50 MB.

1982 CRYSTALLIQUE TREE DECANTER
(right) .5 oz. clear glass tree bottle with bronze color cap. Choice of Foxfire, Timeless or Odyssey cologne. SSP $3 - CMV $3 MB.

1984 VALENTINE BANK & TRUST CHOCOLATE
Red heart design box holds red check book design inter box with 6½ inch chocolate bar in design of bank check. Comes with small pink tube of frosting. Keep cool or will melt. SSP $7 - CMV $7 MB.

1983 FRAGRANCE KEEPSAKE COLOGNES
.5 oz. fan shaped clear glass, with rose red cap. Choice of Somewhere, Here's My Heart, Regence, Rapture, Persian Wood, Brocade, Cotillion. SSP $2 - CMV $2 MB.

1983-84 GINGERBREAD COTTAGE DECANTER
.5 oz. dark amber glass, pink cap. Choice of Sweet Honesty or Charisma cologne. 2'' high. SSP $3 - CMV $3 MB.

1983 LOVE IS SWEET CHOCOLATE HEART
Pink and blue box holds real 4 oz. chocolate candy heart. Must be kept cool or will melt. SSP $7 - CMV $7 MB.

1983 CANDY CANE TREAT EARRINGS
(left) Red and white cane box holds 6'' candy cane and 2 small matching candy cane earrings. SSP $5 - CMV $5 MB.

1983 HOLIDAY GREETINGS CHRISTMAS CANDY
(right) Box holds bag of hard candy. SSP $4 - CMV $4 MB.

1983 SPIRIT OF CHRISTMAS MINT WREATHS
Christmas scene box with see through outer sleeve holds 20 green cream mint candies. SSP $4 - CMV $4 MB.

1982 SEASON'S GREETINGS CHOCOLATE WREATH
4 oz. chocolate wreath sold two campaigns only. This will be very rare as it melts easy. SSP $7 - CMV $4 MB.

1983 PANSY PATCH MINTS
Box holds matching 5" tin can filled with mint candy. SSP $9 - CMV $9 MB.

1982-83 LIP TOPPING LIP GLOSS
Tin box holds choice of chocolate fudge or butterscotch. SSP $1.50 each - CMV $1.50 each.

POMANDERS

1984 MERRY MESSENGER POMETTE
Choice of three different small pomettes.
HAPPY BIRTHDAY MOUSE
THANK YOU RABBIT
KOALA BEAR
Each 1½" to 2" high in display boxes. SSP $4 - CMV $4 each MB.

1982-83 WOODLAND CHARMERS MINI POMANDERS
Small wax figurines. Came in Raccoons, Turtle & Rabbit, Skunk in flower basket. SSP $7 each - CMV $7 each MB.

1982-83 SANTA'S HELPERS POMANDER
Wax elves, choice of girl in red and green or boy. SSP $7 - CMV $7 each MB.

1983-84 CAT NAPPER CERAMIC POMANDER
4" long ceramic cat in basket pomander. Comes with pack of Meadow Morn wax chips. SSP $13 - CMV $13 MB.
1983-84 NATURAL BLEND POTPOURRI
Pink paper box holds dried flowers. SSP $10 - CMV $3 MB.
1983-84 NATURAL BLEND POTPOURRI REFRESHER
Small pink spray container, SSP $3 - CMV $1

1983 LITTLEST BOO POMETTE
1¾" high orange and white pumpkin and ghost wax pomander. SSP $3 - CMV $3 MB.
1983 PUPPY LUV POMETTE
2¼" high wax dog with red heart. SSP $3 - CMV $3 MB.

CANDLES

1983 CALICO GARDEN FABRIC POMANDER
Choice of corn (yellow & green), carrot (orange & green), pepper (green), tomato (red & green). SSP $7 each - CMV $4 each MB.

1978-79 SPARKLING TURTLE CANDLETTE
4½" long clear glass turtle. SSP $7 - CMV $7 MB, $6 BO.

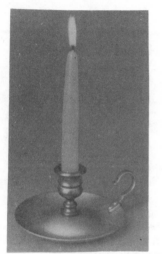

1983-84 CORAL GLOW CANDLE
Clear glass Conch shell design candle. SSP $12 - CMV $12 MB.

1982-84 AMERICAN HEIRLOOM CANDLESTICK & CANDLE
Pewter metal candlestick & 6" red candle. SSP $11 - CMV $11 MB.

1983-84 NATURE'S FRESH PETITE CANDLES
3 miniature candles on connecting wick, choice of strawberry, pine cone, or mushroom. SSP $6 set of 3 - CMV $6 each set MB.

1982-83 TOCCARA SPECIAL EDITION CANDLE
(left) Clear cut glass Fostoria candle. Blue box. SSP $13.50 - CMV $13.50 MB.
1982-83 HARVEST GLOW CANDLE
(right) Clear glass pumpkin shaped candle and lid. SSP $13 - CMV $13 MB.

1983 SNUGGLY MOUSE CANDLE-HOLDER
Ceramic mouse holder base 4¼" wide. Comes with 6" red candle. SSP $13 - CMV $13 MB.

1982 SPICE CUPBOARD CANDLE
(left) 1½" high clear glass refillable candle. SSP $5 - CMV $5 MB.
1983 RAIN OR SHINE GREETING CANDLE
(right) 2" high candle with mouse decal on side. SSP $5 - CMV $5 MB.

1983 HOLIDAY FLOATING CANDLES
Box of 2 candles in choice of Red Poinsetta flowers or green & red wreath, 2½" wide. SSP $5 each set - CMV $5 set MB.

1982 STOCKING SURPRISE CANDLES
Box holds 2 green candles with cat & dog on them. SSP $9 - CMV $9 MB.

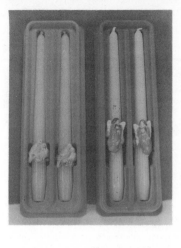

1983-84 LOVE BIRDS TAPER CANDLES
(left) 2 white 10" candles, has 2 ceramic love bird rings. Box has blue birds & felt lined inner box. SSP $10 - CMV $10 MB.

1983 HEAVENLY ANGEL TAPER CANDLES
(right) 10" white candles with 2 ceramic angels rings. Angels on box. SSP $10 - CMV $10 MB.

1983-84 YEAR TO YEAR BIRTHDAY CANDLE
4½" ceramic clown candle holder with yellow candle, 1-2-3-4 on sides. SSP $10 - CMV $10 MB.

1982 LITTLE DRUMMERS CANDLES
Box holds two 10" red candles with boy & girl drummers. SSP $9 - CMV $9 MB.

1982-83 HO HO GLOW "SANTA" CANDLE
5" ceramic red, white & black Santa candle. SSP $16 - CMV $16 MB.

1983-84 AUTUMN HARVEST CANDLES
Box of 2 - 10" brown & beige candles with corn decoration. SSP $9 - CMV $9 MB.

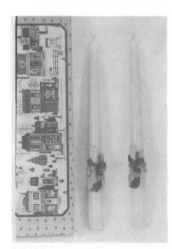

1982 SHADES OF AUTUMN CANDLES
2 - 10" white candles in Christmas box. SSP $9 - CMV $9 MB.

PERFUME GLACE

PLATES

1982-83 ORIENTAL FAN PERFUME GLACE
(left) Yellow & pink plastic, yellow & lavender box. SSP $4 - CMV $4 MB.

1982-83 STRAWBERRY CONE LIP GLOSS
(right) Red plastic fan, black tassel, choice of Timeless or Candid. Red & black box. SSP $4 - CMV $4 MB.

1983 SWEET DREAMS KEEPSAKE PLATE
7 5/8" porcelain plate. SSP $15 - CMV $15 MB.

1982-83 HOSPITALITY SWEETS RECIPE PLATE
3 different 7" metal plates, made to hang on wall, choice of Plum Pudding, Buche de Noel or Blue Berry-Orange Nut Bread. Comes with Avon recipe in box. SSP $6 - CMV $4 ea. MB.

1983-85 CHRISTMAS PLATE
"Enjoying the night before Christmas". 9" porcelain plate. SSP $23.50 - CMV $20 MB.

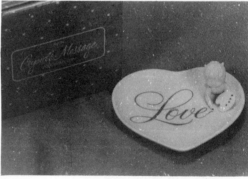

1984 CUPID'S MESSAGE PORCELAIN DISH
White heart shaped dish with Angel & Love in red letters. Red box. SSP $10 - CMV $10 MB.

1982-83 BAKED WITH LOVE PLATE
9" Porcelain plate dated 1982. SSP $18 - CMV $18 MB.

1982-84 CHRISTMAS PLATE "KEEPING THE CHRISTMAS TRADITION"
9" ceramic plate, back says Christmas Memories, 1982. Comes in green & gold box. SSP $23.50 - CMV $23.50 MB.

1983 MOTHER'S DAY PLATE
3rd in series, 5" porcelain plate & plastic stand, dated 1983. SSP $12 - CMV $12 MB.

MEN'S AFTER SHAVE & COLOGNES

1936-49 AFTER SHAVING LOTION
4 oz. maroon cap, maroon & cream colored box. OSP 37c - CMV $30, MB, $22 BO.

1982 COUNTRY CHRISTMAS COLOGNE
2 oz. ribbed, clear glass, green cap & box. Came in Country Christmas set only in men's cologne. CMV $2 MB.

CORDOVAN PRODUCTS

1983-84 CORDOVAN PRODUCTS
2.5 oz. cologne or after shave. SSP $3 - CMV 50c each MB.
MINI COLOGNE & AFTER SHAVE
.5 oz. clear glass. SSP $1 - CMV 50c eachMB.

C.J. PRODUCTS

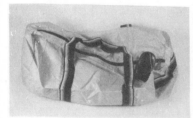

1982 CJ TOTE BAG
Silver bag, black & orange strap, 18" long, 9" high. CMV $8.

1982-83 CJ GIFT EDITION COLOGNE
.5 oz. mini cologne. Clear glass, gray cap, Christmas box. SSP $1.45 - CMV $1 MB.

MUSK FOR MEN

1983-84 MUSK FOR MEN COLOGNE & AFTER SHAVE
Both have 2.8 oz. clear glass. SSP $5.50 - CMV 50c each.

1983-84 MUSK FOR MEN
Shower soap on rope. SSP $3 - CMV $3 MB.
TALC
3.5 oz. brown paper can. SSP $1.75 - CMV 25c.

629

MEN'S SETS OF 1930's

1930 CHRISTMAS BOXES
Special issue boxes came with seven different Avon sets at Christmas, 1931. CMV $25. added to price of set for this box.

1936 ASSORTMENT FOR MEN
No. 1 & No. 2
Avon box holds can of talc for men, tube of Bayberry Shaving Cream and choice of ribbed glass bottle after shave or Bay Rum. OSP $1., CMV $110. MB.

1938 TRAVEL KIT FOR MEN
Tan leather like case with zipper. Holds tube of Styptic Cream, 4 oz. after shave lotion, tube of shaving cream, can of talc for men. OSP $2.16, CMV $80. mint.

MEN'S SETS OF 1940's

1941-42 MENS TRAVELERS SET
Brown leather snap case with maroon & black strip inside case & lid holds 4 oz. After Shaving Lotion, 3½ oz. tube of Brushless Shaving cream, maroon 2 5/8 oz. can of talc for men & tube of Styptic cream. All products came in original maroon & ivory color boxes. CMV $70 MB.

1943 ARMY NAVY KIT
Blue box with eagle holds turquoise can of Elite powder, 4 oz. after shave, and maroon tube of Brushless Shaving Cream. OSP $1.35, CMV $85. MB.

MEN'S SETS OF 1980's

1982-83 HOWDY PARDNERS SET
Box holds 2 oz. Talc & 2 oz. plastic bottle of Buckaroo Cologne with 2 piece blue cowboy hat cap. SSP $5 - CMV $5 MB.

1982 COUNTRY CHRISTMAS COLLECTION FOR HIM SET
Green plastic box with green outer sleeve, holds matching bar of soap, talc 1.5 oz. & 2 oz. ribbed clear glass bottle, green cap cologne in choice of Clint, Weekend, Black Suede or Wild Country. SSP $9 - CMV $9 with sleeve.

BABY PRODUCTS

LAVENDER

1984 BABY'S DREAMING DOOR HANGER
5¾" long scented bear decoration. SSP $8 - CMV $2.

1983-84 CLEARLY GENTLE BABY PRODUCTS
BABY POWDER
7.5 oz. plastic bottle.
BABY OIL
8 oz. plastic bottle.
BABY BATH
8 oz. plastic bottle.
BABY CREAM
2 oz. tube.
CMV 25c each

1934-37 LAVENDER TOILET WATER
4 oz. ribbed glass, gold cap, pink & lavender box. Box shown used 1936-37. OSP 75c - CMV $45 BO, $55 MB.

FANTASQUE PRODUCTS

1982-84 FANTASQUE BY LOUIS FERAUD
Avons 1st designer fragrance. Basic design is black & gold. Plastic bottles in gray or white, gold caps. Choice of PERFUME. .5 oz. SSP $30 - CMV $15 MB. EAU DE COLOGNE SPRAY 1.7 oz. SSP $25 - CMV $4 MB. EAU DE COLOGNE FLACON .5 oz. Purse spray. SSP $13 - CMB $1 MB. PARFUM PENDANT black glass bottle on 38" black cord. Comes in black velvet pouch. SSP $25 - CMV $15.

1983 FANTASQUE GIFT COLLECTION SET
Black box, gray plastic liner holds Eau de Cologne Flacon spray, .5 oz. Perfumed Body Veil, & .5 oz. Perfumed Bath Essence. SSP $6.50 - CMV $6.50 MB.

LIGHT ACCENTS

1983-84 LIGHT ACCENTS PERFUMED TALC
3.5 oz. paper talc, choice of Willow in green, Tea Garden in lavender, Amber Mist in yellow. SSP $2 - CMV 25c each.

1983-84 LIGHT ACCENTS FRAGRANCE
2 oz. spray bottle, choice of Amber Mist, Tea Garden, or Willow. SSP $6 ea. - CMV 50c ea. MB.

1983 LIGHT ACCENTS SAMPLE PACKETS
Small box of 10 sample packets, each fragrance. CMV 25c each box. (Not shown).

1983 LIGHT ACCENTS TRIO SAMPLER
(right) Triangle box holds 3 small sample bottles, sold 2 campaigns only. CMV $1.50 MB.

LITTLE BLOSSOM PRODUCTS

1983-84 LITTLE BLOSSOM & FRIENDS
Shaker talc with puff sets. 2 oz. talc & small hand puff. Choice of
LITTLE BLOSSOM
Pink
DAISY DREAMER
yellow
SCAMPER LILY
Orange
SSP $4 ea. - CMV $4 ea. set
MINI DOLLS
2¼" high soft plastic, choice of Little Blossom, Daisy Dreamer, Scamper Lily. SSP $4 ea. - CMV $2 ea.
DAB O COLOGNE
.45 oz. rollette, choice of Little Blossom in Whisper Soft, Daisy Dreamer in Secret Wishes, & Scamper Lily in Sparkle Bright. SSP $3 ea. - CMV $2 ea.

1983 LITTLE BLOSSOM & FRIENDS IRON ON DECALS
Package of 3 T-shirt decals. SSP 70c - CMV 75c set of 3.

1983 LITTLE BLOSSOM BUBBLE BATH PACKETS
Flowered box holds 10 packets. SSP $2 - CMV $1 MB.

1982-83 LITTLE BLOSSOM LIP & NAIL TINT
Lip tint on left, pink cap, no box. Nail tint in .5 oz. plastic bottle, white cap, boxed. CMV $1 each.

PAVI ELLE PRODUCTS

1983-85 PAVI ELLE PRODUCTS
Frosted glass, goldtone caps, full line of fragrance products.
COLOGNE SPRAY
1.5 oz. CMV 50c.
ULTRA PERFUME
.33 oz. CMV 50c

1982-83 LITTLE BLOSSOM FINGER PUPPET WITH DEMI STICK SET
(left) Box holds small finger puppet & blue, white & pink Demi Stick. SSP $4 - CMV $4 MB.
LITTLE BLOSSOM LIGHT SWITCH COVER
(right) Box holds blue & green light switch plate with pink flowers. SSP $4 - CMV $4 MB.

1983-84 SOFT MUSK PRODUCTS
Full line of fragrance products. All products CMV 25c to 50c.
SOAP
Single bar CMV $1.
5 GUEST SOAPS
CMV $4 MB.

SOFT MUSK

1982-84 SOFT MUSK SOAP
Single 3 oz. bar. SSP $1.50 - CMV $1 mint.

WOMEN'S SETS OF 1980's

1983 APPLE BLOSSOM TIME SET
Fancy box from early Avon days holds .5 oz. bottle of Apple Blossom cologne. Box has outer sleeve. SSP $7 - CMV $7 MB.

1983 GAY NINETIES SET
Fancy box from early Avon days holds .5 oz. of White Lilac cologne. Box has outer sleeve. SSP $7 - CMV $7 MB.

1982 GOLD STAMPS SET
Blue & gold box sleeve holds small bottle of golden fixative & small container of Beauty Dust & plastic stamps. SSP $6 - CMV $6 MB.

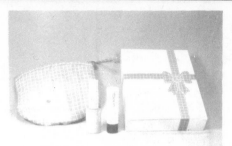

1983 ROARING TWENTIES SET
.5 oz. bottle of Trailing Arbutus cologne. Fancy blue & gold box. SSP $7 - CMV $7 MB, with outer sleeve.

1982 COORDINATES SET
White & red box holds small red checked bag marked Avon. Comes with choice of 2 of 4 different coordinates make up products, lipstick & nail enamel shown. Each boxed seperately. SSP $4.50 set - CMV $4.50 set MB.

1983 HOLIDAY COOKIE KIT SET
Box holds plastic Teddy Bear & Train cookie cutters, 5 gift bags & recipe card. SSP $3.75 - CMV $3 MB set.

1982 HALLOWEEN MAKE A FACE KIT
Carton box holds jar of Make a Face Base, blue lid, 3 pomettes of face color, orange, black & blue. SSP $6 - CMV $6 MB.

1982 GOING TO GRANDMA'S HOUSE SET
Carton box holds 1.25 oz. white plastic bottles with turquoise caps of bubble bath for children & Little Blossom Whisper Soft Cologne, 1 small green childs toothbrush. SSP $5 - CMV $5.

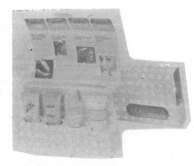

1983 CELEBRATION SAMPLER
Trial size products given to customers 1 campaign only for $7.50 purchase. Box holds trial size tubes of Care Deeply Hand Cream, Aqua Clean Shower Gel, Nurtura Creamy Wash Off Cleanser & small bottle of Naturally Gentle Shampoo. CMV $5 set MB.

1982 COUNTRY CHRISTMAS COLLECTION FOR HER SET
Red & tan plastic box & outer sleeve holds matching soap, talc & .33 oz. cologne. Choice of Odyssey, Timeless, Tasha, Foxfire, Ariane, or Candid. SSP $9 - CMV $9 MB.

1982 NAIL ACCENTS SET
Yellow container box holds .5 oz. top shield & packet of 3 sheets of decals. SSP $3 - CMV $3 MB.

1983 "FANCY FEET" FOOT CARE KIT SET
1 oz. tube of Fancy Feet double action cream, orange stick, emery board, pair of foam toe forms. SSP $3.50 - CMV $2 complete kit, $1 tube only.

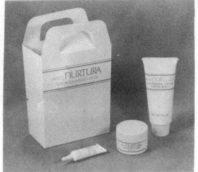

1982 NURTURA GET ACQUAINTED PACK SET
Carry carton holds tube of 2.5 oz. Replenishing body cream, .25 eye cream & 1 oz. jar of Replenishing cream. Short issue. SSP $4 - CMV $4 mint set.

MEN'S SOAP

1983 THAT'S MY DAD DECAL SOAPS
(left) Choice of 3 different decal soaps. "We love you dad" or "You taught me all the important things Dad" or "You're always there when I need you Dad." SSP $2 - CMV $2 each bar MB.

1983 GRANDFATHERS & GRAND-MOTHERS ARE SPECIAL SOAPS
(right) Metal can holds choice of black or white grandfather or black or white grandmother. SSP $6 ea. - CMV $4 ea. MB.

1982-83 ANCIENT MARINER BOX & SOAP
Tin box with bar of compass design soap. SSP $9 - CMV $9 MB.

WOMEN'S SOAP

1983 FIVE GUEST SOAPS
Flower design box holds 5 small bars in Timeless, Candid, Ariane, Tasha, Foxfire, Odyssey or Soft Musk. SSP $4 - CMV $4 MB.

1983 FLORAL BOXED SOAPS
(left) Box has different flower design for each fragrance. 4 flowered bars. Choice of Wild Jasmine "gold" Hawaiian White Ginger "white", Honeysuckle "yellow" or Roses Roses "pink". SSP $4 - CMV $4 MB.

1983 FLORAL GUEST SOAP
(right) Single 1 oz. bar in box. Different color soap for each fragrance. Choice of Roses Roses, Wild Jasmine, Hawaiian White Ginger. SSP 75c - CMV 75c MB.

1983 CHRISTMAS WISHES DECAL SOAPS
3 different boxed bars. Choice of Happiness in pink, Togetherness in green, & Sharing in tan color soap. SSP $1.50 ea. - CMV $1.50 ea. MB.

1983 A MOTHER'S JOY SOAP SET
Blue box holds 2 white mother & child soaps. SSP $4 - CMV $4 MB.

1982 COUNTRY CHRISTMAS DECAL SOAPS
Box holds 2 bars. SSP $4 - CMV $4 MB.

1972-82 RICH MOISTURE BATH BAR SOAP
Single 5 oz. bar, turquoise & white wrapper. SSP $1 - CMV $1 mint.

SOAPS WITH SPONGES

1978 MISTERJAW BATH MITT & SOAP
Blue sponge mitt 9'' long with fish design bar of soap. SSP $5 - CMV $5 MB.

CHILDREN'S SOAPS

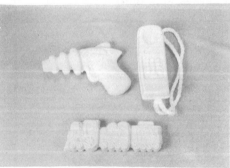

1983 DARLING DUCKLINGS SOAP
Box holds 3 yellow duck soaps. SSP $4 - CMV $4 MB.

1982-83 BUBBLE BLAZER SOAP
(left) Box holds 4 oz. yellow space gun bar. SSP $3 - CMV $3 MB.

1982-83 PARTY LINE SOAP ON A ROPE
(right) Box holds 5 oz. yellow telephone bar on white rope. SSP $4 - CMV $4 MB.

1982-83 TRAIN SOAP
(bottom) 5¾'' long blue train soap, breaks into 3 cars. Must be all together or of no value. SSP $3.50 - CMV $3.50 MB.

CHILDREN'S TOYS

1983 E.T. & ELLIOTT DECAL SOAP
3 oz. blue bar with decal of E.T. on face. Back of bar says "I'll be right there". SSP $3 - CMV $3 MB.

1983-84 E.T. BATH DECANTER
7 oz. blue plastic with tan plastic head. Holds Bubble Bath. SSP $9 - CMV $4 MB.

1983-84 E.T. MUG
4½" high white porcelain mug with E.T. for the handle. SSP $20 - CMV $15 MB.

1984 E.T. & GERTIE DECAL SOAP
3 oz. pink bar. SSP $4 - CMV $3 MB.

1984 E.T. FLOWERS FIGURINE
2½" high hand painted porcelain. SSP $8 - CMV $5 MB.

1983 WABBIT CAR
5 oz. blue plastic car & white rabbit cap. Choice of childrens Bubble Bath or Non-Tear Shampoo. Comes with sheet of stick on decals to decorate. SSP $6 - CMV $4 MB.

1983-84 HERSHEY'S KISS CHOCOLATE LIP GLOSS
(left) Brown plastic, holds lip gloss. SSP $3 - CMV $2 MB.

1983-84 STARRY NIGHT TRINKET BOX
(center) Blue, white, red & yellow plastic box. Lid can be a pin or earrings. SSP $5 - CMV $3 MB.

1983-84 GINGERBREAD MAN SCENTED PIN
(right) Brown gingerbread man pin on cane card. SSP $4 - CMV $2.50.

1982-83 BUBBA LEE BUNNY
6 oz. white plastic rabbit, yellow cap. Choice of Bubble Bath or Non-Tear Shampoo. SSP $5.50 - CMV $3 MB.

1982-83 TWEETHOUSE PAPER CUP TOOTHBRUSH HOLDER
(left) White plastic cup holder with stick on decals & 2 child toothbrushes. SSP $7.50 - CMV $4 MB.

1982-83 FELIX FOX WALL HOOK
(right) White & tan plastic. SSP $3.50 - CMV $1 MB.

1983 SCOOTER SEAL PUPPET
13" long white puppet. Blue sweater & knit hat. SSP $18 - CMV $10.

1983-84 TOOFY THE TOOTH CLOWN
Yellow plastic tube holds 1 Avon toothbrush. SSP $5 - CMV $3 MB.

1983-84 CUTE CHICK PIN & EARRINGS
Yellow plastic egg holds yellow chick pin. Blue egg holds small yellow chick earrings. SSP $4 ea. - CMV $1 ea. mint.

1983-84 LIP SHADES LIP GLOSS
Red plastic sunglasses with lip gloss. SSP $5 - CMV $2 MB.

1982-83 LITTLE RAG DOLL
4" high doll, red dress, yellow hair, green hair ribbons, black shoes. Comes with Demi Stick in Moonwind or Sweet Honesty. SSP $7 - CMV $7 MB.

1982 BABY'S KEEPSAKE BEAR
5" high white stuffed bear. Red hat, green ribbon dated 1982. SSP $7 - CMV $7 MB.

1978 SWEET PICKLES PUZZLES
Set of 3 cardboard puzzles 8" x 6½" size. Sold set for 25c with $3.50 purchase. CMV $3 ea. puzzle.

1982-83 COUNTRY KITCHEN SPICE ANGEL DOLL
Box holds spice fragrance doll 7½" high. SSP $13 - CMV $13 MB.

MISC. AVONS, BOTTLES, ETC.

1983 RAZZLE DAZZLE NAIL ENAMEL
.5 oz. bottle, white cap. SSP $1.75 - CMV 50c MB.

1984-85 ULTRA TOUCH MANICURE PRODUCTS
.5 oz. size. Choice of Nail Fortifier, Quick Nail Dry, Shiny Top Shield, Color Guard Nail Enamel, & Ridge Filling Base Coat. SSP $1.50 ea. - CMV 25c ea.

1983-84 NATURALLY GENTLE SHAMPOO
(left) 24 oz. plastic bottle, yellow cap. SSP $3 - CMV 25c.

1983-84 ALOE VERA SHAMPOO & CONDITIONER
(right) 8 oz. plastic bottles, light green & dark green. SSP $2.30 ea. - CMV 25c ea.

1982-84 EFFECTIVE EYE MAKEUP REMOVER
(left) 2 oz. white plastic bottle. SSP $1.30 - CMV 25c.

1982-84 SAUNA SYSTEM TONING RINSE
(center) 4 oz. white plastic bottle. SSP $2.50 - CMV 25c.

1982-83 SILKEN SOAP
(right) 10 oz. white plastic bottle & pump. Green & red design. SSP $2 - CMV 50c.

1983-84 DESERT SPRING WITH ALOE SOOTHING CLEANSING FOAM
3 oz. tube.
SOOTHING BODY LOTION
5 oz. plastic bottle.
SOOTHING SKIN TONIC
5 oz. plastic bottle.
SOOTHING FACIAL MOISTURIZER
3 oz. plastic bottle.
SSP $2.50 ea. - CMV 25c ea.

1978-80 SKINPLICITY PRODUCTS
Blue & white plastic.
FACIAL TONER
6 oz. bottle.
CREAM CLEANSER
4 oz. jar.
MOISTURIZER AM/PM
3 oz. jar. SSP $2 ea. - CMV 50c ea.
COMPLEXION BAR SOAP
Single bar 3 oz. SSP $1 - CMV $1.
TOTE BAG
Blue & white plastic, marked Avon, given free with purchase of products. Short issue. CMV $3.

1983 EFFECTIVE EYE MAKEUP REMOVER 50% MORE
(left) 3 oz. plastic bottle. CMV 50c.

1983-84 ADAPT SKIN RESPONSE FACIAL CONDITIONER
(center) For combination skin. 3 oz. plastic bottle. CMV 25c MB.

1983-84 ADAPT SKIN RESPONSIVE MAKEUP
(right) 1.5 plastic bottle. CMV 25c MB.

1983 FRESHANCE COOL FINISH MOISTURE SPLASH
8 oz. plastic bottle. Green cap. SSP $3.50 - CMV 25c.

1983-84 CARE DEEPLY HAND CREAM WITH ALOE
(left) 6 oz. white tube. CMV 25c.

1983-84 CARE DEEPLY EXTRA CREAMY LOTION WITH ALOE
(right) 10 oz. white plastic bottle. CMV 25c.

1983-84 MOISTURE THERAPY BATH OIL
(left) 7 oz. clear plastic bottle, blue cap. SSP $5 - CMV 25c.

1983-84 MOISTURE THERAPY BODY LOTION
(right) 7 oz. white plastic bottle, blue cap. SSP $4 - CMV 25c.

1984-85 KEEP CLEAR ANTI-DANDRUFF SHAMPOO & CONDITIONER
(left) 8 oz. blue & white plastic bottles. SSP $2 ea. - CMV 25c ea.

1984-85 NATURALLY GENTLE SHAMPOO & CONDITIONER
(right) Both with Essence of Camomile. 8 oz. frosted bottles with green caps. SSP $2 ea. - CMV 25c ea.

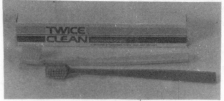

1983-84 TOOTHBRUSHES "TWICE CLEAN"
Red, yellow & white box holds 2 Avon Toothbrushes.

1975-89 MOISTURE SECRET WITH PMB PRODUCTS
All pink plastic.
ENRICHED CREMEGEL CLEANSER
4 oz. jar.
ENRICHED FRESHENER
5 oz. bottle.
ENRICHED NIGHT CONCENTRATE
3 oz. jar.
ENRICHED DAYTIME MOISTURIZER
3 oz. bottle.
SSP $3.33 ea. - CMV 50c ea.

1983 GENTLE BLOSSOMS RINSE-OFF MASK
(left) Box of 3 packets of peach, orange or cherry rinse-off mask. SSP $1.25 - CMV 50c MB.
1983 VICTORIAN BUBBLE BATH CONCENTRATE
(right) Box of 10 packets. SSP $2 - CMV $1 MB.

1982 GOLD STAMP BEAUTY DUST
(left) Small container with blue-green lid.   lid.
1982 GOLDEN FIXATIVE
(right) Small clear glass bottle, blue-green cap. Both came in Gold Stamp. Set only. CMV $1 ea.

SKIN-SO-SOFT

**1983 ON DUTY DEODORANT —
50% MORE**
(left) 3 oz. black & blue.
1983 FEELING FRESH DEODORANT 50% MORE
(center) 3 oz. white & blue.
1983 COOL CONFIDENCE DEODORANT 50% MORE
(right) Lavender.
SSP $1.60 ea. - CMV 50c ea.

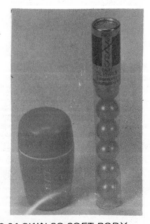

1983-84 SKIN SO SOFT BODY SMOOTHER
(left) 3 oz. turquoise plastic bottle & cap. SSP $4 - CMV 25c.
1982-83 SKIN SO SOFT BATH OIL PEARLS
(right) Clear plastic tube holds 8 bath oil pearl balls. Gold & green cap. SSP $3.50 - CMV $1 full mint.

COLOGNES, MISC.

1983 LIGHT & LAVISH COLOGNE
6 oz. plastic bottle in choice of Timeless, Candid, Ariane, Tasha, Foxfire or Odyssey. SSP $3.75 - CMV 25c ea.

1983 CLASSIC FRAGRANCE NOTE
.5 oz. clear glass, black cap. Cologne in choice of Moonwind, Charisma, Topaze, Occur, Sweet Honesty, Wild Jasmine, Willow, Tea Garden or Amber Mist. SSP $1.80 - CMV $1 MB.

1984 BE MY VALENTINE MINI COLOGNE
His & Her's cologne in 2 seperate ½ heart boxes, .5 oz. clear glass, red cap on hers, black cap on his, choice of Odyssey, Foxfire, Timeless, Candid, Ariane, Tasha, Pavi Elle & Soft Musk for her & Rugger Musk for Men, Black Suede, Wild Country for him. SSP $1.75 ea. - CMV $1.75 ea.

1982 ULTRA FRAGRANCE JEWELS
(left) .33 oz. clear glass jewel shaped bottle, gold cap. SSP $3 - CMV $1 MB.

1982 VINTAGE FRAGRANCE COLLECTION COLOGNE
(center) Pineapple shaped bottle, gold cap. Red & green box. Choice of .5 oz. cologne in Cotillion, Here's My Heart, Regence, Persian Wood, Brocade, or Rapture. SSP $2 - CMV $1 MB.

1982 COUNTRY CHRISTMAS COLOGNE
(right) .33 oz. clear glass. Choice of Foxfire, Odyssey, Timeless, Tasha, Candid, Ariane,. In Christmas box, came in set only. CMV $1 MB.

COLOGNE SPRAYS, MISC.

1983-84 PUFF OF FRAGRANCE
(left) .4 oz. small metal spray can. Choice of Wild Jasmine, gold top. Honeysuckle, yellow top, Hawaiian White Ginger, white top & Roses Poses, pink top. SSP $3 - CMV $1.

ULTRA FLACON SPRAY COLOGNE
(right) .5 oz. clear glass, maroon cap, all fragrances. SSP $3 - CMV $1 MB.

1981 COLOGNE SPRAY LIMITED EDITION
.5 oz. cut glass type bottle. Choice of Charisma, Moonwind, Occur, Topaze, Sportiff, Zany or Sweet Honesty. Short issue. SSP $2 - CMV $1 MB.

1976-77 FLORAL COLOGNE SPRAYS
1.8 oz. clear glass, gold caps. Choice of Raining Violets, Hawaiian White Ginger, Honeysuckle, Field Flowers & Apple Blossom. SSP $3 - CMV $1 ea. BO, $2 MB.

1982 COLOGNE SPRAY CHRISTMAS BOX
Ultra cologne sprays came in special issue Christmas box. Choice of Candid, Ariane, Timeless or Tasha. Add 50c for this box.

PERFUMED TALC, MISC.

1983 "TALC PERFUMED" CHRISTMAS DESIGN
Red & gold Christmas packaging. Choice of Ariane, Odyssey, Tasha, Timeless, Foxfire, Candid & Soft Musk. SSP $2 - CMV $1 ea.

PERFUMES, MISC.

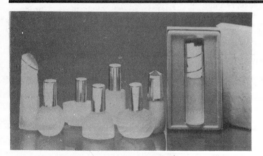

1983-84 ULTRA PERFUMES
All are .33 oz. in frosted glass bottles. Choice of Odyssey, Tasha, Soft Musk, Ariane, Candid, Foxfire, Timeless, Pavi Elle. SSP $10 ea. - CMV $1 ea. MB.

1983 CHRISTMAS PACKAGING
2 different special design boxes for many Avon fragrance products. Red & gold design. Same CMV as regular products.

COMPACTS & LIPSTICKS, MISC.

1983 TROPICAL TREATS LIP GLOSS
Choice of coconut, banana or pineapple. SSP $1 - CMV $1 ea.

1982-84 CARE DEEPLY LIP BALM WITH SUNSCREEN
(left) Black & white.
1982 REFEREE LIP BALM
(center) Red, white & black.
1983 SMOOTH DAYS AHEAD LIP BALM
(right) 1983 calendar on side. SSP ea. $1 - CMV $1 ea.

1983-84 MIDNIGHT MAGIC MAKEUP
Dark blue & silver colors. Lipstick, Nail Enamel, & eye Shadow Compact. CMV 50c ea. MB.

1984 ULTRA WEAR BRUSH ON BLUSH COMPACT
Rose color plastic. SSP $4 - CMV 50c.

1983-84 SLICK TINT FOR LIPS
Rose & silver color. SSP $1.50 - CMV 50c.

1983 SANTA CLAUS LIP BALM
Red, white & blue. SSP $1 - CMV $1.

1982 MAKE A FACE POMETTES
Came in set only. Orange, blue & black. $1 ea.

1982-83 ULTRA WEAR PRODUCTS
all are burgandy in color & come boxed.
MASCARA (left)
BLUSH STICK (back center)
LIPSTICK (right)
EYE SHADOW COMPACT (front center) CMV 50c ea. item MB.

1982-83 ELEGANT TOUCHES COMPACT & LIPSTICK
Both black plastic with flower design. SSP compact $6 - CMV $3 MB. SSP lipstick $2.45 - CMV 50c MB.

1983-84 VERSATILITIES MAKEUP
Black & gray with blue swirl design.
LIPSTICK
SILK TO SATIN NAIL COLOR
WET/DRY POWDER BLUSH
WET/DRY POWDER EYE SHADOW
CMV $1 ea. MB.

1983-84 EYE-LIP CHEEK STACK
(left) 3 small clear top containers of makeup. CMV 25c ea.

1983-84 ULTRATWIST WAND
(center left) Gold tone container holds solid fragrance in Odyssey, Ariane, Candid, Timeless, Tasha, Foxfire or Soft Musk. SSP $5 - CMV 50c MB.

1983-84 ULTRA FRAGRANCE SHIMMER
(center right) Light gray lipstick type tube. 7 fragrances. SSP $3 - CMV 50c MB.

1983-84 COORDINATES SMOOTH TOUCH POWDER EYE SHADOW
(right) Red & clear plastic compact. SSP $2.25 - CMV 25c MB.

1983-84 ULTRA WEAR MAKEUP
All are burgandy color.
LIP 'N NAIL DUO
(left) CMV $1 MB.
LASTING EYELINING PENCIL
(center left) CMV 25c MB.
MASCARA
(center right) CMV 25c MB.
EYE SHADOW BOUTIQUE COMPACT
(right) CMV $1 MB.
All items come boxed.

CREAM JARS, MISC.

BRUSHES & COMBS, MISC.

1983-84 JEWELRY CLEANER
(left) White & blue plastic jar. SSP $1 - CMV 25c.
1983-84 NEW VITALITY NPO CONDITIONING TREATMENT
(center) 6 oz. yellow plastic jar. SSP $2 - CMV 25c.
1983-84 PERFUMED SKIN SOFTENERS FLORAL
(right) 2 oz. plastic jars in Roses Roses, Hawaiian White Ginger or Wild Jasmine. SSP $1.30 - CMV 25c ea.

1973 SCALP & SHAMPOO BRUSH
White plastic Avon brush. OSP $1.25 - CMV $2 MB.

PAPER ITEMS, MISC.

1984 SECRET SCENTED VALENTINES
12 cutout cards, 2 each of 6 different designs. Must be all together to be mint. SSP $3 - CMV $2 mint.

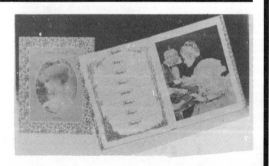

1983 VICTORIAN BOOK OF DAYS CALENDAR
7" x 9" size book calendar. SSP $3.50 - CMV $2.50 MB.

1983 CALENDAR OF ROSES
Hard bound green cover. Comes with outer sleeve. 7'' x 9'' size. SSP $3 - CMV $2 mint.

SHIPPING BOXES
Single carton item boxes for mailing new products to Avon Reps. Boxes shown are 1941. This type of box has been used since 1930's to 1960's. CMV add $5 for CPC box & $3 for Avon box above cost of product inside.

1982 CHRISTMAS SURPRISE CALENDAR
Paper foldout, blue cover. SSP $4 - CMV $1.

1982 SANTA'S MAGIC MIRROR & RECORD
Sold 1 campaign only. SSP $1.50 - CMV $1.50.

1983 MRS. CLAUS' KITCHEN SURPRISE CALENDAR
8'' x 12'' folded 12'' x 15'' open. Six different fragrance on calendar. SSP $5 - CMV $3.

1982 COUNTRY CHRISTMAS RECIPE BOX
Red box holds beige recipe box & pack of recipes from Better Homes & Garden. SSP $3 - CMV $3 MB.

1983 GOODY-VILLE PUZZLE
9½'' x 12'' scratch & sniff puzzle. Comes in blue cardboard envelope. SSP $5 - CMV $1 mint.

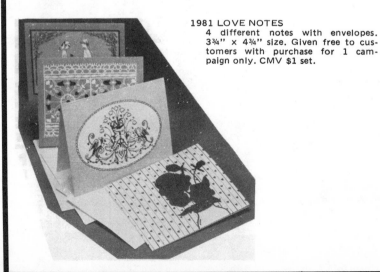

1981 LOVE NOTES
4 different notes with envelopes. 3¾'' x 4¾'' size. Given free to customers with purchase for 1 campaign only. CMV $1 set.

1983 CHILDHOOD MOMENTS CALENDAR
Comes in envelope on left. CMV 50c.

SAMPLES & DEMONSTRATOR KITS

1941 FACE POWDER SAMPLE DOLLAR
(left) 1 metal face powder sample of Tulip "A" design on round card. Silver back says "Avon Products 1 dollar". CMV $6 mint.

1941 FACE POWDER SAMPLE MASTERPIECE
(right) Blue card holds Tulip "A" metal samples of Rose & Ochre Rose. CMV $7 mint.

1982 VERSATILITIES MAKEUP DEMO KIT
Gray box with sleeve & black box lid holds black & gray lipstick & Versatilities nail polish & eye make-up. Used by reps for demo. CMV $5 MB.

1983 HOLIDAY SURPRISE GIFT CARDS DEMO
Green folder holds 6 miniature cards with small vial for fragrance on each. Sold to customers in sets of 3 cards. Demo card CMV $2.50, regular issue set of 3 cards CMV $1.

1930-36 FACE POWDER SAMPLES
Plain box of 30 silver & blue metal samples. With CPC card inside. CMV $30 MB.

1983 COORDINATES MAKEUP DEMONSTRATOR
Plastic display case used by Avon reps to show makeup products. Size 11" x 16". Red & white lip stick sample tubes, nail enamel fan demo, eye shadow, blush colors. Avon rep cost $20 - CMV $20 MB.

1940's FACIAL TISSUES DEMO
Plain box of Avon Tissue used as demo for reps. CMV $20 mint.

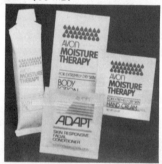

1984 SAMPLE PACKS
Packs of Moisture Therapy & Adapt sample products. CMV 25c per package or box.

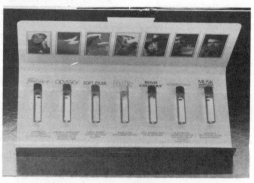

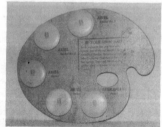

1984 FRAGRANCE SAMPLER
Gold box holds 7 one inch vials of fragrance, 4 womens & 3 mens. CMV $4 MB.

1940's FACE POWDER DEMO PALETTE
Green palette holds 5 Tulip "A" metal samples in Ariel & Vernafleur. CMV $32 mint.

1982-84 ULTRA WEAR NAIL COLOR SELECTOR
Plastic nail polish color demo used by reps. CMV $1.

SPRAY CANS MISC.

1982 FROSTED FANTASY
(left) 4 oz. blue spray can & cap. SSP $2.50 - CMV 50c.

1982-83 COUNTRY BAKER GINGER-BREAD SCENT
(center) 7 oz. spray can, rust color cap. SSP $2 - CMV 25c.

1982-83 COUNTRY BAKER APPLE PIE SCENT
(right) 7 oz. red cap spray can. SSP $2 - CMV 25c.

1983 FROSTED FANTASY
(left) 4 oz. green can of windowpane frost. SSP $2.50 - CMV 50c.

1983-84 COTTAGE FLOWERS ROOM FRESHENER
(center) 7 oz. green can, white cap. SSP $2.30 - CMV 25c.

1983-84 TWICE FRESH BREATH SPRAY
(right) Small .33 oz. white spray can. SSP $1.90 - CMV 25c.

FOREIGN AVONS

AWARDS—FOREIGN

1975 CHRISTMAS ON THE FARM PLATE — CANADA
Same plate as US 1973 Christmas plate only says "Avon 1975" on front of plate & outer sleeve of box. Comes with card from Avon. Given to Avon team leaders at Christmas. Back of plate & card in English & French. CMV $75 MB.

1983 CLOCK - MRS. ALBEE AWARD CANADA
(left) Brass quartz clock. 10 given in each district for top sales. Mrs. Albee face on clock. CMV $150.

1983 CLOCK 5th QUARTER CHAMPIONS - CANADA
(right) Same brass clock as above only all brass clock face. Made by Equity in Hong Kong. Plaque on top says "5th Quarter Champions, Niagara Division 1983". Only 16 given for signing up most new Avon reps. CMV $125.

1982 PRESIDENTS CLUB PIN CANADA
Gold tone stick pin, 4A design cut out in center. Given to top reps. CMV $10 MB.

AVON IN CANADA
By Clark Popham

Many of you would like to know how AVON - Canada started. Following in brief is the story, part history and part from interviews to take you back in time to Montreal in 1914.

in 1914 Mr. Charles C. Stewart, 1888-1949, "TIPPIE", moved to Montreal with his secretary, Miss Murray, and opened the first Canadian office in the Reed Building. Mr. Stewart was born at Suffern, New York, grew up in this small town community, and in 1910 began his life-long career with the Avon Co. then known as the California Perfume Company. He advanced through a series of rapid promotions to the position of Secretary to the Founder of this company, D.H. McConnell, Sr., where he soon acquired an intimate knowledge and wide vision of the company and its work. So it was logical that he should be chosen to assume the managership of the new Canadian Company when it started in 1914.

Mr. Stewart and Miss Murray with a small ten-person staff set up the California Perfume Company in a small office in downtown Montreal.

From the beginning Mr. Stewart built his personality into the operation of the Canadian Company, his management was a friendly one, but it also was a steadfast, hardworking one. Under Mr. Stewart's leadership, Avon of Canada has become one of Canada's biggest cosmetic companies.

East and west from Montreal the company began to spread across this great land. In Winnipeg there still lives a lady, now in her eighty's who worked for the California Perfume Company back before 1920. She belongs in the vanguard of those ladies, who like the original Mrs. Albee, should be known as the Mother of the Canadian Avon Company. Mrs. Marion Verge was employed by the C.P. Co. to recruit and enlist Depot Agents in Western Canada. Operating out of Winnipeg she would travel by train and bus to the cities and towns of Manitoba, Saskatchewan and Alberta to interview ladies to sell the C.P.C. line of products. When I spoke to her she was a member of the Manitoba Avon Bottle Collectors Club and we had a great time as she reminisced about those days. She would arrive in a small prairie town and seek out the local rooming house, and then look for suitable young ladies to employ. Most often she would find that the landlady of the rooming house was the most suitable, as she knew everybody in town and was already a business women. After a quick training period, she caught the train or bus and was on to the next town to repeat the process.

Mrs. Verge spent many years on the road for the company before making her home in Winnipeg and continuing as a representative herself.

In this way the Company continued to grow with all orders going into Montreal for filling and shipment across the country. Over the years C.P.C. became Avon Canada Ltd. and the Company moved to Pointe Claire, a western suburb of Montreal.

Sales representatives sell not only in the Montreal skyscrapers, but in the glacial-bound territories of northern Canada. Some orders, like those for Newfoundland must travel close to 2,000 miles over land and sea to reach representatives. Besides, the unique physical challenges faced, they must accomodate a market that is 75% English and 25% French. Product labels, brochures, and much of the representatives literature must be printed in both languages. The Company service teams speak both English and French.

Canada manufactures just about all of our present product lines except soap, aerosol and jewelry.

1981 PRECIOUS MOMENTS MY 1st CALL AWARD - CANADA
Same as US issue only inscribed in French. CMV $40 MB.
1981 PRECIOUS MOMENTS AWARD "READY FOR AN AVON DAY"
Same as US issue only inscribed in French. Given to reps. CMV $30 MB.

1982 BRACELET TOP TEN AWARD - CANADA
Sterling Silver chain & 4A design pendant. Given to top ten Presidents Club reps. White box says "Top Ten District Award Presidents Club 1982". CMV $75 MB.

1982 ALBEE PICTURE AWARD - CANADA
Rayon & silk picture of Mrs. Albee 1st Avon Lady. French & English on back label. Given to Canada Team Leaders only. CMV $50 MB.

1980 ARKLOW "TEA GARDEN" TABLEWARE AWARD - CANADA
20 piece Honey Stone set with Tea Garden flower design. Given to Reps for sales goals. 3 levels.
COFFEE CUPS
Level 1, set of 4. CMV $10.
SOUP & SALAD BOWLS
Level 2, 4 each. CMV $20 set.
DINNER PLATES & SMALL SAUCERS
Level 3, 4 each. CMV $30 set.

1974 CANADIANA KITCHEN AWARDS - CANADA
Same as American Patchwork awards only Canada label. White ceramic. 4 levels.
STORAGE JARS
Level 1, set of 2. CMV $12.
COOKIE JAR
Level 2. CMV $15.
CANNISTER SET
Level 3, 3 ceramic jars. CMV $25 set.
PRESSURE COOKER
Level 4. CMV $35.

1983 TEAM LEADER AWARD TRAY - CANADA
12¼" size. Chrome plated brass tray. Last gift given to Team Leaders in Canada. CMV $30.

1983 PRESIDENTS CLUB GLASSES - CANADA
Set of 6 glasses with 4A around top of glass. Box sleeve says "You're Better Than Ever" in English & French. Given to Presidents Club reps. CMV $20 set of 6 with box & sleeve.

1974 IMPERIAL GARDEN AWARDS - CANADA
Each is white ceramic & orange flowers. Given to Reps in Canada for sales achievement.
BUD VASE
5¾" high. CMV $10.
CERAMIC VASE
7" high. CMV $16.
GINGER JAR
10¾" high. CMV $25.

1967 PRESIDENTS AWARD PLATE - CANADA
7½" size aluminum plate. Given to Presidents Club members in Canada. CMV $85.

1982 SMILE GLASSES AWARD - AUSTRALIA
Box of 4 Smile drink glasses. Given to Australian Avon reps. CMV $20 set MB.

1982 MUSIC BOX AWARD - CANADA
Wood music box in blue color. Wood trim, gold tassel on key. Bottom label says "President's Club Avon 1982" Club Du President. Made in Italy. CMV $50.

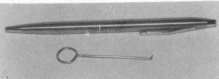

1982 CLOCK PEN - CANADA
Silver tone pen says "Avon 1982" in red letters on side LED clock in top half of pen. Hook is for changing battery. CMV $25 MB.

1982 SNACK SET AWARD - CANADA
Set of 4 chrome plated servers. Pie server & candy dish, 1st level; candy dish & bread tray, 2nd level; tiered snack tray, 3rd level. Avon label on bottom of each tray. CMV $50. Set of 4.

1980 UMBRELLA SMILE AWARD - CANADA
White with red & black design. Given to Team Leaders. CMV $25.

1983 TEAM LEADER BILLFOLD & CALCULATOR - CANADA
Maroon color leatherette has Cities 3660 calculator. Avon on billfold only. CMV $15.

1980 HOT PLATE AWARD - CANADA
White ceramic, red & green holly design. Green & red box sleeve. Given to Presidents Club Reps at Christmas 1980. Box in French & English. CMV $15 MB.

1982 UMBRELLA AWARD - CANADA
Tan umbrella with wood handle. Black letters, red stripe. Given to Team Leaders. CMV $25.

1982 TOCCARA AWARDS - CANADA
Royal blue tote bag. CMV $10.
Cosmetic bag. CMV $5.
Lavender lighted compact. CMV $10.

1983 PARADISE ISLAND HAT AWARD - CANADA
Straw hat with pink Avon band. Given to Presidents Club members on trip to Bahamas. CMV $5.
PARADISE AUTOGRAPH BOOK CMV $5.

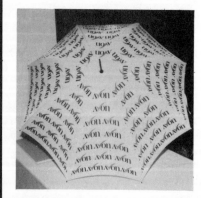

1983 UMBRELLA AWARD - EUROPE
White nylon with Avon in black & red all over it. Black plastic handle. Given to Avon reps in Europe. CMV $30.

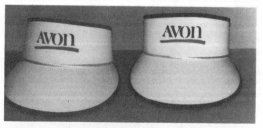

1982 TEAM LEADER HATS AWARDS - CANADA
2 different hats, 1 red trim, 1 blue trim. Given to Team Leaders in Canada. CMV $5 ea.

TUBES MISC.

1983-84 GREEN APPLE FRESH PEEL OFF MASK
3 oz. green tube. CMV 25c.
1983-84 MOISTURE THERAPY HAND CREAM
3 oz. white tube, blue cap. CMV 25c.
1983-84 AQUA CLEAN SHOWER GEL
5 oz. Hang up blue tube and dark blue cap. CMV 25c.

1982 Only STARS & STRIPES TO GO AFTER TAN MOISTURIZER — in 1 oz. plastic bottle, red cap. No box. SSP $1.30 - CMV $1.
SUNTAN LOTION — Factor 4 in 1 oz. tube, red cap, no box. SSP $1.30 - CMV $1.

1982 CLOWNING AROUND BODY SOAP
1.5 oz. tubes in red, yellow or blue. SSP $1.25 each - CMV 50c each.

1983 CLEARLY GENTLE BABY "BEAR" PRODUCTS
Each item has bear in blanket design.
BABY BATH — 1 oz. tube
BABY CREAM — 1 oz. tube
BABY OIL — 1 oz. plastic bottle.
SSP $1.30 each - CMV $1 each.

1982-84 CARE DEEPLY HAND CREAM FOR DRY WORK WEARY HANDS (left to right)
6 oz. white tube. SSP $2 - CMV 25c
Same tube in peach color with Cocoa Butter, CMV 25c.
1982-84 SAUNA SYSTEM FACIAL MASK
3 oz. white tube, red letters. SSP $2.50 - CMV 25c
1982-83 CARE DEEPLY DUO
1 oz. white tube, blue cap. Butterfly design hand cream with cocoa butter. Butterfly design pack of 8 small emery boards. CMV 25c each.

1982 SEASONAL SMOOTHERS HAND CREAM
1.5 oz. tubes in blue, red or green. SSP $1 - CMV 50c each.

1982-84 FRESH AS NATURE HAIR PACK
3 oz. tubes. Choice of Avocado, Lemon, Egg White. SSP $1.50 each - CMV 25c each.

1983 RABBIT LIP BALM AND HAND CREAM
Both have pink caps and rabbit on side. Hand cream is 1.5 oz. tube. No box. SSP $2 for pair - CMV $1 each.

1984 FROSTING
Small pink tube with four hearts. Came in Chocolate Bar. CMV $1.

651

TRAILING ARBUTUS

BABY ITEMS—CPC

1983 TRAILING ARBUTUS COLOGNE
.5 oz. bottle blue label, gold cap. Came in Roaring Twenties set only. CMV $2 BO.

1910 BABY SET
Box with kids playing on lid holds 1905 Baby Powder can, 2 oz. bottle of Violet Toilet Water and box of Baby Soap. OSP 75c - CMV $325 MB.

1902 CALIFORNIA BABY SOAP
Box of one bar. OSP 15c - CMV $75 mint.

CPC BOTTLES, MISC.

POWDER SACHET—CPC

LITTLE FOLKS SETS

1910 SACHET POWDER ENVELOPE
Paper packet of sachet in Violet, White Rose or Heliotrope. OSP 25c - CMV $30 mint.

1910 LITTLE FOLKS SET
Same box as 1908 set, same bottles & labels as 1912 set. OSP 50c - CMV $350 MB.

1910 LAIT VIRGINAL
2 oz. shown, metal crown in cork stopper. Also came in 4 and 8 oz. size. Front and neck labels. OSP 65c, $1.25 and $2 - CMV $100 mint, $125 MB.

REPRESENTATIVE AWARDS/GIFTS

1983 ALBEE FIGURINE AWARD
Purple dress lady given to all Presidents Club reps for top sales. CMV $70 MB.

1982 SMALL TREASURES CURRIER & IVES MINIS AWARDS
Pink box holds mini ceramic Tea Set. Given to reps for Step 2 of sales goal. Made in Japan. CMV $25 MB set.

1983 COME RAIN OR SHINE AWARD
Ceramic Cherished Moments Rabbit with screw on ceramic umbrella. Given to reps for sales goals. 1st of 3 levels. CMV $35 MB.

1982 GOING AVON CALLING AWARD
Yellow ceramic car with rabbit in pink, green base. Given to reps for Recommendation prize. CMV $50 MB.

1982 SMALL TREASURE MINI ROSE AWARD
Pink box holds small green leaf & pink ceramic rose. "The Avon Rose" on base, made in Taiwan. Given to reps for Step 1 of sales goal. CMV $5 MB.

1982 SMALL TREASURE CHERISHED MOMENTS MINI'S AWARD
Pink box holds 3 mini rabbit ceramic figurines. Given to reps for Step 4 sales goals. CMV $30 MB set.

1982 SMALL TREASURES ALBEE MINIATURES
Pink box holds mini Albee figurines of number 2, 3 & 4 Albee Awards. Given to Avon reps for 5th Step sales goal. CMV $35 MB set.

1982 SMALL TREASURES FRAGRANCE BOTTLES IN MINIATURE AWARDS
Pink box holds 3 mini size CPC reproductions with gold caps. Given to reps for Step 3 of sales goals. CMV $15 MB set.

1983 TOWNHOUSE CANNISTER & COOKIE JAR SET AWARDS
Given to reps for sales quota. 1st level, small, CMV $10. 2nd level, CMV $20. 3rd level, CMV $30. 4th level, Cookie Jar (right), CMV $50, or CMV $90 entire set.

1984 WILD VIOLETS COLLECTION WATER GLASSES
Set of 6, 12 oz. clear glass Violet flower design. Given to Avon reps for reaching level 2 of 4 levels. CMV $12 MB set.

1984 WILD VIOLETS COLLECTION TRAY & SALAD PLATES
11" x 17½" white plastic tray & set of 6 clear glass salad plates with Violet flower design. Given to Avon reps for reaching level 4 of 4 sales goal levels. CMV $20 set MB.

1984 WILD VIOLETS COLLECTION PITCHER AWARDS
Clear glass, Violet flower design. Given to Avon reps for level 1 of 4 levels. CMV $12 MB.

1984 WILD VIOLETS COLLECTION DESSERT BOWLS AWARDS
Set of 6, 13.5 oz. dessert bowls. Clear glass with Violet flower design. Given to Avon reps for reaching level 3 of 4 sales goal levels. CMV $15 MB set.

1982 REPRESENTATIVE CHRISTMAS GIFT
Small 4" porcelain dish made by Royal Worcester for Avon. Given to all Avon reps at Christmas 1982. Comes in green box with Avon card. CMV $10 MB.

1981 PYRAMID PAPERWEIGHT AWARD
Clear lucite with gold 4A design on bottom & 2 sides on top. Given to district managers only. CMV $50.

1982 ASH TRAY
Used at Avon plants. CMV $2.50.

1981-82 TIE TAC MEN'S PRESIDENTS CLUB AWARD

Gold tone 4A design Tie Tac given to men's Presidents Club. Comes in Avon box with 2 different backs as shown. CMV $20 MB.

1982 CIRCLE OF EXCELLENCE TRINKET BOX

Small leaded glass box with Rose embossed on lid. Comes with 4A brass coin. Back says "Roman Holiday C of E 1982". Only given to Pasadina Branch managers. CMV $35 box & coin.

1981 TEST DIVISION HEART PENDANT AWARD

(left) Sterling silver & gold heart pendant & silver chain. Given to managers only in Tiffany & Co. box. CMV $150 MB.

1982 ANNIE PENDANT MANAGERS

(right) 14K gold filled pendant & chain. Back marked "I love you" & marked DM on side. Given to district managers. Came in gray Avon box with special card from Avon. CMV $60 MB.

1983 PENDANT -PRESIDENTS CELEBRATION 1980

Sterling silver chain & pendant with 25 blue sapphires around edge. Oak tree in center. Back says "The Presidents Celebration 1980 Avon". Given to 250 top managers in US, 1 per division. CMV $200.

1980's 15 YEAR SERVICE AWARDS

All are marked Avon or has 4A design. Each comes from Tiffany & Co. Given for 15 years service at Avon. Choice of
STERLING SILVER PERPETUAL CALENDAR
6" wide, 4¼" high. CMV $75.
CRYSTAL DECANTER WITH STERLING SILVER TAG
11" high. CMV $75.
STERLING SILVER SALT & PEPPER SET
2¼" high. CMV $75 set.
STERLING SILVER PIN BOX
3" diameter. CMV $75.

1983 PRESIDENTS SALES COMPETITION JEWELRY AWARDS

3 levels, all Sterling Silver made by Tiffany.
BRACELET
Given 10 to a district. CMV $25 MB.
PENDANT NECKLACE
Given 2 to a district. CMV $35 MB.
LAPEL PIN
Given to each rep in top sales group who met individual sales goals. CMV $15 MB.
Each comes in Tiffany box & Avon card.

1981 PRESIDENTS CLUB PIN AWARD

Gold tone pin with 81 in center of 4A design cut out. CMV $10 MB.

1970's DOOR KNOCKER TIE TAC AWARD

10K gold. Given to male executives at Avon. CMV $60.

1980 FASHION HISTORY GLASSES AWARD

Set of 6, 12 oz. glasses marked 1890's, 1920's, 1940's, 1950's, 1960's & 1970's. Given as set to Avon reps for signing up new Avon reps. CMV $30 set.

1980'S 20 YEAR SERVICE AWARDS
Given for 20 years service. All are marked Avon or has 4A emblem on it. All from Tiffany. Choice of
STERLING SILVER PICTURE FRAME 9" high x 7" wide. CMV $100.
QUARTZ POLISHED BRASS CLOCK 2½" square. CMV $100.
CRYSTAL CANDLESTICKS - TALL 9¼" high, 4 1/8" wide base. CMV $75 set.
CRYSTAL CANDLESTICKS - SHORT 4½" high x 4 1/8" wide base. CMV $75 set.

1982 HEART PRESIDENTS SALES CHALLENGE AWARD
Small clear crystal heart on gold tone ribbon pin. Maroon velvet Avon box & outer sleeve. CMV $10 MB with sleeve.

1980's 20 YEAR SERVICE AWARDS
Given for 20 years service. All are marked Avon or has 4A design. All come from Tiffany & Co. Choice of
CRYSTAL PITCHER 5¾" high. CMV $60.
CRYSTAL VASE 7½" wide. CMV $60.
CRYSTAL TULIP WINE GLASSES Set of 6, 8" high. CMV $75 set.

1970's KEY CHAIN SERVICE AWARD 10 YEARS
Gold tone key chain with blue stone in center of 4A design. Comes in Avon white & green lined box. Given to managers. CMV $15 MB.

1981 ROSE STICK PIN AWARD
Small Sterling silver rose, no markings in Tiffany & Co. turquoise box. Given to Avon reps for recruiting & sales goals. CMV $25 MB.

1981 PIN "WATCH US GROW" AWARD
(left) Green & white tie tac type pin. Says "Newark - Watch us Grow". Given to managers. CMV $5.
1982 NEWARK NO. 1 1982 PENDANT AWARD
(right) Gold tone ½" size pendant. Given to managers No. 1 in sales. Brown box. CMV $20 MB.

1982 HOP SKIP & JUMP MEDAL AWARD
Gold tone medal with 4A design on one side & Hop, Skip & Jump Order Count Growth 1982 on back. Hangs on blue & yellow ribbon. CMV $25.

1980's 20 YEAR SERVICE CLOCK AWARD
7" wide x 4½" high Tiffany brass clock. Avon on top. Given for 30 years service at Avon. CMV $75.
1980's 30 YEAR SERVICE PEARL NECKLACE AWARD
17" long cultured pearl necklace with 14K gold Avon marked clasp. Given for 30 years service. Comes in blue holder from Tiffany. CMV $100 mint.

1970'S 45th ANNIVERSARY VASE AWARD
9¾" high x 4" across. Atlantis full lead crystal cut vase. Bottom engraved "45th Avon Anniversary". Given for 45 years of Avon service. CMV $200.

1980 MEDAL - 4A PENDANT AWARD
Silver tone & black 4A design about 2½" on red, white & blue neck ribbon. Given to managers only. Back says "You are a winner 1980" & name. CMV $20.

1982 SUBTLE REFLECTIONS HEART FLOWER VASE & FLOWERS
Small heart shape lucite vase & silk flowers with Avon tag. Given to Presidents Club reps. Does not say Avon. CMV $8.

1974 RECOGNITION AWARD PIN
About 1" size gold tone. Given to branch employees, rare. CMV $35.

1976 CIRCLE OF EXCELLENCE CUP AWARD
Polished pewter cup says "C of E 1976" engraved on side. Given to Circle managers only. CMV $60.

1983 GOLDEN BELL COLLECTION AWARDS
4 small brass bells given for meeting sales goals for C23, C24, C25, 1983. 1st bell has 4A design on top. 2nd bell has Acorn on top, 3rd bell has Avon door knocker. 4th bell was given if all 3 bells were won in all 3 campaigns as a bonus. 4th bell has a rose on top. CMV 1st bell $10, 2nd bell $10, 3rd bell $15, 4th bell $20.

1983 GROUP SALES LEADER PIN AWARD
(left) Red enamel on gold tone tie tac pin. Says "Avon G.L.S. No.1". CMV $10.
1983 REPRESENTATIVE OF THE MONTH PIN
(right) Gold tone pin given to reps for meeting goals for the month. 2 in each district. Passed on to new rep each month. CMV $25.

1964 PRESIDENTS DAY BOWL "LARGE" AWARD
12¼" Oneida silver plate bowl. Center of bowl engraved with big 4A design & says "Presidents Day 1964 - Low Net." CMV $45.
1964 PRESIDENTS DAY BOWL "SMALL" AWARD
9 1/8" Oneida bowl as above. Center says "Presidents Day 1964 - Closest to Pin", 4A design. CMV $40.

1980 VALENTINE ATOMIZER AWARD
Small clear crystal bottle, chrome top & red squeeze bulb. Given to team leaders & district manager. TL on bottom & DM. CMV $10, TL bottle MB. CMV $20, DM bottle MB.

1973 NEWARK FIRST AWARD CLOCK
Alfry electric clock, black face, white painted over brass. Back side says "Newark First 1973" plus owners initials. Given to district supervisors. CMV $40.

1982 PRESIDENTS SALES CHALLENGE AWARD WATCH
Black face, Avon Quartz & small diamond on 12 on face. Gold tone case. Black lizard strap. 1 top rep in each district won. Came in Avon gray felt case & outer sleeve. CMV $100 MB & sleeve.
Same watch only gold face watch & no diamond & black lizard look leather strap in tan felt Avon case & outer sleeve. 20 given in each district to Presidents Club reps only. CMV $50 MB sleeve.

1980 CUSTOMER SERVICE AWARD CLOCK
(left) Brass Tiffany & Co. clock given to Avon managers. Engraved on top "Avon Customer Service Award Conference 1980". Comes in Tiffany box & felt bag. CMV $140.

1981 MILLION DOLLAR INCREASE AWARD CLOCK
(right) Gold tone round Seth Thomas alarm clock. Given to managers for 1 million dollar increase in sales. Engraved on back side "Our First Million $ Increase". CMV $65.

1978 CLOCK 20 YEAR AWARD
(left) Small brass Tiffany & Co. Quartz clock. Top engraved "Avon 20 years & winners initials" Given to Avon managers for 20 years service. CMV $75.

1978 CLOCK AUGUST CONFERENCE AWARD
(right) Brass Relice 400 electronic clock. Given to managers for going to August Conference 1978, bottom engraved. CMV $50.

1982 CIRCLE OF EXCELLENCE AWARD CLOCK
Clear lucite digital clock with engraved name of winning Avon manager. Is not marked Avon. CMV $50.

1982 PRESIDENTS CLUB CARD CASE AWARD
Silver plated card case in Tiffany box & felt bag. Engraved on case "Presidents Club & 4A design". CMV $35 MB.

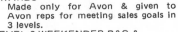

1975 CASTINET AWARD
Given to Circle of Excellence managers only on trip to Spain. Comes with Circle of Excellence orange award card as shown. CMV $25 MB with card.

1982 PARKER PEN AWARD SET
2 gold tone Parker pens. Says Avon on side. Given to managers. CMV $35 MB.

1968 ROOSTER AWARD
Rooster shape leather covered green glass bottom on wood base. Brass plaque says "Rooster Highest Percent Increase, 4A design & all 7 Avon branches". Given to district supervisor. CMV $45.

1983 TELEPHONE PRESIDENTS CLUB AWARD
Red plastic Touch Tone, given to top sales reps only. Made by Webcor. Outer sleeve says "Avon Calling" & Avon Calling on telephone. CMV $35.

1983 RAIN GEAR COLLECTION AWARDS
Made only for Avon & given to Avon reps for meeting sales goals in 3 levels.
LEVEL 2 WEEKENDER BAG & ACCESSORY BAG
Tan color cotton. Both have Avon Rain Gear tags. CMV $15 set.
LEVEL 3 RAIN GEAR RAINCOAT & UMBRELLA
Tan matching coat & umbrella. Avon tags. Raincoat CMV $25. Umbrella CMV $25.

1977 GATEWAY SPRING COMPETITION AWARD
Lucite man on plastic base & nameplate. Given to managers in Morton Grove branch. CMV $35.

1982 ROSE PARADE JACKET AWARD
Avon Products issued 100 Rose Parade jackets in red to people working with Avon float in '82. parade, rare. Same inscription on front. CMV $100.

1981 UMBRELLA LIPSTICK AWARD
White nylon, black & red trim, red plastic handle. Given to Team Leaders. CMV $25.

1980 DIRECTOR'S CHAIR AWARD
White folding chair with green seat & back. Back says "You never looked so good". Given to reps for signing up new Avon reps. CMV $20.

1980'S NECKTIE
Blue necktie with "Avon" in red, white & blue design. Label says "Neatwear Tie London, The Club Tie Specialist". Given to Avon Executives. CMV $25.

1982 BEACH TOWEL AWARD
32" x 59" size, white, black & red. Given to reps. CMV $20.

1982 BEAR PRIDE OF NEWARK AWARD
Small 6" bear hobo name tag with gold tone chain & pendant around neck. Says "Thanks for making us No. 1 & 4A design" on 1 side & "District managers are the pride of Newark" on the other side. Bear must have Avon pendant. CMV $30.

1979 AVON BEAR SMALL TEDDY AWARD
About 6" high brown bear. Made in Korea, given to managers. CMV $50.

1982 MERRI RAT AWARD
(left) White stuffed rat with pink ears & feet, red hat has wood sign around neck "To the best from your N.Y. Buddy". Given to Avon managers just for the hell of it. CMV $20.
1982 TEDDY BEAR SWITCH TO AVON
(right) Small brown & white stuffed bear. Red Avon banner, made by Ruso. Given to winning team in each district. CMV $7.50.

1982 KEY CHAIN NEW YORK AWARD
I Love Avon's New York on front. Given to group sales leaders at Leadership Circle Celebration in N.Y. CMV $15.

1982 KEY CHAIN YOU NEVER LOOKED SO GOOD
White plastic, black letters. Never issued to reps. CMV $5.

1982 SWITCH TO AVON BUTTON
Blue pin. CMV $1.
AVON OPPORTUNITY UNLIMITED 1982 BUTTON
Yellow button. CMV $1.

1981 KEY CHAIN AWARD
Red, white, with black pen insert. Given to reps. CMV $4.

1981 FEEL LIKE A STAR BUTTON
3" blue & white button. CMV $2.

1982 PASADENA SUNGLASSES
Blue sunglasses says "Pasadena '82". Made in the shade. CMV $5.

1983 C OF E SALES GROWING BUTTON
Yellow button. CMV $2.

1982 PASADENA NO. 1 BUTTON
White button with red, white & blue ribbon. CMV $2.

1983 TOTE BAG (WHO COULD SELL AVON)
Beige canvas hand bag, red letters. Given to reps. CMV $5.

1983 MUSK FOR MEN TRAVEL KIT AWARD
Travel kit bag & 2.8 oz. Musk Cologne for men. Comes with Avon letter to reps for metting sales goals. Bag does not say Avon. CMV $15 MB with letter.

1982 TOTE BAGS PRESIDENTS CLUB
Blue & white bag & clutch given to reps at Presidents Club Luncheon. Tote bag CMV $4, clutch CMV $3.

1978 BEAUTY SHOWCASE DEMO BAG
Used to carry demo products in by Avon reps. CMV $3.

1977 CIRCLE OF EXCELLENCE TOTE BAG
White canvas bag, blue letters. CMV $15.

1982 YOU DID IT WALLET AWARD
Blue, white & red purse, in red box. Given to reps for $45 increase in sales. CMV $5 MB.

1976 TOTE BAG
Blue brocade bag used by Avon reps to carry demo products. CMV $3.

TOTE BAG:
9¼" x 4¾" x 12½"

1982 QUICK STAMP
Red Avon box has pink & white plastic name stamp. CMV $8 MB.

1977 BIG BLACK BOOK
Given to managers. Black foldout clip board. Avon on back. CMV $5.

1965 JEWELRY BOX AWARD
White box has 2 lids, blue inside, 4A design & says "Belding Corticelli" inside lid. Given to managers. CMV $15 box only mint.

1983 ORDER BOOK & CALCULATOR
Red Avon box has red Avon order book cover with order book, calculator & calendar. 5 reps in each district won them. CMV $17.50 MB.

1982 FOOT HILL DIVISION HIGHEST DOLLAR SALES INCREASE AWARD PLAQUE
Wood base plaque given to managers only. CMV $40.

1983 PRESIDENTS HONOR SOCIETY AWARD
Plaque in gold tone glass picture frame. Given to reps for top sales. CMV $15.

1983 NOTE PAD TOP TEN
Maroon color real leather. Has 4A design on cover. Note pad & telephone directory inside. Given to top ten reps in Newark branch. CMV $20 mint.

1983 JEWELRY BOX PRESIDENTS SALES COMPETITION AWARD
Black lacquer music box made only for Avon. Bottom says "Presidents Sales Competition 1983". 8" x 4¾" size. Given for sales goals. Comes with Avon card. CMV $25.

1980 TEDDY BEAR AWARD PLAQUE
Certificate in black frame. Given for high sales. CMV $10.
1980 TEDDY BEAR RECRUITING AWARD PLAQUE
Certificate in black frame. Given for recommendation. CMV $10.

1959 MANAGERS CHRISTMAS GIFT
Beige box with blue velvet lining holds French hand made bead purse & Majestic cultured pearl necklace. Given to managers at Christmas 1959. Very rare. Set not marked Avon, but valuable. CMV not established.

1983 CIRCLE OF EXCELLENCE STATIONERY ROME
2 boxes given to all managers on trip to Rome in 1983. CMV $25 MB set.

1981 GREAT AMERICAN SELLATHON PRIZES
Name tag, $1.
Luggage tag, $2.
Menu Presidents Celebration, $2.
Portfolio, $2.

1983 PAVI ELLE MINK PENCIL AWARD
Red Avon pencil with small mink attached. Given to district managers. CMV $7.50

1979 VITAMIN SALES RIBBON
Red ribbon for Avon vitamin sales in test market only. CMV $10.

1979 MOISTURE GARDEN PROMOTION GIFT
Pump dispenser given to Presidents Club reps. Comes in box & envelope shown. CMV $2 MB in envelope.

COIN GLASS HANDCRAFTED BY FOSTORIA
By Ogreta Simmons

The Fostoria Glass Company began operations in Fostoria, Ohio on Dec. 15, 1887. This site was chosen because of a promise of very low cost for natural gas for their furnaces. However, the gas field was short-lived and in 1891, Fostoria moved to Moundsville, West Virginia, its present location.

During the first 10 years, Fostoria made pressed ware. About 1897, oil burning lamps were added to the line and soon became a major part of the production. Today, the lamps are highly prized by antique collectors. As electric lights replaced the oil burning lamps, other handmolded items were created, such as dresser sets, table sets containing tumblers, spoon holders, sugar and creamers and upright celery holders.

Early in the century, Fostoria realized the importance of fine quality blown stemware along with crystal service. They began to concentrate more on glassware for the home. This was, and still is, produced in the "much higher than average" quality of glassware.

When Coin Glass was first produced, the date of 1887 on coins was used, being the year that the Fostoria Company was founded. On the original pieces of coin glass production, real coins were reproduced. Since this was contrary to law, the U.S. Government quickly stopped production and ordered the molds destroyed. Today, the antique flavor of the simulated coins and the lovely old shapes produce collectors items to grace contemporary living. Fostoria Coin Glass is now produced in crystal, amber, olive green, blue and ruby. Fostoria for Avon has only been produced in crystal.

Like collectors of Avon coming together and forming the National Association of Avon Clubs, likewise, there is a Fostoria Glass Society of America, Inc., a non-profit organization, which furnished much of the information for this article. Fostoria, like Avon, has a colorful past history and is a story all of its own. The plant covers 8 acres of ground and has over 450,000 square feet of floor space. About 420 persons are presently employed and there are 90 employees who have been with Fostoria from 25-40 years. Most employees are highly skilled craftsmen that take great pride in their work.

As traditional with Avon wanting to offer their customers only the best, in 1961, Avon selected Fostoria to produce Avon's 75th Anniversary year memento of the founding of the CPC Company. This was the first Fostoria Coin Glass piece offered by Avon and was the Coin Glass Wedding Bowl. In 1977, for the 91st Anniversary of Avon, the Fostoria Company revised the date to 1886 for Avon. This brings up a highly controversial subject about the dates on Coin Glass. Information from Fostoria states that no exclusive items are made for Avon and that Avon does select pieces which are available to Fostoria Dealers around the country. However, for the items selected by Avon, the molds are revised to show the 1886 date. Then, since the molds are owned and retained by Fostoria, the 1886 dates can be found in retail stores on some pieces as Avon does not "own" the 1886 date. For this reason, the cartons and boxes that Fostoria is shipped to Avon Representatives is definite proof that the item is an Avon issue, the collectors should retain the packing box to prove its authenticity status. Each white cardboard box has "Avon" inscribed on it and is your proof that the item came from Avon. However, on the "Coin Glass type" of Fostoria where the Avon motifs are used in lieu of the dated coins, it would appear that these items were made exclusive for Avon you don't need a box to prove that they are Avon.

This article furnished by
Mid America Avon Collectors Club
Ogreta Simmons, Editor
Kansas City, Missouri

Following are some Fostoria Awards given by Avon. There may be others.

1961	Coin Glass Wedding Bowl
1961-72	Coin Glass Covered Compote
1961-72	Coin Glass Oval Center Bowl
1961-72	Coin Glass Candle Holders
1960's	Coin Glass Cake Plate
1960's	Coin Glass Tall Covered Compote
1963	Crystal 77th Anniversary Queen Award (11¼" bowl w/4A design)
1964	Coin Glass 78th Anniversary Salt & Pepper, Cruet and Tray
1970	Crystal Creamer and Sugar, Henry Ford Design
1971	Coin Glass Plate
1971	Coin Glass Short Bud Vase
1971	Coin Glass Handled Nappy
1971	Coin Glass Creamer & Sugar
1971	Coin Glass Salt & Pepper
1973	Lead Crystal dessert plate and bowl, set of 4 each
1977	Coin Glass Footed Compote with AVON emblems
1977	Coin Glass Round Center Bowl, AVON emblems
1977	Coin Glass Candle Holders, AVON emblems
1978	Lead Crystal Plates, came in 2 sets of 4 each
1978	Crystal Candy Dish with 4A design. (Christmas gift)
1980	Crystal Team Leader Recruit-A-Thon Bell

Some of the Fostoria items sold by Avon are as follows: (there may be others)

1969	Salt Cellar w/small silver spoon
1973	Perfumed Candle Holder
1974	Covered Compote w/Skin So Soft bath oil capsules
1975	George Washington Goblet Candle Holder
1975	Candlelight Basket Candle Holder
1976	Martha Washington Goblet Candle Holder
1977	Mount Vernon Sauce Pitcher Candle Holder
1977	Hearts and Diamonds, Soap Dish w/soap
1977	Crystal Egg Soap Dish w/egg-shaped soap
1978	Hearts and Diamonds Loving Cup Candle Holder
1978	Hearts and Diamonds Candlestick for 2 sizes of candles
1979	Crystal Pool Floating Candle
1980	Crystal Bud Vase w/scented carnation
1980	Ring Holder
1982	D A D Paper Weight
1983	Images of Love Picture Frame, Paper Weight
1983	M O M Paper Weight

POINTS OF INTEREST OF EARLY YEARS OF CALIFORNIA PERFUME CO.

In May 1905 each CPC manager who turned in an order of $80 or more received a $5 gold piece. This was a frequent practice.

In May 1905, Mrs. Albert King of Taunton, Mass., was the top selling rep in the nation with $300.80 in sales. She made a profit from this amount of $120.12.

. . . .

September 1905 White Rose was changed to Roses.

. . . .

November 1915 was the first year the president made Thanksgiving a national holiday.

. . . .

In 1905 early day CPC reps were called Depot Managers & the Managers over them were called General Agents.

. . . .

Beginning January 1, 1921 all CPC reps began getting 40% off on all orders.

. . . .

The CPC Co. did not raise a single price on any product from 1914 until May 1, 1917.

. . . .

In July 1906 over 10,000 CPC reps gave out one million samples of Roses Perfume nation wide.

. . . .

In 1909 it cost CPC 5c to print the California Perfume Book Sales Catalog.

. . . .

CPC starting a branch in Kansas City in 1902.

. . . .

In December 1909 to January 31, 1910 a 1910 CPC calendar was given to all customers with an order of 75c or more.

. . . .

CPC first printed product price lists in French in 1910.

. . . .

Start January 1907 on Thursday.

. . . .

The CPC total business doubled from 1905 to the end of 1906.

. . . .

The 119th item to be added to the CPC line was Rose Talcum Powder in February 1907 & sold for 25c.

. . . .

In December 1907 CPC put out a 12 page catalog showing all the special Christmas gift boxes for their line of products.

. . . .

Avon & CPC have been giving Christmas gifts to their reps since 1906.

. . . .

By 1908 most CPC reps were selling $1,000 to $3,000 worth of goods per year.

. . . .

In May 1916 a 9" x 12" picture of the girl on the face of the Sweet Sixteen Face Powder was given with each powder sold.

. . . .

August 1908 was the first introduction of CPC Shaving Soapstick in metal container. It sold for 25c.

. . . .

C.P. sign of quality insignia was first published in August 1908.

. . . .

CPC had a sales Depot Manager selling products in Hawaii in 1908.

. . . .

CPC moved its office in San Francisco to 88 First Street & Mission in November, 1908.

. . . .

CPC moved from 126 Chambers Street in New York in May 1909 to 31 Park Place, New York.

. . . .

AWARDS—CPC

1928 ELEPHANT CRYSTAL JAR AWARD
6" long and 4" high, wrinkled glass to look like skin. Came filled with Vernafleur Bath Salts. Glass top of elephant lifts off. Given to 36 Reps. for highest sales. This will be considered the 1st decanter Avon ever issued. Very rare. CMV $300.

1927 PERFUME ATOMIZER AWARD
Peacock blue opaque crystal bottle with embossed gold top. Silk net over bulb. Given to six Reps. in each district for top sales of gift sets in December, 1927. CMV $125. BO mint, $165. MB.

1923 MISSION GARDEN PERFUME AWARD
8" tall cut glass bottle with sterling silver trim, glass stopper. Given to Reps for tops sales. Very rare. CMV $250.

1916 BROOCH AWARD "GOLD"
Solid gold with one full cut diamond and two pearls. Given to Reps. for $150. wholesale order in four months. CMV $400.

1933 DIAMOND JUBILEE PEARL AWARD
18" long strand of Coro pearls. 14K white gold clasp with diamond inset. Satin lined box and silver metallic cloth outside. Given to 75 top Reps. in U.S. in July, 1933. CMV not established.

1932 PRESIDENTS CUP AWARD
8½" tall silver plate, gold lined. Given to only twenty Reps. in U.S. Engraved on side — winners name, from D.H. McConnell, President California Perfume Co., Inc., July 18, 1932. CMV $300. mint.

1916 PENDANT LAVALLIERE AWARD
Pure gold pendant and chain. Diamond in center of pendant with pearl above. Given to Reps for $150. wholesale order. CMV $400.

1916 SILVER PHOTO FRAME AWARD
Solid sterling silver frame 4½" high by 3½" wide. Oval band is ½" wide, velvet back. Given to Reps. for selling $50. at Christmas. CMV $350.

1915-1917 SILVER TOILET WARE AWARD
Silver plate handle whisk broom made by International Silver Co., and two glass jars with silver plate lids of same design. Hair receiver jar shown with hole in center of lid. Puff jar is same only no hole in lid. Set was given to Reps. for selling $75. order in four month period. CMV whisk broom, $75., each jar $125. each.

1916 OLIVE DISH CUT GLASS AWARD
8 3/8" long by 4 3/4" wide. Genuine crystal cut glass. Given to Reps. for $30. wholesale order. Made only for CPC. CMV $200.

1913 SUGAR & CREAMER AWARD
Glass decorated with sterling silver. Sugar bowl is 3¼" wide by 2¾" high. Creamer is 4" high by 2¾" wide. Given to Reps. for selling 40 packages of Laundry Crystals and Starch Dressing. CMV $100. each piece.

1907 POCKET WATCH AWARD
14K gold filled watch with either Elgin or Waltham movement. Given to Reps. for $200. order in three months. CMV $300.

1913 FLOWER VASE AWARD
Glass vase decorated in sterling silver. Given to Reps. for selling 75 packages of Laundry Crystals and Starch Dressing. CMV $300.

1917 PUFF & HAIR JAR AWARD
Real cut glass jars with cut glass lids given to Reps. for $50. in sales in January 1917. Given as sets only CMV $200. each.

1912-13 CANDELABRA AWARD
Heavy Rogers silver plate. Given to Reps. for selling $75. in four months. CMV $500.

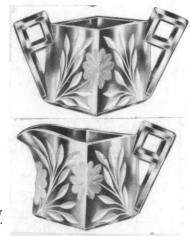

1917 CUT GLASS SUGAR & CREAMER AWARD
Real cut glass set given to Reps. for sales of over $50. in February 1917. CMV $150. each piece.

1913 CLOCK AWARD "1 DAY"
Ormuler gold plate clock with 2" porcelain dial, 10¾" high by 6" wide. From New Haven Clock Co. Given to Reps. for $60. In sales in three month period. CMV $600.

1908 SILVER TOILET SET AWARD
Box holds Rogers silver plated mirror, brush and comb. Given to Reps. for $75. order in three months. CMV $300. set MB.

1913 CLOCK AWARD "8 DAY"
Eight day Ormuler clock from New Haven Clock Co. Gold plate finish beveled edge glass. 10¾" high by 9½" wide. Given to Reps. for $100. In sales in three month period. CMV $750.

1912 COMB & BRUSH SET AWARD
Box holds two silver plated brushes and matching comb. Given to Reps. for $75. order in three months. CMV $300. set MB.

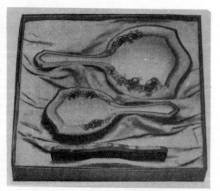

1917 SILVER TOILET SET AWARD
Set holds beveled edge hand mirror of silver plate back and matching silver plate brush and comb. Flower design is Butler Grey pattern. Given to Reps. for selling $96. in four month period in 1917. CMV $300. set, MB.

1906 WATCH AWARD
14K gold filled case, heavy engraved. Choice of Elgin or Waltham jeweled movement. Choice of small ladies or larger mens watch. CMV $350. each.

1936 LAMP AWARDS BY STAFFORDSHIRE
Imported pottery lamps, ivory color with flowers. Shades are shell pink or rose trimmed in rose or gold. Base is gold tone. Given as a pair to top 50 Reps. in U.S. for top sales. CMV $125. each.

1932 SILVER FRUIT COCKTAIL SET AWARD
Silver plate tray and six silver cocktail bowls. Given for $250. order. CMV $75. set.

1932 SILVER CANDLESTICK AWARD
Set of two silver plate candlesticks. Given for $50. order. CMV $40. set.

1906 SILVER TEA SET AWARD
Rogers quadruple silver plate tea set given to CPC reps for selling $100 order. CMV $300 set.

1917 SILVER CLOTH BRUSH AWARD
Silver plate back. CMV $125.
1917 SILVER HAT BRUSH AWARD
Silver plate back. CMV $125.
1917 SILVER JEWEL CASE AWARD
Silver plate jewel box. CMV $200. Each piece has the Butler Grey Flower pattern. Each piece was given to Reps for selling $60. in four month period.

1907 TEA SET AWARD
4 piece Rogers quadruple silver plate serving set. Given to Reps. for selling $125 in three months. CMV $350 set.

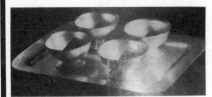

1932 SILVER SHERBERT SET AWARD
Silver plate tray and four sherbert bowls. Given for $200. order. CMV $60. set.

1907 TEA SET AWARD
4 piece Rogers quadruple silver plate tea set. Given to Reps. for selling $75. in three months. CMV $300 set.

1934 LOYALTY BIRTHDAY CELEBRATION AWARD
Three piece W. A. Rogers silver plate tea set given to top 76 Reps. in U.S. during Mr. McConnell's birthday celebration. CMV $85. set.

1932 SILVER SUGAR & CREAMER SET AWARD
Silver plate tray and sugar & creamer. Given to Reps. for $85. order. CMV $75. set.

1931 SALT & PEPPER AWARD
Chrome plated salt and pepper shakers. Given to Reps. for selling eight jars of Rose Cold Cream in January, 1931. CMV $30. set MB.

1932 SILVER PLATTER AWARD
Design only for Avon. Gold lined center. Given to Reps. for $35. order. Silver plate. CMV $35.

1914 CLUTCH POINT PENCIL AWARD
5" long gold filled lead pencil. Given to Reps. for $30. order. CMV $100.

1918 ARMY NAVY PEN
Made by Salz Bros. N.Y. Made of Para rubber with 14K gold pen point. Shaped like a bullet. Given to Reps. for $50. order in September, 1918. CMV $50.

1906 DINNER DISH SET AWARD
Limoges China, 100 piece set. Given to Reps. for $200. order in three months. CMC not established.

1905 DINNER DISH SET AWARD
Made only for CPC. 100 piece set of Limoges fine china dinnerware. Given to Reps. for a $200. wholesale order in three months. CMV not established.

1933 CHINAWARE AWARD
A complete set of china dishes could be won by Reps., a few pieces at a time. Pattern was made only for Avon. CMV not established.

QUICK REFERENCE INDEX

AN AID TO FINDING CATAGORIES QUICKLY

ALPHABETICAL INDEX

If you cannot find the items you are looking for in this Alphabetical Index, check the Quick Reference Index in which it falls.

1984 SUPPLEMENT INDEX

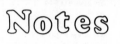

Notes

FREE BONUS ADVERTISING OFFER

DEAR AVONERS!

With this edition of Bud Hastin's Avon Collectors Encyclopedia, you now own the finest book every published on Avon Collectibles.

Even more information is available to you through the "Avon Times". This is the world's largest publication on Avon collecting, published monthly.

We would like to offer you this chance to advertise in a 30 word maximum "FREE" ad; to buy, sell or trade your Avon collectibles in the "Times".

You must send this coupon (a $4.50 value) from this book, along with $1.00 to cover postage and handling to: Avon Times, P. O. Box 9868, Kansas City, MO 64134.

We will also mail you a free sample copy of the "Avon Times" in which your ad appears. All ads over 30 words, please send 15c per word.

Your subscription to "Avon Times" would be welcomed. The rates are $12.00 in U.S.A., $15.00 in Canada, U.S. funds money orders only, for 12 issues sent first class mail. Subscribe today, and see why we are the world's largest Avon Club. You will receive $22.50 worth of "Free Ad Coupons" with each subscription.

------ CUT ALONG LINE ------

Here is my 30 word "Free Ad" to run in your next issue of "Avon Times". Enclosed is $1.00 to cover the postage and handling to mail me an issue in which my "Free Ad" appears.

PLEASE PRINT PLAINLY

. . . .

. . . .

. . . .

. . . .

. . . .

Name. . . . .

Address . . . .

City .State . . . . Zip . . . .

This offer subject to change or revocation without notice. No Free Ads will be accepted that are not on this order forms Send To:

AVON TIMES

P.O. Box 9868   **Kansas City, MO 64134**

Notes

Notes

Notes